D1402005

BIOLOGICAL SCIENCES CURRICULUM STUDY

Publications

Biological Science: Molecules to Man
–Houghton Mifflin Company, Boston

Biological Science: An Inquiry into Life
–Harcourt, Brace & World, Inc., New York

High School Biology: BSCS Green Version
–Rand McNally & Company, Chicago

BSCS Quarterly Tests (two alternate forms)
–available for each Version from the Version publishers

BSCS Comprehensive Final Examination (two alternate forms)
–The Psychological Corporation, New York

Processes of Science Test (for all Versions)
–The Psychological Corporation, New York

Test Booklets (for each Version)
–available from the Version publishers

Biological Science: Patterns and Processes
–Holt, Rinehart & Winston, Inc., New York

BSCS Unit Tests and *Final Examination* for *Biological Science: Patterns and Processes*
–The Psychological Corporation, New York

Biological Science: Interaction of Experiments and Ideas
–Prentice-Hall, Inc., Englewood Cliffs, New Jersey

BSCS Quarterly Tests and *Final Examination* for *Biological Science: Interaction of Experiments and Ideas*
–Prentice-Hall, Inc., Englewood Cliffs, New Jersey

BSCS Laboratory Blocks (13 titles)
–D. C. Heath and Company, Boston

Research Problems in Biology: Investigations for Students,
Series 1, 2, 3, 4–Doubleday & Company, Inc., Garden City, New York

Innovations in Equipment and Techniques for the Biology Teaching Laboratory
–D. C. Heath and Company, Boston

BSCS Techniques Films (9 titles)–Thorne Films, Boulder, Colorado

BSCS Single Topic Inquiry Films (20 titles; others in preparation)
–Harcourt, Brace & World, Inc., New York
–Houghton Mifflin Company, Boston
–Rand McNally & Company, Chicago

The Story of the BSCS (Information Film)–BSCS, Boulder, Colorado

Biology Teachers' Handbook–John Wiley & Sons, New York

BSCS Pamphlet Series (24 titles)–D. C. Heath and Company, Boston

BSCS Patterns of Life Series (8 titles)
–Rand McNally & Company, Chicago

BSCS Bulletin Series (Nos. 1, 2, 3)–BSCS, Boulder, Colorado

BSCS Special Publications (Nos. 1, 2, 3, 4, 5)–BSCS, Boulder, Colorado

BSCS Newsletter–BSCS, Boulder, Colorado

BSCS International News Notes–BSCS, Boulder, Colorado

A revision prepared by: JOHN A. MOORE, *Supervisor*
Department of Life Sciences
University of California
Riverside, California

EDWARD F. DEGENHARDT
Science Department
Niles Township High School, East Division
Skokie, Illinois

BENTLEY GLASS
Academic Vice-President
State University of New York
Stony Brook, Long Island, New York

REV. LUKE HALLENBECK, O.S.B.
Biology Department
The Abbey School
Canon City, Colorado

MANERT KENNEDY, *Associate Director*
Biological Sciences Curriculum Study
formerly, Biology Department
Fraser High School
Fraser, Michigan

WILLIAM V. MAYER, *Director*
Biological Sciences Curriculum Study
Boulder, Colorado

TAMSEN GOODMAN MEYER
formerly, Biology Department
Seminole High School
St. Petersburg, Florida

INGRITH DEYRUP OLSEN
Department of Zoology
University of Washington
Seattle, Washington

WILSON N. STEWART
Chairman, Department of Botany
University of Alberta
Edmonton, Alberta, Canada

Edited by DON E. MEYER
and ROBERT BUCHANAN
of the Harcourt, Brace & World Staff

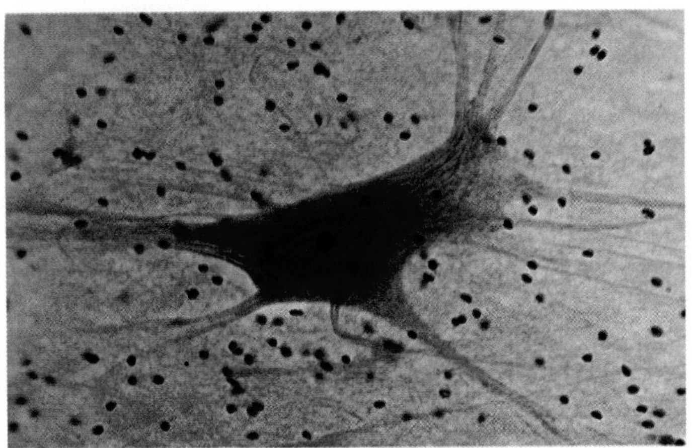

BIOLOGICAL SCIENCE

Second Edition

AN INQUIRY INTO LIFE

Prepared by the Biological Sciences Curriculum Study
with support from the National Science Foundation

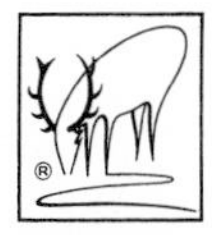

HARCOURT, BRACE
& WORLD, INC.

*New York Chicago San Francisco
Atlanta Dallas*

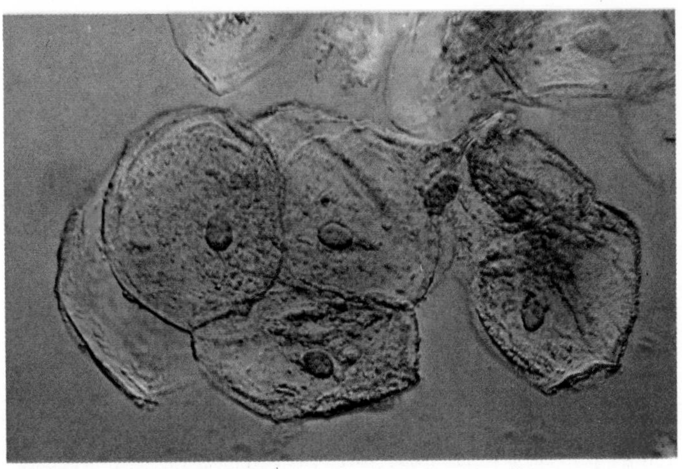

THE BSCS STAFF

DR. ADDISON E. LEE, Chairman, BSCS Steering Committee
DR. WILLIAM V. MAYER, Director
MR. MANERT H. KENNEDY, Associate Director
MR. GEORGE M. CLARK, Assistant Director
MR. KEITH L. BUMSTED, Business Manager
MR. PATRICK E. BALCH, Staff Consultant
DR. THOMAS J. CLEAVER, Staff Consultant
DR. JAMES T. ROBINSON, Staff Consultant
MR. HAROLD A. RUPERT, JR., Staff Consultant
DR. RICHARD R. TOLMAN, Staff Consultant

Illustration Staff

MR. ROBERT F. WILSON, Art Director
MR. LAWRENCE A. STRAND, Assistant Art Director
MISS JANE H. LARSON, Former Art Director*
MISS LINDA G. BOLEY*
MR. JAMES E. BRAMLETT*
MR. EUGENE J. DIODATO, JR.*
MRS. MARGERY A. GARDEPHE*
MR. ELDRIDGE HARDIE*
MR. ROBERT G. HAYNES*
MISS ELAINE HICKS*
MR. GARY J. KEIMIG*
MR. ROBERT T. KUSSEROW*
MRS. SHENG-HING LEE*
MR. RAYMOND S. OROSZ*
MR. KENT PENDLETON*
MR. ROY M. UDO
MR. D. PHILLIP WILLETTE*

*Formerly on Illustration Staff

Cover photograph: A worker honeybee supplying food for the larvae, which are in the cells of the comb. The larvae have hatched from eggs laid by the queen bee. The capped cell contains a pupa, one stage more advanced in development than the larvae. The adult bee that develops from the pupa will gnaw its way out of the cell. (Photograph by Treat Davidson from National Audubon Society)

Title page photographs: Upper view, the cell body of a motor neuron; lower view, human cheek cells from the lining of the mouth. (Both photographs, Harbrace Photos)

Special photographic research by: DAVID FOLLANSBEE, GABRIELE WUNDERLICH

Printed in the United States of America

ISBN 0-15-360800-5

Foreword

We live in an age of science, and it is essential that students of today, who will occupy positions of leadership in the twenty-first century, have the background of a modern and forward-looking program in science. As biology may be the first, last, and only science to which the majority of students are exposed in their formal education, it must be accurate and modern in biological content and must instill a comprehension of both science and the scientific enterprise.

For years, many of our better teachers have been expressing dissatisfaction with the tools with which they have had to work. They wanted to teach modern biology in an imaginative, investigative, and inquiry-oriented fashion, but the texts available to them fostered the rote memorization of lists of names, facts, and dates. This decade has witnessed a spectacular improvement in biological education, and the Biological Sciences Curriculum Study has played an important role in that improvement. The Biological Sciences Curriculum Study was organized to improve biological education at all levels of instruction.

The initial goal of the BSCS was the production of classroom materials for average students in a first course in biology at the secondary school level. The materials were structured around a series of major themes: science as investigation and inquiry, the history of biological concepts, complementarity of structure and function, diversity of type and unity of pattern, change of organisms through time as evolution, genetic continuity, the complementarity of the organism and its environment, regulation and homeostasis, and the biological basis of behavior. These themes were presented through the use of a variety of organisms best illustrating the concept in question. Thus, use of microorganisms, plants, and animals conveys the pervasiveness of these themes in all living things. At the same time, cognizance should be taken of a balanced consideration of all levels of organization of life from the molecule through cells, tissues, organs, individuals, populations, species, communities, and the world biome. It is the interweaving of the themes with organisms and levels of organization that gives biology a structure as a science. Recognition of this structure makes possible a series of patterns that tremendously increases the effectiveness of instruction in biology. Each program includes materials selected for their applicability in the latter half of the twentieth century and their ability to illuminate the principles and concepts that underlie biological science. The BSCS program presents a balanced approach to the science of biology without presenting excessive details. Content has been carefully selected by learned biologists and educators as that most contributory to understanding the basics of biological science.

The first experimental editions of three different versions of BSCS books were completed in 1960 and were tested in approximately 100 schools throughout the country. Based on this experience, the three experimental versions were revised in 1961 and subjected to trials in 500 schools during the 1961-62 school year and in 950 schools the following year. After three years of extensive trials and revisions, these three experimental versions were reorganized to become the commercially published editions that appeared in 1963.

The present book is a complete revision of one of the 1963 versions and is based upon feedback of the last five years together with the most recent scientific information available. The BSCS deeply appreciates the singularly important contributions to the improvement of biological education made by 1,000 teachers and 150,000 students who used the experimental editions and reported their experiences to us. More than two million pupils have studied from the first editions of these books, and to them and to their teachers the BSCS is indebted for many constructive suggestions that have been incorporated in the present volumes.

A unique BSCS contribution to the development of teaching materials for high school biology has been a fruitful cooperation between college biologists on the frontiers of research, and high school teachers on the frontiers of teaching. This cooperation has continued over a period of years. The procedure of producing text materials, with the active involvement of cooperative teams of writers and extensive classroom testing, has obvious advantages over the work of either a single author or of small groups of authors. It could not have been accomplished without the support provided the BSCS by the National Science Foundation.

In addition to the three versions of a first high school biology program (including text materials, integrated laboratory exercises, quarterly tests, a comprehensive examination, and teacher's guides), the BSCS has produced a wide variety of course materials that offer the teacher maximal flexibility in programming, and the student optimal use of his talents.

The BSCS is a continuing curriculum study concerned with the improvement of biological education. It welcomes observations from interested persons. Comments may be sent to the Director at the University of Colorado.

ARNOLD B. GROBMAN
Chairman of the Steering Committee
Biological Sciences Curriculum Study
Rutgers University
New Brunswick, New Jersey 08903

WILLIAM V. MAYER
Director
Biological Sciences Curriculum Study
Post Office Box 930
Boulder, Colorado 80302

Preface

This revision of BIOLOGICAL SCIENCE: AN INQUIRY INTO LIFE was begun during the summer of 1966 at the University of Washington in Seattle. In that unique biological region the members of the writing team produced the manuscript for the volume now in your hands.

If you were familiar with the first commercially published edition, you soon will see that many changes have been made for this second edition. Members of the writing team had many ideas for improving the book and the laboratory inquiries, and we had the advice of hundreds of teachers who had used the previous edition for three school years. We also have been fortunate in receiving advice from many individual reviewers, as well as reports of committees appointed by biological societies for the purpose of making critical appraisals. We are deeply grateful to everyone who has helped, for it is our continuing hope that the biologists of the United States will regard the BSCS books as their responsibility.

In the first section of the book, *Unity*, you will find these major changes. The chapters on cell chemistry and cell physiology have been extensively revised and simplified, and we hope they will be more meaningful to the students. Many teachers asked for a more explicit treatment of inheritance early in the book. We hope that Chapters 7, 8, and 9, which have been almost entirely rewritten for this edition, will satisfy this request.

Again, in response to requests from teachers, the discussion of animal diversity (Chapter 19) has been treated more from the evolutionary point of view. The other chapters in *Diversity* have been updated and revised slightly.

The chapters in *Continuity* have been revised extensively. This became a necessity when part of the material on heredity was put earlier in the book. We have also taken special pains to simplify the chapters on evolution, and especially population genetics.

We have grouped the final chapters in a unit of their own, *Interaction*. You will find here a new chapter on behavior and three completely rewritten and more comprehensive chapters on ecology, one being man's ecology. The last is especially needed in these times when man is making the problems of his own life on this planet so difficult.

Our goal is still fairly simple to state but equally difficult to attain. We should like to present modern biology to the student as an intellectual discipline that will provide a framework to which he can relate the biological experiences that will be his future.

JOHN A. MOORE, Supervisor
BSCS Yellow Version

Guide to the Integration of Text and Laboratory Experiences

The laboratory inquiries in the *Student Laboratory Guide* are correlated with the textbook by the following text references:

Inquiry	Text pages
1-1	6, 165, 178, 244
1-2	6
1-3	6, 50
1-4	6, 53, 184, 199
2-1	18, 19, 165, 178
3-1	41, 43, 299
3-2	47
3-3	47, 48
4-1	74, 107
5-1	88
5-2	88
5-3	91
5-4	101
6-1	107, 226, 396
6-2	107
6-3	107
6-4	112, 342
6-5	93, 112
7-1	128
8-1	152
8-2	155
8-3	167
8-4	173
9-1	183
9-2	188
10-1	198
10-2	199, 200
11-1	205, 215
11-2	221
11-3	226
11-4	227
12-1	230
12-2	233, 235, 237
13-1	239, 241
13-2	233, 248, 249
14-1	252, 258
14-2	254, 272
14-3	268, 271
15-1	280
15-2	280
15-3	280
15-4	284
15-5	284
15-6	284
16-1	296
16-2	301, 302
16-3	304
17-1	311
17-2	316
17-3	317
17-4	321
17-5	321, 454
18-1	332
18-2	337, 338, 360
18-3	337, 338
18-4	337, 338
18-5	337, 338
18-6	337, 338
19-1	355
19-2	362
19-3	366
19-4	370
20-1	396
21-1	407
21-2	412, 416
22-1	425, 438, 467
23-1	435
24-1	441, 652
25-1	463
25-2	464
26-1	477
27-1	495
27-2	478, 502
28-1	514
29-1	521
29-2	522, 527
29-3	524, 527
29-4	532
30-1	548
30-2	565
32-1	579, 592
32-2	579, 592
32-3	578, 594
32-4	579, 594
35-1	648, 653
35-2	652, 674
36-1	677
37-1	713
37-2	713

Contents

Foreword v

Preface vii

PART 1 UNITY

The earth is populated by millions of different types of living creatures. Each has its own way of living, but all share *the only known kind* of structural and chemical organization that means *being alive*. Whatever their dissimilarities, plants, animals, and other creatures solve their big problems—those of being alive—in much the same way. The study of these unifying features will be one theme in Part 1. We will also learn how biologists acquire knowledge of living creatures.

CHAPTER 1 **Biology—What Is It About?** 1

Biology is the sum of man's knowledge about life—his own life and that of all other creatures. This knowledge consists not only of a collection of facts, but more importantly, of the way these facts are associated and interpreted in general theories. An example of a biological investigation is the theme of this chapter. The cause of mankind's most serious disease, malaria, is used as a case history in showing how man attempts to answer his biological questions.

CHAPTER 2 **Life from Life** 19

Less than a century ago scientists debated furiously the question of whether life could arise spontaneously from nonliving substances. The far-reaching implications of this biological question are not necessarily the same for life today and life in its most distant past. But they *are* the same for all kinds of living things, as investigation of this biological problem in terms of life today has abundantly illustrated.

CHAPTER 3 **Basic Structure** 38

Unifying theories relate isolated facts. Science is at its best when it seeks a new theory to organize an accumulation of poorly understood facts. One of the greatest unifying theories of biology is that all, or nearly all, forms of life have a common basic structure. That this is true is not at all obvious: a fish and a tree really do not seem to resemble one another. Yet both are alike in being composed of cells. Cells were first discovered almost 200 years before their nature was understood well enough to lead to the cell theory.

PART 2 DIVERSITY

Diversity among the earth's microorganisms, plants, and animals is more obvious in many ways than the fundamental unity in life. Historically, diversity emerged as modifications upon a common pattern. Unity continues to be shown in the recognition that different organisms are similar chemically, have a common structural basis in cells, reproduce, evolve, respond to stimuli, and constitute parts of an interrelated whole. Yet diversity in life is seen in the millions of different types of living organisms—the three principal groups being microorganisms, plants, and animals. This section of the book will be concerned with the many variations upon the fundamental theme.

PART 2a MICROORGANISMS

CHAPTER 9 **Beginnings—Viruses—Time** 177

Several billion years ago the earth was vastly different from what it is today. The primeval seas may have become rich mixtures of organic molecules. Probably a chance combination of molecules produced a larger molecule (possibly similar to the DNA of today) that had a chemical structure giving it a pattern for exact duplication. Slowly, the duplicating molecules became parts of more complex systems, until they could be called "organisms." From these humble beginnings life spread over the earth and evolved into its innumerable species—each an experiment in living in a particular way. The viruses of today may represent a level of complexity similar to that of some of the earliest forms of life. They cannot live independently but require a living cell for their life and reproduction. This may be analogous to the requirements of the hypothetical first organisms for an environment rich in organic compounds.

CHAPTER 10 **Bacteria—Pioneers of Cellular Organization** 198

The bacteria, more complex than the viruses, are the simplest organisms that can be called cells. They also are the smallest organisms that can be studied with the compound microscope. Their activities are basically those of *every* living organism. Life in the simplest cells can be very complex—even to reproduction by sexual means.

CHAPTER 11 **Small Organisms of Great Importance** 214

Because of their small size, bacteria were discovered only after the invention of the microscope. Their importance became rapidly recognized, for they are organisms that cause spoilage, decay, and disease, but that have many useful activities. The discovery that bacteria cause disease is one of the most interesting examples of the methods of science. Bacteria are beneficial in industry, food preparation, and vitamin production, mostly because of their ability to carry on fermentations that result in valuable byproducts.

PART 2b PLANTS

through the tissues of the roots and the stem. The rapid movement of materials and the support of leaves are aided by the complex conducting systems that have evolved in the vascular plants.

CHAPTER 17 **Reproduction and Development in Flowering Plants** 309

The pinnacle of evolutionary development of the green plants is the large group characterized by flowers. Most of the familiar plants of the world are flower-producing species. It is this group that provides, directly or indirectly, for nearly all of man's needs—his food, his shelter, and most of his clothes and fuels.

PART 2C ANIMALS

CHAPTER 18 **The World of Animals** 329

Green plants are producers; animals are consumers. Given a proper temperature and the necessary inorganic substances, green plants can live wherever there is light. Animals can live only where there are green plants or products derived from green plants. This basic dependence defines the boundaries of the world of animals. The animal way of life—whether of a single-celled organism such as *Amoeba* or of large and complex animals—makes a series of demands on the world of life. These demands can be understood from the study of one kind of animal and its dependence upon other organisms and upon the nonliving environment.

CHAPTER 19 **The Diversity Among Animals—Variations on a Theme** 348

There are probably two million species of animals living today. Fundamentally, all live the same way, but in detail they vary tremendously. The many animal species can be classified into major groups known as phyla. Ten of these phyla include at least 98 percent of all known animals. The known history of animals begins more than a half billion years ago, when all their ancestors lived in water. Much later, some of the animals evolved modifications permitting them to colonize the land.

CHAPTER 20 **Digestion in Multicellular Animals** 388

In animals that have many cells, some degree of specialization, or division of labor, occurs among the cells. Some of the cells may be specialized in capturing food, others in digesting it, still others in coordinating these activities and additional ones. Digestion is carried out in a simple sac (in *Hydra*) or a complex sac (in planarians), a simple tube (in some worms) or a complex tube (in grasshoppers and many other animals, including man). This chapter is a study of one essential aspect of this division of labor—the enzyme-controlled breakdown of food substances.

PART 1

UNITY

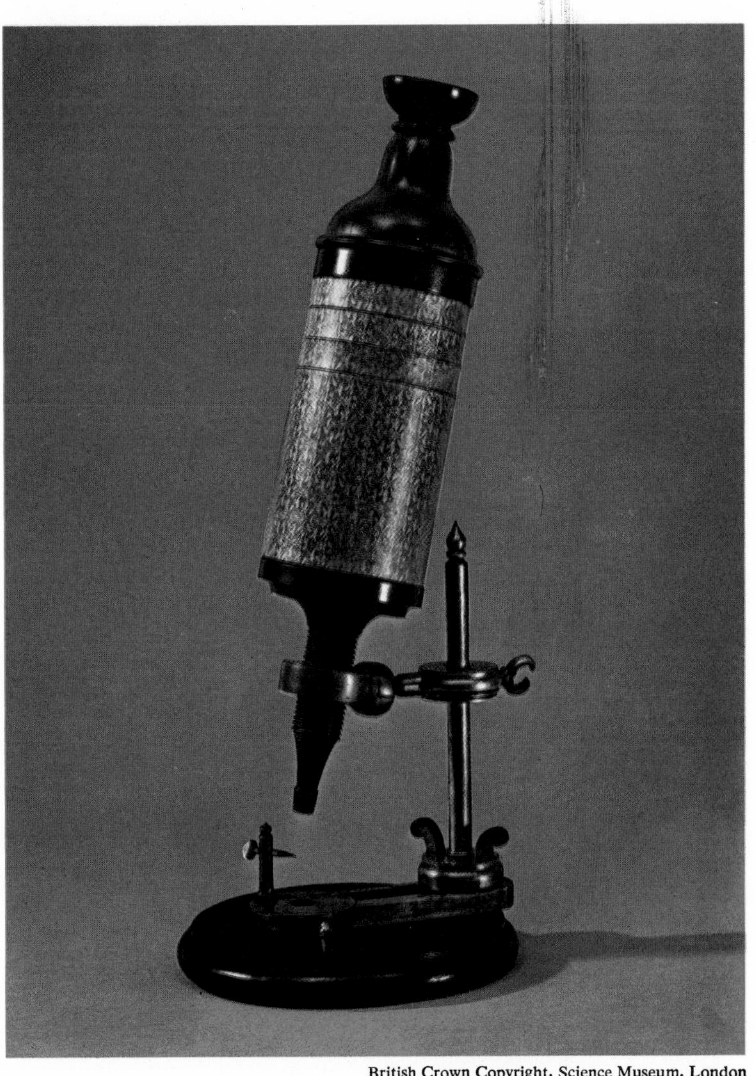

Hooke's microscope

British Crown Copyright, Science Museum, London

1

Biology — What Is It About?

The scientific study of living things is **biology,** from a combination of the Greek words *bios*, meaning life, and *logos*, meaning thought or reasoning. The course you are beginning will be a study of *how man has thought* about living things. Questions about living things have provided problems that man has investigated both to aid his own survival and to satisfy his desire *to know*. To explain what we mean, it will be far better for us to select a biological problem and show you how scientists have sought answers. The example will help to bring out what we most desire to emphasize, *the nature of science and the history of its ideas and social consequences*.

BIOLOGICAL PROBLEMS—AN EXAMPLE: MALARIA

The disease malaria will serve as our biological problem. Like all diseases, it is associated with *many* biological problems. Over man's long history, malaria has been the disease that has most affected his health, economy, and politics. It has killed more people than any other disease.

Malaria is most common in the tropical parts of the world. A century ago it was frequent as far north as Ohio and New York in the United States. Until recently it was even common in parts of Western Europe.

Malaria is a dramatic disease. In a typical attack, the unfortunate victim first experiences a severe chill (Figure 1-1). He feels very cold, even though a clinical thermometer would show that his temperature was above the normal value of 37° C (98.6° F). Gooseflesh forms, and his teeth chatter violently. A pile of blankets will not prevent this feeling of being very cold.

Several hours later the sufferer feels very hot—and indeed he is. His temperature may have risen to 41° C (106° F). He probably has a terrible headache and a feeling of nausea. Still later he begins to sweat profusely. In a few hours he feels much improved—though obviously weak and exhausted. In half a day he may even feel rather well.

If he has not been receiving medical treatment, he will not feel well for long! In a typical case, this whole series of events would be repeated two days later. The attacks will probably occur every other day for several weeks. Eventually the person would appear to be over his disease, but unless he had received medical treatment this probably would not be so. A few months or a year later, there might be a second attack much like the first.

Clearly the person's **physiology** (fiz·ih·OL·o·jee)—that is, *the way the parts of his body are working*—has been greatly upset by malaria. During acute stages of the disease the rates of heartbeat and breathing are increased. Sweat glands are more active. The patient's behavior becomes modified and he may find it more difficult to think. To fully understand malaria we must become familiar with physiology as one of the branches of biology. Physiology is *what living structures do, how they function.*

Our understanding will not be adequate if we only know what the structure *does*; we also must know what the structure itself is like. We cannot really understand how the heart works or why malaria increases the rate of heartbeat until we know about the chambers and valves of the heart and the vessels that carry blood to and from it. Throughout our study of living things we must always attempt to relate structure and function. Just as biologists have a term for function, they also have one for structure: **morphology** (mor-FOL·o·jee).

Malaria in Ancient Times

The ancient centers of civilization in Egypt, Iraq, India, China, Greece, and Italy were all areas where malaria occurred. Some physicians of more than two thousand years ago seem to have been familiar with the disease, although not by its modern name. They described the chills and fevers, and the recurring attacks of the disease. They also noted that the disease was most frequent among people living in low, marshy areas. Somehow the stagnant waters of the marshes were thought to poison the air. As a result of breathing this "bad air," people became ill with malaria. This belief led to the name of the disease. The Italian words for "bad" and "air" are *mala* and *aria*. You may dismiss the belief in "bad air" of swamps and marshes as a silly superstition, but it was an early step toward solving the problem of man's most serious disease. It was an *observation*.

The Romans were not only familiar with the disease but they even attempted to control malaria by draining marshes. They had no successful way to treat persons ill with malaria.

Some historians believe that the decline of Roman civilization (Figure 1-2) was caused partly by malaria—as it may earlier have led to the decline of Greek civilization. In any event, the Western World entered a period lasting more than a thousand years during which little progress was made in solving the problems of malaria—or any other biological problem. In scientific matters, these were truly the Dark Ages in Western Europe.

The Discovery of Quinine

The next advance of great importance, not only in understanding malaria but also in treating it successfully, came in the seventeenth century. At this time a great variety of sub-

1-1 The temperature cycle in malaria. The irregular line of the graph shows changes in body temperature that occur in one common type of malaria. The typical severe chill before each major rise in temperature is shown in the drawings above the graph.

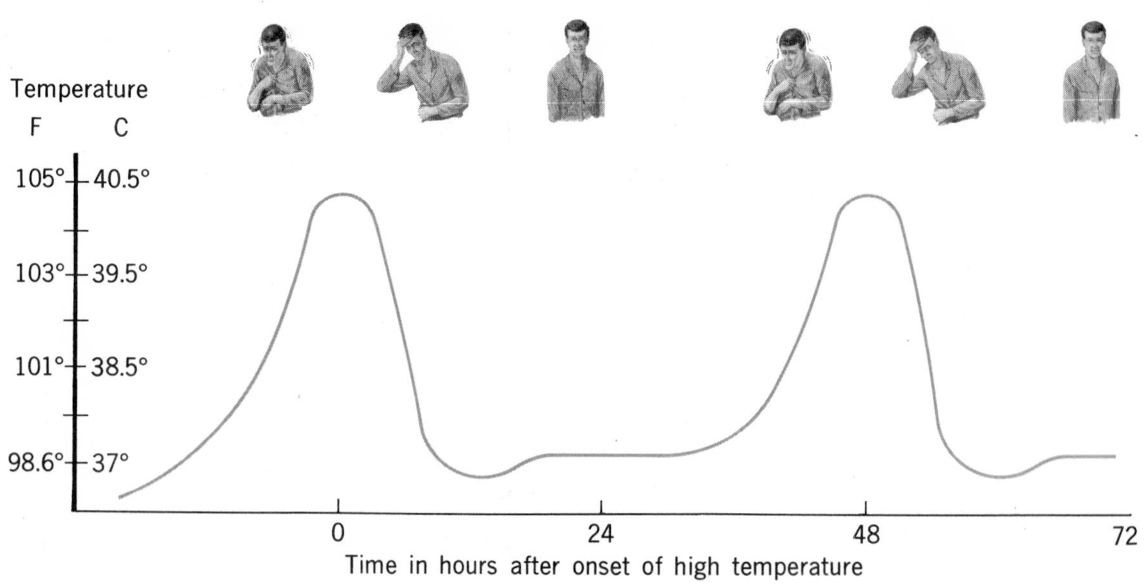

John A. Moore

1-2 The ruins of Ostia, seaport of Rome. Following the barbarian invasions, the land between Rome and the sea fell into ruin. Malaria was so common that the region was almost abandoned. For centuries there was only the crumbling greatness of the port.

stances had been tried and used as medicines. Some were mineral substances; others were derived from animals and plants (Figure 1-3). Most were worthless, and some were even harmful. For example, parts of nettle plants were mixed with the whites of eggs and were placed on the forehead to cure headaches. Toothaches were thought by many people to be cured by cutting up another plant, the spirewort, placing the pieces in the shell of a small snail-like animal, the limpet, and then applying the shell to the patient's temple.

With the discovery of the New World, many previously unknown plants were sent back to Europe to be used as medicines. The bark of a Peruvian tree, known by its native name as **quina-quina** (KEE·na·KEE·na), was thought to be especially suitable for curing fevers. In fact, it was thought to be so good that soon it was impossible to ship enough to supply the demand in Europe. As it became more and more difficult to obtain, some not-so-honest merchants began to substitute the bark of another tree, the **cinchona** (sin·CONE·uh), which closely resembled quina-quina. This mixup was of tremendous value to mankind. Most physicians probably realized that quina-quina was worthless as a medicine. In contrast, the cinchona bark, which was being passed off as quina-quina, was found to be excellent for treating malaria. We now know the reason: cinchona bark contains **quinine** (KWY·nine), a chemical substance that is effective in combating the disease. In fact, quinine was the only effective remedy known for malaria from the seventeenth to the twentieth century.

It is worth emphasizing that this discovery of the usefulness of cinchona was quite accidental. If the supply of quina-quina had been sufficient, cinchona would not have been substituted for it. Thus man narrowly escaped failure to discover quinine—a drug that would serve him so well for three centuries.

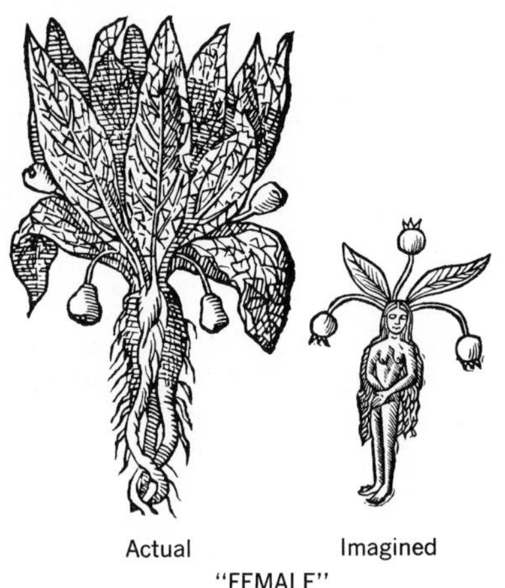

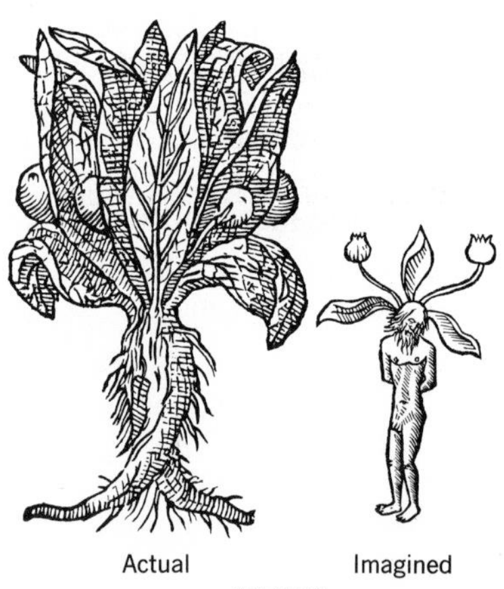

1–3 Before the time of scientific medicine, men used many animal and plant products in attempts to cure diseases. Most were of little or no use. Special powers of healing were attributed to plants with a fancied resemblance to human beings, as shown for the mandrake here. Possibly people believed that a plant resembling a human being should be useful in maintaining human health.

There are numerous examples, similar to the one just given, of important scientific discoveries being made quite accidentally. Time and again, a scientist will be studying one problem when he makes an observation that will lead to an important advance in another branch of science. Now that you have been told about quinine, the next example will interest you. When it was realized that quinine was so useful in treating malaria, chemists attempted to make it in the laboratory. In 1856, William Henry Perkin, a young chemist only eighteen years old, was carrying out such experiments in a crude laboratory in his home. He never succeeded—and no one else did for nearly a century—but accidentally he produced the first **aniline** (ANN·ih·lin) **dye,** one of a group of synthetic dyes now widely used in industry. He failed in his primary purpose to produce quinine, but by accident made the discovery that began the tremendously important aniline dye industry. Elsewhere the investigation of malaria continued.

The Cause of Malaria

Physicians of the seventeenth century treated malaria with cinchona without understanding the *cause* of malaria. The only clue to the cause was the ancient observation that malaria was associated with the "bad air" of swampy places (Figure 1-4). But what in the "bad air" of swamps could be responsible? Possibly experiment would give the answer. Some brave investigators volunteered to drink swamp water from areas where malaria was common. They did not develop malaria. Thus, the illness did not result from drinking *this* particular swamp water. Where should they next look for the cause? The problem could not be studied effectively until there was a better understanding of the biology of disease in general. This came two hundred years later.

During the second half of the nineteenth century, it was found that some diseases are

Walter Dawn

Tet Borsig

1–4 Long before the biology of malaria was understood, some observers noticed that malaria occurred more frequently among people in lowlands than among inhabitants of towns built on hills. This observation suggested a hypothesis: malaria is caused by something associated with low, swampy areas. The town shown here is in Italy.

caused by very tiny living creatures—the **bacteria** (bak·TEER·ee·uh). Once this was discovered, the belief grew that malaria, too, might be caused by a microscopic **organism** (OR·gan-izm—a term that means living thing). The blood and parts of various organs of persons who were ill from malaria, or who had died of the disease, were studied. Some scientists thought that they had found bacteria to be the cause. Others could not confirm this finding.

The Discovery of *Plasmodium*

In 1878 a French army physician named Laveran (luh·VRAHN), who was stationed in Algeria, began to search for the "cause" of malaria. After two years of careful work, he thought he had the answer. He had taken a small amount of blood from a patient ill with malaria, and as he examined it under his microscope he noticed some tiny living creatures. They were long and narrow—like little hairs—and so small that they could hardly be seen under his microscope. In addition, some of the red blood cells contained objects not seen in red blood cells of healthy persons.

Peculiar objects found in the blood of a person ill with malaria are not proof that these objects are causing the malaria. In fact, this first report was not believed by other scientists. But two years later another physician, also in Algeria, saw the same tiny creatures in the blood of another patient ill with malaria. This was interesting but still not sufficient evidence to convince scientists that these tiny creatures were causing malaria. After all, other scientists and physicians did not observe these strange objects in patients ill with malaria.

Five years after the first discovery, the same peculiar creatures were observed for the third time in the blood of a person ill with malaria. This time the place was Italy. The organism was described and given a name—*Plasmodium* (plaz·MO·dih·um). Gradually scientists began to accept the possibility that malaria is caused by *Plasmodium.*

Possibly you wonder whether scientists were just being stubborn in not believing the first report that *Plasmodium* could be the cause of malaria. Actually they were merely using the necessary caution in accepting a new scientific discovery (Figure 1-5). Many new "discoveries" are later shown to be incorrect.

Biologists seeking information about malaria now had several leads. Was *Plasmodium* the cause? Did *Plasmodium* live in swamp water? Both of these questions involved the study of living things that were exceedingly small. Were there other living things that were equally small and could they be associated with malaria and other diseases? What was the nature of this invisible world? These are questions for which you should seek answers. Laboratory Inquiry 1-1 will suggest ways for you to proceed, and Inquiries 1-2, 1-3, and 1-4 will help you use a microscope in your search.

Studying Malaria Experimentally

Think of the situation of a scientist studying malaria in the last part of the nineteenth century. Many *different* causes of malaria were being suggested. How could he be sure which, if any, was the true cause?

Scientists have developed their own methods, which are often little more than common sense, for seeking answers to their questions. One of the methods consists of testing a **hypothesis** (hy·POTH·eh·sis). It starts something like a game. First the scientist uses whatever little information he has to make a statement that *may* be the answer to the question he is asking. This statement is the hypothesis. He does not know whether the hypothesis is true or not, but he accepts that it *may* be true (there would not be much point in his working on a hypothesis that he knows is false).

Suppose we accept, for the time being, the hypothesis:

Plasmodium is the cause of malaria.

Now if this is true, we can make deductions from the hypothesis. A deduction is a logical consequence of a statement or, in this case, of the hypothesis. Since deductions are so important in helping us to answer our questions in science, perhaps we should explain them by a simple analogy. Suppose that you are without a watch or clock and wish to know the time of day. You may recall how long it has been since breakfast and make a hypothesis: "I believe it is noon." If you are right, there are certain other things that must be true. For example, the sun will be at its highest point in the sky, or, if you live in a town where a whistle is blown or a bell is rung at noon, you should hear it at about this time. These "certain other things that must be true" are deductions.

One of the deductions from the hypothesis "*Plasmodium* is the cause of malaria" would be:

If Plasmodium is the cause of malaria, then all persons ill with malaria should have Plasmodium in their bodies.

The next step is to *test* the deduction. We can test it by taking a bit of blood from each of many patients with malaria and examining it with a microscope. If we always find *Plasmodium* present in these individuals, we are on our way to showing that the deduction is correct. Testing one deduction and finding it correct does not necessarily mean the hypothesis is correct. It does mean, however, that we have more evidence for the hypothesis than we had before testing the deduction. We then make other deductions and test them. The more deductions found to be correct, the more probable that our hypothesis is correct.

All this may seem simple, but in biological experimentation things often get complicated. What would you conclude, for example, if you examined the blood of 100 patients with malaria, and 100 patients without malaria, and obtained these results?

In 69 individuals with malaria, *Plasmodium* could be demonstrated; in 31 it could not.

In 7 individuals without malaria, *Plasmodium* could be demonstrated; in 93 it could not.

The cause of malaria was difficult to discover.

It is impossible to estimate the number of scientists who looked for the cause of malaria.

It is not surprising that the task was so hard and took so long. No one was certain that he knew what to look for, or where to look.

So far, we have made these two important observations about malaria:

1. Quinine is an effective remedy.
2. *Plasmodium* may be what causes malaria.

What next?

How Does *Plasmodium* Get into the Blood of Man?

To discover the enemy is not all that is required to defeat it. The next important problem would be to learn more about *Plasmodium.* Where is it found outside of man? How does it get into the blood of man? How can man prevent *Plasmodium* from entering his body?

Malaria tended to occur in marshy areas: this much was known. If we work with another hypothesis:

Malaria is always associated with marshes. . .

then we can make the following deduction:

If we eliminate the marshes we should eliminate malaria.

In some localities this was tried. Marshes were drained, and the disease was greatly reduced, or even eliminated. This seemed to strengthen the hypothesis that in some way marshy areas are associated with malaria. But remember the human volunteers who drank the marsh water from highly malarial regions. They did not get malaria. If these crude experiments were to be believed, it could be concluded that *Plasmodium* was not in the marsh water. But it must be associated with *something* that disappeared when the marshes were drained.

Mosquitoes and Malaria

If the marsh water was not the guilty agent, but if malaria was always associated with marshes, what could be responsible? What would be some of your guesses? If you have

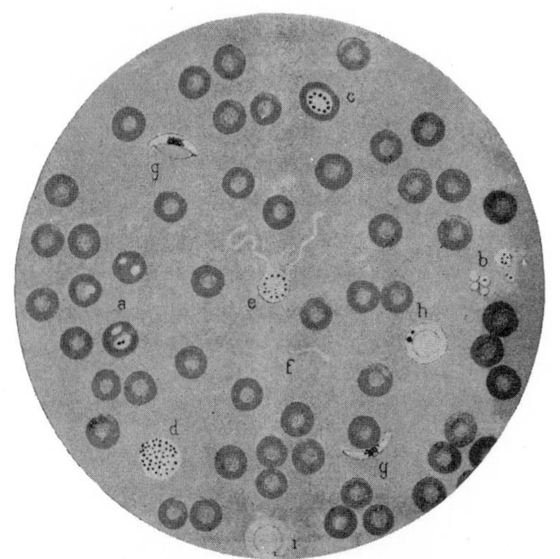

From A. Laveran, *Paludism*, 1893

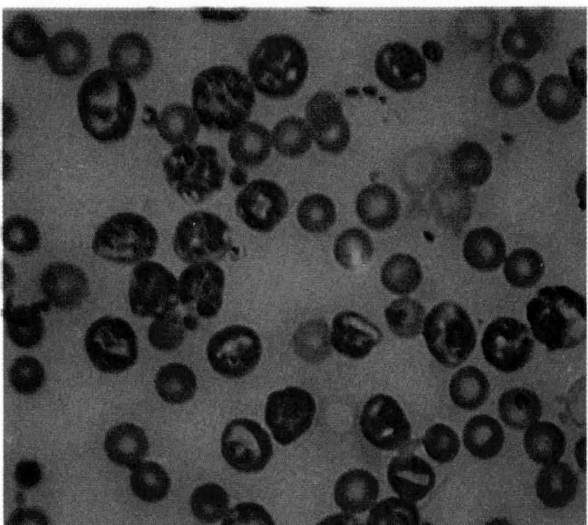

Walter Dawn

1–5 (Left) The discovery of the malarial organism. This drawing of blood from a person ill with malaria is by Laveran, the French army physician who made the discovery. The round, dark bodies with lighter centers are red blood cells. Objects such as those marked **c, d, e,** and **f** were never observed in healthy individuals. A reasonable hypothesis was that these objects caused malaria. Laveran's drawing still compares favorably with today's photographs **(right)** of *Plasmodium* in human blood.

ever visited marshes, what do you remember most vividly? Possibly it is the abundance of insects, and especially mosquitoes.

This idea must have occurred to many scientists. As early as 1717, an Italian scientist suggested that malaria was transmitted by mosquitoes. He knew that malaria decreased when swamps were drained. The mosquito population decreased at the same time; their breeding sites were in the swamp water. No mosquitoes, no malaria—could this be a cause-effect relation?

In the nineteenth century, several American scientists thought the evidence suggested that mosquitoes transmitted malaria. One was a physician, A. F. A. King, who in 1883 listed twenty observations that he believed pointed to mosquitoes as a factor in malaria. For example, he wrote that people who slept out of doors were more likely to contract malaria than those who did not; people who slept under fine nets were less susceptible to malaria than those who did not sleep under nets; malaria seemed to be a disease of the night; and individuals who slept near a smoky fire usually did not get the disease. These observations, and others King listed, were the data he used to suggest this hypothesis:

Mosquitoes are involved in the spread of malaria.

King had this to say: ". . . while the data . . . can not be held to prove the . . . [hypothesis], they may go so far as to initiate and encourage experiments and observations by which the truth or fallacy of the views held may be demonstrated, which, either way, will be a step in the line of progress." (Note he is saying that science advances both by finding out what is true and by eliminating what is false.)

Apparently King's hypothesis was not convincing to many people. Experimental proof was needed.

What might this proof be? Let's begin by rewording King's hypothesis.

Mosquitoes transmit Plasmodium, the cause of malaria.

If so, here are some deductions we can make:

1. *Plasmodium* should occur in mosquitoes.
2. A mosquito can acquire *Plasmodium* by biting a person ill with malaria.
3. If a person is bitten by a mosquito infected with *Plasmodium*, he should develop malaria.

Before continuing our investigation, we should notice that we are involving several types of living things in our study of malaria. We started with man and his disease malaria. Now we find that two other kinds of organisms seem to be involved. One is the microscopic creature, *Plasmodium*. The other is a mosquito. The biologist has a special name for different *kinds* of living things. He calls them **species** (SPEE·sheez or SPEE·seez). Man is a species. There are a number of different species of *Plasmodium* and mosquitoes. A species is a group of individuals that resemble one another fairly closely and form part of the same biological population. That is, they usually interbreed with one another but normally not with individuals of other species.

The Experiments of Ross

The investigation of one or more species of mosquitoes as a possible carrier of *Plasmodium* was first begun by Ronald Ross, a British army physician working in India in the 1880's. Ross first wanted to answer the simple question of whether *Plasmodium* could be found in a mosquito after it had bitten a person ill with malaria. He allowed a mosquito of a group named *Anopheles* (a·NOF·eh·leez), which includes several related species, to bite a person ill with malaria. He killed the mosquito some days later and found *Plasmodium* multiplying in the mosquito's stomach. This was an exceedingly important discovery. It would not have been very important if he had merely found the *Plasmodium* **parasites** (PAIR·uh·sites—organ-

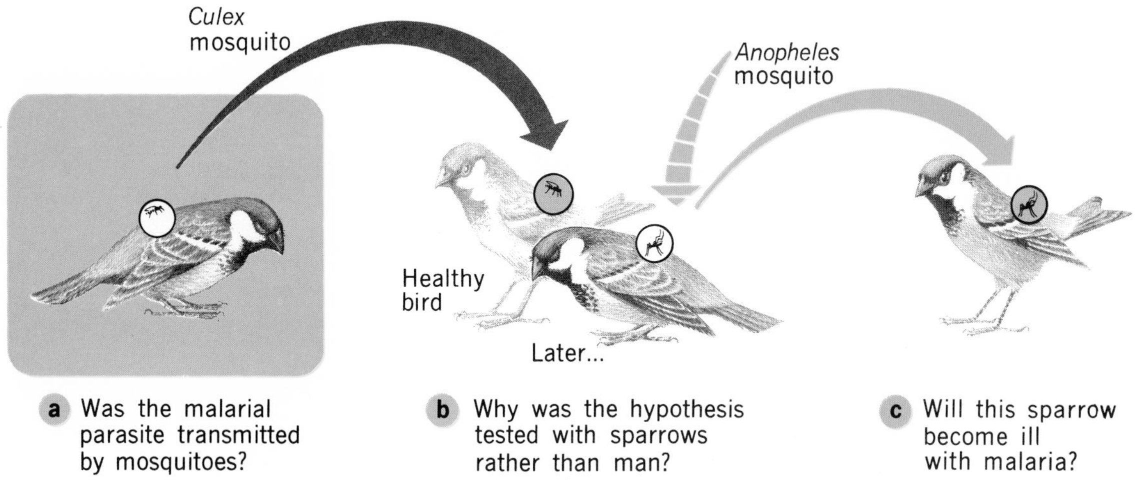
Culex mosquito
Anopheles mosquito
Healthy bird
Later...
a Was the malarial parasite transmitted by mosquitoes?
b Why was the hypothesis tested with sparrows rather than man?
c Will this sparrow become ill with malaria?

1–6 Can mosquitoes transmit malaria in birds? A test of this hypothesis is to let a mosquito bite a bird with malaria (**a**), then bite a healthy bird (**b**). If the experiment is done with a *Culex* mosquito (as in **a** and **b**) the healthy bird will develop malaria. If the experiment is done with an *Anopheles* mosquito (as in **b** and **c**), the healthy bird will not develop malaria. Not all mosquitoes can transmit bird malaria.

isms that grow at the expense of others) in the mosquito's stomach after it had bitten the patient. But the parasites were multiplying—a fact suggesting that the mosquito's stomach was one of their natural homes.

The next logical experiment would have been to allow an infected mosquito to bite a healthy person. If the hypothesis was correct, this person should become ill with malaria. But scientists are most reluctant to use human beings for experiments when the results can be so serious. What should Ross do? He did what biologists have done time after time: if it is difficult or impractical to study the problem in one animal, they study it in another.

Ross used sparrows. It had been discovered that many animals other than man may have malaria. Sparrows are one example. (Nearly all robins have malarial parasites, too.) Ross obtained some birds with the malarial parasites in their blood and allowed mosquitoes to feed on them (Figure 1-6). Some of the mosquitoes were killed and studied at various times after their meal of blood. In each mosquito that he studied, Ross found that the parasites grew and multiplied in the wall of the mosquito's stomach for some days. Later the parasites moved into the mosquito's salivary glands.

Ross did not kill all of the infected mosquitoes. He kept some and allowed these to bite healthy sparrows. When a mosquito bites, some of the fluid of the salivary glands enters the tiny wound. The salivary fluid of the infected mosquitoes contained the malarial parasites, and these entered the sparrows' blood vessels. When Ross examined the blood of these previously healthy birds some days later, he found it teeming with malarial parasites.

Plasmodium in Man

The experiments with birds, mosquitoes, and malaria suggested that a similar relation might exist between man, mosquitoes, and malaria. It was certainly not an identical relation. Ross realized that the malarial parasite of the birds, though very similar, was not ex-

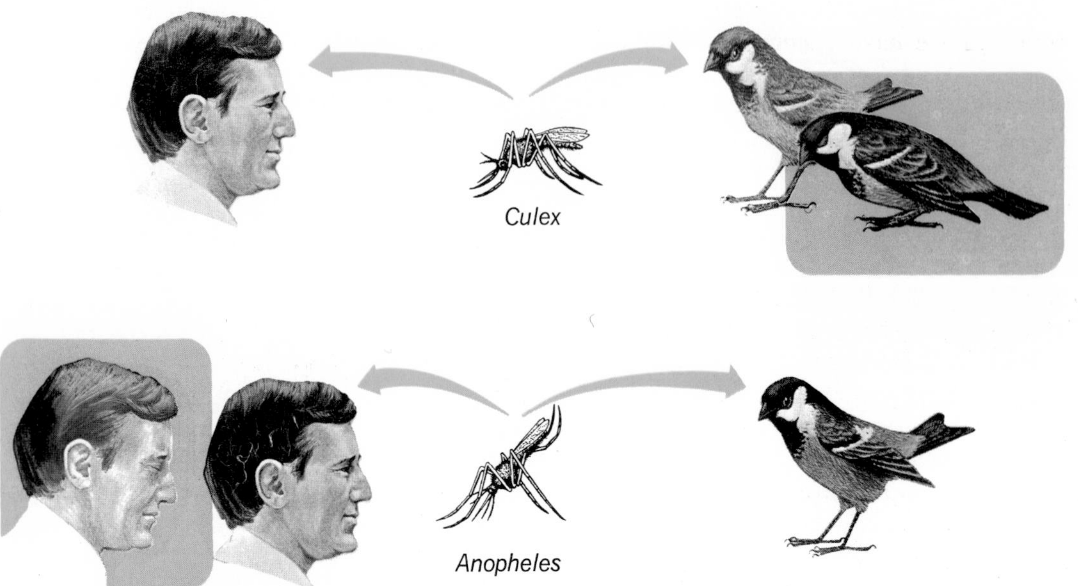

1–7 Malaria in bird and man, as transmitted by *Culex* and *Anopheles* mosquitoes. Malaria in man is transmitted by *Anopheles*, in birds by *Culex*.

actly the same as the one in man. That is, it is a different species. He also knew from his earlier experiments that the human malarial parasite could grow in an *Anopheles* mosquito. In the experiment with the sparrows, however, it was another species of mosquito—one of the *Culex* (CUE·lex) species—that transmitted the parasite.

In the end, the hypothesis that mosquitoes transmit malaria from one human being to another could be tested only by direct experiment. This step was taken in 1898 by some Italian biologists. They allowed an *Anopheles* mosquito to bite a person ill with malaria. The mosquito was kept for a few days, to allow the *Plasmodium* parasites to grow within its body, and then it was allowed to bite a healthy volunteer. This person later became ill with malaria (Figure 1-7).

These early experiments on malaria in sparrows and man were rapidly extended. In a few years the main facts about the biology of malaria were known. Most of the time while the *Plasmodium* parasites are in man, they live in the blood. A parasite enters a red blood cell, and here it reproduces to form as many as one or two dozen parasites. Then the red blood cell bursts and liberates the parasites. Each one of these can then repeat the cycle, entering another red blood cell and reproducing, causing the cell to burst, thus liberating still more parasites.

For reasons that are still not fully understood, nearly all of the parasites in the blood seem to be doing the same thing at the same time. For example, most of the red blood cells with the parasites burst open and liberate the parasites simultaneously (Figure 1-8). At this time the patient experiences the chills and fevers that are so typical of the disease. It takes about 48 hours, in one common type of human malaria, for the parasite to enter a red blood cell, reproduce, and cause the cell to burst, releasing more parasites. This cycle explains why attacks of this type of malaria occur every two days.

We pause again in our investigation of malaria to note that we have encountered two other types of biological events: reproduction and development. **Reproduction** is the biological process leading to the production of new individuals. **Development** consists of the changes that occur between the beginning of an individual's life and the time it reaches maturity. All living things reproduce and show at least some development. Red blood cells containing *Plasmodium* burst when they enter the stomach of a mosquito. The *Plasmodium* then begins to reproduce, and eventually hundreds are produced for every one that entered. Similarly, when a single *Plasmodium* enters a red blood cell of man, it reproduces to form several dozen new individuals. Something more than a mere increase in numbers occurs to the *Plasmodium,* both in man and the mosquito; development also occurs. When a *Plasmodium* first enters the body of man, it must undergo both structural and physiological changes before it can enter a red blood cell. These changes are a part of its development. Further developmental changes occur after the individual *Plasmodium* enters a red blood cell.

In more complex organisms, development is more complex. Thus the mosquito – the carrier of the malarial parasites – begins its life as an egg in the water of a marsh or pool, and develops through several different stages before it becomes an adult (Figure 1-9).

1–8 The temperature cycle in malaria, as related to the life cycle of *Plasmodium*. Changes in the patient's temperature correspond to changes the parasite causes in the blood. High temperatures occur when red blood cells burst, liberating parasites.

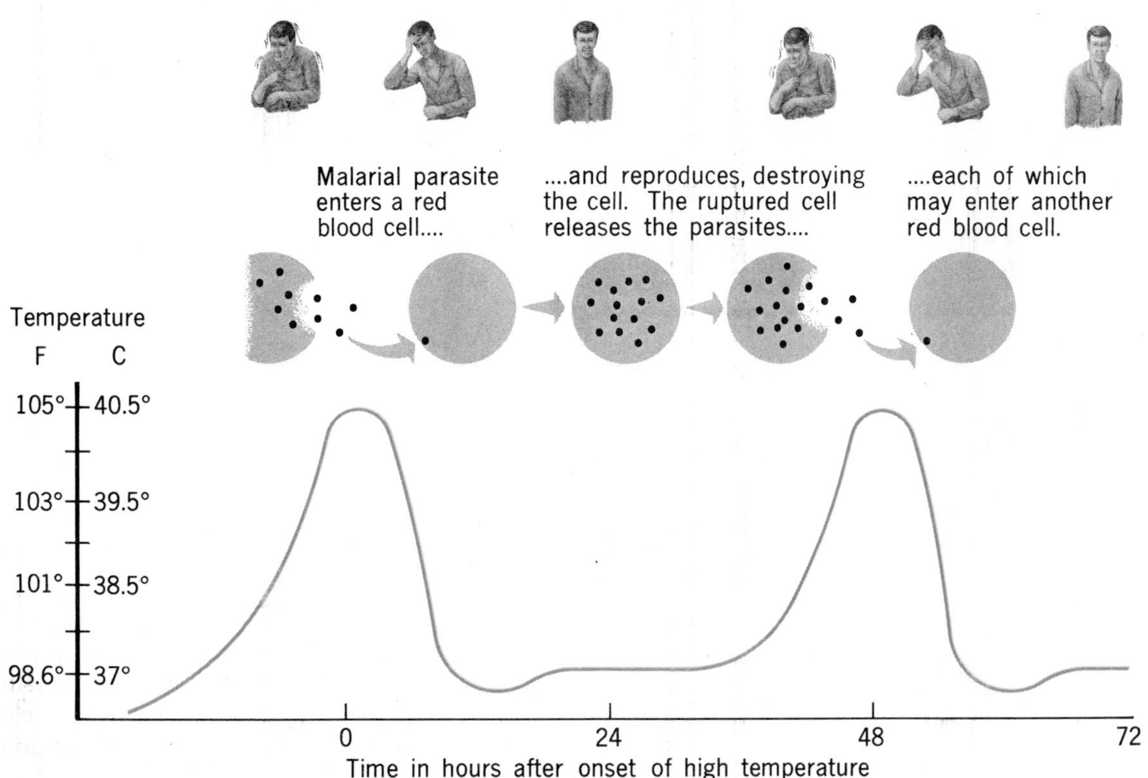
Malarial parasite enters a red blood cell....
....and reproduces, destroying the cell. The ruptured cell releases the parasites....
....each of which may enter another red blood cell.
Temperature
F C
105° 40.5°
103° 39.5°
101° 38.5°
98.6° 37°
0
24
48
72
Time in hours after onset of high temperature

1-9 *ANOPHELES* LIFE CYCLE

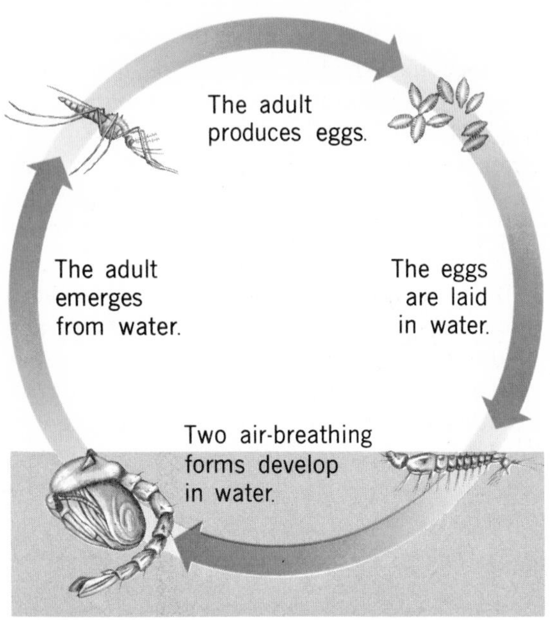
The adult produces eggs.
The eggs are laid in water.
Two air-breathing forms develop in water.
The adult emerges from water.

Preventing Malaria

By the early years of the twentieth century, mankind possessed enough information to control malaria. By destroying breeding sites, such as puddles, marshes, and pools, he could reduce the *Anopheles* mosquitoes in number, or exterminate them. It was not necessary to drain the marshes—a layer of kerosene on top of the water would kill the developing mosquitoes. This would end malaria. If it proved impractical to do this, houses could be screened, and hence the chance of an individual's being bitten by *Anopheles* would be much reduced. Insect sprays were found to be of tremendous value. Another way of controlling the disease was to keep all people with malaria in screened places. When this was done, the mosquitoes could not become infected and spread the disease. Furthermore, persons who already had the disease could be treated with an efficient drug—quinine.

There is frequently a great interval between the time when man first learns how to solve a problem and the time when he has the impulse and the resources to do so. For most of the world, malaria remained a serious problem through the first half of the twentieth century. In some places public health methods did greatly reduce or almost eliminate malaria, as in the northern United States. Yet on a worldwide basis, *Plasmodium* continued through World War II to be man's number one biological enemy. In 1946, in a report prepared for the Division of Medical Sciences of the National Research Council, the following statement was made: "What the actual total malarial incidence is today, no one knows, or can estimate closely. But one would venture to assume that there are not less than 3,000,000 malarial deaths and at least 300,000,000 cases of malarial fevers each year throughout the world." A decade earlier another scientist had written as follows in reference to malaria in northern India: "There is no aspect of life in that country which is not affected, either directly or indirectly, by the disease. It constitutes one of the most important causes of economic misfortune, engendering poverty, diminishing the quantity and quality of the food supply, lowering the physical and intellectual standard of the nation, and hampering increased prosperity and economic progress in every way." And this when man had the knowledge to control the disease!

This story could have a happy ending—malaria is on the way out in many nations. By 1950 the disease was almost eradicated in the United States (Figure 1-10). In 1951 the National Malaria Society was dissolved—the job in this country was considered completed. (Figure 1-10 shows an increase in 1951, and again more recently, but the malaria in these cases was not contracted at home. Where have our armed forces been engaged each time?)

Several centuries from now, when historians look back on the events of our time, they may decide that one important consequence of World War II was that the nations of the world finally decided to join one another and battle their common enemy—malaria. It took the experience of that war to convince them that such a step was necessary. For in World War II, Japan quickly overran the countries of Southeast Asia and the islands off the coast, including the island of Java. What did this have to do with the problem of malaria? In the seventeenth century, cinchona bark, from which quinine is made, was obtained from the bark of wild trees growing in South America. So many cinchona trees were killed by having their bark removed that they became scarce. Attempts were made then to grow them elsewhere. The Dutch in Java were the most successful in this enterprise, and eventually they were producing nearly all of the cinchona bark used in the world.

When Japan conquered Java, therefore, the Allied nations lost their source of quinine. This was most unfortunate, since battles were being fought in parts of the world where malaria is a serious problem – Southeast Asia, the Western Pacific, and North Africa (you may recall that *Plasmodium* was discovered in Algeria). At the time the American army on Bataan in the Philippines surrendered, 85 percent of the soldiers had malaria. During the South Pacific campaign, the armed forces of the United States suffered five times as many casualties from malaria as from combat.

Entomologists (biologists who study insects), physicians, and sanitary engineers went along with the soldiers. They determined the species of mosquitoes that were transmitting the malaria and where the mosquitoes bred. They tried to destroy the adult mosquitoes and the larval stages living in the pools and puddles of the jungle.

You will see that in order to destroy the mosquitoes these biologists had to know a great deal about how mosquitoes live. Where do they breed? Are they present throughout the year? Are they active night and day? How far do they range from the wet areas where they generally live? Questions of this kind, dealing with the relation of a species to its environment, belong to the branch of biology known as **ecology** (ee·KOL·o·jee). The more one understood of the ecology of the mosquito, the easier it would be to plan its destruction.

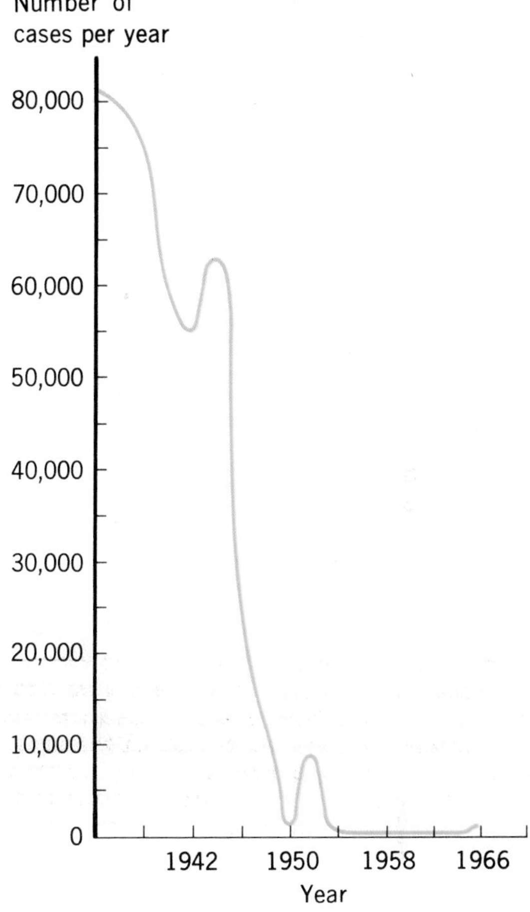

1–10 What factors are responsible for the dramatic decline in the number of people in the United States afflicted with malaria? How can you account for the rise in the curve in 1951–52 and 1966?

While some of the biologists worked to destroy the mosquitoes in the jungles occupied by soldiers of World War II, other scientists back home were trying to make effective insecticides and insect repellents. Still others began a search for effective substitutes for quinine, so needed but no longer available for the treatment of soldiers ill with malaria. Some excellent drugs were eventually discovered, among them **chloroquine** (KLOR·oh·kween). In this search thousands of chemical substances were tried. In fact, more research was undertaken to discover drugs for treating malaria than for any other wartime project except the one that led to the atomic bomb.

The chemical compound DDT, known before World War II but not used as an insecticide until 1939, was found to be effective in destroying the mosquitoes that could carry malaria. When DDT sprays were used in houses, some of the chemical remained on the walls. Months after the house had been sprayed, there often was still enough DDT on the walls to kill any *Anopheles* that happened to rest there.

With an arsenal composed of DDT, chloroquine, and many other chemical substances, it was possible to wage a successful war against *Plasmodium.* By 1960 malaria had been essentially eliminated from entire countries, such as Argentina, Italy, the U.S.S.R., The Netherlands, Venezuela, and the United States. Whereas malaria was responsible for about 3,000,000 deaths per year for the world in 1946, the total had been reduced to about 2,000,000 by 1961. If man continues his current strategy in the war with *Plasmodium*, malaria could become a rare disease.

The Ongoing Battle—Continuity and Change in *Plasmodium*

There are still more subtle points of view, or biological approaches, that one must use in studying malaria. Species of *Plasmodium* that cause disease in man do not cause disease in birds. When the *Plasmodium* of man reproduces, the new individuals that are formed will likewise produce disease in man but not in birds. Thus the new individuals are like the old individuals. Living things produce offspring that resemble their parents, generation after generation. We refer to this as **genetic continuity** or inheritance. The branch of biology involved is **genetics** (je·NET·iks).

Genetics is concerned with inheritance over a few generations. Yet there are long-term questions involved in the study of malaria and nearly all other biological problems. Half a billion years ago, for example, there were no birds and no men on earth. Whether the malarial parasite existed before them at a point in life's history we do not know. Probably it or its ancestors could have infected animals before men or birds existed.

To glimpse the broader picture of life, not only were there no birds or men on the earth of half a billion years ago, but no backboned animals at all. The first backboned animals that subsequently appeared were fishlike (Figure 1-11, pages 16 and 17). Flying insects (but not yet any mosquitoes) also had appeared by 250 million years ago. These and all other forms of life have a similar history, shown by remains of them preserved in the rocks as **fossils.** The beginnings of animals and plants go back to the origin of life itself, and over the course of time their descendants have changed to become the animals and plants of today. This is **evolution,** once hotly debated, but now a well-established theory.

The concept of evolution has been of prime importance in aiding our understanding of the diversity and unity of animals and plants. What they are today is the result of changes that have occurred in the past, changes that on each occasion rendered the possessors slightly better equipped to live in the environments they found—as we now say, made them better **adapted.** Less well-adapted and less fertile forms died out, as fossils of animals and plants that no longer exist abundantly show. The tremendous variety of kinds of animals and plants living on earth today is a consequence of evolution—each kind becoming modified for living in its own way.

Thus, for example, all the different species of *Plasmodium* are thought to have come about through evolution. Long ago, possibly only a single species of *Plasmodium* existed. Over the course of time it probably gave rise to all the different species of *Plasmodium* that live today. We even know that evolutionary changes *still* are occurring in *Plasmodium* today. Thus it is being discovered that in some parts of the world the *Plasmodium* parasites no longer are being killed by the drugs that were previously effective. Biologists have investigated and found that these populations have produced new sorts of individuals. The new individuals, somewhat changed from their ancestors, can resist the drugs better than their recent ancestors could. They have become better adapted to their new environment—an environment that contains the drugs intended to kill them.

CONCLUDING REMARKS

This account of malaria is an example of a biological problem and of how such problems are solved. As with most important biological problems, man has speculated about malaria for centuries. The folklore and imperfect observations of our ancestors provided hints that enabled scientists of the nineteenth century to make hypotheses about the causes of malaria. A laboratory scientist might never have thought of a possible relation between mosquitoes and malaria. But when told that malaria is more common in low, marshy places, he could set up hypotheses to test. Could it be the humidity that promoted malaria, the stagnant water, the decaying vegetation, or some animal associated with marshes? Each hypothesis could be tested by experiment: marsh water could be drunk, mosquitoes destroyed, and so on.

We have learned now that it was the mosquitoes, not the marshes, that were primarily involved. But centuries went by before this hypothesis was proved. How many individuals thought that mosquitoes might be the factor but could never prove it? No one knows. But we do know that the odds against success were tremendous. In all the world there are about 2,000 species of mosquitoes, and we now know that only about 50 of these transmit malaria. Ross failed repeatedly in his early experiments with human malaria. We now know why—he was using the wrong kinds of mosquitoes (Figure 1-7). But he had an essential characteristic of a successful scientist—perseverance. Eventually he found that *Anopheles* was the kind of mosquito in which the *Plasmodium* of man would grow. Control of malaria then became possible. We could try to eliminate the breeding places of the mosquito.

Possibly you were surprised at the slow rate of scientific progress in man's understanding of malaria. As long ago as the early eighteenth century, good reasons were given for believing that mosquitoes transmit malaria. But Ross and others did not prove their hypothesis true until nearly two centuries had passed.

Why such a delay? Many factors are involved. There are endless unsolved biological problems, and far too few scientists to study them. Furthermore, as we will see time and again, progress in the biological sciences was exceedingly slow until the nineteenth century. Few biologists undertook to study malaria, and even these lacked the necessary methods and equipment. The French army physician in Algeria in 1880 needed a very good microscope to see *Plasmodium* in human blood. Microscopes of the quality needed simply were not available to most physicians before about 1860.

What has it taken, then, to study the problem of malaria? Physicians and biologists to recognize the disease; physicians to treat the disease; biologists to study the mosquito; biologists and public health workers to eradicate the mosquito and its breeding places; chemists and biologists to develop insecticides to kill the adult mosquito and its young; other chemists and physicians to develop drugs to treat individuals ill with malaria; schools, books, and teachers to transmit what has been learned; and public officials to organize and direct the many projects involving malaria.

Malaria is everybody's business. All biological problems are.

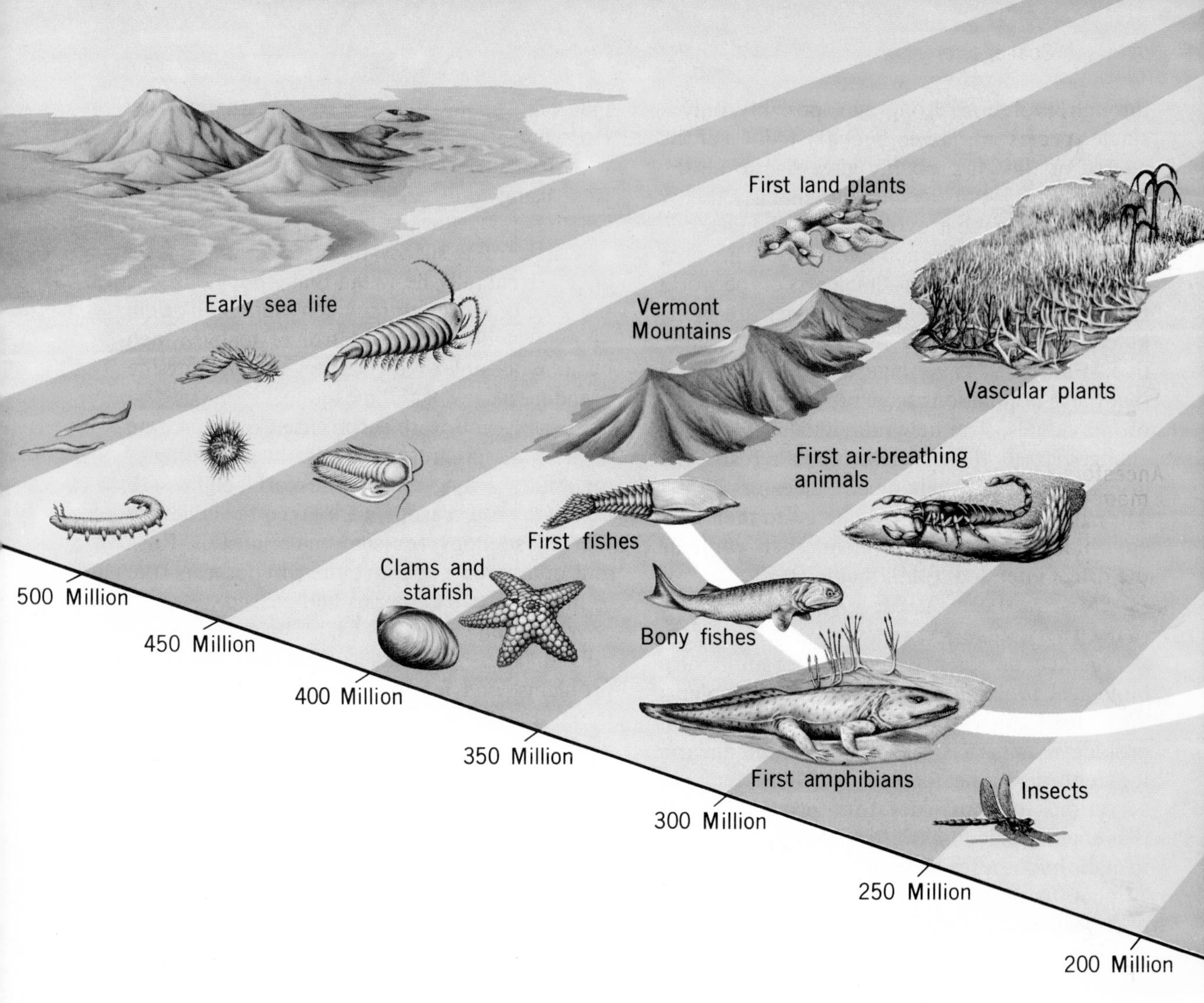

1–11 More than 500 million years of the history of life are indicated by this chart. Life is known to have existed several billion years ago, but most of the variety of life today was evolving during the times shown. The place of mosquitoes in the record of evolution is indicated on the right, 70 or more million years ago, after the emergence of birds and mammals. Whether mosquitoes existed even earlier cannot be demonstrated from evidence so far discovered, although coal-age forests of 250 million years ago are known to have been inhabited by other insects, including roaches and ancestral dragonflies (the latter with wingspans of up to 75 centimeters). No record of the malarial parasite, *Plasmodium*, has been found in the earth's rocks. This is not surprising, since most microscopic life would be expected to decompose, leaving no trace.

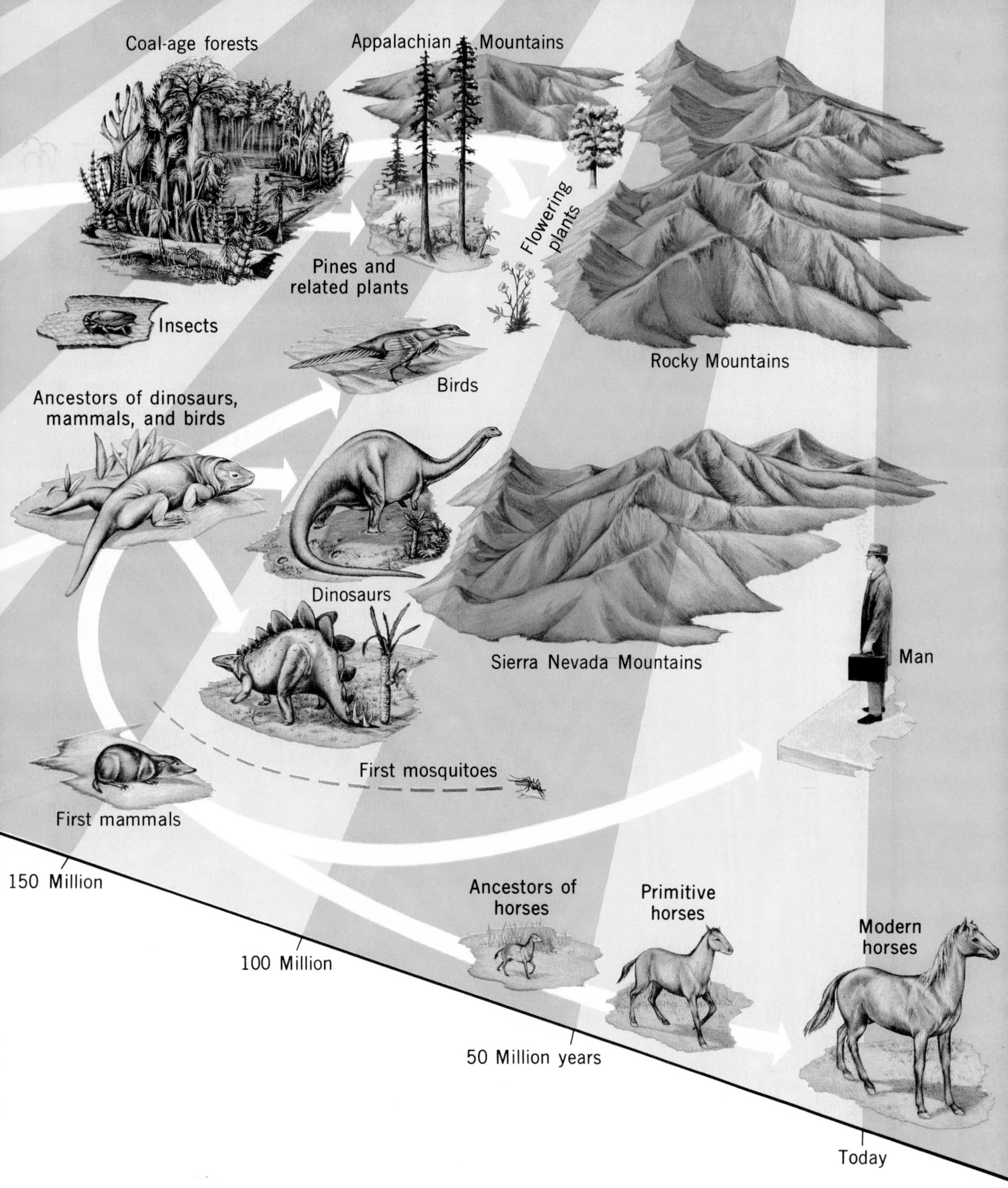
Coal-age forests
Appalachian Mountains
Pines and related plants
Flowering plants
Rocky Mountains
Insects
Birds
Ancestors of dinosaurs, mammals, and birds
Dinosaurs
Sierra Nevada Mountains
Man
First mosquitoes
First mammals
150 Million
100 Million
Ancestors of horses
Primitive horses
Modern horses
50 Million years
Today

Now that we have seen how one biological problem has been studied, let us begin another with Chapter 2. This second problem is one of the most basic in all biology: what is the origin of living organisms? The methods used for studying malaria will be useful for this problem, too. We will also learn other methods that scientists use. Laboratory Inquiry 2-1 will give you some insights into the problem.

GUIDE QUESTIONS AND PROBLEMS

1. Consider how many years passed between the discovery of *Plasmodium* by a French army physician (Laveran) and acceptance of the hypothesis "*Plasmodium* causes malaria."
   a. How can you explain that scientists were slow in accepting this hypothesis?
   b. How is a hypothesis tested?
   c. How could it be demonstrated whether a particular organism causes a particular disease?
2. Explain whether the observations listed by King (page 8) fit the hypothesis "Mosquitoes are involved in the spread of malaria."
3. Suppose one of the early volunteers who drank swamp water had contracted malaria. How much would this fact alone have affected evidence of the cause of malaria?
4. Many people and many birds with malarial parasites in their blood do not show symptoms of the disease. Suggest a hypothesis to explain this and a way to test deductions from it.
5. How does each of the following contribute to solving a scientific problem: data, hypothesis, deduction, experiment, confirmation, observation, equipment?
6. When investigating a problem, a scientist may uncover a number of answers all appearing significant. Marshes, *Anopheles, Plasmodium,* the rupture of red blood cells by *Plasmodium*—each of these may be considered a "cause" of malaria. How do such circumstances affect the investigation of a scientific problem?
7. When a scientist uncovers new factors in a problem, what should he do? For example: U.S. Army physicians working with troops in Southeast Asia have once again been confronted with malaria, in a form resistant to atabrine and chloroquine, and in many cases even to natural quinine. After extensive measures to destroy known mosquito-breeding grounds, the number of malaria cases continued to rise. Servicemen returning to the United States brought the malaria parasite back with them. How would you attack this problem? What areas of biology might you draw upon in your search for an answer?
8. Sometimes unexpected results or accidents in a scientist's experiments lead to new discoveries. Relate this to the importance of keen observation as one of the important "tools" of inquiry.
9. Ecology is becoming an increasingly more important branch of biology—especially as it relates to man. Support this statement with evidence relating to malaria and its control. What might account for the importance of ecology to the solution of scientific problems?
10. Biological knowledge is reported to be doubling every 10 to 15 years. How can this rapid growth of knowledge be explained? What problems does this present to authors of biology textbooks such as the one you are now using?

RELATED READING

Books

For a more complete account of the malaria story...

De Kruif, Paul, *Microbe Hunters,* Harcourt, Brace & World, New York (cloth or paperback) and Pocket Books, New York, 1959 (paperback). See the chapter on Sir Ronald Ross and his work.

For another perspective of the themes in Chapter 1—independent of malaria ...

Bonner, J. T., *The Ideas of Biology,* Harper and Row, New York, 1962.

For other approaches to scientific problems ...

Beveridge, W. I. B., *The Art of Scientific Investigation,* Vintage Books, New York, 1957 (paperback).

Platt, John Rader, *The Excitement of Science,* Houghton Mifflin, Boston, 1962.

Magazines

Alvarado, C. A., and L. J. Bruce-Chwatt, "Malaria," *Scientific American,* Volume 206 (May 1962), page 86.

Butterfield, Herbert, "The Scientific Revolution," *Scientific American,* Volume 203 (September 1960), page 173.

2

Life from Life

When you think of "life," what first comes to mind? Is it movement, a rose, breathing, animals, a beating heart, or something else you associate with things that are alive? Think about this question and then define "life" as carefully as you can.

Now let us test your definition. Will it apply to all animals and all plants that you know? Will it apply to tiny living creatures such as *Plasmodium*, mentioned in Chapter 1? Will it apply to a pea seed, a developing egg of a chicken, a potato? Will your definition distinguish between the pea, the egg, and the potato when alive and after being cooked? Will your definition distinguish between a tree and a piece of firewood chopped from the tree?

The chances are that you did not succeed in making a definition of life that would work in *every* case. No one has ever done so.

When a scientist repeatedly finds himself unable to answer a question, he begins to wonder whether he is asking the right question—or whether he has asked it in the right way. This is our trouble now. The question "What is life?" is too general to be studied easily in a scientific manner. Scientists have learned time and again that it is usually better to ask a very specific question.

For example, we might first have decided that the chief characteristic of life is movement. Probably all the animals with which you are familiar can move—fish swim, birds fly, and dogs run. We could ask our question: "Are all living things capable of movement?" The answer to this question could then be obtained by examining all the living creatures that we could find. Most of the things that we call animals would be found capable of movement. Some might be rather slow about it, however—think of snails. But what about mushrooms and trees? Do they move? Furthermore, a river moves, but is it alive?

Soon we would discover that "the ability to move" is not a very satisfactory definition of life. Some things that are alive do not move. Some things that move are not alive. If we are to define life adequately, all things that are alive must meet our definition, and no things that are not alive can be included.

We can work toward a definition of life that is adequate for nearly all purposes by asking some more questions. "Where do living things come from?" We can all answer that one for familiar plants and animals—they come from their parents. But can you answer the next question: "Do living things come *only* from other living things?" What about tiny creatures such as bacteria and viruses? Do they come *only* from other bacteria and viruses? You will have evidence bearing on these questions after completing Laboratory Inquiry 2-1.

Questions of much the same sort have been asked for at least 2,500 years. You may be surprised, however, to learn that what is now regarded as the correct answer has been accepted for only a century.

HYPOTHESES OF THE ORIGIN OF ORGANISMS

Until the last part of the nineteenth century, living things were believed to originate in three ways. First, they could result from reproduction of other living creatures of their own kind. Second, they could result from the reproduction of very different kinds of living creatures. Third, they could be formed spontaneously, that is, solely from materials that were not alive. Let us trace the history of these three hypotheses,

2-1 THREE IDEAS ABOUT REPRODUCTION

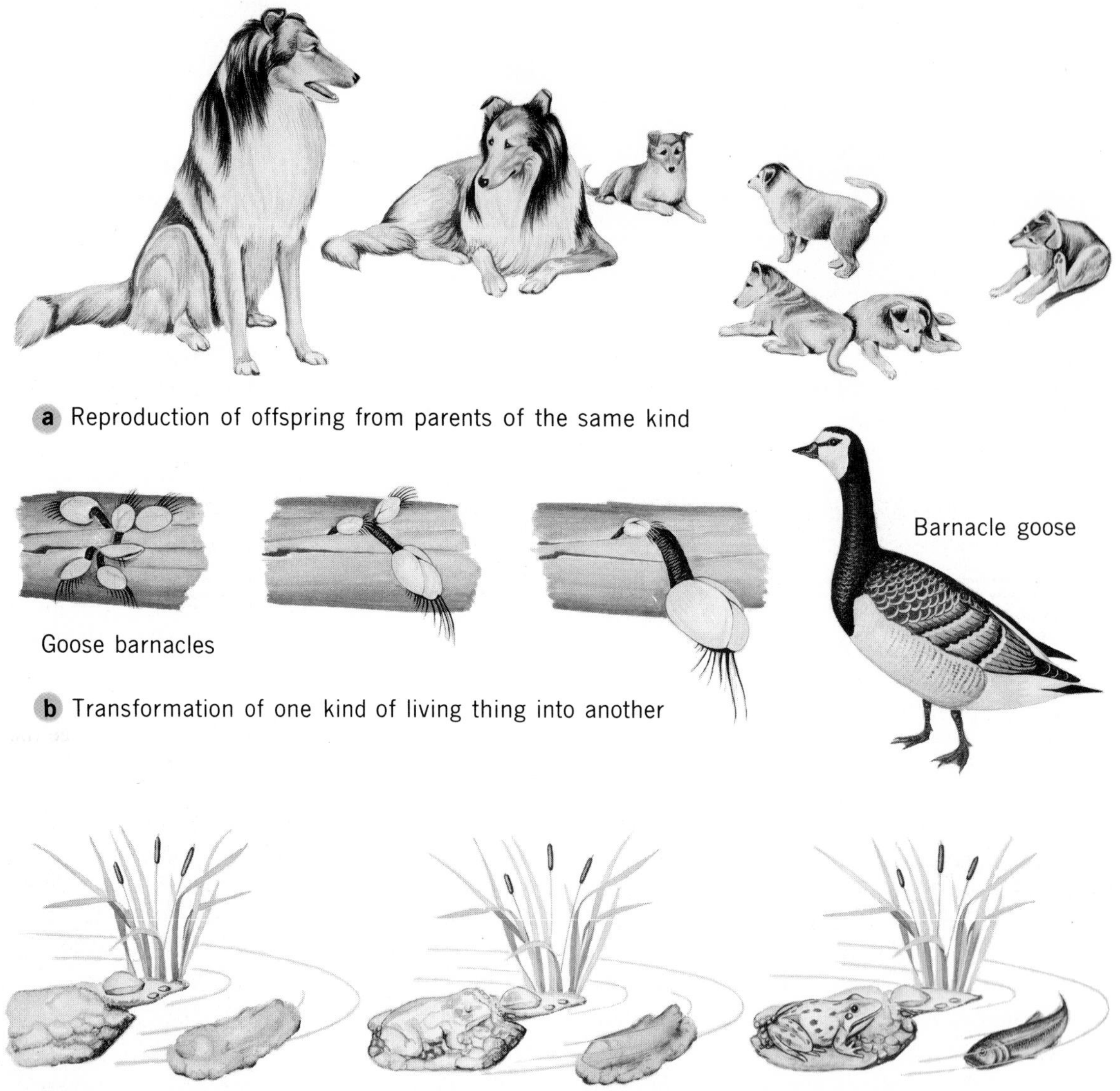

a Reproduction of offspring from parents of the same kind

b Transformation of one kind of living thing into another

c Spontaneous generation from mud or earth or remains of dead plants and animals

for they relate to one of the most fundamental of all properties of living things.

The Barnacle Goose

The idea that offspring are produced by parents of their own kind or species (Figure 2-1a) is a familiar one. "Like produces like," as we say. Another idea, however—that "like produces *un*like"—was regarded by scholars for many centuries as a way of reproduction. The origin of the barnacle goose can serve as one example (Figure 2-1b). We will let a biologist writing in 1657 tell the story (his words have been modernized somewhat).

> There is a bird in Brittany that the English call a Barnacle or a Brant Goose. . . . It is smaller than a wild goose. The breast is somewhat black, the rest is ash-colored. It flies as wild geese do, cries, and haunts lakes, and spoils the corn. Scholars question the origin of it very much. Some say it breeds from rotten wood, some from apples, some of fruit that is like a heap of leaves. . . . Boethius (bo·EE·thee·us) has written as follows: "If you throw wood into the sea, in time worms breed in it, and these gradually grow a head, feet, wings, and lastly, feathers. When they are fully grown, they are as large as geese and they fly upward as other birds do – using their wings to carry them through the air."

[Next the biologist describes an actual case that supports his quotation from Boethius.]

> A great ship, having the name *Christopher*, had been at anchor for three years. It was drawn up on land and the part that had been below the water line was full of holes. There were worms in the holes. Some were unformed and not like birds. Others were perfect birds.

Thus the prevailing view among those interested in animals was that one species of wild goose came from worms that lived in the sea. At the same time it was known, of course, that domestic geese hatched from eggs laid by individuals of the same kind as the young. Clearly nature was using very different methods to arrive at similar ends. There seemed to be little order or reason in nature. Nearly anything seemed possible.

Why was this hypothesis eventually abandoned? You might guess that some biologists began to attack the problem by experiment. They might have brought the worms into their laboratories, subjected them to various experimental conditions, and waited to see if any changed into geese. But remember that this hypothesis dated to the middle of the seventeenth century. It would have been most unusual for anyone living at that time to think of studying a problem by experimentation.

The problem was not solved so directly. However, biologists became more and more familiar with marine creatures. Careful observation revealed no support for the hypothesis that a certain kind of goose develops from worms. Slowly the true story emerged. The worms, which have the common name shipworm, are really not worms at all. They are marine animals related to mussels and clams.

Of even greater interest is the animal known as the goose barnacle. The goose barnacle frequently grows on logs and other wooden objects floating in the sea. If one uses his imagination, he can see that the shape of the goose barnacle does have a vague resemblance to the shape of a bird's head (Figures 2-1 and 2-2).

The shipworm and the goose barnacle are distinctive animals. They do not change into each other or into barnacle geese – any more than cows change into horses, or rye into wheat.

2–2 A cluster of goose barnacles. Can you see the fancied resemblance to birds, as in Figure 2–1b?

D. P. Wilson

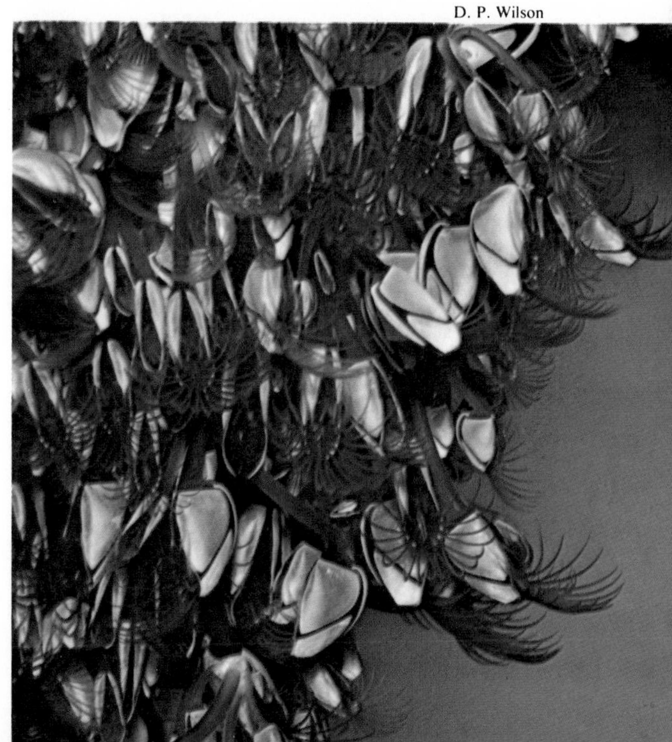

The myth was exploded in part as observers grew better acquainted with shipworms and goose barnacles. Elsewhere, other observers found that the barnacle goose breeds in the Far North—and it lays eggs and the young hatch, just as in the case of the barnyard goose. Why, then, was it necessary to assume a more complicated explanation?

This pleasant myth still lingers in the common names we give to the two principal animals involved: the "goose barnacle" and the "barnacle goose."

There were other tales of organisms of one kind producing organisms of a startlingly different kind. The tree that produces lambs is an example (Figure 2-3). As the years and centuries passed, however, biologists began to reject entirely the hypothesis that one species of animal or plant can suddenly change into another. This method of reproduction was erased from the list of possibilities.

From Henry Lee, *The Vegetable Lamb of Tartary: A Curious Fable of the Cotton Plant*. London, 1887.

2–3 Travelers returning to Europe from the Orient brought tales of "wool" growing on trees! What they had seen or heard about was tree cotton, which they mistook for wool. Tales were told and retold, with inevitable modifications, until this "mutton tree" was drawn by an imaginative artist.

Spontaneous Generation

The third type of reproduction mentioned earlier in the chapter, the formation of living creatures from materials that are not alive, is known as the hypothesis of **spontaneous generation.** It was accepted as a fact by at least some competent biologists until the end of the nineteenth century.

Belief in spontaneous generation is very old. Aristotle (384–322 B.C.), the famous Greek philosopher, scientist, and teacher (Alexander the Great was his student), believed in spontaneous generation. Here are modern versions of some of his statements in the *Historia Animalium*:

> The great majority of fish develop from eggs. There are some fish, however, that develop from mud and sand. A pond near Cnidos dried up—even the mud at the bottom. Later the pond was filled by rain. It was then observed that the pond contained many tiny fishes. The fishes in question are a kind of mullet. From this fact it is clear that certain fishes come spontaneously into existence, not being derived from eggs or from copulation.

The same type of reproduction was thought to occur in insects:

> Some insects are derived from insects of the same kind. Other insects are not derived from living parents but they are formed spontaneously. Some of the latter are formed from dew falling on leaves; others in timber, either green or dry; some in the hair of animals; and still others in the flesh or in the excrements.

Aristotle was a recognized authority. During the Dark Ages of Western civilization, his writings were preserved and studied by Arabian scholars. In the early years of the Renaissance, Western scholars obtained copies of Aristotle's writings from the Arabs. Several centuries followed during which Aristotle's beliefs were accepted as fact by many scholars: one learned about biology more from Aristotle than from personal observation and experimentation. If this seems surprising today, we must recall again that scientific observation and experimentation were rare until recent centuries.

If one believes in the occurrence of spontaneous generation, he cannot strictly believe in an orderly origin of living things, even though he knows, as Aristotle did, that many kinds of living things come from eggs.

Nearly two thousand years after Aristotle wrote of spontaneous generation, biologists were expressing similar views. Jean-Baptiste van Helmont (zhon·bah·TEEST van·HEL·mahnt), in a book published in 1652, stated that if wheat grains and a dirty shirt were put in a pot, mice would be formed from the interaction of the wheat and the dirt of the shirt.

Probably few of van Helmont's fellow biologists followed this recipe for making mice. Yet nearly all of them would have explained some other familiar observations on the basis of spontaneous generation. The most familiar examples had to do with decaying meat (for there were no refrigerators in the homes of those days). What housewife had not observed the appearance of maggots in decaying flesh? In warm weather the carcass of an animal rapidly becomes filled with writhing maggots. Where do the maggots, or "worms" as they are often called, come from? Most biologists of the seventeenth century would have answered, "From the meat through spontaneous generation." One biologist did not, and by so doubting the prevailing belief opened a new chapter in our understanding of life. This biologist was Francesco Redi (fran·CHESS·ko RAY·dee).

The Experiments of Redi

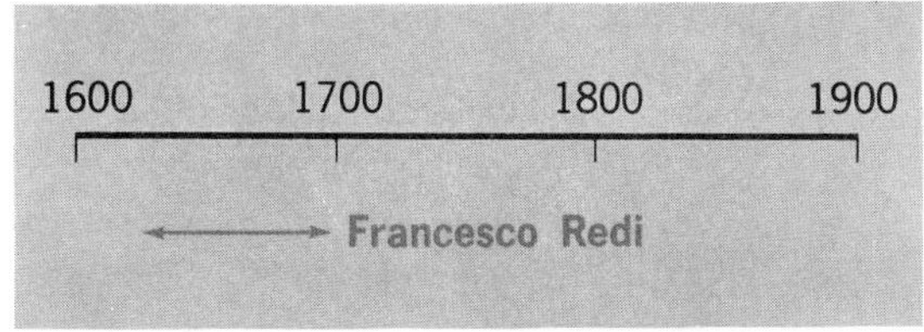

Francesco Redi was a seventeenth-century Italian who was a physician to the family that ruled Florence. Like many physicians of those days, he was also a biologist. He was much interested in the question of the origin of living things, and he was, of course, aware of the belief that maggots are generated spontaneously from rotting meat. To him, unlike others, the belief seemed questionable. He decided to put the matter to a test of carefully controlled experiment and observation. His action was especially noteworthy because he lived in a time when it was customary to seek answers to biological questions in the writings of Aristotle and other ancient authorities. Redi's approach is illustrated by an Arab proverb at the beginning of his book: "Experiment adds to knowledge, credulity leads to error." So he began to experiment. Here is a modified version of Redi's account of his experiments.

> PRELIMINARY OBSERVATIONS. The belief of ancient and modern authorities, as well as the popular belief, is that maggots are generated from decaying bodies and filth. Being desirous of testing this belief, I made the following experiment. I placed three dead snakes in a box and allowed them to decay. In three days the snakes were covered with small maggots. Eventually all of the flesh of the snakes was consumed and only the bones were left. On the nineteenth day some of the maggots stopped moving and behaved as if they were asleep. They seemed to shorten and take on an oval shape, like an egg. Later they became hard little balls, resembling the pupae (PEW·pee) formed by caterpillars.
>
> I put some of these little balls in a glass vessel, which was then carefully covered with paper. After eight days the little balls broke open and out of each came a gray fly. At first the fly moved very slowly and the wings were closed. After a few minutes the wings began to unfold and soon a fly of normal appearance had formed. All the flies matured likewise.

So far Redi had repeated a familiar observation: maggots appear in decaying meat. Others would have interpreted the facts as illustrating spontaneous generation of maggots from decaying meat. But Redi had a different hypothesis.

a Redi prepared four flasks of animal flesh, and left each flask open to flies. ... Same four flasks later

HYPOTHESIS. Having considered these things, I began to wonder if the maggots could be the offspring of flies and not derived from the decay of the meat. Such a hypothesis seemed likely, for I had observed flies hovering over the meat before it became covered with maggots. Furthermore, the flies that hovered over the meat were of the same kind as those that later emerged from the meat.

Redi was here recognizing a rival hypothesis to spontaneous generation. His hypothesis was: the flies observed to hover over the meat may be the parents of those that form in the meat. The maggots could be merely a stage in the development of the flies. Redi made the following deduction from his hypothesis:

DEDUCTION. If adult flies are kept away from the decaying meat, maggots should not form in the meat.

A deduction of this sort can be put to an experimental test (Figure 2-4).

EXPERIMENT 1. Belief would be vain without the confirmation of experiment. Hence I took four wide-mouthed flasks. Into one I put a dead snake, into another some fish, into still another some eels, and into the last a slice of veal. I left these flasks open. I took four other flasks and filled them in the same way. These flasks, however, were closed. Thereafter, it was not long before the meat and fish in the open flasks were covered with maggots. Flies were seen entering and leaving at will. In the flasks that had been closed I saw no maggots, even after many days had passed.

CONCLUSIONS. From these experiments I thought I had proved that the flesh of dead animals could not generate maggots spontaneously. The maggots could only arise if flies laid eggs on the meat and these hatched into maggots.

SOURCE OF POSSIBLE ERROR. There is a possible objection to the experiment, however. The flasks in which no maggots appeared had been closed and the air could not penetrate or circulate. Possibly it was for this reason, and not for the absence of flies, that maggots were not spontaneously generated. Therefore, in order to remove all doubt, I carried out another experiment.

b Four other flasks were prepared identically, except for covers to exclude flies.

... Same covered flasks later

EXPERIMENT 2. I placed some meat and fish in a large vase and covered it with a fine net. This would allow air but not flies to enter the vase. As a further protection against flies, I placed the vase in a frame covered with the fine net.

Maggots never appeared in the meat. It was observed, however, that flies would light on the outside net and deposit maggots there.

Redi conducted many other experiments to test the prevailing belief that spontaneous generation was possible. His general conclusion was as follows:

When meats, fish, and milk products are protected from flies, they do not generate maggots. The same is true for fruits and vegetables, whether raw or cooked.

Just what had Redi proved? Had he shown that spontaneous generation is impossible? The answer, in case you have leaped to a conclusion, is "No." What he had shown was that under the conditions of his experiments maggots did not arise spontaneously in decaying meat. Maggots appeared only if flies were al-

c The final experiment again excluded flies ...

... but admitted air. Why was this modification made?

lowed to lay eggs on the meat. Redi's experiments, of themselves, did not exclude either one of the following possibilities.

1. Spontaneous generation of maggots might be possible under other conditions.
2. Other kinds of living things might be spontaneously generated.

Nevertheless Redi did feel justified in proposing a very broad hypothesis, which if supported by more evidence could become an important theory:

> I shall express my belief that after the first animals and plants were formed on the earth all others were formed by reproduction. There was no spontaneous generation.

Today we agree with this statement of Redi's. It is of interest to note, however, that Redi made other observations which convinced him that spontaneous generation *might* occur. In fact, he believed that some kinds of insects are produced not in the usual way by their parents, but by the juices of plants (Figure 2-5).

The chief importance of Redi's work was that he tested his beliefs with observation and experiment when he found a way to do so. He was one of the first biologists to use an "Experimental Method." At a time when most philosophers believed that answers to biological questions required thought or reading alone, Redi stated that "belief would be vain without the confirmation of experiment." This point of view proved a most fruitful one in the history of the science that came to be known as biology.

Redi's results seemed conclusive, insofar as one man's work can be. But on such an important topic they alone would not have convinced many of his fellow scientists. What was needed was *confirmation*. Others must repeat his experiments or do similar experiments. If the same results were obtained, then Redi's general hypothesis that life comes only from life would be more secure. Many other men performed experiments similar to Redi's. His findings were confirmed time after time.

The hypothesis that living things come only from other living things is called **biogenesis** (by·o·JEN·e·sis). In contrast, the hypothesis that living things can arise from nonliving things can be called either spontaneous generation or **abiogenesis** (ab·ih·o·JEN·e·sis). The work of Redi and others abolished the latter theory—but only for a time. The question was soon to arise again—on a different field of battle.

THE THREE HUNDRED YEAR DEBATE—BIOGENESIS OR ABIOGENESIS?

The entire question of spontaneous generation was reopened by the exciting discoveries of Antony van Leeuwenhoek (LAY·ven·hook). Leeuwenhoek lived most of his life in the Dutch town of Delft, where he often studied objects with microscopes that he himself constructed (Figure 2-6). He made many important discoveries, but the ones that concern us now are those that first revealed the wonder of microscopic life.

Leeuwenhoek's Discovery of Microorganisms

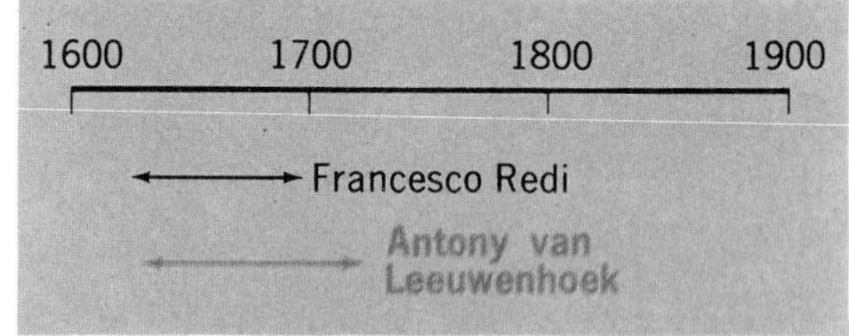

With his microscopes Leeuwenhoek examined drops of water from marshes, from the river at Delft, and from rainwater that had stood in pots. In water from all these sources, he saw numerous tiny living creatures (Figure 2-6). Here was a whole world of living organisms, tiny animals and plants that no one had ever seen before. No one *could* have seen them until the necessary tool—a microscope—was available.

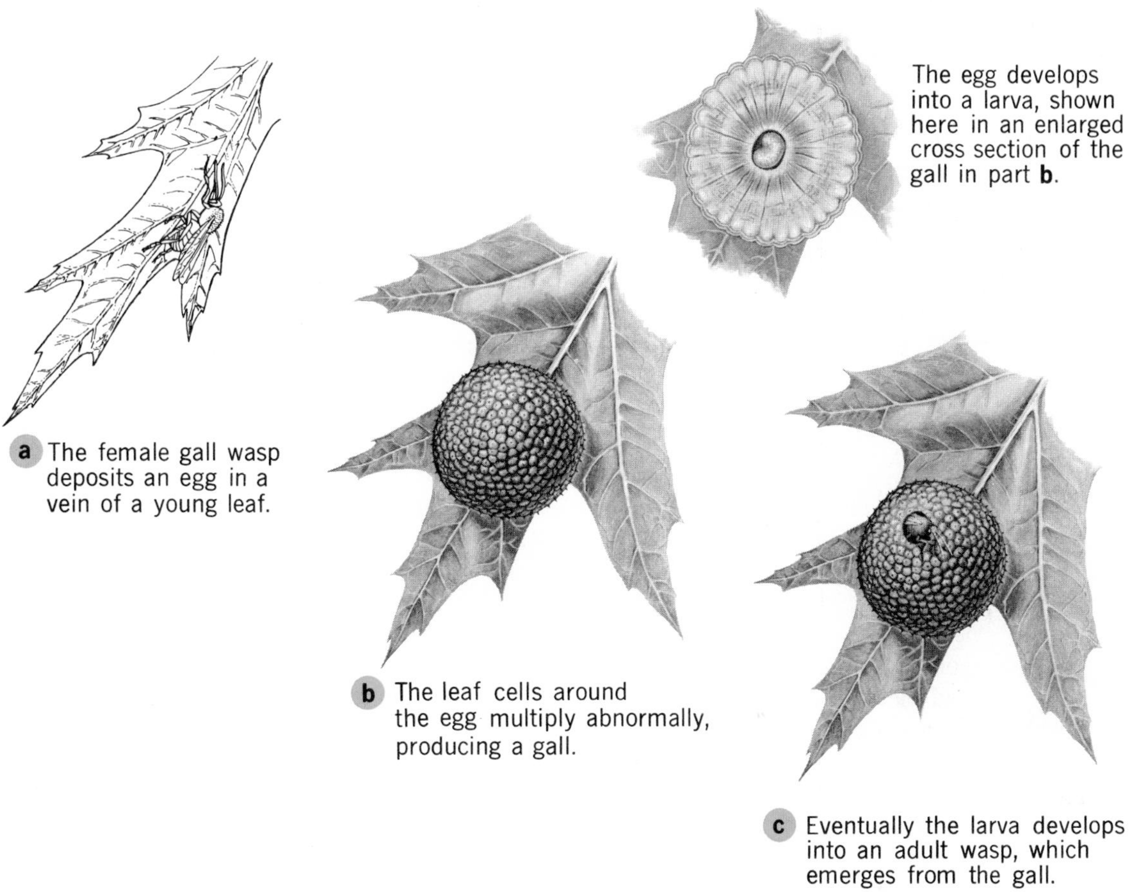

The egg develops into a larva, shown here in an enlarged cross section of the gall in part **b**.
a The female gall wasp deposits an egg in a vein of a young leaf.
b The leaf cells around the egg multiply abnormally, producing a gall.
c Eventually the larva develops into an adult wasp, which emerges from the gall.

2–5 The spontaneous generation of insects? Redi and other biologists were familiar with the strange story of plant galls. These galls were swellings on the plants, which in their mature stage seemed to give birth to tiny wasps (as shown in **c**). Before the wasp was born, the surface of the gall seemed to be without holes. Redi concluded, therefore, that the wasp was formed from the substance of the plant. Do you think that you would have reached the same conclusion on the basis of the data available to Redi? The true story, which was discovered later, is shown in **a** and **b.**

What was the origin of these tiny animals and plants? Leeuwenhoek's opinion of these **micro-organisms** (MY·kro·OR·gan·izms) was clear. His discovery "must surely convince all of the absurdity of these old opinions that living creatures can be produced from corruption or putrefaction."

Other biologists were not convinced. Gradually they gave up the idea that larger animals—mice, worms, maggots, geese, and flies—could be produced spontaneously, but what about microscopic forms? If small amounts of organic matter—for example, chopped hay or a few seeds—were put in pure rainwater, soon there would be a tremendous number of microscopic animals and plants. Were these generated from the materials put into the water? It was easy to see that the question could not be

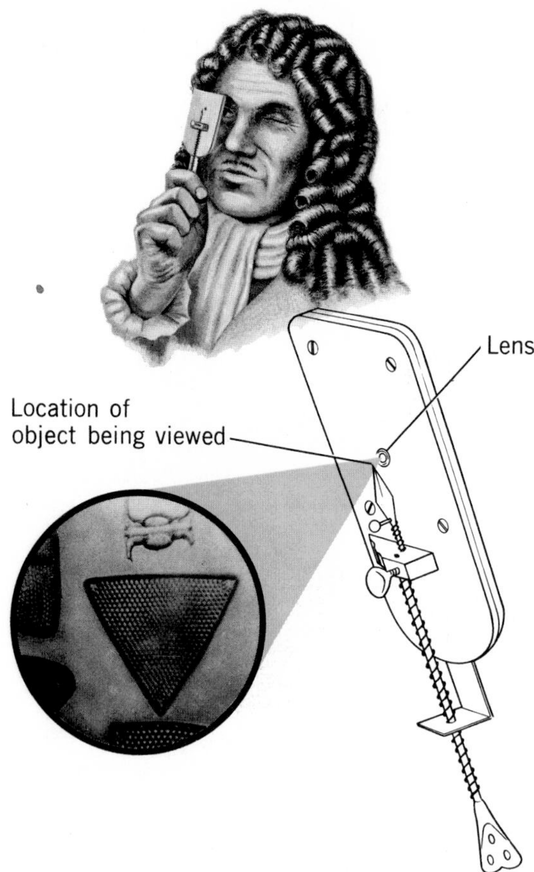

Photo courtesy of J. G. van Cittert-Eymers, Utrecht University Museum

2-6 Leeuwenhoek and one of his microscopes. Notice how different the instrument is from microscopes of today. The photograph is of diatoms (microscopic plants) in pond water; it was taken recently through one of Leeuwenhoek's microscopes.

settled by Leeuwenhoek's *opinion*, or by anyone else's opinion. Redi's remark was still valid: "Belief would be vain without the confirmation of experiment." But experimentation was not yet widely accepted by biologists, and sources of error often went unrecognized. The problem grew greater with forms of life too small to be seen without a microscope.

For the next three hundred years biologists debated fiercely the question of the origin of microorganisms. One group—the abiogenesists—maintained that the microorganisms were produced by spontaneous generation. The opposing group—the biogenesists—maintained that microorganisms were produced by the reproduction of other microorganisms.

Life in a Hay Infusion

Fortunately the debate between the biogenesists and the abiogenesists was usually based on the same general type of observation—the presence of life in a **hay infusion.** It was an observation anyone could make. The recipe is simple. Take a few pieces of hay and chop them up; put the chopped hay in about 500 ml (or 2 cups) of water; boil for 10 minutes; pour the hay infusion into a glass container; and leave it exposed to the air (Figure 2-7).

For the first few days, the liquid in the hay infusion will be clear. If one examines a drop of the liquid under the microscope, no organisms will be seen. After a few more days, however, the liquid will probably appear slightly cloudy. If a drop of the infusion is now examined under the microscope, it will be seen teeming with living creatures. Many will be animals we now call **protozoans** (pro·toh·ZOH·anz). There will also be much smaller creatures—bacteria. Molds, too, will frequently appear.

The believers in spontaneous generation—the abiogenesists—maintained that the protozoans and bacteria must be generated from hay and water. The biogenesists sought another explanation: the infusions were exposed only to air after boiling, and so somehow the air must contain the **spores** of protozoans and bacteria. These spores were thought of as the protozoans and bacteria in some inactive form and so small as to be invisible to the eye. Once they entered the hay infusion they would change into active creatures and reproduce.

The explanation of the biogenesists seemed far-fetched to the abiogenesists. If it was correct, then every time a person took a breath, he could be inhaling all sorts of weird microscopic creatures! Clearly the burden of proof was on the biogenesists.

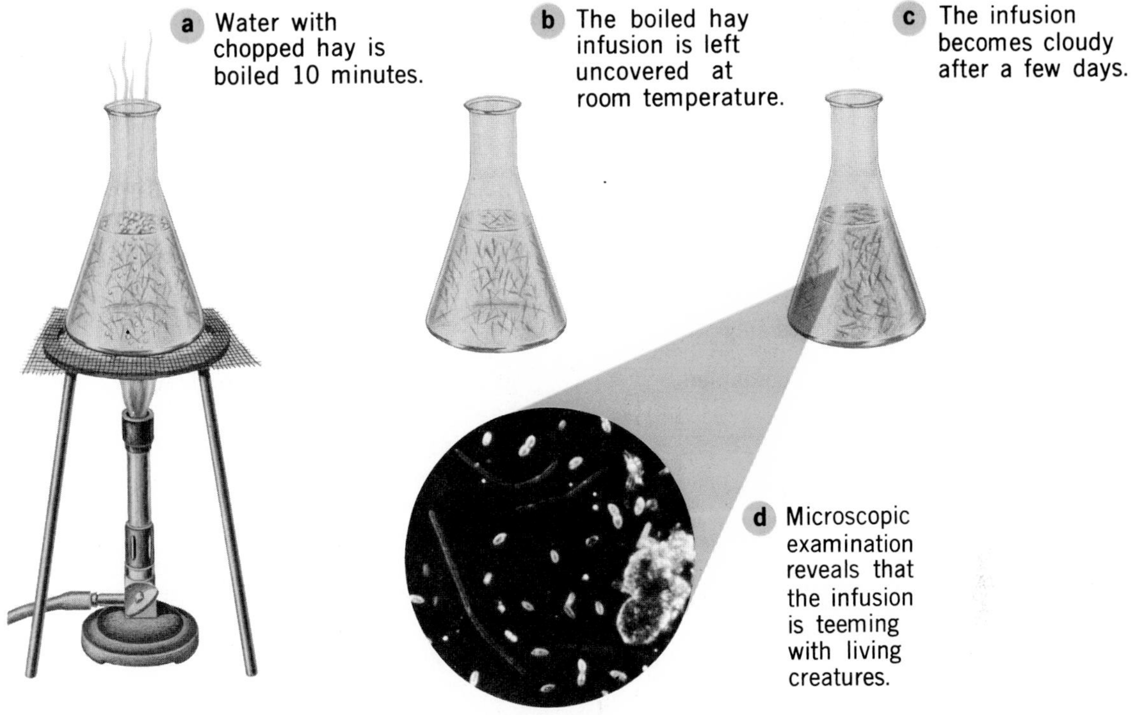

a Water with chopped hay is boiled 10 minutes.
b The boiled hay infusion is left uncovered at room temperature.
c The infusion becomes cloudy after a few days.
d Microscopic examination reveals that the infusion is teeming with living creatures.
Harbrace Photo

2–7 Preparation of a hay infusion. You should repeat this simple experiment, which relates to one of the most important of all questions in biology.

Joblot and Biogenesis

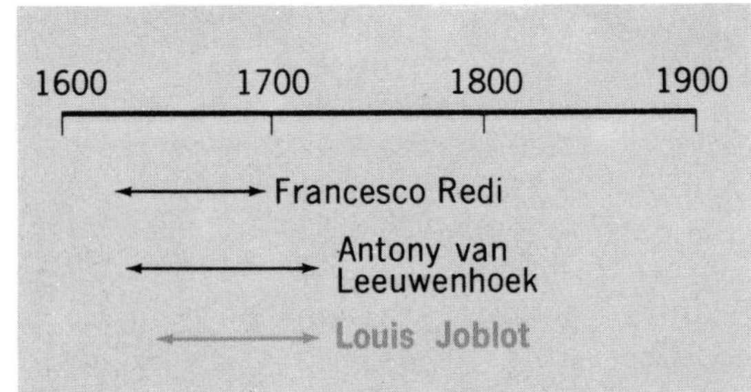

The biogenesists' explanation, strange as it seemed, had one tremendous virtue: *it could be tested by scientific procedures*. Let us try.

HYPOTHESIS. Protozoans and bacteria that appear in a boiled hay infusion come solely from "spores" of these organisms in the air.

If this is true, we can make a useful deduction.

DEDUCTION. If air is prevented from coming in contact with a boiled hay infusion, bacteria and protozoans should not develop in the infusion.

One experiment to test the deduction was performed in 1711 by Louis Joblot (zho·BLOW). A brief account follows, in modern terms:

EXPERIMENT. I boiled some hay in water for half an hour. I then put equal quantities of this hay infusion in two vessels of approximately the same size. Before the infusion had cooled, I closed one of the vessels with parchment. The other vessel was left uncovered. After several days organisms appeared in the open vessel. There were none in the closed vessel. The closed vessel was kept for a considerable time to see if any organisms appeared, but none did.

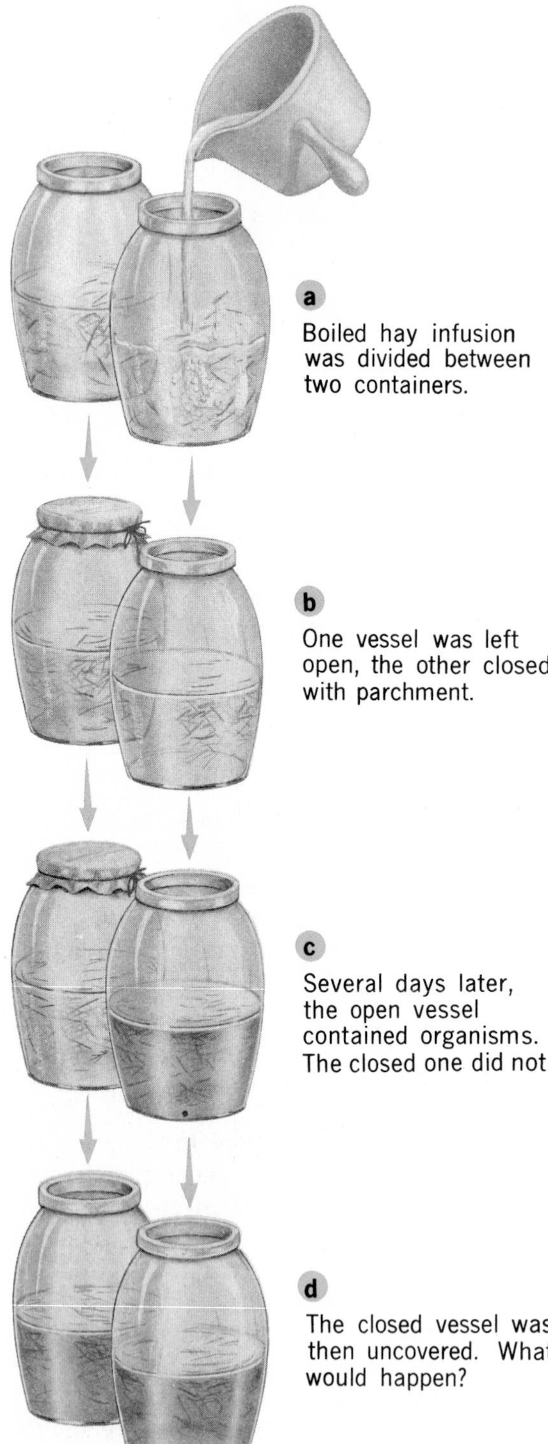

a
Boiled hay infusion was divided between two containers.
b
One vessel was left open, the other closed with parchment.
c
Several days later, the open vessel contained organisms. The closed one did not.
d
The closed vessel was then uncovered. What would happen?

2–8 Joblot's experiment. Which was the experimental vessel and which the control vessel? Why was the closed vessel finally opened?

We can review Joblot's experimental finding in Figure 2-8a, b, and c, and sum up as follows:

> CONCLUSION. In this experiment, no organisms appeared in the vessel from which the air was excluded—but they did appear in the vessel that was open to the air. If the organisms were spontaneously produced by the hay infusion, they should have appeared in *both* vessels. They did not. Therefore the organisms that appeared in the uncovered vessel must have come from the air.

Why did Joblot use two vessels—one closed and one open? If he suspected air as the source of contamination, why was the closed vessel not enough? Joblot realized that if he had used only the closed vessel, fellow scientists could question whether he had proved anything at all. Perhaps the infusion was not suitable for the growth of organisms. Hence he left one vessel open.

The open vessel was the **control** in his experiment. The control vessel and the experimental vessel were identical: they contained samples of the same infusion, were kept at the same temperature, and shared all other conditions identically—except for one. In this and all experiments, a scientist tries to keep his experiments and controls under the same conditions—except for the one condition he is testing. In Joblot's experiment the condition being tested was exposure to air. The experimental vessel was closed; the control vessel was open. Everything else was the same. Suppose that microorganisms had appeared neither in the control vessel nor in the experimental vessel. What conclusions about the origin of microorganisms would have been possible?

If you will look back to Redi's experiments you can apply the same line of reasoning (Figure 2-4). What condition was Redi testing?

Identify his controls. What conclusions would have been possible if he had obtained identical results with both sets of flasks?

Joblot studied his findings and decided to carry his observations one step further. Possibly the hay infusion in the closed vessel had lost some "vital force" by being closed. He could test this by removing the parchment cover. He did so and found that the infusion, which had remained clear for days, soon was cloudy with microorganisms (Figure 2-8d).

Joblot, then, agreed with Leeuwenhoek that air was the source of the bacteria and protozoans that developed in hay infusions. But the opinions of the two are not of equal merit. Leeuwenhoek's opinion was unsupported by evidence. Joblot's opinion was supported by the results of his experimentation.

Needham and Abiogenesis

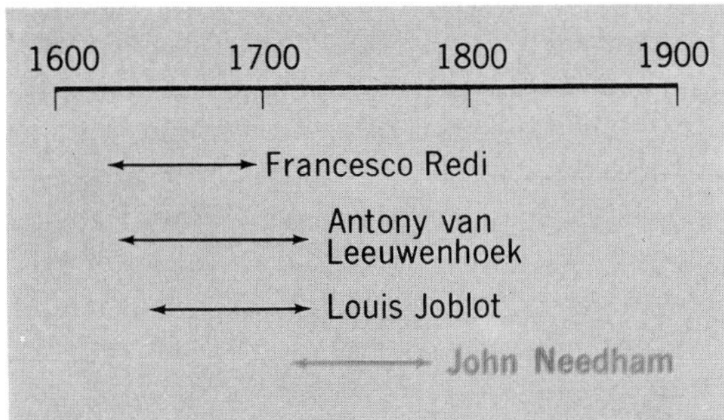

Possibly you are convinced by Joblot's experiments, but the question was far from closed. For the next two and a half centuries, experiments were performed with hay infusions and other liquids, and conflicting results were obtained. The English biologist John Turberville Needham (1713–1781) boiled mutton gravy, poured it into a glass vial, corked the vial, and waited. In a few days the gravy was swarming with living creatures. The same results were obtained when he made infusions by boiling seeds of corn, wheat, and pumpkin. This gave support to the biologists who believed in spontaneous generation.

Spallanzani and Biogenesis

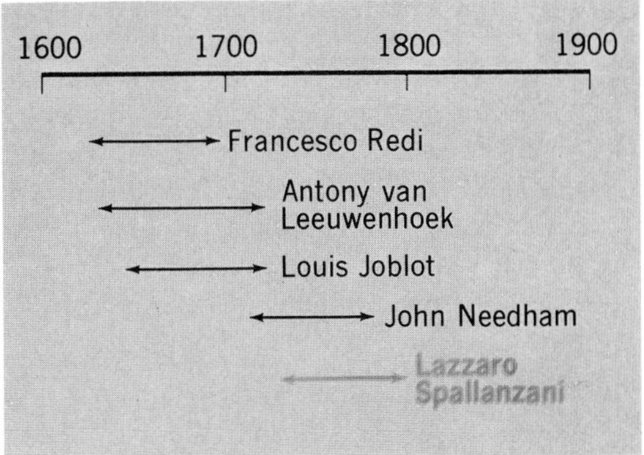

An eighteenth-century Italian biologist, Lazzaro Spallanzani (spahl·lahn·DZAH·nee), repeated Needham's experiments but failed to obtain any evidence for spontaneous generation. When his infusions were boiled and carefully closed, they remained free of microorganisms. But the more Spallanzani worked, the more he realized that these "simple" experiments are not really so simple to perform. First he found that his infusions must be boiled for many minutes to become sterile (free of life). Then the flasks had to be closed so carefully that air could not seep into the vessels. Needham had used corks. These did not make an airtight seal. Spallanzani found it necessary to make airtight seals on his vessels.

Spallanzani then did an experiment that proved to be very important, since it revealed the *source of error* in Needham's work. He put infusions into eight containers and boiled all of them. Four were carefully closed with corks. The other four were closed with airtight seals. The results were dramatic. There were abundant growths of organisms in all the vessels closed with corks. There were no organisms in the vessels with airtight seals.

Was the matter settled? Not at all. Prevailing opinions are hard to change. Those who believed in spontaneous generation were on the defensive, but far from defeated. They suggested that *air* was needed for spontaneous generation to occur! When Spallanzani made airtight seals, he may have been setting up conditions that prevented spontaneous generation.

What a dilemma! The abiogenesists argued that air was necessary for spontaneous generation to occur. Their opponents, the biogenesists, maintained that air was the source of contamination. The abiogenesists needed air to *prove* the theory of spontaneous generation. The biogenesists needed to exclude air to *disprove* the theory of spontaneous generation!

Pouchet and Abiogenesis

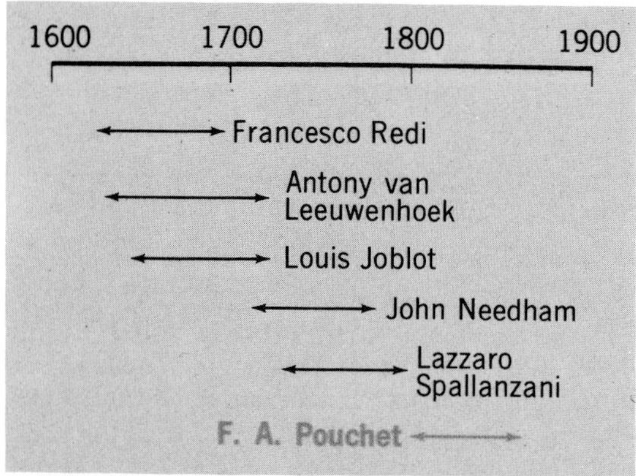

A climax to the long debate came in the last half of the nineteenth century. It began in this way. A respected and skillful French scientist, F. A. Pouchet (poo·SHAY), performed hundreds of experiments with infusions. He knew the criticism of the biogenesists—that natural air was contaminated with spores. To avoid this difficulty, he made his own "air" in one experiment. He prepared a hay infusion and then added nitrogen and oxygen to form an "air" above the infusion. In a few days the infusion was rich with protozoans, bacteria, and molds.

In another experiment, Pouchet even made the water for the infusion! He burned hydrogen gas in air to form water. Then he boiled the water with hay to make the infusion. In spite of all his care to prevent contamination, the infusion soon became filled with organisms.

Pouchet reached the conclusion reasonable to him: spontaneous generation was possible.

Pasteur and Biogenesis

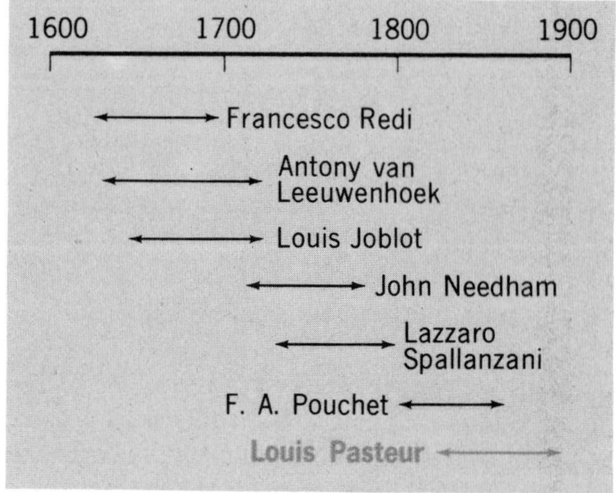

Pouchet's claims did not go unchallenged. One of the greatest biologists of all time, Louis Pasteur of France, challenged him (Figure 2-9).

Pasteur made infusions of yeast and sugar. When exposed to air, they soon had a rich growth of bacteria and protozoans. When he was careful to prevent air from reaching the infusions, however, no organisms appeared.

But how could this solve the matter? Pouchet and Pasteur were both doing the same, or nearly the same, experiments. True, Pouchet generally used a hay infusion, and Pasteur used an infusion of yeast to which sugar was added. Yet spontaneous generation occurred for Pouchet and not for Pasteur.

You must feel by now that this argument is of the "yes it is, no it isn't" type. Each side contradicts the other, and there is no progress. The French Academy of Science sought to hasten a solution by offering a prize for the best essay on spontaneous generation. Pasteur described his experiments and beliefs, and in 1862, was awarded the prize. Pasteur concluded that if air was pure—really without spores—it would not contaminate infusions.

And yet Pasteur had not won his argument. Pouchet and others who believed in spontaneous generation attacked Pasteur's experiments and conclusions. Finally the French Academy appointed a Commission of noted biologists to judge the dispute. In order to make the problem as specific as possible, the Commission agreed on a statement that could be tested. This is a synopsis of what they said:

> It is possible to take the air of certain places, air that has not been subjected to any physical or chemical changes, and demonstrate that this air will *not* cause organisms to grow in infusions.

Pouchet disputed the statement; Pasteur supported it. Rules were agreed upon and the battle began. On June 22, 1864, Pouchet and Pasteur appeared before the Commission of the French Academy. Each was to perform his experiments in the presence of the members of the Commission.

How was Pasteur to get his "pure" air? He began by submitting the evidence of past experiments. In 1860, four years before, he had thought that perhaps the air of the high mountains would be relatively free of the spores of microorganisms. To test this hypothesis, he had carried out the following experiment. Infusions were prepared and boiled in a number of glass flasks. While the infusions were still hot, the necks of the flasks were sealed with a flame. Every infusion remained free of organisms.

Some of the sealed, sterile flasks were then used for a different experiment. Pasteur packed them on a mule and set off for the French Alps. His destination was a point high on a mountain near Mont Blanc, the tallest of the Alps. Here he cut the necks of the flasks open with a file. The infusions were exposed briefly to the air, then the openings in the necks were resealed. The flasks were returned to the laboratory.

What was observed to happen in the flasks subsequently? Of 20 flasks exposed at one place, in only one did organisms grow. The 19 flasks that remained sterile were an impressive demonstration of the probable truth of his hypothesis.

Remember that the experiment had taken place in 1860. Pasteur kept some of the flasks, and on the historic day of June 22, 1864, when he appeared before the Commission of the French Academy, he had three of the flasks with him. He showed them to the judges, who saw that no life appeared to be within them.

But the members of the Commission wanted to know more. Was Pasteur's report of his experiment really accurate? And was there really oxygen, which they knew to be necessary for life, in the flasks? Flask No. 1 was opened and the air analyzed. It contained almost 21 percent oxygen—the normal proportion.

Were the infusions capable of supporting life? Perhaps they had remained lifeless for four years simply because they did not contain the necessary substances for growth of microorganisms. Flask No. 2 was opened and left exposed to the air. In three days it contained a huge population of organisms.

2–9 Pasteur at work in his laboratory. The great French biologist is shown examining a flask that is cloudy with microorganisms. The fluid in the gooseneck flask in his left hand is clear and sterile (see also Figure 2–11).

Flask No. 3 was left unaltered and it remained sterile—as it had been for four years.

Some of the flasks that Pasteur used in his experiments of 1860 are still on exhibit at the Pasteur Institute in Paris (Figure 2-10). A century has passed: spontaneous generation has yet to begin within them!

Pasteur then began his new experiments before the Commission. A total of 60 flasks were prepared. Each contained an infusion of yeast and sugar. The infusions in all the flasks were boiled for two minutes, then the necks of 56 flasks were sealed by flame. (We will return to the other four flasks shortly.) The 56 flasks were used in three groups as follows:

GROUP A: 19 flasks were opened briefly inside the amphitheatre of the building where the Commission was holding its hearings. The flasks were then resealed and set aside.

2–10 Two of Pasteur's original flasks of yeast and sugar infusion, photographed as they appear today. Pasteur opened these flasks high in the French Alps, where he hoped the air would be without spores of microorganisms. He then resealed the flasks and labeled them with the place of exposure and the date. They are now a permanent exhibit at the *Institut Pasteur* in Paris and are still sterile, after more than a century.

Institut Pasteur

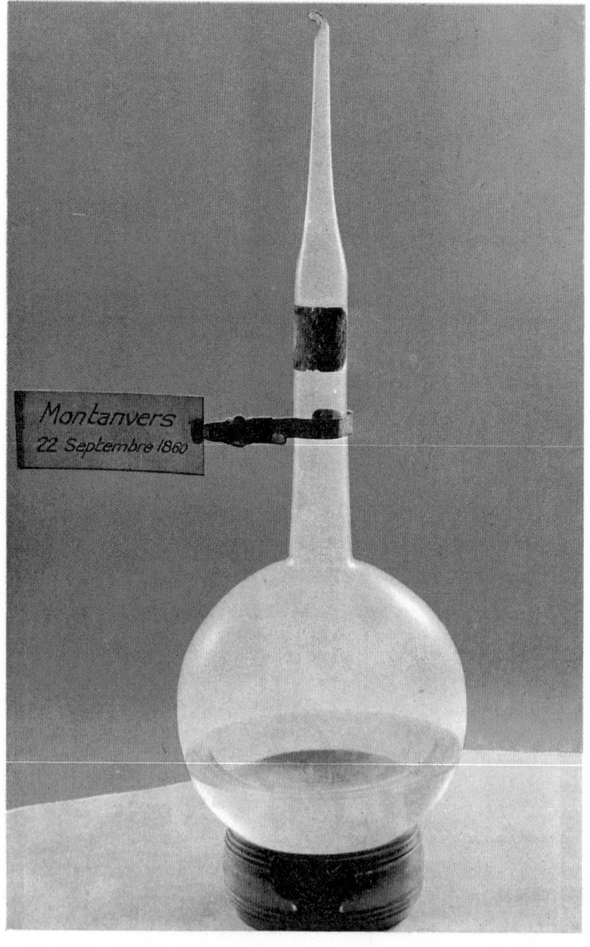

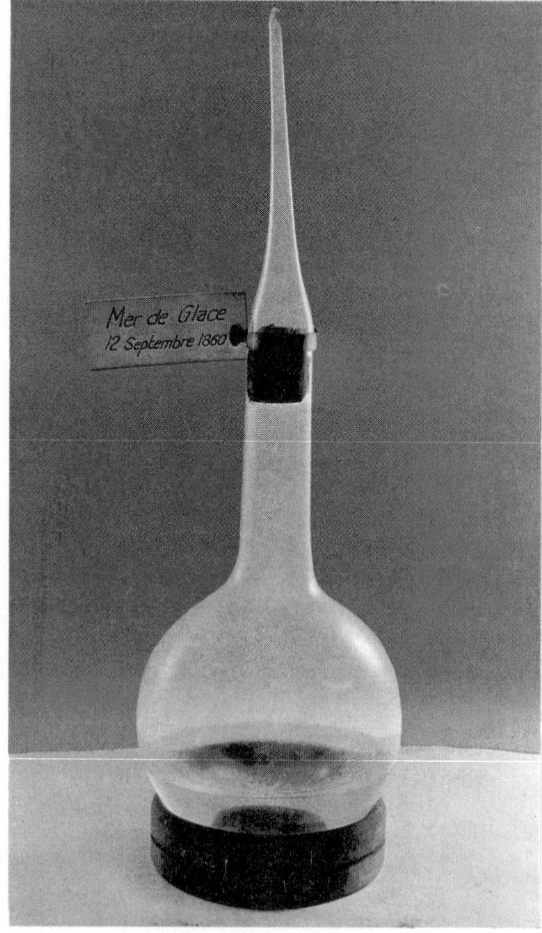

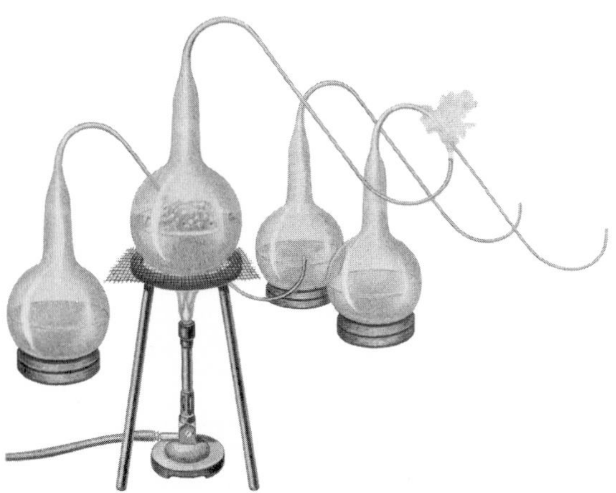

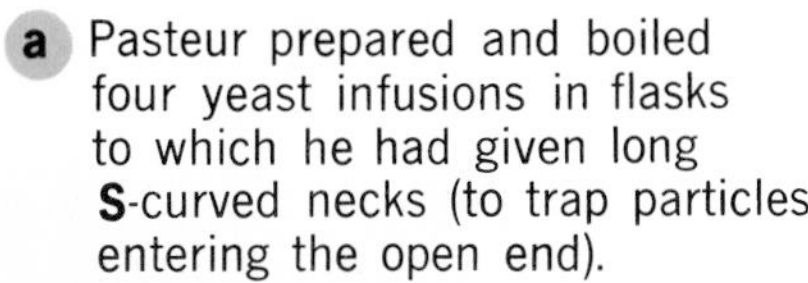

a Pasteur prepared and boiled four yeast infusions in flasks to which he had given long **S**-curved necks (to trap particles entering the open end).

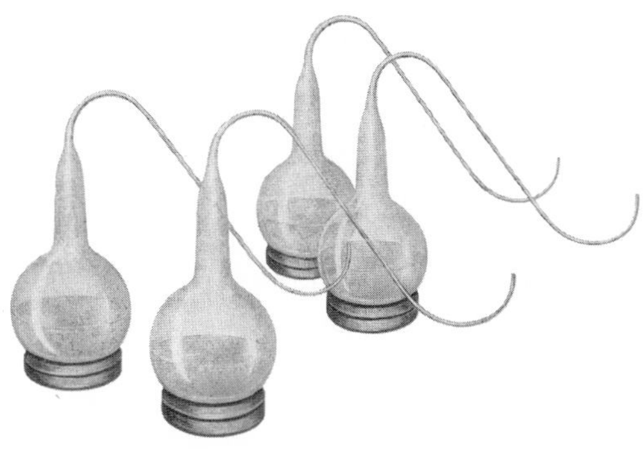

b He left all the flasks open, yet all remained sterile indefinitely. Air without its impurities did not affect the infusions.

2–11 Pasteur's experiments with gooseneck flasks. The abiogenesists maintained that spontaneous generation failed to occur in sealed flasks because fresh air was excluded. To test their hypothesis, Pasteur devised these flasks with long curved necks. The flasks would admit fresh air, but conceivably would trap spores of microorganisms. Why?

GROUP B: 19 flasks were opened briefly high up in the dome of the amphitheatre. These were then resealed and set aside.

GROUP C: 18 flasks were opened outside the building, then resealed and set aside.

The reasoning here was that the air inside the building would be freer of particles than air outside the building, making the chances of contamination less.

The results were as follows:

In group A, 5 flasks (26 percent) developed growths of organisms. In group B, 6 (32 percent) developed growths of organisms. In group C, 16 (89 percent) developed growths.

In every group, some infusions exposed to air remained sterile. *Most* of the infusions exposed indoors remained sterile, but only a *few* of those exposed outdoors did.

It was the four flasks not yet accounted for that proved most interesting of all. From the outset they were handled differently. Pasteur heated the glass neck of each of the four flasks and drew it out into a long curved neck (Figure 2-11). The ends of the necks were left open. Pasteur then boiled the infusions in the flasks and let steam issue out of the neck of each flask. He expected that this live steam would kill any living creatures that might be present in the neck of the flask.

Then the flasks were allowed to cool. The purpose of the long, curved necks will now be apparent. As air entered the necks of the flasks, any particles would tend to settle on the curving walls of the glass. In some cases, at least, no particles should be expected to pass through the curved passage and reach the infusions. As a matter of fact, all four flasks remained sterile! Yet none of the four was sealed!

This concluded Pasteur's demonstrations before the Commission of the French Academy. What did Pouchet do? Although somewhat critical of the way Pasteur had conducted his experiments, Pouchet refused to do any more of his own. He refused to be judged, and the Commission decided in Pasteur's favor.

Pouchet and Pasteur in Retrospect. Pasteur had won a resounding scientific victory when the Commission decided in his favor. He seemed to have established for all time the fact of biogenesis—and to have discredited for all time the theory of spontaneous generation on the earth today. But the outcome might have been very different—in fact it *should* have been very different. Had Pouchet not lost his nerve, it is highly likely that he could have convinced the Commission of the occurrence of spontaneous generation. How could this be?

One should never forget that scientific conclusions are based on observation and experiment. But quite often both the observations and experiments are few in number—possibly not enough to verify a hypothesis. Pasteur, in his experiments, used an infusion made of yeast, sugar, and water. Pouchet, in his earlier work, used a hay infusion. Neither Pasteur nor Pouchet thought this difference was important. The Commission probably did not either. They may have thought it no more important than for the two biologists to use slightly different glassware.

But was the type of infusion really *un*important? It was not, as we know today. Had Pasteur repeated Pouchet's experiments he would have discovered that Pouchet had been "correct"! The hay infusion could have been boiled, closed carefully, and life would nonetheless have appeared!

We now know that both Pasteur and Pouchet made an initial error. Both assumed that boiling would destroy all organisms or spores. Today we know that this is not so. Some species of *Clostridium* (klos·TRID·ih·um), a kind of bacterium, can survive boiling for many minutes or even hours (see the table in Figure 2-12).

2–12 Average Time That Different Organisms (or Their Spores) Can Survive Being Boiled in Infusions

Organisms	*Survival Time (in minutes)*
Protozoa	0
Bacteria	
Most species	0
Bacillus subtilis	14
Clostridium perfringens	20
Clostridium botulinum	360

Dried hay, as used by Pouchet, would be likely to contain spores of *Clostridium* and other highly resistant organisms. Pasteur's yeast and sugar solution would be much less likely to contain them. Hence, both men could have done their experiments equally carefully and reached opposite conclusions!

CONCLUDING REMARKS

After Pasteur's victory, few competent biologists continued to believe that spontaneous generation occurs on the earth today. Had the long line of scientists from Redi to Pasteur actually proved that spontaneous generation cannot occur? Not at all. Perhaps this comes as a shock to you. All that had been scientifically demonstrated was this:

1. All observations and experiments thought to be examples of spontaneous generation were shown to be false.
2. No experiment showed convincingly that spontaneous generation could occur.

All competent biologists today are biogenesists. They accept the view that on the earth today life comes only from life. But wait, have we answered all parts of the question? If life comes only from life, does this mean that there was *always* life on the earth? It must, yet we know that this cannot be so. We know that the world was once without life—that life appeared later. How? We think it was by spontaneous generation! But this was not the same as the events occurring in a flask of boiled hay infusion. We must wait until Chapter 9 to continue this part of the story.

Three hundred years of debate and only a qualified answer. Did all those scientists waste their time? Is the question really that important? For biologists it is. For others, does it matter whether life comes only from life or can arise, at least in a few instances, by spontaneous generation? Yes, for all of us it is tremendously important to have the answer. Consider the problem of bacteria that cause diseases such as tuberculosis and diphtheria. If the disease-producing bacteria arise spontaneously within the sick person, a physician could devote his efforts only to combating the organism within the body of his patient. But the physician now knows that these bacteria come only from other living bacteria. A person becomes ill with tuberculosis or diphtheria only when he is infected from without. Preventive medicine becomes possible with biogenesis.

The next chapter will introduce morphology and physiology. It will begin to answer two more questions of life: "What is it made of?" and "What does it do?" Each of these questions will help us distinguish life from nonlife.

GUIDE QUESTIONS AND PROBLEMS

1. Leeuwenhoek wrote that this new discovery "must surely convince all of the absurdity of these old opinions that living creatures can be produced from corruption or putrefaction." To what extent was the first man ever to see microscopic life justified in his point of view?
2. If microorganisms had not appeared in either the control or experimental vessels in Joblot's experiments (pages 29-30), what conclusions about their origin would have been possible?
3. Nineteen of the twenty sterile flasks Pasteur exposed briefly to the "pure" air of the Alps remained sterile; microorganisms later began to grow in only one. Pasteur concluded that spontaneous generation does not occur. Could he just as reasonably have concluded that spontaneous generation occurs, but only rarely—about 5 percent of the time?
4. Can spontaneous generation be disproved entirely? How would you explain that biologists today no longer are undertaking experiments similar to Redi's and Pasteur's?
5. One reason spontaneous generation was "observed" by Aristotle and "confirmed" by so many others for 2000 years is the reliance people place on *what they can see for themselves.* Is "seeing believing"? Name as many examples as you can to support your answer.
6. How did Pasteur's evidence for his convictions about spontaneous generation compare with and contrast to Aristotle's?
7. All life as we know it today comes from preexisting life: why is this a theory and not a fact? How do such theories contribute to development of new knowledge and new ideas?
8. If you were asked to criticize the conclusion reached by Boethius (page 21) on the origin of barnacle geese, on what errors or omissions would you base your criticism?
9. You have read that a great deal of controversy existed as biologists conducted experiments relating to the origin of life. Controversy of this sort exists today in all branches of biology and is considered to be a vital element in development of biological knowledge. Why is the controversy so valuable?

RELATED READING

Books

For Leeuwenhoek's own account of his discovery of microscopic life . . .

Dobell, Clifford (editor), *Antony van Leeuwenhoek and His "Little Animals,"* Dover, New York, 1962 (paperback). Translations of Leeuwenhoek's letters.

For more detailed accounts of the work of Redi, Spallanzani, Needham, Joblot, Pouchet, and Pasteur . . .

De Kruif, Paul, *Microbe Hunters,* Harcourt, Brace & World, New York (cloth or paperback) and Pocket Books, New York, 1959 (paperback).

Schwartz, George, and P. Bishop (editors), *Moments of Discovery,* Basic Books, New York, 1958 (2 volumes).

Dubos, René, *Pasteur and Modern Science,* Doubleday, New York, 1960.

3

Basic Structure

Man has always been a biologist of sorts. He had to be in order to live. Early in his history he was a hunter of animals and a gatherer of fruits, seeds, roots, and berries. The more he knew about animals and their habits, the more successful he was as a hunter. The more he knew about kinds of plants, the better his chances of distinguishing the edible from the nonedible. The penalty for being a poor biologist was a severe stomach ache, or worse!

Early Knowledge of Plants and Animals

Primitive man used many wild plants for food, shelter, medicine, tools, and other purposes. Frequently his knowledge of varieties of plants and their usefulness was staggering. As an example today, the Indians of Brazil are known to use at least 66 different species of plants as fish poisons alone. Each of these plants contains some substance that makes the fish sluggish, or that paralyzes them. The plants are mashed and thrown into a stream. Soon the fish float to the surface and are easily caught. (Can you think of any reason why the Indians may have found it advisable *not* to use certain of their available poisons in catching fish for food?)

The Plains Indians of western North America depended largely upon a single species of animal—the buffalo, or American bison (Figure 3-1). The flesh was their main source of food. It could be eaten fresh or preserved. After a successful hunt, there was a feast of fresh meat. Blood was used as a soup. The surplus meat was dried, usually by being exposed in thin slices to the hot sun. The dried meat could be saved as it was or used to make pemmican. Here is the Indian's recipe for pemmican: pound the meat into a powder, then mix with crushed cherries, marrow, and melted fat. Dried meat and pemmican lasted almost indefinitely, tiding the Indians over periods when other food was not available.

Buffalo skins were used in many ways. Robes, tepee covers, storage sacks, war shields, and ropes and thongs were all made of skins. Some tribes also used skins to make boats—the skins were stretched over a wooden frame. Even cooking vessels were made of skins! One way of doing this was to dig a hole and line the bottom and sides of the hole with a buffalo skin. Water and food were then put into the skin. Finally, rocks were heated in a fire and put into the water. In this manner the food was cooked.

Buffalo stomachs were another source of cooking vessels; they were used also as buckets.

Buffalo heads, complete with horns, were used as headdresses in Indian ceremonies. Horns were used separately to make spoons, arrowheads, and cups. Other tools were made from bones: a shoulder blade, for example, could be attached to a stick to make a hoe. Children made sleds from the ribs.

The tendons, especially the long ones extending down the back, were used as sewing thread and bow strings. A glue was obtained from the hoofs. The brains were used in the hide-curing process; they were rubbed into the hides to help soften them. The skin of the rough side of the tongue was dried to make a comb.

Finally, the dried dung, which came to be known as "buffalo chips," was the principal fuel in a region that had few trees.

Thus it was that the Plains Indians relied upon the buffalo for most of their food, clothing, shelter, and fuel. Little of a slain animal was wasted, for the Indians possessed a great store of knowledge about this species which had come to be so necessary for their existence.

All primitive peoples had a detailed knowl-

3–1 The Indians of the North American Plains depended heavily on the buffalo. How many of the articles shown here do you think were obtained from the buffalo? What would you guess is the significance of the painting on the first tepee? This illustration is reproduced from a painting by George Catlin, who visited many Indian tribes in the nineteenth century and left a valuable pictorial record of the Indians' way of life – a way of life that depended on considerable biological knowledge of the environment.

American Museum of Natural History, Painting by George Catlin

edge of the plants and animals in their immediate world. They were dependent on these living things for their own well-being. Not infrequently they seemed to have a feeling of awe for life itself. Thus, in some tribes the warrior performed a brief ceremony after the hunt – apologizing to the spirit of the animal he had killed. He was sorry to take a life, but he must to preserve his own. The warrior referred to the animal as "little brother," which implies an understanding that life in man and life in beast were not so very different after all.

Scientific Knowledge

Was primitive man's tremendous knowledge of animals and plants *science*? Think about this. *Science* is so common a term today that we should not be surprised that it has many meanings. But for us it has a clearer, useful meaning. Above all it implies *organizing* our knowledge of natural phenomena. To do this for so many separate facts requires relating the facts by discovery of general principles. We have already had one example: in spite of the many different kinds of organisms and the many ways they are produced, biogenesis accounts for all of them that live on the earth today.

Science is knowledge based upon data derived from observation and experiment. Sometimes the knowledge seems to be "impractical" – gained solely to satisfy someone's curiosity. We will find, however, that what seems to be impractical knowledge at one time may eventually provide the basis for other important discoveries.

Were our fishermen and our buffalo hunters scientists? Not in the strict sense of the word. There is no evidence that they *organized* their knowledge of living organisms the way a biologist would. Their knowledge of plants and animals can better be described as *technological*. Technology is *practical* knowledge, which is, of course, the kind primitive man had to possess to survive.

The technical knowledge that flocks of wild geese appeared in the marshes at specific times every spring and fall was of great importance to a hunter who had to feed his family. But we must begin to ask such questions as "Why do geese migrate?" – and seek answers to these questions for the sake of knowledge – before we can be considered scientists.

Necessity is the mother of technology: curiosity is the mother of science.

Micrographia, New York Public Library

3–2 When Robert Hooke used a microscope (Figure 3–3) to study a common fly, this is what he saw. Microscopes have revealed a wealth of biological knowledge that otherwise would have eluded our understanding. (The letters on the fly and its wing refer to structures Hooke described in his book *Micrographia*, published in 1665.)

The distinction between what is science and what is not rarely is as sharp as we have implied. The first Indian warrior to note that animals with hair also nursed their young, and had other characteristics in common, had the gleam of a scientific idea—the classification of organisms based upon natural groupings. He was recognizing a group we call **mammals.**

Biological science began independently all over the world, in the chance observations of primitive man. The ancient Greeks were the first to make comprehensive attempts to *organize* the data of the natural world. Aristotle and others of the fourth century B.C. were so superior as scientists to all who came before them that we sometimes tend to think of science as a Greek product. Of course, much that Aristotle wrote is incorrect—recall his observations on spontaneous generation of fish and insects (Chapter 2). His lasting contribution was his awareness that all knowledge of animals and plants somehow could be related. He was not satisfied with answers to the question "What?" He also wanted to find the answers to "How?" and "Why?"

Aristotle died in 322 B.C., and science began a long decline. The Romans came and went, adding no one of Aristotle's worth to biology. Europe declined into its Dark Ages. Not until late in the sixteenth century did biological science again approach the level at which Aristotle had left it.

THE DISCOVERY OF CELLS

Perhaps you see that the main theme of the preceding discussion is that observations do not become scientific observations until they are organized—until they are related to a question. Consider the history of one important question:

> Is there a fundamental unit of structure shared by all organisms?

By this we mean, "Is there any evidence that microorganisms, plants, and animals are constructed of the same parts?"

This is an example of a scientific question. We are seeking knowledge for knowledge's sake. When we first ask the question there seems little likelihood that the answer will have practical value. But the answer to this question has proved most important, not only for the advance of science but also for many problems of medicine.

At the moment this is being written, the author is also eating a pear. Author and pear are both alive—but the life expectancy of the pear is brief! One could examine both carefully and conclude that there is no morphological similarity between man and pear. That is, each appears to be constructed in a different way. There is no trick here. This *is* the answer to the unaided eye. The question is whether other methods of study yield the same answer.

Early Work with the Microscope

Crude microscopes seem to have been made for the first time in Holland, shortly before 1600. By about 1610, Galileo (gal·ih·LAY·oh), the Italian astronomer and physicist who supported the theory that the earth revolves around the sun, had made a microscope and used it to observe very small animals. He was followed by many others, among them Leeuwenhoek, who discovered microscopic life, as we learned in Chapter 2.

The microscope revealed that animals so small that the details of their structure could not be seen by the unaided eye, have a complex morphology (Figure 3-2).

There must have been a tremendous feeling of excitement when biologists began using microscopes for the first time. (Did you have similar feelings when you first looked at things under a microscope?) Magnified images revealed a hidden world and answered questions that could not have been answered before. One biologist in 1630 wrote that he was learning about matters unknown even to Aristotle. That was about as far as one could go in 1630!

Hooke's *Micrographia*

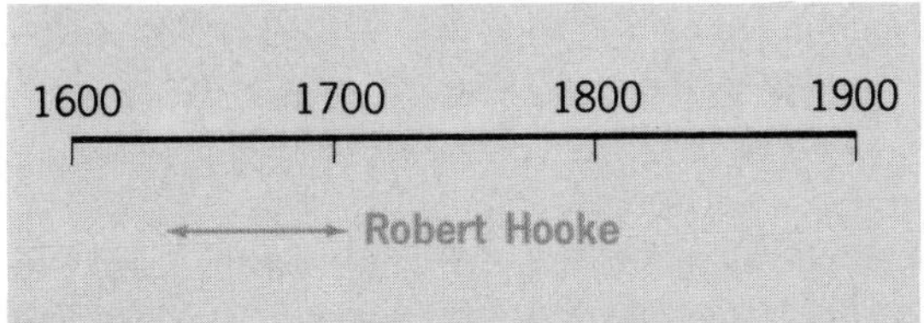

In 1665, Robert Hooke published a book entitled *Micrographia*. Hooke was an English scientist and inventor, who in his youth served as a laboratory assistant for a chemist you will read about in Chapter 4. He constructed a compound microscope (Figure 3-3), which was much better than the crude models available in his day. He examined many things with his microscope – minerals, textiles, and small plants and animals (Figure 3-2 is from his book). One of the things he examined was cork. If you can, examine some cork (see Laboratory Inquiry 3-1) before reading on. Cork is part of the outer bark of the cork oak (Figure 3-4). Hooke's description of it occupies so prominent a position in the history of man's attempt to understand the basic structure of living things that you may wish to read what he had to say. The printer's type used in *Micrographia* is quaint, but once you notice that an *s* is often much like an *f*, you ſhould have little trouble underſtanding it.

3–3 Hooke's microscope. It was shown in color introducing Part I of your textbook. Hooke's design was a vast improvement over that of Leeuwenhoek (Figure 2–6). In several ways Hooke's microscope is similar to the one you use today.

The Bettmann Archive

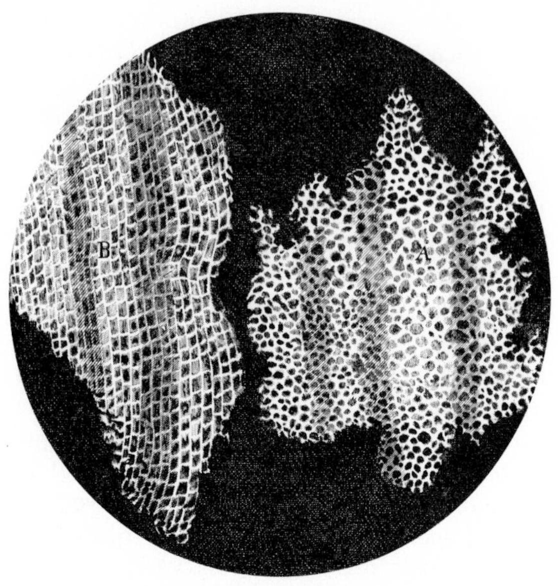

Micrographia, New York Public Library

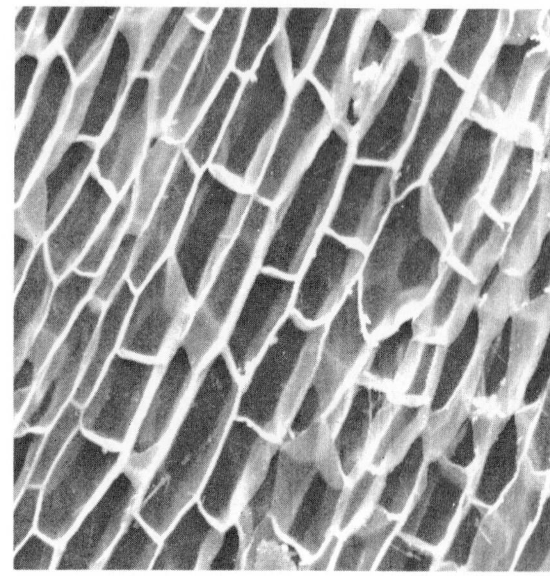

Delbert Philpott

3–4 (Left) The microscopic structure of a piece of cork. This illustration, like Figure 3–2, is from Hooke's *Micrographia*. Contrast it to a recent photomicrograph of cork cells **(right).** What finer structure can you see with the greater magnification (1750 ×) and sharper image obtained with the modern microscope?

* Try not to trouble about obsolete words you run across. Most of their meanings are clarified by the words around them. "Schematisme" means *structure* here.

Obſerv. XVIII. *Of the* Schematiſme* *or* Texture *of* Cork, *and of the Cells and Pores of ſome other ſuch frothy Bodies.*

You share Hooke's difficult problem of *laboratory technique* in Laboratory Inquiry 3-1. It would be useful if we could reach across the years and ask him to demonstrate how he learned to hold the cork *just so*, to slice it thinly enough to admit light under the microscope.

I Took a good clear piece of Cork, and with a Pen-knife ſharpen'd as keen as a Razor, I cut a piece of it off, and thereby left the ſurface of it exceeding ſmooth, then examining it very diligently with a *Microſcope*, me thought I could perceive it to appear a little porous; but I could not ſo plainly diſtinguiſh them, as to be ſure that they were pores, much leſs what Figure they were of: But judging from the lightneſs and yielding quality of the Cork, that certainly the texture could not be ſo curious, but that poſſibly, if I could uſe ſome further diligence, I might find it to be diſcernable with a *Microſcope*, I with the ſame ſharp Pen-knife, cut off from the former ſmooth ſurface an exceeding thin piece of it, and placing it on a black object Plate, becauſe it was it ſelf a white body, and caſting the light on it with a deep *plano-convex Glaſs*, I could exceeding plainly perceive it to be all perforated and porous, much like a Honey-comb, but that the pores of it were not regular; yet it was not unlike a Honey-comb in theſe particulars.

The first use of the word *cells* for the structures Hooke writes of finding with his microscope (see asterisk in text). Is the comparison to six-sided honeycomb cells really reasonable? Get out your microscope and look into these puzzling "pores" (Laboratory Inquiry 3-1).

Firſt, in that it had a very little ſolid ſubſtance, in compariſon of the empty cavity that was contain'd between, as does more manifeſtly appear by the Figure A and B of the X I. *Scheme*, for the *Interſtitia*, or walls (as I may ſo call them) or partitions of thoſe pores were neer as thin in proportion to their pores, as thoſe thin films of Wax in a Honey-comb (which encloſe and conſtitute the *ſexangular cells*) are to theirs.

Next, in that theſe pores, or cells,* were not very deep, but conſiſted of a great many little Boxes, ſeparated out of one continued long pore, by certain *Diaphragms*, as is viſible by the Figure B, which repreſents a ſight of thoſe pores ſplit the long-ways.

Why did Hooke check with others and read their work? Was it only to be sure that the discovery was his, or is there better reason?

I no ſooner diſcern'd theſe (which were indeed the firſt *microſcopical* pores I ever ſaw, and perhaps, that were ever ſeen, for I had not met with any Writer or Perſon, that had made any mention of them before this) but me thought I had with the diſcovery of them, preſently hinted to me the true and intelligible reaſon of all the *Phænomena* of Cork; As,

Hooke relates his discovery to other facts already known. What does this have to do with science?

Firſt, if I enquir'd why it was ſo exceeding light a body? my *Microſcope* could preſently inform me that here was the ſame reaſon evident that there is found for the lightneſs of froth, an empty Honey-comb, Wool, a Spunge, a Pumice-ſtone, or the like; namely, a very ſmall quantity of a ſolid body, extended into exceeding large dimenſions.

No wonder cork floats! And no wonder it is "springy" and makes such excellent bottle-stoppers, as Hooke is commenting. Check the last three lines of this section to find out whether Hooke may be guessing too far afield. Cells in "almost all other kinds of vegetable substances"?—if this is what the statement means, use your microscope again to conduct your own examination of plant materials.

Next, it ſeem'd nothing more difficult to give an intelligible reaſon, why Cork is a body ſo very unapt to suck and drink in Water, and conſequently preſerves it ſelf, floating on the top of Water, though left on it never ſo long: and why it is able to ſtop and hold air in a Bottle, though it be there very much condens'd and conſequently preſſes very ſtrongly to get a paſſage out, without ſuffering the leaſt bubble to paſs through its ſubſtance. For, as to the firſt, ſince our *Microſcope* informs us that the ſubſtance of Cork is altogether fill'd with Air, and that that Air is perfectly encloſed in little Boxes or Cells diſtinct from one another. It ſeems very plain, why neither the Water, nor any other Air can eaſily inſinuate it ſelf into them, ſince there is already within them an *intus exiſtens*, and conſequently, why the pieces of Cork become ſo good floats for Nets, and ſtopples for Viols, or other cloſe Veſſels.

And thirdly, if we enquire why Cork has ſuch a ſpringineſs and ſwelling nature whem compreſs'd? and how it comes to ſuffer ſo great a compreſſion, or ſeeming penetration of dimenſions, ſo as to be made a ſubſtance as heavie again and more, bulk for bulk, as it was before compreſſion, and yet ſuffer'd to return, is found to extend it ſelf again into the ſame ſpace? Our *Microſcope* will eaſily inform us, that the whole maſs conſiſts of an infinite company of ſmall Boxes or Bladders of Air, which is a ſubſtance of a ſpringy nature, and that will ſuffer a conſiderable condenſation (as I have ſeveral times found by divers trials, by which I have moſt evidently condens'd it into leſs then a twentieth part of its uſual dimenſions neer the Earth, and that with no other ſtrength then that of my hands without any kind of forcing Engine, ſuch as Racks, Leavers, Wheels, Pullies, or the like, but this onely by and by) and beſides, it ſeems very probable that thoſe very films or ſides of the pores, have in them a ſpringing quality, as almoſt all other kind of Vegetable ſubſtances have, ſo as to help to reſtore themſelves to their former poſition.

Hooke previously gave descriptive data and now is adding *quantitative data*—what to look for in terms of size and numbers. Consider how to calculate the size of a tiny structure under the microscope, when you are not sure how much the microscope has enlarged the image you see!

A cell hypothesis for numerous other plants!—not cork alone. What do your *own* investigations indicate?

> ... to return to our Obſervation. I told ſeveral lines of theſe pores, and found that there were uſually about threeſcore of theſe ſmall Cells placed end-ways in the eighteenth part of an Inch in length, whence I concluded there muſt be neer eleven hundred of them, or ſomewhat more then a thouſand in the length of an Inch, and therefore in a ſquare Inch above a Million, or 1166400. and in a Cubick Inch, above twelve hundred Millions, or 1259712000. a thing almoſt incredible, did not our *Microſcope* aſſure us of it by ocular demonſtration; nay, did it not diſcover to us the pores of a body, which were they *diaphragm'd*, like thoſe of Cork, would afford us in one Cubick Inch, more then ten times as many little Cells, as is evident in ſeveral charr'd Vegetables; ſo prodigiouſly curious are the works of Nature, that even theſe conſpicuous pores of bodies, which ſeem to be the channels or pipes through which the *Succus nutritius*, or natural juices of Vegetables are convey'd... are yet ſo exceeding ſmall, that the *Atoms* which *Epicurus* fancy'd would go neer to prove too bigg to enter them, much more conſtitute a fluid body in them.

Hooke found no passages from one cell to another, although he looked for them. What have *you* found?

> ... though I could not with my *Microſcope*, nor with my breath, nor any other way I have yet try'd, diſcover a paſſage out of one of thoſe cavities into another, yet I cannot thence conclude, that therefore there are none ſuch, by which the *Succus nutritius*, or appropriate juices of Vegetables, may paſs through them; for, in ſeveral of thoſe Vegetables, whil'ſt green, I have with my *Microſcope*, plainly enough diſcover'd theſe Cells or Poles fill'd with juices, and by degrees ſweating them out: as I have alſo obſerved in green Wood all thoſe long *Microſcopical* pores which appear in Charcoal perfectly empty of any thing but Air.

Note that Hooke really could foresee a future of improved microscopes. Make your own prediction about the passages between plant cells.

> Now, though I have with great diligence endeavoured to find whether there be any ſuch thing in thoſe *Microſcopical* pores of Wood or Piths, as the *Valves* in the heart, veins, and other paſſages of Animals, that open and give paſſage to the contain'd fluid juices one way, and ſhut themſelves, and impede the paſſage of ſuch liquors back again, yet have I not hitherto been able to ſay any thing poſitive in it; though, me thinks, it ſeems very probable, that Nature has in theſe paſſages, as well as in thoſe of Animal bodies, very many appropriated Inſtruments and contrivances, whereby to bring her deſigns and end to paſs, which 'tis not improbable, but that ſome diligent Obſerver, if help'd with better *Microſcopes*, may in time detect.

Although the last paragraph may have suggested to you that Hooke was extending his cell hypothesis to animals, he actually was not doing so. He was comparing the *work*—not the structure—of a column of plant cells to veins and vessels of animal bodies.

Scientific Publications and Societies

Hooke narrowly escaped having to publish *Micrographia* at his own cost. In his day authors generally paid their publishers, instead of the other way round. Why publish at all under such circumstances? To answer the question, we must pause to consider an important aspect of science: how does scientific knowledge become generally known? If Hooke had looked at cork, but had failed to report what he saw, his observations would not have contributed to science. Of course, most people probably would not have been very interested in Hooke's report, but how could Hooke communicate with those who might share his interests?

In the 1640's a group of men interested in science began meeting informally each week in London. They would discuss topics that interested them and report any observations or experiments. In 1660 the group was organized more formally, and in 1662 it was given a charter by King Charles II. It was to be called the "Royal Society of London for Improving Natural Knowledge."

The Royal Society was one of the first scientific societies. Among early members we find Robert Hooke, Isaac Newton, the chemist Robert Boyle, and the architect Christopher Wren. Antony van Leeuwenhoek was elected as a foreign member when the Society was quite young. The Society provided a place where those interested in science could meet and discuss their problems. Not infrequently, members actually performed experiments at the meetings.

The Royal Society was of enormous influence in stimulating science in still another way: it arranged to publish the observations by its members and other scientists. These appeared in *Philosophical Transactions*, which was the Society's journal. Publication began in 1665, supported by funds from the royal treasury. During that first year, the Royal Society published Hooke's *Micrographia* and many other books on scientific subjects. By 1968, volume number 254 had been reached.

Other societies soon were formed, and the number has increased through the years. It is difficult to obtain an accurate estimate of the total number of such societies in the world. In the United States there are now hundreds devoted to all aspects of science. The American Association for the Advancement of Science is one of the largest. It has more than 100,000 members.

Scientific societies typically hold meetings at which the members can discuss their problems and discoveries. The societies also publish articles having scientific value. Living as we do in an age of tremendous scientific activity, it is not surprising that the number of articles being published is enormous. In one recent year alone, it was estimated that 50,000 scientific journals containing a total of about 2,000,000 articles were published around the world.

Now that we have seen how scientific information, from the time of Hooke onward, has been made known to all who might help one another in studying scientific questions, we can return to a group of men (beginning with Hooke) who did help one another in just this way. The questions they asked related directly to Hooke's discovery of cells.

THE CELL THEORY

It took a century and a half to progress from Hooke's initial observations on the structure of cork to what you will learn in one or two days. As more and more scientists were able to obtain microscopes, they examined many different animals and plants. They knew what to look for because Hooke had published his observations; they had but to read his book, *Micrographia.*

Accumulation of the Evidence

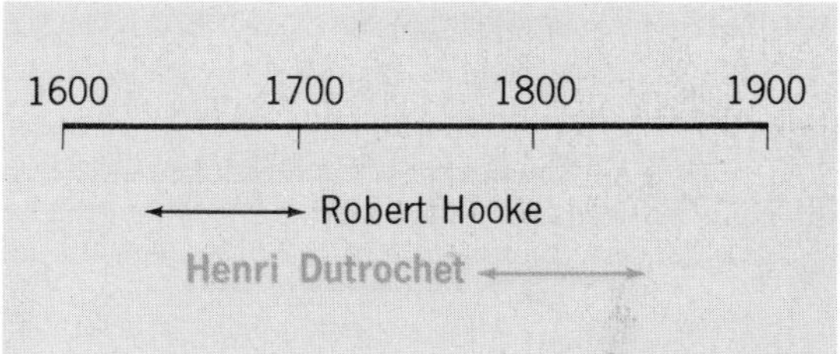

Early in the nineteenth century, a mature concept began to crystallize. Could it be that *all* living things are composed of cells? A French botanist, Dutrochet (doo·troh·SHAY), published some data in 1824 that suggested this was so. He found that when plant material was boiled in nitric acid it broke up into tiny pieces. When examined with a microscope, the tiny pieces were seen to be boxlike units similar to those Hooke had described as cells.

More and more plants were found to be composed of cells. *But what about the animals?* When bits of animal matter were examined, no heavy-walled, boxlike structures of the type so common in plants could be seen. It was difficult to make out anything at all.

The Interpretation by Schwann and Schleiden

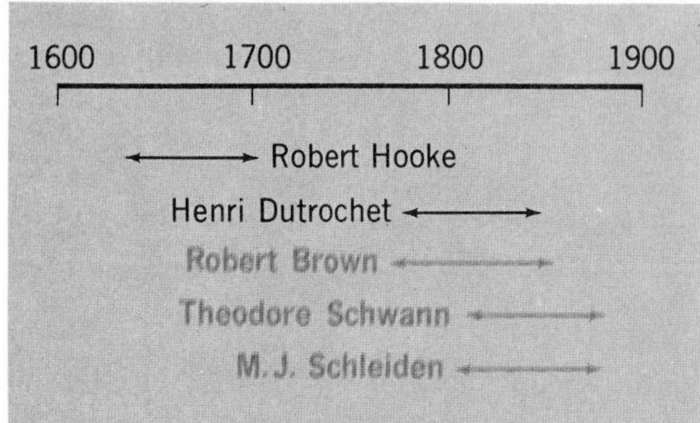

The next major advance was made in 1839 by a German zoologist, Theodor Schwann (SHVON or SHWON). His contribution was not *what* he saw, but *how he interpreted* what he saw. In a sense he changed the definition of "cell." Previous investigators had emphasized the walls of the box. He emphasized what was inside the box.

It had earlier been discovered that within the boxlike cells of *living* plants was a little sphere, the **nucleus** (NEW·klee·us). We owe this discovery to Robert Brown (see time scale, left) who first observed nuclei in cells of orchids. But compared to cell walls, nuclei were difficult to see. It was only natural to continue to identify plant cells on the basis of their heavy walls.

When Schwann looked at little bits of animals under his microscope, he observed that nuclei were present, although cell walls were not. The nuclei were surrounded by a watery substance, and usually by a very thin outer membrane as well (Figure 3-5). There was little here that seemed much like plant cells with their conspicuous walls. But Schwann thought there might be a fundamental resemblance. Possibly one should think of the substance *within* the walls of plant cells as corresponding to what he saw in parts of animals. Nuclei, for example, were present in both. In Schwann's opinion, a cell could be said to consist of a nucleus, with its surrounding substance, plus some sort of a wall or membrane. The thick walls of plant cells could then be considered a characteristic of

3–5 The microscopic structure of small parts of animals as seen by Schwann. The cluster of six cells at the right is from a fish. The oval cell is from the nervous system of a frog. The long cell at the bottom is from the muscle of an unborn pig. The spindle-shaped cell at the left is also from an unborn pig. Do you think you would have seen or suspected a unifying principle in such different objects?

Redrawn from Th. Schwann, 1839

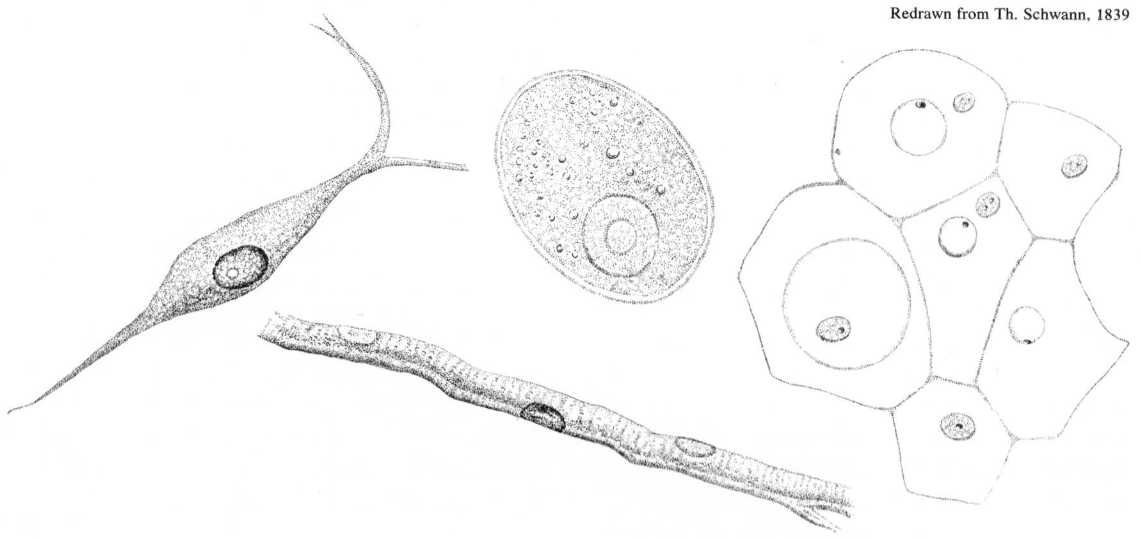

plant cells alone, and not of *all* cells. (You can judge the evidence for yourself in Laboratory Inquiries 3-2 and 3-3.)

Thus, Schwann developed a concept of the cell as a structure with a nucleus, rather than as a structure with a thick wall. He then proposed a fundamental hypothesis:

> The bodies of animals and plants are composed of cells and the products of cells.

A German botanist, M. J. Schleiden (SHLY-den) also came to this conclusion at about the same time. From the observations of Schwann and Schleiden, as well as those of others, the cell theory was born.

Schwann had proposed a hypothesis—the cell hypothesis. It led to a theory—the cell theory. What is the difference? For our purposes let us say that a hypothesis is a statement to be tested; it is a possibility. Schwann and others could test the hypothesis by making observations on the microscopic structure of numerous kinds of animals and plants. If they found the hypothesis true, that is, if all the animals and plants examined were found to be composed of cells, we could speak of the cell theory. But a theory is more than just a true or tested hypothesis. A theory is a body of *interrelated* facts. If observation had shown that only cork was composed of cells, we would not speak of this as the *theory* of cork cells. We would merely say that cork is composed of cells. But when cork, frogs, carrots, man, wheat, fish, and all other living things examined seem to be composed of cells, we have a body of important and interrelated facts which can be called a theory.

It was clear to Schwann and others that cells are tremendously varied in appearance, especially in animals (Figures 3-5 and 3-9). But in both animals and plants these microscopic structures are found, whatever their form. Each structure has a nucleus, together with surrounding substance and an enclosing membrane (animals) or wall (most plants). Cells were apparently the building blocks of life.

The Origin of Cells

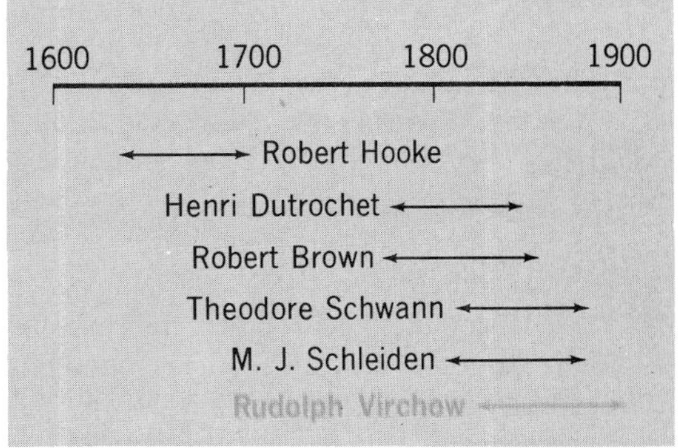

A new question immediately arose. Where do cells come from? Using the crude methods and microscopes of the early nineteenth century, biologists could not be sure. Schwann believed that new cells formed spontaneously of living substance, much the way crystals form in an evaporating solution of salt. He was wrong.

Other biologists noticed occasions when one cell seemed to divide into two (Figure 3-6). Was this the way new cells are formed—by the parent cell dividing into two parts? Many biologists thought so. Their view was expressed concisely in 1855 by the German biologist

3–6 Two cells from one. A sea urchin's egg is about to complete its first division. Additional cell membrane will form where the daughter cells adjoin, and a nuclear membrane will re-form around each daughter nucleus. Observation of similar divisions of cells suggested to nineteenth-century biologists that all cells come from pre-existing cells.

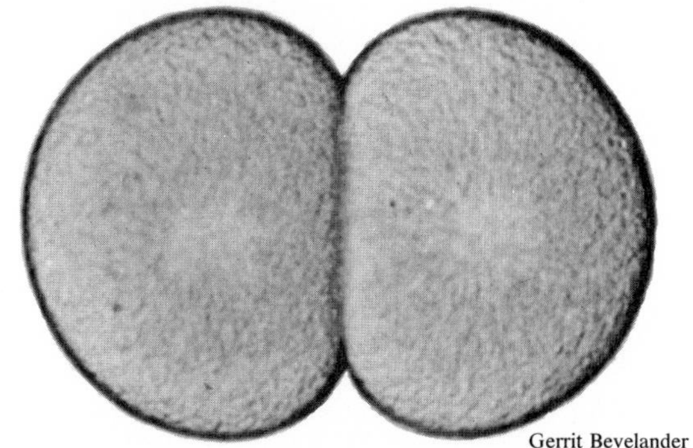

Gerrit Bevelander

Rudolf Virchow, who wrote, *"omnis cellula e cellula"* (all cells from cells).

Now this was a difficult hypothesis to establish. If one observes a cell dividing into two, does it mean that other origins of cells are impossible? Some observers believed that cells could form in several ways. For example, it was claimed that the cells in young embryos are carved out of the substance of the egg. This was similar to Schwann's belief. Gradually this view was abandoned. With better microscopes and more careful observations it was found that cells in embryos arise by cell division.

There were, of course, other scientists who believed that living cells could arise by spontaneous generation. We have already considered this hypothesis in Chapter 2.

Today all biologists accept the cell theory of Schwann and Schleiden and Virchow's hypothesis that all cells come from pre-existing cells. While some animals and plants are single-celled (**unicellular**—u·nih·SEL·u·ler), the ones you are most familiar with are usually made up of many cells of numerous kinds.

Techniques of Study—Fixation and Staining

There are limits even with the best microscopes to what one can observe in living cells. Usually dead cells are more revealing—but not just any dead cells, for they must be killed and treated in special ways. The methods used are designed to preserve the cells with as few structural changes as possible, and to stain the parts to make them more easily visible.

Briefly, the methods used are these. First, the cells are *fixed*. This means that they are treated with chemical agents that solidify the normally jellylike parts. The various parts are thus fixed in position (and of course, the cells are killed by the fixation process). Second, if the cells are in thick masses (making it nearly impossible to observe details within individual cells), means must be found for making them easier to study. Sometimes they can be spread out in thin sheets. Otherwise it is necessary to make very thin slices of the material. Third, the cells are *stained* with one or more of a variety of dyes. It has been discovered, largely by trial and error, that some dyes will selectively stain specific structures in cells. Thus, a dye known as **hematoxylin** (hee·ma·TOK·sih·lin) will stain the nucleus much more than other parts of the cell. Other dyes will selectively stain other structures. Until recently, most of our information about structures in cells was based on observing cells that had been fixed and stained as described here.

Animal Cells

Biologists today realize that cells are more than just the structural units of organisms. They are also units of function, each kind of cell performing specific tasks. Muscle cells are specialized in contracting, nerve cells in carrying messages from one part of the body to another, gland cells of the intestinal lining in aiding the digestion of foods, and some of the cells of the eye in responding to light. Blood cells are another major type; you will study them in Laboratory Inquiry 3-3.

In spite of their great variability, however, cells do have much in common. What are these common features? Let us begin with an animal cell (Figure 3-7). The nucleus is the most conspicuous structure that one observes within the cell. In some cells the nucleus is spherical; in others, irregular in shape. The nucleus of a *living* cell, when examined with an optical microscope, may appear almost transparent, with little visible internal structure.

When a cell has been fixed and suitably stained, the nucleus no longer appears to have so little internal structure. Within the nucleus, usually one or two small spherical bodies, the **nucleoli** (new·KLEE·o·lye; singular, **nucleolus**—new·KLEE·o·lus), can be seen. The rest of the nucleus may appear to contain a network of threads. Around the outside of the nucleus is seen a thin membrane, the **nuclear membrane.**

Our methods of preparing cells for study lead to an incorrect impression about the apparent network within the nucleus. There is, for example, considerable indirect evidence (from genetics; see Chapter 31) to suggest that in the living nucleus there is no actual *network* of the threadlike material. Instead the data indicate *separate* threads, the **chromosomes** (CROW·muh·zomes). They are plainly visible when cells divide, as we will see in Chapter 7, but not at other times. The chromosomes are independent structures – they do not fuse to form a network.

Chromosomes are of tremendous importance. They control the activities of the cell. In addition, they are the structures of the cell that are of the greatest importance in inheritance.

With few exceptions (such as sex cells), the nucleus of every cell in the body of an animal or plant has the same number of chromosomes. For example, most of the cells of your body contain 46 chromosomes. This number is characteristic for man. A frog's cells have 26. A chimpanzee's cells have 48.

The portion of the cell substance outside the nucleus and within the cell membrane has been named the **cytoplasm** (SY·toh·plaz'm). It is a *region* and not a single substance any more than the nucleus is a single substance. Like the nucleus, the cytoplasm is relatively fluid in living cells. It contains a variety of structures,

3–7 All cells have many structures in common. Differences exist, however, between most animal cells and most plant cells. Both the similarities and the differences are shown in this illustration of a generalized animal cell and a generalized plant cell. Have you observed all the cell structures shown here in your laboratory study of plant and animal cells? If you have not, what do you think could be the reasons?

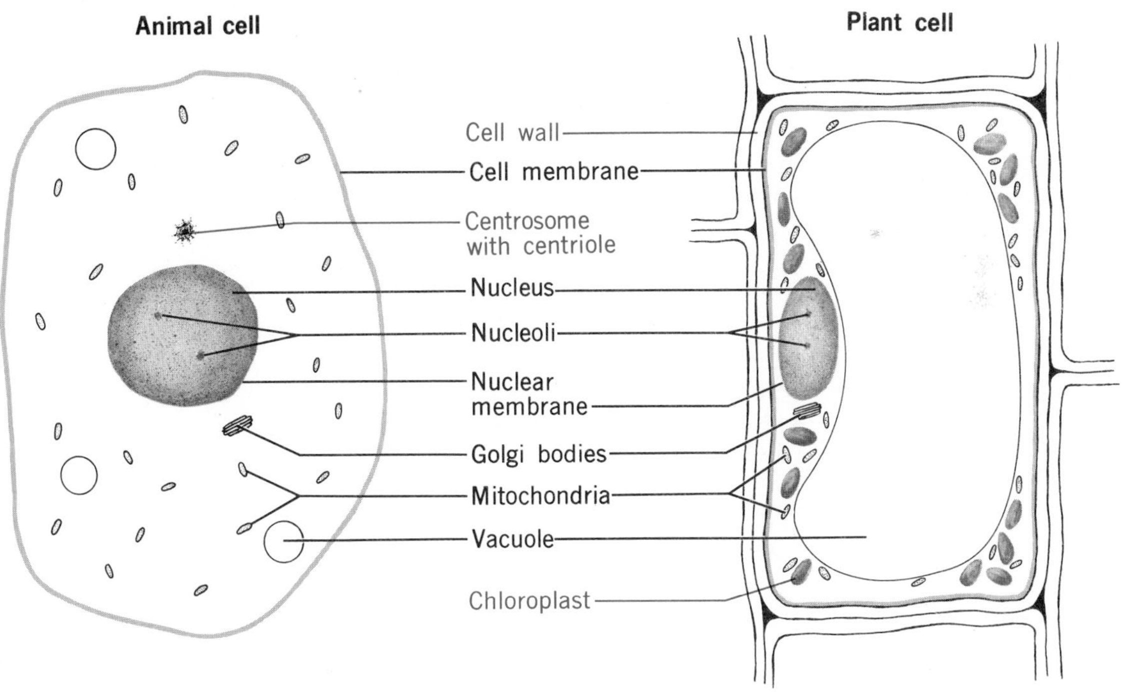

identifiable on the basis of their shape, staining properties, and chemical activities. The more important will now be mentioned.

The **mitochondria** (my·toh·KON·drih·uh) are common structures in the cytoplasm. In some cells they are short rods; in others they may be long filaments. In recent years the function of mitochondria has been discovered: they are important in providing energy for the cell.

The **Golgi** (GOL·jee) **bodies** are a collection of tiny platelike structures in the cytoplasm. Their function has not been established definitely. There is evidence that they are concerned with cell **secretions** (sih·KREE·shunz). Secretions are products formed within the cell and then passed to the outside.

The cytoplasm also contains a number of small granules. Some, such as the **ribosomes** (RY·boh·zomes), are too small to be seen with the compound microscope—one must use the electron microscope. Ribosomes are necessary for the cell to make its proteins.

A thin **cell membrane** covers the cell. Everything that enters or leaves the cell must pass through it.

We remember that all cells come from preexisting cells by a process of division. The animal cell we have been describing was not in the process of dividing. Other structures make their appearance when a cell is dividing (Figure 3-8). At this time, for example, the chromosomes become clearly stainable. The chromosomes of dividing cells are situated in a structure called the **spindle.** At each end of the spindle there are one or more tiny granules, the **centrioles** (SEN·trih·ohlz), surrounded by fibrous **asters.** These structures important in cell division will be discussed further in Chapter 7.

Plant Cells

So far we have looked closely at an animal cell. When we examine plant cells, many similarities to animal cells will be apparent. There will also be some differences between the two.

A plant cell (Figure 3-7) typically possesses a nucleus, one or more nucleoli, mitochondria, Golgi bodies, ribosomes, and a cell membrane. In these respects it resembles an animal cell. Generally, plant cells differ from animal cells in having thick **cell walls** and *large* central **vacuoles** (VAK·yoo·ohlz); animal cells frequently have numerous *small* vacuoles. The plant cell walls were the prominent structures that were first observed by Hooke in cork. They form a relatively rigid outer case for the rest of the cell. The vacuoles are large liquid-filled structures bounded by a membrane. Frequently these are in the middle of the cell and so large that the bulk of the cytoplasm is pushed into a thin film next to the cell wall.

The cell membrane is ordinarily close to the inner surface of the cell wall. It usually cannot be seen unless one uses some method to shrink the contents of the cell away from the cell wall.

Many of the cells of green plants contain **chloroplasts** (KLOR·o·plasts). These are microscopic bodies which contain the green pigment **chlorophyll** (KLOR·o·fill). Chloroplasts are of enormous biological importance; they are key structures in the plant's manufacture of food—not only food for the plant, but ultimately food for the entire animal kingdom. Nearly all living creatures, plant and animal, are dependent on the food-producing activities of plant cells that contain chlorophyll.

When a plant cell divides, the chromosomes and spindle are prominent (Figure 3-8), as in the case of animal cells. However, in nearly all the plants with which you are familiar, the cells lack centrioles and asters.

Sizes of Cells

Most cells are very small. White blood cells of man range from about 8 to 12 microns in diameter. (A **micron** [MY·kron] is about 1/1,000 the thickness of a dime. Refer to Laboratory Inquiry 1-3 for a discussion of measurements.) A nerve cell's width at its widest point is—like that of white blood cells—measured in microns, but its length may be more than a meter! (A meter is about 39 inches—slightly more than a yard.) Single nerve cells, for ex-

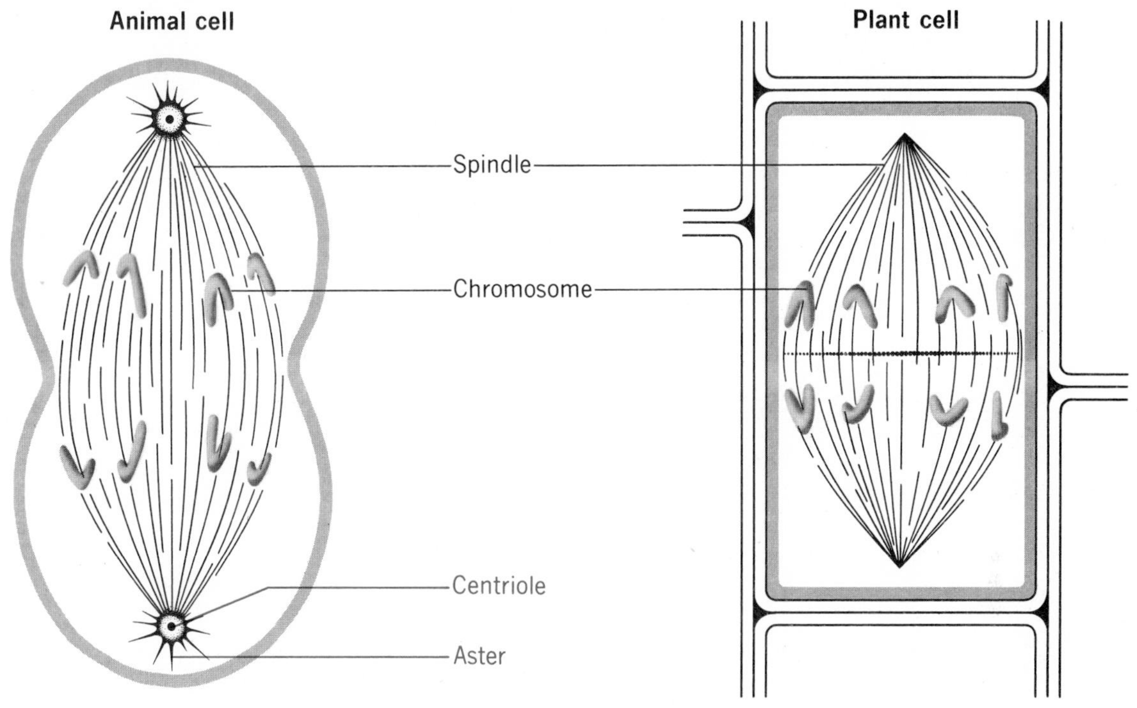

3–8 Cell division at a similar stage in a generalized animal cell and in a generalized plant cell. Only structures closely associated with cell division are shown.

ample, extend from the lower end of your spinal cord to the muscles that move your feet.

The largest cells are the yolks of birds' eggs. Before a young bird begins to develop, the yolk of the egg is a single cell. In the course of time, this single cell forms the young bird.

CONCLUDING REMARKS

With a microscope we can see that there is a basic similarity in the structures of living things. Nearly all are composed of cells. There are a few exceptions, such as viruses (Chapter 9) and slime molds (Chapter 12). There are so few exceptions, however, that one can recognize a general theory, the cell theory. It is one of the basic theories of biological science.

The intellectual steps from Hooke's observations to the cell theory were numerous and difficult. Hooke stumbled upon cells, so to speak, when he was using his microscope to look at common objects. Cork happens to show cell walls clearly. Hooke sought to relate cells to at least one function – the passage of juices through plant stems. Neither he nor others in the seventeenth century built a cell hypothesis into a successful cell theory.

It was exceedingly difficult to recognize cells as the common structural basis of living things. The reason is that cells differ tremendously in appearance. Most plant cells are surrounded by prominent cell walls, and the cell membrane is not readily seen. Most animal cells are sur-

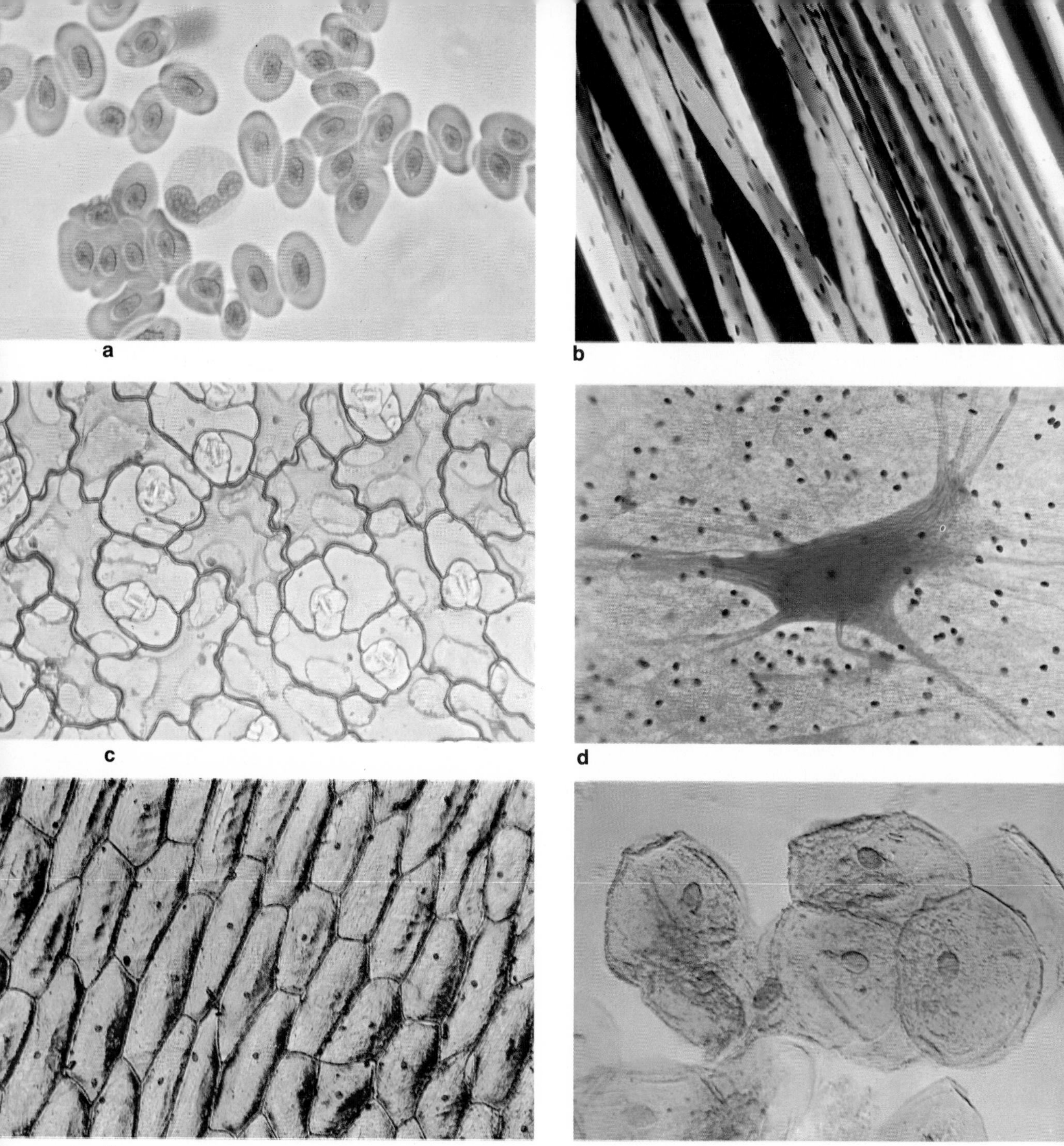

3–9 Variety in animal and plant cells: **a,** blood cells of the frog; **b,** muscle cells; **c,** cells from the surface of a plant leaf; **d,** a cell body of a nerve cell; **e,** cells of onion skin; **f,** cells from the lining of the cheek. If you had been asked to look at these photographs before reading about the cell theory, what conclusions would you have reached? What evidence do you see now for classifying all of them as cells?

rounded by a delicate cell membrane alone. Some cells are flat, others are spheres, still others are long and narrow (Figure 3-9). It is unlikely that anyone would unite all these various structures in a class of similar objects. In external appearance, cells are *not* similar.

It was Schwann's lasting contribution that gave us a new way of defining cells. To him it was not the general shape and form that made a cell, but the nucleus and the surrounding living matter—all enclosed in a wall or a membrane.

Hooke and his microscope started biologists along a fruitful line of inquiry, leading to the recognition that cells are the structural units of living matter. Today an understanding of cells is necessary for all branches of biology that deal with morphology and physiology. Our digestive juices are secreted by cells. Vision, taste, and hearing are all made possible by cells. The contraction of a muscle is the cumulative effect of the contraction of its individual cells. Much in embryonic development is understandable in terms of interactions of cells. As Virchow was first to emphasize, a physician studies the cells of a sick person and can often identify the disease. Hooke's discovery of cells, of little value at first, is now of great importance.

If there is a basic unit of structure, are there also basic *similar* functions in living cells? That is, can one discover any activities common to all living organisms? We shall go on to see.

GUIDE QUESTIONS AND PROBLEMS

1. In what ways was early man more technologist than scientist in learning about the world around him? What kinds of pursuits indicated his becoming a scientist? What is the distinction between science and technology?
2. Of perhaps almost two million animal species on earth, most have not been examined microscopically. Indeed, many lived long ago and are now extinct. Why is it reasonable to assume that these unexamined species are, or were, cellular?
3. Careful study of cells of many thousands of kinds has led scientists to the conclusion that almost all cells have many structures in common. What is the significance of this? What structures do most cells have in common? Why is it reasonable to assume that these structures share functions in common?
4. Why is it necessary to base your study of the cell upon *living* material as well as upon fixed and stained materials that have been prepared especially for use in the laboratory?
5. Hooke discovered microscopic walls in plants and named the spaces they enclosed *cells* for their partitioned appearance. What difficulties of microscopic observation made Hooke's idea of cells so different from the later one of Schleiden and Schwann, who described cells mainly in terms of their *contents*? When you take into account staining techniques, the electron microscope (Inquiry 1-4), and chemical tests, what are some of the observational difficulties you would associate with cell parts that remain to be discovered today or in future years?
6. Even the most significant scientific observations are valueless without accurately recorded data and communication of results. A discovery is not enough; it must be made available to other scientists. How does the development of the cell theory illustrate the importance of communication in science? In what ways has the theory led to new research?

RELATED READING

Books

For a compact account of cells and techniques of cell study . . .

Swanson, C. P., *The Cell*, Second Edition, Prentice-Hall, Englewood Cliffs, N. J., 1964.

For more on structures and functions of cells . . .

Butler, John A. V., *Inside the Living Cell*, Basic Books, New York, 1959.

Gerard, Ralph W., *Unresting Cells,* Harper and Row, New York, 1961.

Mercer, E. H., *Cells: Their Structure and Function*, Doubleday, New York, 1962.

Magazines

Scientific American, Volume 205 (September 1961). An issue devoted entirely to cells.

The Living Cell, Readings from *Scientific American*, W. H. Freeman & Co., San Francisco, 1965. Reprints of *Scientific American* articles, 1958–1965.

4

Basic Functions

Have you ever seen an animal die? Possibly you have seen a bird accidentally fly into a closed window of a building, or a beetle drown in a puddle. All of us have noticed plants dying. Flowering plants wither in the late summer. The leaves of trees turn brown and die in the autumn. If you examine an organism before and after it dies, it is often impossible to detect an immediate, obvious change in structure. The unfortunate bird that flew into the building probably broke its neck. But you might have to examine it very carefully to show that this was so. The part of the bird actually damaged might be much less than 1 percent of the whole bird.

The change occurring in this less than 1 percent leads to vast change in the rest of the organism. In a moment life has gone. What happened? If we were to weigh an organism immediately before and after death, we would detect no difference. We could conclude that whatever the organism lost when it died was not a material that we could weigh. In fact, a series of elaborate experiments and observations would show that the "lost" property had none of the known characteristics of matter. Our failure to detect what was lost narrows the problem, but if anything, makes it more difficult.

Once again, as in Chapter 2, page 19, we are faced with the basic question, "What is life?" You have learned many things that contribute to an answer. In Chapter 1 you learned that one of the most important properties of the living state is the ability to reproduce. In Chapter 2 you learned that life, whatever it is, is part of a genetic process—living organisms of today are the descendants of other living organisms. In Chapter 3 you learned that living organisms have a basic structural similarity—they are composed of cells and the products of cells. None of these properties explains what happened to the bird in the few seconds that passed between the time it was alive and flying and was no longer living, falling to the ground with broken neck. To help understand what happened we must look for other important features of life.

TWO EXPLANATIONS OF LIFE—VITALISM AND MECHANISM

Life and death have puzzled human beings for so long that we have no record of when people first began to ask questions about them. For thousands of years even the most intelligent people had little to help them in answering these questions. They realized that in one way the living and the no-longer-living seemed related to the earth itself. That is, an organism died, decayed, and left a residue that seemed identical with other substances in the earth's crust. At one moment in time, the same substance was alive; at another, not. Yet the difference between the living and the nonliving seemed obviously so great that it was reasonable for people to guess that there must be some special quality or force in living things, beyond the substance of which they were built. Aristotle (Figure 4-1, left), the great Greek philosopher of 23 centuries ago, believed in such special living forces, which he called **psyches** (SY·keez). He and generations of people following him believed that substance is alive when it contains psyche. If we followed this way of explaining, we could say that the bird mentioned in the preceding paragraphs was alive until it broke its neck, thus losing its psyche, the living force which made it alive.

But what are psyches? What does the idea of special living forces do to help us really understand life? Actually this idea performed

Kunsthistorisches Museum, Wien

Giraudon

4–1 Aristotle **(left)** and Descartes **(right).** Aristotle was a vitalist; he believed that life involved a unique force. Descartes believed otherwise; he was fundamentally a mechanist and sought to explain living phenomena by the laws of physical nature.

a very useful service for many centuries. It provided a basis for discussion among philosophers. You must remember that there were no scientists and very few useful data on either the living world or the earth and universe.

The next useful step in the study of life did not come until the seventeenth century, when Redi (pages 23-26) and others developed the experimental method of inquiry. Hypothesis, deduction, and experiment provided a powerful tool—often displacing the "evidence" of our own eyes! But how could one experiment with a vital force if it could not be identified by weight, or location, or activity?

A very different sort of hypothesis about life helped to resolve the difficulty. The ideas of René Descartes (day·KART), a great philosopher and an early biologist (Figure 4-1, right), will help us to understand this hypothesis.

Criticism of Vitalism and Reasons for Mechanism

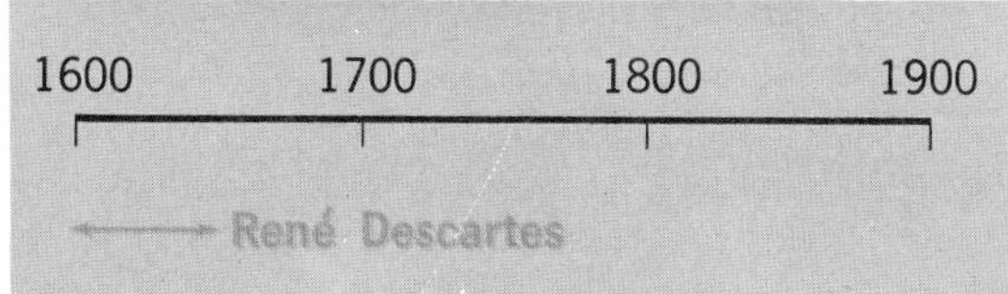

Descartes was a young man living in France when the first European colonists were landing on the east coast of what is now the United States. At this time astronomers and physicists such as Kepler and Galileo (who also used the microscope—page 41) were having considerable success studying the movements of the planets, the swing of the pendulum, and the rise and fall of the tides. In each instance it proved possible to describe the physical world in mechanical and mathematical terms.

Descartes was interested in these studies, and he was also interested in life. He attempted to explain all the activities of living organisms in terms of mechanics. The movement of fluids within the body, the contraction of muscles, the pumping of the heart, were obvious examples. Descartes went on to explain how the brain and nerves could act on mechanical principles. To him, life could be understood in terms of the laws that applied to nonliving objects. There was no need to invoke a special psyche.

Descartes' arguments did not convince everyone. He had made a remarkable guess or hypothesis. Unfortunately the hypothesis could not be tested fully because too little was known about physics and chemistry at that time. So for many generations people continued to argue and believe that life depends on special life forces. We call this belief **vitalism,** a term that can be understood from the word *vital,* which means living or alive.

But Descartes' position yielded one great advantage—it was subject to experiment. To consider this, take the example of heartbeat. Vitalists, if they considered the psyche or vital force localized at all, often wondered if it was located in the heart. You can see why. Place your hand upon your heart—and think—and you truly can share your ancestors' wondrous feelings about this throbbing presence within their chests. What *makes* the heart beat? Only a few men in Descartes' time had associated heartbeat with the movement of fluids in the body. You will understand, then, that depending on your point of view you might or might not ever learn anything more about heartbeat than you can discover by placing your hand over your heart and wondering (see Figure 4-2).

Would either of the two approaches in Figure 4-2 ever lead to an answer? Descartes and others believed that one eventually might—and time proved them right. Again and again parts and processes of living things proved to be approachable experimentally, and in the same way that parts and processes of the nonliving world were studied experimentally. This direct association of the study of life with the study of any other phenomenon of the earth and universe came to be known as **mechanistic.** (You see the title "Mechanism" over one of the approaches in Figure 4-2.)

With this approach in mind, let us see how scientists tried to solve a very basic problem in biology.

What Makes a Willow Tree?

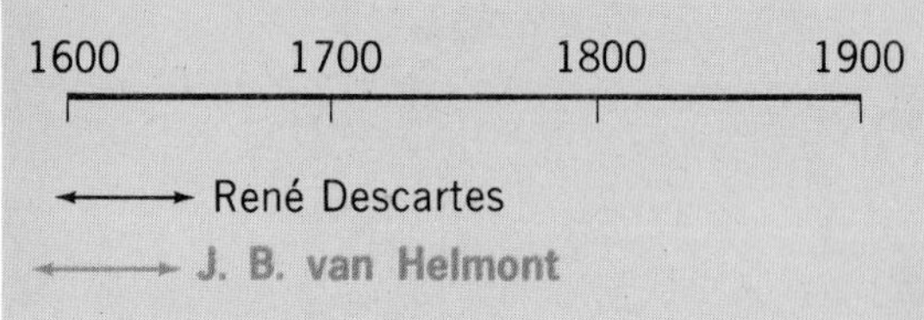

Biologists are quite aware of the role of food. Without it they or other animals do not grow, or even maintain themselves. Instead they waste away and finally die.

What about plants? They do not eat, yet they maintain themselves and grow. When they grow, the living material increases in amount. An acorn may weigh less than an ounce; an oak tree may weigh more than ten tons. When the acorn grows into the oak, where does all the extra material come from?

Aristotle had suggested an answer. The earth manufactures the food, which enters through the roots. This explanation correlated well with some of the facts known to farmers. If crops were grown year after year in the same field, the yield dropped, as though the earth could not make plant food rapidly enough.

Aristotle's idea could lead to this logical hypothesis:

> If a plant grows in a container of earth, the earth should lose weight—because the food it produces will enter the plant. The plant should gain the weight the earth loses.

An experiment testing this deduction was performed by J. B. van Helmont, whom we first encountered in the controversy over

4-2 DIFFERENCES IN APPROACH

VITALISM	MECHANISM
Question: What causes the heart to contract?	Question: What causes the heart to contract?
Hypothesis: A "vital force"	First hypothesis: If the nerve from the brain to the heart is responsible....
Deduction: ?	Deduction: ....then cutting the nerve will stop the heartbeat.
How can experimental deductions be made and tested?	Test: In an experimental animal, the nerve is severed; the heart continues to contract.
	Second hypothesis: If the cause is....

spontaneous generation (page 23). Here is a paraphrased account of his experiment:

> I dried 200 pounds of earth in a furnace and then put it into a large pot. The earth was then moistened with rainwater and a small willow tree was planted. At this time the willow tree weighed five pounds. The earth was kept moist with rainwater or distilled water. Nothing else was added. In order that no dust would get into the pot and add to the weight of the earth, I put a cover on the pot, leaving a hole for the tree trunk.
>
> After five years the entire tree was removed and found to weigh 169 pounds and 3 ounces.

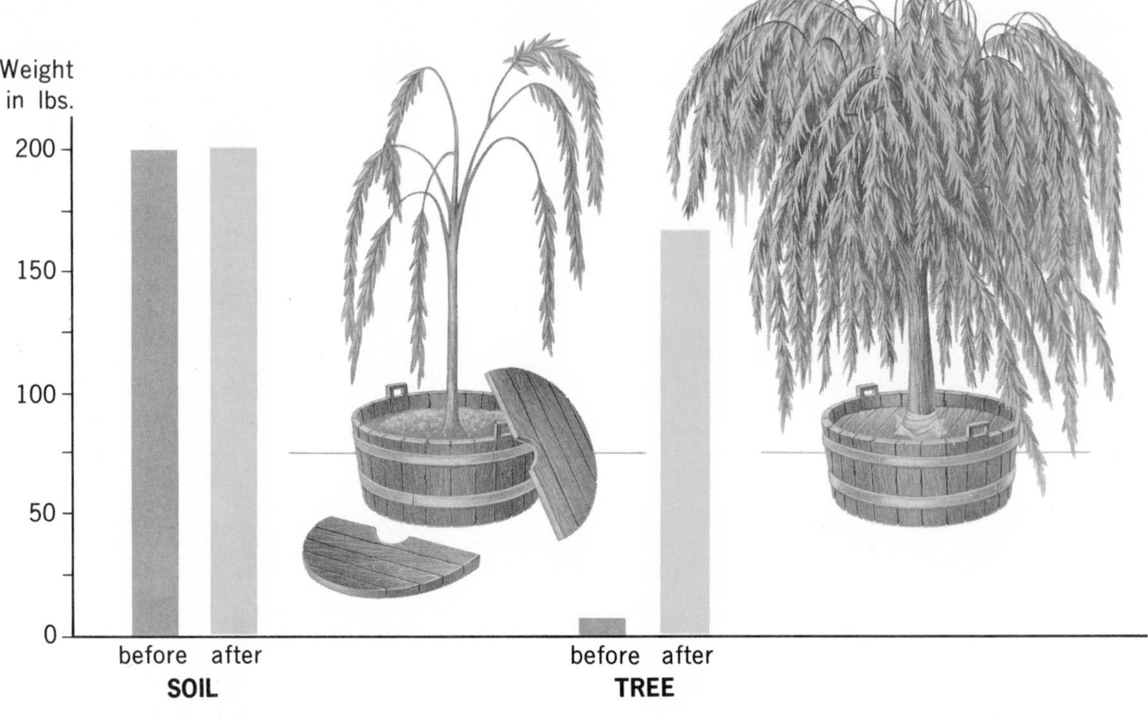

4–3 The growth of a willow tree. As van Helmont's little tree grew, its increase in weight was *not* associated with an equivalent decrease in weight of the soil. Of what importance to his experiment was the cover for the container of earth?

> Since the tree had weighed five pounds at the start, the gain in weight was more than 164 pounds.

If Aristotle was correct, there should have been a great decrease in the weight of the earth —possibly a 164-pound decrease. However, as van Helmont reported:

> I removed the earth from the pot, dried and then weighed it. It weighed 199 pounds and 14 ounces.

Thus, while the earth had lost two ounces, the tree had gained 164 pounds. Clearly, earth-food was not being converted into willow tree in the way Aristotle had suggested. But where did the 164 pounds of willow tree (Figure 4-3) come from? The conclusion van Helmont reached seemed the only logical one to him.

> Therefore, 164 pounds of wood, bark, and roots were formed out of water only.

According to van Helmont, then, water can be converted into living matter—in this case a willow tree. At the time, this seemed an unassailable conclusion, since all that he had added was water. Remember also that he added *pure* water (either rain or distilled water), so that there could be little or no source of error in added substance dissolved in the water.

Robert Boyle (briefly mentioned on page 45—also the chemist whom Robert Hooke served as an apprentice, mentioned on page 41) did similar experiments and obtained the same results, except that he was not sure the earth decreased even a trifling amount in weight.

How could these results be interpreted? Van Helmont thought the water was converted into the living substance of the willow tree. The water was nonliving; the willow tree was living. Somehow the nonliving substance had been transformed into the living.

How? It seemed obvious that more knowledge of the chemistry and physics of the process was necessary.

EARLY CHEMISTRY

In every science there is an attempt to reduce the complex to the simple; to get down to the basic facts. We have had one example—the quest for some unit of structure common to all living creatures. Biologists looking for this unit discovered cells and the cellular nature of both plants and animals.

Could there be units of structure in the nonliving world as well? Many people thought so—in fact, ideas of this sort can be traced back to the days of the Greeks and Romans. Aristotle thought that all matter was composed of varying proportions of earth, water, air, and fire. This could easily be seen in some instances. Thus, when wood was burned, the fire left the wood. Smoke (air) was formed. If the wood was burned near a cold wall, moisture condensed on the wall, showing that water had been in the wood. Finally only ashes (earth) were left. Thus wood was a combination of fire, air, water, and earth.

These four substances were supposed to be **elements**—that is, substances that could not be altered, or destroyed, or divided into simpler substances. The belief that all matter was composed of varying proportions of these four elements lasted for two thousand years. It was still widely accepted in the seventeenth century. Boyle, however, thought the view to be sheer nonsense and suggested that scientists should base their knowledge upon more careful observation and experimentation.

Chemists and physicists ("natural philosophers") of those times had little understanding of the fundamental laws applying to the structure and activity of nonliving matter. Biologists had correspondingly little knowledge of the fundamental laws applying to living organisms. The analysis of one problem—the nature of burning—was of tremendous help to both (Figure 4-4).

The Burning Question

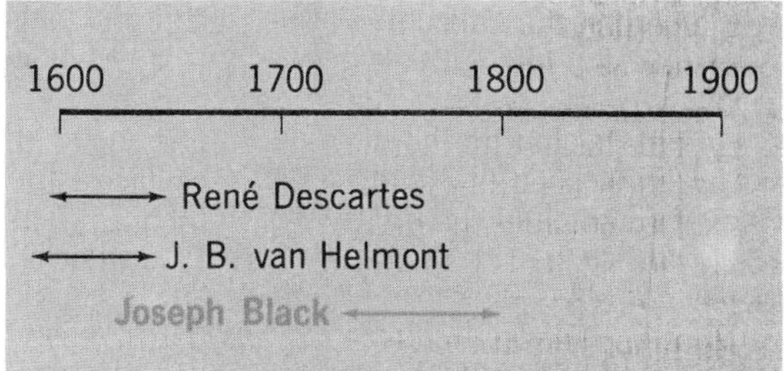

One of the most dramatic activities of the nonliving world is fire. It may be violent. It can be associated with tremendous destruction and with tremendous pain. Is it a substance, an activity, or both? It is so striking that it would be easy to imagine that fire is a special substance, and for years many people felt that this was so. You will recall that fire was one of Aristotle's "elements." Many complicated ideas grew up around this belief.

As it turned out, another early idea—that air is an element—was closely linked to the understanding of fire. Observations and experiments showed that there are many kinds of "air," or *gases* (a name suggested by van Helmont). How, then, could air be thought of as an unchanging element? And matter, reacting with fire (heat), could change in a way that suggested relationship to living processes. Specifically, in 1755 an English chemist, Joseph Black, collected a gas produced by burning charcoal. It was the gas now known as carbon dioxide. The same gas was found by Black to make up a noticeable part of the air coming from people's lungs. Thus, the burning of charcoal and some reaction in the human body were producing the same result—formation of carbon dioxide. What was the significance of these observations? Clearly further study was needed.

4-4 THE BURNING QUESTION

Was fire a FORCE...

Most of man's work for many centuries was accomplished by fire–supporting the concept of fire as a *force*.

1. Fire heated the home.
2. Fire cooked the food.
3. Fire smelted the ores.
4. Fire shaped the metals.

No other known "force" could do this work.

...or CHEMICAL REACTION

Some substances *gained* weight when burned.

Other substances *lost* weight when burned.

In both of these conditions, a part of the air seemed involved, either being taken up by a burning substance or converting part of the substance itself to "spent" air.

...or an ELEMENT ?

Many substances when burned – however unlike they may have appeared before – seemed always to yield common products:

1. the fire itself
2. earth (the ashes)
3. air (the smoke)
4. water (the moisture appearing on cool surfaces exposed to the vapors of fire)

Lavoisier and Burning Phosphorus

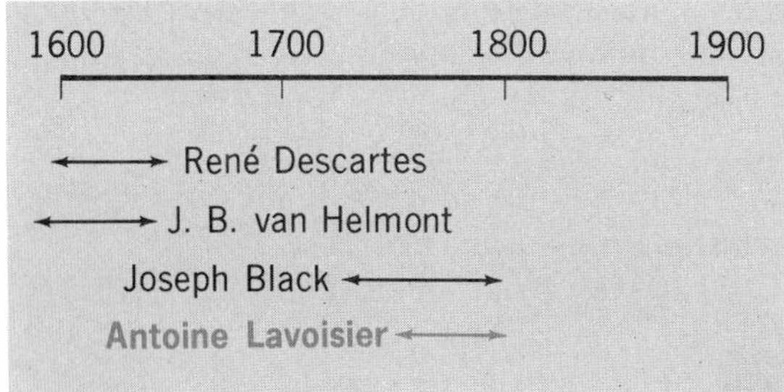

Many further insights into the nature of burning, and into what air really is, came from the French chemist Antoine Lavoisier (luh-VWAH·zee·ay). In one of Lavoisier's experiments, red phosphorus, a very reactive substance, was allowed to burn in a closed vessel containing air. In the process it was converted into a white powder. After the phosphorus had burned, Lavoisier found that one fifth of the air (by volume) had disappeared. Furthermore, by varying the amounts of phosphorus in the container, he found that there was a limit to the amount of phosphorus that would burn in the closed container.

Lavoisier was an exceedingly careful experimenter. Among other things he did was to weigh each of the substances he used, both before and after an experiment, as few others of his time did (Figure 4-5). Let us analyze his experiment.

1. For convenience, we will call the weight of the maximum amount of phosphorus that can burn in the closed container X.
2. After the phosphorus has burned and produced the white powder, we weigh the powder. Let us call this weight Y. We find that Y is considerably greater than X. Therefore, the difference in weight before and after burning is $Y-X$.
3. Let us call the weight of the air in the closed vessel before the phosphorus is burned A.

4-5 Careful observations and measurements are basic to scientific inquiry. Chemical reactions that early investigators witnessed repeatedly with little understanding began to appear more meaningful when the substances were weighed before and after the reactions. Even the gases used or produced by the reactions had to be weighed!

4. After the phosphorus has burned, we find that one fifth of the air (by volume) has disappeared. Let us call the weight of this air B. The difference in weight before and after will be A – B.
5. Lavoisier found again and again that Y – X = A – B. That is, the gain in weight of the phosphorus was exactly equal to the loss in weight of the air.

How can we interpret these results? It would seem that some substance in the air had combined with the phosphorus.

This leads us to another question (as all answers in science do). Why did only one fifth of the air disappear when the phosphorus burned? Why didn't the addition of more phosphorus cause all of the air to be used up? Repeated experiments showed that this was never so: no matter how much phosphorus was used, only one fifth of the air disappeared. We might therefore reach this tentative conclusion, as Lavoisier did: air consists of two parts – one part that will combine with phosphorus, and another that will not.

Priestley, Candles, Mice, and Mint

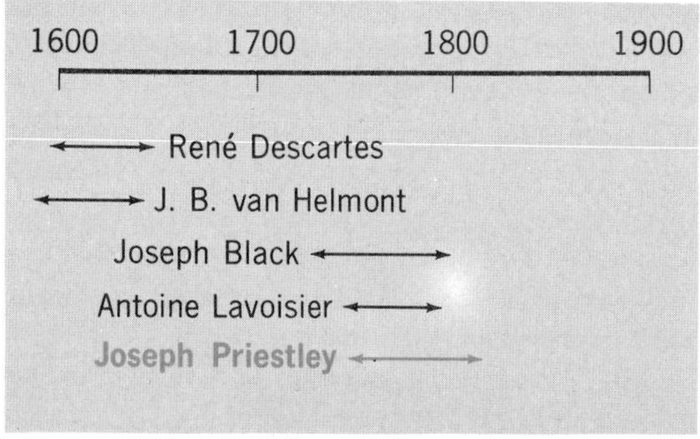

In the same year that Lavoisier published the results of his experiments – 1774 – he was visited by an English parson who was a spare-time chemist, Joseph Priestley. Priestley had been performing similar experiments. Neither Priestley nor Lavoisier had been making rapid progress while working alone. When they discussed their experiments with one another, however, they began to understand things that had been confusing before. New ideas suggested new experiments. New experiments gave new insight. Old questions were answered and new ones took their place. The endless cycle of scientific progress – question, answer, question, answer – continued.

What was Priestley able to tell Lavoisier? Early in his scientific life, Priestley lived in a house next to a brewery. It was wholly accidental that he happened to live near a brewery, but the fact that he did was of enormous importance for both biology and chemistry. He became interested in events occurring within the brewery. He noticed, for example, that bubbles of "air" came from the fermentation vats. He collected some of the air and found it to be the gas we now call carbon dioxide. (Priestley was unaware that Black had previously discovered this gas.)

Carbon dioxide, then, was produced by fermentation. Here was an isolated fact that neither Priestley nor we would seem to be able to do much with – but let us "file and *not* forget."

Priestley found that carbon dioxide could also be obtained by heating limestone or by mixing acid and chalk. (He used the carbon dioxide so produced to make the first artificial carbonated water!) Experiment showed that the new gas differed in many ways from ordinary air. Candles would not burn in carbon dioxide, and a mouse placed in a container of it died quickly. A frog held for six minutes over a fermenting vat became inactive and seemed to be dead. It recovered after being removed to fresh air.

Other experiments showed that ordinary air was changed by a candle flame or a mouse. When a candle was placed in a closed container of air, it burned for a while, but then the flame went out. When a mouse was placed in a closed container of air, the mouse died after some time.

In an interesting double experiment, a lighted candle was placed in the container in which the mouse had died. The flame went out quickly.

4-6 PRIESTLEY'S FIRST EXPERIMENTS WITH AIR

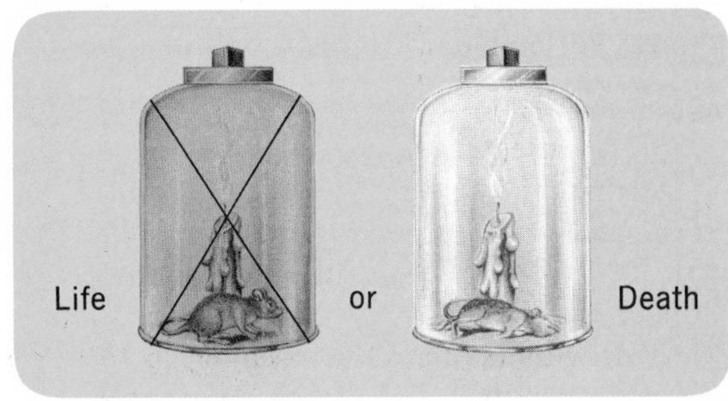

a Priestley uncovered one of the great relationships in chemistry and in life with a mouse and a candle...

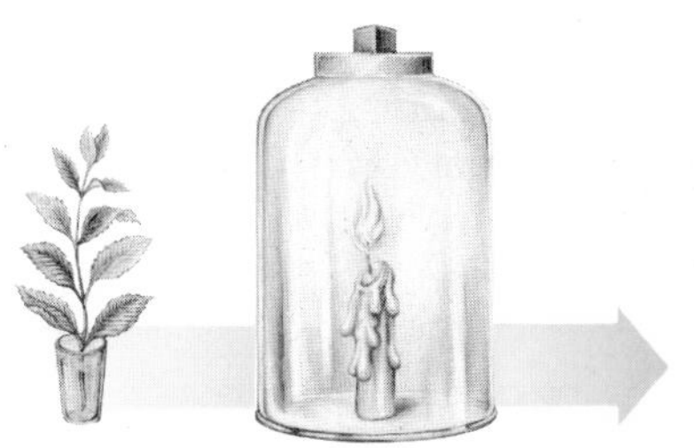

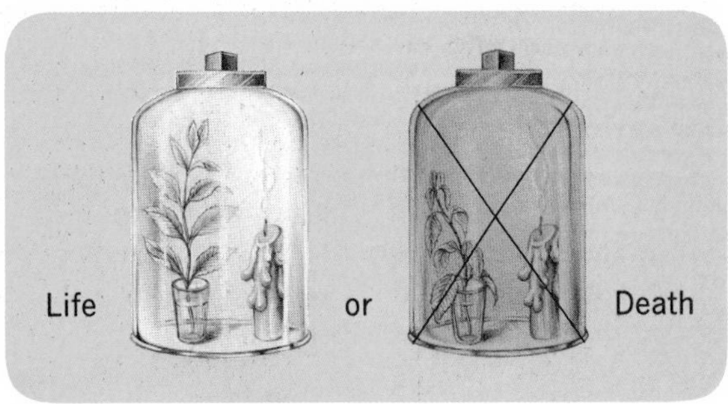

b ...and a sprig of mint and a candle. Why did the mint live but the mouse die?

c Why could the candle be made to burn again after the mint had been in the jar for several days? Could a mouse have breathed the air "renewed" by the mint?

The mouse and the burning candle must have been using something in common from the air (Figure 4-6). Air that they had used was made "worthless" in some manner. But think what this seems to mean. We and many other animals are breathing all the time. Eventually we would destroy the life-supporting portion of the air. This point puzzled Priestley, too, until he made another important discovery, reported in an article in the *Philosophical Transactions* for 1772 (refer to text page 45):

> It is evident . . . that there must be some provision in nature for this purpose, as well as for that of rendering the air fit for sustaining flame; for without it the whole mass of the atmosphere would, in time, become unfit for the purpose of animal life, and yet there is no reason to think that it is, at present, at all

less fit for respiration than it has ever been. I flatter myself, however, that I have hit upon [a method] employed by nature for this great purpose.

. . . on the 17th of August, 1771, I put a sprig of mint [plant] in a quantity of air in which a wax candle had burned out, and found that on the 27th of the same month another candle burned perfectly well in it. This experiment I repeated, without the least variation in the event, not less than eight or ten times in the remainder of the summer. Several times I divided the quantity of air in which the candle had burned out, into two parts, and putting the plant into one of them, left the other in the same exposure, contained, also, in a glass vessel immersed in water, but without any plant [this was Priestley's control]; and never failed to find, that a candle would burn in the former but not the latter. I usually found that five or six days were sufficient to restore the air.

Priestley wrote to an American friend, Benjamin Franklin, to tell him of the experiments and received this summarizing statement in reply:

That the vegetable creation should restore the air which is spoiled by the animal part of it, looks like a rational system. . .

Priestley was able to tell Lavoisier about these interesting observations on mice, candles, mint, and carbon dioxide. But he had another observation that interested Lavoisier more.

The Discovery of Oxygen

Priestley had taken a chemical substance, known now as red oxide of mercury, and heated it by focusing sunlight upon it with a "burning glass." The heated chemical produced mercury and gave off a gas—a gas unlike air or carbon dioxide. As Priestley reported:

. . . what surprised me more than I can express, was, that a candle burned in this air with a remarkably vigorous flame . . . I was utterly at a loss how to account for it.

Furthermore, when a mouse was placed in a container with this new gas, it lived twice as long as did a mouse in another container of the same size containing ordinary air. Priestley breathed some of the gas and reported:

. . . my breast felt peculiarly light and easy for some time afterwards . . . who can tell but that, in time, this pure air may become a fashionable article in luxury. Hitherto only two mice and myself have had the privilege of breathing it.

Priestley was not the first man to discover the new gas, but to him must go the credit for the usefulness of the discovery. He published his results promptly, unlike another chemist who really discovered the gas first. Here we meet again one of the necessary conditions of science: making a discovery is not enough—it must be made known to other scientists.

Priestley's new gas, so invigorating for him to breathe, proved invigorating in an entirely different way to Lavoisier. As Priestley related his findings to his French host, Lavoisier's mind ticked rapidly through a comparison of Priestley's work with his own. A new theory began to emerge in his thoughts. Could the one fifth of air used up by his burning phosphorus (or Priestley's mice and candles?) be identical to Priestley's invigorating new gas?

Shortly afterward, in an experiment brilliant in its directness and simplicity, Lavoisier confined air and pure mercury together and slowly heated the mercury. At first nothing happened, then slowly—over a period of days—a change began to take place. The mercury was changing in appearance—and the volume of air began to decrease! At the end of twelve days, the reaction stopped. Almost one fifth of the air had been used up, and the mercury had been converted back to red oxide of mercury—the substance Priestley had used to obtain his "pure air"!

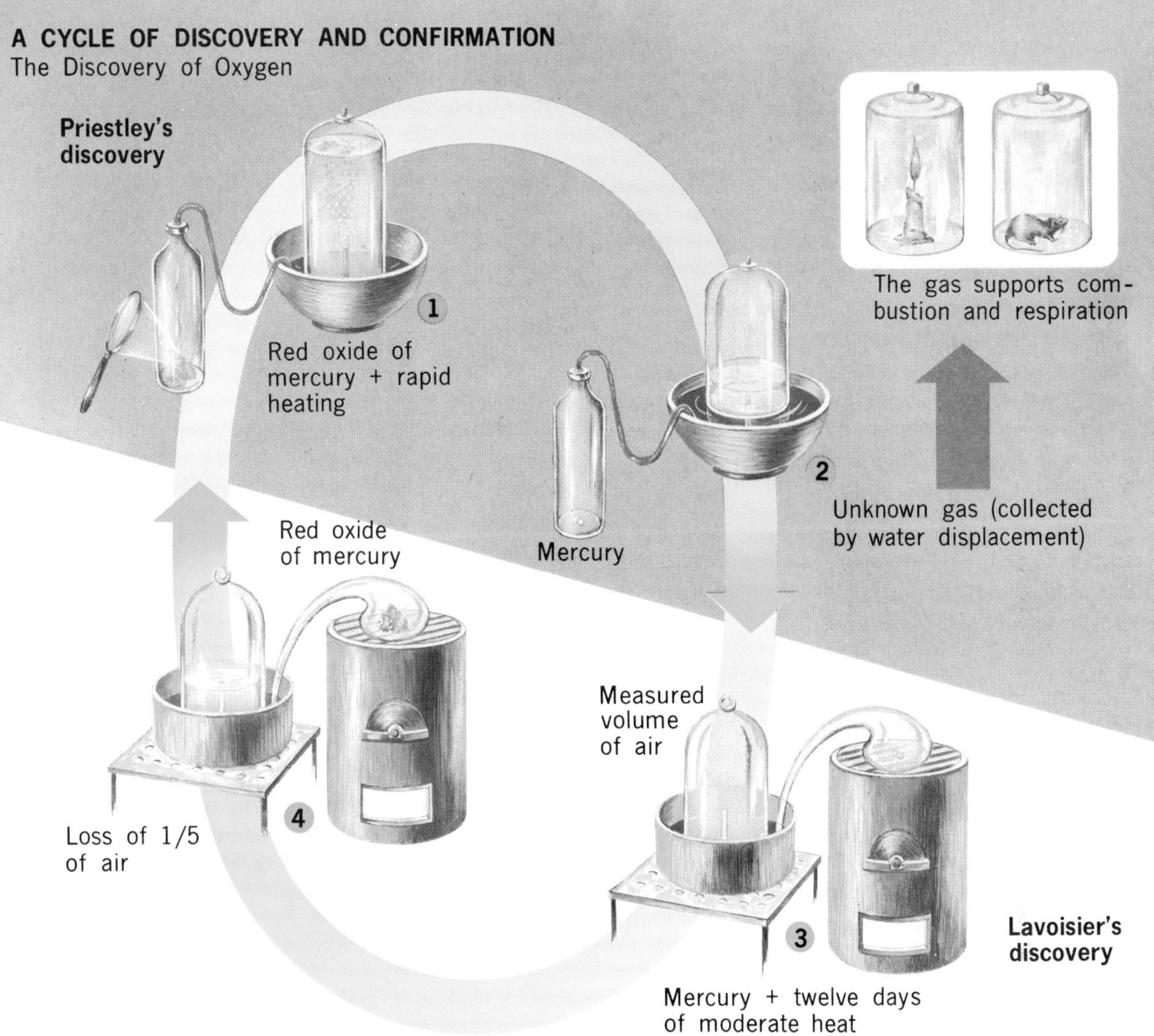

4–7 Priestley evolved an unknown gas by concentrating the sun's rays upon red oxide of mercury. From the properties of the gas as Priestley described them, Lavoisier guessed at its nature and tested his hypothesis by trying to reverse the reaction, using mercury and ordinary air. Lavoisier's genius lay in his realization that his work with burning substances, and Priestley's work with the unknown gas, were related.

There was no longer any doubt (Figure 4-7). *Oxygen,* as Lavoisier named the invigorating gas, was a part of air. It supported combustion and respiration alike. Combustion and respiration were alike, too, in another way – in the flame and heat of the burning charcoal and phosphorus, and in the "animal heat" of the mouse. This was a tremendous concept. A living process – **respiration** – was being interpreted in the same way as a chemical reaction. Respiration was close to life itself. If it stopped for more than a moment, life ceased.

Could anything so fundamental to life be explained by the laws of the nonliving world? Lavoisier was answering "Yes." This was one of the first examples of the successful explanation of a biological problem in mechanistic terms.

The Law of Conservation of Mass

Before we leave Lavoisier we must emphasize another of his magnificent contributions to science. He measured and weighed with the finest analytical balances that he could obtain. He observed that the total weight of all the substances at the end of each reaction was the same as the weight of all the substances at the beginning. This fact also had been observed in many carefully performed experiments done years before Lavoisier's lifetime. Van Helmont, for example, had observed the same constancy of total weight.

These experiments suggested that matter could not be destroyed—though of course it could be changed. The total **mass**, or quantity of matter, remains the same. This fundamental principle became known as the

> *Law of Conservation of Mass:* Matter can neither be created nor destroyed. The mass of the substances present before and after a reaction or change is the same.

Matter: Transformable and Nontransformable

During the seventeenth and eighteenth centuries some exceptionally useful ideas about chemistry were emerging. Robert Boyle (pages 45, 58) suggested a theory that, with many modifications, eventually proved true.

According to Boyle, there were two sorts of chemical substances—**elements** and **compounds.** The *elements* were the ultimate kinds of matter. They could not be divided into simpler substances, nor could they be changed into one another. The *compounds,* on the other hand, were composed of two or more elements, chemically united.

As time went on, more and more chemists regarded this as a good working hypothesis. Lavoisier added to it. He found that the elements in air seemed to be *physically* but not chemically united. Air, then, was a simple **mixture.** Unlike the elements in compounds, the parts of air seemed to separate or come together again without evidence of chemical reaction.

So there were elements, mixtures, and compounds. Compounds were those substances that could be broken down chemically into the simpler elements. Mixtures could simply be "unmixed." Elements could not be broken down at all. Thus gold, sulfur, silver, lead, copper, mercury, and carbon were regarded as elements. Air was a mixture. Sulfuric acid, mercuric oxide, and limestone were compounds.

The definitions seemed to be clear and untroublesome. In practice they were not. How could a chemist know whether an unknown substance was an element or a compound? He could not look it up in a book! Suppose that he took a substance X and used it in many experiments. He might find that it would combine with many other substances, but that no matter how he tried, he could not divide X itself into simpler substances. Could he safely conclude that X is an element? No. All he could conclude would be that on the basis of his experiments, X behaved as an element. It could be possible that X is really a compound, and that he did not perform the proper experiments to prove this.

Thus, often in the early days there was doubt about whether a substance was an element or a compound (Figure 4-8). Water is a good example. Repeated efforts to divide it into simpler substances failed. Then, near the end of the eighteenth century, it was found that hydrogen could be burned in the presence of oxygen to yield water. Water, therefore, was shown to be a compound composed of the elements oxygen and hydrogen. Efforts to break water down continued to fail, until electricity could be applied to the problem.

As one chemist expressed it in 1857, "The elements count as simple substances not because we know that they are, but because we do not know that they are not!"

Dalton and the Atomic Theory

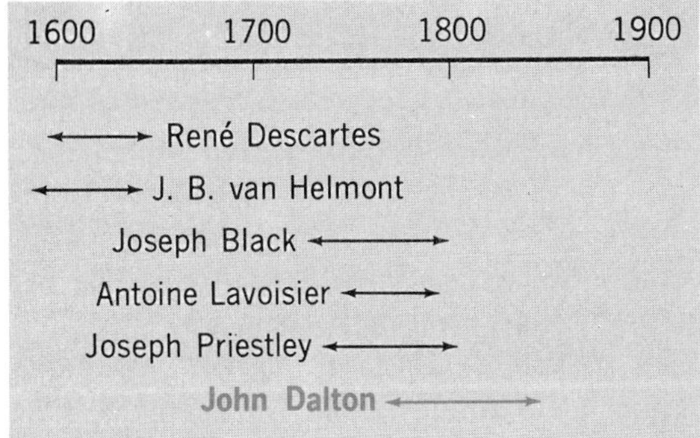

Other chemists followed Lavoisier's lead, and soon many interesting facts and relations were discovered. Lavoisier himself did not live to take part in these developments; he was executed during the French Revolution. But the Englishman John Dalton pursued Lavoisier's doctrine of careful measurement and established the Atomic Theory.

We begin to approach the concept of an atom when we ask this question: what is the ultimate structure of matter? Boyle, Lavoisier, and others spoke of elements, but what are the elements really like? If one could examine carbon, mercury, oxygen, and hydrogen with a tremendously powerful microscope, would there be basic units of structure in the same sense that cells are units of living structure?

The compound microscope gives one answer: No. The highest magnifications available, even today, reveal no unit of structure common to all elements. Oxygen and hydrogen are invisible. Both carbon and mercury have their own peculiar microscopic appearances. No chemical "cells" common to even two of these four elements are revealed by the microscope. But careful work with the chemists' balance has shown that there are other ways of "looking" at chemical substances.

4-8 ELEMENT OR COMPOUND?

a For the eighteenth-century chemist, one test of whether a substance was an element or a compound was whether it could be decomposed by heat.

b Chemical tests also were made. Could the substance be broken down into simpler substances in this way?

c Even physical means were tried. Hammers, chisels, mortars and pestles, and other tools were called into use.

d Sometimes the evidence came in a surprising way. Efforts to decompose water, for example, failed, but what happened when the gas *hydrogen* was burned in air?

If you measure very carefully the weights of the different elements that react to form a compound, you can find an important relationship: the ratio of weights is always the same. In water, for example, the oxygen always weighs 8 times as much as the hydrogen. If we burn 1 gram of hydrogen in 8 grams of oxygen, we get 9 grams of water. If we start with 2 grams of hydrogen and 8 grams of oxygen, we still get 9 grams of water—this time with 1 gram of hydrogen left over. The elements in a compound are in constant proportion by weight.

The same elements that form *one* compound may combine in a different way to form another. For example, oxygen and hydrogen form not only water but also another compound, hydrogen peroxide. The weights of the hydrogen and oxygen in this case are in the proportion 1 (hydrogen) to 16 (oxygen).

Notice the difference. In water the ratio of hydrogen to oxygen is 1 to 8. In hydrogen peroxide it is 1 to 16. In other words, the relative weight of oxygen is exactly twice as great in the case of hydrogen peroxide.

The same relation was observed repeatedly with other elements in many different compounds. Under one set of conditions, 3 grams of carbon plus 4 of oxygen will yield 7 grams of carbon monoxide. Under other conditions, 3 grams of carbon plus 8 of oxygen will yield 11 grams of carbon dioxide. Again notice the ratio of the weights of oxygen to the constant weight of carbon. In carbon dioxide, as compared with carbon monoxide, there is twice as much oxygen in proportion to the carbon.

Note more closely the ratios by weight in the two sets of examples:

Water:	1 (hydrogen)	to	8 (oxygen)
Hydrogen peroxide:	1 (hydrogen)	to	16 (oxygen)
Carbon monoxide:	3 (hydrogen)	to	4 (oxygen)
Carbon dioxide:	3 (hydrogen)	to	8 (oxygen)

In each *pair* of ratios, the left-hand members remain unchanged. The right-hand members change in what appears to be *their own ratio of small whole numbers*. For example, the two oxygen ratios—8 to 16, and 4 to 8—are both 1-to-2 relationships. It is important to notice that the ratio is *exactly* a whole-number ratio (1 to 2). Neither member of the ratio is a fraction, such as $^7/_{18}$ to 1, or $^{29}/_{11}$ to 2, or 1 to $^9/_{17}$.

What does all this mean? How can we use these data obtained by chemists with their balances?

Let us suggest an answer to these two questions by asking two more. Have you noticed from the examples that *either* 1 part of hydrogen *or* 3 parts of carbon can combine with 8 parts of oxygen? Suppose the carbon and hydrogen were combining with one another instead of with *the same amounts* of oxygen. Can you predict the proportions of carbon and hydrogen that might combine to form a carbon-hydrogen compound?

The chances are you guessed correctly. The smelly compound methane (or marsh gas) consists of 1 part by weight of hydrogen and 3 parts of carbon!

In 1808, data of this sort were put together by John Dalton in what is known as the Atomic Theory. Dalton suggested that:

1. Matter is composed of particles which are indestructible, indivisible, and discrete. He used the name **atoms** for these particles.
2. All atoms of a single element are the same. That is, all oxygen atoms are alike, especially in having the same mass.
3. The atoms of different elements differ from one another. That is, oxygen atoms, hydrogen atoms, and carbon atoms differ from one another, especially in having different masses.
4. Compounds are formed by the union of atoms, and only *whole* atoms can combine in this way.

Dalton's theory gives us an explanation of the interesting relation between the relative proportions of oxygen in carbon monoxide and carbon dioxide, or in hydrogen peroxide and water. Let us assume that small particles of carbon monoxide are each made of one atom of carbon and one of oxygen. We know that the ratio by weight of carbon to oxygen in carbon monoxide is 3 to 4. Our reasoning now leads us to suggest that the union of one carbon atom and two oxygen atoms would give us carbon dioxide, with its carbon to oxygen ratio of 3 to 8. The ratio could not be 3 to 6, or 3 to 10, for according to Dalton only whole atoms can combine.

In Chapter 5, we will see that Dalton's ideas about atoms proved to be very helpful in leading to other questions about matter. The possibility was opened up for asking why atoms should differ in size and in ways of reacting with other atoms. This in turn led to understanding of the structure of atoms themselves. But in 1808, Dalton's theory was only a *possible* explanation. It suggested that the data of chemistry could be interpreted in terms of indestructible atoms.

THE BEGINNING OF BIOCHEMISTRY

The Atomic Theory threw doubt on van Helmont's conclusion regarding the willow tree experiment. Could water *alone* be transformed into the substance of a willow tree? Water is *oxygen* and *hydrogen*. A willow tree is composed of compounds of oxygen, hydrogen, and *many other elements, including carbon and nitrogen*. If Dalton was right, van Helmont had to be wrong; indestructible atoms of oxygen and hydrogen in water could not yield all the different atoms in willow trees.

Lavoisier's and Dalton's new ideas in chemistry were exceedingly helpful in understanding many chemical phenomena. At first, however, they were not of much help in accounting for the activities that take place in plants and animals. It was true that the relation between respiration and combustion was established, involving reaction with oxygen.

It proved to be exceedingly difficult to study the chemistry of living organisms. For the most part, they seemed to consist of a tremendous variety of different compounds unanalyzable by the available chemical methods.

Not only were living organisms almost entirely unanalyzable, but in the early years of the nineteenth century chemists could not *make* in their laboratories any of the substances known to occur in living creatures. They might be quite skillful in juggling Dalton's atoms to produce the chemical compounds of the nonliving world. They could even obtain alcohol or sugar from living materials and determine its composition in terms of elements. They could not, however, take the elements and make alcohol or sugar. This inability was all the more distressing when it was found that sugar was composed only of the elements carbon, hydrogen, and oxygen. It would seem easy, wouldn't it?

A justifiable conclusion in 1825 would have been this: living organisms are made, at least in part, of chemical substances that can be **analyzed** (divided into parts) and shown to consist of the common elements, but it is impossible to **synthesize** (or unite from parts) these substances from the elements of which they are made. This synthesis, it was supposed, can be accomplished only by living creatures and seems to involve some kind of a "vital force." Had the experimental method gone so far only to prove its rival philosophy?

The unique substances in organisms were named **organic compounds.** Chemists soon found that all of these organic compounds contained carbon. In addition, most of them contained oxygen and hydrogen. Other elements were less frequent.

Compounds which were not restricted to living organisms were named **inorganic compounds.** Some inorganic compounds contained carbon, but this was not so frequently the case.

Wöhler's Synthesis of an Organic Compound

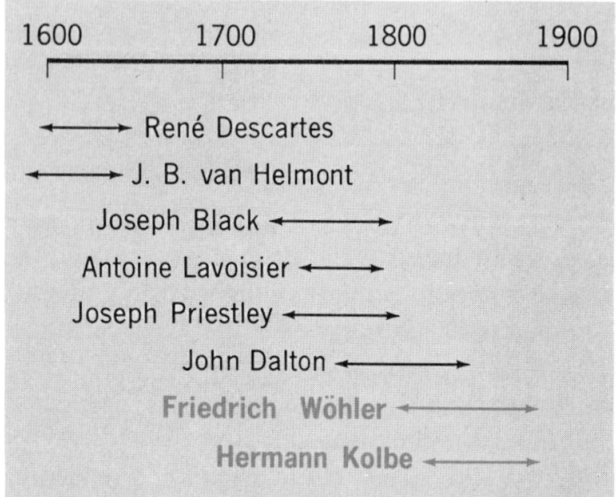

In 1828 Friedrich Wöhler (VIUL·er) suggested it was not the "vital force" in an organism but the ignorance of the chemist that prevented successful laboratory synthesis of organic compounds. He discovered one organic compound that could be produced in the laboratory. Wöhler heated a solution of a substance known as ammonium cyanate. A new substance was formed which on further study was found to be **urea** (yoo·REE·a). Urea is a compound found in urine and, as such, is a product of living organisms. Until Wöhler had performed this experiment, urea could be produced only by living cells.

Wöhler had not quite done the critical experiment, namely, to produce an organic compound using only *in*organic materials. Although ammonium cyanate would generally be classed as an inorganic compound, Wöhler had made it from substances obtained from animals. It remained for one of Wöhler's students, Hermann Kolbe (KOHL·beh), to complete the achievement. Using the elements carbon, sulfur, and chlorine—plus water, which chemists knew could be produced by uniting the elements hydrogen and oxygen—he produced **acetic** (a·SEE·tik) **acid** in 1844. This appears to be the first case of an organic compound's being made solely from inorganic materials.

Urea and acetic acid were humble beginnings, but their synthesis in the laboratory was a triumph of scientific endeavor. At least *some* organic compounds could be produced without the assistance of a vital force. Gradually more and more chemists and biologists began to suggest that perhaps all organic compounds could be made in the laboratory. *Knowledge* was what was required—not a vital force!

Let us continue to be cautious, however. Even if chemists could synthesize some organic compounds in the laboratory, it did not follow that all the activities of organisms were explainable by the laws of chemistry and physics. There were some obvious difficulties. Chemical reactions in the laboratory usually occurred with at least *some* noticeable changes. Few were violent in the sense that combustion so often was—but nearly all produced a change that could be detected readily (even if it required observation over a period of days, as with Lavoisier's synthesis of red oxide of mercury—see page 65). Perhaps the most noticeable change would be in color, or solubility in water, or taste, or change of state (from solid to liquid or liquid to gas, or vice versa, in association with some other property). The point was that *a change would be noticed.*

Disappointingly, no such changes were observed in living cells examined under the microscope. Furthermore, the temperatures in organisms did not even approach the range necessary to activate most of the chemical changes that took place in the laboratory.

In spite of this it appeared that chemical changes were occurring in cells. How else could organic compounds originate?

Clearly there was some immense flaw in the understanding of chemistry as it applied to living organisms. It was unthinkable that two opposing points of view were *both* correct—that complex chemical changes could take place in living organisms that apparently could *not* provide the conditions necessary for those changes (Figure 4-9). Some important piece of information was missing.

4-9 THE MISSING LINK

Chemistry in the Laboratory	Chemistry in the Body
Oxygen was found to be required for many reactions in the laboratory—chiefly combustion and other oxidation reactions.	Similarly, oxygen was found to be required by the body of a man or a mouse or other animal during respiration.
If a piece of charcoal was burned, carbon dioxide would be given off.	Carbon dioxide was given off by the body during respiration.
Combustion in the laboratory was almost never a self-starting process. An increase of temperature to the proper ignition temperature was required.	Respiration seemed to take place in the body without change in temperature; no "ignition" temperature appeared to be involved at all.
Combustion in the laboratory yielded visible or measurable light and heat—and often smoke.	Respiration seemed to yield no light, no measurable heat (above the normal body temperature), and no smoke.

Was it possible that similar processes could be taking place under different conditions in the laboratory and in the body?

Spallanzani and Gastric Juice

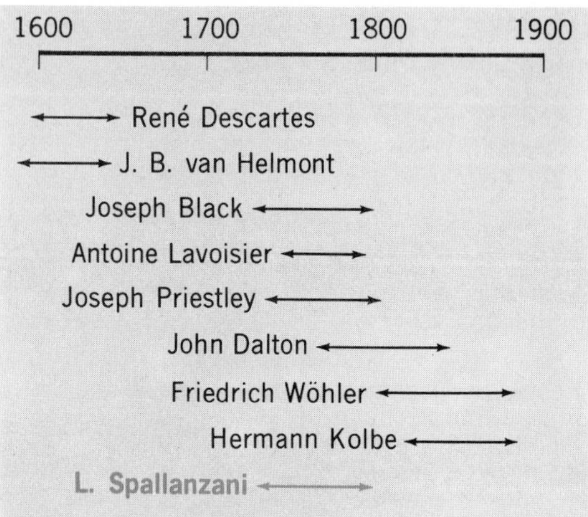

During the period when Priestley and Lavoisier were performing their experiments in England and France, in Italy Lazzaro Spallanzani was studying digestion. (Recall from page 31 that he was also interested in the question of spontaneous generation.)

It was already known that foods such as meats and vegetables become liquid in the stomach and intestine. Was this a chemical reaction? And could it occur only in a living organism?

Spallanzani noticed a fluid, which he called **gastric juice,** in the stomachs of birds that he studied experimentally. He speculated that this gastric juice might "dissolve" the food. He tested the hypothesis as follows:

> I have found the gizzards of turkies and geese most abounding in gastric juices, probably on account of their superior size. I was induced by the quantity they afforded to attempt an experiment . . . It consisted in trying, whether these juices retain their solvent power out of the stomach. For this purpose, I took two tubes sealed hermetically at one end, and at the other with wax: into one I put several bits of mutton, and into the other several bruised grains of wheat, and then filled them with the gastric liquor. In order that they might have the condition which in these animals precedes digestion, they had been macerated in the craw of a turkey cock. And as the warmth of the stomach is probably another condition necessary to the solution of food, I contrived to supply it by communicating to the tubes a degree of heat nearly equal, by fixing them under my arm-pits. In this situation I kept them at different intervals for three days, at the expiration of which time I opened them. The tube with the grains of wheat was first examined; most of them now consisted of the bare husk, the flour having been extracted, and forming a thick grey sediment at the bottom of the tube. The flesh in the other tube was in great measure dissolved (it did not exhale the least putrid smell), and was incorporated with the gastric juice, which was hence rendered more turbid and dense. What little remained had lost its natural redness, and had become exceedingly tender. Upon putting it into another tube, and adding fresh gastric liquor, and replacing it under my arm-pits, the remainder was dissolved in the course of a day.
>
> I repeated these experiments with other grains of wheat bruised and macerated in the same manner, and likewise upon some flesh of the same kind, but instead of gastric juice I employed common water. After the two tubes had remained three days under my arm-pits, I found that the grains, where they were broken, were slightly excavated, which was occasioned by an incipient solution of the pulpy substance. The flesh had also undergone a slight superficial solution, but internally it appeared fibrous, red, firm, and in short, had all the characters of flesh. It was also putrid; and wheat too had acquired some acidity, two circumstances which did not take place in the grains and flesh immersed in the gastric liquor.
>
> These facts are then irrefutable proofs that the gastric juice retains even out of its natural situation the power of dissolving animal and

vegetable substances in a degree far superior to water.

This was a very important discovery. The process of digestion, whatever it might involve, *could take place outside of the body.* This meant that the process could be studied under the controlled conditions of the laboratory. One could then try to isolate from gastric juice a substance that had the power of digesting food.

From Ferments to Enzymes

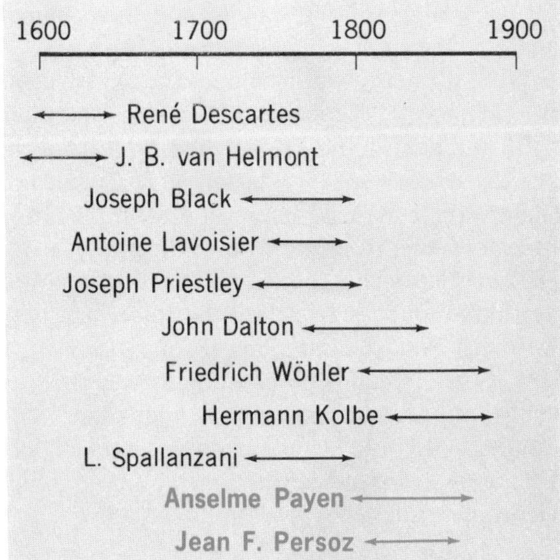

During the early part of the nineteenth century, two French chemists, Payen (pie·OHN) and Persoz (pehr·SOHZ), ground up barley seeds in water to make a crude mixture that would digest starch. Payen and Persoz gave the name **diastase** (DY·a·stays) to whatever it was that digested the starch. They did not know whether it was a substance or a vital force. If it was a substance, it might be possible to isolate it in a relatively pure form. If it was a vital force, it could not, of course, be separated from the living barley seeds.

Their problem was to begin with the crude mixture of barley seeds in water and try to extract a pure diastase. The first thing they did was to *filter* the mixture. That is, they poured the mixture into a funnel that was lined with a good grade of paper known as filter paper. The paper was designed to hold back particles even as small as cells, but to allow the water and substances dissolved in it to pass through. The material that passed the filter was known as the **filtrate** (FIL·trayt).

The first step in their purification was the separation of the active mixture into two parts—the filtrate and the part held back by the filter paper. Which fraction was active? They tested each on starch and found that the liquid portion or filtrate was active. They knew, therefore, that diastase could be removed from the crushed barley seeds.

What should they do next to purify their material? There was no guide for them to follow—no previous experiments to suggest how they might proceed. Their approach would have to be hit-or-miss. They heated the active filtrate to 70° C. The heat coagulated some of the material in the filtrate. They filtered it again. Once more they found that the activity was present in the filtrate. The materials caught by the filter paper were inactive.

Would a higher temperature purify the diastase more? The active filtrate was heated to 100° C. More substance was coagulated and removed by filtration. Tests showed that the coagulated material was inactive. What about the filtrate? It also was inactive. Too bad! This experiment had destroyed the diastase.

They had to start all over. This time they were careful not to heat the material to 100° C. The seeds were ground up in water, the mixture filtered, and the filtrate heated to 70° C as before. The filtrate was active. At this point they tried something else. Alcohol was added, and it produced a precipitate in the filtrate. Filtration then was used to separate the precipitate from the filtrate. Both the precipitate and the filtrate were tested, and this time only the precipitate was active. The precipitate, diastase, was a white, solid material. It could be purified further by dissolving it in water and precipitating it again with alcohol.

The purified diastase was very active in digesting starch. One part of diastase, dissolved in water, could digest 1,000 parts of starch in ten minutes!

The digestive action was found to be definitely a chemical change (and not a matter of dissolving). Payen and Persoz had shown that the chemical change depends upon a substance. More important, this substance could be extracted and purified (Figure 4-10), then used to carry out its activities in the laboratory apart from a living system. These observations of Payen and Persoz were of the greatest importance for our understanding of living chemistry. Today, it is useful to repeat and even extend their work, and we suggest that you carry out Inquiry 4-1 in the laboratory at this point.

Diastase and similar substances provided a key to the understanding of many activities of organisms. Reactions that at first seemed impossible for the chemist to carry out were made possible with the aid of these substances isolated from living organisms. In 1879 the name **enzyme** (EN·zyme) was suggested for such a substance and it is the name we still use today. Diastase was one of the first enzymes obtained in a partially purified form. Two of the characteristics of diastase were found to be true of all enzymes: first, a temperature of 100° C destroys them; second, the enzymes are active even when present only in traces. Recall that 1 part of diastase could digest 1,000 parts of starch.

Enzymes provided the answer to why certain chemical changes can take place rapidly in the absence of high temperatures.

As the nineteenth century progressed, biologists came more and more to the view that the many activities in cells are controlled by enzymes. Most of these activities are so complex that even today the chemist cannot duplicate them in his laboratory without using enzymes. No vital force is involved—the chemist uses enzymes as tools, knowing that these enzymes are simply chemical compounds, though of special and complicated structure.

There is more to the enzyme story, and we shall return to it in Chapter 6 and again in Chapter 8. What we must consider now is a more basic question: why is chemical activity necessary to living organisms?

Chemical Activity for What?

When Priestley and Lavoisier compared the activity of a mouse and the activity of a burning candle, they suggested an important relation. The candle and mouse both used oxygen in reactions that liberate **energy**—the heat and light of the candle and the "animal heat" of the mouse.

What is energy and why does the mouse need it? Is *energy* a specific something? Neither light nor heat could be weighed on a balance. A closed container of water at 0° C has the same weight as at 50° C, even though the latter has more energy in the form of heat.

The relationship of energy to reactions did not make much sense until the following facts were discovered. Under one set of experimental conditions, chemical substances A and B could combine to form AB. Under other conditions, AB could be broken down into A and B. In other words, the reaction was reversible. We can express these relations as follows:

$$A + B \rightarrow AB$$

$$AB \rightarrow A + B$$

Careful observations and measurements showed that if heat was *needed* to make A and B combine, then heat would be *liberated* when AB changed into A + B. Heat, as noted, is a form of energy, so we will abbreviate it as "e." We can rewrite our equations as follows:

$$A + B + e_1 \rightarrow AB$$

$$AB \rightarrow A + B + e_2$$

The amount of heat required for the one reaction was found to be exactly the same as the amount liberated in the reverse reaction. In other words, $e_1 = e_2$. This relationship soon was verified for other chemical reactions.

4-10 THE SEARCH FOR THE MISSING LINK

Birds and barley provided the clue to differences between chemistry in the laboratory and in living organisms.

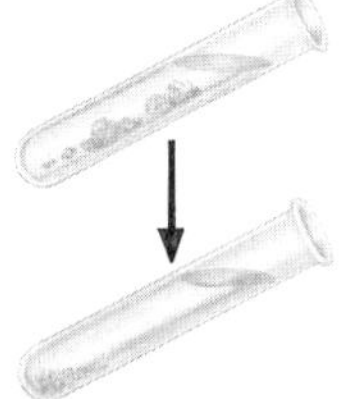

Spallanzani found that gastric juices of turkeys and geese would decompose meats and grain even in the laboratory.

Payen and Persoz found that barley grains would digest starch. They ground some barley and mixed it with cold water:

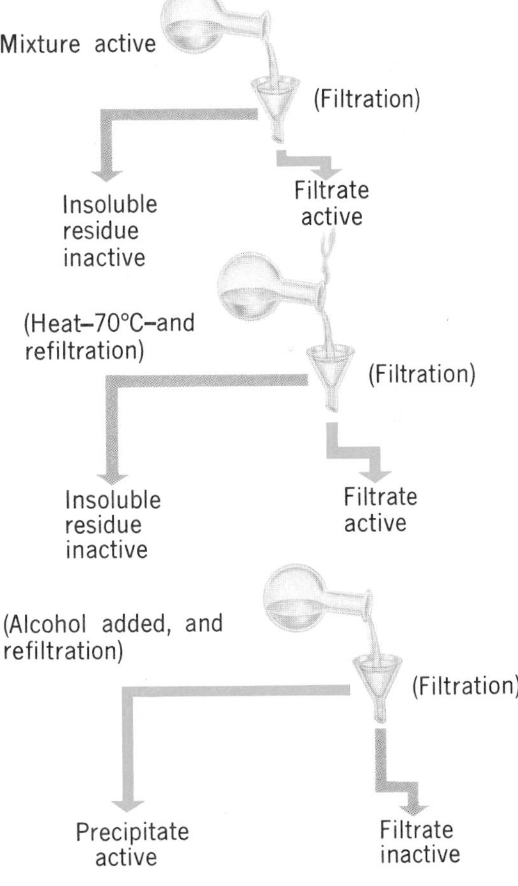

(Diastase—the first enzyme to be purified)

Energy and Its Varieties

In the nineteenth century, chemists and physicists came to realize that there was a relationship between heat, light, and—once it was discovered—electricity. *All* are forms of energy. But again, what *is* energy? About the best general, though not really satisfactory answer that could be given at that time was that *energy* is the ability to do work.

There are many situations with which you are already familiar where energy is required to get things done. Perhaps you live in a community where the electricity is generated from water power. Even if you do not, we could illustrate the point by considering a power plant near a waterfall. The water has the ability to do work as it drops from the top of the falls to the bottom. We could show this to be the case by putting a waterwheel in the falls. The wheel would be rotated by the falling water.

In former times, waterwheels of this sort were used to operate mills. First, a dam was constructed across a stream to provide the site for the waterwheel. The wheel was mounted in the waterfall and was attached to an axle. The axle was attached to heavy millstones which turned and crushed the grain (Figure 4-11). This was work!

A wheel of this sort could also be attached to a generator. In this case, the energy released by the falling water would be used to generate electricity.

Not only water, but any mass of substance which can fall downward has energy of this sort; as opposed to heat or light or electricity we term it *mechanical energy*. As in the case of the waterwheel, mechanical energy can always be turned into *electrical energy*.

Now think of the many kinds of work that *electricity* can do. It can be used to *mechanically raise* a heavy elevator from one floor to another. It can be used to *light* our homes. It can be used to produce *heat* in electric stoves. So electrical energy can be turned into other forms—mechanical, light, and heat.

Electricity can also do *chemical* work. You will remember that a chemical reaction $A + B \rightarrow AB$ can take place if energy is added in the form of heat. In much the same way, electrical energy can be used to give energy to a chemical reaction. Let us look at a particular case. With electricity we can separate ordinary table salt (sodium chloride) into sodium and chlorine.

$$\text{sodium chloride} + e_1 \rightarrow \text{sodium} + \text{chlorine}$$

If we let the sodium, a solid, and the chlorine, a gas, come together again, they react very quickly to form sodium chloride, releasing energy:

$$\text{sodium} + \text{chlorine} \rightarrow \text{sodium chloride} + e_2$$

The amount of energy released is exactly the same as the amount needed in reaction 1. Once again, $e_1 = e_2$. It is important to note that in this example, e_1 was supplied as *electricity*, and e_2 was released as *heat*.

These examples show how all forms of energy can be changed into one another. True, this does not *define* what energy is—it is difficult to define in words—but in terms of heat, light, motion, electricity, and chemical work, energy does seem partly understandable. Physicists have found out how to measure amounts of energy, and have also made the important discovery that the total amount of energy always stays the same no matter how often it may be changed from one form to another. So it has become possible to add to the Law of Conservation of Mass (page 66) a similar law for energy.

Law of Conservation of Energy: Energy can neither be created nor destroyed, but it may be changed from one form to another.

There is a postscript to be added to the Laws of Conservation of Mass and of Energy. Physicists have discovered that matter and energy, which seem so different to us in terms of our day-by-day experience, are really not basically different at all. This is part of the problem in describing energy in words. Today we are aware that in reactions involving very great changes in energy, matter can change into energy, and energy into matter. But these are concerns of the physicist, with his nuclear reactors and linear accelerators, and of the astronomer, who seeks to learn more of what goes on inside the sun. So far as the reactions in chemistry and in living organisms are concerned, the Laws of Conservation of Mass and Energy as stated still suffice.

We began this discussion of energy back on page 74 by asking, "Why does the mouse need energy?" The mouse uses energy in many different ways. It uses chemical energy to build chemical compounds, and mechanical energy to move about. Heat is important to the mouse—just as it is to you—in keeping the body warm. Even electric current may be detected in it, with sensitive instruments. Some living organisms give off visible light and shocking amounts of electric current—perhaps you have seen or read about fireflies and electric eels.

Where do organisms get their energy? Quite early, biologists realized that living things can use only one form of energy as a direct source for their activities of living. This form is chemical energy, the energy stored in chemical compounds. They can change this chemical energy to all other forms as they move about, build up new chemical compounds, give off heat, and do other things characteristic of life. But they cannot make energy go the other way—for instance, from mechanical or heat energy into chemical energy. This is why you must take in energy stored in complex chemical substances we call foods. All of this is a rather complicated way of saying something which you know already from your own experience. When you need energy you are hungry. You cannot satisfy your hunger by sitting in the sunlight or next to an open fire or radiator. Though your body receives lots of energy from the sun, fire, or radiator, light and heat energy are useless as far as your living activities are concerned. You want food when you are hungry—and food is the source of chemical energy, the only kind which your body cells can use.

But if, like you and the mouse, all organisms constantly need new supplies of chemical compounds as they use energy in various ways, there must be a huge supply of these compounds. Where does all the energy needed by life come from? These questions have been answered by a series of observations and hypotheses made by many scientists during the last two hundred years. The source of almost all the energy used by living organisms is the sun. We will ask later (Chapter 15) how this is known, but even now you may find the statement strange, since you know that you yourself cannot use sunlight as a source of energy for living activities. Nor can other animals. But green plants differ in one important way from animals. They have special methods of capturing the energy of light and turning it into chemical energy in complex compounds they make from carbon dioxide and water. Do you remember the difference between the mint plant and the mouse in Priestley's experiment (pages 62-64)? This seemed to be a difference involving only chemical substances—oxygen and carbon dioxide—but we know now that it involved energy as well. Plants can store energy by building foods. They make more food than they need for their moment-by-moment use, and this extra supply can then be used by other living things.

4-11 Energy from falling water. The waterwheel is connected to the grinding machinery of the mill. Man alone has used mechanical energy extensively. All living organisms depend upon energy in one form or another, but while energy is a familiar concept, its nature is still being probed.

The story of energy in *any* system is fascinating—and in living systems perhaps most fascinating of all, involving enzymes and other compounds of which we shall learn more.

CONCLUDING REMARKS

In this chapter you have covered a lot of ground—from questions about living to some answers that have to be given in terms of chemical substances, energy, and exchange of matter and energy between the nonliving world and living things, and between plants and animals.

Three hundred years ago, Descartes began suggesting that the activities of animals and plants could be understood in mechanistic terms. His statement was only a hypothesis. There was very little that animals and plants do that he could explain. In fact, there were really no useful laws known at the time that would explain even the data of physics and chemistry. It was a little premature, therefore, to attempt to explain the activities of living organisms in terms of laws that were not known!

Gradually the nature of the chemical and physical universe was discovered. The old idea that matter is composed of the elements fire, air, earth, and water was found to be inadequate. Lavoisier and others began to recognize the elements that we know today: oxygen, carbon, hydrogen, sodium, and so on. Dalton suggested that one could explain much of the data of chemistry by assuming that all matter was composed of atoms—tiny particles far too small to be seen. An oxygen atom could on one occasion combine with hydrogen to form water, or on another combine with carbon to form carbon monoxide, but it always would maintain its identity. It could be recovered from water or carbon monoxide and shown to be pure oxygen.

In the nineteenth century, the previously mysterious chemistry of living organisms was found to be approachable. It was discovered that organisms contain a large number of carbon compounds. The reactions of these and other compounds in living systems were found to be controlled by enzymes.

The physicist supplied the biologist with the concept of energy. Energy required to keep an organism working was supplied by its food.

It all began with studies of a candle, a mouse, and a sprig of mint. Biologist, chemist, and physicist were soon to realize that the problems of living matter and nonliving matter were basically the same. When an ever-increasing number of plants and animals was studied, it was found that there are activities that are basic to all life: somehow everything that is alive must obtain chemical compounds for maintenance and growth of its own substance and for the energy it requires.

By the end of the nineteenth century, this is how man stood on the question of mechanism versus vitalism:

> There was no basic activity of life that could not be at least considered by way of the methods of chemistry and physics. Not everything was known—far from it—but every biological problem was approachable by the laboratory scientist.

Scientists showed that it was unnecessary to invoke a vital force to explain the data of the physiology of cells and organisms. Vitalism was not really disproved; it just was not needed in explaining biological activities.

Clearly an understanding of the nature and behavior of matter and energy is essential for an understanding of biology. In this chapter we have laid a background, and in the next two we will learn enough to help us understand ourselves and other living organisms.

GUIDE QUESTIONS AND PROBLEMS

1. Van Helmont's experiment on tree growth seemed to lead to a sound conclusion about the source of the material making up 164 pounds of tree.
    a. How would his experimental results have been interpreted by a vitalist? by a mechanist?
    b. What chemical knowledge of water and of willow tree compounds would have revealed an error in van Helmont's findings?
2. How does van Helmont's conclusion about materials for plant growth illustrate that conclu-

sions in science are subject to reinterpretation as further knowledge is acquired? Apply the same reasoning to Lavoisier's conclusion that air consists of two gases—one that supports combustion and one that does not. Why were new types of experiments needed as a further test of Lavoisier's findings? of van Helmont's?

3. Compare the ideas of vitalism and mechanism by suggesting the relative influence each may have had on the development of biological science.
4. What kinds of discoveries from the seventeenth to the end of the nineteenth centuries made the concept of vitalism unnecessary to the study of physiological problems?
5. Criticize this statement: "Priestley and Lavoisier demonstrated that respiration in living organisms and burning in nonliving systems are the same process."
6. The ability of nineteenth-century chemists to analyze some of the simpler organic compounds into elements, but their *in*ability to synthesize the organic compounds from these elements outside a living organism, seemed to add to the indication of a vital force associated with life. How did the discovery of enzymes reverse this indication?
7. Using enzymes in the laboratory, chemists can synthesize organic compounds as they are synthesized in living organisms. From the text on page 74:

   "No vital force is involved—the chemist uses enzymes as tools, knowing that these enzymes are simply chemical compounds, though of special and complicated structure."

   But what if "the vital force" of life is in the enzymes? Did Payen and Persoz take into account the possibility that if life has a vital force, it may reside in the complex enzyme systems of the living organisms? What kind of experiments would test this possibility?
8. Study Spallanzani's account of his work on page 72 and identify the following factors in his investigation of special chemical abilities in gastric juice: known facts, hypothesis, experimental design, control, results or data, and interpretation or conclusion.

RELATED READING

Books

For other accounts of the work of van Helmont, Black, Priestley, Lavoisier, Wöhler, and Payen and Persoz . . .

Gabriel, M., and S. Fogel, *Great Experiments in Biology*, Prentice-Hall, Englewood Cliffs, N. J., 1955. Includes work of van Helmont, Priestley, and Payen and Persoz.

Schwartz, George, and P. Bishop, *Moments of Discovery*, Basic Books, New York, 1958 (2 volumes). Includes accounts of Black, Priestley, Lavoisier, and Wöhler.

For extensions of ideas introduced in this chapter . . .

Moore, Ruth, *The Coil of Life*, Knopf, New York, 1961. Chapters 1, 2, 4, and 7.

For an account of the methods of science, appropriate in reviewing and extending concepts of inquiry . . .

Lastrucci, C. L., *The Scientific Approach*, Schenkman Publishing Company, Cambridge, Mass., 1963. Includes problem formulation, reasoning, principles of research, data collection, and scientific analysis of data.

5

Living Chemistry

Chapters 3 and 4 are tremendous concepts, taking you immediately to questions of cell makeup and chemical events in any unfamiliar organism you see. Now we must look at these ideas more closely. In this chapter we will ask two kinds of questions: What chemical substances are formed into living things? What can we learn about living processes by knowing about living chemistry?

A visitor from Mars could ask exactly the same sorts of questions about a house in any American town or city. What materials make up the house? What could the Martian learn about the functions carried on in the house by knowing about these various substances? He might begin by listing all the different materials in the house—concrete, brick, metal in the form of tubes and sheets, glass, cloth, plastics, water, soap flakes, wax, sugar, salt, pepper, and so forth. Studying the properties of these materials would tell the Martian a lot about what they do in the complex organization of the house. Bricks and concrete are strong, hard, heavy, and not soluble in water. It would seem very reasonable that these materials are used to form the outer protective layers—the walls of the house. Would cloth, water, sugar, salt, or pepper serve as well? The Martian could easily find out that they would not. On the other hand, bricks and concrete, though very useful in walls, could not be made into comfortable pillows, nor would they be very tasty if served for lunch. You can see that description of the special properties of each of the materials in a house, and what happens to them as people live in the house, would tell the Martian a lot about their special functions. Any complex organization, whether a house, a machine, or a man, is built up of different materials with many different characteristics. Just as in the case of the house, understanding of the structure and function of the chemical substances in living organisms can tell us a lot about the organisms. We must begin our study of living chemistry with a careful look at the matter of which all living things—like houses and everything else we know about—are built.

COMBINATIONS OF ATOMS AND ELEMENTS

We will begin by comparing three examples of matter: air, water, and a diamond. We shall think of all three of these substances in terms of Dalton's suggestion of discrete, uniform particles—the atoms. What can air, water, and a diamond reveal to us of the ways in which atoms associate with one another?

Air

Air is invisible, odorless, colorless, and tasteless. It is so light in weight that you may think of it as next to nothing. Yet we can pump it into tires where it will support the weight of an automobile. You are also familiar with the fact that air contains something that we need in order to live, and that a candle needs in order to burn.

Air is a gas. At first, chemists believed it was an element. But when Priestley and Lavoisier removed oxygen from the air, they still had gas left. The remaining gas accounted for about four fifths of ordinary air. After many experiments, the properties of this gas became known. It was named nitrogen.

Air, then, was shown to be about one fifth oxygen and four fifths nitrogen. Careful analysis later showed that there are tiny quantities of other gases in air. Carbon dioxide, which is exhaled in breathing and is produced by burning carbon compounds (such as wood and coal), is present. There is not much, to be sure—about 0.03 to 0.04 percent. Traces of other gases, such as helium, neon, and argon are also present. There are also varying amounts of water vapor.

Could we think, then, of a small container of air as a huge number of nitrogen atoms, many oxygen atoms, and fewer atoms of other kinds? The answer is a mixed one—partly yes, partly no. Helium, neon, and argon *do* exist in air as individual atoms. The nitrogen and oxygen, however, are *not* present as individual atoms. The oxygen atoms react with one another chemically to form pairs. Chemists refer to this arrangement as O_2. The "O" is the symbol for an oxygen atom, and the "2" means that two atoms of oxygen have formed a **chemical bond** between them. The nitrogen atoms of air also react with one another to form pairs; hence chemists refer to atmospheric nitrogen as N_2.

When two or more atoms form chemical bonds in the manner of O_2 and N_2, chemists call the resulting particle a **molecule.**

Air, then, is made up of molecules of nitrogen, molecules of oxygen, atoms of helium, atoms of argon, and atoms of neon—together with traces of carbon dioxide and water vapor, themselves molecules. It is important to realize that the atoms and molecules in air are *separate*. They do not influence one another except for an occasional collision.

In the last chapter, we learned that Lavoisier spoke of air as a *mixture* of gases. We speak of it in the same way today—and for the same reason. The gases found in air do not react chemically with one another. To look at this idea another way, suppose we put some flour and salt in a bowl and stir them. What we have is still salt and flour; there would be no chemical interaction.

In a mixture of substances, the amounts of different ingredients can vary. Thus you could make an artificial air by mixing 49 percent nitrogen, 49 percent oxygen, and 2 percent carbon dioxide. Any proportions of these substances will mix.

Water

Water was originally regarded as an element, since scientists were unable to divide it up into simpler substances. The clue to its identification as a compound, rather than an element, came when hydrogen was burned in the presence of oxygen. A clear, odorless liquid was formed. Simple tests showed that this liquid was water, identical with the water in rain, streams, and lakes.

Chemists soon found that water is composed of hydrogen and oxygen in the ratio of two atoms of hydrogen to each atom of oxygen. Here again the two gases will *mix* in any ratio, but if a spark is applied to the mixture we find that the reaction is selective. It will combine two parts hydrogen with one part oxygen as long as it can (which is very quickly, an explosion really). Then it stops. Upon checking we find out that it used up one gas and left the surplus of the other unchanged. The ratio is always the same. We represent the molecule as H_2O. *Constant proportions* characterize all compounds. This was one of the observations that led Dalton to the Atomic Theory.

If H_2O is a molecule, is it like O_2? Yes and no. H_2O is also a compound, a term that we do not use for O_2. What is the distinction? A *molecule* is a particle formed by a chemical reaction between two or more atoms. These atoms may be of the same element, as in O_2, or different elements, as in H_2O. A *compound*, on the other hand, *always* is composed of atoms of two or more different elements. Water is a compound because it is composed of the elements hydrogen and oxygen chemically bonded to one another.

Diamond

A diamond was the third substance on our original list of materials to study. With it we encounter a new situation. All the methods of the chemist could be used, but it would be impossible to separate the diamond into other substances. It would still be a diamond—pure crystalline carbon.

The Elements

Studies of air, water, and a diamond have given different results. Air is composed of oxygen, nitrogen, and other gases. It is a mixture. Water is composed of hydrogen and oxygen. It is a compound. The diamond is pure carbon. It is an element. No chemical method can divide it into simpler substances.

Can oxygen, nitrogen, and hydrogen be divided into simpler substances by chemical means? The answer is "No." No matter how the chemist tries to divide them, they still remain oxygen, nitrogen, and hydrogen. Like carbon, they are elements.

The *three* samples of matter (air, water, and a diamond) that we have analyzed have revealed *seven* (or more) elements—hydrogen, oxygen, carbon, nitrogen, helium, neon, argon, and traces of other elements in air. If we analyzed three *thousand* substances, would we come up with roughly seven *thousand* elements in the same ratio? When the search for the elements began, almost two thousand years ago, Aristotle was looking for a *simple* explanation to a complex world: it would have been beautiful if there were only four elements, as he thought. But it is beautiful anyway—for in all substances, living or not, scientists have found fewer than 100 elements. These occur over and over in different patterns to make everything we know. By exact count there are 92 of these elements in nature. Others produced in the laboratory are not known elsewhere in the world.

Here are just a few of the most common elements in air, land, oceans, and organisms:

Air	*Land*	*Oceans*	*Organisms*
Nitrogen	**Oxygen**	**Oxygen**	**Oxygen**
Oxygen	Silicon	**Hydrogen**	Carbon
	Aluminum	Chlorine	**Hydrogen**
	Iron	Sodium	**Nitrogen**
	Calcium		Sulfur
			Phosphorus

Elements common to two or more columns are shown in **boldface** type.

Chemical Activity of the Elements

Atoms are now popular everywhere—on advertising billboards, in textbooks (Figure 5-1), on television, and even in cartoons and comics. Always these basic units of the elements are shown with swarms of **electrons** busily circling a nucleus made of **protons** and **neutrons.** It is the swarms of electrons that interest us most. Examine the list of twenty elements in the following table, with numbers of electrons and chemical activity shown for each. These are the simplest elements known, and among them are all of the most common elements in living organisms. Try not to read the list too carefully—look only for a pattern if one is there.

	Number of Electrons	*Chemical Activity*
Hydrogen	1	Reactive
Helium	2	Very stable
Lithium	3	Reactive
Beryllium	4	Reactive
Boron	5	Reactive
Carbon	6	Reactive
Nitrogen	7	Reactive
Oxygen	8	Reactive
Fluorine	9	Reactive
Neon	10	Very stable
Sodium	11	Reactive
Magnesium	12	Reactive
Aluminum	13	Reactive
Silicon	14	Reactive
Phosphorus	15	Reactive
Sulfur	16	Reactive
Chlorine	17	Reactive
Argon	18	Very stable
Potassium	19	Reactive
Calcium	20	Reactive

Note numbers 2, 10, and 18. Number two (helium) has 2 electrons and is very stable—it does not change, nor does it react with other atoms except in very special circumstances.

Number ten (neon) has 10 electrons and is very stable, also. Number eighteen (argon) has 18 electrons and is stable. These three nonreactive elements – helium, neon, and argon – are the rare gases we found traces of in air (page 81). There seems to be something about the electron numbers 2, 10, and 18. When atoms have electrons in these numbers, they are extremely stable.

The numbers 2, 10, and 18 become even *more* interesting when we put the following pair of elements together:

Sodium	11	transfer 1 electron?	$11-1=10$
Chlorine	17		$17+1=18$

Do the two elements react? Yes, the sodium gives up its electron to form the arrangement 10, and thus becomes more stable. The chlorine takes the extra electron to form the arrangement 18, and thus becomes more stable. The compound formed is sodium chloride, the salt you use at the dinner table.

Try this one:

Magnesium	12	transfer how many electrons?
Sulfur	16	

Yes again. The magnesium reverts to 10, and the sulfur takes the two electrons and goes to 18. The compound is magnesium sulfide. The atoms have reacted predictably.

Let's go all the way back to the first two elements in the table:

Hydrogen	1
Helium	2

The helium is stable, but what about the hydrogen? Will two hydrogen atoms follow a $1 + 1 = 2$ pattern and react with one another? Yes. Very rarely, though, does one atom get both electrons. Instead they tend to share them. The electron cloud of one atom overlaps with the electron cloud of the other, and the two electrons associate with both nuclei! Each atom in the H_2 molecule has the two electrons on a shared basis.

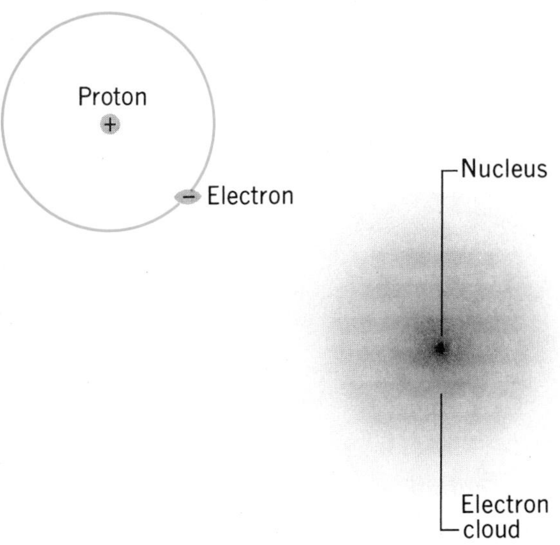

5–1 An atom of the element hydrogen. The two illustrations are highly diagrammatic. Both represent the same atom, but they convey different impressions of it. How does the cloud model on the right modify the impression conveyed on the left? If you could see hydrogen, greatly magnified, what would you expect its appearance to be?

Chemical Bonds

When the atom of sodium gives up an electron to react with an atom of chlorine, the reaction leaves both particles electrically charged. The sodium (11 electrons) normally has no charge, because for each of its electrons *there is a corresponding proton in the atomic nucleus.* A proton has a charge of +1, an electron a charge of −1. Eleven protons and eleven electrons come out neutral.

But sodium's electron number decreases to ten when it reacts with chlorine to make table salt. It still has eleven protons in its nucleus, but only ten electrons. The sodium has become +1 in charge. It no longer is a neutral atom, but an **ion** (ɪ·ahn). We abbreviate it Na^+, with the "Na" coming from the Latin name for sodium – *Natrium.*

What has happened to the sodium also happens to the chlorine, but in the opposite way.

Harbrace Photo, model courtesy of the American Museum of Natural History

5-2 A model of a crystal of sodium chloride. The larger balls represent the chloride ions, the smaller balls the sodium ions. In the actual crystal, are the chemical bonds ionic or covalent?

Chlorine has 17 electrons. Its nucleus has 17 protons that balance the charge. The atom is neutral. But when chlorine takes an electron from sodium to go to an arrangement of 18 electrons, its 17 protons no longer balance the charge. The chlorine becomes −1 in charge. It, too, is an ion. We abbreviate it Cl^-.

The kind of chemical bond formed between sodium and chlorine is called **ionic** (i·AHN·ic). What holds the sodium and chlorine ions together as table salt is chiefly a force of *attraction between opposite charges.*

It is not the same with the hydrogen molecule, H_2. The two electrons are shared, and each atom tugs at *both* electrons in what you might call a compromise toward a heliumlike arrangement with two electrons. Neither atom gives up, and each gets both electrons on a shared basis. In this way, the atoms are bonded together. The bond is **covalent** (co·VAY·lent), and the H_2 molecule has no charge.

Hereafter when we say *molecule*, you will know that a covalent bond has been formed. It may be a molecule of an element (as H_2) or a molecule of a compound (as H_2O, water). In the latter, each hydrogen atom shares its one electron with the oxygen in return for also sharing *one* of the oxygen's electrons. Thus each hydrogen tugs in a $1+1$ sort of way toward the stable number, 2. The oxygen (eight electrons) tugs also, in an $8+1+1$ sort of way toward the stable arrangement of 10 electrons.

When a compound forms and no one mentions "molecule," an *ionic compound* has been formed. In dry, crystalline form, these compounds hold together well, too—opposite charges attract (Figure 5-2). But dissolve the table salt in your soup, and the Na^+ particles will go one way, the Cl^- particles another. Nothing has overcome the rule of opposite charges attracting—it is just that there are *other* opposite charges in your soup!

The attraction of opposite charges is very important in the behavior of atoms. Otherwise, would Na^+ stay in even the same part of the world with Cl^- and make table salt? Many of the chemical substances in living things are ionized; the attraction between opposite charges—and a repulsion between similar charges—play an important part in the organization of living cells. We can't really begin to list all the events that no longer would take place, both in nonliving and living systems, if opposite charges did not attract.

All this is associated with what happens to electrons of atoms. Your table of twenty elements can be revised in a useful fashion for your reference if you think of stable and reactive electron arrangements as *recurring patterns*. The table in Figure 5-3 will help you whenever you need to think about a reaction—or when you need to think about a molecule or ionic compound produced by a reaction. All of the most common elements found in materials of living cells are here. Some of the relationships the table suggests truly are amazing in helping you predict or analyze reactions:

1. *Recurring patterns.* Number 3, lithium, tends to give up the lone electron listed in its *second* column of electron number. Number 11, sodium, tends to give up the lone electron listed in its *third* column of electron number. Number 19, potassium, tends to give up the lone electron listed in its *fourth* column of electron number. It is as if the elements had sorted themselves out along a street or avenue. In the first house on each block are found elements that react alike – giving up one electron. In the second house on each block are other chemical "cousins" that give up two electrons in reaction (elements numbers 4, 12, and 20). And so it goes on each block; in the seventh house on one block is fluorine, and in the next block, chlorine – both tend to *gain* one electron. And in the eighth house on each block lives an unneighborly fellow – neon on one block, argon on another – having no interchanges with their neighbors. Only the first block on the street is short; even here, one element is reactive (hydrogen), and the other an unneighborly fellow (helium).
2. *Are reactions "imitative"?* Withdraw four entries from the table, as follows:

Neon (Ne)	2	8		Very stable	10
Sodium (Na)	2	8	1	Reactive (toward)	10
Chlorine (Cl)	2	8	7	Reactive (toward)	18
Argon (Ar)	2	8	8	Very stable	18

5–3 Elements with 1 to 20 Electrons

Element and Symbol	*Electron Number 1 or 2*	*. . . plus*	*. . . plus*	*. . . plus*	*Chemical Activity*	*In Reaction, Tends Toward Electron Total . . .*
1. Hydrogen (H)	1				Reactive	2
2. Helium (He)	2				**Very stable**	
3. Lithium (Li)	2	1			Reactive	2
4. Beryllium (Be)	2	2			Reactive	2
5. Boron (B)	2	3			Reactive	2
6. Carbon (C)	2	4			Reactive	10
7. Nitrogen (N)	2	5			Reactive	10
8. Oxygen (O)	2	6			Reactive	10
9. Fluorine (F)	2	7			Reactive	10
10. Neon (Ne)	2	8			**Very stable**	
11. Sodium (Na)	2	8	1		Reactive	10
12. Magnesium (Mg)	2	8	2		Reactive	10
13. Aluminum (Al)	2	8	3		Reactive	10
14. Silicon (Si)	2	8	4		Reactive	10 or 18
15. Phosphorus (P)	2	8	5		Reactive	10 or 18
16. Sulfur (S)	2	8	6		Reactive	18
17. Chlorine (Cl)	2	8	7		Reactive	18
18. Argon (Ar)	2	8	8		**Very stable**	
19. Potassium (K)	2	8	8	1	Reactive	18
20. Calcium (Ca)	2	8	8	2	Reactive	18

When the sodium (2 8 1) reacts with chlorine (2 8 7) to form an ionic compound, table salt, the situation changes:

Neon (Ne)	2	8	
Sodium ion (Na^+)	2	8	
Chloride ion (Cl^-)	2	8	8
Argon (Ar)	2	8	8

Now all the electron arrangements appear stable. But are sodium and chlorine *really* imitating the "unneighborly" eighth elements on these two blocks—neon and argon? Our analogy with relationships among neighbors along a city street suggests that it might be a mistake to assume this too readily. Sodium and chlorine may only like the way that self-sufficient neon and argon "keep their yards." Inside their houses, they are different and have even hung out an invitation to neighbors to drop by (the + and − charges attract opposite charges). All this suggests that chemists still are investigating why elements react toward electron configurations with 2, or 10, or 18 electrons.

The amazing thing about the table in Figure 5-3 is that we do not *fully* understand why patterns of chemical reactions are as simple as they appear. It is true that chemists know much more than we have reported about electrons and their atomic configurations—the last few words alone sound grand and carefully chosen. But in the end there is always another question *why* that is not yet answered.

But you can have a profitable time in living chemistry without much more background than this table.

How Do Neutrons Fit In?

We have accounted for protons and electrons, but not for neutrons. Neutrons make less difference chemically. They occur in the nucleus and have no charge. The carbon atoms in the diamond you examined earlier are usually very neatly numbered in their component particles—6 protons, 6 neutrons, 6 electrons. While the proton and electron numbers remain 6 each in all carbon atoms, the neutron number can vary—and does. Carbon atoms may have five, six, seven, or eight neutrons and still be carbon. Strangely, you wouldn't want to own the diamond at all if its carbon atoms had eight neutrons. It could be lovely and large and blue-white, but it would be radioactive. We say these different forms of carbon are **isotopes** (ı·sotohps) of one another. *Every* element has isotopes (with different neutron numbers). Some of these isotopes are stable, while others are unstable and break down and release electrons or other pieces of the atom. They are radioactive. The **radioisotopes** are very valuable, because we can follow them around with instruments like Geiger counters—even through a living organism, to see what becomes of particular atoms in something the organism takes in for its use.

Extending the Chemical Concepts

As one way of expressing real events, chemistry can be very complex. But as a *pattern* it usually is understandable in the way you have just experienced. Suppose, for example, that many atoms come together to make a molecule. *Molecule* suggests that all the bonds are covalent, even though the formula looks complex. $C_6H_{12}O_6$ is the formula for a molecule of a sugar. There are 24 atoms in the molecule, but every bond is covalent. The molecule is neutral.

Because molecules have varying dimensions they can be neutral as a whole, yet charged in some of their neighboring parts. In other words, the proton and electron charges are equal, but not evenly distributed. In water, H_2O, the electrons of the covalent bonds are shared a bit unevenly; the oxygen pulls strongly at them. The oxygen part of the molecule acquires a slight negative charge, the hydrogen parts of the molecule a slight positive charge (Figure 5-4). This is largely why the salt in your soup separates into Na^+ and Cl^- ions. Each Na^+ ion is attracted to the *slightly negative* oxygen parts of a group of neighboring

H_2O molecules. Each Cl^- ion is attracted to the *slightly positive* hydrogen parts of other neighboring H_2O molecules. As the H_2O molecules move around, so do the attracted ions. The Na^+ and Cl^- go different ways.

Can a molecule also be an ion? What if it should lose an electron at one of its bonds, or acquire an extra one? The charges would no longer be equal for the whole molecule. Molecules can be ions in this event. Even gigantic molecules, containing many thousands of atoms, may form ions, and then they attract or repel one another according to the charges they carry. Opposite charges attract; like charges repel.

In a big molecule, just as in H_2O, there may be atoms which are not really ionized, but which have attracted electrons a little more than nearby atoms, or have let one or a few of their own electrons slip away a bit. These, too, are regions of slight charge—regions of the big molecules which tend to attract or repel other charged particles and therefore to form bonds, though these are of a very weak sort. Like ionic bonds, these weak bonds play a part in the moment-by-moment organization of molecules within the living cell.

An atom in one molecule may even tear an electron completely away from an atom in another molecule. Often a big energy change is involved in such a reaction. In these conditions, the atom losing the electron is said to be **oxidized** (ox·ih·dyzed) and the atom gaining it is said to be **reduced.** The reaction as a whole is called an *oxidation-reduction reaction.* Why is this particular way of exchange of electrons important in biology? Because reactions of this type are the basic energy-supplying reactions of cells. *Enzymes* (recall the one first discovered by Payen and Persoz—Chapter 4, page 75) are involved in these reactions. Green plants have remarkable enzyme-containing structures which can use the energy of sunlight to separate electrons from relatively stable molecules. With these electrons they build unstable compounds which act as a storehouse of chemical energy. In all living things, reactions beautifully regulated by enzymes are used to carry the electrons back to stabler arrangements, thus freeing the stored chemical energy for all the processes of life. You have met these oxidation-reduction reactions before, without knowing it—they were the basis for the chemical activities of the mint plant, mouse, phos-

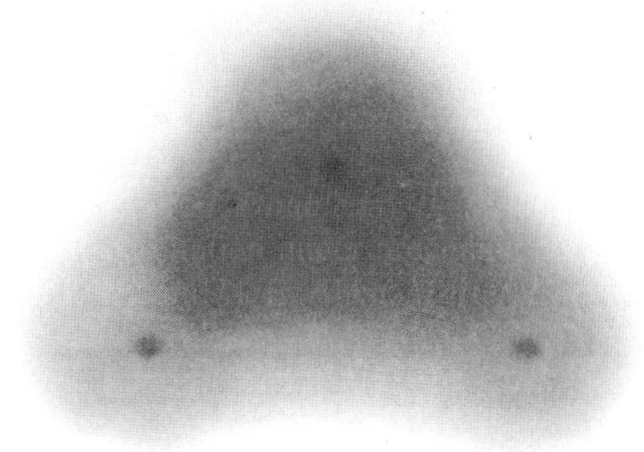

a The darker area indicates that the electrons are held more closely by oxygen than by hydrogen....

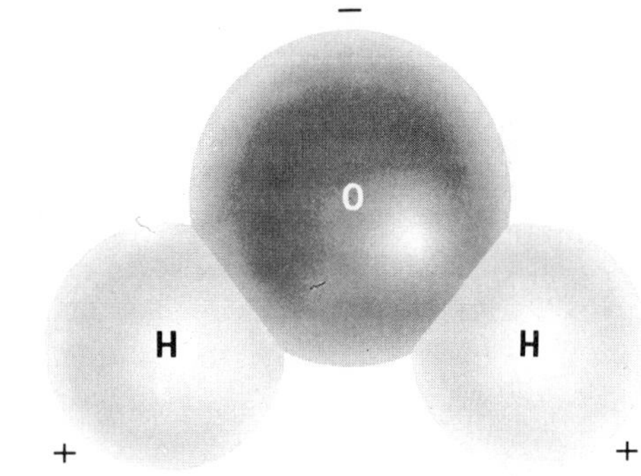

b ....giving the water molecule areas of negative and positive charge. Bonds to ions and to other molecules of unbalanced charge occur. These ions or molecules are said to be hydrated.

5–4 Two diagrams of a molecule of water. In the cloud model, the darker tones indicate that the shared electrons spend more time in their molecular orbitals nearer the oxygen than to the hydrogen. At the bottom is a Stuart model, another type of representation. What impression does it convey?

phorus, and candles of Chapter 4. We will come back to them again later in this chapter.

But at this point you might stop and ask "How do we know so much about the structure of atoms and the compounds – molecular and ionic – which they form?" Chemists have spent many years studying chemical substances, designing countless experiments to discover the data and build the hypotheses and theories we have suggested here. It is a pity that we cannot take time to describe some of this work in this book, for it represents one of the finest achievements of human thought. But perhaps you will take a chemistry course in a year or two, and then you will learn about these methods and experiments. As biologists, we must save our energy for finding out as much as we can about what is known about the various molecules which make up living organisms.

One problem we have in biology that is not so great in chemistry is expressing chemical events in a convenient way. When we explained that sodium and chlorine react to form table salt, we described what chemists would note in this way:

$$Na + Cl \rightarrow Na^+Cl^- + \text{energy}$$

You could also write the formula for the compound as NaCl, without the signs, but these show quickly that the bonds are ionic rather than covalent.

When the salt was dissolved in your soup, it dissolved in the water of the soup. Here is the simplest notation:

$$Na^+Cl^- \xrightarrow[\text{solution}]{} Na^+ + Cl^-$$

Actually energy was involved here, too, but we have not written it into the reaction because it was only a small amount.

When two hydrogen atoms and an oxygen atom combine, the reaction may be written as

$$2\,H + O \rightarrow H_2O + \text{energy}$$

although usually we double the amounts because we know that both the hydrogen and the oxygen enter the reaction as molecules instead of as individual atoms:

$$2\,H_2 + O_2 \rightarrow 2\,H_2O + \text{energy}$$

Here the product formed is molecular, and a great deal of energy is involved.

Reactions of these sorts are relatively simple, but in most of the reactions in the living cell, thousands of atoms take part in so many ways that chemical equations would not make things appear simpler to you. We will use equations later in this book only in special cases, though if you go on to study more biology you will use them often. You will also find that energy changes are almost always involved in reactions in living systems. In Laboratory Inquiries 5-1 and 5-2 you can study some reactions involving changes in heat energy.

Organic Molecules

The molecules found in living organisms vary tremendously in all ways including complexity. Usually they vary from complex to *more* complex! A molecule of table sugar, which comes from sugar cane or sugar beets, is composed of 45 atoms: 12 of carbon, 22 of hydrogen, and 11 of oxygen. Its chemical formula is $C_{12}H_{22}O_{11}$. Starch molecules, which are found in all plants, contain thousands of atoms of carbon, hydrogen, and oxygen. Protein molecules are often much larger still.

These large molecules are called **organic** molecules. All organic compounds contain carbon, in addition to other elements.

As you learned in Chapter 4 (page 69), many chemists of the eighteenth and early nineteenth centuries felt it was impossible to learn much about organic compounds. They felt that these complex compounds could be made by an animal or plant but not by a chemist in his laboratory. Only after Wöhler synthesized urea and Kolbe synthesized acetic acid (page 70) did these beliefs change.

It was found that urea was made of carbon, hydrogen, oxygen, and nitrogen in the proportions expressed by the formula CON_2H_4—a molecule of eight atoms. For reasons that will become clear shortly, this is better written as $CO(NH_2)_2$. As study progressed, it became apparent that a simple formula for a compound is not always sufficient. For example, three different sugars were found with the same formula! They are composed of the very same numbers of the same atoms. How then, do they differ? The answer eventually was found. The characteristics of an organic molecule depend not only upon its *numbers* and *kinds* of atoms, but also on the *positions* the atoms occupy.

Suppose we compare words and molecules. The same letters a, e, and t, can be combined one way to form "ate" and another to form "tea." Just as the positions of letters determines the word, so the positions of atoms determines the type of molecule.

The formula $CO(NH_2)_2$, for urea, does not fully indicate the position of each atom relative to the other atoms. A better way of showing what we know of the makeup of the urea molecule is to use a *structural formula:*

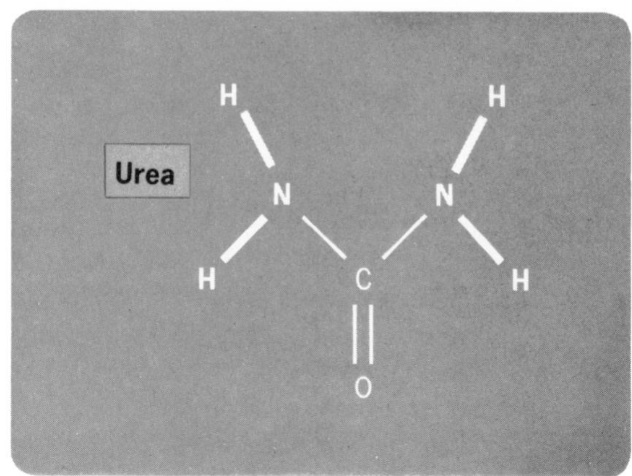

The two distinctive NH_2 groups are shown at each end. They are attached to a central carbon. A single oxygen atom is also attached to the carbon. Altogether there are eight atoms in the molecule.

The bonds in this molecule are indicated by lines. We will not often stop to figure out what such bonds mean, but one example may be fun. Your earlier tables of the first twenty elements give this information for the atoms in the urea molecule:

	Number of Electrons	*Chemical Activity*
Hydrogen	1	Reactive
Carbon	6 (or 2 + 4)	Reactive
Nitrogen	7 (or 2 + 5)	Reactive
Oxygen	8 (or 2 + 6)	Reactive

Except for hydrogen, each atom will tend to move toward a configuration giving it 10 electrons in all. The double line between the central carbon atom in the urea molecule and the oxygen atom indicates that carbon is sharing 2 of its electrons with oxygen—and in return is getting a share of 2 of the electrons of the oxygen atom. This moves oxygen satisfactorily from 8 to 10, the stable arrangement, but it changes carbon only from 6 to 8. How does the carbon go on to 10? Check the bond lines with nitrogen.

Similarly, the nitrogen atoms have three bond lines. Each of the three represents *giving* a share of an electron, and *getting* a share of an electron from another atom in return. Thus nitrogen goes from 7 to 10, the stable arrangement.

Hydrogen has only one electron. It needs one more to reach the stable arrangement, 2. It, too, shares its electron and gets a share of another in return, from another atom.

Each bond line in the urea structural formula indicates a shared *pair* of electrons, with one of the pair coming from each atom.

Hereafter, if you wish to analyze the bonds in a molecule on your own, you may take a shortcut. Take the electron configuration for each atom and simply add the number of its bond lines. Thus, for the carbon in the urea molecule, you start with 6, add a double-bond line and the two single lines, and you have reached 10.

You can see that this method of representing organic compounds and analyzing their bonds is most useful. Structural formulas do have one serious limitation, however. Molecules have three dimensions, while the paper on which the structural formulas are shown is only two-dimensional. And even when shown in three dimensions, a structural formula is not a true picture. Think of a urea molecule dissolved in water. You can imagine each of its atoms, with fast moving electrons in orbit about the nucleus. Where two atoms are shown by letters connected with lines, you must imagine instead the quick back-and-forth movements of shared electrons. Each electron and the atom as a whole is vibrating, perhaps rotating—the whole collection of atoms in constant motion in the water solution. When the molecule is very cool, the movements are fairly slow, but if it is heated, energy is absorbed by the combination of atoms and all the movements become faster and faster. Sometimes all these movements become so fast that a piece flies off the molecule!

Later, as we describe other molecules, we will not be able to take the space to give this same sort of description. If we could, we would design diagrams of molecules to jump out of the printed pages. The electrons would fly all about, and the bonds shorten and lengthen and swing about as you watched. It would make an exciting but rather messy book. We will have to continue showing atoms and molecules in two dimensions, in the symbols of letters and lines. Can you use your imagination to supply the action? If you can, you will have a much better understanding of chemistry and of the processes of living things.

Carbon and Life

All organic compounds contain carbon (in addition to other elements). This simple but very important statement is based on the research of chemists and biologists who have isolated many thousands of compounds to discover what atoms they are built of and how the atoms are put together. They have found that carbon is always present. This work has also given us some understanding of why carbon should have such a central part to play in building the chemical foundation for life. Because carbon needs to gain four electrons to achieve a stable arrangement of its atoms, it is able to combine with four other atoms at once, or with three, or two, or only one. Thus, it has the greatest versatility. Carbon atoms also have the most amazing ability to link up with each other, forming long chains and rings of various sizes. Within a carbon chain, each carbon atom is attached by covalent bonds to two neighboring carbon atoms, and two other covalent bonds can be formed with hydrogen or other atoms. In the case of carbon attachment to hydrogen, each of these bonds is a potential source of chemical energy. Energy may be released when electrons and protons (that is, hydrogen atoms) are removed in an oxidation-reduction process. One can just look at the structural formula of a carbon chain compound rich in hydrogen and see that it is a storehouse of chemical energy, fuel for the needs of life, food for uncountable hungry organisms.

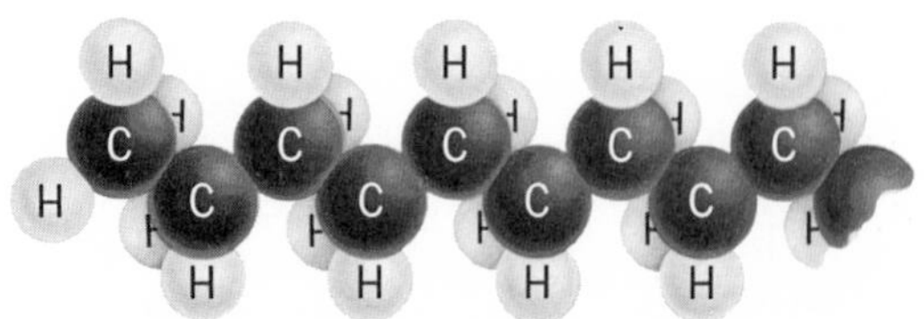

Carbon atoms can combine with atoms other than hydrogen, of course, making all sorts of atomic combinations with their four covalent bonds. Some of these molecules are so unstable that they last for only the briefest time, then break down, releasing energy. These compounds are often used by organisms for energy transfer. In other cases, molecules built with carbon skeletons may be so stable that they hardly react at all, and are so big that they cannot dissolve in water. Such compounds make up the wood of trees, lasting for more than a thousand years. Because of these special properties and reactions of the carbon atom, we can almost guess the answer to the question—"Could there be life without carbon?"

THE PRINCIPAL COMPOUNDS OF CELLS

Living cells are composed mostly of water and organic compounds grouped together as proteins, carbohydrates, fats, and nucleic acids. In addition, there are many other kinds of substances about which you will learn in time, such as vitamins, steroid hormones, and mineral salts. In the laboratory, you can see for yourself that the chemical composition of living material is very complex (Inquiry 5-3).

Water in Cells

The amount of water in living cells varies, but it is usually at least 65 percent, and in some organisms may be 96 percent or more of the total substance. Water is *by far* the most abundant compound in organisms. The activities of cells, therefore, are activities that occur in the presence of water.

Water is not an organic compound, of course, since it does not contain carbon. Its properties, however, make it enormously important in living activities.

One of its properties is this: it is the best solvent known. That is, more chemical substances dissolve in it than in any other liquid. What is the importance of this fact? The answer has to do with the way in which chemical substances react. In most cases substances react best if they are mixed thoroughly and are in very small particles, such as individual molecules or ions. Both the separation into small particles and the mixing occur when substances are dissolved. Water, therefore, makes it possible for many chemical reactions to occur—reactions that would not occur if the substances were dry.

This mixing is partly explained by the motion of molecules. All the molecules in a water solution are continuously moving about, mixing and bumping into each other and thus having many chances to react together. Also, many substances ionize when they are dissolved in water, as you saw with the salt in your soup. In the ionized state the substances can react more readily. Their ions are charged and are attracted to particles of opposite charge.

The movement of molecules and ions, as a result of their own motion or of being hit by other molecules and ions, is known as **diffusion** (dih·FEW·zhun). The movement is in all directions. Eventually, it leads to an even distribution of substances—even though they were not evenly distributed at the outset. We say, then, that the *net* result of diffusion is movement of substances from areas of greater concentration to areas of lesser concentration. In living cells this diffusion is partly the result of molecules and ions being hit and moved by water molecules.

Another important property of water is that it is a relatively *stable* compound. Imagine what would happen if this best-of-all-solvents happened to be *un*stable. With hundreds of reactions constantly going on in a cell—reactions dependent upon the presence of water—it would be disastrous indeed if the water were to decompose easily into hydrogen and oxygen!

Water does take part in many reactions within cells, but not in the uncontrolled manner of an unstable compound. Almost all reactions are controlled by—and indeed, made possible *only* because of—specific enzymes within the cell.

We can begin to see what *relative* stability means when we consider what we now know of water:

1. To serve as a good solvent, it must have chemical stability.
2. To take part in enzyme-controlled reactions, however, it cannot be inert (that is, *completely* stable under all conditions).

We can now add another important property of water to our understanding of its relative stability. You may be surprised to learn that among the substances which ionize in water is *water itself*! To a very slight extent—that is, to the extent of about one in 550 million molecules—water ionizes. The few ions produced among millions of water molecules are very important to cells.

A water molecule ionizes into H^+ and OH^- ions. The H^+, or hydrogen ion, is actually nothing more than a single proton (a hydrogen nucleus). Its missing electron is held by the OH^-, or hydroxide ion, which consists of an oxygen atom, a hydrogen atom, and the extra electron. Chemists will tell you that the H^+ ion, and perhaps also the OH^- ion (they are not yet sure), exists *hydrated*—that is, bonded to a water molecule. In other words, H_2O plus H^+ yields an H_3O^+ ion. This idea is not new; the salt dissolving in your soup was hydrated by association of the Na^+ and Cl^- ions with *many* water molecules. For our purposes we

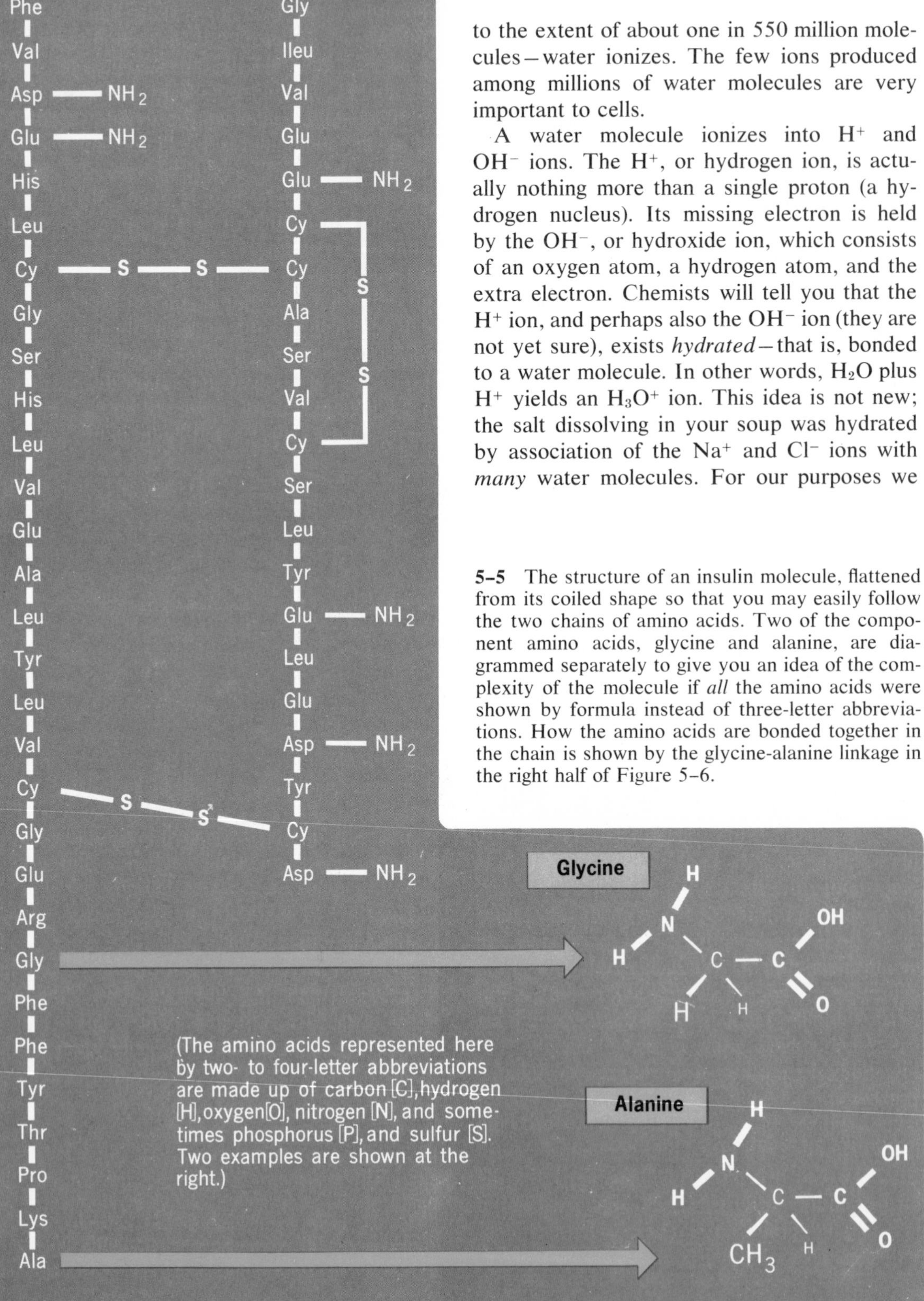

5–5 The structure of an insulin molecule, flattened from its coiled shape so that you may easily follow the two chains of amino acids. Two of the component amino acids, glycine and alanine, are diagrammed separately to give you an idea of the complexity of the molecule if *all* the amino acids were shown by formula instead of three-letter abbreviations. How the amino acids are bonded together in the chain is shown by the glycine-alanine linkage in the right half of Figure 5–6.

may ignore the hydration of H^+ ions and represent the ionization of water as follows:

$$H_2O \rightarrow H^+ + OH^-$$

The reaction is reversible, so the equation may be written:

$$H_2O \rightleftharpoons H^+ + OH^-$$

H^+ and OH^- ions affect, and take part in, many of the reactions that occur in cells. If, as a result, more H^+ than OH^- ions remain in the solution, we say that the solution is **acidic.** (Such a solution is sour to our taste.) If more OH^- than H^+ ions remain in solution, we say that the solution is **basic.** (Such a solution is alkaline.) The relative concentration of H^+ and OH^- ions in living cells is very important, because the reactions controlled by enzymes each take place most readily at definite concentrations of H^+ and OH^- ions, as you will discover for yourself in Laboratory Inquiry 6-5.

Proteins

The most abundant organic compounds in plants and animals are the proteins. So important are these compounds that when they were named a century ago, the term chosen was based upon the Greek word *proteios,* meaning "prime" or "first." The word seems to suggest a sense of mystery about these compounds.

In living organisms, proteins serve a wide variety of functions. They are the principal organic substances within cells. Here many of them build structure, while others are those amazing tools, enzymes. Proteins make up much of the substance of seeds and other plant parts. They also provide the bulk of the material of which skin, muscles, hair, and nails of familiar animals are made.

Hemoglobin (HEE·mo·glow·bin), the oxygen-carrying compound of red blood cells, is protein; every cell in our bodies depends upon red blood cells and their hemoglobin for oxygen. Proteins play a key role in contraction of muscles, in digestion of foods (including other proteins!), in clotting of blood—indeed, there seems no limit to the variety of functions that proteins perform in living organisms. In each instance, the ability of a protein to serve a specific biological role is a consequence of its molecular structure.

Proteins are very large and complex molecules. This may be illustrated by the formula for human hemoglobin, which is $C_{3032}H_{4816}O_{872}N_{780}S_8Fe_4$. If you count all the atoms in this single molecule, you will get a total of 9,512!

Amino Acids

The proteins are built of various combinations of more than 20 kinds of organic compounds called **amino** (a·MEE·noh) **acids.** For example, insulin contains 16 different kinds of amino acid subunits. In Figure 5-5, some idea of the complexity of an insulin molecule is given. Each of the two-to-four-letter abbreviations (*Gly, Val, Asp,* etc.) represents one of the 16 different kinds of amino acids. You can see that some of these are used more than once in the molecule, which has a total of 51 amino acids in two chains, plus other components as well.

The molecule looks very complex, but not nearly as complex as it really is. For example, suppose that in place of the two-to-four-letter abbreviations of the amino acids, we showed the structural formula of each one, as we did earlier for urea. At the bottom of Figure 5-5 are structural formulas for just *two* of the amino acids. There would not be room on a page to "map" the whole insulin molecule! It might take you a whole day to analyze the bonds that you checked in just a few minutes in the urea molecule.

Each amino acid is a distinctive kind of organic compound with both an **amino group** and a **carboxyl group** chemically bonded to the same carbon atom. The amino group is made up of a nitrogen atom and two hydrogen atoms bonded together ($—NH_2$). The carboxyl group is made

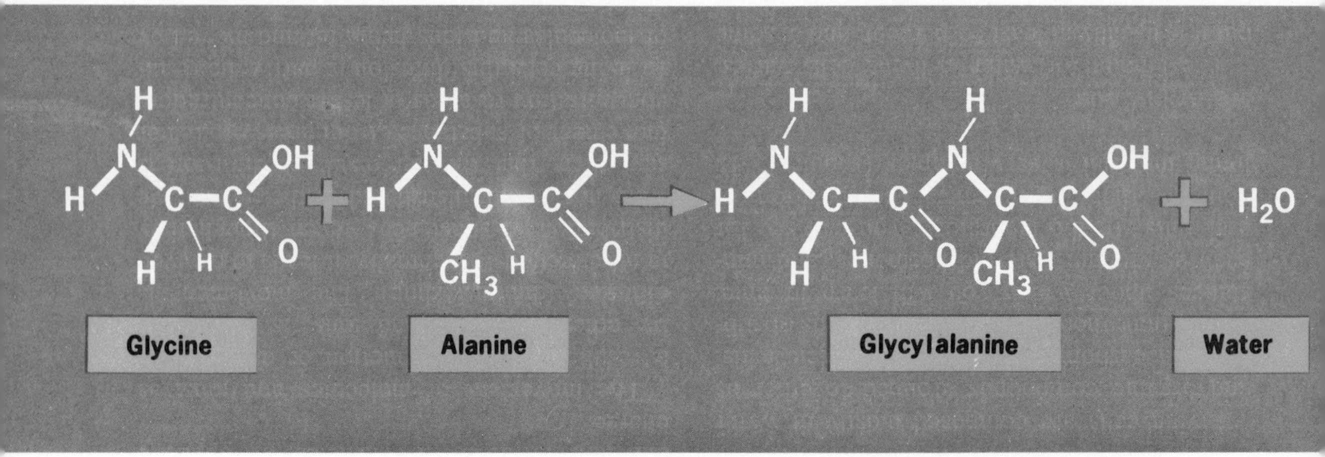

5–6 If you compare the glycine and alanine at the left with the glycylalanine at the right, you will find the source of the OH and H of the water. Biologists and chemists have found a way to link amino acids in this way in the laboratory. In the living cell it is quite another story, but one feature is the same: a bond between amino acids is formed, leaving an amino group intact at one end and a carboxyl group at the other end. At these points a living cell adds other amino acids to the chain.

up of carbon, oxygen (two atoms), and hydrogen (—COOH). The simplest amino acid is **glycine** (GLY·seen), one of the two shown at the bottom of Figure 5-5. Note the amino and carboxyl groups.

The other amino acids differ from glycine in having one of the hydrogen atoms (which in glycine are attached to the central carbon) replaced by some other combination of atoms. The amino acid **alanine** (AL·a·neen), for example, is shown along with glycine at the bottom of Figure 5-5. At what one point in the alanine molecule does it differ from glycine?

Proteins (the insulin of Figure 5-5, for example) are formed by the chemical linkage of amino acids in a characteristic manner. We can illustrate this with our molecules of glycine and alanine (Figure 5-6). These and other amino acid molecules can be linked together as shown, by special methods in the laboratory. Note that the reaction involves the removal of one molecule of water. The carboxyl group contributes an OH; and the amino group, an H. When these are removed, a chemical bond extends from the carbon of the carboxyl group to the nitrogen of the amino group. The new compound is **glycylalanine.**

Notice in Figure 5-6 that after the glycine and alanine have formed glycylalanine, there is still an amino group at the left and a carboxyl group at the right of the molecule. The amino group at the left can be bonded to the carboxyl group of a third amino acid. The carboxyl group at the right can be bonded to the amino group of a fourth amino acid. This method of "chain-building" always leaves one free amino group and one free carboxyl group. Thus, there is an opportunity of building an ever larger molecule.

In living cells, proteins are built up by hundreds or even thousands of linkage reactions somewhat like these, although for every amino acid added, many more steps are involved than we are able to explain until some of the complexity of a living cell is familiar to you. Energy is required for these reactions, and enzymes and other cell components take part in the selection of special amino acids, and in their arrangement to form the specific protein molecules of the cell. We will have more to say about this in Chapter 8.

The molecules of the majority of proteins are built of 300 to 3,000 amino acid subunits. With so many individual amino acids in the protein molecule, and usually 20 kinds of amino acids to choose among, you can imagine the enormous number of possible protein molecules which might exist in plants and animals.

Once again an analogy may help to make the point. The number of kinds of amino acids found naturally is only a few less than the number of letters in the English alphabet. You are aware of the tremendous number of words that it is possible to construct with 26 letters. Remember also that the average number of letters to a word is fewer than ten. If words consisted of 300 to 3,000 letters, just as proteins consist of 300 to 3,000 amino acids, the possible number of words would be staggering. We can learn something more from this comparison between words and protein molecules. A word has a *particular meaning* because of the way its letters are put together. Similarly, a protein molecule functions in a *particular way* because of the way its amino acids are put together. Remember the hemoglobin molecule? Biologists have discovered that sometimes a person may develop an abnormal type of hemoglobin which has just two of the 574 amino acids in the molecule different from normal. This alone may so disturb the oxygen-carrying function of the protein that it can cause the death of the unfortunate person.

The cells of any one species of animal contain thousands of different kinds of protein molecules. Each kind of animal and plant has among its proteins numerous kinds found only in its own species. Some may be found only in a single individual—you, for instance. However, the more closely related two organisms or species are in an evolutionary sense, the more their proteins are alike.

Complex protein molecules are constantly being broken down within organisms. For example, in digestion, protein molecules in foods are decomposed into amino acids. The bond between the N of a modified amino group and the C of a modified carboxyl group is broken by enzyme activity. Simultaneously, the equivalent of a water molecule is introduced to fill out the amino and carboxyl groups at the point of the broken bond. An H is bonded to the N, and an OH to the C. We call this process **hydrolysis** (hy·DROL·ih·sis). The term means "to break with water." The hydrolysis reaction can be imagined using Figure 5-6. All one has to do is to reverse the arrow!

Only a few proteins have been studied so intensively that their structure of amino acid units is fully known. The first was insulin, a protein that aids our use of sugar in the body. When not enough is present, the result is the disease **diabetes** (dy·a·BEE·teez). Insulin is a relatively small protein molecule, and therefore relatively easier to study than bigger ones, even though it has 51 amino acids in its two chains. In one of the most remarkable achievements of biochemistry, Frederick Sanger of Cambridge University was able to determine completely the structure of insulin. His research required years, but at the end, in 1954, he knew the precise position occupied by each amino acid in the molecule, as you saw in Figure 5-5.

Sanger's feat of analysis has been duplicated for only a few other kinds of protein molecules. Let us pause a moment to see what such achievements mean. Remember that the proteins are among the most important of all organic molecules. Many of the properties of life are reflections of the structure and functions of proteins. A fuller understanding of the living processes must therefore be based on an intimate knowledge of proteins. In view of this, it is sobering to realize that we know the structural details of so few proteins. Clearly this important branch of biochemistry is still in its infancy.

The *size* of a protein molecule depends upon the kinds and total number of amino acid molecules that have been bonded together. The *shape* of the molecule, however, depends upon the manner in which separate chains of amino

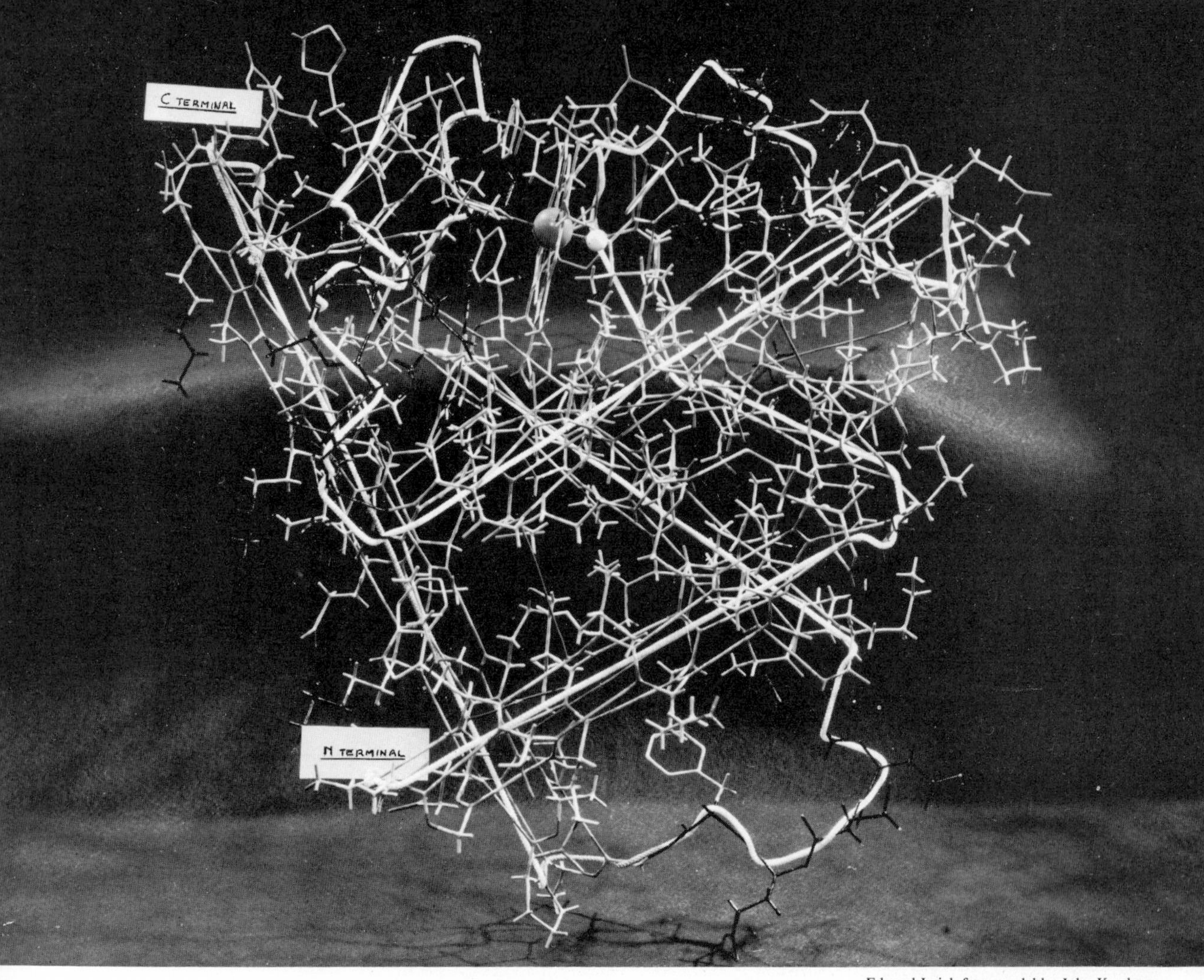

Edward Leigh from model by John Kendrew

5–7 A model of a myoglobin molecule, a protein of your cells. The active or functional part is seen edge-on, almost vertical, near the upper middle, with an oversize iron atom (dark ball) at its center and an oversize oxygen atom (light ball) attached. The two ends of the main chain of amino acids are labeled at the left; the N terminal is the amino end, the C terminal the carboxyl end. In your cells, myoglobin temporarily accepts the oxygen delivered by the hemoglobin of your blood.

acids have been connected, and *which* specific amino acids are present in the chains. Some proteins are long, thin fibers, such as those which form hair and silk. Others are globular, like hemoglobin and other proteins in our blood. They appear to have their amino acid chains coiled up into a ball. Still others exhibit shapes resembling a cigar or a sausage.

What is the significance of coiled or folded structure in a protein molecule? One can see from the structure of insulin, Figure 5-5, that it has at two places cross-linkages (bonds involving two sulfur atoms) that hold the two chains of the molecule together and in a particular shape. There is also a third such linkage between two different parts of one of the chains.

Larger protein molecules are folded back and forth many times and held in shape by similar linkages between the folded chains. In protein molecules there is a remarkable range of groups which can react to form covalent bonds, ionic bonds, or weak bonds with other atoms or molecules. This makes proteins the most versatile of all chemical tools. In fact, there is no substance known in living organisms—from the smallest gas molecules to gigantic molecules of carbohydrates and nucleic acids—with which some protein molecule will not react. Enzymes of some organisms will even react with such improbable things as paper, old shoe leather, and jet plane fuel!

But the structure and shape of a protein bring out another feature. The molecule pictured in Figure 5-7 will help you see this. The functional part of the molecule (upper middle in Figure 5-7) is held in a particular position by the coils of the remaining parts of the molecule. The ability to combine with another molecule and transport it or modify it obviously depends upon the overall structure of the protein molecule. If the active or functional part were tucked away too deeply inside the molecule's coils, its chemical activity would be greatly reduced and possibly eliminated altogether.

Proteins, therefore, are not quite so mysterious as they once were. Their enormous molecular size, however, does create great problems in studying them. As we proceed with our study of biology, we will encounter many specific proteins in both plants and animals. It will be useful to remember that each kind of protein has its own arrangement of amino acids, as well as a characteristic size and shape and range of possible chemical reactions. It is these properties that make it possible for the protein to do its specific job for the plant or animal in which it is found. The correlation between structure and function, a prominent feature of all living organisms, is nowhere more striking than in the case of proteins, which include both structural compounds and the enzymes of the cell.

Carbohydrates

Carbohydrates are another class of organic compounds in all living organisms. Their name, expressed as "hydrated carbon," comes from the fact that in addition to carbon, they contain hydrogen and oxygen *in the same ratio as in water* (2 to 1). This fact helps us remember their chemical structure.

Glucose is a common and important carbohydrate. It is a sugar—you know it chiefly from the sweet taste of honey and fruits like grapes. It can be found in almost all living organisms. It occurs in the blood of all people, where its concentration is so critical that if it falls to half the normal value the person rapidly loses consciousness and will die unless given treatment at once.

Glucose has the formula $C_6H_{12}O_6$. The 24 atoms of each of its molecules can be arranged as shown in Figure 5-8. From its formula alone we could predict something about the function of glucose in cells—it contains carbon linked to hydrogen (page 90), and therefore should be a good energy source. As organic compounds go, it is not a large molecule, and it dissolves easily in water, which makes it available for reactions throughout the living organism.

Glucose and similar "small" carbohydrate molecules can be linked together in the cell to form much larger molecules. Chemical energy is used under close control by enzymes in carrying out these linkage reactions. The gigantic molecules which are formed may contain thousands of carbohydrate units, and are extremely stable. The molecules are so large that unlike the glucose of which they are made they cannot dissolve in water; an example is starch. Because of their large size and insolubility in water these large molecules serve two main functions in living organisms. They act as storage molecules for the small carbohydrate units, like glucose, that the cell actually uses in its chemical reactions. And they are excellent building materials for solid protective structures of living organisms. A good example of the latter is *cellulose*. Without a doubt it is the most abun-

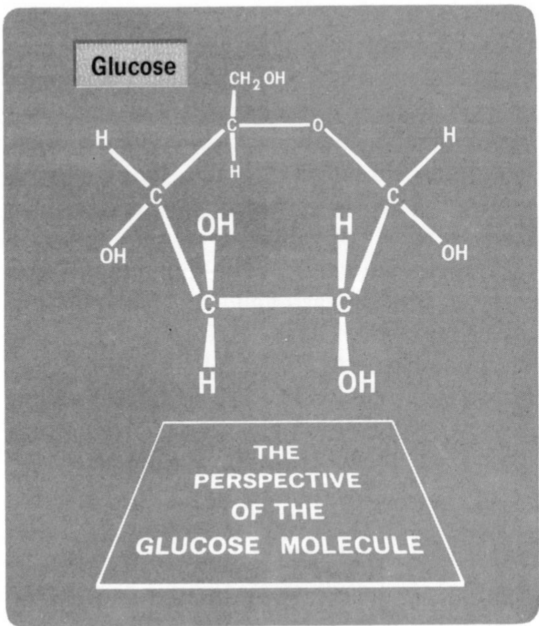

5–8 You can picture a glucose molecule as a hexagonal plate to which various H and OH are attached, along with a CH_2OH. Like all other molecules, glucose is best imagined in constant motion. The ring of C and O atoms may break at a C–O bond, spring open, then form into a ring again in the same or slightly different form. Though very stable when dry and isolated from other compounds, glucose is highly reactive in the presence of enzymes.

dant carbohydrate in all of nature. Its subunits are made of glucose. Cellulose is found in plants, where it makes up most of the material of plant cell walls. Pure cellulose is familiar to us as cotton fibers formed in the cotton plant. Wood is very largely cellulose. So is the paper of this printed page in your book.

Fats

Fats are familiar to us in several forms—as butter (the fat of milk), as the solid fat in meat, and as the oils from cotton seeds, olives, and peanuts. The term *fat*, like the term *carbohydrate,* indicates a group of related compounds rather than any one compound. The main feature that they have in common is a basic skeleton built of long chains or rings of carbon atoms combined by many covalent bonds with hydrogen. (A part of one such chain appears on page 90.) Other atoms are often built into these molecules, but we can explain the common biological functions of fats and related compounds in terms of the carbon skeleton with hydrogen atoms attached. Molecules built in this way are not soluble in water, and are lighter than water. You have probably observed something about these properties in your daily life, for they explain why cream separates from natural milk, and why the oil in a vinegar-and-oil salad dressing rises shortly after mixing. (Skim milk and vinegar are largely water.)

In the living cell, molecules with these properties take part with proteins in building structures that cannot dissolve in water, and thus divide the cell into regions where different chemical reactions can take place without interfering with one another. Such organization in the cell is absolutely necessary.

Fats and similar molecules have another very important property. Because they contain so much carbon linked to hydrogen, they are a rich source of stored chemical energy. Again, this is something with which you are probably familiar already—if you know anyone who is dieting because he has too much energy stored in his body as fat, you know that he has to avoid eating fatty foods like cream, butter, and nuts.

Nucleic Acids and Nucleotides

Not long ago, **nucleic** (new·KLEE·ik) **acids** and **nucleotides** (NEW·kle·o·tides) were scarcely discussed. Only recently have biologists come to understand their importance in the life of cells and organisms.

Like the proteins, nucleic acids are long chains made from simpler units by linkage between the units. The units are not amino acids, as in the case of proteins, but nucleotides. Each nucleotide molecule, as you will learn in Chapter 8, is a rather complicated and stable structure built from rings of carbon and nitrogen associated with other atoms of hydrogen, oxygen, nitrogen, and phosphorus. In the "language of the cell," where each protein "word" may be built of 20 kinds of amino acid "letters," each nucleic acid "word" is built of only four kinds of nucleotide "letters." Yet, as in the case of proteins, the order of structure of units is of the greatest importance.

Two major types of nucleic acids are recognized. **Deoxyribonucleic** (dee·OKS·ee·ry·boh-new·KLEE·ik) **acid,** or DNA for short, is characteristic of the cell nucleus. **Ribonucleic** (ry·boh·new·KLEE·ik) **acid,** or RNA, is found in many places in the cell. DNA has a key role in inheritance. It is the substance that, passed down from one generation to another, controls development. One egg develops into a kitten and another into a human baby because each contains different and specific types of DNA: cat or human DNA's.

We have excellent reasons to believe that DNA molecules work by guiding enzymes in making RNA. RNA molecules in turn guide the enzymes that make proteins. Do you remember about the hemoglobin molecule with two fatally wrong amino acids (page 95)? The thing that went wrong in making this protein was a change in DNA, which caused a wrong form of RNA to be made. With this wrong RNA as their guide, the enzymes making hemoglobin went wrong, too. You can see that this is a fascinating story, and we will explain it more fully in Chapter 8.

Nucleotides also play other important roles in the cell. In Chapter 6 we will see how some of them, including **adenosine triphosphate** (a-DEN·O·SEEN try·FOS·fayt), or ATP, has a key role in providing energy for the cell's activities.

Looking back over this range of organic compounds in cells, you can see how each of the four main classes—proteins, carbohydrates, fats, and nucleic acids and nucleotides—plays two major kinds of roles in cell function: the building of structure, and the supplying of energy.

This is not the full story of the principal compounds of cells. The chemical substances we have described do not lie around in a cell like stuffed animals in a museum display. Stored chemical energy is constantly made available to cells by oxidation-reduction, and is used to build compounds so unstable that they would break down and could not be formed again without the use of energy. The small, very reactive nucleotides are made in this way, and they in turn can transfer energy to the cell's various activities, including the building of other compounds. Some of this energy goes into making giant protein or nucleic acid molecules from the small amino acid or nucleotide units. Energy can be used to change carbohydrates into fats or proteins, or build carbohydrates from proteins or fats, depending on the cell's moment-by-moment needs. The chemistry of cells is a very lively business—individual molecules are constantly being built, torn apart, rebuilt, and moved from place to place. Enzymes regulate these processes so that hundreds of thousands of reactions go on in a single cell with nearly unbelievable control. If you had to direct the chemical traffic in just one of your own cells—a liver cell, for instance—you certainly would not have time to learn anything else about biology!

ENERGY SUPPLY

Now that we have established a background of knowledge of the chemical compounds in living things, it is wise to look once again at the sources of energy for living processes. Earlier in this chapter we pointed out that oxidation-reduction reactions are the direct source of this energy. Remember that oxidation-reduction involves exchange of electrons between atoms. How, you might ask, can electrons serve as a source of energy?

The answer can be given in terms of a similar question—when can water on the surface of the earth serve as a source of energy? It can if it is in a waterfall, but not if it is in the Dead Sea. In a waterfall, water goes from a region of high to a region of low stored energy (mechanical energy), and as it does so, energy can be changed into other forms (for instance, into electrical energy). In the Dead Sea, water has no place to fall, so it cannot be a source of energy. In the same way, different atoms have different degrees of electron attraction, forming more or less stable electron configurations. The movement of electrons from an atom where the electron attachment is less stable to one where it is more stable results in energy change. Here, too, energy can be converted to other forms (for instance, into the energy of mechanical movement, molecule building, or other activities of living organisms).

Imagine, then, a glass of water sitting on the ground. You really cannot call it a source of energy. Now lift this glass of water as far as you can over your head—it has become a source of energy (where did its energy come from?). You could demonstrate this to yourself by pouring the water from the glass in a stream through a very small generator, thus producing enough electric energy to light a tiny flashlight bulb. Electrons can be an energy source because of *where* they are, in an arrangement of atoms—just as water can be an energy source in terms of *where* it is in relation to the surface of the earth. An association of electrons with oxygen is not likely to be a good energy source because it is so stable. But if electrons are dragged away from oxygen and attached to something else—carbon and hydrogen, for instance—they become a source of energy. They will tend to move back to oxygen if possible, or to other atoms which can become more stable by taking up electrons. When this happens, energy is released or changed to another form.

By now it would be quite reasonable for you to be wondering why the terms *oxidation* and *reduction* are used for processes involving electron loss or gain. *Oxidation* seems to suggest something about the element oxygen, and yet our definition of oxidation—the loss of an electron by an atom—does not say anything in particular about oxygen atoms. But many of the reactions involving oxidation which were first recognized by scientists *did* involve oxygen, because oxygen atoms form exceptionally stable associations with two extra electrons. We can say this in another way—oxygen is one of the most common and most powerful of the electron-attracting substances in our world. A familiar example is the rusting of iron. Atoms of the dull, dark silvery metal iron give up electrons to the far more electron-attracting atoms of oxygen in oxygen molecules of the air. The result is the formation of charged (by electron loss) iron atoms which react with charged (by electron gain) oxygen atoms. The two kinds of charged atoms attract one another to form molecules containing both iron and oxygen—iron oxide, the familiar reddish compound rust. Early scientists recognized that rust formation was caused by reaction of iron with *oxygen*—no wonder they called this sort of process *oxidation.* They also knew of ways to recover metallic iron from rust—simplifying it, or reducing it, as they might say, to its original form. The reducing process, or *reduction,* freed the iron from combination with oxygen—and, as we now know, restored to the iron the electrons previously lost to oxygen.

The events of oxidation and reduction always occur together, just as *giving* and *receiving* do. You cannot give something to another person unless he accepts it. In the same way, when we say that food materials are oxidized by an organism, we should always remember to think of—and even to mention—the substances (oxygen and others) which are reduced at the same time. Oxygen is not necessary for every oxidation-reduction process. (Think of your previous Na^+ and Cl^-, forming table salt.) Even in human body cells, oxidation-reductions take place without oxygen. It is only the final steps in the pattern of cell oxidation-reductions that require oxygen. People and many other animals must breathe in air and get the oxygen their cells need to keep electrons "flowing." But what about organisms that live in tropical swamps, or inside the intestines of animals like ourselves—can they get oxygen from the air? The answer is either no, or at most they get very little oxygen. They do not need it because they are able to use compounds other than oxygen to take up electrons in their oxidation-reduction reactions.

Since oxidation-reduction does not necessarily involve oxygen, why do we keep a term like "oxidation," which suggests that oxygen is present? Partly because the word has been used so long that it is generally accepted by scientists. But you will also find that it is a useful word in helping you remember what actually happens in energy exchanges in most cells. Although oxygen (and hydrogen) are not *always* involved in oxidation-reduction, they *often* are in living organisms. We say that a molecule has been oxidized, then, when it has *lost electrons, lost hydrogen atoms*, or *gained oxygen atoms*. A molecule is *reduced* by just the opposite changes—*gain of electrons, gain of hydrogen, or loss of oxygen atoms.* These changes always involve change in stability of molecular arrangement, so energy changes occur in these reactions. We cannot *see* a molecule lose or gain electrons, or lose or gain a hydrogen atom, yet we know that oxidation-reduction reactions take place in both living and nonliving systems. What evidence do we have to support this knowledge (Inquiry 5-4)?

In Chapter 6 we will tell more about how these reactions occur in cells.

ENERGY WASTE

As you can see, we seem to have found a way to start explaining the structure and functioning of organisms in chemical terms. The structure depends on special chemical compounds built from atoms. The energy comes mainly from oxidation-reduction reactions. Organisms can store the chemical energy made available in oxidation-reduction reactions by building unstable organic compounds. Then they can regain the energy and convert it for various uses when the unstable compounds are broken down. But there is one other important fact which we must take into account, although we do not understand why it should be true. Scientists have discovered by experiments and observations for many years that whenever an energy change takes place in a chemical reaction, some of the energy is turned into a form in which it can never be used again. Part is likely to be changed to heat which cannot be trapped and turned to any other form. We often speak of this change of part of the energy to useless form as "loss of energy." But this does not mean real loss—you remember from the Law of Conservation of Energy that energy is never created or destroyed in chemical reactions. "Energy loss" only means that some energy is changed to a form which cannot be used.

Although we do not know why such energy loss or waste should occur in every process involving energy change, we accept it in our everyday life and build all our machines with this in mind. The car's engine changes part of the chemical energy stored in gasoline to mechanical energy in turning the car's wheels, but part of the energy is turned to heat. The car has a radiator to help get rid of this extra heat. So when you buy gasoline, you are paying partly for useful mileage and partly for waste heat. Living organisms, like the car and all other energy-converting machines, could not operate long if energy waste were not taken into account. How do you take it into account in your own body? Your cell processes, appetite, habits, and behavior do this for you. In a way, you always eat for two—for your own activities, and for the energy you have to waste in carrying out these activities.

CONCLUDING REMARKS

Although we know so much now about the chemistry of living things, there is still a vast amount to be learned. An architect can make a complete "chemical picture" of a house, describing all the materials (brick, concrete, glass, and others) of which it is built. But you could not make such a "chemical picture" of your own body, because we do not know all of the substances that are built into even a tiny division of the human body—we do not even know the full chemical structure of a toenail, a hair, or a blood cell. As a matter of fact, there is not a single living organism that we can yet describe in terms of its chemical structure!

Still, there is a great deal which we do know about living chemistry. All of it is interesting, for it is basic to our understanding of the various processes of life. We have described only a few kinds of compounds in this chapter, but you can learn about others in the laboratory and on pages 759-60 of this book. And you are sure to learn more about organic compounds all your life as you read books, magazines, newspapers, or watch television. These compounds are so important in understanding human life and disease, and so important as food materials, vitamins, drugs, and so forth (Figure 5-9), that discoveries in biochemistry are part of the news of the day.

Biological processes really could not be explained if we did not have some knowledge of chemistry. The question "What is a living thing made up of?" can be answered in terms of atoms and the characteristic molecules they form. The questions "What does a living thing do? What processes does it carry out?" can be answered in terms of the ways in which atoms of the living system share or exchange electrons, bond together, attract or repel one another, store energy, and change stored energy from one form to another by changing the structure of atoms and molecules.

Yet we need other kinds of information. We need to know how the chemical substances are put together to form the structure of living cells, and how, when built in this way, these structures function. Then we must ask how cells are put together to build different organisms. We will start to look for answers to some of these questions in Chapter 6.

5–9 Only a few of the chemical compounds important in your life are suggested by this illustration of kinds of compounds you might find mentioned in a single issue of the newspaper, with its news reports and advertisements. One way to be alert to the chemical nature of your world is to look for the underlying meanings in the news.

Foods: organic compounds, salts, vitamins, water
Soft drinks: organic compounds, water, carbon dioxide
Low-calorie foods and drinks (relatively few fats and carbohydrates)
Clothes and other textiles: complex carbohydrates, proteins
Medicines and drugs: organic compounds, aspirin, antibiotics, etc.
Also: organic compounds... gasoline car oils heating oils rubber
...and inorganic compounds hair sprays plant "foods" (salts) mouthwashes

GUIDE QUESTIONS AND PROBLEMS

1. What have "patterns" to do with solving biological problems? (Page 86: ". . . we do not *fully* understand why patterns of chemical reactions are as simple as they appear," referring to numbers of electrons as guides to reaction of the elements listed in Figure 5-3. For examples from earlier chapters: a *pattern* of malaria near swamps; a suspected *pattern* of structure in plants and animals—but difficult to establish from Hooke's description of cells in terms of cell walls, which were not found in animals.)
2. Explain the difference between a solution of salt in water and a solution of sugar in water; then extend your explanation to suggest why most starches and many proteins do not dissolve in water. In the laboratory, where you have looked at cells under a microscope, what kinds of compounds would you reason are built into the cell structures that you see (the cell membrane, the nucleus, and the visible structures and granules in the cytoplasm)?
3. Proteins in cells of a bean plant differ from proteins in cells of a dog; yet both organisms build their proteins from similar amino acids. How can the differences be accounted for?
4. You are almost 70 percent water—one of the best *solvents* known. How do you keep from dissolving in it? How are you able to maintain your structure and continue to produce more cells and tissues?
5. If you were to design a molecule to store in your cells for future use as a source of energy, what are some of the characteristics you would build into it?
6. The sugars glucose, galactose, and fructose all occur in living organisms and all have the same formula—$C_6H_{12}O_6$. They are distinctly different in their chemical reactions and behave differently in the organisms in which they occur. How can you account for this?
7. Molecules of the type you designed in Question 5 are not the *immediate* energy source of cells. Instead, the stored molecules are broken down while the cell is using energy from unstable compounds, and the energy from the stored molecules is transferred to renew the supply of the unstable compounds. What advantage is there in this method of energy transfer and use?
8. How can the transfer of electrons from one substance to another be a means of making chemical energy available to a cell for its synthetic activities and other life processes?

RELATED READING

Books

For an extension of your introduction to chemistry . . .

Bronowski, J., *et al, Doubleday Pictorial Library of Science*, Doubleday, New York, 1960. Beautifully illustrated historical account of physics, astronomy, and chemistry, including the "Chemistry of Living Things."

Grunewald, E., and R. H. Johnson, *Atoms, Molecules, and Chemical Change*, Prentice-Hall, Englewood Cliffs, N. J., 1960. A modern account, for readers without a background in chemistry.

Lagowski, J. J., *The Chemical Bond*, Houghton Mifflin, Boston, 1966. The historical development of ideas of atoms and how they combine, presented by direct quotations from publications of the period.

Lessing, L., *Understanding Chemistry*, New American Library, New York, 1959 (paperback). A popularized account of man's discoveries in chemistry.

For an extension of your introduction to biochemistry . . .

Bronowski, J., *et al, Doubleday Pictorial Library of Science* (see citation under preceding heading).

Baker, J. J. W., and G. E. Allen, *Matter, Energy, and Life*, Addison-Wesley, Palo Alto, Calif., 1965. Introduces general chemistry, enzymes, and the chemistry of life.

Magazines

Stein, W. H., and S. Moore, "Chemical Structure of Proteins," *Scientific American*, Volume 204 (February 1961), page 81.

Thompson, E. O. P., "The Insulin Molecule," *Scientific American*, Volume 192 (May 1955), page 36.

6

The Physiology of Cells

Not far away from your biology classroom is a laboratory used for investigations in chemistry. Stored there in separate cabinets are groups of bottles whose labels include such carefully worded warnings as:

"Store in a DRY place away from acids."

"CAUTION—reacts violently with water, releasing heat rapidly. Spattering may cause severe burns."

"Strong oxidizing agent—store separately from combustible substances and organic compounds."

—and many other precautionary statements. On the open shelves of the laboratory are a limited number of chemicals that the chemistry teacher stores with less concern. Although accidental breakage and mixing may occur, he does not expect chemical reactions among these substances—unless at a rate that would take months or more to occur.

If a cell in your study of biology has seemed little more to you than a small box of assorted chemical parts subject to occasional modifications, think of it now as it is—a *powerfully*-stocked little living laboratory. All its chemicals are there together—and yet *not* together, really. For just as the chemist has separate cabinets, so does the cell build structures of membranes and keep chemicals it is using in one job here, and others there.

It isn't easy—for how can a cell keep certain chemicals in a dry place when its most plentiful chemical is water? Many of its substances also cannot easily be kept away from acids, especially if the cell is one that produces substances of significant hydrogen ion (acid) level. To carry the comparison with the chemist's laboratory further, you would find among the cell's chemicals several that with no more than a loss of an electron would react "violently." And finally, among the chemicals in the cell are oxidizing agents, which like those in the chemistry laboratory readily accept electrons from organic compounds; you already know that most of the compounds inside the cell *are* organic compounds.

What makes a cell survive under conditions that would make your school's chemistry laboratory unsafe?

Nor is this all that is to be considered. Some of the types of substances that chemists would keep on "open shelves" react with one another in the cell!

You can put two and two together and guess "who" many of the chemists in these living laboratories are—the *enzymes*—and what these amazing proteins must somehow accomplish in living cells:

1. They draw many substances safely away from reactive encounters the chemist might expect. They apparently do this by *speeding them along paths* of reactions that the chemist would *not* ordinarily expect, and that will not harm the cell.
2. They cause other reactions, particularly among substances that the chemist considers relatively stable or slow-to-react, *to take place rapidly* enough to be of use to the cell.

You can see that the two statements are consistent in an important respect—how the enzymes work. In either situation, enzymes *speed up* the reactions that actually take place in the cell. Other reactions do *not* take place to any significant extent.

ENZYMES

You can't be invited into a cell to watch enzymes at work. To begin to appreciate *how* small a "laboratory" the enzymes occupy, start by imagining a cubic container 1 mm × 1 mm × 1 mm. Can you guess how many objects the size of human body cells could be packed into it? Or how many the size of protein molecules? Or the size of water molecules? Make your guesses and check your answers with the estimates in Figure 6-1. The numbers there may give you a fair idea of the sorts of difficulties biologists face when they try to discover ways to investigate the microscopic structures and the functions of living cells.

In energy changes, too, the biologist's scale is special. We are not concerned, as the chemist is, with how many grams or kilograms of one substance must react with another to free so much energy. We are concerned with how many *individual molecules* must react to make energy available on one cell's scale!

Some of the chemical events that may be important to us can involve only a single molecule—or a very few.

Our difficulties go even beyond *size* and *numbers,* and *measures of energy.* Consider

6–1 You would have a difficult time indeed if you had only one way to study the chemical events in cells. Investigating events on a molecular level inside a single living cell would be on a scale nearly unimaginably smaller than shown for the millimeter cube here. Fortunately biologists have discovered ways to extract enzymes and other cell components from vast quantities of similar cells in living tissues. The chemical events then can be studied on a larger scale in the laboratory.

This cube could contain about 250,000 liver cells of average size...
or-
1X10^{15}= 1,000,000,000,000,000 protein molecules of average size...
1mm cube
or-
3X10^{19}= 30,000,000,000,000,000,000 water molecules

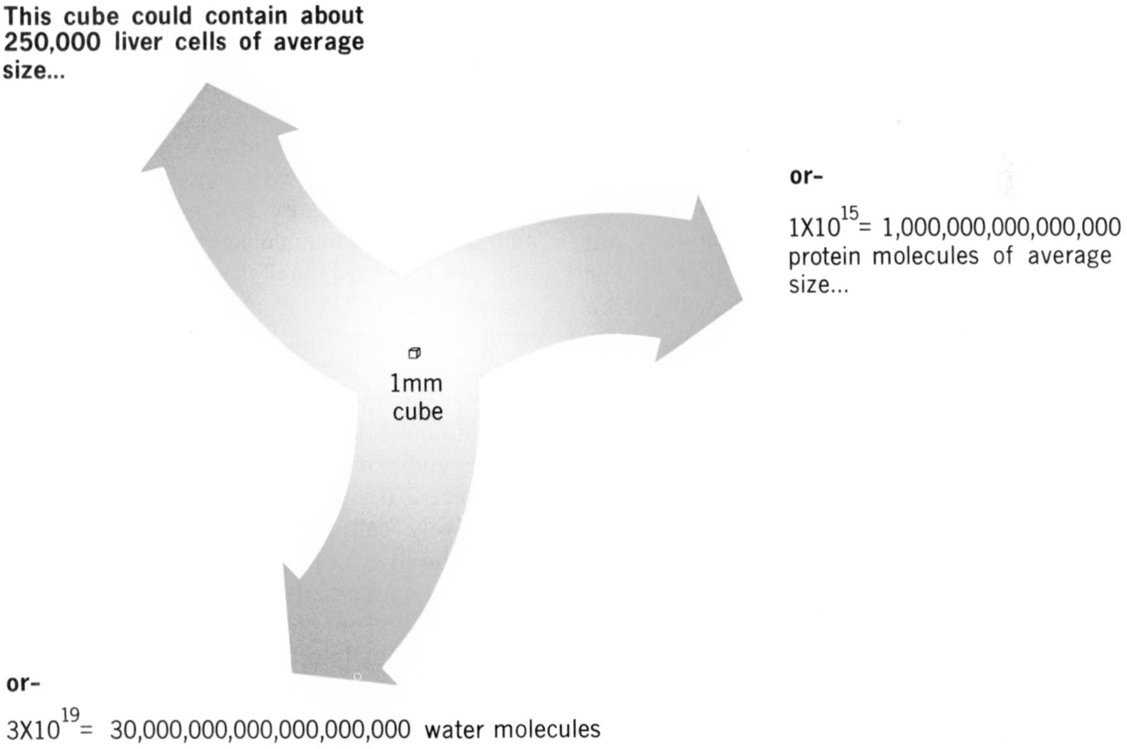

amounts of time. A single enzyme molecule may break down other molecules of a particular kind at rates of more than 100,000 molecules per second! If we wish to observe such events taking place, we must have instruments that are *very* sensitive and extremely accurate.

You can see that the problems biologists study are not easy to solve. You also will understand that our methods are not yet perfect. Perhaps you will *not* wonder why the experiments you undertake often seem so complicated.

To study enzymes in living cells, or **in vivo** (VEE·voh or VY·voh) as this is termed, you would encounter all the problems of cell and molecular size just discussed. Fortunately you can study enzymes **in vitro** (VEET·roh or VYT-roh), which means "in glassware" in our laboratories. Payen and Persoz, whom you remember from Chapter 4, first showed that an enzyme can be isolated and used in the laboratory. Today we have hundreds in fairly pure form. Dozens of these have been crystallized; this is important because we know that in crystals the enzymes are fairly pure. That is how we can say with confidence that enzymes are proteins. They are made up of thousands of atoms, but still only a handful of the elements from your table in Figure 5-3 (page 85). You can determine for yourself which elements enzymes contain if they are proteins. They rarely have more than one or a few atoms of any element you will not be able to name from a review of what you have read in Chapter 5 about proteins.

Enzymes at Work

If enzymes work such marvels in making *their* chemical events the rule in cells, you will not be surprised that they have help. Other substances that we call **coenzymes** (KOH·en·zymes) assist. They are not proteins and usually are much smaller than proteins.

Enzyme-coenzyme pairs carry out various kinds of reactions. One example is oxidation-reduction, which you read about in Chapter 5 (page 87). In this case the enzyme removes electrons rapidly from food substances and transfers them to the coenzymes in the cell (much as oxygen removes electrons—or hydrogen—rapidly from the fuel that burns in your basement furnace). But there is only so much of the coenzyme to accept the electrons the enzyme is removing (while in the basement a continuing supply of oxygen in air reaches the basement furnace). The coenzyme cannot continue to accumulate electrons; it cannot hold them. Other enzymes pass the electrons on to other coenzymes. From there they go on to oxygen. Without this cooperation among the enzymes and coenzymes, activity would stop.

One of the most striking things about almost all enzymes is that they are *specific*. An illustration of this is that horses, cows, and sheep can eat grass and prosper; you cannot. In the digestive systems of these animals, certain one-celled organisms live and form the enzyme **cellulase** (CELL·yoo·lace). Cellulase breaks up cellulose in grass and makes the glucose of which it is built available to the horses, cows, and sheep. You do not have an enzyme like cellulase. Grass will not satisfy your need for food.

For another illustration of enzyme specificity, consider the two amino acid molecules you know from Figure 5-6, page 94. Glycine and alanine look much alike in molecular structure. It is also hard to tell them apart by ordinary chemical tests. Yet the enzymes in the cell that react with glycine, in building this amino acid into protein molecules, are quite different from the enzymes the cell uses with alanine—or any other amino acid, for that matter.

The study of enzymes, coenzymes, and the substances they cause to react—which we collectively call **substrates** (SUB·strayts)—occupies the lives of thousands of biologists who are investigating activities of living cells. You can profitably enrich your *own* study of enzymes by going into the laboratory. There you can investigate some questions like the three in the list that begins the next page.

1. How do hydrogen ions affect the cell environment? (Laboratory Inquiry 6-1)
2. What difference can you detect between a reaction going on when an enzyme is present and when it is not? (Laboratory Inquiry 4-1) What clues to enzyme action are left in body products? (Laboratory Inquiry 6-2)
3. Since enzymes are proteins, how do factors that affect proteins affect enzyme action—factors such as temperature, hydrogen ions, and larger ions that combine with proteins? (Laboratory Inquiry 6-3)

Certain other problems about enzymes are harder to solve. The first of these is the question: *What happens to an enzyme when it takes part in a chemical reaction?*

No enzyme can "force" a reaction to take place. This would amount to changing the nature of the substances involved. If a reaction can take place at all—however slowly—a specific enzyme can make it go faster. An enzyme may speed up a reaction that otherwise would go so slowly that it might just as well not happen at all. You remember our example of the horses, cows, and sheep that use cellulose as an energy source. They are able to do so because of the enzyme cellulase, which splits cellulose into thousands of small sugar molecules. But a cellulose molecule would break down even without any enzyme to help—if you could wait long enough! By "long enough" we mean years—perhaps thousands of years, although we really do not know how long it would take. In any case, it would be far too long for a starving animal to wait for those sugar molecules! Speed is always of the greatest importance in biology, and enzymes can give speed to chemical reactions.

Another point about enzyme function helps to explain why they are so important in determining the reactions that take place in living processes. Enzymes are not just *in* the cell; they are in organized structures of the cell. Thus, several different kinds of enzymes may work closely together to speed several very slow reactions that can result in a complex reaction we would not have predicted from our knowledge of chemistry alone. We can illustrate this point with a comparison, asking the question—is it likely that an orange will roll down the steep surface of a glacier? You might say that this is very unlikely, because oranges grow on trees in the warmest parts of the world, but glaciers exist only in the coldest regions. Therefore, although you would expect an orange to roll down any steep surface, it seems almost impossible that it would ever have a chance to roll down a glacier. But of course a man could take an orange to a place where there are glaciers. This very unlikely event—an orange rolling down a glacier—can occur easily if human action is taken into account. In a similar way, very unlikely chemical events can occur in cells if enzyme action is taken into account.

A Model for Enzyme Action

How can we account for all the properties of enzymes? Trying to answer this question, biologists began making careful measurements of the relationship between enzyme concentration, substrate concentration, and rate of reaction. They saw that they could give a good explanation of the data if they assumed that an enzyme and a substrate molecule must combine as a first step in the reaction. The very unstable *enzyme-substrate molecule* thus formed could then break down, according to this hypothesis. When this happened the substrate would be changed into different substances—the products of the reaction. Meantime, the enzyme would be freed in its original form, and could start the whole process over again by combining with another substrate molecule. This hypothesis would explain why enzymes are specific. Thus, a given reaction could take place only if the enzyme had just the right reacting groups to combine with the substrate. It would be easy to see why anything that changed these groups would change enzyme function. *Anything,* in fact, that

6-2 A MODEL FOR ENZYME ACTION

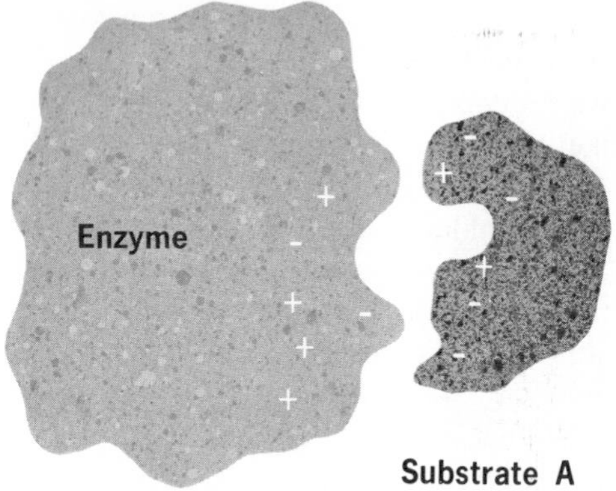

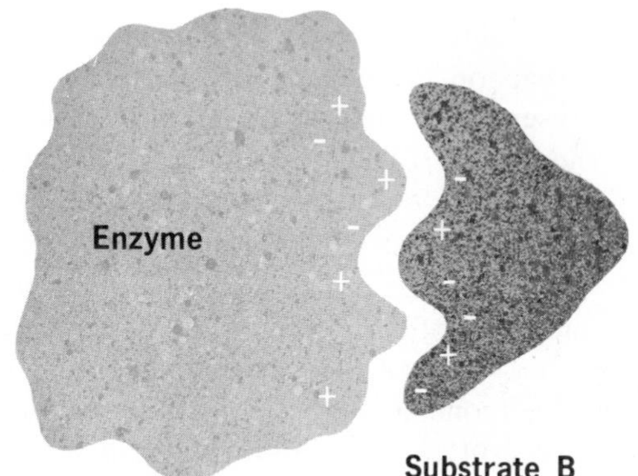

a Weak bonds — like those formed by attraction of "+" for "−" groups of atoms — may cause molecules to combine. Are the positions of combining groups effective in that way here?

b If neighboring groups of atoms fit together well enough to form *numerous* weak bonds between two molecules, the cumulative effect of the bonds temporarily links the molecules.

changes protein structure could alter the structure of enzymes and change their function. These ideas can be built into models, or descriptions, of enzyme action. An enzyme and a substrate combine because they "fit" together well enough for certain weak bonds to be effective. This combination with an enzyme can affect greatly the reactiveness of the substrate. When it is combined thus with the enzyme, changes in the structure of the substrate take place easily. In Figure 6-2 we have given a picture of such a model. Though the substrates shown are imaginary, they could be real substances like the two amino acids in Figure 5-6, page 94.

Biologists have found experimental evidence to support this hypothesis, or model, of enzyme action. Using very sensitive methods, they can detect slight changes in some enzyme molecules *during* a reaction—but not before or after! These changes are direct indications that the enzyme has combined chemically with its substrate during the reaction.

As we go on to various aspects of cell physiology, keep in mind that enzymes are involved. An individual enzyme molecule may catalyze its specific reaction several hundred or even many thousand times in one second. Enzymes are involved in all sorts of reactions: those in which large molecules are synthesized from smaller ones; those in which molecules are decomposed into smaller ones; those in which atoms are exchanged between molecules; and those in which the atoms of a molecule are rearranged. The sum of all these reactions is called **metabolism** (meh·TAB·o·liz′m).

STRUCTURE AND FUNCTION IN CELLS

You already know a surprising amount about structures found in cells. With no more than you learned in Chapter 3, you can ask two very important questions about them. The first question is: what are the structures—cell membranes and walls, vacuoles, granules, rods, and so forth—made of? The second is—what do they *do* in the cell—that is, what are their *functions*?

Biologists have worked out experimental methods to answer the first question. You

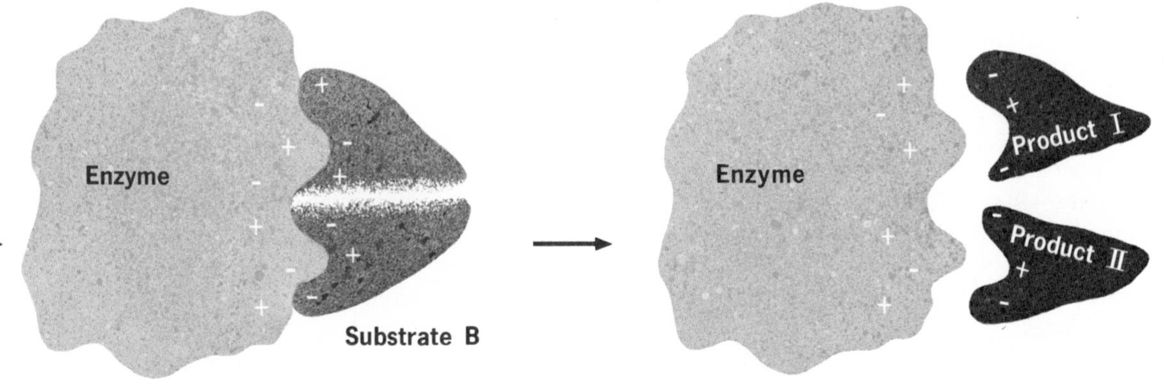

c The numerous weak bonds affect the nature of other bonds in the enzyme-substrate complex. Changes in bonds of the substrate take place more easily.

d As the substrate changes, the weak bonds between enzyme and substrate change, too. The products of the reaction are freed from the enzyme molecule.

can guess that they use the ideas of chemistry introduced in Chapter 5 to analyze what these structures are made of. There will be more about it in this chapter. Thus we can say, in part, that the structures of the cell are built from proteins (including enzymes), carbohydrates, fats, nucleic acids, and other compounds. These compounds form rods, membranes, and so forth when they are attached to one another by chemical bonds—the covalent, ionic, and weak bonds you read about in Chapter 5. You can see, then, that the cell membrane, the ribosomes, the mitochondria, and other cell parts have specific compositions that can be studied in terms of the kinds of organic compounds of which you are aware.

The second question—what the structures *do* in the life of the cell—must be attacked in many different ways. So far, it looks as if most of the membranes and other structures of cells are distinctive organizations of enzymes and other compounds that work together to do a particular job. In this sense, a cell can be compared with a service station—the oil cans, gas pumps, wrenches, and so forth are there because they are used to do particular things needed to keep cars running and in good order. In somewhat the same way, cells are made up of organizations of enzymes, coenzymes, and other substances with which they build chemical compounds, take energy from foods, and repackage the energy for use in all the cells' activities.

We could also compare a cell with a house. A house is divided into different rooms where different activities can be carried out at one time without interfering with each other. In the kitchen, a woman can be busy cooking dinner, as near her in another room a man listens to a radio, and a baby sleeps undisturbed in the bedroom. Similarly, membranes and other structures in a cell divide it into places where special activities are carried out. Thousands of chemical reactions take place in different areas of a cell at the same time—both building up and breaking down chemical compounds. All the different processes are kept in order, which is lucky, for otherwise there would be great confusion and waste of energy. In fact, there would be no life.

THE PARTS OF CELLS

By the early 1950's biologists began to obtain useful electron microscope pictures of cells. Naturally, their excitement rose to a high pitch as they discovered more and more details of structure which had never been seen or imagined before. You can share in these discoveries as you examine illustrations in this and several other chapters of your textbook. Centuries of study with the light microscope provided little or no evidence of some of these discoveries.

Biologists use not only the electron microscope but also other methods to get more information about the organization and function of cells. For instance, cells or parts of organisms can be ground up for mechanical separation by **centrifugation** (sen·trif·yoo·GAY-sh'n). A centrifuge is an instrument for separating substances or structures of different **densities.** Perhaps an example will best illustrate the meaning of density. If one allows whole milk to stand, the cream rises slowly to the top. The cream is *less dense* than the skim milk; that is, its particles occupy more space but weigh less per unit of volume than those of the skim milk. The separation of the cream and skim milk can be speeded greatly—and indeed this is done in milk-processing plants—by centrifugation. The whole milk is put into a centrifuge machine, which whirls it around at high speeds. The heavier skim milk is thrown to the bottom of the container, and the cream comes to the top.

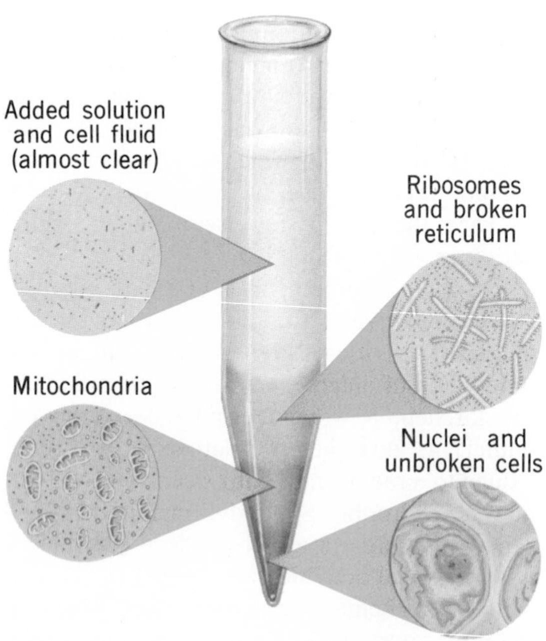

6–3 The separation of cell structures by centrifugation. Cell fractions are in successive layers. More fluid than shown would be added before cells are centrifuged, with the result that the top layer would be of proportionately greater volume.

Using this technique let us suppose that we wish to study the liver cells of a mouse. We can remove the liver from the animal and put it in a solution of salts or sugars of known density, then grind it up so fine that even most of the individual cells are broken. We will then have separate cell structures in a liquid medium. We put this into a centrifuge tube. Next we put the tube in the centrifuge and whirl it around for some time. After about 20 minutes we can stop the machine and remove the tube. The ground liver will have separated into several layers (Figure 6-3). We can examine the material in these layers with a compound microscope or with an electron microscope. Also, the separated parts can be studied chemically with tools and tests which show whether they contain proteins, fats, or other kinds of organic compounds. Does a particular cell part contain enzymes? If so, what can these enzymes do, what reactions in the cell do they control? If you can discover the functions of these individual parts, can you put different parts together and show that they carry on a related series of the normal activities of cells? Answers to these and similar questions give us ideas about cell structure and function in terms of biochemistry.

Today we are fortunate because we can use everything that has been discovered with so

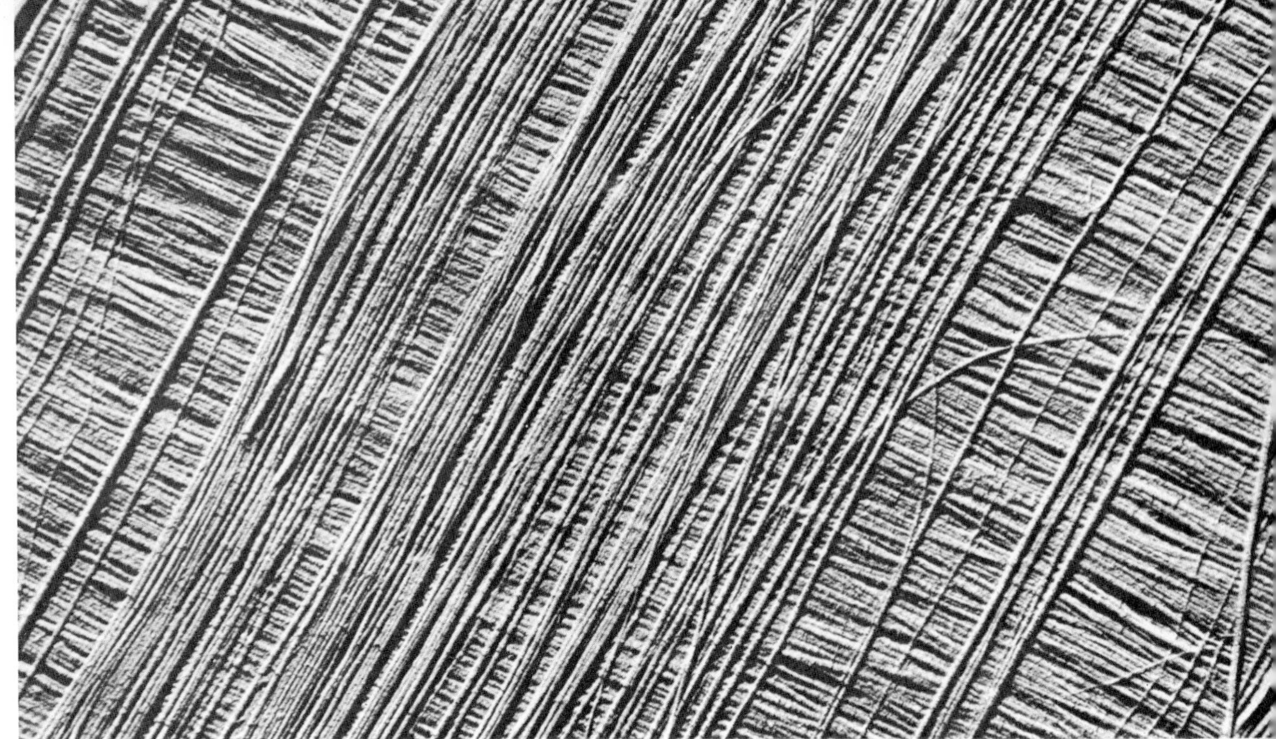

Eva Frei & R. D. Preston

6–4 The secret of the strength of plant structures, including the lumber used for many centuries in building furniture and houses, is revealed by electron microscope photographs of plant cell walls. The cellulose fibers are arranged in layers, with the fibers of each layer at an angle to those of other layers. Some of the fibers in the uppermost layer shown here have been removed. (35,000 ×)

many different experimental methods to build our working picture of the living cell. Of course we know that the picture will change as more experiments are carried out in the future, using new methods and testing new hypotheses. But today's ideas are our best basis for the growth of new ideas.

We will begin our description of parts and processes at the outer cell boundary and work our way inward from there.

The Cell Wall

In most plant cells, the outermost structure is the cell wall. The electron microscope shows that the wall is a network of fibers (Figure 6-4). Chemical tests show that it consists of the carbohydrate cellulose and some other substances. Although plant cells almost always have walls, in *some* experiments the cell wall can be separated from the cell or removed completely without killing the cell. And you know that the cell walls remain when the cell dies—when there is no longer a living cell, as in cork or your wooden pencil. Therefore, biologists say that the cell wall is nonliving. In woody plants it often becomes very thick. In these cases the fibers are arranged in layers. In any single layer most of the fibers will be parallel to one another. The adjacent layer will also have its parallel fibers, but these will be at an angle to those in the first layer. This crisscross arrangement gives the cell wall great strength—this is the basis for the tremendous strength of the wood of trees. In woody tissues the cell wall is impregnated with minerals and organic materials so that it is mechanically tough and resists the movement of water and of dissolved substances.

The Cell Membrane

The cell membrane lies next to the cell wall in plants. In animal cells, and in those plants without cell walls, it is the outer boundary of the cell. Everything that enters or leaves the cell must pass through it. Membranes are of such importance in the life of cells that you will understand biology much better if you have a clear understanding of membranes. This is why we ask you to carry out Laboratory Inquiries 6-4 and 6-5 when you go into the laboratory.

The cell membrane has some interesting characteristics, in both structure and function. In structure, as seen with the electron microscope, the cell membrane appears as layers of materials. Chemical tests show that it contains closely associated molecules of protein and the fatlike materials, **lipids** (LIH·pids).

The materials of the membrane, and their difference in interaction with chemical substances, are associated with the control the membrane exerts over what enters and leaves the cell. Thus, while in general very large molecules cannot pass in or out, molecules that associate with fats—that is, molecules like ether and alcohol—pass through easily even though of fairly large size. And ionic charge affects the way in which substances cross the membrane. Some small molecules pass through easily—water, oxygen, carbon dioxide, and urea are examples. Our hypothesis for this selective behavior of the cell membrane is that it may involve pores, limiting the molecules that can pass through it by size and electrical charge, and by the presence of fatlike materials in the membrane's structure.

We recognize these properties of the membranes of living cells by saying that the membranes are **differentially permeable** (PUR·me·a·b'l). This means that they allow some but not all molecules to pass. To learn something of the traffic of molecules through membranes let us consider the movement of oxygen and carbon dioxide molecules through them. Cell membranes are very permeable to both of these substances. The cell is constantly using oxygen, as you have read about in enzyme-coenzyme work, as electrons are removed and transferred in oxidation-reduction reactions. This use lowers the supply of oxygen within the cell. A higher concentration of oxygen molecules exists *outside* the cell. As a result, many more oxygen molecules will move into the cell than will tend to move out.

Carbon dioxide, on the other hand, is produced in the cell. It is at a higher concentration in the cell than outside it. Therefore, more CO_2 leaves the cell than enters it.

The movement of molecules—the net result of which is a more even distribution of each kind of molecule—is called diffusion. You are already acquainted with the diffusion of dissolved substances in water (page 91). Now you see that diffusion can take place across a membrane.

Water molecules move across the cell membrane in a rather similar way. The *direction* of their movement could easily be explained in terms of diffusion through pores in the membrane. But measurements of the *rate* at which water moves do not fit in well with this simple explanation. In other words, it moves faster than we might expect, chiefly because of the association between water molecules. We can measure the actual rate at which water molecules move by using a supply of water made of oxygen and **tritium** (TRIT·ee·um), a hydrogen isotope. This is "heavy water," which can be detected because the tritium is so much heavier than ordinary hydrogen. The results confirm that water often moves much faster between solutions of different concentrations (of water) than would be predicted from our knowledge of simple diffusion. Therefore, biologists use the special term **osmosis** (ahs·MOH·sis) to describe the movement of water across membranes.

Osmosis raises some interesting problems. Consider one-celled animals that live in fresh water. These aquatic animals contain a great deal of water with a certain amount of dissolved material. The cell membrane is permeable to the water, but not to much of the dissolved material. What will happen to these one-celled animals in the fresh water in which they live?

Fresh water contains traces of dissolved materials, but the amount is so small that we can say the water is about 100 percent pure. Inside the one-celled animals the amount of dissolved material is greater, lowering the relative concentration of water in their bodies to perhaps around 98 percent. More water molecules will, therefore, move from the fresh water into the cell than will leave the cell. This movement is a consequence of the differences in concentration of water: 100 percent outside and 98 percent inside. If there is nothing to counteract this movement, the cell will swell. However, the one-celled organisms in question do have a way of getting rid of the excess water, as you will find when you study Chapter 18. As a result, they remain about the same size.

Not all cells have a means of getting rid of excess water. If, for example, you place some blood cells of a frog (or your own) in pure water, the cells will swell and burst. The water concentration will be greater on the outside of the cells than within. Consequently, more water enters the cells by osmosis than leaves them, until their cell membranes rupture.

For some cells the problem is reversed. They may accidentally be surrounded by solutions so rich in dissolved materials that water begins to leave the cells, and the solid contents of the cells become more and more condensed. Activity is disturbed and life itself may end. This is the reason that placing a cell such as a bacterium in a concentrated solution of salt or sugar may kill it.

For all organisms, the activities of life depend upon keeping the internal concentration of water fairly constant. A few marine organisms retain concentrations of urea in the body fluids that balance the heavy concentration of salts in ocean water. Balance in the human body is maintained by blood and tissue fluids in which the concentration of dissolved substances is kept at a level suitable for the cells. Changes in the concentration of substances in the tissue fluids and the blood are regulated by kidney action and by a variety of other mechanisms. We will come back to osmotic problems when we discuss in later chapters the physiology of plants and animals.

In many one-celled organisms, there are vacuoles that pump excess water out of the cell. We do not understand how this process is carried out. We do know that it requires a large part of the energy of living in these organisms.

Not only in one-celled organisms but in all other organisms studied by biologists it has turned out that diffusion and osmosis are not the only ways in which materials can cross the cell membrane. Many cells actively use energy to bring substances into the cell and to move other substances out. We do not know how they move, or *transport,* substances in this way, although it is quite certain that enzymes are involved. Often biologists refer to such processes for using energy to move a particular substance into or out of a cell as **active transport.** As you will see later (in Chapters 18, 21, and 23, for instance) active transport plays a major part in the normal functioning of cells and organisms.

The Endoplasmic Reticulum

Figure 6-5 shows a small portion of a cell as seen with the electron microscope. You see part of the nucleus at the bottom, and two mitochondria near the top. We will learn more of these later. For now, notice the many tube-like structures of the cytoplasm. These are part of the **endoplasmic reticulum** (EN·doh·PLAZ·mik re·TIK·yoo·lum). Recent evidence suggests that the endoplasmic reticulum is a network of tubes extending throughout the cytoplasm. Some of the tubes seem to open on the cell membrane; thus, they appear to be continuous with the fluid surrounding the cell. Tubes of the endoplasmic reticulum also connect inside the cell with the nuclear membrane.

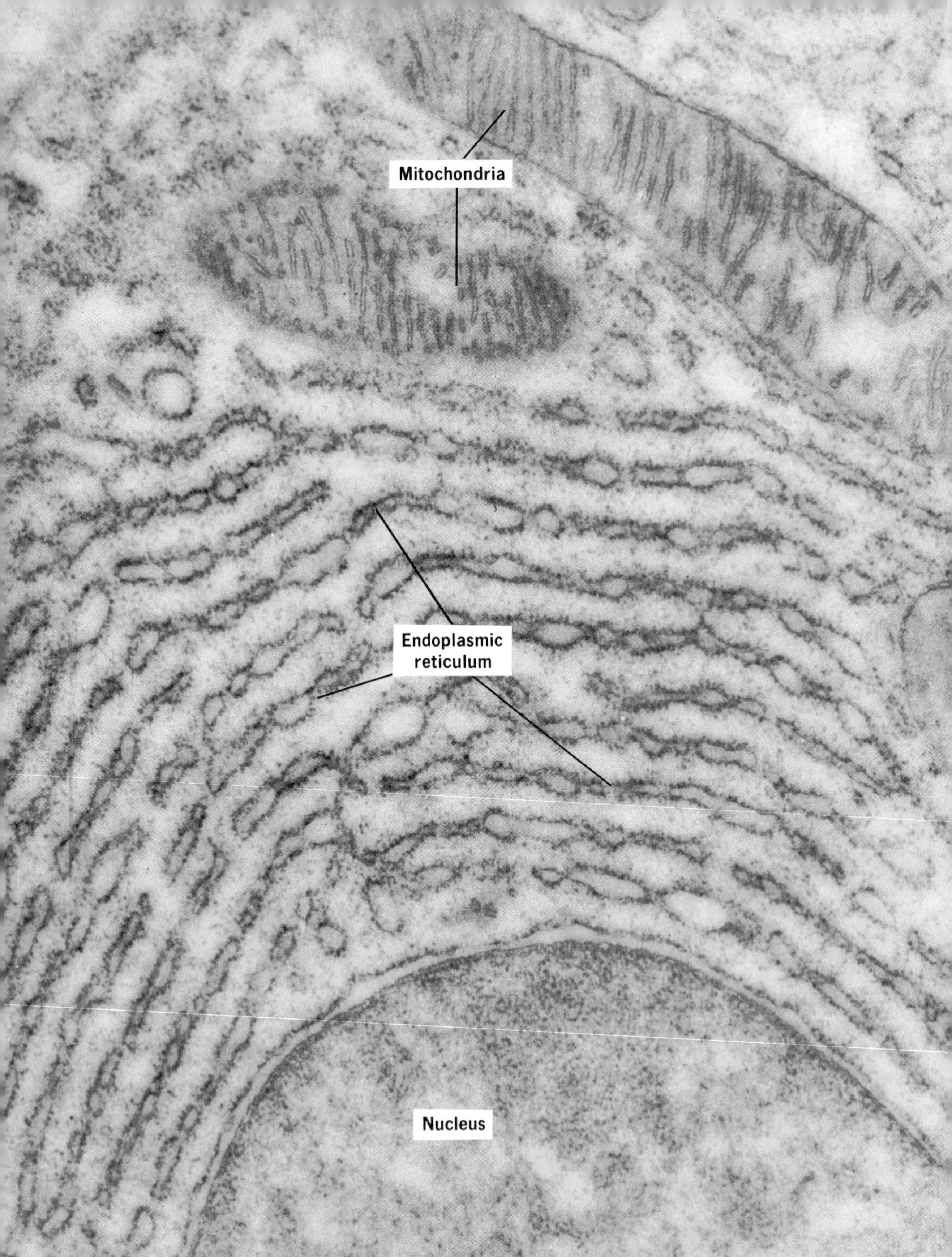
Mitochondria
Endoplasmic reticulum
Nucleus

The function of the endoplasmic reticulum is not adequately known. It probably plays an important part in the movement of materials throughout the cytoplasm. There is good evidence also that it helps organize chemical reactions in the cell. We can explain this better by considering important cell structures of another kind, the **ribosomes** (RY·boh·sohmz).

Ribosomes—Formation of Proteins

If you examine Figure 6-5 closely, you will see that some of the endoplasmic reticulum is coated with tiny granules. The granules are so small that they may not look important, but they are now known to have a major function in the cell. They are called *ribosomes* because they are known to be composed largely of ribonucleic acid, or RNA (page 99). They also contain protein.

What do the ribosomes do? As you know, cells require food for two general purposes: to provide energy to maintain life, and to provide materials to be converted into more living matter. How do cells synthesize the special proteins of their living matter?

Proteins are made *within* the cell from amino acids. This is not surprising, since almost none of the proteins have molecules small enough to pass from the outside through cell membranes into cells. Amino acid molecules can enter cells, however, and once inside they are linked chemically to form proteins. But the process is more complicated than just hooking amino acids together. We learned earlier that there are many kinds of proteins in every cell. The amino acids, then, have to be chemically bonded to one another in very definite ways. It is at the ribosomes that the pattern for arrangement of amino acids is established. The ribosomes, then, are concerned with the synthesis of proteins from amino acids. Later, in Chapter 8, we will have a lot more to tell about this important process, for it determines that you make human proteins and not other types. What we must consider now is that this is an energy-requiring process. We need to know something about how the energy is supplied.

MITOCHONDRIA—ENERGY FOR THE CELL

Chapter 3 first mentioned mitochondria in the cell—as small bodies shaped like rods or filaments. That is how they appear when we examine cells with light microscopes. When the far greater magnification with the electron microscope became available, it was discovered that mitochondria have a complicated inner structure of folded membranes, as you see in Figures 6-5 and 6-6. The membranes are built chiefly of protein and lipid molecules, and include many of the enzymes, coenzymes, and other organic compounds of which the mitochondria are built. This remarkably complicated structure alone could suggest to you that the functions of mitochondria may be quite complex. You might also guess that their functions are of great importance just from the fact that they are present in almost all cells. Even before biologists had good electron microscope pictures of mitochondria, they began to get clues that these structures are a major center for the cell's oxidation-reduction reactions. They are not the only place where these reactions take place. In fact, enzymes in the fluid part of the cytoplasm, in the endoplasmic reticulum, and in other cell structures may

George E. Palade

6–5 (Facing page) An electron micrograph (as an electron microscope photograph is sometimes called) showing a small, central portion of an animal cell. The existence of the endoplasmic reticulum, and the detailed structure of mitochondria, were unknown until the electron microscope came into use. If the entire cell could be shown at this magnification (52,500 ×), how large a photograph would you expect?

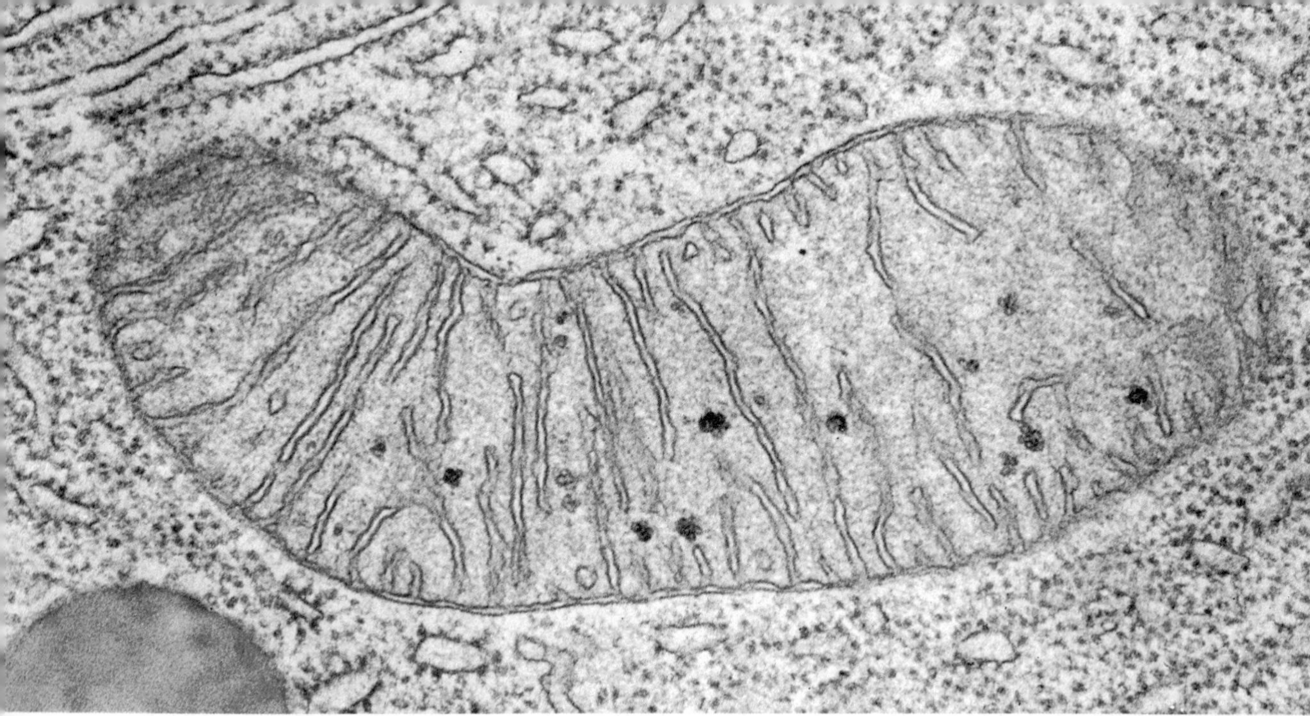

Keith Porter

6–6 An electron micrograph of a mitochondrion in an animal cell. (77,500 ×) The outer layer of membrane conforms to the shape of the mitochondrion. The complexly folded inner layer of membrane contains enzymes, coenzymes, and other compounds. Mitochondria are vital in supplying energy for a cell's use. The oxidation-reduction reactions that result in energy exchange occur elsewhere in the cytoplasm as well as at mitochondria, but the most *efficient* exchange occurs at the mitochondria. Apparently these structures even carry their own DNA and can be reproduced independently of DNA replication in the cell's nucleus, which otherwise controls reproduction.

carry out oxidation-reduction. Yet mitochondria have a key role in cell metabolism because here the great majority of the cell's energy is converted for its use.

This is such an important point that it is worthwhile to stop and recall from Chapter 5 that oxidation-reduction reactions are the direct source of energy for all the cell's activities. Consider the case of the oxidation of glucose, which we can abbreviate as follows:

$$\underset{\text{glucose}}{C_6H_{12}O_6} + \underset{\text{oxygen}}{6\ O_2} \rightarrow \underset{\text{carbon dioxide}}{6\ CO_2} + \underset{\text{water}}{6\ H_2O} + \text{energy}$$

Note that the number of atoms remains the same: on both the left side and the right side of the arrow there are 6 carbon atoms, 12 hydrogen atoms, and 18 oxygen atoms. The arrangement of the atoms changes, however. In glucose the arrangement of atoms had more stored chemical energy than the new arrangement in carbon dioxide and water. There were many C–H (carbon-hydrogen) bonds in glucose, but there are none in the products. Thus, when the atoms in glucose react with oxygen to form carbon dioxide and water, chemical energy becomes available. Is this a very special reaction, or one which is common enough to be worth studying in detail?

When one thinks of the tremendous variety of cell types, it is natural to think that there might be an equal variety of biochemical patterns. This is far from true. Much to the surprise of everyone, including the biochemists, the basic biochemical events in all cells are much alike. Untold numbers of cells in a vast variety of organisms use glucose as an energy source in the way shown in the reaction. The way your liver cells work is much the same as the way your muscle cells work. Many of the reactions that occur in your cells also occur in those of frogs, mice, earthworms, mushrooms, radishes, and rats. There is a surprising uniformity of cell functions in all living creatures. We can recognize a unity of life that is far more apparent than one would gather from comparing the external appearance of animals and plants.

One of the fortunate aspects of this unity is that it has given biologists a chance to study cell oxidation-reduction reactions in detail in simple organisms, and then apply the results to more complex forms—even to man. It also makes it worthwhile for you to study these processes carefully, for in this way you will learn some very basic processes of living organisms.

Look again at the reaction:

$$C_6H_{12}O_6 + 6\,O_2 \rightarrow 6\,CO_2 + 6\,H_2O + \text{energy}$$

The molecules taking part in the reaction—glucose, oxygen, carbon dioxide, and water—are all familiar to you. But exactly how does the energy fit into the picture? Biologists were not able to answer this question until the results of many different kinds of experiments showed clearly that much of the stored chemical energy of glucose is trapped by cells and used to build special unstable compounds. These unstable compounds can then be broken down in steps closely controlled by enzymes. The energy that had been trapped in them is transferred at the same time to energy-requiring processes of cells. This, then, is one of the major functions of mitochondria—to build up unstable energy-transfer compounds. The best known and perhaps the most important of these is adenosine triphosphate, ATP.

ATP is a nucleotide (Chapter 5, page 99). It is a key substance in the life of cells, apparently occurring in every living organism and in every cell. But it was years before biologists recognized this, because ATP is so unstable that they were unable to find it. At last special methods were worked out which made it possible to isolate ATP and discover how it was built. Its universal role in energy storage and supply was emphasized only in 1941, by Fritz Lipmann. The Nobel prize was later given to him.

ATP is not very complicated—as organic molecules go. Figure 6-7 shows a simplified diagram of the structure of this important molecule, and if you wish you can find it in much more detail on page 760 of Chapter 39. The "triphosphate" part of the name comes from the three groups each of which contains a phosphorus (P) atom. You will notice them on the left side of the diagram. Figure 6-7 gives some idea as to how ATP can serve as an energy-storing compound. It is a very unstable compound and energy must be used when it is built from ADP (adenosine *di*phosphate) by addition of a phosphate group. As a matter of fact, ADP is also unstable, and energy must be put into the reaction which builds ADP from AMP (adenosine *mono*phosphate). These compounds differ only as their names suggest: *tri-* denotes three phosphate groups; *di-*, two phosphate groups; and *mono-*, one phosphate group. When cells use energy to build ATP from ADP, or ADP from AMP, they are really storing energy—as you might put money in a bank.

Some years ago, the important discovery was made that breakdown of glucose by cells cannot occur unless they have available some chemical energy to start the reaction. And only the chemical energy of ATP will do. Once started, the metabolism of glucose runs quickly to completion. The main product, besides carbon dioxide and water, is chemical energy stored in the form of more ATP. But does this mean that the cell must have an enormous supply of ATP always on hand? At first you might guess that this would be so. But experiments have shown that only tiny traces of ATP are

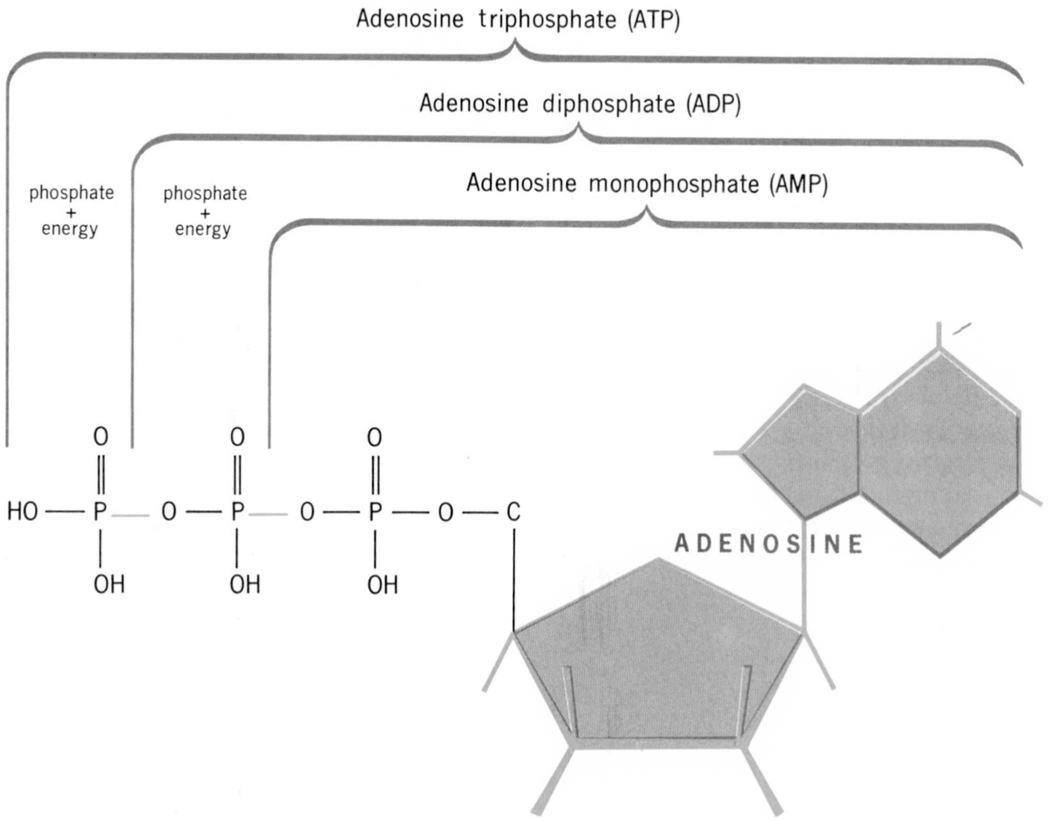

6–7 The structural relation of ATP, ADP, and AMP. The basic nucleotide is the same in all three. The difference is one or more phosphate groups. Each of the last two phosphate groups shown at the left forms an unstable bond (represented by color) with the rest of the molecule. Breaking the bond transfers energy.

present in cells. How can this be explained? It turns out that energy transferred from glucose to ATP is quickly used by other cell processes, so that the ATP is broken down. More cell oxidation of glucose then supplies more energy to form ATP from ADP, and these new ATP molecules are again broken down as the energy is used by the cell. The buildup and breakdown of ATP is a process continuing in a circle – we speak of such a series of reactions as a *cycle*. You can gain a general understanding from Figure 6-8 of how this ATP cycle serves to transfer energy from glucose oxidation to the living processes of cells.

Energy from Glucose

As we continue our description of the functions of mitochondria, we must give more details about how glucose serves as an energy source for living cells.

How have biologists discovered the details of such a process? One plan of attack is to let the process run for a while, but stop it before it is finished and see by chemical tests what you find.

We can give a comparison to help explain this method. Imagine that you knew nothing about how a cake is made, but suddenly wished to find out about this process by direct observa-

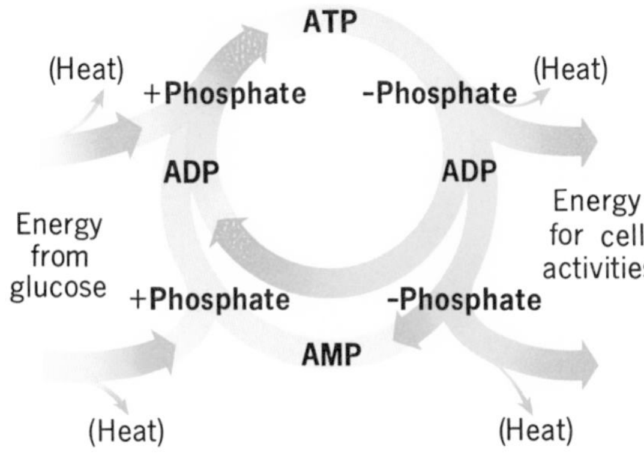

6–8 The energy-transfer cycle involving AMP, ADP, and ATP. The cyclic relation shown here complements the structural relation diagrammed in Figure 6–7. What part of the energy in the cycle cannot be used for the cell's activities?

tion. You would probably begin by trying to discover the starting materials and the general pattern of the reaction. After some research, you would make observations that would lead you to this equation for the reaction:

$$\text{flour} + \text{eggs} + \text{milk} + \text{sugar} + \underset{\text{(spices, chocolate, etc.)}}{\text{trace substances}} \xrightarrow[\text{energy}]{} \text{cake}$$

But just how does it happen that the different starting materials can turn into the single organization of a cake? A good way to attack this problem would be to stop the cake-making process at various stages and analyze what is present at each stage. You might discover steps like these: at the beginning of the reaction, all the starting materials, but no cake, would be present. Ten minutes later you would find flour + milk + sugar + trace substances unchanged, but the eggs would have taken on a surprising new form—the shells would be gone and the rest of the egg would appear as a foamy yellow liquid. Twenty minutes later *all* the original starting materials would have disappeared, and you would discover instead a thick, brownish fluid. If you analyzed it, you could show that it contained all the starting materials in constant proportions. After some other steps, involving the use of energy (when the cake mix is in the oven), the final product, a cake, would appear. As a scientifically minded observer, you would of course have to analyze the source and use of energy in this reaction. You would also ask—is there an enzyme or other such substance involved? If so, what is it? Using all the different kinds of information you could collect, you would develop a logical picture of what happens in the formation of a cake. This is the sort of approach biologists have used in attacking problems of cell metabolism.

Biologists have stopped processes of metabolism at different stages, often by using cold or poisons to interfere with the action of enzymes. They have then separated organic compounds from the reaction mixtures and studied their chemistry. They have also used radioisotopes to label particular kinds of molecules and follow the ways they change in metabolism, somewhat as you might follow the changes in one reactant, the eggs, in your observations of cake formation. Another approach you already know—the discovery of the enzymes needed in cell metabolism and how they work. Using the data of all these different methods of study, biologists have built hypotheses to account for all the reactions in the metabolism of important compounds like glucose. There are at least 22 compounds known to take part as steps in a single metabolic path of glucose to carbon dioxide and water! And as for enzymes, do you remember the statements of how enzymes affect the reactions in a cell, from the first page of this chapter? In diverting the oxidation of glucose from a single, direct reaction with oxygen to a pathway involving at least 22 brief, rapid steps and the resulting *controlled* conversion of the energy, *each* of the many steps is carried out by its own enzyme, often working with special coenzymes.

To help you gain an understanding of the pathway of glucose oxidation, but without studying each step in detail, we ask you to look

DURING CELL METABOLISM OF GLUCOSE, THESE CHANGES TAKE PLACE IN...

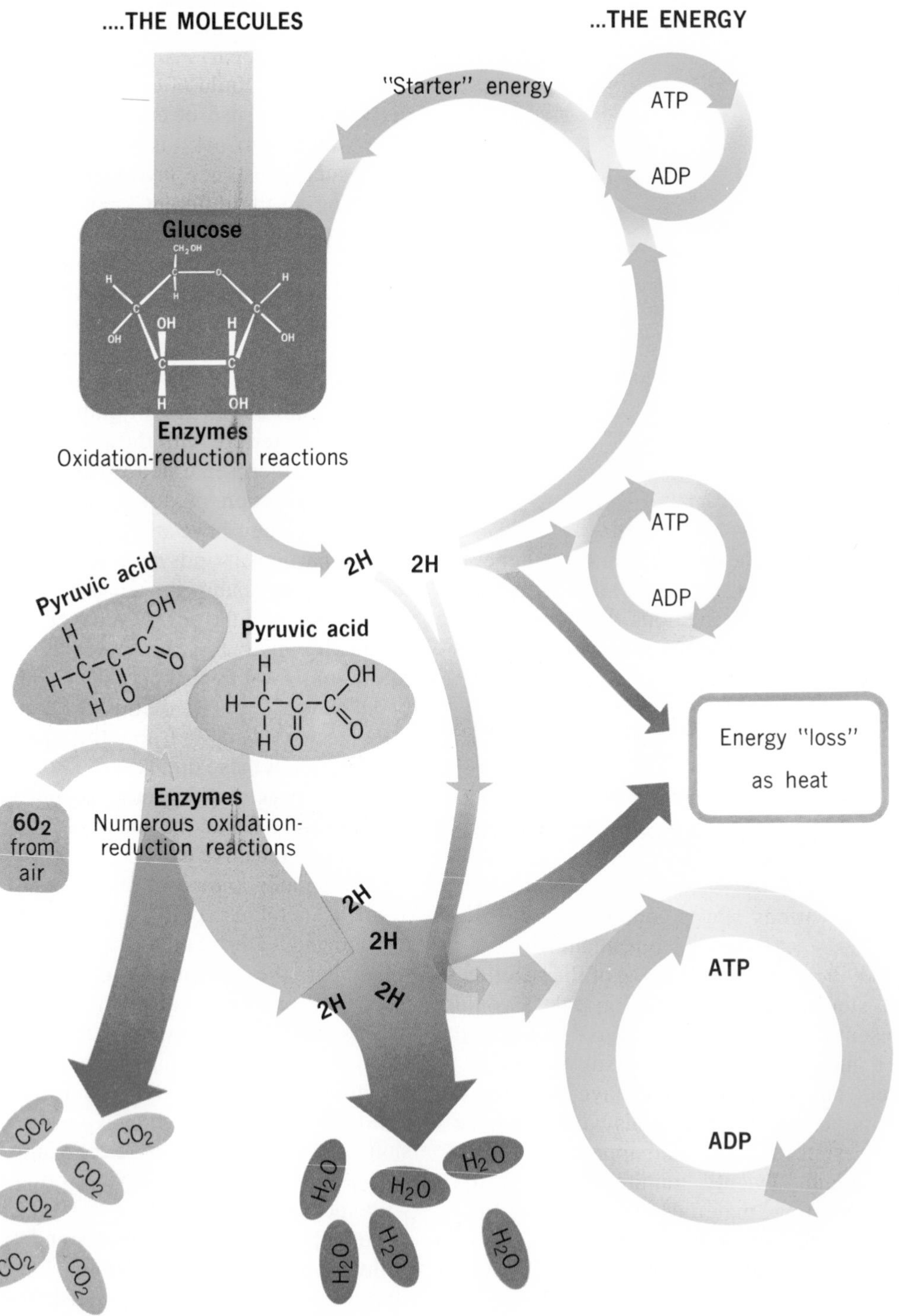

carefully at the diagram in Figure 6-9. It shows the three major kinds of reactions that take place. These include 1) breaking of the carbon chain; 2) oxidation-reduction reactions, beginning with oxidation of carbon (removal of hydrogen from carbon), and ending with linkage of oxygen with carbon and with hydrogen; and 3) the formation of ATP and similar energy-transfer compounds.

It is important to look further into two of the major kinds of reactions involved. One of these is oxidation-reduction. The other is the synthesis of ATP and other energy-transfer compounds. Let us consider them one at a time.

The Electron Transport Chain

In the oxidation-reduction reactions, electrons and hydrogen ions are removed from association with carbon. But just what does this mean—where do the electrons and hydrogen ions go? In other words, what is *reduced* when the substrate is oxidized? You can answer this from the discussion on page 106. An enzyme removes electrons (and hydrogen ions) from the substrate and transfers the electrons to a coenzyme working closely with it. The substrate (glucose or one of the partial products of its metabolism) is oxidized by the removal of the electrons; the coenzyme is reduced by its acceptance of the electrons. Other enzymes then transfer the electrons from this coenzyme to a series of closely cooperating enzymes and coenzymes. These react together, passing the electrons from one to another until, at the end of the sequence, an enzyme reacts with oxygen. In this step, the enzyme passes to oxygen the electrons removed many steps before from glucose. This is the end of the line for those electrons—they are unlikely to find any association more stable than this association with oxygen. The "electron-rich" oxygen atoms formed in this way attach to hydrogen ions. You remember that hydrogen ions, like electrons, were removed from the substrate at the start of the process. The final product is the stable and familiar molecule, water. Here, then, is a case of electrons moving from atoms where they are attached less stably (in glucose) to atoms where they are attached more stably (in water). In Chapter 5, we described such electron "flow" as the main source of energy for cellular processes. Now you see the sequence of reactions involved. The transfer of electrons through this cooperating association of enzymes and coenzymes of mitochondria is indeed a rich source of chemical energy. Quite reasonably, we often call such an enzyme-coenzyme association an **electron transport chain.**

6–9 (Facing page) The changes that take place as glucose is oxidized in a living cell are very complex, involving many steps not shown in the diagram. The main pattern of arrows for the oxidation-reduction reactions is on the left of the page, descending vertically. At each point labeled "Enzymes" and "Oxidation-reduction reactions," many intermediate compounds are formed before the next step shown by the diagram. The initial breakdown of glucose to pyruvic acid involves the transfer of electrons from only a few of the hydrogen atoms split from their bonds with carbon in the glucose molecule. (See the labels "2H" above and to the right of the pyruvic acid molecules.) These first steps occur both at mitochondria and elsewhere in the cytoplasm. Note that they transfer energy in relatively small amounts (represented by the two small ADP-ATP cycles at the middle and upper right). The subsequent steps involved in breaking the carbon chains and C—H bonds of the pyruvic acid molecules occur only at the mitochondria and are responsible for most of the energy transfer in the cell (as represented by the much larger ADP-ATP cycle at the lower right). As a result of these last oxidation-reduction processes, all the carbon and all the hydrogen are removed from glucose and its intermediate product, pyruvic acid, and ultimately are combined with oxygen as carbon dioxide and water.

The Formation of ATP and Other Energy-transfer Compounds

Has our description of events yet told you exactly how mitochondria make ATP, using the energy of glucose? If so, we have explained to you something we do not understand ourselves! This is such an important problem that its study is one of the most active fields in biological research today. So far no one has been able to explain satisfactorily how mitochondria trap the chemical energy of oxidation-reduction. Apparently the processes involved depend on a very exact arrangement of enzymes, coenzymes, and other reactants within the mitochondrion, for almost anything which changes the structure of a mitochondrion can disturb or stop altogether its formation of ATP. This makes a problem for biologists—how can you study mitochondria without disturbing them?

Fortunately, there are some clues in spite of the problem. We can explain some of these clues by describing a much simpler case of ATP formation. In the cytoplasm outside the mitochondria, relatively small amounts of ATP are made when glucose is oxidized to **pyruvic** (py·ROO·vic) **acid.** You can see from Figure 6-9 that this is only a small part of the complete oxidation of glucose that takes place in the mitochondria. Some of the substrates formed in this oxidation of glucose to pyruvic acid involve unstable bonds to phosphate. Quickly enzymes cause ADP molecules to react with these unstable substrate-phosphate molecules. The ADP takes the phosphate group so that ATP is formed. The chemical energy which had been briefly stored in the unstable substrate-phosphate molecule is transferred to the ATP.

It may be molecular reactions of this kind that mitochondria use in trapping energy from oxidation-reduction and forming ATP. However, instead of substrates being used directly for these processes, it seems as if molecules built directly into the structure of mitochondria are used. We do not know the details of this arrangement, but it probably accounts for the remarkable capacity of mitochondria to make so much ATP. Thus, if we compare mitochondria with the cytoplasmic enzymes that can also extract energy from glucose for building ATP, we find an important difference. For every molecule of ATP that the cytoplasmic enzymes can make during oxidation of a single glucose molecule, the mitochondria can make nearly 20 molecules! This is why we said on page 116 that mitochondria have a key role in cell metabolism.

Other Sources of Energy

The proteins, fats, and other organic compounds that enter the body as food can also be used for energy. Like glucose, they are carried along special metabolic paths by enzymes, and many of these paths are located in mitochondria. For instance, when proteins are used for energy, they first are converted to amino acids. Later their amino groups are removed. The structure of the amino acid alanine is given in Chapter 5. When alanine has its amino (NH_2) group removed, the middle carbon atom is oxidized. That is, its H atom is replaced by an O atom. The molecule is then pyruvic acid, the same 3-carbon-atom compound that figures in glucose oxidation. Pyruvic acid molecules formed in this way from protein are broken down in the mitochondria. Their energy is used to make ATP from ADP.

Other Functions of Mitochondria

Supplying energy to cells is not the only function of mitochondria. They can *build* organic compounds, as well as break them down. For instance, starting with small organic molecules, enzymes in mitochondria can synthesize the long chains of carbon atoms found in fats. Building up these chains is an energy-requiring process, and as you might expect, the energy is supplied by breaking down ATP molecules. No wonder a biologist sometimes feels that he is not as good a chemist as a single one of the mitochondria in one of his own liver cells!

Some Unsolved Problems in Mitochondrial Function

In our description of mitochondria as major sites of the energy-supplying reactions of cells, we left two important questions unanswered. The first question is this—when chemical energy has been stored in ATP, how can it be transferred from the mitochondria to all the other places in the cell where it is needed for living processes? Biologists are working to solve this problem, and it seems very likely that mitochondria can move about from place to place in the cell, taking their stored energy "packages" with them wherever they go. But we do not know whether ATP or other energy-transfer compounds can pass from mitochondria to other cell structures.

A second question of the greatest importance is this: how do mitochondria regulate the *rate* of their metabolism? A single cell may contain hundreds of mitochondria, and the function of each mitochondrion must be controlled in some way to meet the moment-by-moment energy needs of the cell. You can easily recognize that chemical reactions in your own body must take place at different rates depending on how active you are. If you need more energy—when you are running or working hard, for instance—your metabolism is faster than when you are resting. Your everyday experiences suggest this to you, for when you run or work hard you get hot and breathe fast, taking larger than normal quantities of oxygen into your lungs. Usually you feel tired and hungry after exercise. But how do your body cells "recognize" the need to carry out chemical reactions more rapidly when you are exercising, or less rapidly when you are at rest and do not need so much energy? Even though we put these questions in terms of you as a person, they are very fundamental questions which could be asked about any other organism or about any single cell. We are far from knowing the answers, but we are beginning to get some clues. For instance, it appears that the products which are formed when ATP is broken down, ADP and AMP, affect the structures of some of the enzymes involved in glucose oxidation. By changing the enzyme structure, they can actually speed up the formation of ATP! Since ATP is made from AMP and ADP, the concentrations of AMP and ADP must decrease as ATP increases. Therefore the enzyme-control is itself controlled! We will often speak of control later in this course, especially in the chapters devoted to multicellular animals. This is an exciting area in biology today, for it is full of unsolved problems of the greatest importance in the life of organisms.

THE CELL NUCLEUS

Nearly all the events we have been describing occur in membranes and various other structures of the cytoplasm of the cell. You may have wondered if the nucleus has any function at all. It does, and a most important function it is.

The nucleus controls the life and activities of the cell. (The evidence for this will come later, largely in Chapter 8 and Chapters 29 and 30.) The key structures in this control are the chromosomes, which are composed largely of **deoxyribonucleoprotein** (dee·OKS·ih·ry·boh-NEW·klee·oh·pro·teen). This is a combination of protein and deoxyribonucleic acid (DNA).

There is ample reason to believe that DNA is one of the most vital substances in our cells because of the part it plays in inheritance. We are human beings because we have DNA of the human type. A rabbit is a rabbit because it has rabbit-type DNA.

But how can DNA and the protein associated with it carry out such important functions? We have much evidence now that they do so by controlling the synthesis of specific types of RNA. These various types of RNA then leave the nucleus and enter the cytoplasm, where they associate with the ribosomes and control the synthesis of all the specific types of proteins, including the enzymes.

There is a special structure in the nucleus, the nucleolus (Chapter 3, page 48), which is composed largely of ribonucleoprotein. Perhaps it is the storage place for some of the RNA before the RNA leaves the nucleus to enter the cytoplasm. But we will not continue with this story here, for it deserves a chapter to itself. You will learn about the interaction of DNA, RNA, and protein in Chapter 8.

CONCLUDING REMARKS

Figure 6-10 is a schematic diagram of an animal cell. In most respects, it could also be considered a plant cell without the wall.

It can serve as the basis for our summary of cell structures and functions.

The cell membrane is more than a mere covering of the cell. It is a living structure that regulates the passage of materials into and out

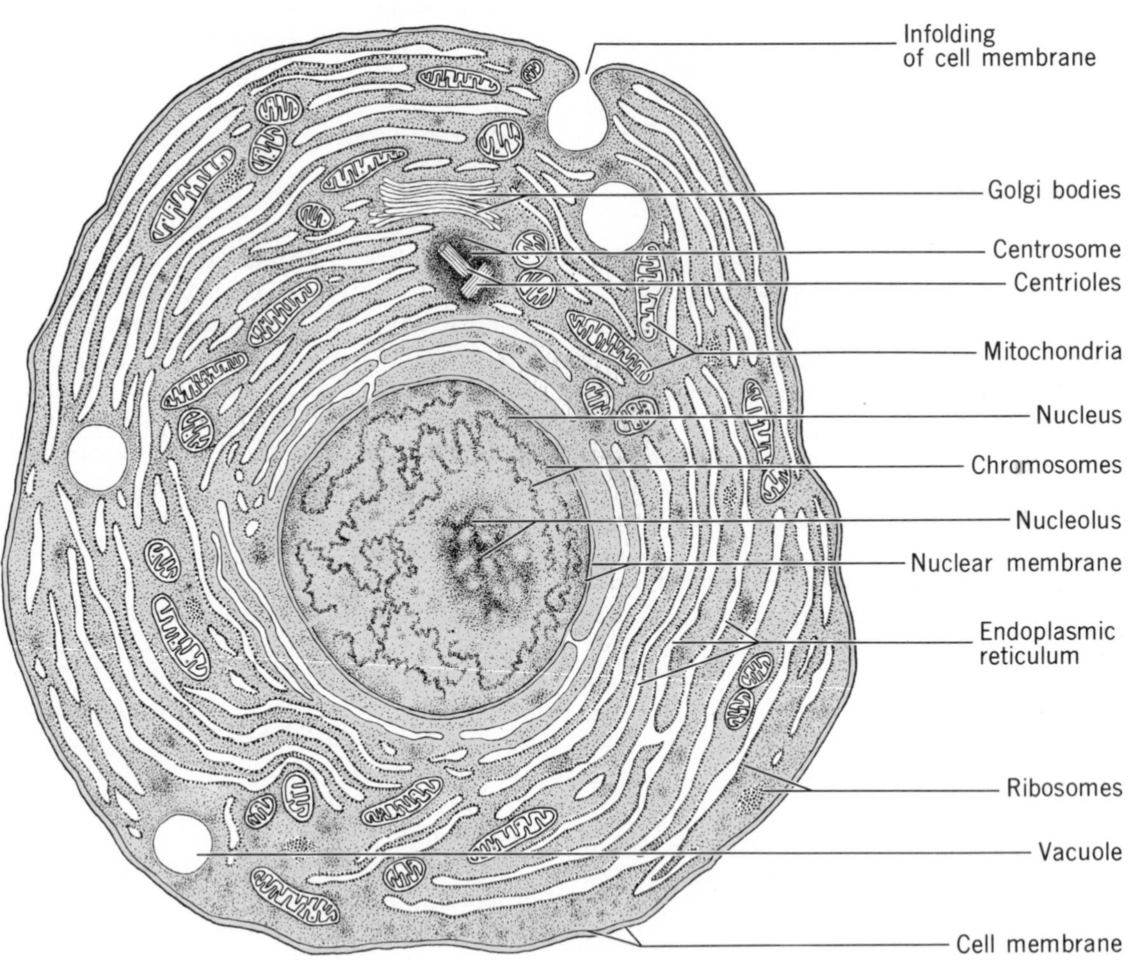

6–10 Probably no cell looks exactly like this one, yet most animal or plant cells would have the structures shown. The sizes are not meant to be accurate. For example, the centrioles and mitochondria, if drawn to size, would be tiny dots, and the ribosomes and endoplasmic reticulum would be too small to show. Our knowledge of the structure of cell parts stems largely from the electron microscope.

of the cell. Some substances pass across by diffusion and osmosis; others are taken in by energy-requiring processes. The amino acids, simple sugars, vitamins, minerals, oxygen, and other substances that enter the cell are used to synthesize living material, as sources of cell energy, and for regulation of the chemical structure of the cell itself.

The cell membrane may have pores that open into the endoplasmic reticulum. Many biologists believe that the endoplasmic reticulum transports materials throughout the cell. It is also involved in organizing reactions. In many cases, ribosomes are attached to the endoplasmic reticulum. The ribosomes are the chief sites at which proteins are made in the cytoplasm of the cell.

Several mitochondria are shown in the illustration. They are the "powerhouses of the cell." Their enzymes and coenzymes transfer the energy of food molecules to ATP and similar energy-transfer compounds. Mitochondria also play a part in the wide range of synthetic processes in the cell.

The nucleus is the sphere near the center of the cell. It contains the chromosomes, whose DNA controls the cell's activities. The DNA controls the formation of RNA, some of which is found in the nucleolus.

The centriole and centrosomes are concerned with the reproduction of cells. More will be said about them in the next chapter.

We are not too sure of the function of the Golgi bodies. The best evidence is that they are concerned with the formation and storage of special compounds secreted by cells. For instance, in mammals one of the organs of digestion, the pancreas, secretes granules which contain enzymes that aid digestion. The Golgi bodies seem to have a role in the formation of these granules.

Living cells require energy for their activities. The *ultimate* source of this energy is sunlight. The energy is captured in the C–H bonds of glucose and other organic compounds by special chemical processes of plants. Later, within cells of all living organisms these organic compounds are oxidized in small steps with the transfer of large amounts of energy. The energy is used to make compounds like ATP. These compounds are then the *immediate* source of energy in the cell.

The chemical reactions within cells occur rapidly in closely regulated ways because they are controlled by enzymes.

GUIDE QUESTIONS AND PROBLEMS

1. Oxidation of glucose by mitochondria in a cell differs from oxidation of glucose (burning) in the laboratory. Explain the difference in terms of your understanding of how enzymes work in the oxidation-reduction reactions in the cell.
2. a. One *mole* of glucose (the molecular weight of the glucose molecule taken in grams) when completely oxidized can yield an estimated 680,000 calories of energy (calories are a measure of heat energy). When the mitochondria of your body cells oxidize a mole of glucose they transfer the energy to about 38 moles of ATP molecules (the same ratio as one molecule of glucose to 38 molecules of ATP, explained in the text). As your cells break down the ATP to ADP, an estimated 12,000 calories of energy are released per mole of ATP. All in all, you recover about 456,000 calories of energy (12,000 calories × 38) from the ATP made from one mole of glucose. What happens to the 224,000 calories of energy not accounted for?

   b. How efficient does this indicate that your cells are in their ability to recover energy from glucose?
3. What is the source of the heat used to maintain your body temperature?
4. We know that enzymes are affected by heat. Predict what would happen to a person whose body temperature rose to 45° C.
5. Enzymes and their substrates must fit together properly for the substrates to undergo reactions necessary to a cell's life. Certain compounds *that resemble some of the cell's substrates in structure* often block enzyme function upon those substrates. For example, sulfanilimide, a sulfa drug, blocks an enzyme's action in bacterial

cells infecting your body, and prevents the bacteria from reproducing. Explain how this blocking action might work.

6. Normally your red blood cells are in the shape of a flat disc, almost hollowed out in the center. If these cells are placed in a 9 percent sodium chloride (NaCl) solution, they shrink and change shape. Why is this? The same cells placed in only a 0.1 percent sodium chloride solution will swell, become round, and finally burst. Again, why is this?
7. What would happen to a cell if its activity was suddenly changed so that diffusion was the only process operating to move substances from outside the cell to inside the cell?
8. *Active transport* is carried on by *living* cells, greatly increasing the rate of supply of certain materials beyond what diffusion can supply. From this statement and what you know of cell walls (in plants), what evidence can you suggest for the probable existence of pits or pores in the heavy cell walls of many plants? Here is an opportunity to form a hypothesis that you can try to confirm in the laboratory (and in a later chapter of this book).
9. If the enzyme *catalase* (CAT·a·lace) is placed in some hydrogen peroxide, a fast release of gas bubbles occurs. However, if the enzyme diastase (Chapter 4, page 73) is placed in some hydrogen peroxide, nothing obvious happens. How would you account for these different results?

RELATED READING

Books

For extension of topics on the chemistry of life . . .

Baker, J. J. W., and G. E. Allen, *Matter, Energy, and Life*, Addison-Wesley, Palo Alto, Calif., 1965. A continuation of the reading in this text suggested at the end of the preceding chapter.

For extension of topics on both cell structure and cell chemistry . . .

Butler, John A. V., *Inside the Living Cell*, Basic Books, New York, 1959.

Mercer, E. H., *Cells: Their Structure and Function*, Doubleday, New York, 1962.

Swanson, Carl P., *The Cell*, Second Edition, Prentice-Hall, Englewood Cliffs, N. J., 1964 (cloth or paperback).

Magazines

Brachet, J., "The Living Cell," *Scientific American*, Volume 205 (September 1961), page 50.

Allfrey, Vincent G., and A. E. Mirsky, "How Cells Make Molecules," *Scientific American*, Volume 205 (September 1961), page 74.

Green, David E., "The Mitochondrion," *Scientific American*, Volume 210 (January 1964), page 63.

Hokin, Lowell, and Mabel Hokin, "The Chemistry of Cell Membranes," *Scientific American*, Volume 213 (October 1965), page 78.

Lehninger, A., "How Cells Transform Energy," *Scientific American*, Volume 205 (September 1961), page 62.

7

Reproduction —of Cells —of Individuals

Life for you began in a single cell. All the cells of your body are descendants of it. All cells come from pre-existing cells: who was credited for this recognition (page 48)?

One cell divides and becomes two. The division is a *fact*. But *how* they divide is a puzzle.

If you tried to divide a watch or an automobile in half, the result would be two piles of parts—neither pile able to function as a watch or an automobile. It is very different when a cell divides. Each daughter cell has all the parts (nucleus, ribosomes, mitochondria, and others) that were present in the original cell, and each can carry on all the activities of the original cell. To be sure, each daughter cell has only half the volume of the parent cell. In most cases it soon grows to the size of the original cell, however, and so we end with two cells exactly like the original.

Thus we have to account for the doubling of all the complexity of the original cell. It does not just *happen*—with a division of the cell's contents in *any* manner. It is possible for the body of some **protozoans** (pro·toh·ZOH-ans)—animals whose body usually is a single cell—to be cut in half with a tiny knife in such a way that both halves survive surgery. If the cut is made so that one half contains a nucleus and the other half does not, the survival of the two will be very different. The half with the nucleus heals quickly, then slowly grows back into a normal animal. It continues to live and reproduce as though nothing had happened to it. Not so with the half lacking a nucleus. It too heals, but it never grows and restores the missing parts. Gradually it wastes away and dies. In these single cells, therefore, the nucleus is necessary for life and reproduction.

One of the best places to observe dividing cells is in developing embryos. In most organisms, embryos begin life as one cell, the **fertilized egg,** formed by the union of an **egg cell** from the female parent and a **sperm cell** from the male. The fertilized egg soon begins dividing into daughter cells. Frequently the divisions are regular—that is, the one cell divides into two, the two into four, the four into eight, and so on.

The problem is this: how can a single cell, the fertilized egg, have the ability to form all the cells of the adult?

Genetic Continuity

Nor is the problem yet fully stated. It is not a matter of the food and oxygen that are required, for these and other things in the environment do not direct the outcome. Rather, it is the problem of how a cell can produce another cell of its own kind instead of some other kind. For example, a fertilized egg of a frog and one of a toad can be placed in the same dish, and the embryos can be given the same food, but in every case the one becomes a frog and the other a toad. There is no environment in which a fertilized frog egg will develop into a toad, or in which a fertilized toad egg will develop into a frog.

Somehow the knowledge, "How to become a frog," must be carried in the fertilized egg cell. Furthermore, this knowledge is transmitted from generation to generation. We speak of this as **genetic** (je·NET·ik) **continuity**—the production, generation after generation, of offspring that are similar (though not identical) to their parents. Genetic continuity applies not only to the individuals but to the cells as

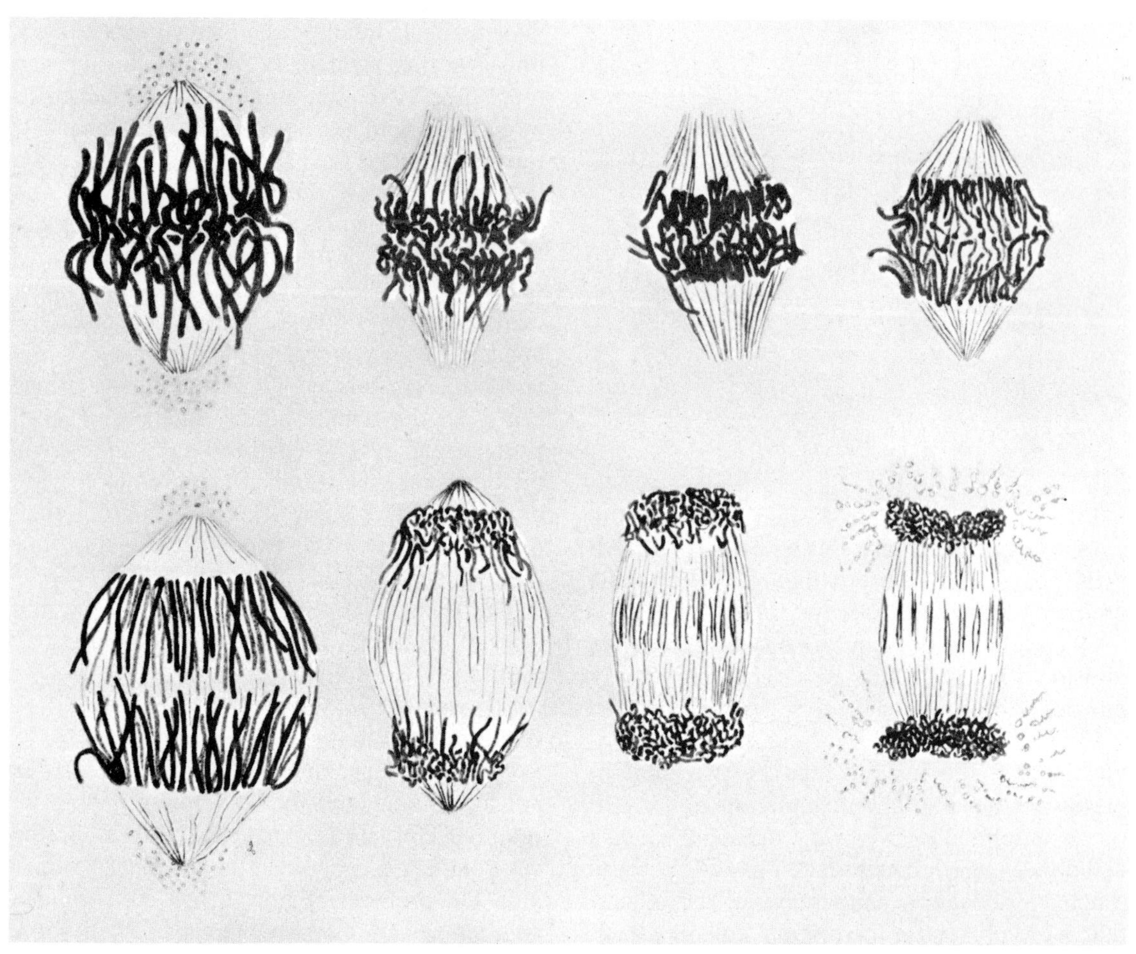

7–1 Almost a century ago, the events of mitosis and cell division were observed and recorded by Walther Flemming. His drawings of mitosis in *stained* cells of a lily are reproduced above; similar events in *living* cells from the skin of a larval salamander appear on the facing page. The sequence of events on both pages is from left to right, beginning at the upper left and ending at the lower right. The drawing at the end of the second line

well. When a frog cell divides, the daughter cells that are produced are frog cells.

Think of it in this way. A single cell, the fertilized egg, develops into a frog. This frog becomes an adult. If it is a female, it produces egg cells. If it is a male, it produces another type of cell, sperm cells. When the mature frog mates with another frog, **fertilization** again occurs – that is, an egg cell and a sperm cell fuse to form a single cell, the fertilized egg cell. This fertilized egg will also develop into a frog. *What insures that it will?*

So far we have been engaging in speculation; in science it is a means of questioning, directed toward an end – greater understanding. It is not an end in itself. It will be more profitable now for you to go to the laboratory and observe dividing cells (Inquiry 7-1).

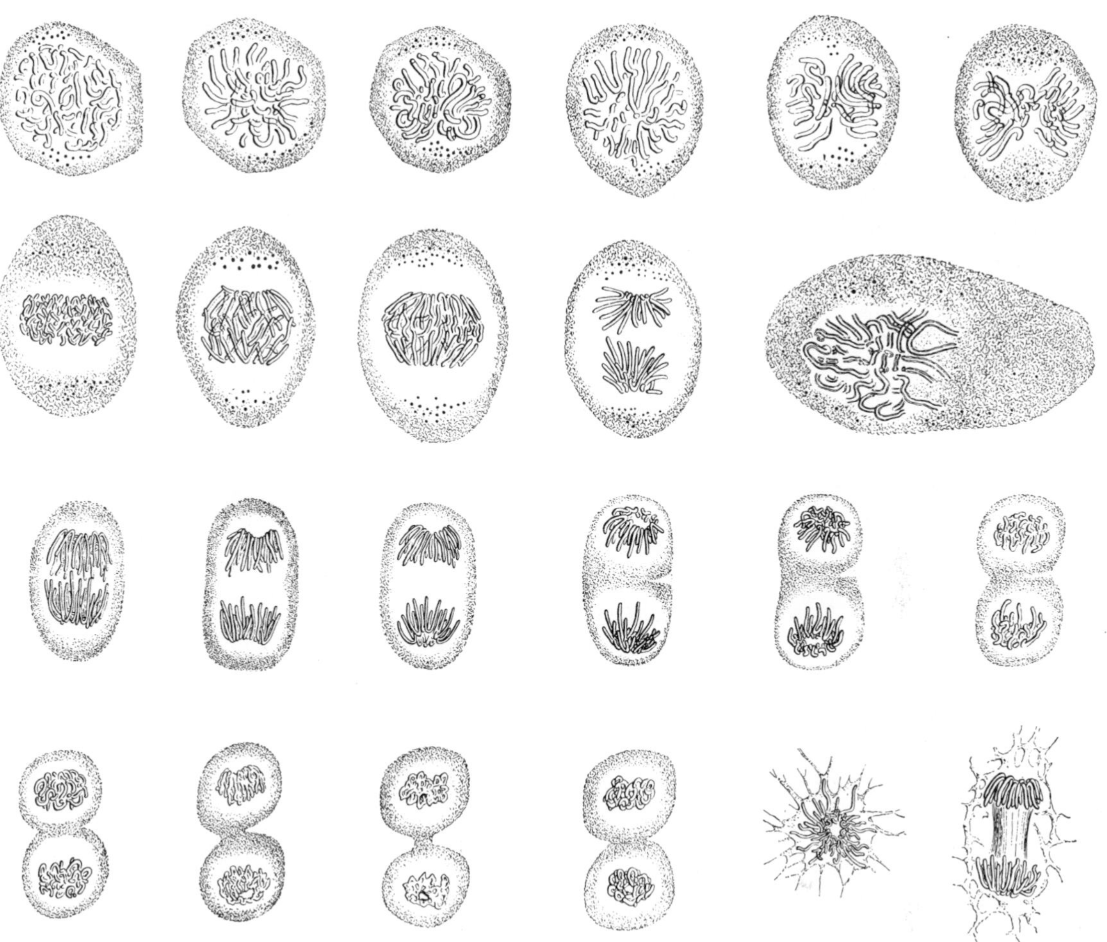

From Walther Flemming, *Zellsubstanz, Kern und Zelltheilung*, Leipzig, 1882

on this page (above right) shows one of Flemming's most important discoveries: each of the cell's chromosomes at this time appeared "double." *What was the significance of this observation?* The last two drawings above show how differently things appear when viewed from one *end* of the spindle (next to last drawing), then from one *side* of the spindle (last drawing). Why was it important to study living *and* stained cells?

Your microscope and the techniques available to you will probably be better than those available to many of the early scientists, but you will soon discover one serious obstacle: many of the things in cells are too small to be studied with your compound microscope. Mitochondria and centrioles are no more than tiny dots. Ribosomes are invisible: their discovery had to await the electron microscope.

MITOSIS

But there are important things that you *can* observe, as was also true for the biologists who first studied dividing cells. As it happened, one of the cell's most important structures—the nucleus—is large enough to be seen. One could then ask: what happens to the nucleus when the cell divides (Figure 7-1)? The first

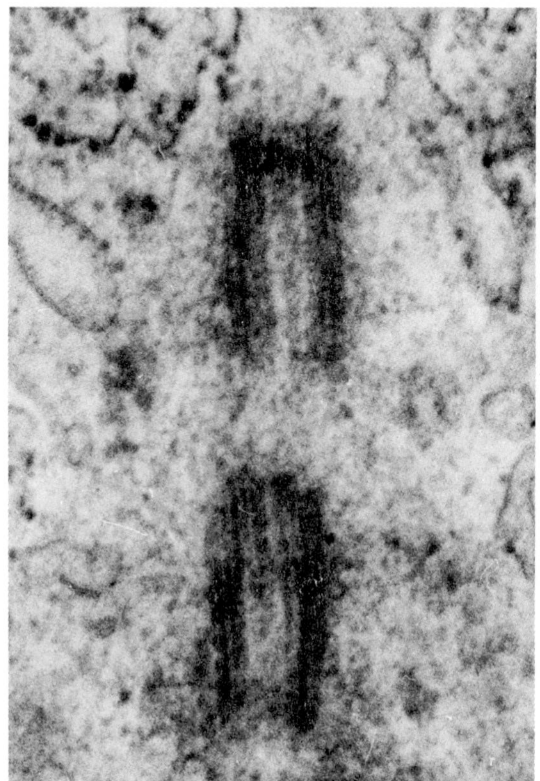

J. André

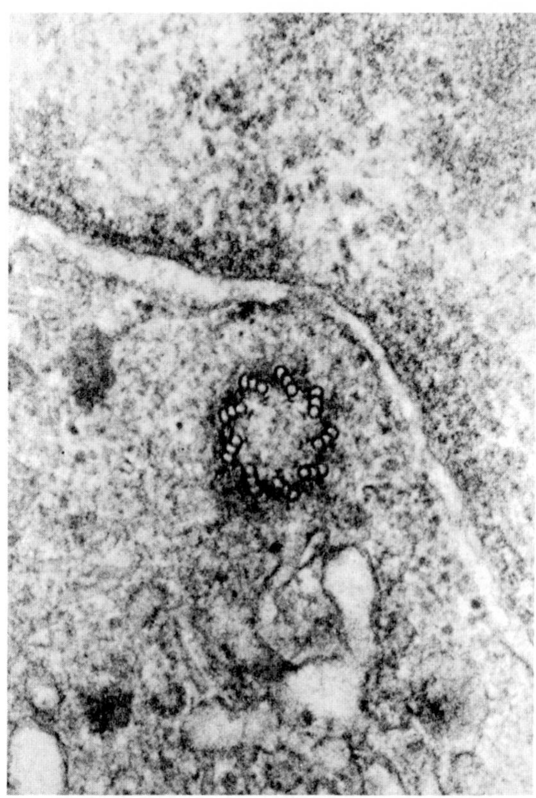

J. André

7–2 The structure of a centriole. Studies made when only the light microscope was available suggested that the centriole was just a dot. The electron microscope reveals that it has a complex structure. The photograph at the left shows a pair of centrioles in side view. The photograph on the right shows a cross section of one centriole. Can you relate these two points of view? (Both magnifications, 80,000 ×)

person to give an accurate and detailed account in answer to this question was a German biologist, Walther Flemming, in the 1880's.

The compound microscopes of Flemming's day were reaching a high degree of perfection. Methods for fixing and staining cells also were good and becoming better (Perkin's aniline dyes were available, for example; see page 4). A generation earlier it would not have been possible for anyone to do the work that Flemming did. He lived at the time when he or someone else could use recently improved tools and newly devised techniques to make meaningful observations about the internal events during cell division. Technology was supporting science, as it almost invariably does.

But Flemming was more than lucky to be living at the right time. Cell division occurs throughout the living world, yet its secrets are not revealed equally well in all cells. Flemming examined many kinds of animal and plant cells and selected those that showed the details of dividing cells most clearly. And although he was interested in events in *living* cells, he knew that it is easier to see structures in fixed and stained cells than in living cells. Yet herein lay a danger: when one sees a structure in a *dead* cell, can he be sure that it is part of the *living* process? You can understand the danger from an example. When a hen's egg is boiled, there are changes much like those occurring in fixation. You could study the boiled egg and reach some conclusions regarding its structure. To what extent would these conclusions be true of the *living* egg?

Flemming carefully studied fixed and stained cells *as well as* living cells. He made it a rule never to believe what he saw in fixed and stained cells unless he could observe it also in living cells. As a result, he made observations that have stood the test of time. Other biologists have confirmed what he observed.

Thus Flemming observed that in a dividing cell the nucleus passes through an orderly series of changes (Figure 7-1) which he called **mitosis** (my·TOE·sis). In all the cells he studied, both animal and plant, the nuclear events were approximately the same. There seemed in this, as in other features of organisms, *a unity of life*. Let us study the process for information on which to base further questions.

A Study of a Cell Undergoing Mitosis

In an animal cell just before division there is a central nucleus with one or more nucleoli. Usually no chromosomes are visible within the nucleus. Outside the nucleus the cytoplasm contains mitochondria, Golgi bodies, and various granules, many of which are almost impossible to study with the compound microscope. Only one will be considered further: the centriole (page 50). To biologists using the compound microscope, the centriole of a cell is a tiny granule. Sometimes it is contained in a **centrosome** (SEN·tro·soam). The electron microscope has revealed considerable complexity. A centriole is a tiny cylinder made up of nine clusters of two or three tubules per cluster (Figure 7-2). What is the relation of this highly organized structure to the function of the centriole? No one yet knows. However, the first indication that a cell is about to divide is generally given by the centriole and centrosome as the centriole divides into two, forming two daughter centrioles (Figure 7-3). The daughter

7-3 The division of the centriole and centrosome. Before mitosis begins, the centriole appears as a small granule within the centrosome. Actually, most animal cells have two centrioles at this time, as shown in Figure 6-10 (page 124), but they are so small that they can be seen as separate structures only with the electron microscope (Figure 7-2, left view). Slowly the two centrioles move to opposite sides of the nucleus, and each characteristically doubles again. (What begins to occur in the nucleus during the migration of the centrioles to opposite sides of the cell?)

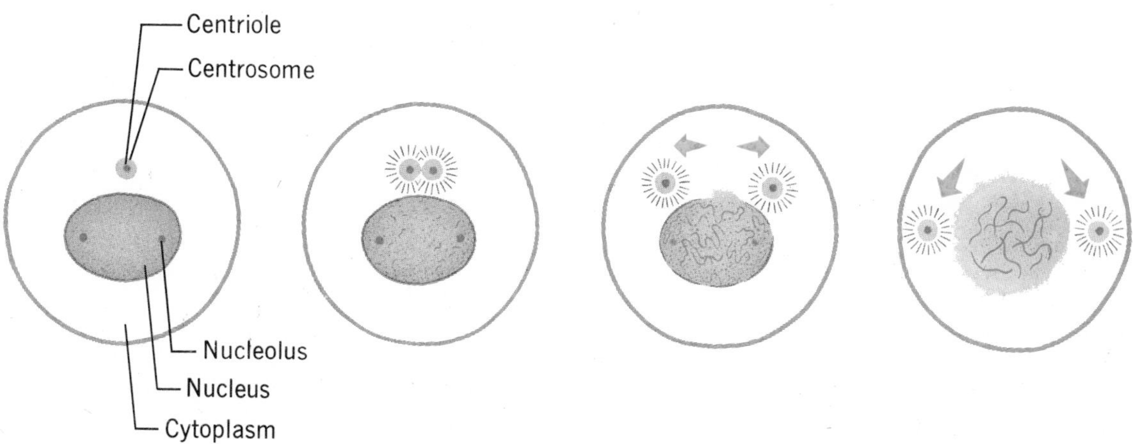

centrioles then migrate, each with its surrounding centrosome, to opposite sides of the nucleus. The nucleolus, a prominent feature of the nucleus in *non*dividing cells, gradually disappears at this time.

The first photograph of Figure 7-4 shows a cell at the beginning of mitosis. The nucleus appears as a sphere containing darkly stained threads, the chromosomes. The two darker spheres, to the right and left of the nucleus, are the centrosomes. (The centrioles within the centrosomes are difficult to see in the whitefish. They do not show in the photographs.)

The most striking events in mitosis concern the chromosomes. Nearly always invisible in nondividing cells, they become increasingly easy to see as mitosis gets under way.

In the second photograph of Figure 7-4 the chromosomes appear as tiny, dark rods (dark because they have been stained). The membrane surrounding the nucleus has disappeared. It will not re-form until the end of mitosis. The centrosomes are prominent. A series of fibers extends from one centrosome to the other, forming what is known as the **spindle.** The spindle has roughly the shape of a football, and the chromosomes are situated *within* the spindle. One specialized part of each chromosome, known as the **centromere** (SEN·tro·meer), seems to be attached to the fibers of the spindle. Centromeres cannot be seen in these photographs.

In the third photograph of Figure 7-4 the chromosomes appear to be separating into two groups. One group is moving through the spindle toward one centrosome; the other group is moving toward the other centrosome.

A close examination of the part of the cell immediately surrounding each centrosome will reveal fibers. These are easiest to see in the third photograph, surrounding the centrosome on the right. The fibers appear to extend from the centrosome to the edges of the cell. This group of fibers surrounding each centrosome is the **aster.** It actually appears earlier than the stage of mitosis shown in photograph 3—look carefully at photographs 2 and 1. The centrosomes, together with their centrioles, the spindle, and the asters, are known as the **mitotic** (my·TOT·ik) **apparatus.**

Discouragingly little is known of the way the mitotic apparatus functions. Even its structure is not well understood. The spindle contains a number of fibers that extend from one end of the spindle to the other. These are easy to see in fixed and stained cells, as in Figure 7-4. For many years it was not possible to see them in living cells, but now we know definitely that they are present. Most of the spindle fibers are of a single kind of protein. There are also traces of RNA in the spindle.

The asters also seem to be composed of protein fibers.

The entire mitotic apparatus forms one organized structure in the cell. If the surrounding cytoplasm is dissolved away, the mitotic apparatus remains intact (Figure 7-5).

In photographs 4 and 5 of Figure 7-4, the two groups of chromosomes have moved progressively farther apart, and in the last photograph, number 6, we approach the end of mitosis. The original cell has divided into two. The cell membrane has grown inward to cut across the spindle, pinching the cell in two. Each daughter cell has a full set of chromosomes. The asters and the spindle have become indistinct.

At a time somewhat later than represented by photograph 6, a nuclear membrane forms around the chromosomes in each new cell. The chromosomes become progressively less distinct, and the nucleus in each new cell assumes the appearance characteristic of nuclei in nondividing cells. Nucleoli re-form within the two daughter nuclei. The asters and spindle disappear. The centrosomes decrease in size, and one remains, with its centriole, in each daughter cell.

In some cells the entire process of mitosis (nuclear division) and subsequent cell division is completed in about 15 minutes; in others it may require hours.

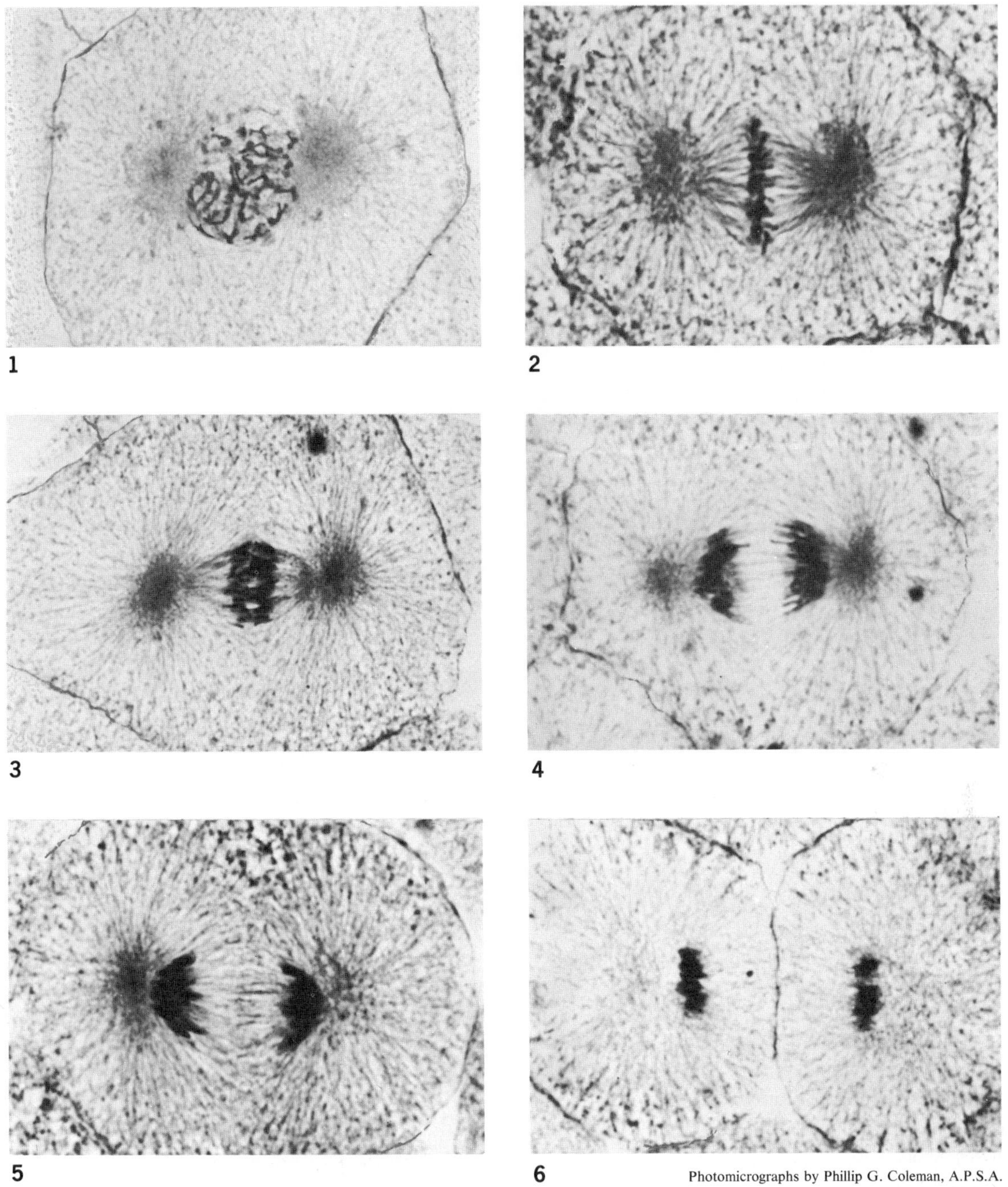

Photomicrographs by Phillip G. Coleman, A.P.S.A.

7–4 Mitosis in cells of a whitefish embryo. These photographs, taken through a compound microscope, show six stages of mitosis and cell division. The spindle's axis is horizontal in each photograph. How do the events recorded here compare with Flemming's drawings of mitosis in skin cells of a larval salamander (Figure 7–1)?

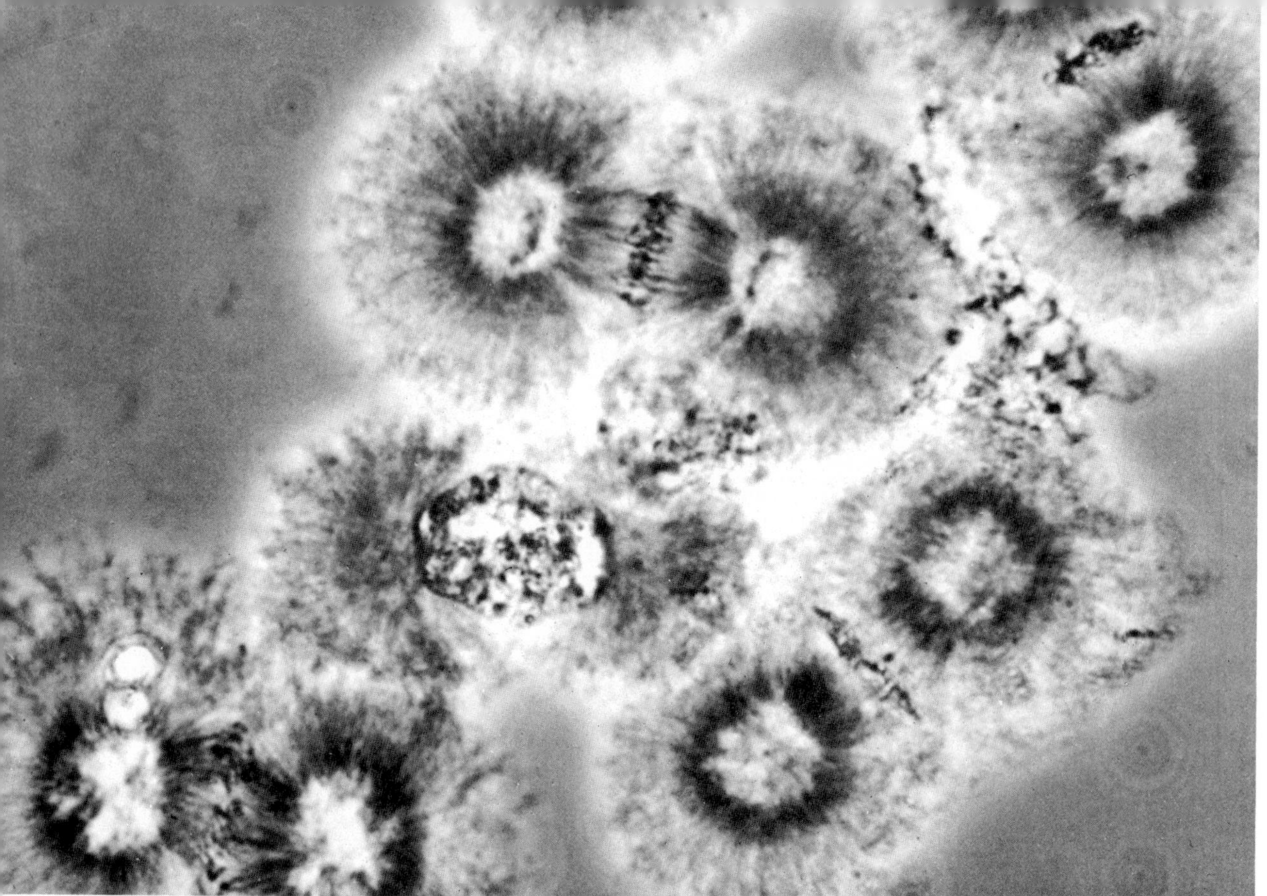

D. Mazia

7–5 Isolated mitotic apparatus of sea urchin eggs. The white spherical areas are centrosomes. The darker areas surrounding the centrosomes are the asters. Between each pair of centrosomes is a spindle with chromosomes upon it (most clearly seen near the top of the photograph). The centrioles are not visible.

By now you will have examined many kinds of cells in the laboratory. How many have you seen dividing? The chances are that you may not have seen *any* dividing. You could examine thousands of cells from most parts of your own body and not find one dividing. There are several places where mitosis would be common —your skin and the lining of your intestine are two. In both places cells are constantly being worn away and replaced by the division of the remaining cells.

Mitosis and subsequent cell division in the cells of complex plants (such as the onion root tip in Figure 7-6) is much the same as in animal cells. The chief points of difference are these: there are no centrioles or asters in such plant cells. Furthermore, the cell does not pinch in two. Instead, a new cell wall forms across the middle of the spindle.

The formation of the cell wall is complex. Tiny swellings appear on the spindle fibers at the middle of the spindle. These swellings fuse to form a partition that cuts across the cell, dividing the original cell into two daughter cells. This partition is not the new cell wall but a cementing substance that will hold the daughter cells together. The cytoplasm of each daughter cell lays down a new cell wall of several layers adjacent to the central partition. The cell walls consist largely of cellulose (Figure 6-4, page

111). In the walls of some plant cells there is also **lignin** (LIG·nin), the substance that gives hardness to wood.

What is the *meaning* of mitosis to the life of new cells? To seek more information we must turn to a closer study of the chromosomes within the nucleus.

Chromosome Reproduction

The more Flemming and others studied mitosis the more convinced they became that the nucleus is not merely divided. Instead both reproduction *and* division are involved. At least this seemed to be true of the chromosomes. This was almost a requirement since the nucleus appeared the same after each division. If it had divided in half, each daughter cell would contain only half a nucleus with half the number of chromosomes. Yet as well as the early observers could tell, the number of chromosomes seemed to be the same in all cells of a given species.

In some exceptionally fine microscopic preparations (such as that illustrated in the drawing on the far right of the second row of Figure 7-1) each chromosome seemed to be double. Flemming believed this to be an important clue, and this is how he interpreted the observation: since the number of chromosomes in each cell is the same before and after each division, *there must be a doubling of the chromosomes* at some time before division. So far as he could tell, each chromosome was *single* when it moved to the poles of the spindle in the last part of mitosis. Then the chromosomes seemed to disappear when the nuclear membrane reformed. When they appeared again at the beginning of the next mitosis, they were *double*.

It was regrettable that the chromosomes could not be observed during this important time. All one could do was to make a hypothesis to account for the events. He could assume that each chromosome became two during the "blackout" period between the preceding and the succeeding mitosis. Thus if an organism has 46 chromosomes, as does man, these 46 would each reproduce and so form 92. At the next mitosis and cell division these 92 would be divided between the two daughter cells, each receiving 46. Figure 7-7 shows part of this process for human chromosomes. You can count the 46 chromosomes and, in most cases, see that each is double. (This illustration will be confusing until you realize that the cell was prepared in a special way. It was flattened and broken to spread out the chromosomes. Stains affecting only the chromosomes were used. Other parts of the cell do not show.) You can also see that the

7–6 Mitosis in cells of the growing tip of an onion root. At the time the cells were fixed and stained, some were in the process of dividing, others not. Note the prominent nucleoli in the nuclei of non-dividing cells. Why do some of the cells appear to be without nuclei? (550 ×)

Harbrace Photo

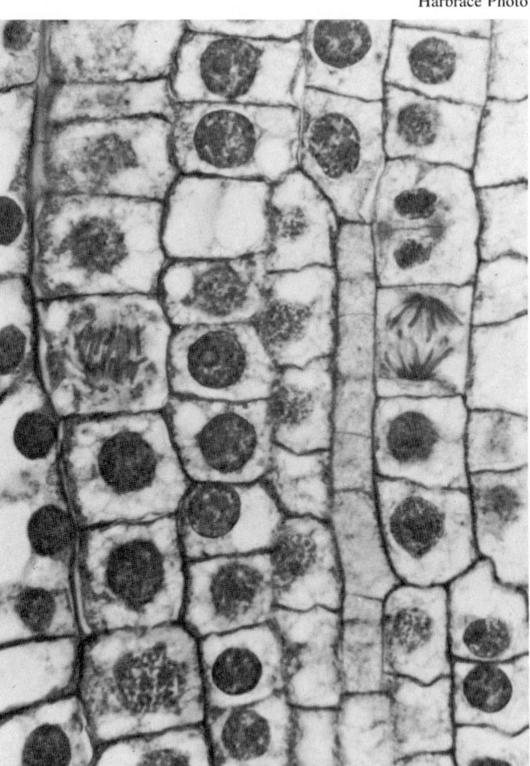

two parts of each chromosome seem to be held together at one place. This is the centromere, which at this time is undivided. At a slightly later stage than is shown in the photograph, the centromere divides. Then each of the 46 "double" chromosomes separates into two daughter chromosomes. Thus two complete groups of chromosomes are formed, each with 46 single chromosomes. Each group has one chromosome of each kind that was present in the parent nucleus.

It took a great amount of observation and experimentation by Flemming and those who followed him to establish the hypothesis of these events as "highly probable." Figure 7-8 illustrates what is believed to happen.

For many of the other cell structures it was assumed that during cell division they were divided in a roughly equal way between the daughter cells, and that the original quantities were subsequently restored by the growth of

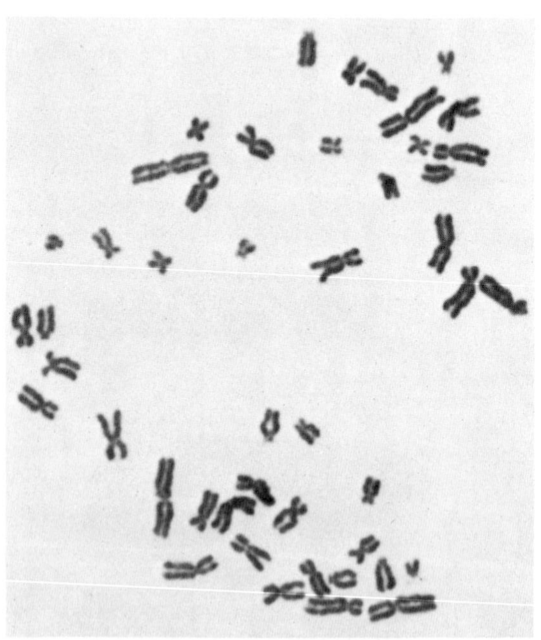

J. H. Tjio and T. T. Puck, P.N.A.S. *44*, 1229, 1958.

7-7 A normal set of human chromosomes. How many are shown according to your count? What is the significance of their double structure?

each daughter cell. Some observers believed that the centrioles were reproduced and divided in a manner somewhat like the chromosomes, but other observers disagreed. (The reason for this debate was the great difficulty in making observations of centrioles, which were so very small and difficult to study.) One could only be sure that the chromosomes were reproduced in a precise and orderly manner during mitosis and cell division.

In the years after Flemming made his observations, and especially since 1953, we have learned a great deal about the structure of chromosomes, and of *how* they divide. They are composed mainly of DNA and protein. The role of protein in chromosome structure and function is just beginning to be known. On the other hand, we know much about DNA—enough to make us believe that *it* is the material in the chromosomes that ultimately controls the cell's life and reproduction. What a cell is and what a cell does, therefore, depends on the kind of DNA it has. The kind of DNA in your cells is what makes you a human being, and a frog is a frog because its cells contain another specific sort of DNA. Furthermore, the DNA in all of your cells is believed to be essentially the same.

DNA can have these important properties only if it passes intact from parent cell to daughter cell.

The cell contains a remarkable mechanism for producing replicas, in an exact way, of the DNA of its chromosomes. During mitosis the *replicated* DNA is divided between the two daughter cells. Each new cell receives DNA like that of the parent cell. We can then say that the basic importance of mitosis is this: it supplies daughter cells with DNA that is *usually* identical to that of the parent cell.

Mutation

The phrase "*usually* identical" brings us to another important point about DNA. Occasionally a mistake is made: when the DNA of a

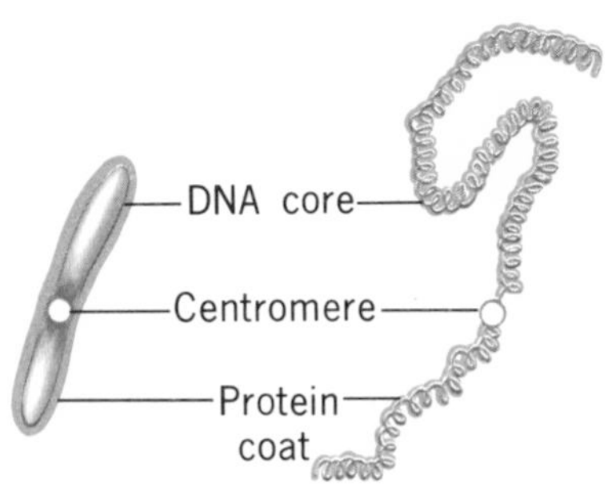

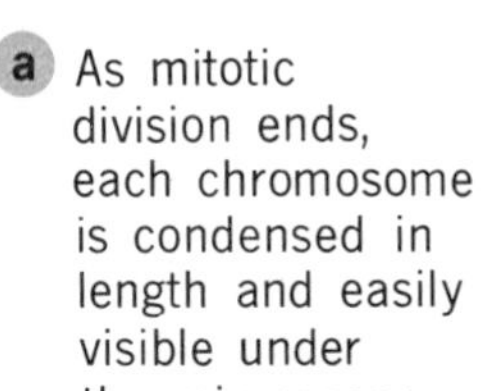

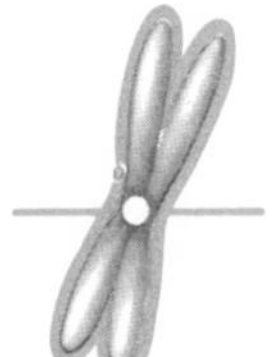

a As mitotic division ends, each chromosome is condensed in length and easily visible under the microscope.

b The chromosome uncoils in the new daughter cell and disappears from view. Replication begins at this stage.

c The chromosome becomes visible when another mitotic division begins. It is now double, with replication completed except for the centromere.

d The double chromosome becomes attached to the spindle at the centromere. Finally the centromere divides, and ...

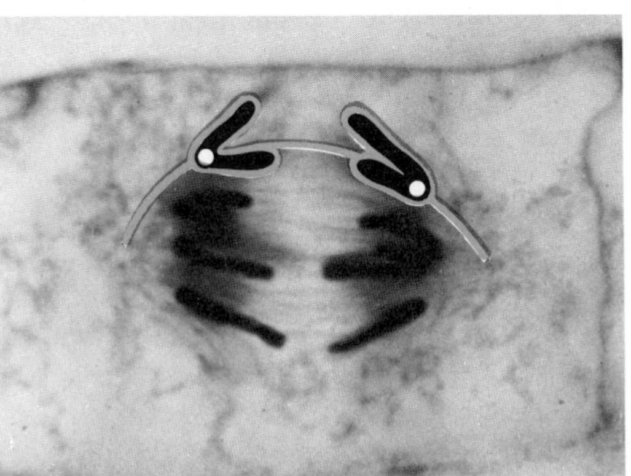

...each half-chromosome becomes an independent chromosome, one going to each pole of the spindle.

Photo by General Biological Supply House, Inc., Chicago

7–8 One chromosome becomes two. Five stages of the process are illustrated here. Each chromosome is replicated before the cell divides. Drawing **a** shows a chromosome at the end of one mitotic cycle; **b, c,** and **d** show stages ending in replication of the chromosome early in the next mitotic cycle; the final photograph shows the separation of the replicated chromosome and others in the succeeding cell division.

chromosome is replicated before mitosis, a tiny part of the new DNA might not be exactly the same as the original DNA. The altered DNA may have been so changed that it no longer can support the life of a cell. Or it can change less drastically and the cell will live but function in a different way. This change of a tiny part of the DNA is known as **mutation** (mew·TAY·shun). The fact that DNA can change is of tremendous significance, for it is the basis of all the variability that occurs in organisms. We will learn, for example, in Chapter 13 that there is strong evidence that at one time long ago the only green plants were single-celled organisms. We call them the algae. These algae were the ancestors of all the green plants on the earth today – the trees, the flowers, the grasses, the ferns, the mosses, and so on. Over the course of time some of the algae changed and eventually produced these other kinds of plants. These changes with time are *evolution*. Evolution is made possible by the slight alterations, or mutations, that occur in successive generations of organisms.

Mutation is such an important process, and it influences so many biological processes, that we will return to it again and again. We will study it in relation to viruses (Chapter 9), bacteria (Chapter 10), and repeatedly in the chapters on genetics (Chapters 29-30) and evolution (Chapters 31-32).

In the next chapter we will continue with the molecular basis for the replication of chromosomes and with their role in the life of the cell. But before leaving this chapter we must discuss some additional problems associated with the replication of chromosomes in cells that are to divide.

MEIOSIS

The chances are you have begun to question whether the number of chromosomes *always* remains the same when cells divide. Biologists also began to wonder about this, once Flemming and others had established the basic fact of the constancy of the number of chromosomes in mitosis.

This was the problem: let us assume that when cells divide, the daughter cells *always* have the same number of chromosomes as the parent cell. In other words, let us assume that cell division is always preceded by mitosis. In the case of man, this will mean that egg cells and sperm cells, like other cells, must receive 46 chromosomes. But if this were so, then the union of the egg nucleus and the sperm nucleus, which takes place at fertilization, would produce a total of 92! The fertilized egg would then undergo mitosis and all of the cells in the new individual would have 92 chromosomes.

The same process would be repeated each generation. The grandchildren would have 184 chromosomes per cell, the great grandchildren 368. Observation of cells from successive generations of animals and plants shows that this is not the case. The chromosome number remains the same.

Let us review our dilemma:

HYPOTHESIS. If the number of chromosomes remains constant in all cell divisions, including those that produce sperm cells and egg cells . . .

DEDUCTION . . . then we would expect the individuals of the next generation to have twice the number of chromosomes their parents had.

This deduction, like all deductions, is a logical consequence of the hypothesis.

TEST OF DEDUCTION. We carefully examine a variety of plants and animals but find that successive generations of a species have identical numbers of chromosomes.

CONCLUSION. We have checked the deduction and found it to be false. Therefore, the hypothesis cannot be correct as stated.

In every careful study of mitosis and cell division in animals and plants, the chromosome number in successive cell generations *does* remain constant. Obviously we have overlooked some important factors.

Let us recall the details of the test: what was actually done? Developing embryos and the growing roots of plants were fixed and stained, and the cells were studied. It was found that the chromosome number remained the same. Actually we studied only *some* cells, and these during a *limited time period* of the individual's life. On the basis of these data we assumed that in all parts of the body and at all periods of life the number of chromosomes remains constant. In other words we have looked at a *few* cell divisions and assumed that *all* cell divisions are the same. Is this justifiable?

Arguments similar to these were advanced during the 1880's when biologists were first learning about mitosis and cell division. August Weismann (1834–1914) was one of these biologists. Because his eyesight was poor, it was difficult for him to use a microscope to study cells. But there were other things that

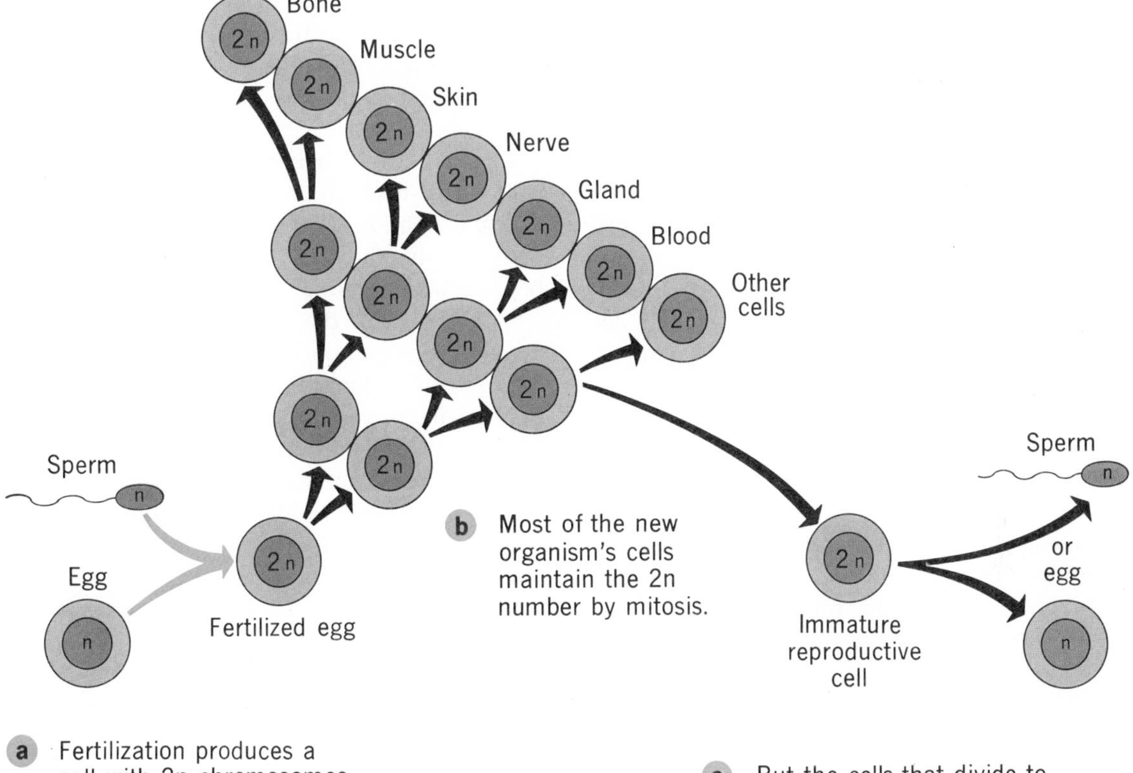
Bone
Muscle
Skin
Nerve
Gland
Blood
Other cells
2n
Sperm
n
Egg
Fertilized egg
b Most of the new organism's cells maintain the 2n number by mitosis.
Immature reproductive cell
Sperm
or egg
a Fertilization produces a cell with 2n chromosomes— the diploid number.
c But the cells that divide to produce sperms or eggs halve the chromosome number by meiosis.

7-9 Two kinds of cell division in the life of an individual. The chromosome numbers $2n$ and n are respectively the number of chromosomes following mitosis ($2n$) and half that number (n) following meiosis—the type of division predicted by Weismann.

he could do. Science is not advanced only by the collection of data. Someone must *think about* and interpret the data. Weismann's poor eyesight forced him to spend time thinking.

He considered the apparent facts:

1. In successive generations, individuals of the same species have the same number of chromosomes.
2. In successive cell divisions, the number of chromosomes remains constant.

Weismann realized, just as we have come to do, that both statements 1 and 2 cannot *always* be true. There was one way out: perhaps not *all* cell divisions are the same. Weismann then suggested this hypothesis: there must be a kind of cell division in which the chromosome number is halved (Figure 7-9).

Let us see what the hypothesis means in terms of the cells of man. The normal number of chromosomes, 46, is doubled to give 92. Mitosis and cell division then allot 46 chromosomes to each daughter cell. But assume that there is one situation where the chromosome number is not doubled before cell division. If so, 23 would be given to each daughter cell.

If this "other" type of division would occur during the formation of eggs and sperms, then all the facts could be explained. The egg would have 23 chromosomes. The sperm would also have 23 chromosomes. When egg and sperm combined, the sum would be 46 chromosomes again. The fertilized egg would then divide by the usual sort of mitosis and every cell so formed would have 46 chromosomes.

Weismann's prediction was soon verified. Biologists carefully studied the cells that developed into eggs and into sperms. They found that just before the mature egg and the sperms are formed, the chromosome number is halved. This process is called **meiosis** (my·OH·sis). As a result of meiosis, the sperm and the egg in human beings each have 23 chromosomes.

Meiosis occurs in all animals and plants that reproduce sexually. In animals it occurs before eggs and sperms are formed. In plants it characteristically occurs when spores are formed, as you will find in Chapter 13.

The general events are these: eggs and sperms nearly always have half the number of chromosomes found in other cells. We speak of this number as the **monoploid** (MON·o·ploid) **number** (or use the abbreviation *n*). When the egg and sperm, each with a monoploid number of chromosomes, unite, a fertilized egg with the **diploid** (DIP·loid) **number** of chromosomes (abbreviated *2n*) is the result. The gross relations are shown in Figure 7-9, where meiosis and mitosis are compared.

The Events of Meiosis

The details of meiosis are complex but, once again, the process is so important for the understanding of so many biological processes that its general aspects must be described. Biologists were relieved to discover that meiosis is much the same in all animals and plants. Thus when we learn about meiosis in one organism we can apply this knowledge to other organisms. There are variations, but the general mechanism is the same in all plants and animals that reproduce sexually.

Meiosis begins with diploid cells, which undergo two specialized cell divisions. The result is four cells, but each has only the monoploid number of chromosomes. This is what we must investigate.

Let us discuss meiosis in a male human being, where it occurs as part of the process of sperm formation. The cell that will form sperms contains 46 chromosomes—the diploid number, as with other cells. If one examines the chromosomes at the time of an ordinary cell division (Figure 7-7), they seem to vary greatly. They may be long or short; the centromeres may be in the middle or near the ends. However, if one *arranges* the chromosomes according to these structural features, he finds they can be paired. There are not 46 different kinds of chromosomes but only 23 (this is not strictly correct for the human male, since the pair at the lower right in Figure 7-7 has one long and one short member; these are the sex chromosomes, to which we shall return in Chapter 30).

The pairs of chromosomes are shown in Figure 7-10, where the individual chromosomes have been arranged according to size and other structural features such as positions of the centromeres.

To simplify our discussion let us concentrate on only two of these pairs of similar chromosomes. If we find out what happens to them during meiosis, we shall know (or know how to find out) what happens to other pairs as well. Let us designate one pair as 1^a and 1^b and another pair as 2^a and 2^b (Figure 7-11a). 1^a and 1^b, as well as 2^a and 2^b, are said to be **homologous** (ho·MOL·oh·gus) **chromosomes.** The two members of a homologous pair, as 1^a and 1^b, are the same kind of chromosome. They are not, however, *exactly* alike. By analogy, two animals can be of the same kind, as German shepherd dogs. However, two individual dogs could vary in many particulars. Thus chromosomes 1^a and 1^b would have DNA that is much alike but not exactly alike. The differences would be the result of mutations that have occurred in the past.

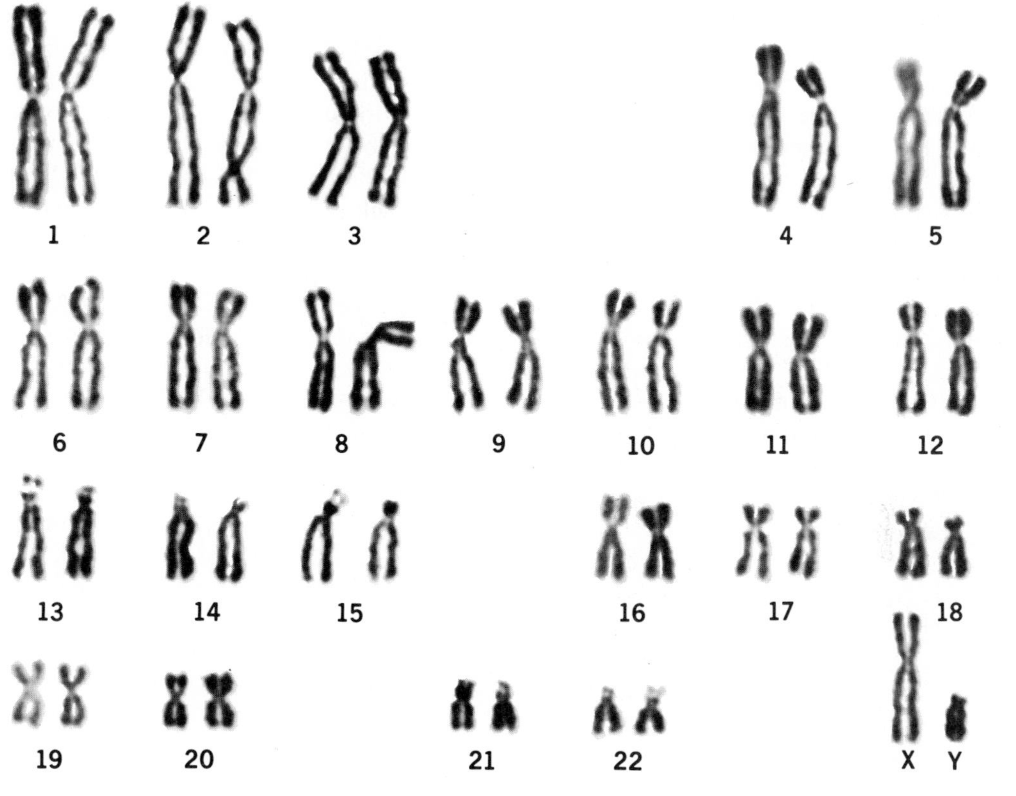

Margery Shaw, M.D.

7–10 A normal set of human chromosomes arranged by pairs. Compare Figure 7–7, shown at lower magnification, with this photograph. Strictly speaking, one of the pairs of chromosomes shown here is not a pair—which one? What is its significance?

At the beginning of meiosis each of the chromosomes reproduces at all places except the centromere (Figure 7-11b). In our example the result is $1^a \bullet 1^a$, $1^b \bullet 1^b$, $2^a \bullet 2^a$, $2^b \bullet 2^b$. We are using the • to represent the undivided centromere. We speak of each unseparated replica of the original chromosome as a **chromatid** (CROW-muh·tid). Thus $1^a \bullet 1^a$ signifies that one 1^a chromatid is joined by a centromere to another 1^a chromatid.

The next major event that occurs is **synapsis** (sin·NAP·sis): the homologous, now *replicated* (or doubled) chromosomes come together in pairs. Thus $1^a \bullet 1^a$ comes together with $1^b \bullet 1^b$, and $2^a \bullet 2^a$ comes together with $2^b \bullet 2^b$ (Figure 7-11c). Each pair of synapsed chromosomes will consist of four chromatids but only two centromeres. Such a structure is called a **tetrad** (TEH·trad) because it consists of four elements.

The original homologous chromosomes, 1^a and 1^b, or 2^a and 2^b, are genetically somewhat different because of mutations in the past. But when 1^a replicates to form $1^a \bullet 1^a$, the two 1^a chromatids will be identical except for those *very* rare cases when a mutation again occurs.

In a similar way the two 1^b chromatids will be identical with one another. Thus the $1^a \bullet 1^a$ $1^b \bullet 1^b$ tetrad will consist of two, not four, genetically different kinds of chromatids.

The tetrads are now in the spindle (Figure 7-11d). One of the centromeres with its two attached chromatids moves to one pole of the spindle and the other centromere moves to the other pole (Figure 7-11e). There are two possibilities so far as the daughter cells are concerned. One daughter cell could have $1^a \bullet 1^a$ together with $2^a \bullet 2^a$, and the sister cell $1^b \bullet 1^b$ together with $2^b \bullet 2^b$. Or, one daughter cell could have $1^a \bullet 1^a$ together with $2^b \bullet 2^b$, in which case its sister cell would have $1^b \bullet 1^b$ plus $2^a \bullet 2^a$. Only the second possibility is shown in Figure 7-11f. This is the end of the first meiotic division, of which there are two.

In the second meiotic division only the centromere is duplicated. This means that the $1^a \bullet 1^a$ pair of chromatids now separates to become two independent 1^a chromosomes, each with its own centromere. The same happens for each other pair of chromatids (Figure 7-11g).

One chromosome of each former pair of chromatids goes to one pole and the other goes to the opposite pole. The result is four cells each with the monoploid number of chromosomes (Figure 7-11h). The chromosome number has been reduced.

The events of meiosis can be understood better if the diagrams in Figure 7-11 are studied carefully. If you compare Figure 7-11a with Figure 7-11h, you will see that the two meiotic divisions have produced four cells, but that each is now monoploid. It has only *one* member of each original *pair* of chromosomes, instead of both as in the original diploid cell. It would also be profitable to contrast Figure 7-11 with the earlier description of mitosis (pages 131–33).

Each of the cells shown in Figure 7-11h will now develop into a sperm cell. Eggs are formed in the female in essentially the same way. The result also is four cells, but only one becomes an egg. The other three degenerate.

Thus meiosis produces sperms and an egg with the monoploid number of chromosomes. In man this would be 23 for the sperm cells and 23 for the egg cell. When a sperm and egg cell unite, the diploid number of 46 is restored. As the embryo develops, the increase in cell number is through cell divisions preceded by *mitosis*; each cell in the body will have 46 chromosomes. Not until the embryo reaches maturity and begins producing sperms or egg cells will meiosis occur again.

Does all this complexity have a function?

The Significance of Meiosis

Meiosis, followed by the union of a sperm and an egg, provides for a mixing of some of the hereditary materials from each parent in each of their offspring. This mixing produces new combinations of hereditary materials; some of these combinations may result in better adapted individuals.

Let us reconsider the example we have just used. Chromosomes 1^a and 1^b were slightly different from each other and very different from 2^a and 2^b. The different sperms formed in our example had these kinds of chromosomes: 1^a plus 2^a; 1^a plus 2^b; 1^b plus 2^a; 1^b plus 2^b. Let us now consider the egg cells produced by a human female. In the diploid state her cells will have a pair of homologous chromosomes of type 1 and a pair of type 2. Again, because of mutations that occurred in the past, the members of each pair will be slightly different from one another. They will also be different from the chromosomes of the male. Let us designate them as 1^c, 1^d, 2^c, and 2^d. The female will produce egg cells of four types with respect to just these two pairs of her 23 pairs of chromosomes—but not all at one time, as in the male, for only one daughter cell survives to become an egg after each occurrence of meiosis. Thus, at different times, the female can produce eggs of these types: 1^c plus 2^c; 1^c plus 2^d; 1^d plus 2^c; 1^d plus 2^d.

With four types of sperms and four types of egg cells, how many different types of fertilized

7-11 MEIOSIS—REDUCTION OF CHROMOSOME NUMBER

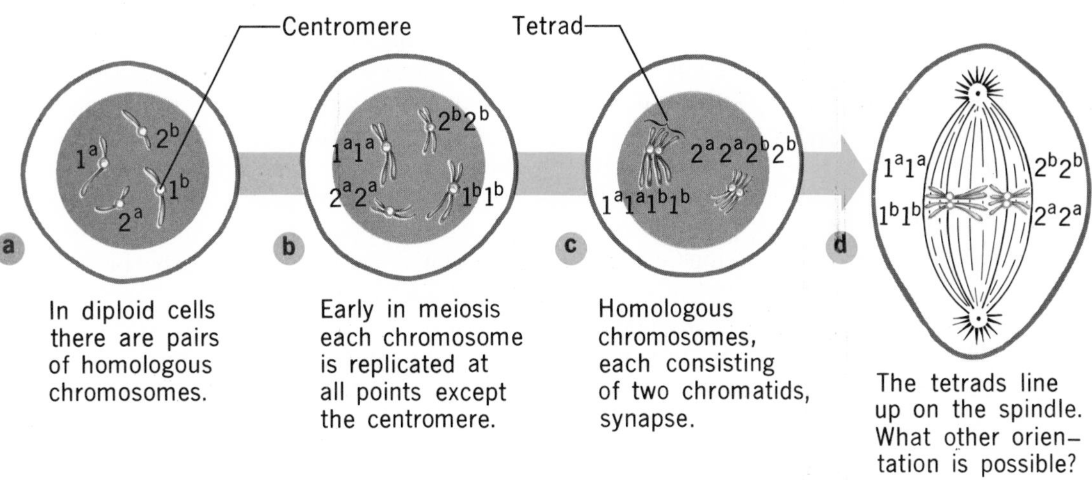

a In diploid cells there are pairs of homologous chromosomes.

b Early in meiosis each chromosome is replicated at all points except the centromere.

c Homologous chromosomes, each consisting of two chromatids, synapse.

d The tetrads line up on the spindle. What other orientation is possible?

1^a1^a 2^b2^b 1^b1^b 2^a2^a

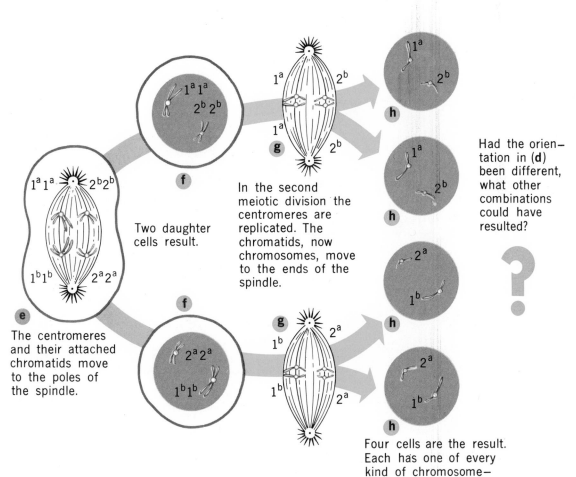

e The centromeres and their attached chromatids move to the poles of the spindle.

1^a1^a 2^b2^b — 2^a2^a 1^b1^b

f Two daughter cells result.

1^a 2^b 1^a 2^b — 1^b 2^a 1^b 2^a

g In the second meiotic division the centromeres are replicated. The chromatids, now chromosomes, move to the ends of the spindle.

1^a 2^b — 1^a 2^b — 2^a 1^b — 2^a 1^b

h Four cells are the result. Each has one of every kind of chromosome—the monoploid number.

Had the orientation in (**d**) been different, what other combinations could have resulted?

?

eggs are possible? What will these types be? Biologists have developed a scheme that they frequently use for genetic problems to obtain the answers to both questions (Figure 7-12). We make a checkerboard with the types of sperm cells listed on one side and the types of egg cells on the other. This simple device shows all possible combinations of egg cells and sperm cells. By counting the squares, you will know the number of possible combinations. Then if you combine the chromosome types of the egg cells and the sperm cells, as has been done for several of the squares, you will know the genetic types of the offspring. Is the genetic type different in each of the squares?

As you can see, many different genetic combinations are possible even in the simple model that we are using. Now consider 23 pairs of chromosomes instead of two, and you will have one of the keys to the variability among human beings, even in the same family. All of this means that many different sorts of hereditary materials can be tried out in numerous combinations. Throw in mutations and other events to be considered in later chapters, and the variability seems almost endless. In any natural population of sexually reproducing organisms, these events are the basis of the genetic variability that occurs.

It has been said that every human being is genetically unique (with the exception of identical twins). That is, there is no other human being who has exactly the same genetic material: *you* are at least slightly different from everyone alive today. Furthermore, there was probably never in the past, nor will there be

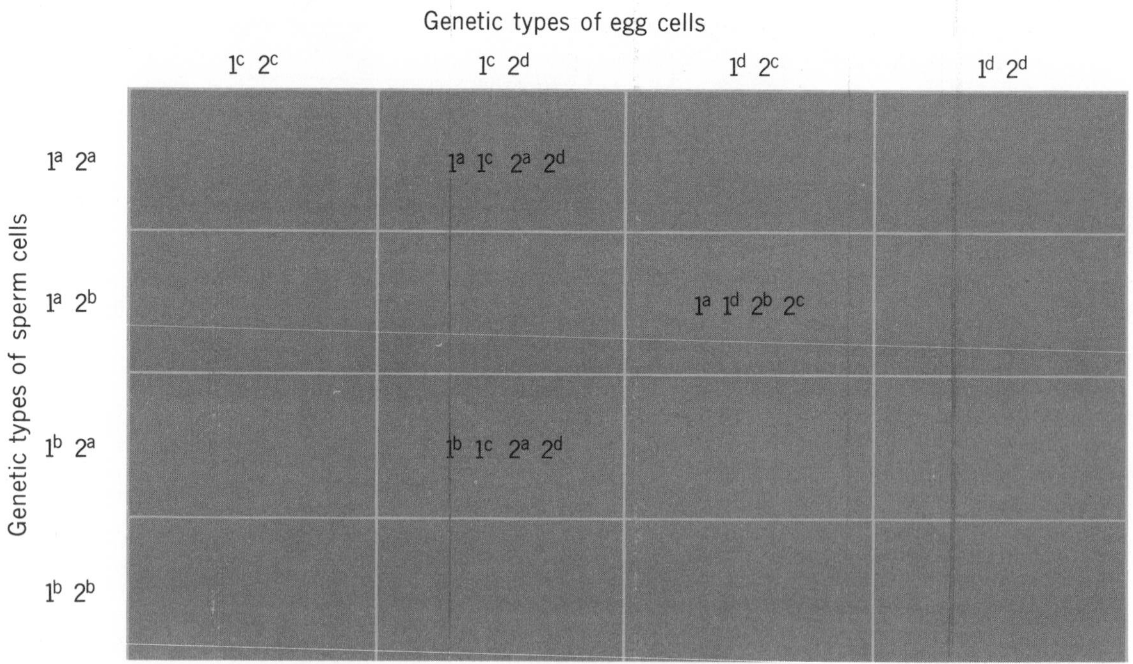

7–12 A genetic checkerboard. This device will show you how many different genetic combinations are possible between four kinds of egg cells and four kinds of sperm cells. Make your own copy of the table and complete it. How many *different* combinations do you find? Use another checkerboard to determine how many different combinations would be possible with four kinds of egg cells and two kinds of sperm cells.

in the future, another individual with exactly your hereditary make-up. You may find this statement hard to believe and, of course, there is no way of proving it rigorously. You may be surprised, however, that you can convince yourself that it is at least possible: refer to Problem 10 at the end of this chapter. You will need to use mathematics as you proceed, but you will come to appreciate something about genetic variability in natural populations. In all probability you are unique. Be careful when you cross the street—there may never be another you!

CONCLUDING REMARKS

In Chapters 3 through 6 we learned something of the tremendous complexity of cells. Their molecules are the largest and most complex associations of atoms known. Furthermore, cells undergo ceaseless activity. Molecules are being built up and broken down in fractions of a second. Biologists today have only a superficial understanding of the structure and function of a living cell. They understand enough, however, to be tremendously impressed by the mechanism that divides cells. Somehow the living, organized cell divides itself—and does so without being destroyed. More than that, in nearly every case the daughter cells have all the structure and potentialities of the parent cells.

The exact, or almost exact, replication of cells is made possible by a type of internal specialization and control, centered in the nucleus. The chromosomes, built of organized protein and DNA molecules, are the most important controlling elements. The structure and behavior of a cell is dependent on its specific DNA. The DNA contains the instructions necessary for the cell to carry on its vital activities.

In mitosis, each chromosome is replicated; the two identical chromosomes that result separate during cell division, with one going to each daughter cell. The replication of the chromosome involves a replication of its DNA. The rest of the cell is more or less equally divided. Each daughter cell, then, contains half of the original cell material but receives a *full* quota of the instructions in the DNA. With these instructions the daughter cell can grow and live as the parent cell did. It has all the information it needs.

Chromosome number remains constant from generation to generation. This is made possible by another type of division—meiosis. At some stage in the life of all plants and animals that reproduce sexually, there is a cell division without the replication of chromosomes. Meiosis halves the number of chromosomes to form the monoploid number. The full diploid number is restored again at the time of fertilization.

Meiosis is important in two ways. First, it provides for the precise transmission of genetic material from one generation to another. Second, it provides for a huge amount of genetic variability. Genetic variability is found in all organisms. It means no more than that the individuals of a given species differ from one another. Yet these differences are the basis of the evolutionary changes that occur with the passage of time. Some of the individuals will have hereditary characteristics that will allow them to survive a little better and to leave more offspring than individuals with less favorable hereditary materials. In the long run this will allow the population to become increasingly better adapted to its environment.

GUIDE QUESTIONS AND PROBLEMS

1. The nuclei of cells of different organisms undergo a similar process, mitosis, before cell division. What is the basic significance of mitosis that makes it equally important to a radish or a rat?
2. Mitosis is both a process of reproduction and of nuclear division. How are these two processes related?
3. Flemming's work on the division of the nucleus was the basis for scientific observation of the mitotic process. For what reasons has his work continued to be considered of great value?

4. Distinguish between the monoploid and diploid number of chromosomes in cell division.
5. In what ways are mitosis and meiosis expressive of genetic continuity in living organisms?
6. In cancer there is uncontrolled cell division. In what way might an understanding of mitosis contribute to the search for possible causes or cures of cancer?
7. Before scientists had discovered and observed the process of meiosis, they had predicted the occurrence of this type of cell division. How was it possible to predict that meiosis occurred before there was actual evidence for it?
8. If *either* the monoploid or the diploid number of chromosomes will result in an organism with similar physiological and morphological characteristics, what advantages for the organism might be provided by the diploid number of chromosomes?
9. Suppose you are discussing the nature of life with one of your friends who has never studied biology. You first make the statement, "I am a human being because my cells have DNA of the human type." Your friend replies, "Nonsense. You are a human being because your father and mother are human beings." How can this argument be resolved?
10. Are you genetically unique? First consider the number of genetic types of sperms or eggs one parent can produce. If two pairs of homologous chromosomes can yield four genetically different types of sperms or eggs, and three pairs of homologous chromosomes can yield eight genetic types of sperms or eggs, how many genetic types can 23 pairs of homologous chromosomes produce? Express this as a fraction: $1/x$ (the figure you calculate). Now multiply this fraction by itself, since you must calculate the still more unlikely probability that *one particular genetic type of sperm* and *one particular genetic type of egg* will come together at fertilization.

    What you have calculated is only the unlikely possibility that your own parents could produce another you—but even this is not quite correct. There is a process known as crossing-over which results in a single pair of homologous chromosomes producing not four but possibly hundreds of different genetic combinations. In how many of the pairs of chromosomes of your father, then of your mother, could crossing-over occur (or have occurred in the past, perhaps resulting in you!)?

    You should consider all the other parents in the world who possibly could produce sperms or eggs genetically like those that led to you—perhaps involving crossing-over. The low probability that such possible parents exist should be multiplied by the low probability that they might meet and marry. The result can then be multiplied by the probability figure you obtained from considering your own parents. Finally, this product can be added to the probability figure obtained for your parents.

    Obviously you can calculate no further—or even this far!—but perhaps you have reached a conclusion: are you genetically unique?

RELATED READING

Books

For original papers on mitosis . . .

Hall, Thomas S., *A Sourcebook in Animal Biology*, McGraw-Hill, New York, 1951.

For mitosis and meiosis in photomicrographs . . .

McLeish, J., and B. Snoad, *Looking at Chromosomes*, Macmillan, New York, 1958. Excellently illustrated.

For a modern account of cell structure, functions, and processes of cell division . . .

Swanson, C. P., *The Cell*, Second Edition, Prentice-Hall, Englewood Cliffs, N. J., 1964 (cloth or paperback).

Magazines

Mazia, Daniel, "Cell Division," *Scientific American*, Volume 205 (September 1961), page 100.

Baserga, Renato, and W. E. Kisieleski, "Autobiographies of Cells," *Scientific American*, Volume 209 (August 1963), page 103.

8

The Hereditary Materials

Reproduction occurs at several levels in biological systems: 1) individuals can produce other individuals, their children; 2) cells can divide into daughter cells, essentially the same as the parent cells; 3) chromosomes are replicated, producing daughter chromosomes; and, as this chapter will show, 4) some molecules also are replicated.

We should not reach the hasty conclusion that reproduction occurs at all levels of biological organization. A stomach does not divide into two stomachs—one for the parent and one for the baby! Neither do all cell structures reproduce. Mitochondria are believed to, but the nucleolus, the spindle, and the asters are formed anew at each cell reproduction. The nucleolus, for example, disappears early in mitosis; a new one is formed after mitosis.

Individuals, their cells, and cell structures are composed largely of molecules, along with other particles such as ions. In some way all the molecules must reproduce or be produced in new cells and individuals. Let us suppose that a cell has 1,000 molecules each of protein A, fat B, carbohydrate C, and so on. After it divides, and the daughter cells have grown to full size, *each* will have about 1,000 molecules of protein A, of fat B, and of carbohydrate C. Are these new molecules formed from the parent cell's old molecules of the same type, or are they formed in another way? If they are formed by the reproduction of old molecules we might imagine ways in which two daughter molecules would be identical to a parent molecule. At least the original molecule could serve as a model for the daughter molecules. But if the molecules are formed anew—that is, when no similar molecules are present—how are the new molecules made in the proper manner?

Genetic Continuity

Our questions can be made more definite when asked in relation to a specific problem. In Chapter 5 two important protein molecules were mentioned: hemoglobin and insulin. In our bodies hemoglobin is produced only in the red blood cells. Insulin is produced only in cells of the pancreas. Both proteins are essential in our bodies.

Our parents had hemoglobin and insulin, we have hemoglobin and insulin, and our children will have hemoglobin and insulin. Careful study of egg cells and sperm cells, however, would show that neither hemoglobin nor insulin is present. We are left with these observations:

1. The only living materials that link the generations are egg cells and sperm cells.
2. Egg cells and sperm cells do not contain hemoglobin or insulin.
3. As the new individual develops from the fertilized egg (egg cell + sperm cell), some of its cells will begin to make hemoglobin and others to make insulin.

We can only conclude that the egg cell or the sperm cell, or both, must transmit the capacity to make hemoglobin and insulin. Or we may say that they carry the instructions, the "know-how," for making these molecules.

Thus, there must be two kinds of genetic continuity, or transmission from generation to generation (Figure 8-1).

1. *Direct genetic continuity.* Some structures reproduce and pass directly to the daughter cells. Chromosomes are a key example.

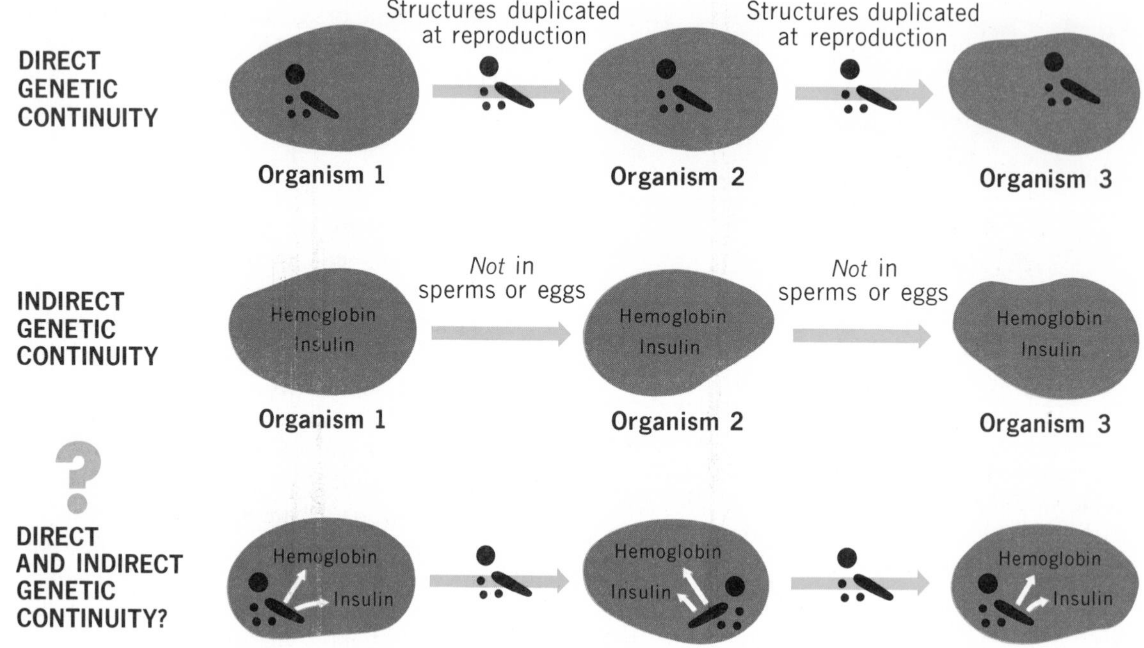

Could the structures that are duplicated at reproduction determine what forms in the next generation?

2. *Indirect genetic continuity.* Some structures appear in every generation, yet are not reproduced and passed on to the daughter cells. Hemoglobin and insulin are examples. You probably can guess that most structures are in this category. Egg cells and sperm cells do not contain hair, teeth, bones, brains, stomachs, arms, or legs. But if these structures are not transmitted directly then *instructions* for producing them must be transmitted.

This argument may seem reasonable enough to you that we can formulate a hypothesis:

A biological mechanism exists that transmits the instructions for making the structures of the succeeding generation.

If there *is* such a mechanism, clearly it is very important. What is it? How does it work? By now you are familiar with one way we obtain answers to our questions. We make deductions from our hypothesis and test these deductions. Let us first make deductions about "What is it?" Later we will use the same methods for "How does it work?"

A SEARCH FOR THE HEREDITARY MATERIAL

If we tentatively accept as true the hypothesis that a biological mechanism exists that transmits hereditary instructions, here are some deductions we can make:

1. *The instructions must be exact.* You have already learned (page 95) how even a small change in the hemoglobin molecule can result in illness or death. Many similar examples could be given.

That is, small changes in proteins and other molecules can abolish or change their normal functions.

2. *The instructions must be permanent and constant.* That is, they are transmitted intact from one generation to another. They are probably in all cells of the individual. Certainly they are in the sperm cells and the egg cells, as suggested by the observation that a child seems to inherit characteristics sometimes from his father and sometimes from his mother.
3. *The instructions must be of the same general kind in all organisms.* This is suggested because inheritance follows the same general rules in all organisms. (Chapter 29 deals with this evidence.)
4. *Only the hereditary instructions should be capable of transmitting all the information for making the individuals of the next generation.*

As you can see, we have used "instructions" interchangeably with "hereditary material." We have assumed that the instructions are a molecule or molecules, present in all cells and transmitted to the next generation in egg cells and sperm cells.

In Flemming's time biologists began to assume that the cell's nucleus had the primary responsibility for inheritance (pages 135-36). Expressed in our modern usage, the nucleus contains the hereditary instructions. This conclusion was based on simple observations and simple experiments. Recall the consequence of cutting a single-celled organism so that one half has the nucleus and the other half does not (Figure 8-2). No matter what other parts of the organism are present, the half without the nucleus dies without reproducing.

So we tentatively assume that the cell's nucleus carries the hereditary instructions. Is the whole nucleus, or some part of it, primarily responsible? A nucleus consists mainly of a nuclear membrane, nucleoli, chromosomes, and a semifluid portion without definite structure. Both the nuclear membrane and the nucleoli seem to disappear during cell division. This also seems true of the semifluid portion of the nucleus. At least it has no structures by which we have been able to trace it after the nuclear membrane disappears. It seems to merge with the cytoplasm of the cell.

8–2 Are the hereditary instructions of a cell carried by the nucleus, the cytoplasm, or by both?

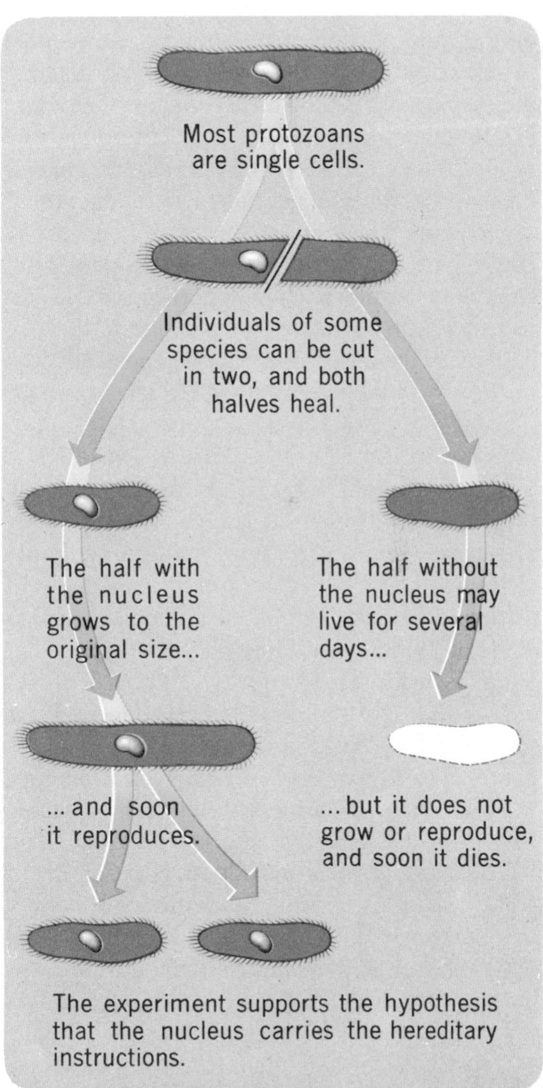

Most protozoans are single cells.
Individuals of some species can be cut in two, and both halves heal.
The half with the nucleus grows to the original size...
The half without the nucleus may live for several days...
... and soon it reproduces.
... but it does not grow or reproduce, and soon it dies.
The experiment supports the hypothesis that the nucleus carries the hereditary instructions.

In contrast to lack of permanence of these parts of the nucleus are the chromosomes. The work of Flemming and those who followed him suggested that chromosomes are permanent cell structures. Although they could not be seen easily (except by use of special techniques) between one mitosis and the next, they were there and were replicated in an exact way before the cell divided. Was this suggestive? Many biologists thought so.

Of course, we have not excluded the possibility that the nuclear membrane, the nucleoli, or the fluid portion of the nucleus is involved in transmitting the hereditary instructions. Neither have we shown that the chromosomes *are* involved. But we have tried to predict the properties of the hereditary material. One of these properties is permanence (deduction 2 preceding). The chromosomes *appear to be* permanent cell structures. The nucleoli, nuclear membrane, and fluid portion of the nucleus *appear not to be*. This suggests that we first study the chromosomes for a possible connection with the hereditary material.

Narrowing the Search – DNA or Protein?

You have read twice before of the composition of chromosomes (pages 123, 135). They are made mainly of protein and deoxyribonucleic acid or DNA. The protein is made up of dozens or hundreds of other molecules – amino acids of 20 different kinds. DNA, on the other hand, is made up of only six kinds of molecules. One is the carbohydrate **deoxyribose** (dee·OKS·ih·ry·bose), a sugar. Another is phosphate. The other four are the bases: **adenine** (ADD·eh·neen), **cytosine** (SY·toh·zeen), **guanine** (GWAH·neen), and **thymine** (THY·meen). You have had a partial introduction to some of these molecules. Adenine and **ribose** (RY·bose – another sugar differing in only one atom from deoxyribose) form adenosine. Adenosine combined with three molecules of phosphate is ATP (Figure 6-7, page 118).

Results of further chemical study of DNA showed that the six basic molecules of which DNA is composed combine in only four specific ways. For example, adenine is always joined to deoxyribose and phosphate:

adenine – deoxyribose – phosphate

The other three types of molecules are:

guanine – deoxyribose – phosphate
cytosine – deoxyribose – phosphate
thymine – deoxyribose – phosphate

These four resulting molecules are collectively called **nucleotides** (NEW·klee·oh·tides). The four individual nucleotides are

adenine nucleotide
guanine nucleotide
cytosine nucleotide
thymine nucleotide

In these early studies, the data suggested that DNA is a very large molecule even though it is composed of only four different sorts of nucleotides. Huge numbers of the nucleotides were thought to be combined in some unknown way to form a DNA molecule.

What could the next step be? We have tentatively made the assumption that the chromosomes are responsible for inheritance. We could modify the hypothesis to ask whether only one of the components of chromosomes, the protein or the DNA, is responsible for inheritance. We have learned a little about the chemistry of each (all that biologists knew until recently). Is there any way that we could decide which type of molecule is the most important in inheritance? If you were to make a guess, you might reason, as did nearly every biologist before 1940, somewhat like this:

1. The hereditary material must carry all of the instructions for the life of a cell. The instructions are probably in the chromosomes.
2. Since the life of a cell is very complex, the instructions must be very complex.
3. DNA is made of only four kinds of nucleotides, but proteins are made of 20 different kinds of amino acids.

4. Since more different kinds of molecules can be made from 20 units than from 4 units, there can be far more different kinds of proteins than DNA. (Think of the huge numbers of words that you could make with an alphabet of 20 letters, compared with the few you could make with an alphabet of 4 letters.)
5. Therefore it is more probable that proteins, rather than DNA, are the hereditary material.

Reasonable, perhaps, but still speculation. At this point in the analysis, progress was determined more by what *could* be done experimentally rather than by what *should* be done. You might have assumed that one should study intensively the proteins of chromosomes. Many biologists tried, even before the turn of this century. But proteins are difficult to analyze—they are so complex, and adequate methods for studying them were not available. Neither were adequate methods for studying DNA available until fairly recently, when methods were developed for accurately measuring DNA even in single nuclei (Figure 8-3). As it happened, DNA then became easier than proteins to study. The *practical* thing to do, therefore, was to go ahead and study DNA until more suitable methods for studying proteins became available.

A staining technique had been discovered to stain chromosomes. The stain used is basic **fuchsin** (FOOK·sin). Later analysis showed that it stained specifically for DNA, in a reaction that is known as the **Feulgen** (FOIL·ghen) **reaction.** Cells could be treated chemically in such a way that the deoxyribose combined with the stain. The combination between the sugar and the purplish stain was strictly quantitative—that is, the more deoxyribose, the more deeply the cells would be stained. The amount of stain in a cell, therefore, would be a measure of the amount of DNA.

As studies were carried out, all or nearly all of the stain was found to be localized in the nucleus. Eventually a method was developed to measure the amount of stain in nuclei by means of a microscope with a photoelectric cell fitted over the eyepiece. A meter in the setup registers the amount of electric current produced by the photoelectric cell as light coming up through the microscope strikes it. The greater the amount of deoxyribose in the nuclei of cells, the more densely the nuclei are stained and the more light they absorb (that is, the less light can be transmitted through the microscope to the photoelectric cell, and the less current is produced). The amount of light absorbed by the nuclei is taken as the measure of the deoxyribose present. Fortunately, deoxyribose is found only in DNA, and always in a definite proportion to the other components of DNA.

8–3 Amount of DNA in the Nucleus for Different Kinds of Cells

Tissue and Organism	*Amount of DNA* (in billionths of milligrams)
Red blood cells	
Chicken	2.3
Carp	3.3
Shad	2.0
Liver cells	
Dog	5.3
Pig	5.2
Chicken	2.4
Beef	6.4
Carp	3.3
Shad	2.0
Kidney cells	
Chicken	2.4
Beef	6.4
Pig	5.2
Pancreas cells	
Chicken	2.6
Beef	6.6
Sperm cells	
Chicken	1.3
Beef	3.3
Carp	1.6
Shad	0.9

Therefore, a measure for deoxyribose also measures DNA. In another approach against which the Feulgen reaction could be checked, biologists learned to extract DNA directly and measure its amount. You can try this in Laboratory Inquiry 8-1.

Look back again at the data biologists obtained for the amounts of DNA in different kinds of nuclei (Figure 8-3). The amounts of DNA vary widely. Do you see any general relations? Possibly not. Now try this: arrange the data on a sheet of paper *according to kinds of organisms* rather than kinds of cells. That is, put all measurements for chicken cells together, then beef cells, and so on. Now do you see any relations between the amounts of DNA in cells? Is there a relation between the amount of DNA in sperm cells and in other cells *of the same kind of animal?* As you answer these questions, consider what you learned in Chapter 7 about the numbers of chromosomes in sperm cells and in other cells in the body. Do you find evidence of *constancy* and *permanence* in DNA? Reread the second deduction on page 149 and decide if DNA can be considered further as the possible hereditary material.

Probably you have decided that this is most interesting and suggestive. A far more critical experiment was yet to be made, however.

Today we hear a great deal about the exceedingly small organisms we know as *viruses* (Figure 8-4). Some cause diseases in animals and plants. Some even cause disease in bacteria; these particular viruses are known as **bacteriophage** (bac·TER·ih·o·fayj), or more simply as **phage** (FAYJ) **viruses.** A number of different strains of phage viruses attack colon bacteria (so-called because they are common in the human colon, a part of the large intestine). Figure 8-5 shows photographic evidence of this process. In the upper photograph the tiny virus particles attack a large bacterium. Somewhat later the bodies of bacteria are seen to contain many virus particles—as in the lower photograph. Still later the bacterium bursts and liberates many phage viruses.

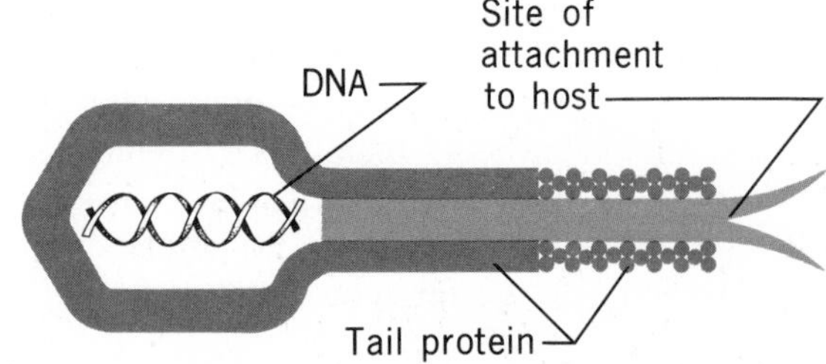

8–4 A diagram of the structure of a phage virus. In what way does the virus resemble a chromosome?

The electron microscope made possible this photographic evidence. For our purposes one of the important points of the evidence is this: for every virus particle that enters a bacterial cell, many are released when the cell bursts. Tests would show that the daughter viruses are the same as the parent viruses. Thus there has been reproduction and genetic continuity of the viruses.

A phage is almost diagrammatic in its simplicity. There is an outer coat of protein and an inner core of DNA—nothing more except a simple "tail" composed of several additional proteins (Figure 8-4). Yet even this simple organism transmits instructions for "how to make a virus." We have to reach this conclusion because the daughter viruses are like the parent viruses.

Since the phage virus, not unlike chromosomes, is composed only of protein and DNA, we can ask whether the protein or the DNA is responsible (or whether both are) for the transmission of the instructions. We were trying to answer this question for the chromosomes, but so far we have found no way. Perhaps we can for the virus, using some information from Chapter 5. There you were introduced to the idea of slightly different atoms of the same element—isotopes. Some isotopes are radioactive and can be detected by instruments that measure radioactivity. For example, there is a radioisotope of sulfur called S^{35}, and one of phosphorus known as P^{32}.

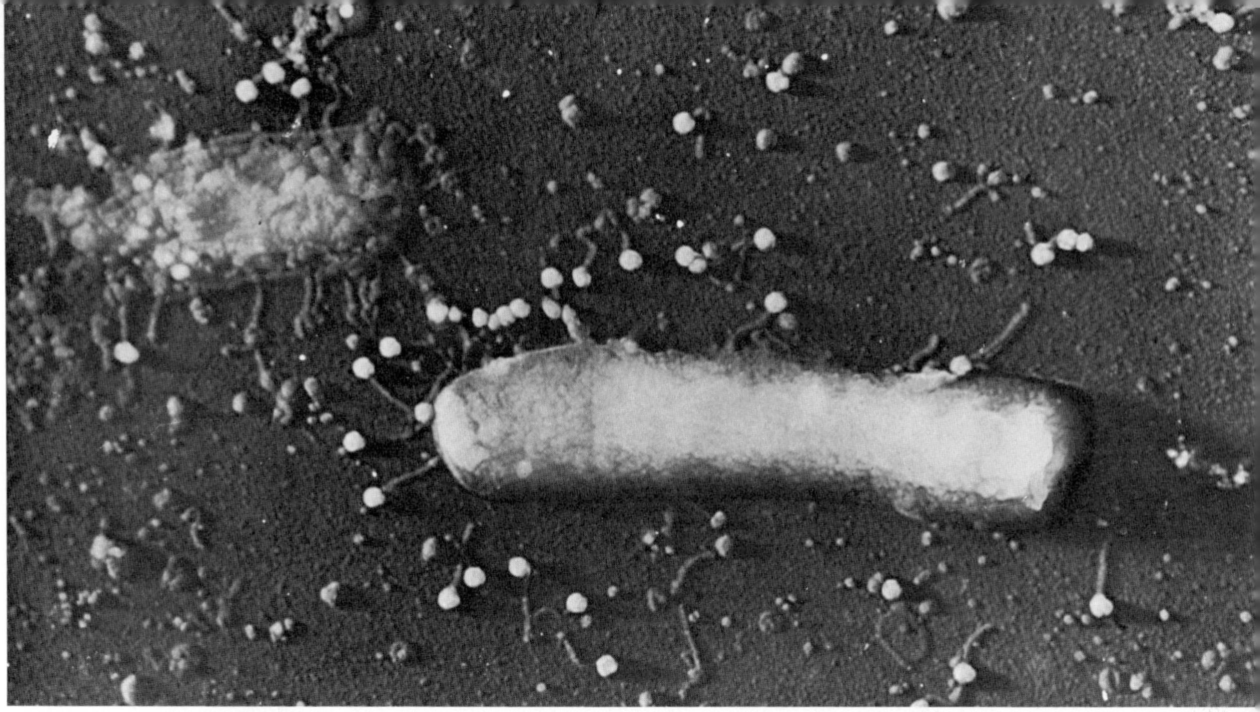

G. Penso

8–5 Two electron micrographs of stages in virus replication. **(Top)** Phage viruses attached by their tailpieces to a bacterium. Note the remains of another bacterium destroyed by the viruses. (30,000 ×) **(Bottom)** A very thin section through a bacterium containing reproducing phage viruses. Heads of new viruses appear black. (55,000 ×)

E. Kellenberger

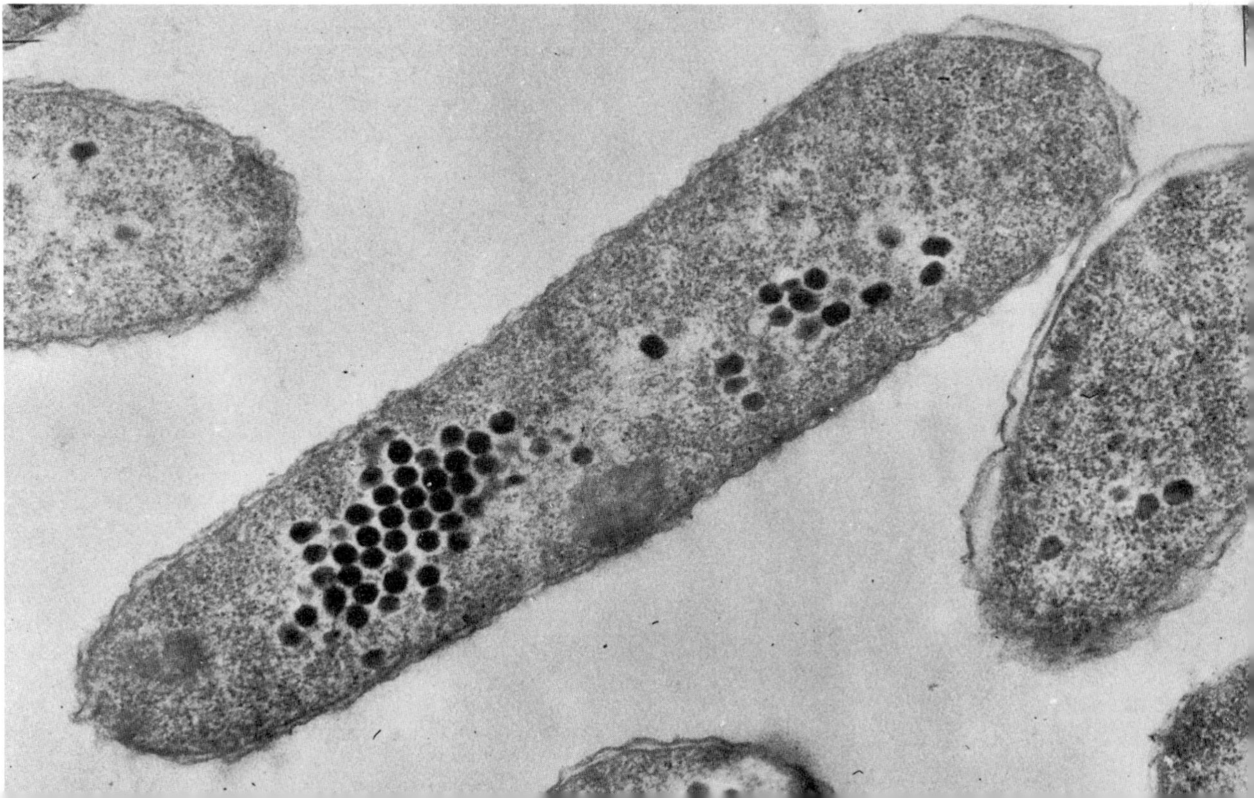

8-6 IDENTIFICATION OF THE HEREDITARY MATERIAL OF PHAGE VIRUSES

Part of the material of phage viruses enters bacteria and reproduces. Radioisotopes were used to investigate further.

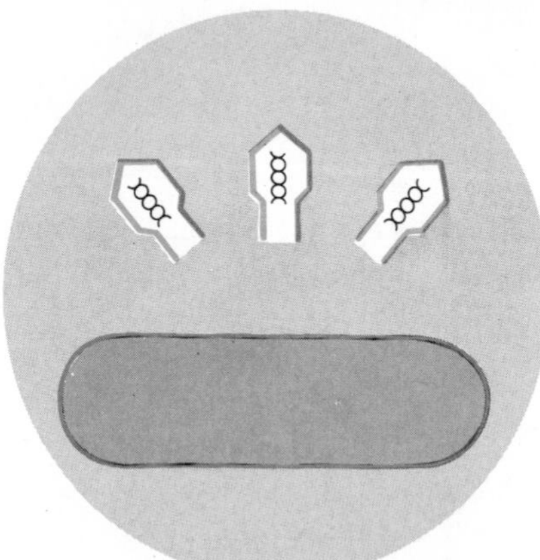

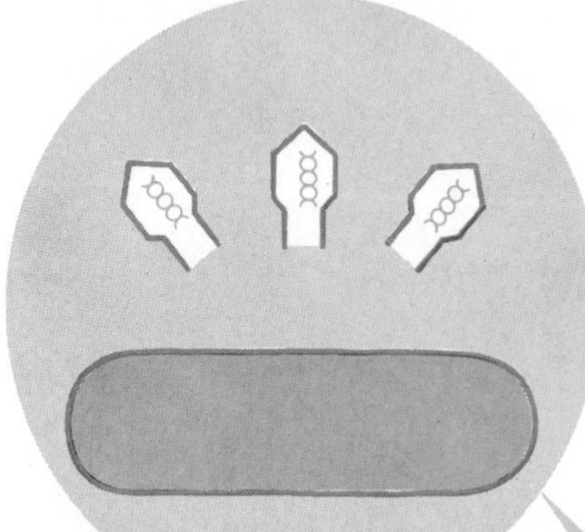

Bacteria were exposed to phage with S^{35}–labelled protein coats.

Other bacteria were exposed to phage with P^{32}–labelled DNA cores.

(Bacteria washed after contact with phage)

The bacteria did not become radioactive, implying that infection of the bacteria is not caused by phage protein coats.

The bacteria became radioactive, implying that infection of the bacteria is caused by injection of the DNA cores of the phage.

Visual evidence on this small scale was difficult to acquire, even with the electron microscope. The events were first demonstrated indirectly, with radioisotopes.

A visual model for what occurred

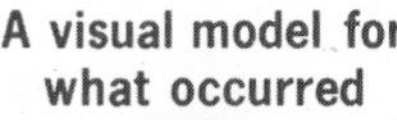

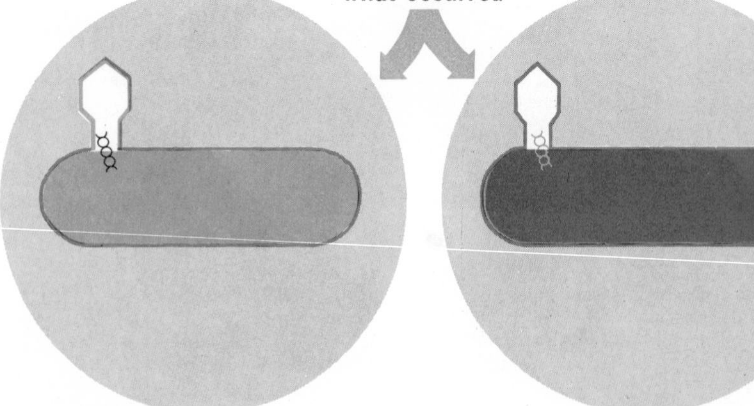

Sulfur occurs in protein but not in DNA. Fortunately, phosphorus occurs in DNA but not in protein. If phage viruses are allowed to grow in the presence of S^{35}, their protein coats, but not their DNA, will contain some of this isotope. Alternatively, if they are allowed to grow in the presence of P^{32}, their DNA, but not their protein coats, will be labeled with this isotope. It is possible, therefore, to label separately the protein coat and the DNA. We could use this method to determine whether phage DNA, or proteins, or both, enter the bacterial cell. If only DNA or proteins, but not both, enter the cell, the one that enters must be responsible for the transmission of hereditary information.

The experiment was done (Figure 8-6). First, phage with protein coats labeled with S^{35} were allowed to infect bacterial cells. In a second experiment phage with their DNA cores labeled with P^{32} were allowed to infect bacterial cells. A sufficient period of time was allowed for the phage to reproduce in the bacterial cells, but not enough time for the cells to burst. Then the bacterial cells were washed to remove any phage that might not have entered. Finally the radioactivity was measured.

The results were clear-cut. The bacteria that had been infected with the S^{35}-labeled phage were *not* radioactive. On the other hand, the bacteria that had been infected with the P^{32}-labeled phage were highly radioactive.

What was one to conclude? These data suggested that *only* the DNA of the phage enters the bacterial cell. The protein coat must be left on the outside. This belief was confirmed by studies with the electron microscope. It was found that the phage attaches to the wall of the bacterial cell. The protein coat remains on the outside, but the DNA core passes into the bacterial cell, as suggested by Figure 8-6. Within the bacterial cell it reproduces: more virus DNA and more virus protein coats are made. Since the DNA alone is sufficient to bring about these syntheses, it must transmit the hereditary characteristics!

This experiment, carried out jointly by Alfred Hershey and Martha Chase at the Cold Spring Harbor Biological Laboratory, New York, was one of the most important in biology in our century. It showed that DNA is the material of heredity in these phage viruses. Biologists rapidly extended this conclusion to other organisms as well. This far-reaching study was made possible by the cooperation of a great many people—numerous biologists who worked on viruses, other biologists who worked on bacteria, geneticists concerned with all the problems of inheritance, physicists and chemists who prepared the isotopes, and engineers who made the instruments for measuring radioactivity. Nor should we forget the administrators who were willing to devote large sums to the research before knowing how it would turn out, or whether it would be that important. This *does* take vision and courage, for in one respect it must seem foolish to offer large sums of money for research on sick bacteria!

Last, but not least, we must pay our respects to the phage virus. If it so happened that the *entire* virus, coat and core, entered the bacterial cell, we could never have reached our important conclusion. All we could have said is that either DNA, or protein, or both, were the carriers of the hereditary instructions. But the virus leaves its coat at the door, so to speak, and so makes it possible to answer a most important question in biology.

The tiny viruses, too small to be observed without the electron microscope, yield important biological data partly *because* they are so simple in their organization. They have become extremely valuable organisms in research, and you should begin your own laboratory study of them at this time. Laboratory Inquiry 8-2 is a good place to start. Chapter 9 will have additional material on viruses, but you will want to undertake your investigations of these simple organisms without delay, if possible, in order to have the amounts of time you will need to devote to your studies.

DNA—The Answer and the Problem

We can now work with the hypothesis:

DNA transmits the hereditary instructions.

If this is so, DNA must fulfill all four of the deductions that were made for the composition of the biological mechanism that transmits the instructions (pages 148-49):

Deduction 1 concerned the exactness of the instructions. So far we have not been able to investigate this deduction. We need to know how the molecules of DNA are constructed, and how faithfully the construction is replicated when a cell divides.

Deduction 2 concerned the permanence and constancy of the hereditary material. This now is answered with a high degree of certainty. The data of the table in Figure 8-3 (page 151) suggest that the different cells of the same species contain the same amount of DNA. There is, however, an interesting exception. Sperm cells contain only half the amount. We know also that sperm cells contain the monoploid number of chromosomes instead of the diploid number as with other cells. Thus, the quantity of DNA parallels the quantity of chromosomes.

Deduction 3 concerned the general occurrence of the instructions in all organisms. Again, the data of the table in Figure 8-3 suggest DNA may be present in all types of cells, or at least animal cells. This deduction can be checked for any cells we wish to investigate. (Indeed it *has* been checked by biologists for cells of many kinds of plants, animals, and microorganisms.)

Deduction 4 concerned the ability of the hereditary materials alone to transmit the instructions. This was shown to be true in the case of phage viruses. Our evidence is based on the experiment conducted by Hershey and Chase (Figure 8-6); they found that the DNA alone enters the bacterial cell with the instructions, "How to make a virus."

These data and arguments seemed to make a very strong case for DNA being the material of inheritance. But remember we have attacked only half the problem (page 148). Possibly we have discovered the answer to "What is it?" but not to "How does it work?" Some of the additional deductions we could make concerning the way the hereditary material must function are

5. *There must be a mechanism for reproducing the instructions exactly at each cell division.* Why do we make this deduction? We know that all of the instructions are present in the fertilized egg. The fertilized egg divides repeatedly to give all the cells of the adult. Some of the adult's cells will become sperm cells or egg cells. The simplest way of accounting for all this is to assume that the instructions must be in the cells *at all times* and be reproduced, in some way, when the cell divides.
6. *Cells must have mechanisms giving them the capacity to follow the instructions.* Thus, if the instructions say: make a molecule of hemoglobin, the cell must have, or be able to obtain, the materials and to have the tools required.
7. *Although the instructions must be reproduced exactly nearly all of the time, there must be a basis for errors.* We know that mutations are errors.

Thus, we must discover how the hereditary material can be reproduced exactly, how it transmits its message in the cell, and how it mutates. Before we can answer any of these questions we must know far more about the composition of the hereditary material. It is not enough merely to know that it is DNA. We must know the structure of DNA before we can understand how it can reproduce, how it can act, and how it can change.

Let us begin with the awesome problem: how can a cell begin with DNA and make two molecules exactly like the original molecule?

THE QUESTION OF REPLICATION —HOW IS IT DONE?

The important advances now to be described were made by two young scientists who used little more than their brains, paper, and pencils. They were J. D. Watson, now at Harvard University, and F. H. C. Crick, at Cambridge University in England.

When Watson and Crick began their work, biologists had much data suggesting that DNA was the hereditary material. No one knew the structure of the DNA molecule, however. These were the principal observations Watson and Crick had to work with:

1. DNA is made up of four nucleotides—the adenine, guanine, cytosine, and thymine nucleotides.
2. The available chemical data suggested that the nucleotides are joined to form long strands. Normally these strands occur in pairs, forming a double strand.
3. This double strand of DNA is far too small to be seen with an optical microscope. X-ray studies, however, suggested that it has a uniform diameter.
4. The available data also indicated that the nucleotides of each long strand are joined together as shown below:

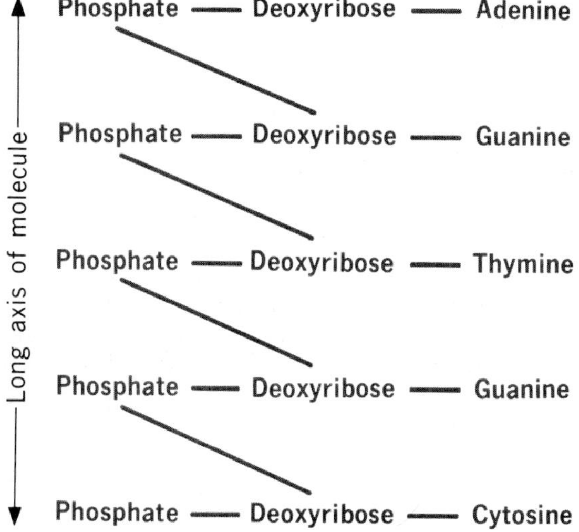

We might think of DNA as a long line of nucleotides, joined by the deoxyriboses and phosphates. The bases—adenine, guanine, cytosine, and thymine—would then be sticking out on the side.

The problem for Watson and Crick was to show how the double strand of DNA could be constructed. How could all the nucleotides be made to fit together to form a double strand of uniform diameter? It became necessary for them to know the sizes of the nucleotides. The phosphates in the four nucleotides are the same size. So are the sugars. But this is not true of the four bases (Figure 8-7). Cytosine and thymine are small; they are compounds of a type known as **pyrimidines** (pih·RIM·ih·deenz). Adenine and guanine are larger; they are **purines** (PURE·eens). These four bases join with deoxyribose and phosphate (as shown for one of the four bases in Figure 8-8) to form the nucleotides. Thus the nucleotides containing cytosine and thymine are smaller than the nucleotides containing adenine and guanine.

You can take the next step. Place a piece of paper over Figure 8-8 and make a rectangle by drawing two parallel lines, one below the bottom OH and H of the deoxyribose and the other above the top NH_2 of the adenine. Draw two other parallel lines (these will be perpendicular to the first two), one to the left of the HO group at the left of the phosphate and the other to the right of the CH on the right side of the adenine. Cut out the rectangle and label it "adenine nucleotide."

Next make rectangles for the other three nucleotides. This will require that you replace the adenine in Figure 8-8 with cytosine, thymine, and guanine from Figure 8-7. The guanine should be joined to the deoxyribose by the N at the lower left of the molecule. The cytosine and the thymine should be joined by the N at the bottom of each molecule.

The four rectangles you have made will indicate roughly the sizes of the four nucleotides. Make and label three copies of each.

Cytosine

Thymine

Adenine

Guanine

8–7 Comparative diagrams of the four bases that are equivalent parts of the four different nucleotides in DNA. The bases fall roughly into two sizes, the smaller pyrimidines (cytosine and thymine), and the larger purines (adenine and guanine).

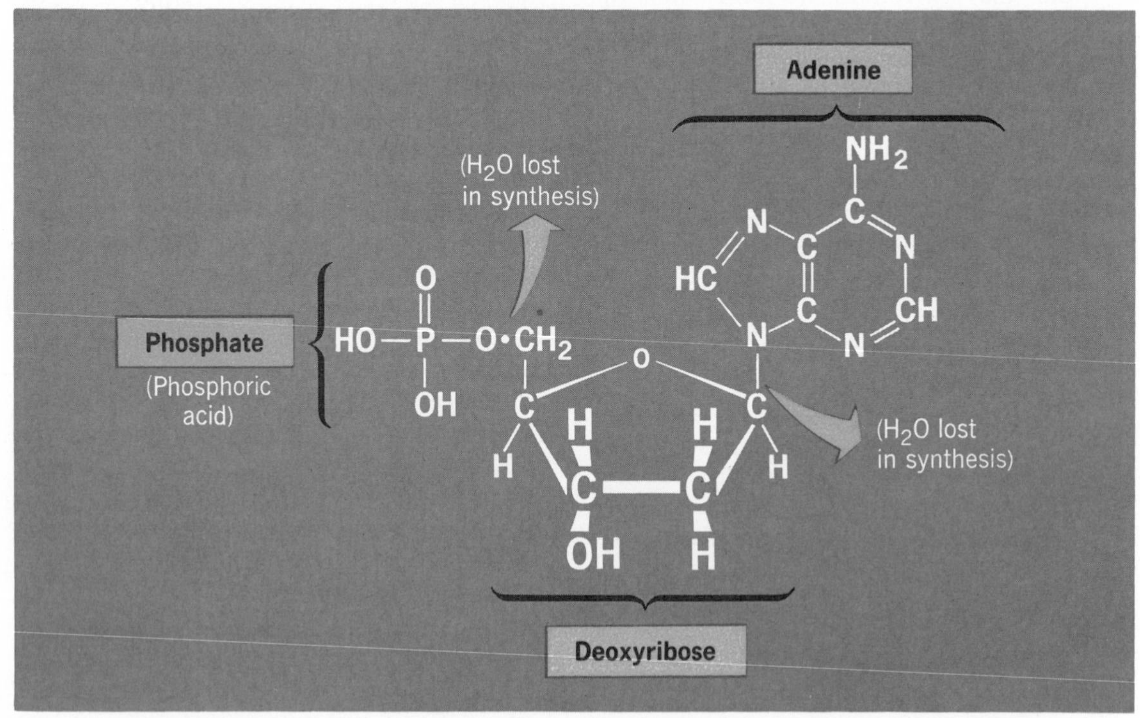

8–8 A diagram of a nucleotide containing adenine. This and the three other kinds of nucleotides (with guanine, cytosine, and thymine, respectively) are the components of DNA. Each nucleotide is synthesized from three molecules: a base (such as adenine), the sugar deoxyribose, and phosphoric acid. Enzymes control the synthesis.

Let us try to put together the parts of the puzzle. Remember the data indicated that DNA is a double strand *of uniform diameter.* Now try arranging your cutouts in two parallel rows with the longer side of each rectangular cutout kept at right angles to the direction of the rows. Arrange to have the cutouts of the right and left rows meet in the center.

How can the cutouts be arranged so that the width of the two rows is always the same? You should soon find that the cutout that you have in one row will determine what can be opposite it in the parallel row. List all the possibilities as hypotheses—remembering to keep the total width of the two rows constant.

Test your hypotheses one by one. Here are some hints. Suppose you have found that if nucleotide A is in one vertical row, the other vertical row can have either nucleotide C or D (we will not use the names of the nucleotides since that would give the game away). There would then be these possibilities:

1. If A is in one row then C must be in the other.

or, 2. If A is in one row then D must be in the other.

or, 3. If A is in one row then C *or* D must be in the other.

Using this approach, work out the possibilities for the four nucleotides.

How can we determine which possibility is correct? Eventually we will need data, but it is not yet obvious what data we need.

Let us try possibility 1 as a hypothesis. If A is *always* paired with C and C with A, what deduction can you make about the relative amounts of A and C? Write this down.

On to possibility 2. If A and D are always paired with each other, what deduction can you make about the relative amounts of A and D? Write this down.

Finally, if A is always paired with C *or* D, what deduction can you make about the relative amounts of A and of C+D? Write this down.

To test these deductions we need data on the amounts of the four nucleotides, or even of their bases, in a variety of cells. Such data are given in the table in Figure 8-9. Once

8–9 Percent of Adenine, Guanine, Thymine, and Cytosine Molecules in Different Cells

Tissue and Organism	*Adenine*	*Guanine*	*Thymine*	*Cytosine*
Thymus cells				
Man	30.9	19.9	29.4	19.8
Sheep	29.3	21.4	28.3	21.0
Pig	30.9	19.9	29.4	19.8
Spleen cells				
Man	29.2	21.0	29.4	20.4
Sheep	28.0	22.3	28.6	21.1
Pig	29.6	20.4	29.2	20.8
Liver cells				
Man	30.3	19.5	30.3	19.9
Sheep	29.3	20.7	29.2	20.8
Pig	29.4	20.5	29.7	20.5
Sperm cells				
Man	30.7	19.3	31.2	18.8
Sheep	28.8	22.0	27.2	21.0
Colon bacterium	26.0	24.9	23.9	25.2
Yeast	31.3	18.7	32.9	17.1

again, there are lots of numbers, but our task is *to find relationships*. It may be wise to re-arrange these data according to species. So first copy down the values for man alone. Do you find any relation between the percentages of the different molecules? Are there pairs of similar percentages? If you find a seemingly constant relation for man, does this also hold for the sheep, pig, colon bacterium, and yeast? These data will tell you which of your deductions can be correct.

Hopefully you have followed this long, and not very easy, analysis. If so, you may now have the answer to the way the nucleotides are arranged in the double strands of DNA. Watson and Crick were awarded the Nobel prize for being the first to reach the answer.

You should not read beyond this point unless you are satisfied with your solution to the problem of the structure of DNA. If you have difficulties, you may overcome them in a classroom discussion. Scientists, too, discuss problems with one another. A fellow scientist may suggest new experiments to try, different interpretations of data, or even an entirely fresh way of looking at a problem. The same can happen in your classroom.

The Watson-Crick Model of DNA

Let us try to summarize the data and hypotheses.

Taking into account all the facts known at the time, Watson and Crick proposed their model for the structure of DNA. X-ray analysis strongly suggested that the DNA molecule consists of two strands twisted about one another in the form of a double **helix** (HEE·lix). A double helix can best be pictured by imagining a ladder as shown in Figure 8-10.

Now let us unwind the ladder and take a closer look at its parts. In Figure 8-11, the key shows us that the uprights of such a ladder are made entirely of the phosphate and deoxyribose portions of the nucleotides. The "rungs" are made only of the purines and pyrimidines. Each rung consists of a purine matched with a pyrimidine. Adenine is always paired with thymine; guanine is always paired with cytosine.

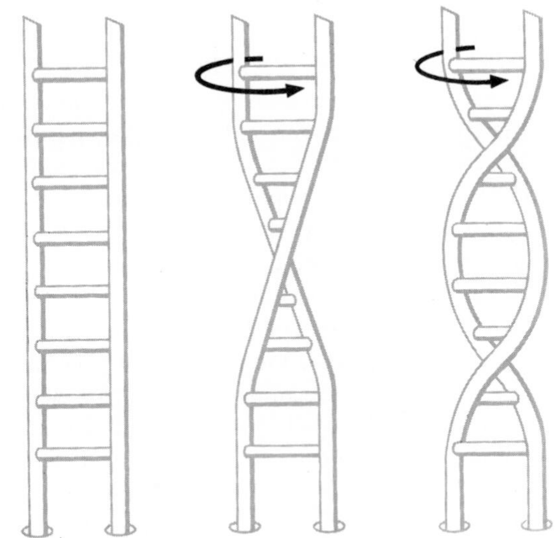

8–10 A model of DNA structure can be made with a flexible ladder. As the ladder is twisted it comes to assume the double helix form of a portion of a DNA molecule. The nucleotides in the double helix are identified in Figure 8–11.

Thus when the order of nucleotides is established for one side of the ladder, the order on the other side will follow of necessity: an adenine nucleotide must *always* pair with a thymine nucleotide; and a guanine nucleotide must *always* pair with a cytosine nucleotide. Notice, too, that the uprights of the ladder—the backbone of the molecule—are the same along the entire length: an almost endless repetition of . . . deoxyribose-phosphate-deoxyribose-phosphate. . . . The *distinctive* part of each DNA molecule is the particular sequence of purine and pyrimidine groups.

According to the Watson-Crick model, then, the DNA molecule is made of two strands wound about one another. The two strands are held together by weak bonds between each purine and its pyrimidine partner. Even though each of these bonds is weak, there are thousands of them. Thus the total force of these weak bonds holds the two strands together.

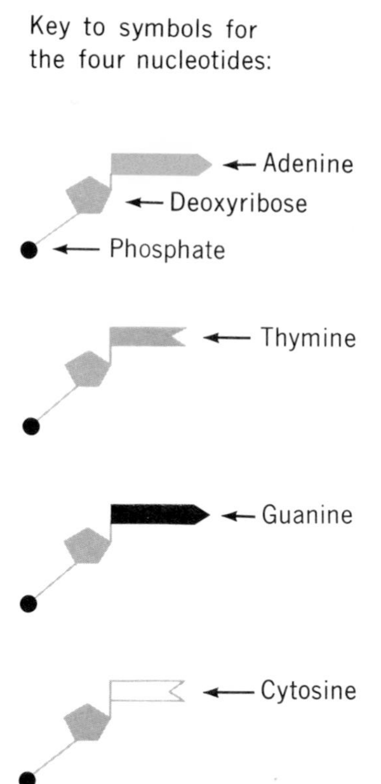

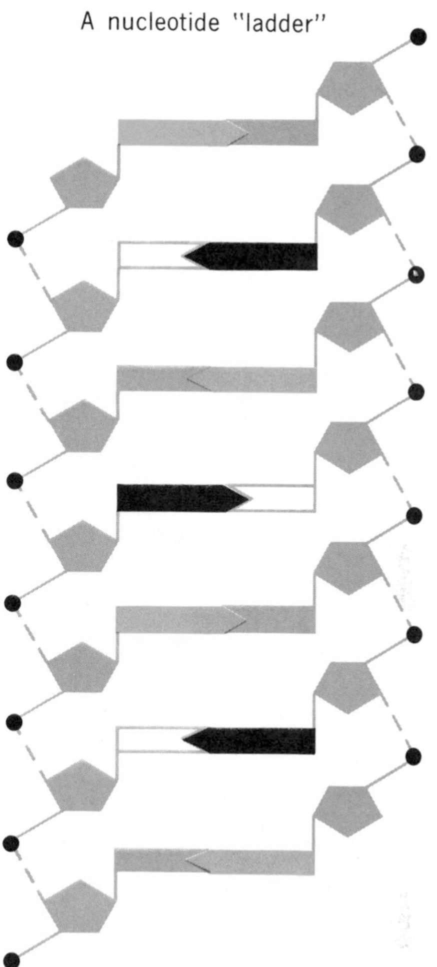

8–11 Another model of a small part of a DNA molecule, unwound for your study. The ladder of Figure 8–10 is now a nucleotide ladder. The dash lines represent bonds between nucleotides.

The Direct Replication of DNA

The data we have gathered suggests strongly that DNA carries the hereditary instructions. If this is so, DNA must meet deduction 5 (page 156), having to do with exact reproduction. But before we could consider how it might reproduce, we needed to know what it is. The Watson-Crick model fits the known chemical properties of DNA. Can we use this model to propose a mechanism for the reproduction of DNA?

We know that both the nature and the amount of DNA in similar kinds of cells remain constant from generation to generation. This means that our mechanism must insure that both the *quantity* and *quality* of the DNA be duplicated in cells derived from the same parent cells. The puzzle is this: how can we get two identical DNA molecules—each one a double helix—starting with only one such molecule?

It is very hard to imagine how it can happen unless first the two coils of the DNA molecule somehow come apart. Suppose the weak forces that hold together the double helix of DNA are released, starting from the ends like a zipper. One by one, each purine then separates from its pyrimidine partner. Each separation leaves an unmatched purine and pyrimidine, which can be "satisfied," or complemented, only by the addition of the proper partner of

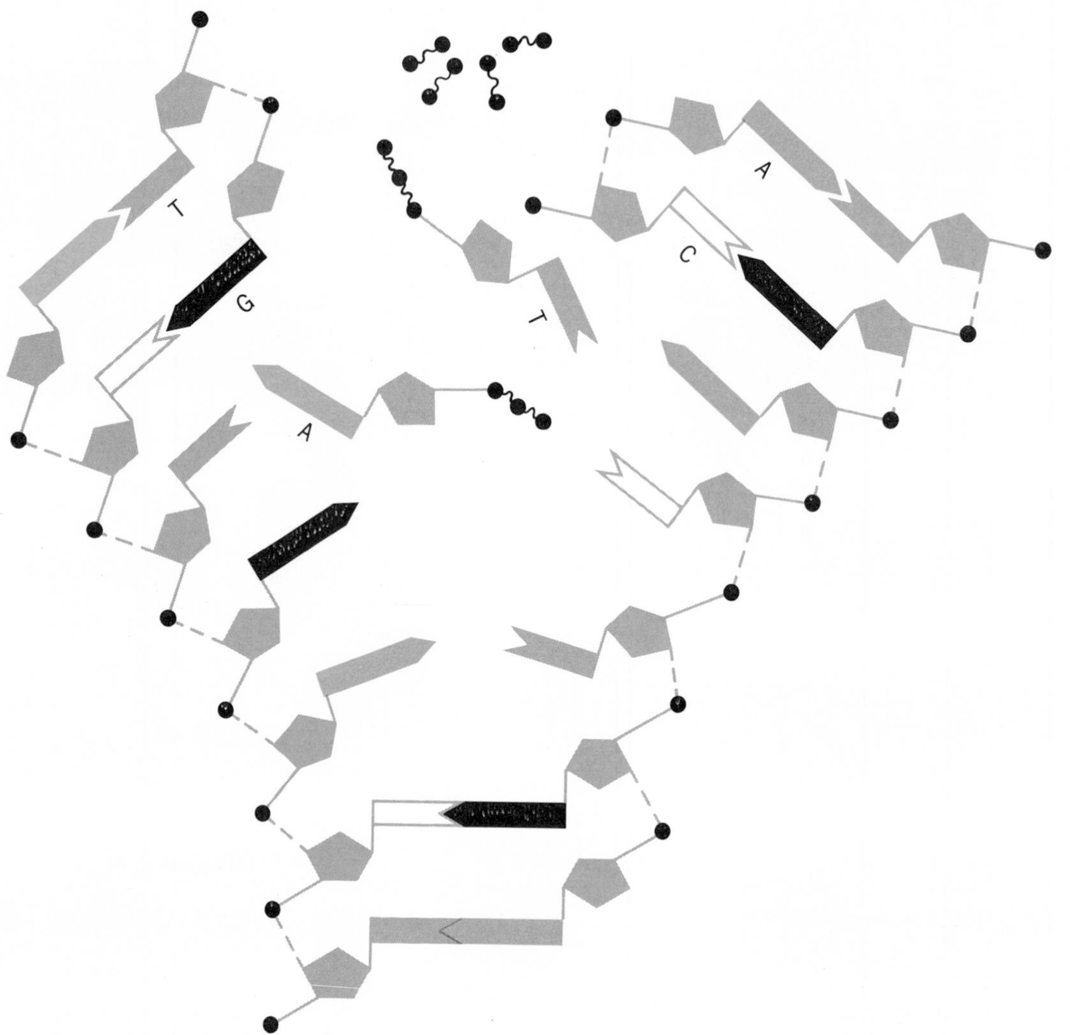

8–12 A diagram of the replication of DNA (see Figure 8–11). The two strands of the DNA molecule begin to "unzip," and new nucleotides of the proper kind are brought into place. Each new nucleotide initially has *three* phosphate groups, as you are familiar with in ATP. The extra phosphate groups are split off, yielding energy that is used in bonding the nucleotides to one another in the two new sequences.

the same kind as before. How this process would proceed is shown in Figure 8-12. An adenine group would make a new bond only with a new thymine group, and a guanine only with a cytosine. In the cell's storehouse of raw materials, there are a variety of nucleotides, each like ATP with three phosphate groups. These would be used to make the new DNA. A *new* nucleotide of the proper kind for each vacant position would then fall into place.

Little by little the double spiral would continue to "unzip" along its length, and each new nucleotide of the proper kind—the only kind able to make the proper bonding—would be added to the separated chains (Figure 8-12). The extra phosphate groups on the new nu-

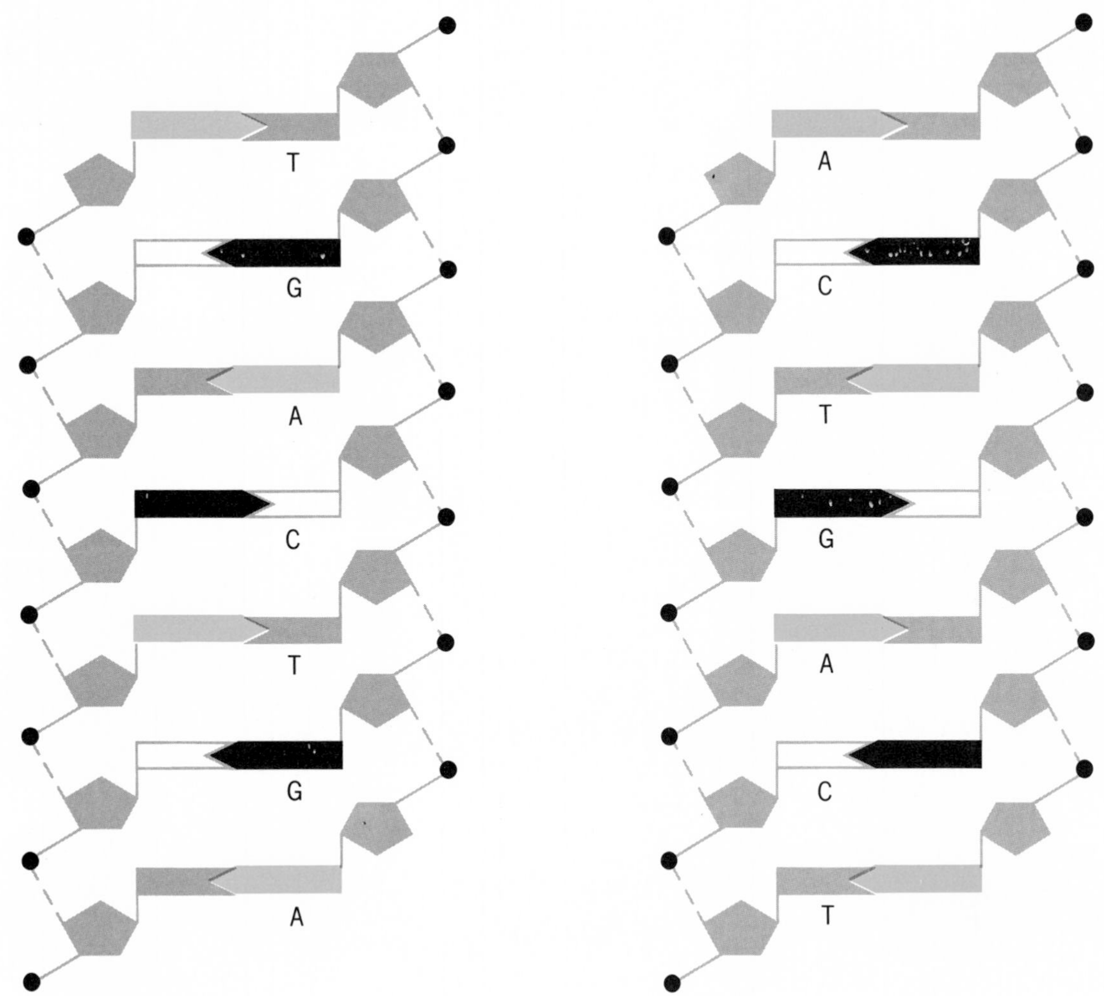

8–13 The replication process undergone by the DNA of Figure 8–12 has now been completed. The two *new* nucleotide sequences are labeled here and in Figure 8–12 with the letters of their purine (A and G) and pyrimidine (C and T) components. Examine both of the replicated DNA double strands. Are they identical? How do these two double strands of DNA compare with the original portion of the molecule in Figure 8–11?

cleotides would be split off, and the energy used in attaching the deoxyribose group of one nucleotide to the phosphate group of the next nucleotide. Through these steps, closely controlled by enzyme molecules, a new upright would be supplied for each ladder.

By the time the end of the spiral is reached, the two *original* strands of the DNA will have separated. Each strand will have replaced the nucleotide partners it has lost with new ones of exactly the same kind (Figure 8-13).

Now we come to the test of the model and the hypothesis. Have we formed *two* double strands where we had but *one* before? Look very carefully at both of these new molecules (Figure 8-13) to see if they are *exactly* like the original molecule (Figure 8-11). If we compare the new products with the original, we see that indeed we have been able to manufacture two *exact* replicas of the original, by using the model. Thus our *replication* process, based on the Watson-Crick model, has met its first test: it is able to provide an explanation of how a huge, complicated molecule can be copied exactly (deduction 5 on page 156). Every descendant cell will get an *exact* copy of the hereditary instructions of its parent cell.

The best evidence that this is what really happens as the DNA of the chromosomes is replicated was supplied by a very ingenious experiment reported in 1958 by two young Americans, M. Meselson and F. W. Stahl, working at the California Institute of Technology. They used a heavy isotope of nitrogen (N^{15}) to label nucleotides made by bacteria while the bacteria were reproducing (and thus making new DNA molecules). There are nitrogen atoms in both the purines and the pyrimidines, so that after many generations, the bacterial DNA became heavier than normal, and this was possible to measure. Next the bacteria with heavy DNA were supplied with ordinary nitrogen (N^{14}), from which they synthesized all their nucleotides. *After one cell division, all the new bacteria had DNA that was exactly halfway in weight between the heavy DNA and ordinary DNA.* Each new strand of DNA that was made in the replication process therefore must have been "light"; and each new molecule of DNA must have consisted of a double helix made up of one light strand and one heavy strand. In the next cell division half the bacteria had one heavy and one light strand; the other half, two light strands. This is exactly what the model of the DNA molecule and its replication predicts.

In Figures 8-11, 8-12, and 8-13, let us assume that the original strands have purines and pyrimidines with heavy nitrogen in them. The nucleotides of the new strands that are made have the letters A, G, C, T shown for them in Figures 8-12 and 8-13. Let us assume further that these new strands have light nitrogen in them. See if you can make a diagram to represent the results found by Meselson and Stahl in the next cell division. Start with one half of the diagram of Figure 8-13, and remember to use light-weight nucleotides (letters A, G, C, T added) as raw material for the replication.

FUNCTION AND CHANGE IN THE HEREDITARY INSTRUCTIONS

We have found in DNA a substance that will account for nearly all of the requirements for the hereditary instructions. We have considered all of the deductions (pages 148-49 and 156) except 1, 6, and 7. We must postpone Number 1 until Chapter 31. Number 6 is the problem "How do the hereditary instructions act in cells?" Number 7 is the problem "How do the hereditary instructions change or mutate?"

Let us raise a typical problem about the action of the hereditary instructions. If a person inherits from his parents the instructions for brown eyes, how are brown eyes made? The problem is certainly very complex from a biochemical standpoint. Somehow the instructions in the **iris** cells of the eye are able to organize the chemicals that form dark pigment, which in turn is deposited in a particular concentration; the result is brown iris color.

Another person might inherit the instructions for blue eyes. Blue eyes do not contain a blue pigment; the iris appears blue because longer wavelengths of light are absorbed and shorter wavelengths are reflected back from the framework of the iris.

When we discuss the specific things that the hereditary instructions do—for example, control the formation of brown eyes or blue eyes—we have a useful term, **gene** (JEEN). Thus the portions of the hereditary material that control the formation of brown eyes are known as genes for brown eyes. Similarly, the portions that control the formation of blue eyes are known as genes for blue eyes.

Gene Action in *Neurospora*

It is difficult to trace the actions of as many genes, or different portions of hereditary material, as are involved in a structure as complicated as a brown or blue eye in a large and complex organism. It is easier to obtain information about gene action at the cellular level, as in microorganisms. Bread molds are an example. The salmon-pink bread mold *Neurospora* (new·ROS·po·ra) has been widely used for such studies. This mold grows luxuriantly in a test tube containing only a dilute mixture of salts, some table sugar, and one vitamin—**biotin** (BY·oh·tin). It reproduces by producing spores. Each tiny spore can grow into a new colony of the mold. You may be familiar with *Neurospora* or similar molds from Laboratory Inquiries 1-1 and 2-1.

If we analyze this mold chemically, we find that the mature organism consists of a whole range of complex proteins, carbohydrates, fats, a large number of vitamins, nucleic acids, pigment, and so on. The mold evidently synthesizes for itself, from the simple raw materials in the test tube, a large number of very complex chemical compounds. Furthermore, these compounds are put together in a particular way, for each individual mold organism closely resembles, in its chemical composition, the parent mold that originally supplied the spores. This again is genetic continuity.

In the 1940's it was learned that microorganisms may lose some of their synthesizing abilities. That is, the hereditary instructions (or genes) become so changed, by mutation, that they no longer can direct the normal syntheses. The affected or **mutant** (MEW·tant) genes result in mutant *Neurospora* being produced. G. W. Beadle and E. L. Tatum at Stanford University, California, treated spores of *Neurospora* with X rays or ultraviolet rays and tested the treated spores to determine if they had been changed in any way. Beadle and Tatum were particularly interested to see if any of the abilities of the mold to synthesize complex organic substances had been impaired.

They found mutant spores that could not grow at all on the usual medium. These spores could survive, however, if nutritional supplements, such as amino acids and vitamins, were added to the medium.

Over a period of time, Beadle and Tatum found that virtually every substance normally synthesized by the mold is subject to genetic control. The gene or genes responsible for any particular biochemical synthesis of a substance can be damaged (made nonfunctional) by radiation. Figure 8-14 diagrams a typical experiment with *Neurospora*.

Beadle and Tatum found some mutations that seemed to affect a series of related chemical syntheses. We might designate the compounds synthesized in such a series of steps as O, C, and A, for the time being. (As the story unfolds you will learn that these letters refer to specific substances.) Careful experiments revealed that:

Mutant 1 would grow if either O, C, or A was added to the minimal medium of salts, sugar, and biotin.
Mutant 2 would grow if either C or A was added to the minimal medium.
Mutant 3 would grow *only* if A was added to the minimal medium.

Various explanations for these observations are possible. Certainly the compounds must have some relationship to one another. The hypothesis suggested by Beadle and Tatum was that each mutation alters a single gene that controls *one step* in the synthesis of a particular kind of molecule.

We might diagram such a chain of reactions as follows:

$$\text{Some prior substance} \xrightarrow{\text{Gene 1}} \text{O} \xrightarrow{\text{Gene 2}} \text{C} \xrightarrow{\text{Gene 3}} \text{A}$$

This diagram suggests that gene 1 functions by converting some prior substance into O; gene 2, by converting O into C; and gene 3,

8-14 IDENTIFICATION OF INDUCED MUTATIONS IN *NEUROSPORA*

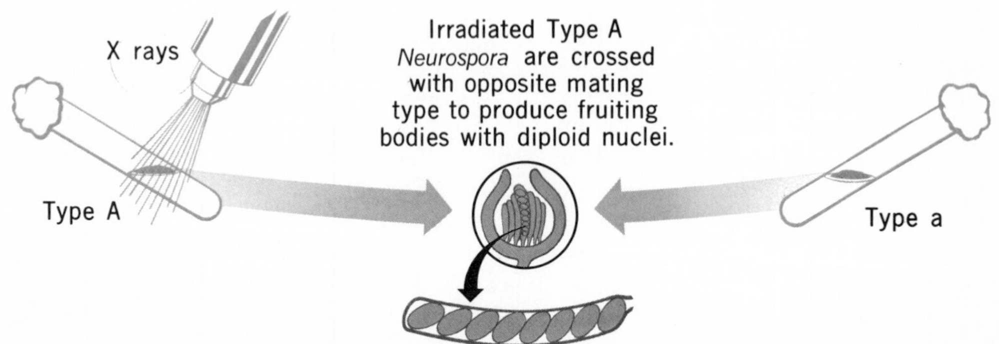

Irradiated Type A *Neurospora* are crossed with opposite mating type to produce fruiting bodies with diploid nuclei.
Type A
Type a

After meiosis, 8 monoploid spores develop in each spore sac.

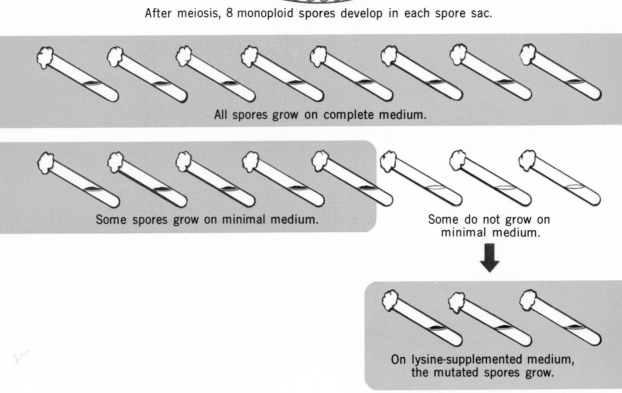

All spores grow on complete medium.

Some spores grow on minimal medium.

Some do not grow on minimal medium.

On lysine-supplemented medium, the mutated spores grow.

by converting C into A. If gene 1 were damaged by X rays, then the mold could no longer grow, unless its normal function of making O were compensated for. This could be done by adding product O to the minimal medium. But note that we could also take care of this deficiency by adding either C or A. We would just be supplying the compound in a somewhat more advanced stage of synthesis, thus bypassing the normal functions of genes 2 and 3.

If gene 3 mutates, however, we cannot fill this deficiency by adding substances O or C. Gene 3 is responsible for converting C to A, and we have no alternative except to add A to the medium. By reasoning like this, we can arrange a series of chemical steps in the proper order. We simply have to know what supplementary substances added to the minimal medium will permit the mutated mold to grow.

Beadle and Tatum found their hypothesis to be true. They had succeeded in isolating a series of related steps in synthesis and showing that a different mutation affected each step. These experiments were of great importance in showing that the functions of genes could be investigated at the chemical level.

Genes and Enzymes

From studies such as this we can learn about the *kinds* of biochemical reactions that genes normally control. It turns out that these are very often the reactions that take place in living cells at a sufficient rate to supply useful amounts of products *only because specific enzymes are present to speed up otherwise ineffective reactions*. Enough evidence has now accumulated to suggest strongly that genes often do their work through their effects on enzymes. Genes also control the formation of those proteins that are not enzymes.

The relationship demonstrated between genes and enzymes has been called the "one gene–one enzyme" hypothesis. It has been a very productive idea for suggesting additional experiments to learn more about gene action. George Beadle, now Chancellor of the University of Chicago, shared a part of the 1958 Nobel prize in medicine and physiology with E. L. Tatum for these experiments using *Neurospora* to attack this most important problem of genetics.

In the light of this hypothesis we can refine our earlier diagram a bit to include the role of the enzymes controlled by the genes:

	Gene 1		Gene 2		Gene 3	
	↓		↓		↓	
	Enzyme 1		Enzyme 2		Enzyme 3	
Some prior substance	↓ ⟶	O	↓ ⟶	C	↓ ⟶	A

Is this relationship between genes and enzymes in controlling the steps of synthesis of substance A purely hypothetical? You can be quite sure that geneticists and biochemists were soon looking at mutant types of *Neurospora*, and of bacteria and even humans, to see whether a particular enzyme is absent or reduced in activity once the specific biochemical step blocked by a mutation had been identified. Many cases were found.

We can get an even clearer idea of what genes do by looking in detail at the compounds O, C, and A, which we used in our theoretical discussion. Actually, these letters stand for three amino acids that are very similar to one another—**ornithine** (OR·nih·theen), **citrulline** (SIH·trul·een), and **arginine** (AR·jih·neen). Let us now substitute the actual chemical structures of these three molecules for their abbreviations (Figure 8-15). It is easy to see that the three molecules all have the same basic structure, except for the group of atoms outlined in the dotted boxes. Unless we know precisely what molecule has preceded ornithine in the synthesis, we cannot be sure just what enzyme 1 has done. Enzyme 2, however, quite clearly affects the addition of four atoms, in a particular arrangement, to the molecule of ornithine: one atom each of carbon, oxygen, nitrogen, and hydrogen. Or, to put it in a more detailed way, it has substituted a urea group—$CO(NH_2)_2$ *less* one hydrogen atom—for an amino group, NH_2. Enzyme 3, in turn, acts to replace the atom of oxygen with a nitrogen and a hydrogen atom. This series of compounds—ornithine, citrulline, and arginine—whose story has been worked out in *Neurospora*, also occurs in many other species, including man. The compounds are synthesized by the same steps, too. We have gained a greater understanding of man's biochemistry, and the effects of genes upon it, by studying a mold!

You will undertake somewhat similar inquiries in the laboratory, as you study differences in peas and investigate whether the cause is environmental or hereditary (Inquiry 8-3).

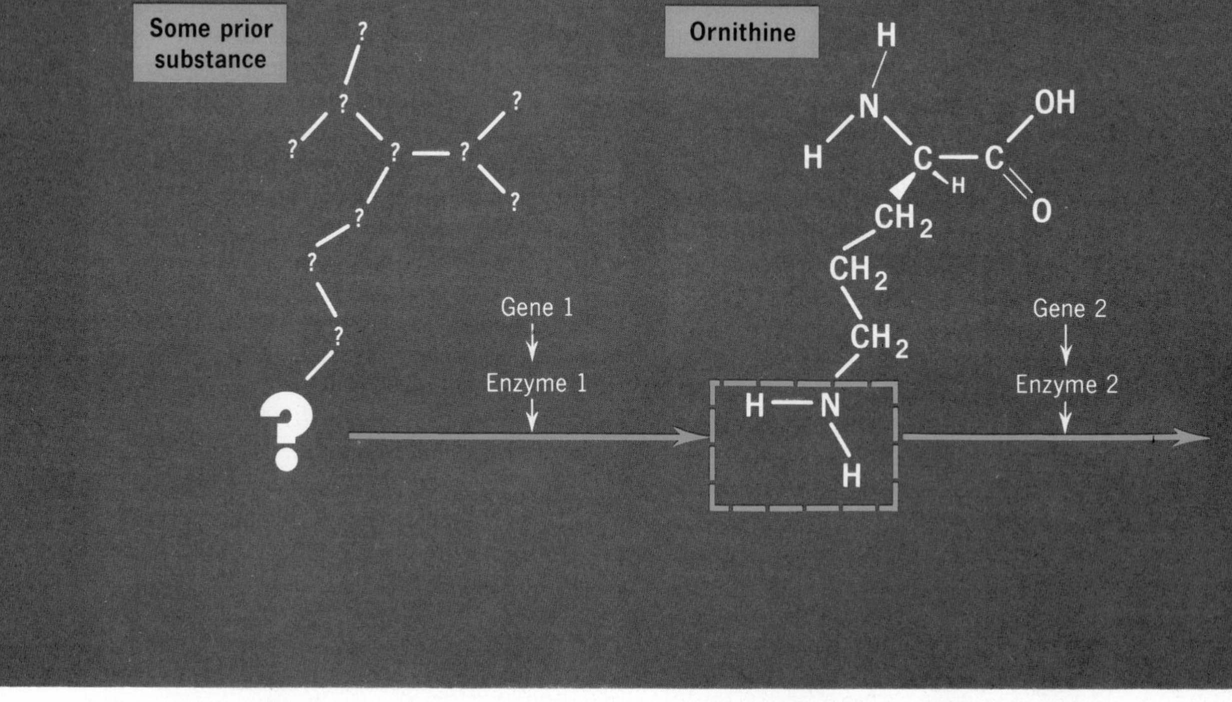

8–15 In the pink bread mold *Neurospora*, ornithine is converted to citrulline, and citrulline to arginine. Each step is controlled by a specific enzyme. Each enzyme is the product of a synthesis controlled by a specific messenger RNA made by a specific gene. The same

Gene Action in Man

Pages ago we raised questions about the "inheritance" of hemoglobin. It is important to note that genes are involved in the synthesis of hemoglobin. One example will be given. It is based on the studies of Vernon Ingram and his former associates at Cambridge University in England. In persons affected by the inherited defect called sickle-cell anemia, the red blood cells become distorted (shaped like sickles) when the oxygen concentration is low. This suggests a connection with hemoglobin, the red cell part that carries the oxygen.

When we study the chemical structure of hemoglobin in normal individuals and in those with the sickle-cell trait, we find that there is a slight chemical difference between the two kinds of hemoglobin. The abnormal hemoglobin is produced under the direction of a mutant gene. If we could identify the slight chemical difference, we would know exactly what role the mutant gene must play in the manufacture of the hemoglobin molecule.

The hemoglobin molecule is made up of two halves, each of which contains about 4,000 atoms arranged in a chain of nearly 300 amino acids of 19 different kinds. (There are 574 amino acids in the whole molecule.) Ingram's goal was to break this molecule down, bit by bit, until he could detect the difference in amino acid units between normal hemoglobin and sickle-cell hemoglobin.

This careful work showed that one chain or half-molecule of sickle-cell hemoglobin differs in only *one amino acid* from normal hemoglobin. At one place in the chain of amino acids, **glutamic** (gloo·TAM·ic) **acid** is replaced by **valine** (VAY·leen), an amino acid essential to

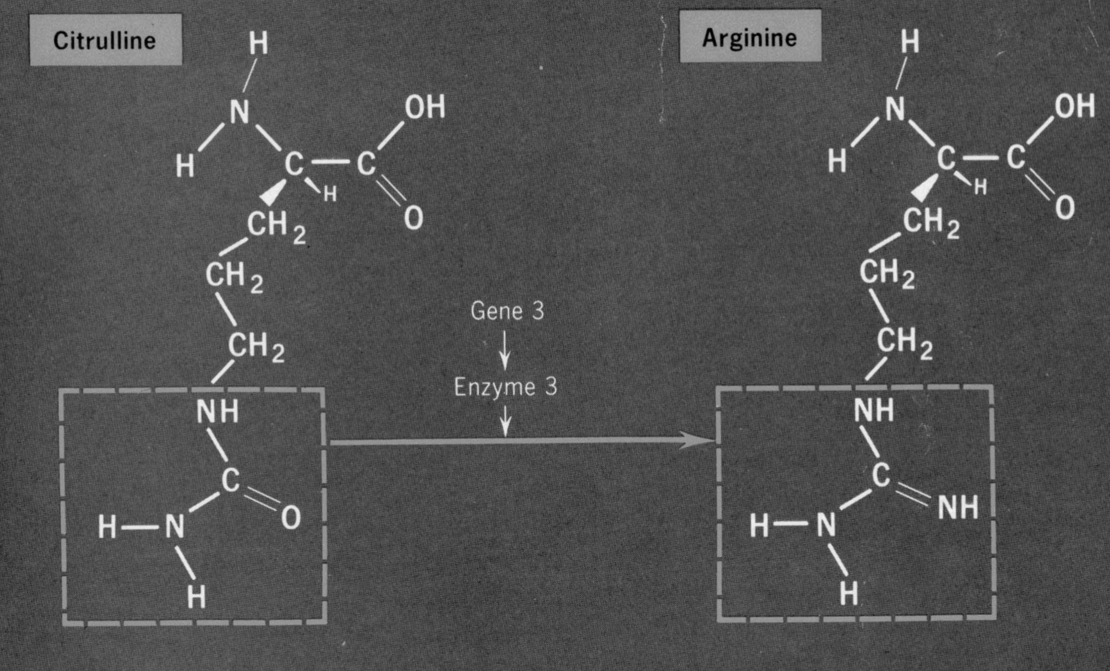

steps occur in the liver of man, as part of the ornithine cycle leading to the formation and excretion of urea (shown in the diagram on page 89). Could this mean that man and *Neurospora* have some genes in common?

many proteins, including hemoglobin, but disadvantageously located at this particular spot.

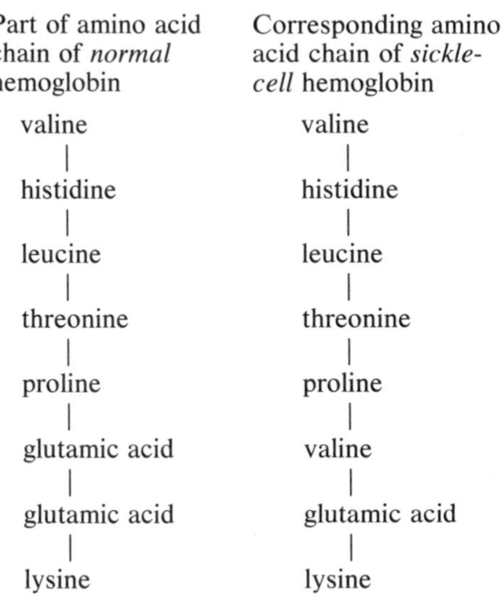

Part of amino acid chain of *normal* hemoglobin	Corresponding amino acid chain of *sickle-cell* hemoglobin
valine	valine
histidine	histidine
leucine	leucine
threonine	threonine
proline	proline
glutamic acid	valine
glutamic acid	glutamic acid
lysine	lysine

The evidence is clear that the mutant gene causes a valine unit to be substituted for a glutamic acid unit at one point in the half-molecule. Only one amino acid unit among about 300 in the half-molecule, or among almost 600 in the whole molecule, is affected by the mutant gene. This discovery suggests that a gene mutation is able to change a single unit of a very large molecule without altering the rest of the molecule at all. We also know something else, perhaps just as important: the substitution of a single amino acid unit in the normal hemoglobin molecule can have a profound effect on the blood cells of an individual with this hereditary trait.

We have come very close to learning what a single gene may do. Again, a gene seems to determine the *unique structure* of a molecule, or of one part of a molecule.

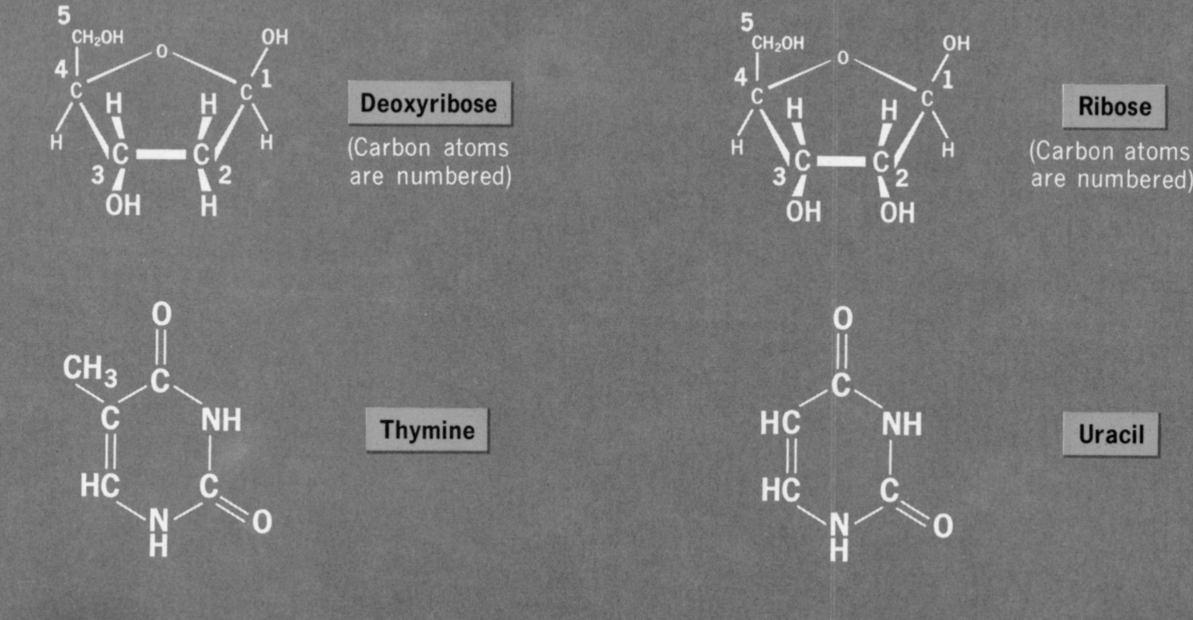

8–16 The units that differ in DNA and RNA. On the left are deoxyribose and thymine, found in DNA. On the right are ribose and uracil, found in RNA. What is the difference in structure between deoxyribose and ribose, and between thymine and uracil? What other four units not shown are parts of *both* DNA and RNA?

THE ROLE OF DNA AND RNA

By now we have a picture of the close relationship that must exist among genes, the enzyme and other protein molecules they control, and all the molecules affected by enzyme action. More questions naturally arise in our minds. How does a gene control an enzyme? How does a change (mutation) in a bit of DNA in the nucleus bring about the insertion of a different amino acid at one particular place in a protein molecule?

Recent experiments have thrown considerable light on the problem. We believe that genes themselves do not act directly in most of the chemcial reactions that take place in the cell. There is a fairly simple reason for thinking this: the genes are in the nucleus of the cell, while most of the chemical reactions occur in the cytoplasm.

What is the link between the "boss" genes in the nucleus and the "worker" enzymes—or other proteins—in the cytoplasm? We have the answer to this question.

In addition to DNA, there is another type of nucleic acid: ribonucleic acid, or RNA (page 99). For years its function was a mystery. There were reasons to suspect that it might have important roles in the life of the cell. Some of these reasons were

1. RNA was discovered in all cells that were examined, often in fairly large amounts. In the nucleus, for example, the nucleolus is largely RNA. Even greater amounts of RNA occur in the cytoplasm.
2. In chemical structure, RNA closely resembles DNA. Since DNA is known to be very important, it was hard to imagine RNA as present solely to fill up the cell.

RNA is composed of four nucleotides, as is the case with DNA. And, once again, the nucleotides are made up of six smaller units:

In DNA	In RNA
phosphate	phosphate
deoxyribose	ribose
cytosine	cytosine
adenine	adenine
guanine	guanine
thymine	uracil

As you can see, there are two main differences. The sugar in DNA is deoxyribose; in RNA it is ribose. In RNA there is no thymine. In its place is a similar pyrimidine, **uracil** (YUR·uh·sill). In Figure 8-16 you will see these four molecules that differ in DNA and RNA. You may conclude that they really are not very different. But you will soon see that the two nucleic acids play very different, though closely related, roles in the cell.

Nearly all of the DNA is in the cell's nucleus. RNA, on the other hand, is present in the nucleus and in the cytoplasm. The ribosomes in the cytoplasm were found to have large amounts of RNA. In addition, some of the RNA seemed to be in smaller molecules that were dissolved in the fluid portion of the cytoplasm.

What else do we know about RNA? Besides the fact that we find RNA in all cells, we know that there is more in some cells than in others. Cells with the most RNA actively engage in protein synthesis. Pancreas and liver cells, for example, synthesize large quantities of proteins; and in these cells we find large amounts of RNA. In the silk-gland cells of the silkworm we also find large amounts of RNA, in agreement with the function of those glands, which is to produce a protein, silk. Yet nerve cells contain very large amounts of RNA and perhaps synthesize little protein. Maybe RNA does something else, too.

Where in the cell does protein synthesis actually occur? By using techniques that break down cells into their components, biologists have learned that the ribosomes of the cytoplasm (page 115) contain most of the cellular RNA. These small particles are made up of about half RNA and half protein.

All of our evidence now points to the conclusion that RNA plays an essential role in protein synthesis. Using a number of different techniques, especially those in which radioactive atoms are incorporated into molecules, it is possible to trace the main steps (Figure 8-17).

1. The gene in the nucleus, a portion of a DNA molecule, controls the synthesis of specific RNA. This RNA is known as **messenger RNA.** The messenger RNA carries instructions, in the form of its own chemical make-up, from the DNA to the cytoplasm. Here it becomes associated with the ribosomes.
2. Other sorts of RNA, already free in the cytoplasm, are acted on by enzymes so that they pick up individual amino acids and carry them to the ribosome-messenger RNA sites. This RNA that carries amino acids is called **transfer RNA.** There is a different transfer RNA and a different enzyme for each of the twenty or so different amino acids used in making protein.
3. The transfer RNA molecules, along with their amino acids, assume positions momentarily with the ribosomes on the messenger RNA, in a specific order determined by the surface pattern of the RNA.
4. Enzymes link the amino acids to one another in a specific order to form a new **polypeptide** (pol·ih·PEP·tide) chain. A part of a protein molecule has been synthesized.
5. The transfer RNA molecules are freed and each one again becomes available for picking up another amino acid of a particular kind.

You have been presented with a small portion of the evidence that has convinced biologists that DNA is hereditary material. It,

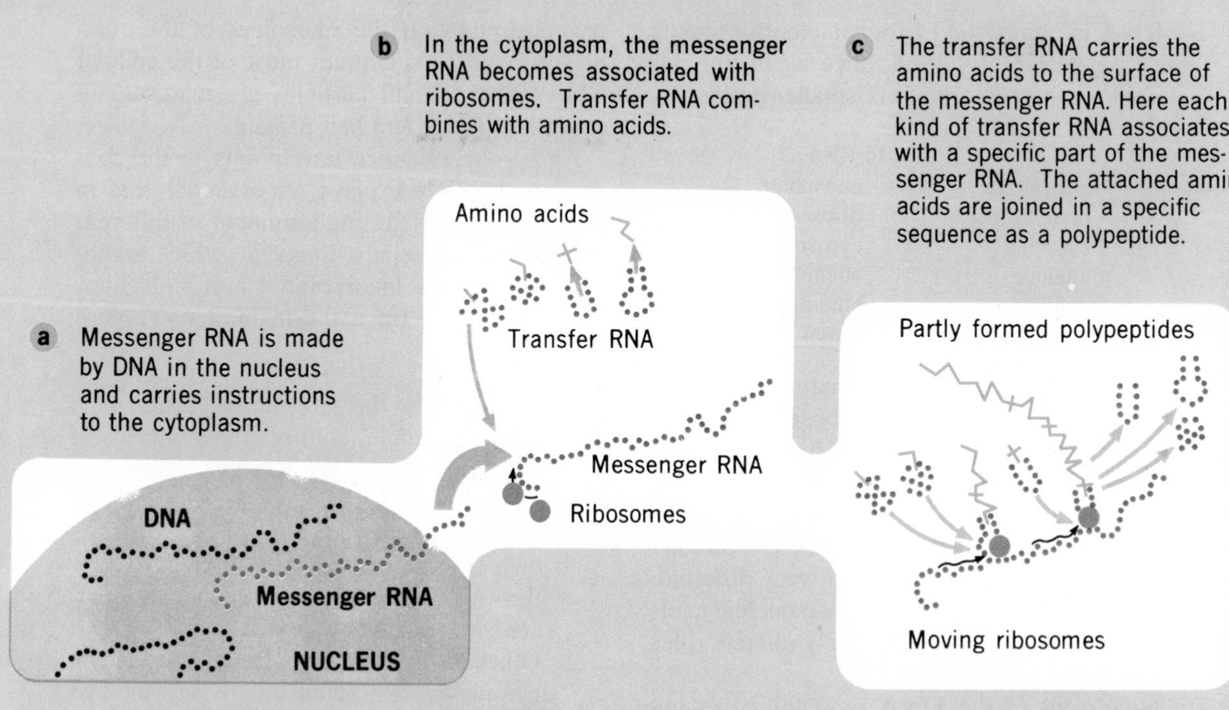
b In the cytoplasm, the messenger RNA becomes associated with ribosomes. Transfer RNA combines with amino acids.
c The transfer RNA carries the amino acids to the surface of the messenger RNA. Here each kind of transfer RNA associates with a specific part of the messenger RNA. The attached amino acids are joined in a specific sequence as a polypeptide.
Amino acids
Transfer RNA
a Messenger RNA is made by DNA in the nucleus and carries instructions to the cytoplasm.
Partly formed polypeptides
Messenger RNA
Ribosomes
DNA
Messenger RNA
NUCLEUS
Moving ribosomes

8–17 Steps in protein synthesis, beginning in the cell nucleus. It is not possible to indicate in one diagram all the cell activity that affects protein synthesis. Indeed a great deal is still unknown. But ATP and specific enzymes are necessary, as each step requires expenditure of energy and very precise chemical control.

and it alone, is believed to carry the hereditary instructions from generation to generation. Not only is it responsible for transmission between generations, but in each cell it sends out the instructions that determine the synthesis of proteins, and indirectly of other substances as well.

It would now be profitable for you to list the seven deductions (pages 148-49 and 156) that we made from the hypothesis:

A biological mechanism exists that transmits the instructions for making the structures of the succeeding generations.

Then list the data that suggest that DNA is the mechanism.

CONCLUDING REMARKS

Man has wondered about the nature of inheritance for generations. Many of his questions were answered in general ways in the years following 1900. These will be considered when we study genetics further in Chapters 29-30. The answers in terms of cellular functions began to come much later. In the decade beginning in 1953, tremendous progress was made. Earlier experiments had suggested strongly that DNA is the hereditary material. In 1953 Watson and Crick published their description of a model for the structure of DNA. Their model accounted for the known chemical characteristics of DNA as well as for the genetic characteristics of any hypothetical hereditary material. Since then the data have accumulated so rapidly that we say with considerable confidence that DNA is the hereditary material for most organisms (in a few viruses the genetic material is RNA).

The hereditary instructions of DNA are transmitted to the cytoplasm by messenger RNA. Ribosomes on the messenger RNA serve as a site for the synthesis by enzymes of specific protein molecules. It is these proteins—enzymes and other sorts of molecules—that dominate the life of the cell.

There is now a partial answer to the problem of indirect genetic continuity (page 148). How can it be that hemoglobin is present in parent and offspring but never in egg cell or sperm? The egg cell and the sperm both contain DNA with the instructions "how to make hemoglobin." The *instructions* are inherited.

Have you noticed a common problem in Chapters 2, 7, and 8? In Chapter 2 we dealt with the origins of individuals and found that they always arise from other individuals. Under the conditions on earth today there is no spontaneous generation of life. In Chapter 7 we investigated the origins of cells. We found that cells always arise by the division of cells. Finally we have learned that DNA also arises from other DNA. These are all examples of genetic continuity: of individuals, of cells, of molecules. Each example is similar to the others, but at a different level of biological organization. Laboratory Inquiry 8-4 will help familiarize you with different levels of organization and serve as a useful introduction to the chapters that follow.

GUIDE QUESTIONS AND PROBLEMS

1. What caused biologists to suspect that chromosomes were involved in the transmission of hereditary material?
2. What reasoning first led biologists to suspect that protein, rather than DNA, was responsible for the transmission of hereditary traits? What caused the biologists to turn their attention to DNA in search of an explanation of heredity?
3. How does the Watson-Crick model of DNA satisfy the requirement that hereditary instructions must be reproduced in an exact way? In what way does experimental evidence support the theory of how this model works?
4. New techniques often affect the status of unsolved problems. How did the Feulgen staining reaction contribute to the hypothesis that DNA is the hereditary material of living organisms?
5. What was the importance of the Beadle and Tatum experiments with *Neurospora* to the study of hereditary materials of cells?
6. Experiments of seemingly restricted importance often lead to far-reaching evidence affecting scientific hypotheses. How do experiments with viruses and bacteria illustrate this statement?
7. You have studied the molecular basis for gene mutations. When would molecular changes have to occur for a newly mutated gene to be found in all the cells of a given organism?
8. Suppose that the nucleus is removed from a cell. How would this affect the ability of the cell to synthesize new protein?

RELATED READING

Books

For more details of DNA and chemical control of the cell's life . . .

Barry, J. M., *Molecular Biology and the Chemical Control of Living Cells*, Prentice-Hall, Englewood Cliffs, N. J., 1964 (cloth or paperback).

Borek, Ernest, *The Code of Life*, Columbia University Press, New York, 1965.

Crick, F. H. C., *Of Molecules and Men*, University of Washington Press, Seattle, 1966.

Watson, James D., *The Double Helix*, Atheneum, New York, 1968.

Magazines

Crick, F. H. C., "The Genetic Code," *Scientific American*, Volume 207 (October 1962), page 66.

Nirenberg, Marshall W., "The Genetic Code—II," *Scientific American*, Volume 208 (March 1963), page 80.

Rich, Alexander, "Polyribosomes," *Scientific American*, Volume 209 (December 1963), page 44.

Holley, Robert W., "The Nucleotide Sequence of a Nucleic Acid," *Scientific American*, Volume 214 (February 1966), page 30.

PART 2

DIVERSITY

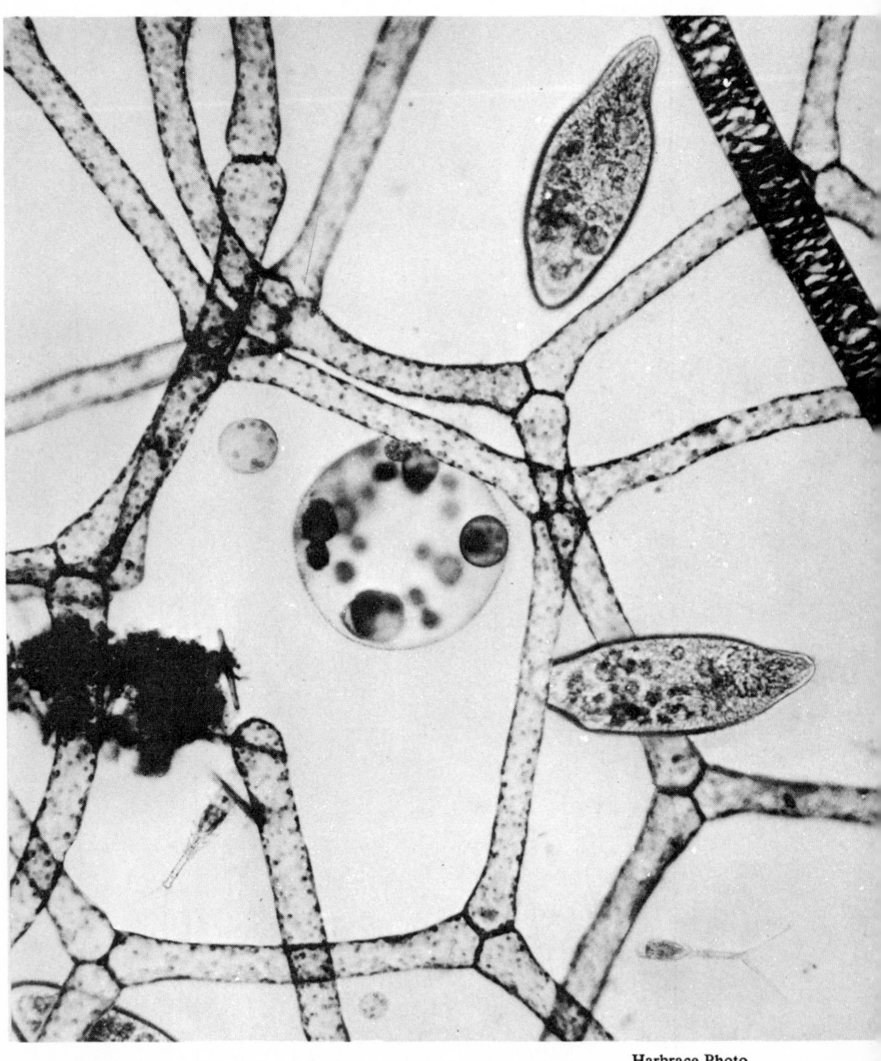

Harbrace Photo

PART 2a
MICROORGANISMS

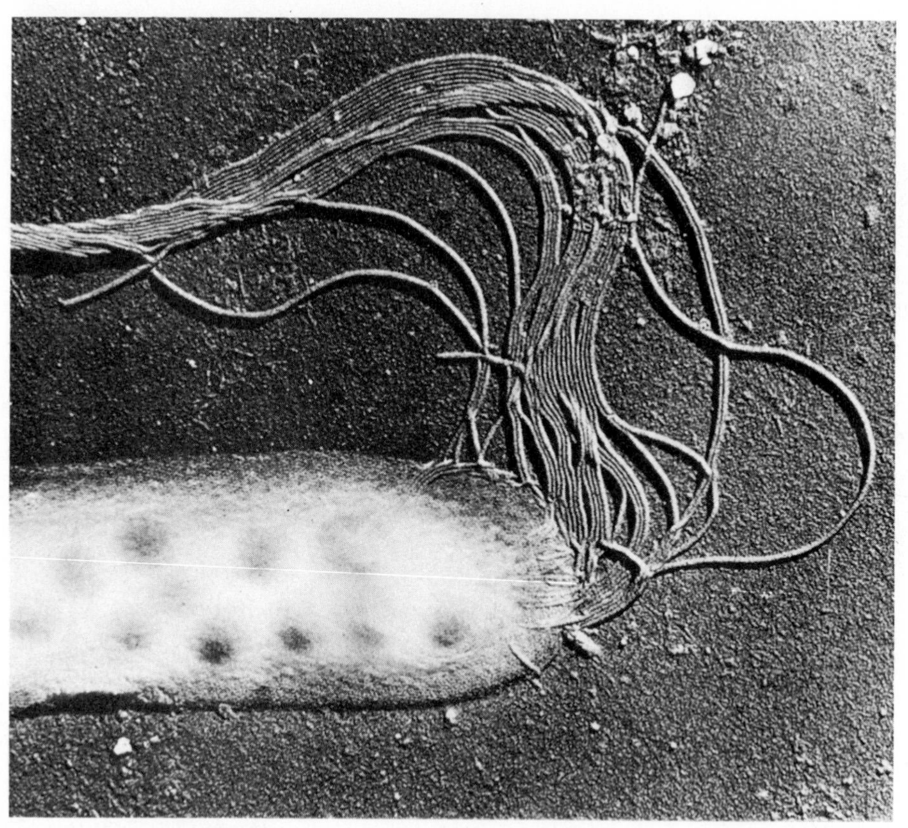

A. L. Houwink

9

Beginnings — Viruses — Time

Biologists debate among themselves those questions for which the observations and experiments do not suggest clear answers. But one question they no longer debate: "Is it possible for life to appear spontaneously on the earth today?" The answer that all competent biologists give is "No!" Such an abrupt answer is a short way of giving the proper answer. A biologist would be more accurate if he were to say, "All of the observations and data known to me suggest that the living organisms of today arise only from other living organisms; no observations or experiments known to me demand spontaneous generation as an explanation for the life we see around us."

But biologists also believe that "No" cannot be the complete answer. During the past century their fellow scientists in geology, astronomy, and physics were telling them something else: there was a time when life could not have existed on the earth. Why was this? The best evidence suggests strongly that the earth has not been in existence forever. It too had a beginning, which is estimated to be about 5 billion years ago. When the earth began, the conditions were such that life as we know it would have been impossible. For example, the evidence suggests that there was no oxygen and probably no carbon dioxide in the atmosphere. You can imagine what this would have done to the animals and plants familiar to you; they could not have survived.

We can summarize the available evidence with three statements:

1. There was a remote time when the earth was lifeless.
2. At the present time there is life on the earth.
3. Life must have appeared in the interval between 1 and 2.

THE ORIGIN OF LIFE

There are three hypotheses that could be suggested for the origins of life on the earth.

1. Living things could always have existed on the earth. For the reasons just given, this possibility seems unlikely.
2. Living things could have come from some other world, that is, from outer space.
3. Living things could have appeared on earth at some remote time in the past.

With hypothesis 1 contrary to available evidence, we are left with hypotheses 2 and 3.

Life from Other Worlds

A favorite way of explaining the origin of life on earth has been to suggest that life was introduced by way of dust particles or meteorites from distant parts of the universe.

There are two objections to this hypothesis. First, it explains only the appearance of life on earth. We are still left with the problem of explaining how life arose on some distant planet.

The second objection comes from our knowledge of outer space. The tremendous extremes of heat and cold, the excessive radiations, and the lack of an atmosphere in outer space cannot be tolerated by any known forms of life. Furthermore, meteors would make poor vehicles to carry life. The meteors often seen at night are particles of stone or metal that burst into flame as they plunge into the earth's atmosphere. Surely, bacteria hitching a ride on one of these shooting stars would come to a blazing finish in the upper atmosphere. That is, if they had not been destroyed already by deadly radiation or by the violent extremes of temperature in outer space. Nevertheless, scientists have not given up looking for evidences of life in the inside of meteorites.

With the possibility of being able to travel in space, scientists are busily making plans to look for evidence of life in space, as well as on the moon and any planets that can be investigated. It will be difficult to study the origin of life on other worlds. It may be more profitable to ask if life could have arisen on the earth.

The Origin of Life on Earth

How can a biologist study questions such as: "When did life first begin on the earth?" "What were the first organisms like?" "Are some of the first organisms still alive or have they been replaced by others?"

Our attempts to answer these questions will introduce us to a different way of studying biological problems. So far in this course many difficult questions have been asked, but in every case we arrived at answers that could be reasonably well substantiated by observation and experiment. This will not happen with questions involving the origin of life and this is why: biologists suspect that life began on the earth at some very remote time. It is, of course, impossible to study directly those events that took place long ago. Biologists simply arrived on the scene several billion years too late! The very best they can do is to suggest ways in which life *might have* begun. Think how different this is from studying biological events that are occurring at the present. Today one can study the origins of new cells by mitotic cell divisions or even the origins of DNA molecules from existing DNA molecules. Observations, measurements, and speculations about these current events can lead to conclusions that are based on verifiable data. But, so far as the origin of life on the earth is concerned, there is nothing left to study directly! It is all over (see Figure 9-1).

In spite of these difficulties it is still true that questions about the origin of life are some of the most interesting that a human being can ask. In seeking answers, biologists can make some suggestions and even do a few experiments, but in the end all that results are hypotheses as to how life might have begun. It will never be possible to substantiate these hypotheses as "true beyond a reasonable doubt."

Some of the earliest hypotheses began with this question, "What is the minimum structure and physiology required for an object to be alive in a nonliving world?" In other words, what is the simplest living organism that can survive in the absence of other living organisms? The phage virus is the simplest organism that you have been introduced to so far. Yet it cannot be the model we are seeking since a phage virus cannot live alone. It is unable to use the inorganic substances found in nature as food. It can carry on an active life and reproduce only in the complex environment of the interior of a bacterial cell. It never could have survived in the oceans when the earth was young. We must look elsewhere.

Since we are seeking a model organism that can live in an environment without other living organisms, and hence without living sources of energy and raw materials, we should consider the green plants. A typical green plant can live solely on inorganic salts, water, and carbon dioxide, if there is light. Some biologists of a few generations ago reasoned that life must have begun with some "simple" cell that contained chlorophyll.

You have probably observed tiny green algae in cultures of pond water (Inquiries 1-1 and 2-1). These are single-celled organisms that can live solely on nonliving materials. If organisms something like this appeared as the first organisms, they could have survived. With the passage of time they could have evolved into the plants and animals of today.

A reasonable hypothesis? Hardly. You have probably spotted the error in the argument. How does one get that first cell? It did not seem quite so difficult a few generations ago. Not very much was then known about the structure and physiology of cells. It was possible to think of a small cell as "simple." But think of what you know about cells—their complex physiology and their complex structure. Today we cannot imagine a cell so simple that it could "just happen" by some chance collision of atoms. Yet that is what is required. If there is to be a spontaneous appearance of life, the beginnings must be some chance association of atoms.

There is still another serious error in this line of speculation. We have assumed that the earth's crust at the time life started was about the same as it is today. Such is no longer believed to be the case. If not, what was the earth like long ago when life started?

Let us cease our speculation for a moment and ask the astronomers, geologists, and chemists what they believe the young earth was like. These scientists are reasonably sure that the earth condensed from cold gases and became a molten mass at a fairly early stage in history. At such temperatures atoms combine, separate, and recombine in a variety of ways. But they cannot combine to form the huge organic molecules that are characteristic of life.

As the molten earth slowly cooled, new chemical compounds were formed. Enough is known about the behavior of chemical sub-

9–1 Will ideas about the origin of life always remain speculation? Research continues to give us new information. In 1965, Professor Elso Barghoorn of Harvard University described some fossils, shown at the right, in Pre-Cambrian rocks from Ontario. These organisms, which he named *Kakabekia umbellata*, lived about two billion years ago and are examples of some of the earliest forms of life known. Professor Barghoorn knew of nothing alive today that resembled them . . .

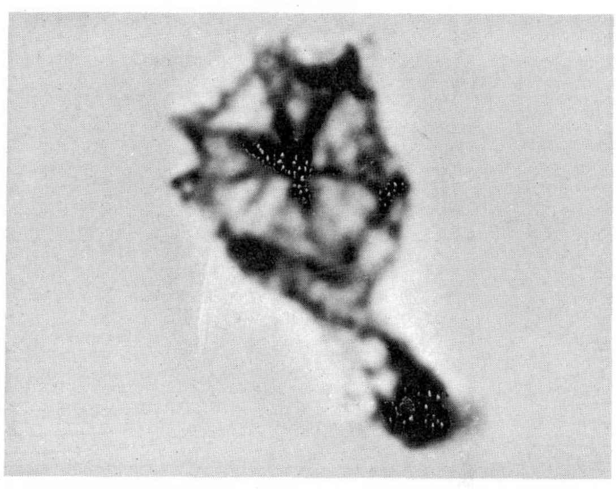

E. S. Barghoorn

S. M. Siegel & Constance Giumarro

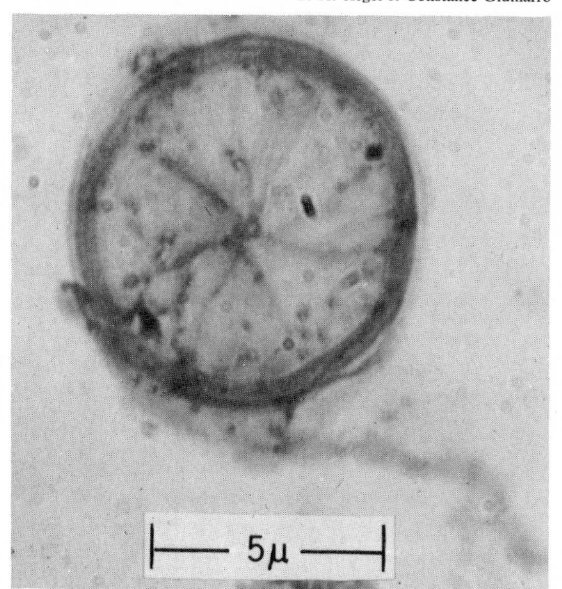

. . . but in 1966, two scientists, S. M. Siegel and Constance Giumarro, reported the results of an interesting experiment. What would happen if soil was placed in an atmosphere like that thought to be present on the earth at the time of the origin of life? Would any of the numerous organisms present in the soil be able to live? The researchers took soil samples from many parts of the earth and cultured them in atmospheres of methane and ammonia. One of the few organisms that lived was new to them. It is shown at the left. Close study showed that it was very similar to *Kakabekia.* Is this *Kakabekia*-like form a survivor from life's beginnings? If it is, a careful study would tell us a great deal about the structure, physiology, and way of life of a very primitive organism. Are there other organisms, still alive, which are as closely related to ancient species?

stances at high temperatures for us to be sure that the earth's crust was very different from its present state. The atmosphere, for example, is believed to have been totally different.

Today our atmosphere is composed of nitrogen, oxygen, carbon dioxide, water vapor, and traces of other gases. When the temperature of the earth was very high, however, these gases could not have existed in the atmosphere. The oxygen would have combined with hydrogen (to form water) and with elements of the earth's crust—such as silicon, aluminum, and iron. Similarly, nitrogen would have combined with hydrogen, forming ammonia (NH_3), and with elements of the earth's crust. The oxygen and nitrogen, therefore, would be present in the atmosphere only in the form of reduced compounds, not as free gases (O_2 and N_2). Even today, oxygen exists in the atmosphere largely because it is released by the photosynthesis of green plants.

United Press International

9–2 Harold Urey, whose interest in events on the primitive earth encouraged Stanley Miller to study the interaction of materials thought to have existed in the primitive atmosphere. See Figure 9–3.

The primitive earth probably had an atmosphere of methane (CH_4), ammonia (NH_3), water vapor (H_2O), hydrogen sulfide (H_2S), and hydrogen (H_2). It is believed that these relatively simple substances gradually combined into increasingly complex molecules. Finally these complex molecules associated to form systems or organized groups of molecules that had a unique feature: they served as models for organizing chemical substances around them into other systems of molecules like themselves. Life had started.

What could these molecules have been? Having no direct evidence, we can only guess. Since our hypothetical molecules could reproduce, possibly they were a nucleic acid like DNA or RNA. Of all the biological molecules we know today, only DNA and RNA can be replicated directly. Could the first "living" molecules have been a nucleic acid? Possibly. And if they were, we would have a wonderful explanation of why DNA or RNA is the basis of inheritance in all organisms.

You could rightly conclude that we have taken a lot for granted by inventing a replicating molecule. Is there really any evidence that this could have happened? Here we can do some experiments. It is assumed that conditions on the earth before life started were different from today. Yet no scientist believes that the principles of physics and chemistry that we know today did not apply to the earth at that time. Thus we should be able to duplicate in the laboratory the conditions we believe prevailed when life began.

Harold Urey (Figure 9-2), a Nobel prizewinner then at the University of Chicago, had become interested in the evolution of chemical compounds under primitive earth conditions, and he discussed this with one of his students, Stanley Miller. In May 1953, Miller published

United Press International

9–3 Stanley Miller, shown with apparatus designed for the now famous experiment that demonstrated amino acid synthesis in a simulated primitive atmosphere.

in *Science,* a famous scientific journal, an article entitled "A Production of Amino Acids Under Possible Primitive Earth Conditions." The article begins as follows:

> The idea that the organic compounds that serve as the basis of life were formed when the earth had an atmosphere of methane, ammonia, water, and hydrogen instead of carbon dioxide, nitrogen, oxygen, and water was suggested by Oparin [a Russian scientist]. In order to test this hypothesis, an apparatus was built to circulate CH_4, NH_3, H_2O, and H_2 past an electric discharge.

Figure 9-3 shows the basic design of the apparatus used by Miller in his experiments. The apparatus contained water in a flask, and the application of heat caused the water to boil continuously. The rest of the apparatus was filled with methane, ammonia, hydrogen, and water vapor.

The electrical discharges were intended to duplicate conditions that we assume were present on the primitive earth—violent electrical storms, much more severe than any occurring today. Actually, ultraviolet radiation should have been used too, since it was probably a prevalent form of energy on the primitive earth. But in this particular experiment, the principal requirement was intense bursts of energy.

Miller allowed the experiment to continue for a week. At the end of that time his originally colorless solution had turned red. He analyzed the solution and found that a great variety of organic molecules was present. Some he could not identify with certainty. However, some of the molecules present were *amino acids*. All of these acids contain carbon, hydrogen, oxygen, and nitrogen. Amino acids are the structural units of proteins (page 93).

And so it may have started. The gases of the primitive atmosphere, exposed to lightning and ultraviolet light, could have combined to form simple organic compounds. As the earth continued to cool, the water vapor would have condensed to form pools, lakes, and oceans. Simple organic substances would begin to accumulate in these waters as millions of years passed.

The compounds of this soup could be expected to react with one another, producing a variety of chemical substances. For example, the way amino acids might have been combined to form the first protein molecules was suggested by Sidney W. Fox of the Institute of Molecular Evolution, University of Miami. Fox took a mixture of 18 to 20 amino acids and heated it to the melting point. When the mass was allowed to cool, he discovered that many of the amino acids had bonded together to form chains not unlike those characteristic of proteins. In a paper given in 1957 during a conference on the origin of life, Fox stated:

> The prebiochemical distance from such organic compounds as amino acids to the origin of life, however, must be quite large. . . . The work to be described in this paper, however, began with an attempt to understand only the prebiochemical origin of protein. The experiments yielded a succession of unexpected results and stimuli for new experiments such that a unified theory of biochemical origins is emerging.

Another example comes from the work of Melvin Calvin of the University of California. He was able to show that gamma radiation, acting on a mixture of methane, ammonia, hydrogen, and water, produces molecules of amino acids and sugars. Also produced are some biologically important compounds tentatively identified as purines and pyrimidines.

Somewhat later other investigators heated mixtures of amino acids and obtained the purines—adenine and guanine. Ribose and deoxyribose were produced in other experiments. Of even greater interest, it was found that the nucleotides could be produced under conditions thought to be like those of long ago when the earth was young.

It is no longer far-fetched to imagine a slow evolution of organic molecules in a primitive ocean. Direct replicating molecules have yet to be produced in the laboratory, but scientists are close—they are at the nucleotide stage as this is being written. And these syntheses are being done without the use of enzymes, which are necessary for nucleotide molecules to be produced in cells.

Ten years after reporting on biochemical origins, Sidney Fox and his associates today are reporting on the results of experiments into pre-cell structures. Evidence for a remarkable degree of self-assembly of amino acids into structures that appear *and grow* as microscopic spheres is accumulating. Some of the characteristics of cells, including a membranelike outer boundary, are associated with these microspheres; the most astonishing of these is the apparent growth. Careful experiments have ruled out that the "growth" is attributable to water (by osmosis). Yet these primitive structures have no nucleic acids!

Once a system can take the next step beyond growth and be reproduced from raw materials of the environment, we can say that it is alive. In life today this requires nucleic acids. The primitive systems of living matter probably were formed and disintegrated on many occasions. But some systems survived, and from these, life on the earth originated.

A living mass would have come to contain many proteins (including enzymes), and nucleic acids. Possibly it would be broken into smaller parts from time to time. Each sub-glob could then start a new living mass. It is reasonable to suppose that the systems that were best organized and most stable, that grew the fastest, that divided most frequently, and that transmitted their own qualities most effectively to their descendants would survive and displace the others.

Life at this time would depend on a rich supply of organic molecules in the environment. Later, as the conditions of the earth changed, and as a new kind of atmosphere arose, organic compounds would cease to be produced spontaneously. Life would have gradually become difficult. It would have finally become impossible if the supply of organic materials in the primitive oceans had been exhausted.

This dilemma must have been avoided by the evolution of a photosynthetic process. Once we can assume that this step was taken, we can make reasonable guesses about the major steps leading to the evolution of the primitive organisms.

While we cannot consider that the hypothesis just outlined has been fully established—or ever will be fully established—it has offered us an opportunity to demonstrate the kind of speculative thinking that precedes the creation of sound hypotheses. More than that, it has given us a chance to see how scientists try to accept only those hypotheses that can be tested by experiment and that will account for all of the known and relevant facts.

We have used our knowledge of DNA and RNA to suggest the characteristics of the first replicating molecules. In a similar manner we might ask what are the simplest organisms alive today. Possibly they would suggest what the early organisms might have been like.

The simplest living organisms today are the viruses. You have already learned about one type, the phage virus. Consisting as it does of only a DNA core and a protein coat (Figure 8-4), it is about as simple as one can imagine. Possibly something like a virus represented an early stage in the evolution of organisms. Recall that the phage virus cannot live alone. It depends on the bacterial cell for energy and the raw materials for its life and reproduction. This may be analogous to life in the primitive oceans. We have assumed that the early forms of life used the organic compounds of the surrounding ocean for their life and reproduction.

So let us study the least complex living organisms known to us. They are interesting and important in themselves and possibly they will help us to understand some of the problems of the earliest living organisms. At the same time, in the laboratory, you should begin to become familiar with microbiological techniques (Inquiry 9-1). As you have found in Inquiry 8-2, you will not be able to observe viruses directly, but you can work with microorganisms somewhat more complex, and with the effects of viruses upon them.

DISCOVERY OF VIRUSES

If you look up the word *virus* in the dictionary, you will find that it is derived from a Latin word meaning "poison." This use of the word goes back many hundreds of years, long before anyone really knew what a virus was, or that it even existed as we know it today. It was generally believed that these "viruses," or poisons, were carried in the night air and could cause many unexplained diseases.

By the late 1800's Louis Pasteur, Robert Koch, and other pioneer bacteriologists had demonstrated that many diseases of man and other organisms were caused by bacteria. Some diseases puzzled them, however, because they could find no bacteria or other organisms that were responsible for the disease symptoms. One such disease was found to occur in tobacco plants. It causes the leaves to wrinkle and become mottled. The mottled effect has the appearance of a mosaic, and the disease soon was called **tobacco mosaic disease.**

It was soon discovered that a virus could be transmitted from an infected organism to a healthy organism of the same kind. This was first demonstrated in 1892 by a Russian biologist named Iwanowsky. He extracted the juice from an infected tobacco plant and strained the juice through a very fine filter made of porcelain. The idea was to remove all the bacteria from the juice, leaving a bacteria-free filtrate—the juice that passed through the filter. Next, Iwanowsky rubbed some filtrate on leaves of a healthy tobacco plant. The healthy plant soon showed symptoms of the disease (Figure 9-4a).

By 1900, similar disease-producing substances had been discovered in many organisms, both plant and animal. In 1898 it was demonstrated that foot-and-mouth disease of cattle could be transmitted by using bacteria-free filtrates made from blisters produced on diseased stock. The name filterable virus was given to these substances. The list of **filterable viruses** (viruses that can pass through a filter which has pores too small for bacteria to pass through) was growing. Today the list is long. Viruses cause many of the major diseases of plants, animals, and man. We have already mentioned that the tobacco mosaic virus (TMV) causes an important plant disease. Other viruses that cause plant diseases are the Y virus of potato, cucumber mosaic virus, mosaic virus of lettuce, and many others. In man, such diseases as yellow fever, influenza, poliomyelitis, the common cold, German measles, mumps, and chicken pox can be listed. Fever blisters are also caused by a virus.

Not all viruses cause disease in the sense they they bring about the death or serious malfunction of the organism in which they live—the **host.** In some species of fig trees and ornamental plants, the leaves are mottled because of a virus. In these organisms, the virus has little or no harmful effect that we can detect. It may destroy chlorophyll, but usually more than enough remains for the leaf to continue its photosynthetic activity.

If so many viruses were discovered during the early part of our century, then surely, you might suppose, someone must have seen them to prove their existence. No one had. By 1930 most people interested in viruses believed that the viruses were present as small particles, but *too* small to be seen with the compound microscope. (See Laboratory Inquiry 1-4 for a discussion of the limitations of the compound microscope.) No one had even succeeded in obtaining a pure sample of viruses from the cells of a host—the only place, apparently, where viruses reproduced and increased in amount.

Isolation and Observation of Viruses

The year 1935 was important in unraveling the story of what viruses really are and how they behave. After many unsuccessful attempts, W. M. Stanley, an American microbiologist, succeeded in isolating TMV viruses from the host cells. Under the compound microscope, the isolated virus mass appeared as sliver-shaped crystals (Figure 9-4b). Within a short time it was shown that the virus crystals were nucleoproteins, closely resembling the nucleoproteins found in the chromosomes of plants and animals.

By 1935 a new kind of microscope—the electron microscope—had been constructed. (See Laboratory Inquiry 1-4.) It was capable of producing magnifications far greater than the best compound microscope. When Stanley's isolated TMV crystals were observed with an electron microscope, they were found to be composed of many rod-shaped structures (Figure 9-4c).

In the isolated, purified condition, removed from the cells of the host, TMV seemed quite dead. Many attempts were made to get the virus to reproduce outside the tobacco plants. All failed. Again the question was asked: "Are viruses really living?" Stanley took a very small amount of the purified TMV, dissolved it in water, and rubbed it on the leaves of healthy tobacco plants. The leaves soon showed the mottled condition characteristic of tobacco mosaic disease. The diseased plants were then extracted for TMV. It was found that the amount of the virus had increased greatly. This result showed conclusively that reproduction of TMV occurred in living cells of the host species.

Many biologists have since tried to get viruses of different kinds to grow and reproduce outside the living cells of their hosts.

9–4 **a.** A tobacco plant showing the symptoms of tobacco mosaic disease. The virus causes a mottling of the leaves. **b.** Crystals of the purified virus are shown as they appear under the compound microscope. Each crystal is composed of many rodlike virus particles, but these are not visible under the compound microscope. **c.** Several of the virus particles are shown as photographed with an electron microscope. (72,500 ×)

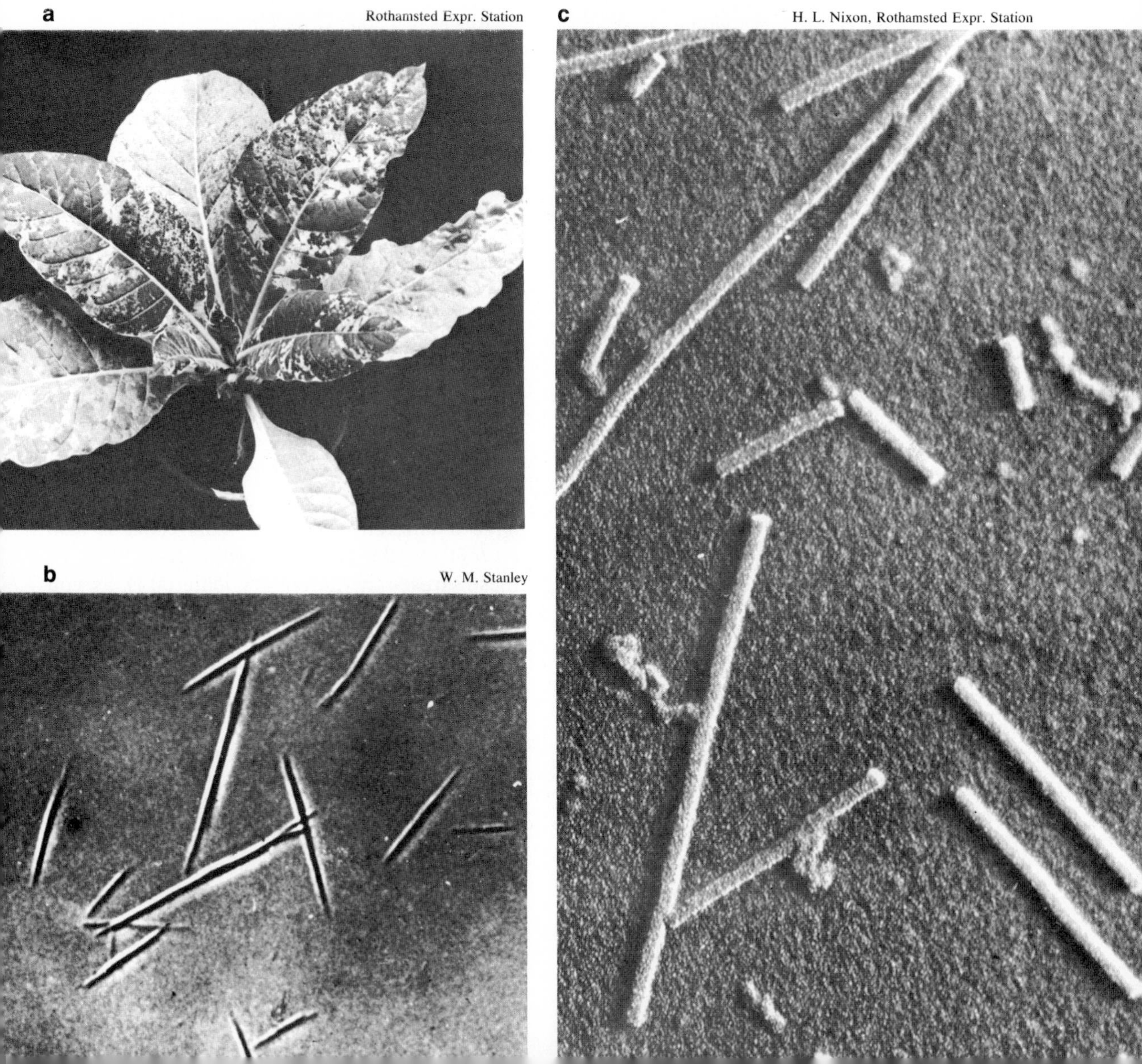

a Rothamsted Expr. Station

b W. M. Stanley

c H. L. Nixon, Rothamsted Expr. Station

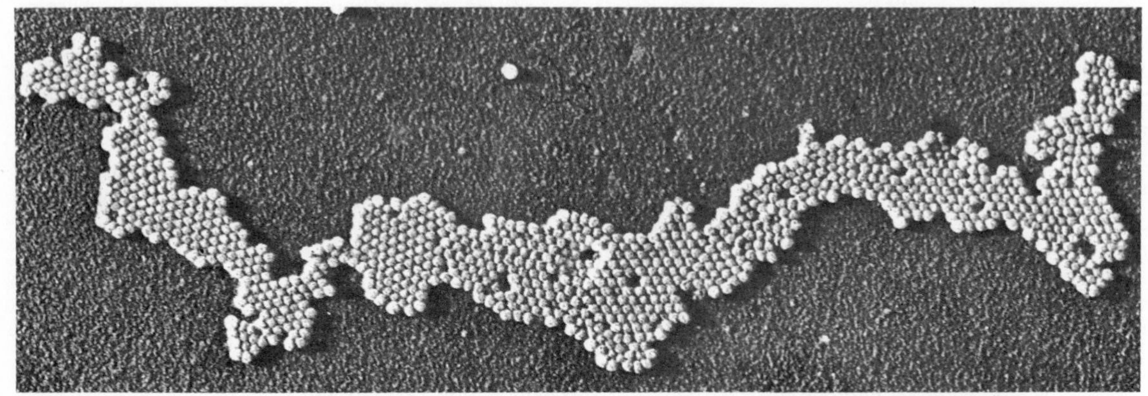

A. R. Taylor, Parke, Davis & Company

9–5 An electron micrograph of sphere-shaped particles of a polio virus. (56,500 ×) Polio is a disease of man. The viruses you first became familiar with in Chapter 8 were phage viruses that attack bacteria. How do the polio viruses compare in shape with tobacco mosaic viruses (Figure 9–4c)? with the phage viruses in Figure 9–6?

All attempts have failed. Thus it has been shown that viruses are strict **parasites,** requiring for their life processes the enzyme systems present in the living cells of other organisms. How should we interpret this phenomenon? Are viruses primitive living particles that have not yet evolved the enzyme systems required for an independent existence? Or were they once more complex living structures, which during the course of time have lost their capacity for an independent existence? We may never know. However, if we agree that viruses are alive, at least while in living cells of their hosts, where they reproduce, then they represent the simplest forms of life that we know.

Virus Size and Shape

Nearly all viruses are so small that as individual particles they cannot be seen with a compound microscope—a fact which means that most of them must be smaller than 210 millimicrons (mμ). Actually, viruses range in size from about 17 mμ to 450 mμ or even more. We might expect all such particles to look like no more than indistinct blobs even under the electron microscope. However, a photograph of polio virus (Figure 9-5), taken with the electron microscope, shows the virus particles as little spheres that look like tiny golf balls. Tobacco mosaic virus (Figure 9-4c) is rod-shaped, while some phage viruses of bacteria look like little tadpoles (Figure 9-6).

Virus Structure

We have already learned about the structure of the phage virus (page 152). Most of the viruses that live in animal cells are similar: they have a core of DNA and a protein coat. A few of the viruses that live in animal cells and all that live in the cells of higher plants have a different structure. Their coat is also protein but the core is RNA (Figure 9-7). In these viruses the hereditary material is, as you might suspect, the RNA.

VIRUSES AND THEIR WAY OF LIFE

Most plant viruses are spread by insects, with aphids and leafhoppers heading the list. Other plant viruses are transmitted by the mechanical rubbing of one leaf of a plant against another. Still others are spread by contact between the roots of different plants of the same species. The roots grow together to make a natural graft, a bridge from the infected plant to a neighboring healthy plant.

In a few cases, seeds of plants are known to carry virus particles and thus to transmit the virus from one generation to the next. This is true of lettuce mosaic disease, mentioned earlier. Vegetative parts of plants, such as leaves and cuttings of stems, may also harbor viruses. When the leaves or cuttings are used for propagation, the viruses are transmitted.

Animal viruses also are transmitted in a variety of ways. Viruses that cause infection of the respiratory tract are expelled in droplets by coughing, sneezing, or talking. Some common diseases spread to susceptible hosts in this way are virus pneumonia, the common cold, influenza, mumps, common measles, and German measles.

Some animal and human viruses, such as the polio viruses and the viruses of infectious hepatitis, are excreted in feces. Flies may carry the viruses to food, which is later ingested by human beings, or to water supplies used for drinking. This is one reason we should strive for the very best sanitary conditions in our communities.

Animal and human viruses can also be transmitted by direct contact. It is suspected that warts and fever blisters are transmitted in this way.

Virus Reproduction

What happens to a virus in a host organism? And what happens to the cells of a previously healthy host, once the transmission of a virus from an infected organism has taken place? We already know that viruses are completely inactive outside of the host's living cells. Once inside the host's cells, however, the virus DNA or RNA (depending on the kind of virus) assumes control of the cell's biochemical activities. The host cells, instead of making their own characteristic nucleic acids and proteins, begin to make different ones specifically appropriate for the virus. The situation is somewhat like a master-slave relationship. As soon as the virus—the master—enters the host cell, it changes the activities of the cell and makes

9–6 An electron micrograph of phage viruses of bacteria. (55,000 ×) Compare this micrograph with the diagram shown in Figure 8–4.

E. Kellenberger

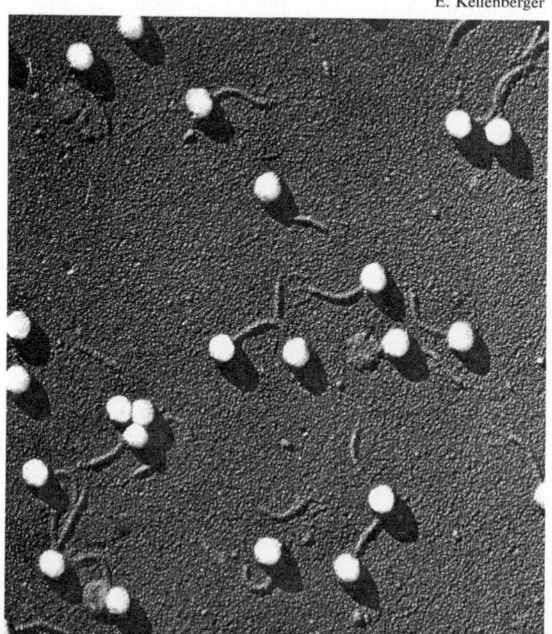

9–7 Tobacco mosaic virus particles with their protein coats partly removed, exposing the core of ribonucleic acid. (75,000 ×)

H. Fraenkel-Conrat

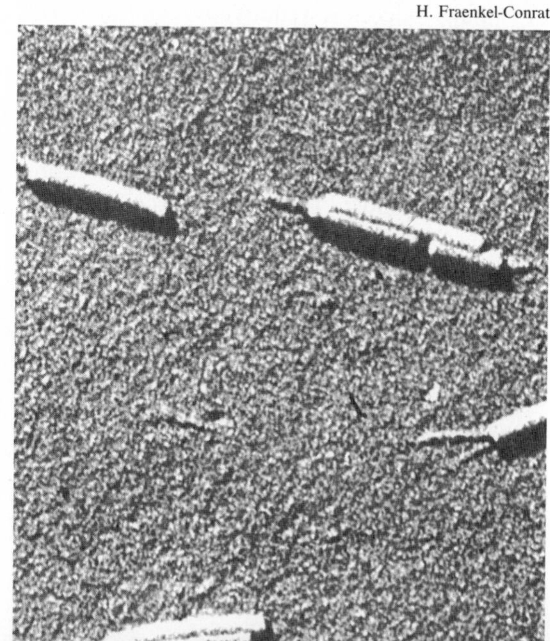

it a slave to the needs of the virus. In this changed cell environment, the virus replicates. Hundreds of virus particles may be produced, all exactly like the original virus that infected the host cell.

The phenomenon of virus reproduction has been studied in detail as it occurs among the phage viruses. (You will learn more about these viruses in Laboratory Inquiry 9-2.) In some way phage particles are attracted to cells of bacteria, where they become attached by their tailpieces to the cell wall, as we have already seen (pages 153 and 154). At the point of attachment to the bacterial cell wall, a phage particle injects its DNA, and *only* its DNA, into the bacterial cell. In a remarkably short time, the DNA of the phage organizes the enzymes of the host so that they produce more phage DNA and protein sheaths for the phage.

The introduction of phage DNA into a bacterium does not always have such violent results. Apparently the DNA of phage and bacterium can combine or associate in peaceful coexistence; many new generations of bacteria can be produced without any harmful results. Instead of a master-slave relationship, something more like a host-guest relationship results. The replication of the phage is evidently geared to be exactly in time with the growth cycle of the bacterium. Sometimes, however, the phage becomes reactivated and destroys the bacterium by reproducing rapidly in its helpless host. The outline of this cycle is shown in Figure 9-8.

How can the replication of the phage be timed so nicely to correspond to the reproduction of its host? It has been discovered that the DNA of the parasitic phage may become attached to the chromosome of the host. One interesting example of this phenomenon occurs in the bacteria long thought to cause diphtheria. It has recently been discovered that only those diphtheria bacteria that contain a specific phage DNA produce the poison which causes the disease. Is the bacterium, then, the cause of the disease? Or is the phage the cause?

Some scientists have suggested that a similar relation between our body cells and viruses may explain some types of cancer. This is just one of numerous ideas about causes of cancer now being investigated in many laboratories.

Variability of Virus Types

One of the characteristics of living things is their ability to produce offspring that may differ from the usual or normal parent type. These changes may be spontaneous and unpredictable in time. We call them mutations (pages 136-38, 165-69), if they are changes in the hereditary materials of the cell.

Many kinds of viruses are known to undergo mutations. Mutations in disease-producing viruses of plants can result in diseases with different symptoms. Other mutations are known to occur in the bacteriophages (page 152), which we have been calling the phage viruses. In fact, after only a decade of study, the known mutations of some phages are more numerous and better understood than are those of any other living things.

Certain kinds of mutant phage can be grown along with normal phage in the cells of susceptible bacteria. After the phage offspring have burst from the host cells, the virus particles can be isolated and their hereditary characteristics tested. It has been discovered that not only are the two parental types of phage (mutant and normal) present among the offspring, but also new forms in which characteristics of the parent viruses are combined. This reshuffling of heritable materials is called **genetic recombination** and is another important characteristic of living things. You were introduced to this concept in Chapter 8. It is interesting to note here that such simple structures as viruses display the same hereditary principles found in the most complex organisms. There is unity to life!

We may summarize this information about the viruses by saying that they show many of the properties of living organisms. Among these is the property of replication, though in the

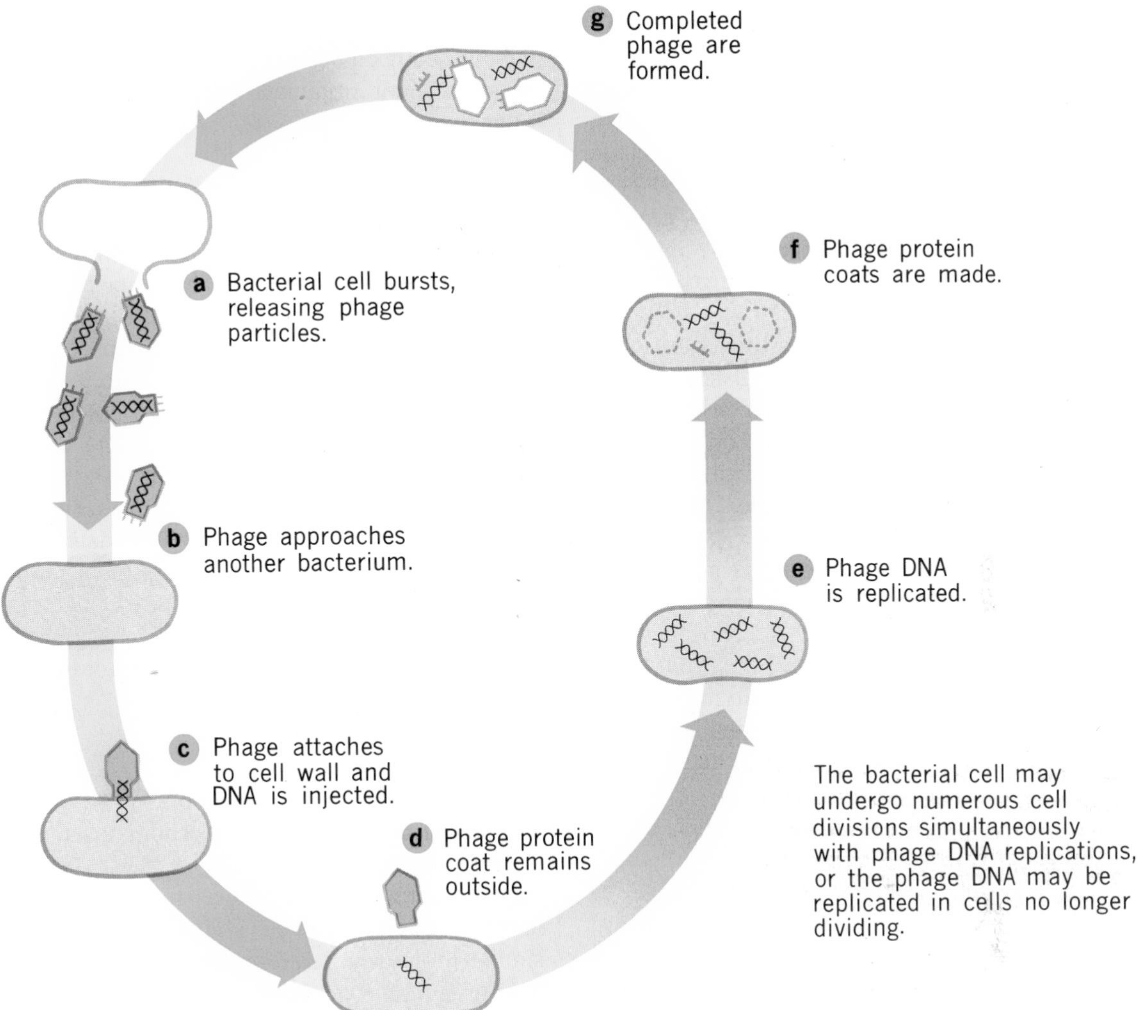
g Completed phage are formed.
f Phage protein coats are made.
a Bacterial cell bursts, releasing phage particles.
b Phage approaches another bacterium.
e Phage DNA is replicated.
c Phage attaches to cell wall and DNA is injected.
The bacterial cell may undergo numerous cell divisions simultaneously with phage DNA replications, or the phage DNA may be replicated in cells no longer dividing.
d Phage protein coat remains outside.

9–8 The phage "life cycle" in cells of bacteria. Compare the stages in this diagram with the electron micrographs in Figure 9–6 and Figure 8–5. What is the function of the tail-piece of a phage particle, as you would describe it?

case of viruses this occurs only in the cells of a host. Viruses with their core of DNA or RNA surrounded by a protein sheath somewhat resemble the chromosomes of higher plants and animals. The hereditary instructions – the genes – of viruses can mutate or be recombined when two different strains of viruses are brought together in the same host cell. This is characteristic of living things.

Where in the scale of organization do we reach the level of life? Is it at the lower end occupied by atoms or simple molecules? We all know that an atom of carbon, hydrogen, or oxygen has none of the properties of life shown by a virus. Atoms, even when they are combined into certain kinds of molecules – glucose ($C_6H_{12}O_6$), for example – cannot replicate in a living cell. The more complex molecules of the nucleic acids, however, do have the remarkable capacity of replication in living cells, a feature they share with viruses. Thus, as we go up the scale to the level of the most complex molecules, we approach the level of life. Viruses are only a little above this level.

Viruses are not as complex as cells, if for no other reason than their lack of the enzymes found in cells. We therefore place viruses below the level of cellular organization.

How have viruses achieved their position in the scale of organization? We ask again: do they represent the starting point in the evolution of other living things? Or, on the other hand, have they been derived through the degeneration of some more complex cellular organisms, such as bacteria?

No matter what our hypothesis may be, we can see that among living organisms viruses stand at the very threshold of life. Does this also mean that viruses were the first living creatures? We do not know, but in the absence of convincing evidence we can consider them a hypothetical model for an early stage in the evolution of living organisms.

EVIDENCES OF LIFE IN THE PAST

You have probably been given the impression that we have little real information about organisms that lived long ago—since they are dead. This is not always the case. Many remains of ancient animals and plants have been preserved as **fossils** (Figure 9-9).

Fossils are formed in several ways. One of the commonest ways can be described as follows. The dead organism sinks to the bottom of a swamp, lake, or mouth of a river and becomes covered with mud. The soft parts, such as the flesh of animals, decay. If conditions are just right, some of the hard parts—the bones of animals or cell walls of plants—become fossilized. Mineral substances in the water or mud penetrate the bones or cell walls and gradually the entire mass becomes hardened into stone. The remains of the organisms become **petrified,** which means changed into stone. Any remains of an ancient organism preserved in this or other ways is a fossil.

Perhaps you have visited or read about the Petrified Forest National Monument in Arizona or the Dinosaur National Monument on the Utah-Colorado boundary. In one you can see the fossil remains of trees. The other contains the fossilized bones of huge reptiles, the dinosaurs. Most natural history museums exhibit fossils, such as those shown in Figure 9-9.

Only an exceedingly small proportion of animals and plants die in places where conditions are suitable for fossilization. In addition, not all have hard parts that make preservation probable. Nevertheless, paleontologists (scientists who study life of the past) have found numerous examples of fossils of nearly all types of animals and plants. Even some very small and delicate creatures have been fossilized.

Earliest Fossils

We have no fossil evidence of organic molecules or of viruses living in a primitive sea rich in organic compounds. The earliest known organisms to be preserved as fossils were almost certainly cellular. They were probably similar to modern microorganisms, particularly blue-green algae (primitive plants that will be discussed in Chapter 13) and bacteria.

Fossil remains of both algae and bacteria are known from rocks older than 3.1 billion years. Although bacteria are difficult to recognize in a fossil state, many geologists believe that the vast iron ore deposits in northern Minnesota are the results of bacterial activity about a billion years ago. Iron pyrite is a common chemical product of bacteria. The fossil algae resemble the blue-green algae still living.

Although the evidence is still inconclusive, it suggests that for more than a billion years, the dominant and perhaps the only forms of life on earth were microscopic organisms such as algae, bacteria, and molds.

Both photos by John A. Moore

9–9 A great deal of energy and time go into the study of life in the past. Fairly reliable accounts of the influence of ancient organisms upon life today are often reconstructed from fossil evidence. In the photograph below, the fossil bones of a dinosaur are being unearthed. At the right is a section of a petrified tree trunk, and above is an imprint of a dinosaur footprint.

Dinosaur National Monument

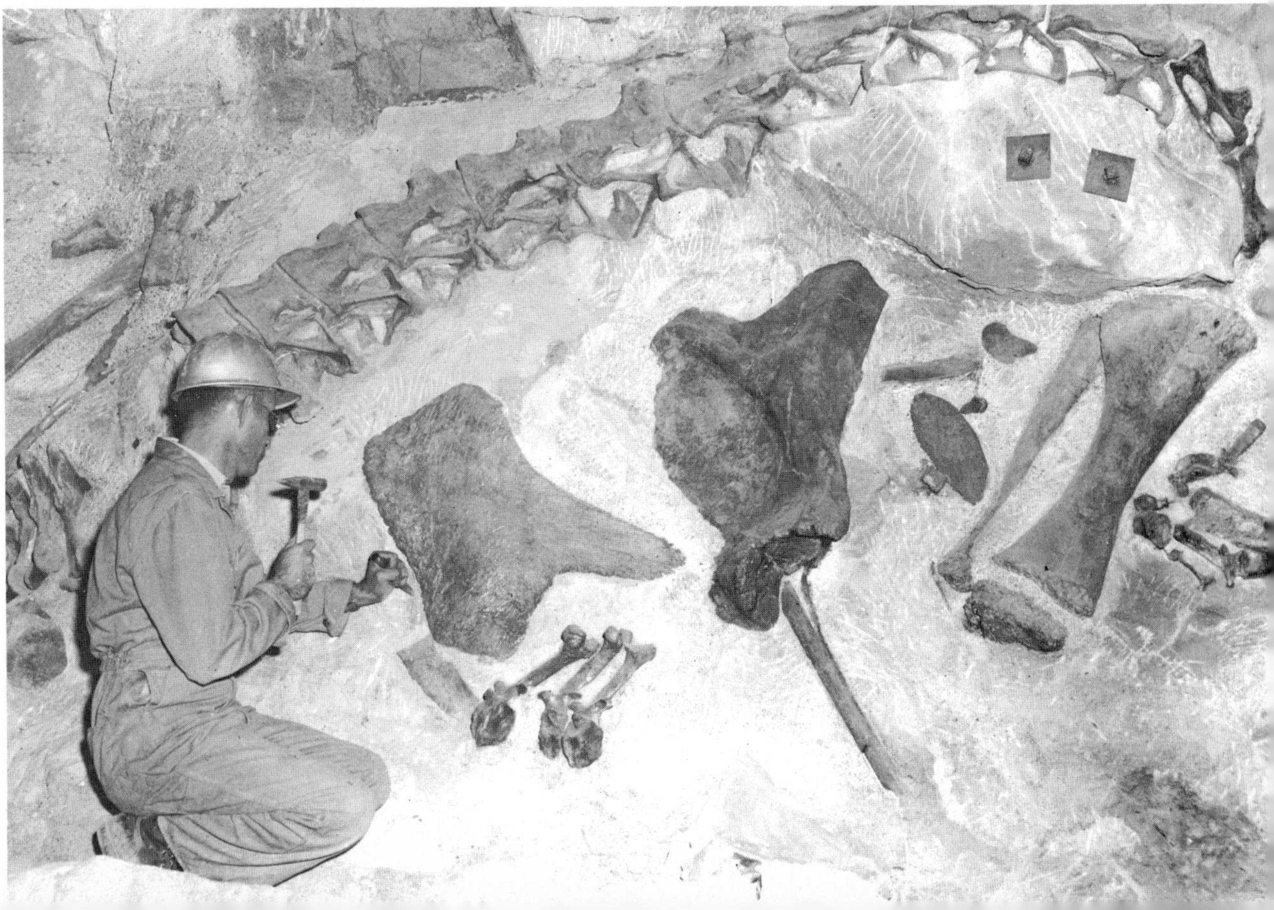

We know that cells of blue-green algae and bacteria differ from even the simplest of protozoans and molds in lacking a well-defined nucleus. The genes of these bacteria and blue-green algae are arranged on a threadlike structure, usually one thread per cell. Even the most powerful microscopes have not revealed in these organisms well-defined nuclear membranes or mitotic spindles. One might say that at this level of organization, division of labor between nucleus and cytoplasm, so characteristic of higher organisms, is poorly developed.

Blue-green algae carry out photosynthesis. However, their chlorophyll is scattered through the cytoplasm in the form of small granules, rather than in elaborately constructed chloroplasts like those found in other algae and in all green land plants.

These facts lead us to believe that the first great advances made by organisms after the appearance of living cells were the evolution of a well-organized nucleus, a division of labor between nucleus and cytoplasm, and the development of the mitotic spindle, asters, and other structures associated with mitosis. These evolutionary advances may have been completed more than two billion years ago.

How to Tell Time by the Rocks

You are probably asking what is the justification for stating that an event occurred one billion years ago. Surprisingly enough, there are instances where the time of some event that occurred in the remote past can be estimated with a fair degree of accuracy. One method is to measure the accumulation of certain isotopes (see Chapter 5) of lead and other elements that are products of the disintegration of radioactive materials originally present when the rocks were formed. This method is called the radioactive clock method and is the most accurate way to measure the age of **igneous** (IG·ne·us) rocks of the earth's crust. Igneous rocks are formed from molten materials such as the lava which comes from the outflow of volcanoes. It is presumed that the oldest rocks in the earth's crust are igneous, having been derived from molten materials formed fairly early in the history of the earth.

Many igneous rocks contain lead-206 (Pb^{206}), which is a stable isotope of lead derived from the disintegration of radioactive uranium-238 (U^{238}). The disintegration of U^{238}, like the disintegration of any radioactive substance, is unaffected by factors of the environment such as temperature, humidity, and pressure. The rate of disintegration is constant and is expressed in units of time called **half lives.** Perhaps the best way to understand a half life is to give an example.

Let us imagine that we have purified some U^{238}, and then taken exactly 2,000,000 atoms of U^{238} and sealed them in a bottle where there were no atoms of any other elements. We place a label on the bottle marking the year 1968. The U^{238} atoms in the bottle would continue to disintegrate at a given rate, so that at the end of 4.5 billion years there would be only 1,000,000 U^{238} atoms left, or just one half the number we started with. At the end of another 4.5 billion years the U^{238} atoms would be reduced by one half again, and so on, as shown below.

Date	*Number of Atoms of* U^{238} *in Sample*
A.D. 1968	2,000,000
A.D. 4,500,001,968	1,000,000
A.D. 9,000,001,968	500,000
A.D. 13,500,001,968	250,000

Thus the halflife of U^{238} is 4.5 billion years, which means that only half of the atoms of U^{238} present at a given moment will be on hand 4.5 billion years later.

As the U^{238} atoms in our sample disintegrate, a series of new radioactive substances forms, each with a specific half life, until the final stable product, Pb^{206}, is produced. Since Pb^{206} represents the "end of the line" of the disintegration process that started with U^{238} atoms, each atom of Pb^{206} therefore represents an atom of U^{236} in the "original" sample. Let

9-10 FOSSILIZATION

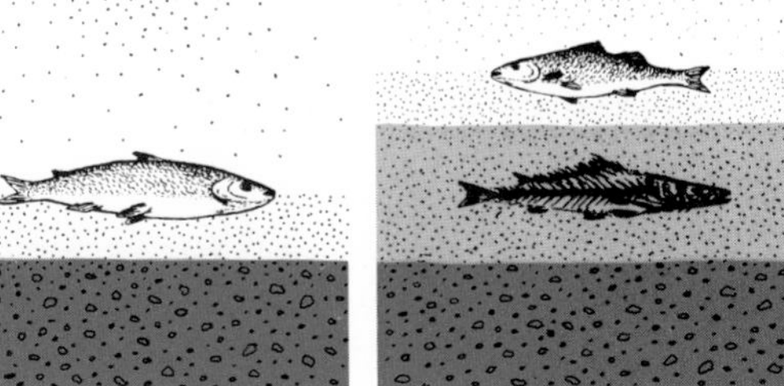
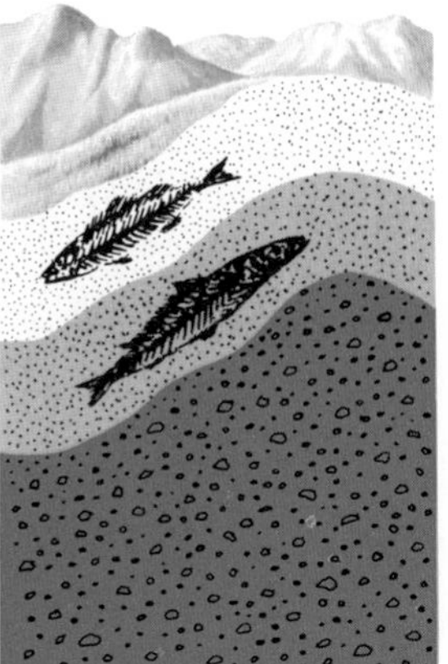

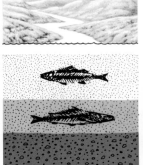

a A fish dies and is covered by sediment washed down from the mountains.

b Slowly the fish's remains are fossilized. Other fishes die and are covered.

c Different layers of sedimentary rocks have fossils of different ages.

d The positions of the sedimentary rocks and their fossils may be changed, and surface erosion may expose the fossils.

us suppose that our sample is a piece of igneous rock containing U^{238} and Pb^{206} atoms. We discover that the ratio of uranium to lead is approximately 2 to 1. How old would the rock be if we assumed that only U^{238} atoms were present at the time the rock was formed? By using the radioactive clock method, the age of some of the oldest igneous rocks has been determined to be about 3 billion years.

Fossils nearly always occur in a different kind of rock. Let us return to the example of fossils being formed in the mud at the bottom of some body of water. Figure 9-10 illustrates the process. The earth carried down by the river shown in the background becomes deposited as sediments (mud, gravel, etc.). The sediments cover the remains of the fishes and are slowly changed to rock by the pressure of the sediments that continue to form above them. Thus the sediments become converted to **sedimentary rocks.** As you can see, the sedimentary rocks are deposited in layers. You may have seen them exposed on cliffs or on highway or railroad cuts (Figure 9-11).

You have probably concluded that some useful information about the relative ages of sedimentary rocks and their fossils can be obtained merely by observing their positions. It is far more difficult to determine absolute age. In some cases, however, it can be done. Because particles of which sedimentary rocks are composed have many different origins, it is impossible to use the radioactive clock method to date them. However, sedimentary rocks are often associated with dated igneous rocks in such a way that the age of the sedimentary rock can be inferred. Such an association occurs where molten igneous materials have filled the cracks and spaces in sedimentary rocks. Since the sedimentary rocks were formed first, they must be at least as old as the intrusive igneous material. Knowing the age of the igneous material, we can determine the minimum age of the sedimentary rocks.

There are also a few instances where one can make a more accurate determination of the age of sedimentary rocks. For example, geologists know of a few places where a layer

New York Thruway Authority Photo

9-11 Strata of sedimentary rocks that have been exposed by a road cut. The letters **x**, **y**, and **z** indicate strata formed at different times. What is their relative age? Dating fossils by the relative positions of the strata is an important technique of geologists. How else may fossils be dated?

of molten igneous material spread over a layer of sedimentary rock in the process of formation. In this case the ages of the sedimentary rocks and the igneous rocks would be nearly the same.

A running diary of the earth's history is preserved in its rocks. The geologist has been able to determine the main events of the past by studying these rocks.

You should be able to look at Figures 9-10 and 9-11 and deduce some very useful information about the dating of layers of rocks. What will be the relation between the time the fossil is formed and the time the layer of rock is formed? Is there any way of telling the relative ages of the different layers? For example, would you conclude that the layer identified as X in Figure 9-11 is older or younger than the layer identified as Y? And what are the ages of these relative to Z? Once you have answered these questions, try this one. How do you think the time interval between X and Y compares to the interval between Y and Z? What are some of the assumptions that you are making in arriving at your answers?

The earth is thought to be exceedingly old. For most of its long history there is no evidence of life. In fact, the evidence of *abundant* life goes back only about 600 million years – about one-ninth of the total span. But there are good reasons to believe that the origin of life took place much earlier. There are fossils of blue-green algae and bacteria that are at least three billion years old. But even before these relatively simple organisms were present, there must have been a very long period of evolutionary change. Four billion years ago, more or less, the first complex organic molecules probably formed (possibly as described earlier in this chapter). Or possibly our hypothetical nucleic acid-type molecule appeared about this time. Untold eons then passed before the inhabitants of the earth were as complex as even the simplest virus. And the step from a level of organization such as the virus to the bacteria and blue-green algae seems so great that we can only assume that it required a very long period of time.

The oldest sedimentary rocks are about 600 million years old. It is only in the sedimentary rocks that fossils are abundant. Already in these oldest sedimentary rocks there is a rich variety of primitive plants and animals. These are so far advanced in organization over the bacteria and blue-green algae that we must assume that it took a huge amount of time for their evolution. Some of the highlights of the evolution of life are shown in Figure 9-12.

CONCLUDING REMARKS

It is generally believed that the earth's life originated here, but scientists have only hypotheses for the how's and the when's. Recent experiments have shown, however, that organic molecules, such as nucleotides, can be produced under conditions thought to resemble those of the primitive earth. The oceans of the young earth may have slowly accumulated a rich assortment of organic compounds. At some stage there must have appeared a molecule with unique abilities: in the presence of other molecules it could be duplicated directly. Such a molecule would have had the properties of the nucleic acids of today. Possibly primitive life passed through a stage similar to viruses, the simplest organisms today.

As the earth grew older, more advanced types of animals and plants appeared. There are three main groups: the bacteria, plants, and animals. The bacteria will be the subject of the next two chapters. Then we will study the plants—beginning with the primitive forms—and learn about their evolution into the great variety we see today: algae, mushrooms, ferns, mosses, trees, and flowers. Then, many chapters later, we will study the group to which we belong—the animals.

We should not end this chapter without noting some interesting things about the methods of science. One of the topics we have dealt with, the origin of life, is an example of a scientific problem for which there are no sure answers. We can only guess what might have happened. To be sure we can experiment with what-might-have-happened. But the results of the experiments could only tell us that what-might-have-happened *might have happened.* The results could never prove that what-might-have-happened *did happen.*

Not only does the problem of the origin of life appear to be insoluble, but there are reasons to believe that we will never have direct evidence for the events that occurred. The rocks that represent the time when life first might have appeared have been so altered that the record has been destroyed.

There have been many times in science when problems seemed impossible to solve. One example will have significance for us. A hundred years ago, geologists despaired of ever being able to measure accurately the age of rocks. They could tell by position which of two sedimentary rocks was older. *But how much older*—a million years or a hundred million years? They could only speculate and have the hopeless feeling that accurate measures would never be possible. Then the solution came from an entirely different field of science. Shortly after the Curies and others began exploring the mysteries of radioactivity, another scientist saw that radioactive uranium could be used to measure the age of rocks. So we must never conclude that a scientific problem is insoluble. Possibly some day we will be able to reconstruct the early evolution of life. We may not see a possible solution to the problem today, but tomorrow. . .

GUIDE QUESTIONS AND PROBLEMS

1. Would it be reasonable to assume that the earliest form of life on earth was a cellular organism containing chlorophyll?
2. What characteristic must man-made molecules possess before we can be satisfied that life has been created in a "test tube"?

9-12 A SYNOPSIS OF EARTH HISTORY

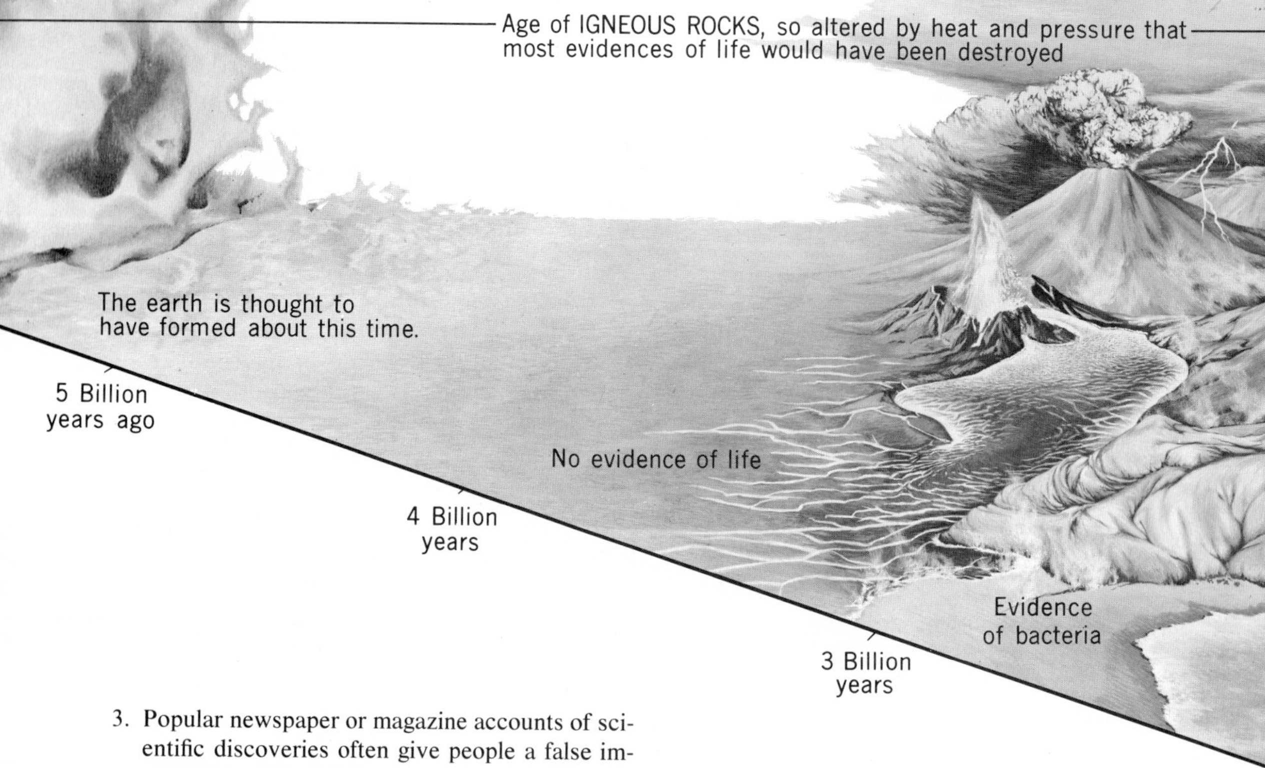

Age of IGNEOUS ROCKS, so altered by heat and pressure that most evidences of life would have been destroyed
The earth is thought to have formed about this time.
5 Billion years ago
No evidence of life
4 Billion years
Evidence of bacteria
3 Billion years

3. Popular newspaper or magazine accounts of scientific discoveries often give people a false impression. For instance, the title of an article might be: "Scientist Discovers How Life Originated on Earth." Why is such a title misleading?
4. The experiments of Miller, Fox, and Calvin all included the input of energy. What were the sources of energy in each of their experiments? Are these the same forms of energy that serve as the basis of life today?
5. Why is the evolution of a photosynthetic process thought to be a necessary step in the evolution of life on earth from primitive molecules?
6. What properties do viruses have that would lead us to say that they are living things? Why aren't viruses classified as cells?
7. What similarities exist between cell division (mitosis) and virus reproduction?

RELATED READING

Books

For a more complete account of the fundamental problems of studying viruses and the diseases they cause . . .

Burnet, F. M., *Viruses and Man*, Penguin Books, Baltimore, 1953.

Smith, K. M., *Beyond the Microscope*, Penguin Books, Baltimore, 1949.

Stanley, W. M., and E. G. Valens, *Viruses and the Nature of Life*, Dutton, New York, 1961.

Weidel, W., *Virus*, University of Michigan Press, Ann Arbor, Mich., 1959.

For an authoritative account of fossils and the study of fossils . . .

Fenton, C. L., and M. A. Fenton, *The Fossil Book: A Record of Prehistoric Life*, Doubleday, Garden City, 1958.

Simpson, G. G., *Life of the Past: An Introduction to Paleontology*, Yale University Press, New Haven, Conn., 1953.

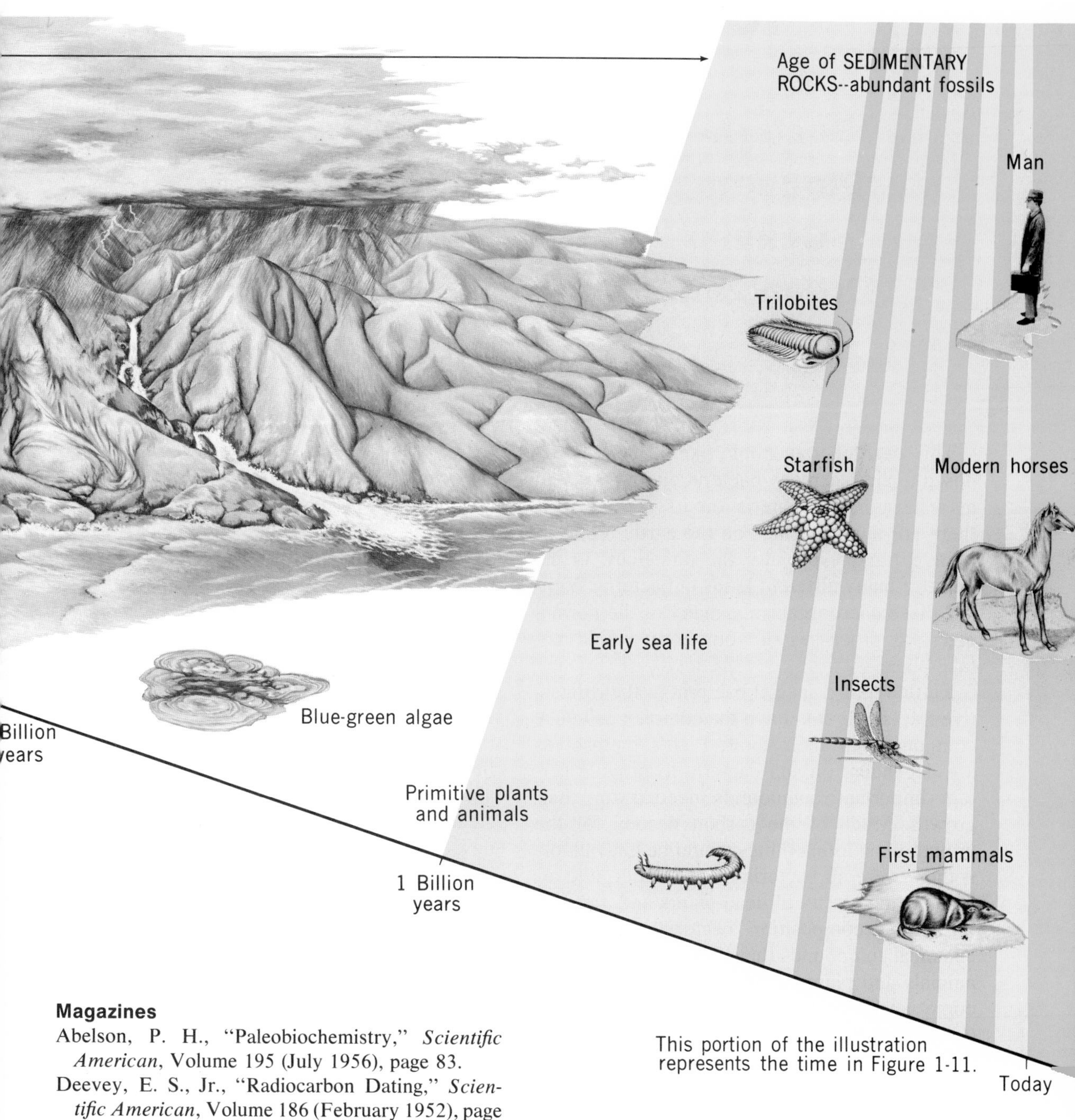

Magazines

Abelson, P. H., "Paleobiochemistry," *Scientific American*, Volume 195 (July 1956), page 83.

Deevey, E. S., Jr., "Radiocarbon Dating," *Scientific American*, Volume 186 (February 1952), page 24. (A correction to this article appears in the April 1952 issue, page 2.)

Fraenkel-Conrat, J., "Rebuilding a Virus," *Scientific American*, Volume 194 (June 1956), page 42.

Horne, R. "The Structure of Viruses," *Scientific American*, Volume 208 (January 1963), page 48.

Lwoff, A., "The Life Cycle of a Virus," *Scientific American*, Volume 190 (March 1954), page 34.

10

Bacteria — Pioneers of Cellular Organization

This page of your book, like all objects exposed to air, has many bacteria on it. Your skin may have more bacteria on its surface than there are human beings on the earth. Your digestive tract, especially the intestines, is the home of many different kinds of bacteria. Without these microorganisms, many of the normal digestive processes of your body would not take place.

Cattle require special bacteria in their digestive tracts to break down the complex cellulose compounds in their food. Plants themselves are dependent on soil bacteria to provide certain important compounds needed for their growth. Much of the carbon needed for the growth of all living things would be unavailable if there were no bacteria in soil, water, and air to cause the decay of dead plants and animals. By this decomposition bacteria release the chemical compounds that composed these dead animals and plants. These chemicals then become available for use by living organisms (Chapter 36).

Bacteria are found in the depths of the oceans. They have been collected miles above the earth. They have been isolated from the ice packs of the Arctic and Antarctic, and from the hot, humid rain forests of the tropics. It would be virtually impossible to name a part of the earth's land surfaces or oceans where bacteria are *not* found (Inquiry 10-1).

It is obvious that bacteria must be small in size to be present in such large numbers in so many places, yet not be seen with the unaided eye. How do we know that bacteria are so universally present? How do we know that bacteria exist at all, for that matter?

DISCOVERY OF BACTERIA

Advances in our understanding of living things often depend on the invention of special instruments. Because of their extremely small size, viruses could not be detected by the optical microscope. Their presence was assumed, however, from evidence of their effects on living tissue. The electron microscope later *confirmed* their existence. It was not so with bacteria. Before the invention of the optical microscope, men lived in ignorance of the presence of these microorganisms.

Leeuwenhoek—the First Bacteriologist

A man who must seem like an old friend by now, Antony van Leeuwenhoek, was the first to observe microorganisms. In much the same way that you and I might become interested in photography or stamp collecting, Leeuwenhoek became interested in lens grinding and the construction of microscopes. Suppose that you, instead of Leeuwenhoek, had just completed a new instrument that would magnify small objects many times and make them clearly visible for the first time. What would you choose to look at? Where would you start? The list would be endless, but it would have only a limited number of possibilities as imaginative as Leeuwenhoek's choice—a drop of water! You already know part of the story: we first encountered Leeuwenhoek in Chapter 2, where we learned of his role in the biogenesis-abiogenesis debate.

Leeuwenhoek discovered life in a form that was unexpected. He was amazed at the variety of tiny living objects he saw wriggling and dart-

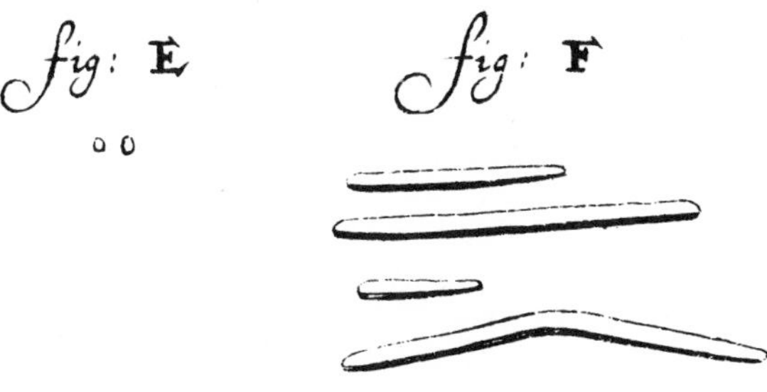

From *Arcana Naturae*, Detecta ab Antonio van Leeuwenhoek, 1695

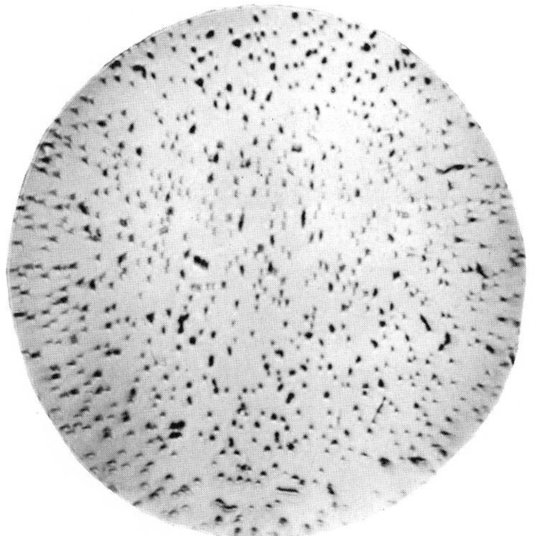

J. G. Van Cittert-Eymers

10–1 (Top) Drawings of bacteria made by Leeuwenhoek and published by the Royal Society of London in 1695. **(Bottom)** Photographic evidence that Leeuwenhoek could see the shapes he recorded in his drawings. The photograph was taken recently, using one of Leeuwenhoek's original microscopes (see Figure 2–6). Although the photograph may seem fuzzy, if you look closely you will see many small rounded shapes and several rodlike ones, similar to the enlarged drawings above the photograph.

ing across the field of his little microscope when he examined drops of various kinds of water (Figure 10-1). He became so enthusiastic about what he saw that he wrote several letters to the Royal Society in London. One letter with an account of what he saw was published by the Society in 1677. This article included the very first description of bacteria.

In 1695 Leeuwenhoek submitted another letter with additional drawings of bacteria (labeled "fig. E" and "fig. F" in Figure 10-1). Compare his drawings with the drawings of bacteria made with the aid of a modern microscope (Figure 10-2).

Bacteria – Shape and Size

Until the structure and reproduction of viruses were clarified, bacteria were considered the smallest living things. When we talk about sizes of viruses we use a scale of millimicrons. Bacteria are measured in microns (Inquiry 10-2, and for comparative sizes of viruses and bacteria, Inquiry 1-4). Bacteria range in size from about 0.2 micron (μ) to 2μ in width, and from 2μ to 10μ in length. (For one type of bac-

10–2 Three basic shapes of bacteria. Some bacteria occur as single cells; others form colonies in pairs, chains, or irregular clusters. How do bacteria compare in size and shape with viruses?

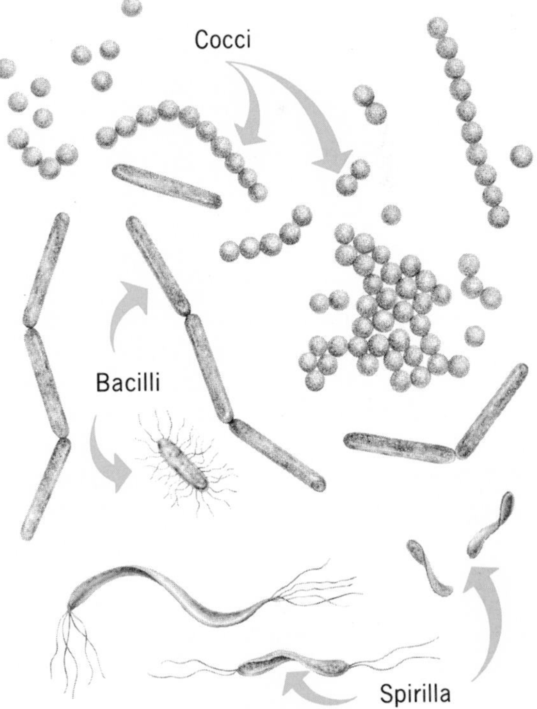

teria, the terms "length" and "width" do not apply; these bacteria are sphere-shaped and can be described by a single dimension, their diameter.) All of the dimensions cited are within the range of the compound microscope.

Three basic forms of bacteria have been recognized. You will look for these in Laboratory Inquiry 10-2. There are rod forms (**bacilli**—ba·SIL·i), spheres (**cocci**—KOK·si), and spiral or corkscrew forms (**spirilla**—spy·RIL·a). These forms are illustrated in Figure 10-2. Although bacteria are unicellular organisms, the cells of some species may remain associated after cell division and form groups or colonies (Figure 10-2). Rod-shaped bacteria may form colonies that look like threads or filaments. These colonies are composed of the rod-shaped cells placed end to end. Sphere-shaped bacteria may occur in pairs, in groups of four, in irregular grapelike clusters, or in beadlike chains. Spiral-shaped bacteria seldom form colonies.

STRUCTURE AND NUTRITION OF BACTERIA

Bacteria appear at the level of cellular organization—and immediately above the viruses. In many ways, however, a bacterium is much simpler in structure than the cells of the multicellular plants and animals which you may have examined.

Cell Structure

Biologists generally agree that bacteria do not have nuclei of the type found in cells of higher plants and animals. In the cells of these more complex organisms, the nucleus contains a nucleolus or two, is bounded by a visible membrane, and divides by mitosis. In bacteria there are no nucleoli, no nuclear membrane, and no typical mitosis. Yet, it has been demonstrated repeatedly that there is some kind of mechanism in bacteria for the transmission of hereditary characteristics.

Experiments have shown that the bacterial hereditary determiners have an arrangement that is also characteristic of more complex organisms. Could it be that instead of a complex nucleus, the bacteria, in contrast to more complex organisms, have a "nucleus" which is composed of a single chromosome?

Let us try another attack on the problem. We know that DNA comprises the genetic material of living cells. Perhaps we can answer the question by studying the DNA and its location in bacteria.

To locate DNA in a cell, special stains specific for DNA can be used. The results obtained from staining different kinds of bacteria vary. Some forms have their DNA concentrated in one or two deeply staining bodies (Figure 10-3a). Shortly before a bacterium divides, these DNA bodies divide and are equally distributed to the daughter cells. In this way the DNA bodies resemble chromosomes replicating in a dividing cell. More critical observations of bacterial "chromosomes" have been made by studying ultra-thin sections of bacteria under the electron microscope (Figure 10-3b). Here the strands of DNA can be seen packed into a bacterial chromosome. It has been determined for some species of bacteria that the DNA molecule is about 3 millimicrons ($m\mu$) wide and as much as 1,200 microns (μ), or more than 1 mm, long! A bacterial DNA molecule is thus more than 500 times as long as the bacterial cell that contains it! To make these measurements, bacterial chromosomes have been removed from the cell. In this condition the replicating strand of DNA has been observed to be in the form of a circle. Within the cell the circle of DNA appears to be twisted and folded as in Figure 10-3b. Are these structures similar to the chromosomes of more highly evolved organisms? Some investigators think they are. But until we know more about the fine structure of both kinds of chromosomes, it is difficult for us to determine their degree of resemblance.

Other structures of a bacterial cell (Figure 10-4) are small vacuoles, ribosomes, and granules of stored food. (The ribosomes are too

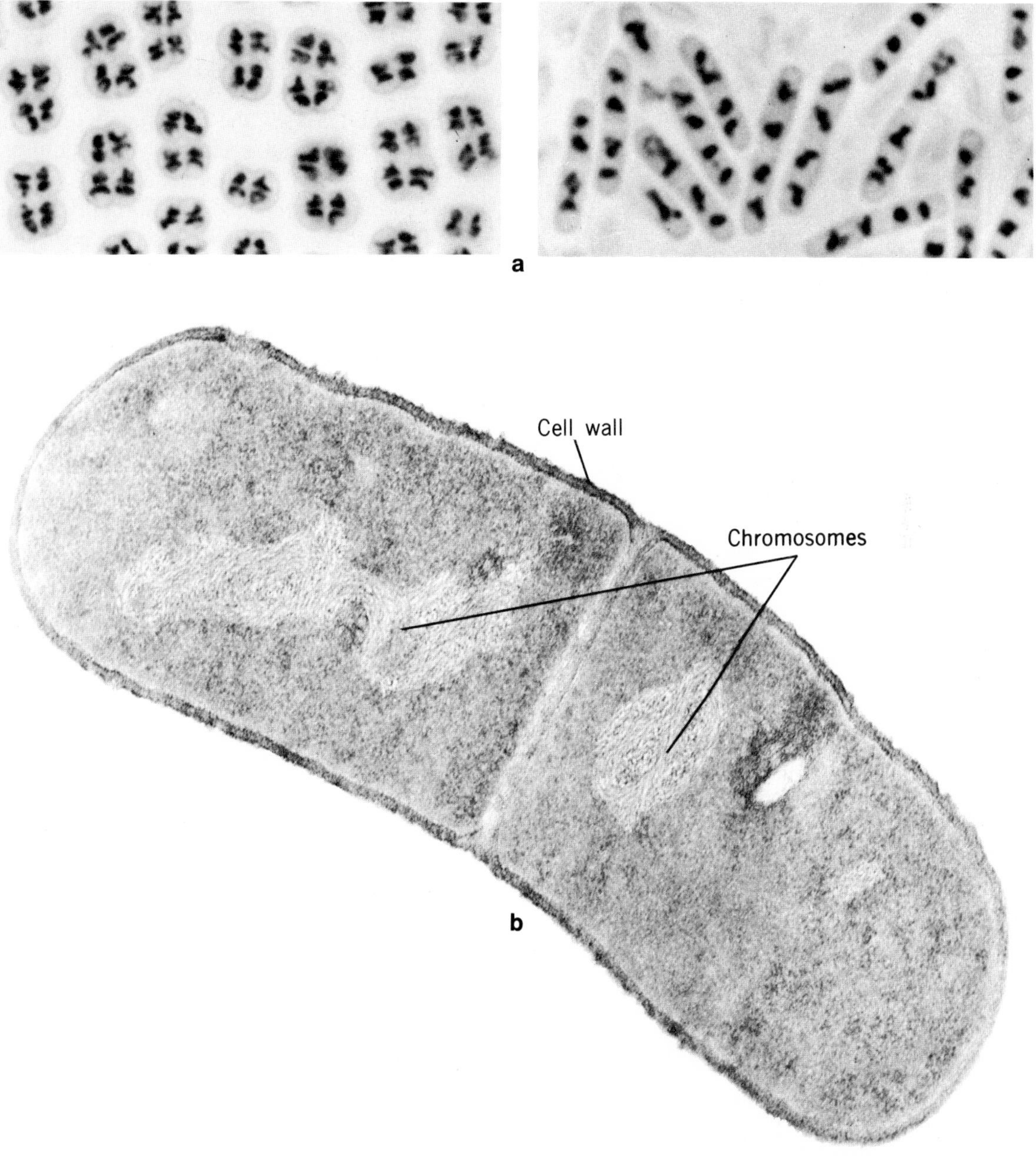

All photos by C. F. Robinow

10–3 **a.** Bacteria of two of the basic forms (cocci and bacilli) prepared with a special stain to reveal their DNA. The DNA is localized in discrete bodies—the bacterial chromosomes—shown in various stages of division. The photographs were made through a compound microscope. **b.** An ultrathin section of a dividing bacterium, photographed with an electron microscope. The sectioned bacterial chromosome in each daughter cell shows as twisted, contorted strands of DNA. (87,000 ×)

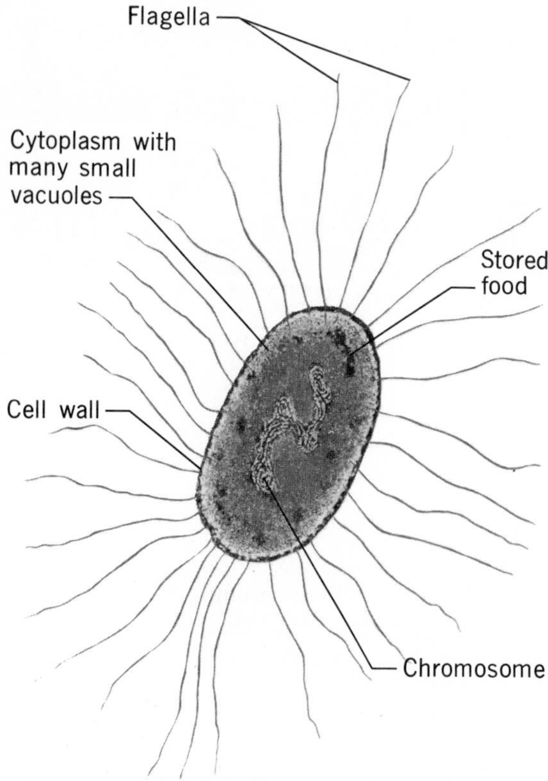

10–4 A diagram of a generalized bacterium. According to its shape, how would you classify this bacterium—as a bacillus, coccus, or spirillum (Figure 10–2)? Note that the flagella are embedded in the cytoplasm, inside the cell wall (see also Figure 10–6). Are all bacteria flagellated? What structure of this bacterial cell is like that of a plant? Is there also a structural resemblance to an animal? Which structures would you expect to find, in similar form, in both plant and animal cells?

small to show in Figure 10-4.) Water, of course, is an important constituent of bacterial cells. As much as 90 percent of the cell is water. The movement of dissolved materials in and out of the cell is regulated by a cell membrane, formed by the cytoplasm that lies next to the inner face of the cell wall. Structurally, the cytoplasm of a bacterial cell is quite similar to cytoplasm found in the living cells of more complex organisms.

In view of the importance of mitochondria in the oxidative reactions of the cell (Chapter 6), we might expect to find them in the cells of all organisms. Bacteria, however, lack mitochondria—at least of the sort found in most cells. Some bacterial species have structures that vaguely suggest mitochondria. In other species of bacteria the enzymes normally found in mitochondria are localized on or near the cell wall.

The bacterial cell wall (Figure 10-3b) is a complex structure composed of some proteins and many carbohydrates. Unlike the cell walls of plants, however, cell walls of most bacteria do not contain cellulose. Some bacteria may have a slime capsule surrounding the cell wall. Among bacteria that cause infections, those with capsules seem to be more resistant to the defenses of the body than those without capsules. The encapsulated forms, therefore, are more likely to cause disease. The bacterium causing pneumonia is an excellent example of a capsulated form that causes disease. The same bacterium without capsules does not cause pneumonia.

A unique feature of some bacteria is their ability to form highly resistant **endospores** (EN·doe·sporz—Figure 10-5). Endospores are produced when part of the living substance of a bacterium is surrounded by an almost indestructible wall. Mature endospores occur singly in the bacterium. They look like tiny spheres or ovals occupying either the center or one end of the old cell in which they are formed. When an endospore germinates, it gives rise to a single bacterium. Endospores can survive the most adverse environmental conditions. Long periods of drying seem to have little or no effect upon them. In one experiment, endospores were kept in a dry condition for sixty years. At the end of this time, they readily germinated when they were provided with water and proper nutrients and kept at a suitable temperature.

Most bacteria are killed by boiling water (100° C), but endospores resist this rough treatment. A temperature of 121° C (250° F) for a period of fifteen minutes is required to kill endospores of bacteria. Do you recall Pasteur, Spallanzani, Needham, and other early investigators of spontaneous generation (Chapter 2)? If they had known about endospores and their resistance to boiling, the mystery of whether or not spontaneous generation had occurred in "sterile" flasks would have been easier for them to solve.

Many diluted chemicals such as chlorine, "Merthiolate," and iodine may kill bacteria—but not their endospores. Even deepfreezing will not kill them. During recent expeditions to Antarctica, biologists isolated and germinated endospores obtained from snow and ice deposited centuries ago. What remarkable little bits of life endospores are to withstand such drastic treatment! Nothing else in the world of living things seems to be quite so resistant to adverse conditions of the environment. We can hardly escape the conclusion that endospores have survival value for the bacteria that form them.

Many kinds of bacteria are motile—they can move. Motile bacteria have slender, whiplike threads called **flagella** (fla·JEL·a—Figure 10-6), which propel the bacteria through the water in which they live.

The diameter of a single flagellum is approximately 12 mμ—about the same dimension as the diameter of a molecule of some proteins. Because of their small size, the flagella of bacteria are invisible under a compound microscope unless first specially treated and stained. Studies using the electron microscope show that the flagella of most bacteria consist of a single strand (Figure 10-6). Chemical analyses have shown the substance of the strand to resemble the contractile proteins responsible for the contraction of animal muscle cells. The presence of the protein gives us an explanation of the physical basis for bacterial propulsion, just as it explains muscle contraction. (Propulsion by means of flagella will be discussed along with other types of locomotion in living organisms in Chapter 25.)

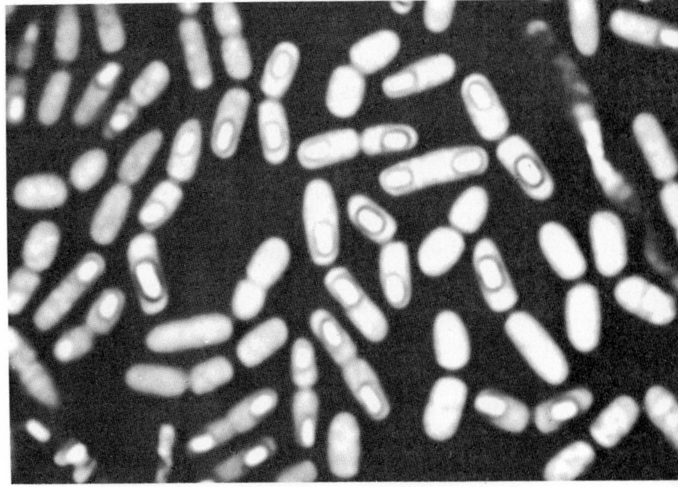
C. F. Robinow

10–5 Bacteria with endospores. A single, thick-walled endospore is produced by each bacterial cell. In what way is an endospore of importance in the life of a bacterium? (2550 ×)

Nutrition of Bacteria

Like all other living organisms, bacteria need energy for their growth, their maintenance, and their reproduction.

Most bacteria are **heterotrophic** (het·er·o-TROF·ik) in their nutrition. That is, they cannot synthesize their organic compounds from simple inorganic substances. They require many complex organic materials such as amino acids, glucose, and vitamins, in addition to inorganic substances. Since most bacteria are not photosynthetic, they cannot use light, as green plants do, to synthesize the substances they need. There is only one other source of energy readily available—the organic compounds in the environment. For example, the soil is full of organic compounds in the form of **humus,** which is the material resulting from the partial decay of plants and animals. Many soil-inhabiting bacteria have very extensive enzyme systems that break down the complex substances of humus to simpler compounds. The bacteria can then absorb and utilize these simpler compounds as a source of energy.

Organisms capable of obtaining their nutrition from organic compounds in this way are called **saprophytes** (SAP·ro·fites). Bacterial saprophytes cause decay of dead animal and plant material as they convert complex organic compounds to simpler ones.

Some bacteria lack certain complex systems of enzymes. They depend on enzymes of other living organisms (hosts) to synthesize glucose, amino acids, vitamins, and other substances for growth. These bacteria are parasites. Many parasitic bacteria cause disease and sometimes the death of their host, a topic discussed in the next chapter.

Some kinds of bacteria are **autotrophic** (aw-toe·TROF·ik)—that is, they can synthesize organic compounds which are necessary for their structure and metabolism from simple inorganic substances. A few of the autotrophic species are photosynthetic. Photosynthetic bacteria have a pigment very similar in molecular structure to the chlorophyll which is found in more complex green plants. Unlike most green plants, which have their chlorophyll in chloroplasts, bacterial chlorophyll is dispersed in the bacterial cell. Other autotrophic species of bacteria obtain their energy from oxidation of some inorganic substance such as iron, sulfur, atmospheric hydrogen, or nitrogen compounds. No matter what the source of energy, some of it is directed to the production of new bacterial cells—that is, to reproduction.

10–6 A tuft of flagella at the end of a bacillus. This electron micrograph confirms that the base of a flagellum is in the cytoplasm of the cell. (47,500 ×)

A. L. Houwink

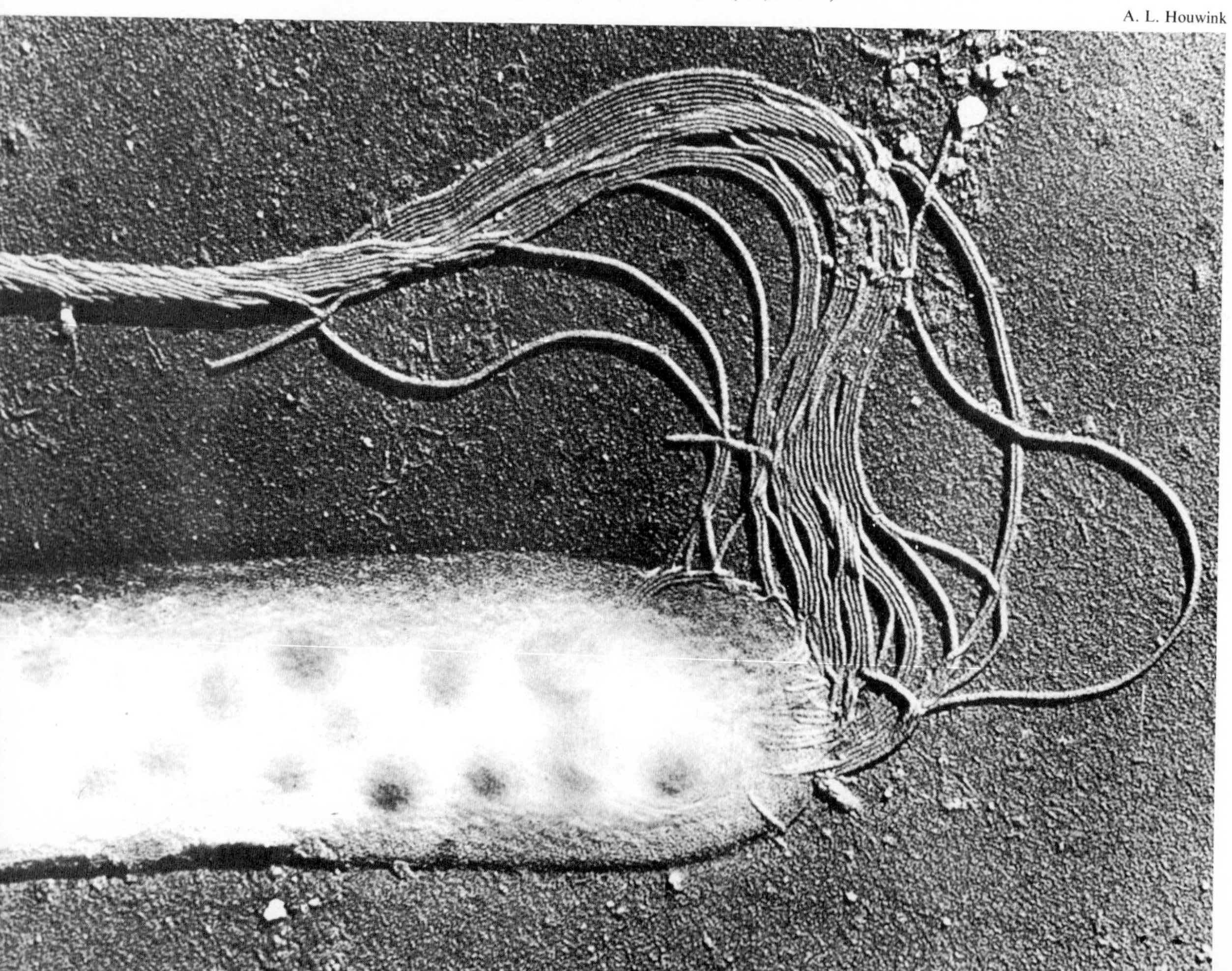

REPRODUCTION OF A UNICELLULAR ORGANISM

Using your microscope in the laboratory, you will look at cultures of living bacteria. In the same way that Leeuwenhoek and Pasteur saw them, you can see countless thousands of tiny cells. You might wonder, as they did, about the origin of these little cells. If all of them arose from preexisting cells, as Pasteur and others suggested long ago (Chapter 2), then bacteria must have a rapid method of reproduction. Cell division is that method.

Cell Division in Bacteria

In multicellular organisms, the cells produced by cell division generally remain together, and larger organisms are the result. A bacterium, however, is a single-celled organism. It divides and produces two cells, both of which become independent organisms. This kind of reproduction is **asexual** (ay·SEK·shew-al), meaning that it does not involve the union of sex cells in the manner characteristic of so many animals and plants.

When there are sufficient amounts of water and nutrients, and when the temperature is favorable, bacteria can divide very rapidly. A bacterium can divide, and the two daughter cells can grow and start dividing—all in a period of twenty minutes. If we were to start with a single bacterium, it soon would divide to form 2 cells, then approximately twenty minutes later each of the 2 cells would divide simultaneously to form 4. Each of the 4 would divide to form 8, then 16, 32, 64, 128, 256, and so on—doubling every twenty minutes. If this kind of cell increase, called a geometric increase (Figure 10-7), continued once every twenty minutes for twenty-four hours, a mass of bacteria weighing approximately 2,000 tons would be produced from a single cell! Actually this would never happen. The bacteria would soon run out of sufficient water and nutrients needed for their reproduction. (You will be able to observe the rate at which a colony develops from a single bacterium, and the size to which such a colony grows, in Inquiry 11-1.) Also, as a bacterial population grows, the bacteria usually produce substances, such as alcohol or acids, which are poisonous to them. The accumulation of these substances can cause a decrease in the rate of reproduction, so that the number of new cells produced is about equal to the number of cells that die. As time passes, even greater concentrations of poisons accumulate. These can cause the death rate of cells to exceed the rate of reproduction, and sooner or later all the cells may die. Figure 10-8 is a graph showing changes in rates of reproduction of bacteria resulting from the changes in the environment described above.

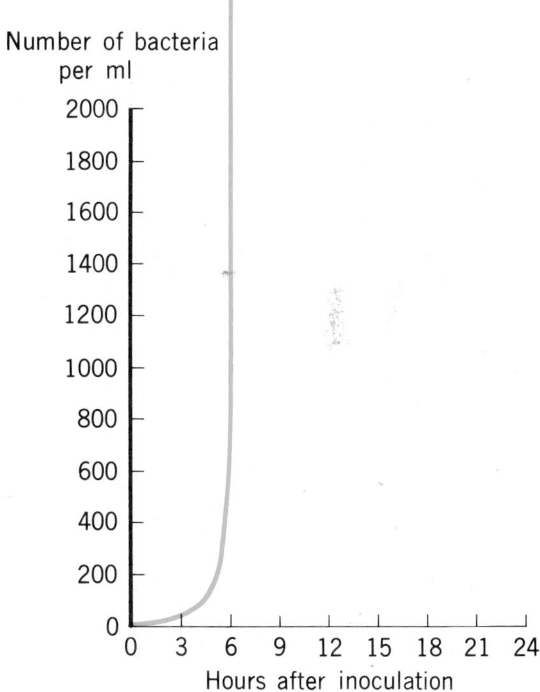

10–7 Initial growth of a population of bacteria. The almost vertical ascent of the yellow line illustrates graphically the rapid reproduction of bacterial cells under ideal conditions. Could the increase go on indefinitely, as indicated by the yellow line that runs off the top of the page?

The Life Cycle—The Beginnings of Sexual Reproduction

Do bacteria reproduce sexually, that is, do they ever form sex cells, or **gametes** (GAM·eats), that unite with one another in the production of offspring? These questions have been asked for many years, but until recently the answers were very elusive. Many descriptions of a sexual stage in bacteria were published, but these descriptions differed so much that they only emphasized the fact that no one was quite sure about the life cycle of bacteria.

It had long been known that bacteria mutate. Futhermore, it was found that mutations could be induced by exposing bacteria to high-energy radiation (X rays or ultraviolet radiation) or certain chemicals. Could an experiment be devised to combine two mutant strains of bacteria so that they would have the opportunity of exchanging or making new combinations of the mutant genes?

Such an experiment was undertaken in 1946 at Yale University. The investigators were Joshua Lederberg and Edward L. Tatum, who later were awarded the Nobel prize for this and other researches. First they had to obtain the two different bacterial strains that they hoped to cross. To do this, they first selected a "wild type" of bacteria capable of synthesizing the substances it needed for growth. Using irradiation to produce mutations, Lederberg and Tatum obtained a "triple nutritional mutant"—a strain that was unable to make three of the substances required for its growth (Figure 10-9). If this mutant was to grow at all, it had to be supplied with the three substances which it could

10–8 What would happen to the bacterial population in Figure 10–7 can be seen by using the logarithm of the number of bacterial cells present in the culture. The result is a graphic illustration of the growth and decline of the large population of cells. What point on this graph corresponds to the point at which the yellow line measuring population growth ran off the page in Figure 10–7?

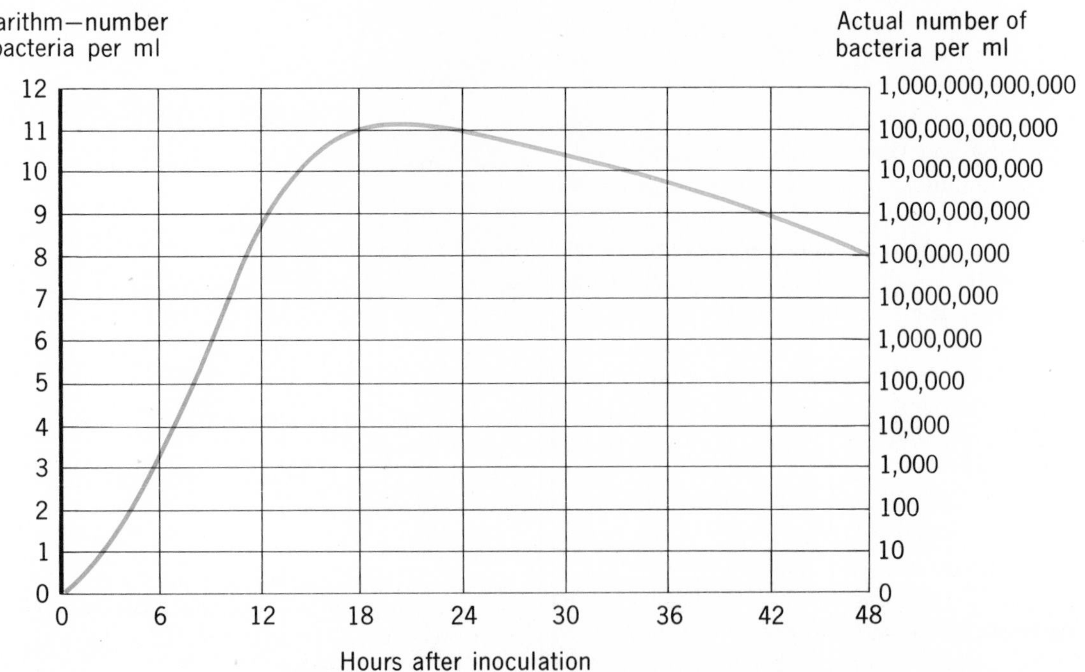

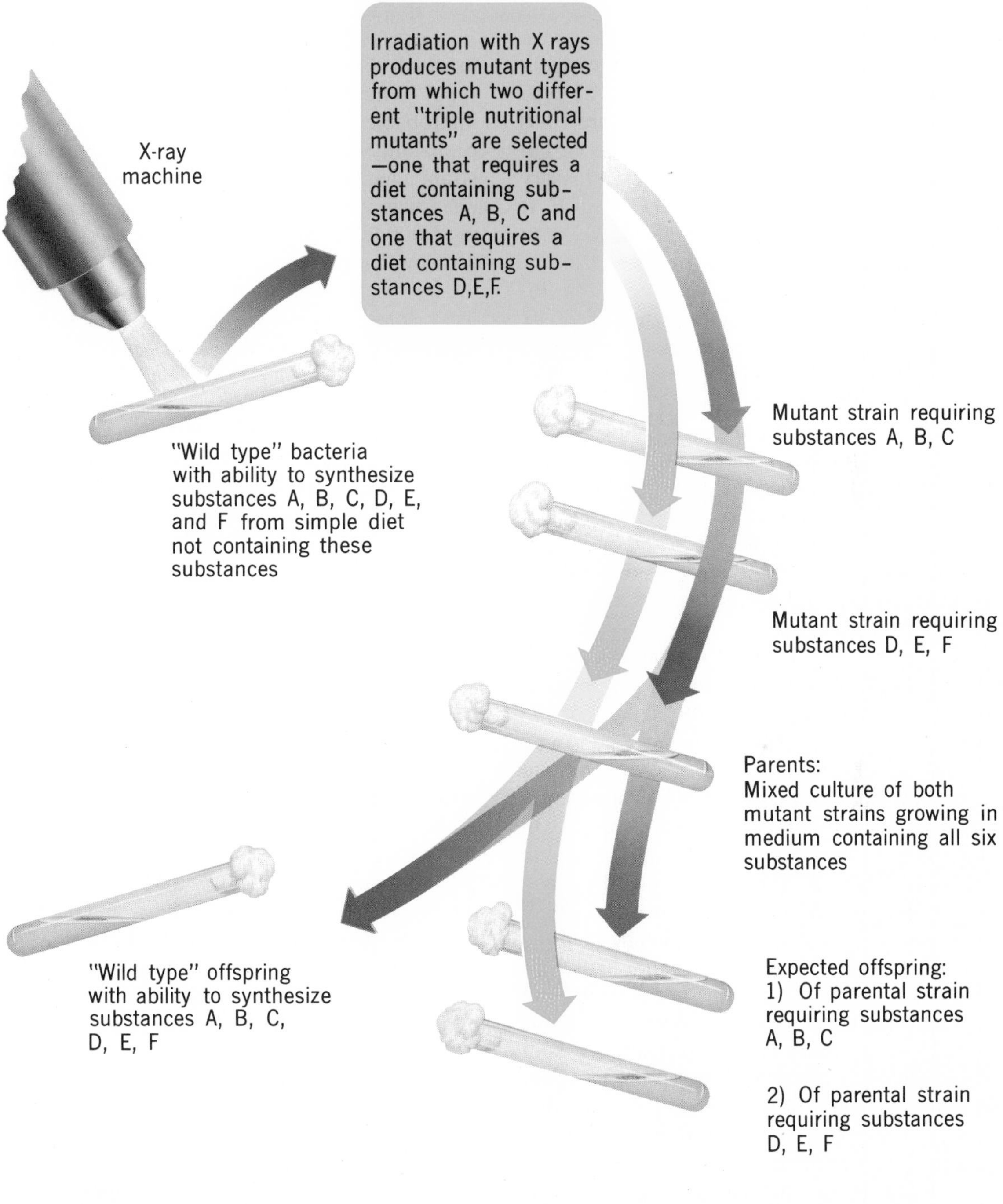

Irradiation with X rays produces mutant types from which two different "triple nutritional mutants" are selected —one that requires a diet containing substances A, B, C and one that requires a diet containing substances D,E,F.

X-ray machine

"Wild type" bacteria with ability to synthesize substances A, B, C, D, E, and F from simple diet not containing these substances

Mutant strain requiring substances A, B, C

Mutant strain requiring substances D, E, F

Parents:
Mixed culture of both mutant strains growing in medium containing all six substances

"Wild type" offspring with ability to synthesize substances A, B, C, D, E, F

Expected offspring:
1) Of parental strain requiring substances A, B, C

2) Of parental strain requiring substances D, E, F

10–9 The principal steps of the Lederberg-Tatum experiment. In what respect does the experiment offer convincing evidence that some bacteria do exchange genetic material and produce offspring with new combinations of genes?

not make for itself. For convenience let us call these substances A, B, and C.

A second triple nutritional mutant was obtained by once again irradiating the wild type bacteria. The second mutant (also Figure 10-9) could synthesize substances A, B, and C, but could not synthesize three other necessary compounds, which we will call D, E, and F. It appeared that six genes had been made to mutate, three in each mutant strain.

The two mutant strains could be grown together if the growth medium contained all six substances—three that one mutant needed and three that the other needed. If sexual reproduction could occur at all, it would be detected in the mixed culture of the two mutant strains. Thus, if any cells were formed that had the mutant genes combined in new ways, we would suspect sexual reproduction as the cause.

The experiment proceeded in this way. The genetically different strains were brought together for several hours and given the opportunity to grow and reproduce. The next step was to isolate single cells from the mixed culture and test them for their nutritional requirements. What might we expect to find as a result of these tests? It would be no surprise to find strains of offspring exactly like the mutant parent strains—that is, some offspring requiring substances A, B, and C for their growth and others requiring D, E, and F. If these were the only kinds of offspring we could isolate, we would conclude that probably no sexual reproduction—no exchange of genetic material—had occurred. On the other hand, if such an exchange *had* occurred, we might expect to find new kinds of offspring. Two new kinds would be (1) bacteria requiring all six substances for growth, and (2) bacteria that could synthesize all six substances. The second kind would be like the wild type; it could grow on a medium without supplements.

For Lederberg and Tatum, the testing of offspring proved rewarding. They isolated the wild type of bacteria from the mixed culture! But was this really an example of genetic recombination, resulting from sexual reproduction, or was it simply a case of "back mutation" in which the mutant genes reverted to the wild type? The latter explanation seemed most improbable to the investigators, because the probability of *three* genes of either mutant strain changing back to the wild type all at once was very, very slight—about one chance in 1,000,000,000,000,000,000. All biologists are now convinced, as a result of these experiments, that recombination *does* occur in at least some species of bacteria. This is best interpreted to show that some kind of sexual process is responsible.

This conviction was later confirmed by visual evidence. Electron microscopes were used to photograph cells in mixtures of two mutant strains, which could be distinguished by their structure. It was discovered that pairs of bacterial cells, one of each type, form little conjugation tubes (Figure 10-10), which make possible the physical transfer of genetic material from one cell to the other. It seems that we have been introduced to a simple means of sexual reproduction in the evolution of primitive organisms. In later chapters we will also see to what extent sexual reproduction has evolved in plants and animals more complex than the bacteria.

Transduction

With your knowledge of the structure and reproduction of viruses (Chapter 9) and the role of DNA (Chapter 8) you will find it easy to understand the process of **transduction.** In addition to conjugation, genetic material can be relayed from one bacterium to another by a "third party." The third party in our story is a bacteriophage.

You will recall that certain kinds of bacteria are used by some strains of bacteriophage as a substrate in which the phage particles can multiply. When multiplication is complete the phage may destroy its passive host and escape. We will call the host bacteria the **donors.** Donor bacteria "give" some of their genetic material to the multiplying phage particles (Figure 10-11). Thus after reproduction of the phage in the donor is complete, new phage particles are released that contain the genetic material of the phage plus a little of the genetic material of the donor. In a way, the virus is a "go-between," carrying a "genetic message" from one bacterium to another of the same species. The bacterium receiving genetic material from the donor via the phage is called the **recipient.** The recipient is a bacterium that the phage will attack but will not destroy as it destroyed the donor. After the phage attaches to the recipient it injects phage and donor genes into the recipient. Thus the recipient contains three complements of genetic material; that of the phage, the donor, and its own. The genetic material of the donor becomes a part of the genetic material of the recipient bacterium. The genetic material of the phage may multiply in the recipient, but it does not seem to hurt its host.

The recipient divides and forms daughter cells. Some of these daughter cells will receive genetic material that was derived from the donor and will have the characteristics of the donor bacterium instead of the recipient bacterium. So here is another way that an exchange of genetic material can be accomplished

10–10 Visible evidence of a possible basis for the exchange of cell materials between bacteria. This electron micrograph reveals a little tube between bacteria of two different strains. Biologists believe that genetic material may move from one cell to the other through the tube.

T. F. Anderson

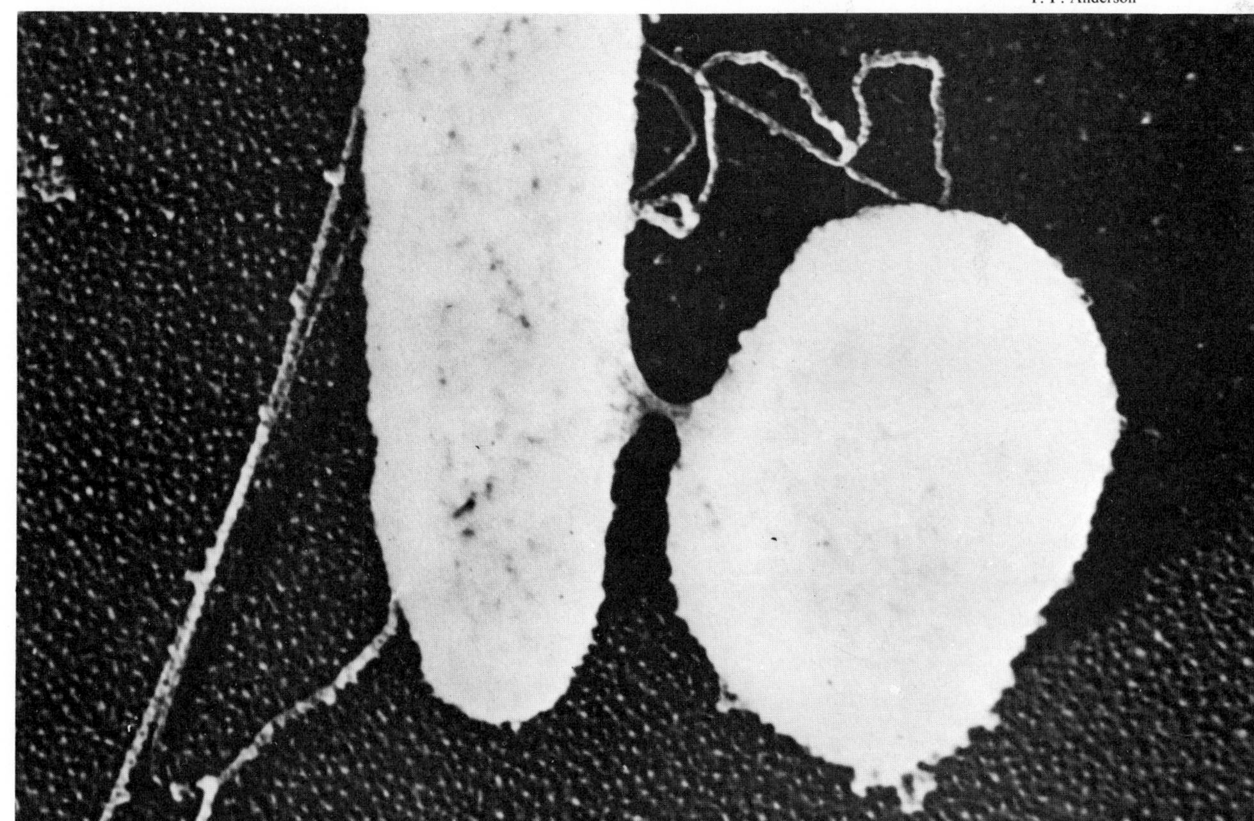

10-11 TRANSDUCTION IN BACTERIA

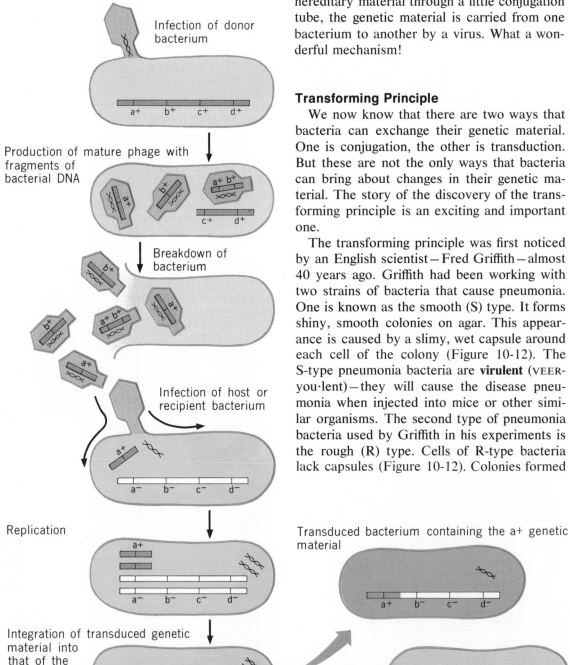

Infection of donor bacterium

a+ b+ c+ d+

Production of mature phage with fragments of bacterial DNA

Breakdown of bacterium

Infection of host or recipient bacterium

a− b− c− d−

Replication

Integration of transduced genetic material into that of the recipient bacterium

in bacteria. But instead of direct passage of hereditary material through a little conjugation tube, the genetic material is carried from one bacterium to another by a virus. What a wonderful mechanism!

Transforming Principle

We now know that there are two ways that bacteria can exchange their genetic material. One is conjugation, the other is transduction. But these are not the only ways that bacteria can bring about changes in their genetic material. The story of the discovery of the transforming principle is an exciting and important one.

The transforming principle was first noticed by an English scientist—Fred Griffith—almost 40 years ago. Griffith had been working with two strains of bacteria that cause pneumonia. One is known as the smooth (S) type. It forms shiny, smooth colonies on agar. This appearance is caused by a slimy, wet capsule around each cell of the colony (Figure 10-12). The S-type pneumonia bacteria are **virulent** (VEER-you·lent)—they will cause the disease pneumonia when injected into mice or other similar organisms. The second type of pneumonia bacteria used by Griffith in his experiments is the rough (R) type. Cells of R-type bacteria lack capsules (Figure 10-12). Colonies formed

Transduced bacterium containing the a+ genetic material

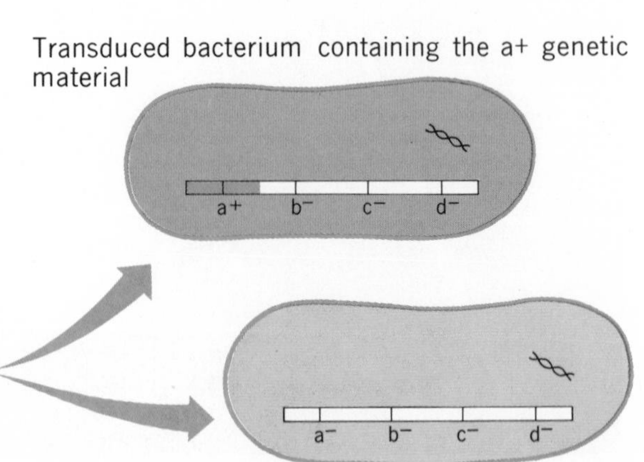

by these bacteria are easy to distinguish from the S-type. The R-type colonies appear to be dry and have an irregular (rough) surface. When injected into experimental animals they fail to cause pneumonia. These bacteria are nonvirulent.

With rare exceptions, the S-type cells with their capsules divide and produce daughter cells which also have capsules. Similarly, R-type cells, which lack capsules, produce offspring which also lack capsules. The presence or absence of capsules on the bacterial cells, therefore, can be said to be inherited.

Making sure that mutation of one kind of bacteria into another would not affect his results, Griffith proceeded with his experiment. He injected a small quantity of R-type bacteria into a mouse (Figure 10-12). At the same time he injected a larger quantity of heat-killed S-type bacteria into the same mouse. We might guess that the mouse would go on leading a normal, healthy life. There was no reason for it to get pneumonia because the R-type was nonvirulent, and the virulent S-type had been killed with heat. But the mouse did get pneumonia and died. In determining the cause of

10-12 THE TRANSFORMING PRINCIPLE

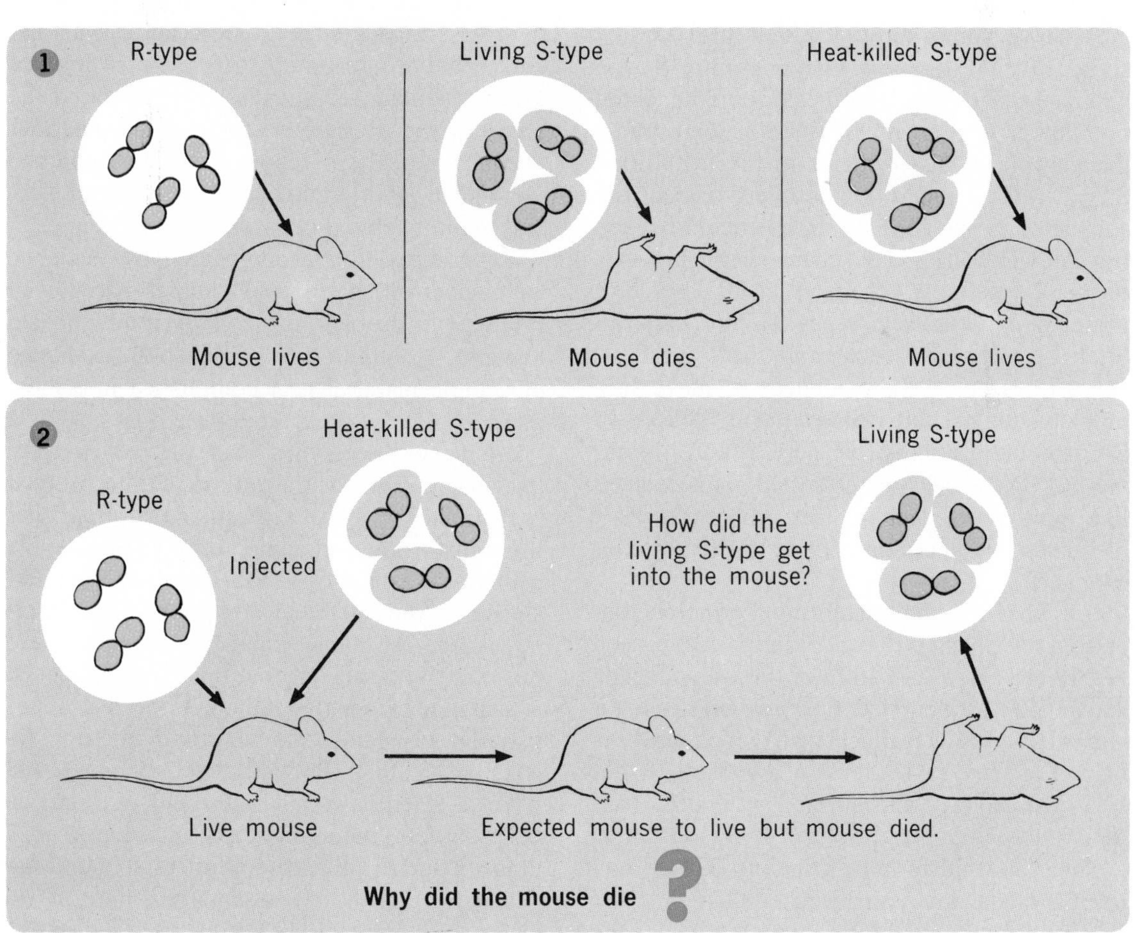

death Griffith made a discovery that was difficult to explain. In addition to the R-type that he expected to find, Griffith found living, virulent, S-type bacteria in the mouse. Where did they come from? What kind of hypothesis could he give to explain this unusual change? It could not be mutation. He had been careful to eliminate this possibility. He used only healthy mice. His control animals never got pneumonia. Perhaps the heat-killed S-type bacteria produced some kind of poison that killed the mouse. But this could not be. For when only heat-killed S-type bacteria were injected, no pneumonia developed, nor were any living S-type bacteria found in the mouse (Figure 10-12).

It seemed to Griffith that there was only one other explanation. The dead S-type bacteria must have some substance that transformed some of the harmless R-types into S-type killers. Perhaps this hypothesis could be tested by another experiment. If there is some transforming chemical substance in the heat-killed S-type cells, it might be possible to isolate the substance in the form of an extract. This extract should bring about a change in the heredity of the R-type cells—changing at least some of these into virulent S-types (Figure 10-12). Such a change did occur and the hypothesis was supported by the evidence. To make sure of his results, Griffith isolated the newly formed S-types and grew them in pure culture. Nothing but S-type cells were formed. This seemed like good proof that the hereditary materials of the R-type had indeed been transformed or changed.

But what was the transforming principle that caused this unusual change? Many years passed before the chemical nature of the transforming substance was identified. Can you guess what it was? It was a substance with which you became familiar in Chapter 8— a substance that had been isolated and purified by another scientist more than 70 years ago. It was DNA.

Since the transforming principle (DNA) had itself brought about an inherited change in the R-type bacteria, could it be that DNA *was* the chemical substance of hereditary material not only in bacteria but in other organisms as well? Subsequent investigation has shown the answer to be yes. What an important "yes" this has been when we remember that these are the experiments that have led to our understanding of the gene and how it works!

CONCLUDING REMARKS

Since the first description of bacteria in 1677, we have learned much about the structure and reproduction of bacteria. Their small size is no longer a factor limiting what we can learn about them. The electron microscope and other special kinds of instruments have made possible the discovery of the nature of the bacterial cell wall with its variety of carbohydrates, flagella structure and activation, and bacterial chromosomes with their strands of DNA. Staining techniques have permitted the study of the division of the chromosome that accompanies the division of the cell and the identification of endospores and stored substances in bacterial cells.

Experimentation accompanied by evidence from electron microscope studies has solved the age-old problem of sexual reproduction in bacteria. In addition to conjugation, exchange of genetic material is accomplished in a most unusual way by a bacterial virus that acts as a "go-between" carrying bacterial genes from one bacterium to the other. Perhaps most spectacular of all was the demonstration that the transforming principle, found in pneumonia bacteria, was really DNA and that this substance is the chemical compound that determines the heritable characteristics of these bacteria. With this information it has since been possible to show that DNA is the hereditary material in plants, animals, and microorganisms other than bacteria. But it all started when a scientist wondered about the unusual behavior of pneumonia-causing bacteria in a mouse! Such is the true spirit of scientific investigation. How it will start or where it will lead us, no one can predict.

GUIDE QUESTIONS AND PROBLEMS

1. What would happen if the world were suddenly left without bacteria?
2. How did the death of a mouse help lead Dr. Griffith to the discovery of the importance of DNA?
3. New discoveries in science often depend on instruments that extend the range of man's senses. In what ways, other than those you have learned about in this chapter, has man improved his ability to sense things beyond his normal range? What instruments and discoveries can you name as examples?
4. In obtaining its nutritional requirements, which do you suppose will use the greater number of extracellular enzymes, a parasitic bacterium or a saprophytic one? Explain.
5. Lederberg and Tatum had to consider "back mutation" as well as a genetic recombination while interpreting the results of their experiments with nutritional mutants. Why were they justified in concluding that genetic recombination had occurred? Why do scientists use such words as "might be," "probably," or "possibly," rather than words that imply certainty when interpreting the results of experiments?
6. In the research done on the problem of transformation in bacteria, it was found that digested DNA (free nucleotides) would not bring about transformation, while intact fragments of DNA would do so. What does this finding tell us about DNA and genetic messages?
7. The following graphs are based on the bacterial growth curves. Interpret these graphs and state the conditions under which they might exist.

RELATED READING

Books

For a source of the original reports of pioneering discoveries in microbiology . . .

Brock, Thomas, *Milestones in Microbiology*, Prentice-Hall, Englewood Cliffs, N. J., 1961.

De Kruif, Paul, *Microbe Hunters*, Harcourt, Brace & World, New York (cloth or paperback) and Pocket Books, New York, 1959.

Dobell, Clifford (editor), *Antony van Leeuwenhoek and His "Little Animals,"* Dover Publications, New York, 1962.

For an inspiring account of Pasteur's life and work . . .

Dubos, René, *Pasteur and Modern Science*, Doubleday, New York, 1960.

For a discussion aided by recent electron micrographs of the form, structure, and activities of microbes . . .

Dubos, René, *The Unseen World*, Rockefeller Institute, New York, 1962.

For a more advanced discussion of microbiology . . .

Sistrom, W. R., *Microbial Life*, Modern Biology Series, Holt, Rinehart, and Winston, New York, 1962.

Magazines

Cairns, J., "The Bacterial Chromosome," *Scientific American*, Volume 214 (January 1966), page 36.

Zinder, N. D., "Transduction in Bacteria," *Scientific American*, Volume 199 (November 1958), page 38.

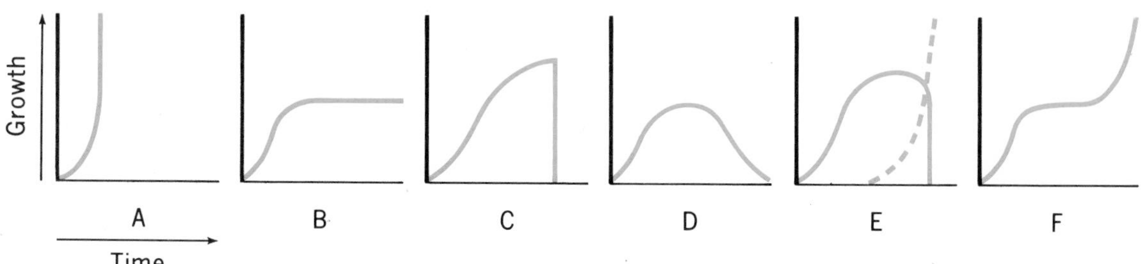

11

Small Organisms of Great Importance

There are many ways in which microorganisms have a direct effect on our everyday living. Imagine, if you can, a world where there was no decomposition. It is not a very pleasant thought. About the only way we could get rid of dead organisms would be by burning them. Burying them or dumping them in the sea would offer only a temporary solution. But more important than the inconvenience of accumulated bodies of plants and animals is what would happen to the balance of nature if there were no decomposition. All compounds that make up living things contain the element carbon that has its ultimate source from the CO_2 in the atmosphere. Even now there is a short supply of atmospheric CO_2. But this supply would soon be depleted if decomposition ceased. All of the carbon would soon be fixed or "tied up" in the compounds of nonliving organisms. There would be none left for the growth and reproduction of new organisms. In other words, life on earth would cease.

HARMFUL BACTERIA

Other than their indirect importance as decomposers, bacteria have many other direct effects, both helpful and harmful. Among the harmful aspects are diseases. The following account describes how the theory that bacteria cause disease was first proposed.

As is often the case in scientific investigation, observations and experiments in one field of knowledge help us to gain understanding in seemingly unrelated areas. So it was in the late 1800's when Pasteur was conducting his famous experiments on the causes of fermentation. In the process of proving that yeasts and bacteria were responsible for fermentation (we will learn more of this later in the chapter), Pasteur noticed, as others had previously noticed, that frequently wine became "sick," or sour, and that certain kinds of bacteria were responsible. The bacteria produced acid, causing the wine to turn to vinegar. Pasteur reasoned, without good proof, that if bacteria could have such an adverse affect on wine, perhaps they could cause sickness or disease in animals and man.

It was *less than one hundred years ago* that Pasteur developed this hypothesis, which later became known as the Germ Theory of Disease. There was much opposition to this revolutionary idea, and Pasteur was hard pressed to defend himself. Such opposition is not unusual. New ideas are rarely well supported by data, so scientists are cautious in accepting them.

Koch's Postulates

Support for Pasteur's ideas came from Robert Koch (KAWK) a young German physician who was a contemporary of Pasteur. Koch had become interested in a lethal disease called anthrax, which had caused 528 human deaths and over 56,000 deaths among horses, cows, and sheep during a three-year period in a single district of Novgorod, Russia. A bacillus could always be found in the blood of diseased animals. Was it the cause of anthrax? Koch discovered that the bacillus multiplied rapidly in the **aqueous** (AY·kwee·us) **humor** (the fluid in the front part of the eye) of an ox's eye, and that he could watch its stages of development in extracts of aqueous humor under a microscope. As the bacillus aged, little dots developed in the cells. These, we now know, were endospores. Although Koch had discovered the life cycle of the organism, he had not yet proved any relationship between the organism and the disease anthrax. What would happen, however, if blood containing the bacteria was taken from an animal showing symptoms of anthrax and injected into a healthy animal? There was only one way to find out. Koch began to inoculate living animals—guinea pigs, rabbits, and mice. Invariably they died of anthrax within 20 to 30 hours.

If blood containing the bacillus was dried, it lost its **virulence**—its ability to infect—after about five weeks. If spores were present and these were dried, however, then for at least five years the bacterium retained its virulence. By these experiments, Koch provided final proof that bacteria do cause disease in animals.

In 1882 Koch completed another study, his monumental work, which demonstrated that another bacillus causes a disease of man—tuberculosis. In this particular work he devised experimental methods, based in part on his earlier work with anthrax. These methods of inquiry soon became rules for all who studied **pathogenic** (path·o·JEN·ik—disease-producing) organisms. The rules are usually called *Koch's postulates* (Figure 11-1). However, he never set them forth in a list of the kind that follows:

1. The organism believed to cause the disease must *always* be present in the host when the disease occurs. (Koch certainly realized that the anthrax bacillus was *always* present in cattle, mice, and rabbits diseased with anthrax. He had never failed to observe it under his microscope in blood from these diseased animals.)

2. The organism believed to cause the disease must be isolated from the host and grown in pure culture. (A pure culture of bacteria is one in which there is only one species of bacteria. The pure culture technique you will be using in the laboratory [Inquiry 11-1] is essentially the same as that devised by Koch.)

3. The organisms obtained from pure culture, when inoculated into healthy hosts, must

11-1 KOCH'S POSTULATES

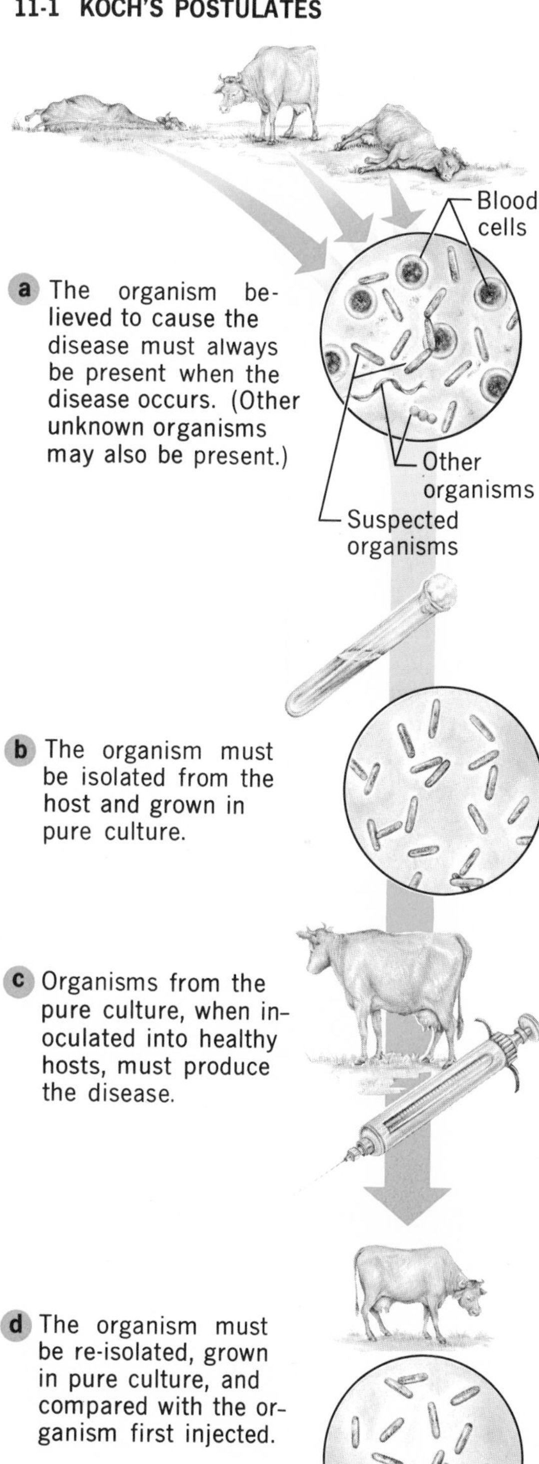

Blood cells
a The organism believed to cause the disease must always be present when the disease occurs. (Other unknown organisms may also be present.)
Other organisms
Suspected organisms
b The organism must be isolated from the host and grown in pure culture.
c Organisms from the pure culture, when inoculated into healthy hosts, must produce the disease.
d The organism must be re-isolated, grown in pure culture, and compared with the organism first injected.

produce the characteristics of the disease. (In his early work on anthrax, Koch used the technique of inoculation when he injected blood from animals infected with anthrax into healthy animals; the blood was not a pure culture, though, since it probably contained other organisms.)

4. The organism believed to cause the disease must be re-isolated, grown in pure culture, and compared with the organism first injected and must be shown to be the same. (This addition to the postulates was made at a later time by Erwin F. Smith of the U.S. Department of Agriculture.)

We have seen how Robert Koch succeeded in proving Pasteur's hypothesis that bacteria can cause disease in animals and man. It was not long after Koch's epoch-making discoveries that Thomas Burrell (1829–1916), a botanist at the University of Illinois, demonstrated that a disease—fire blight of pears—was caused by bacteria. Since his discovery, more than one hundred diseases of plants have been attributed to bacteria. These hundred or more plant diseases, added to numerous diseases of animals and man caused by bacteria, further emphasize the important role bacteria play in our lives. But are bacterial diseases of humans as important now as they were one hundred years ago? Let us look at the list.

Here are some of the bacterial diseases of humans:

> Anthrax, bacterial pneumonia, botulism, bubonic plague, cholera, diphtheria, bacterial dysentery, syphilis, leprosy, meningitis, scarlet fever, septic sore throat, tetanus, tuberculosis, tularemia, typhoid fever, undulant fever, and whooping cough.

How many of these diseases have you or members of your family contracted? There are probably many of them that are not even familiar to you—yet all of them have at one time or another been important human diseases within the last two hundred years.

Tuberculosis was of major concern to every family until twenty years ago (Figure 11-2). To have tuberculosis meant a long period of rest, isolation, and treatment in a sanatorium, with only a remote prospect of complete recovery and a useful life. Bacterial pneumonia

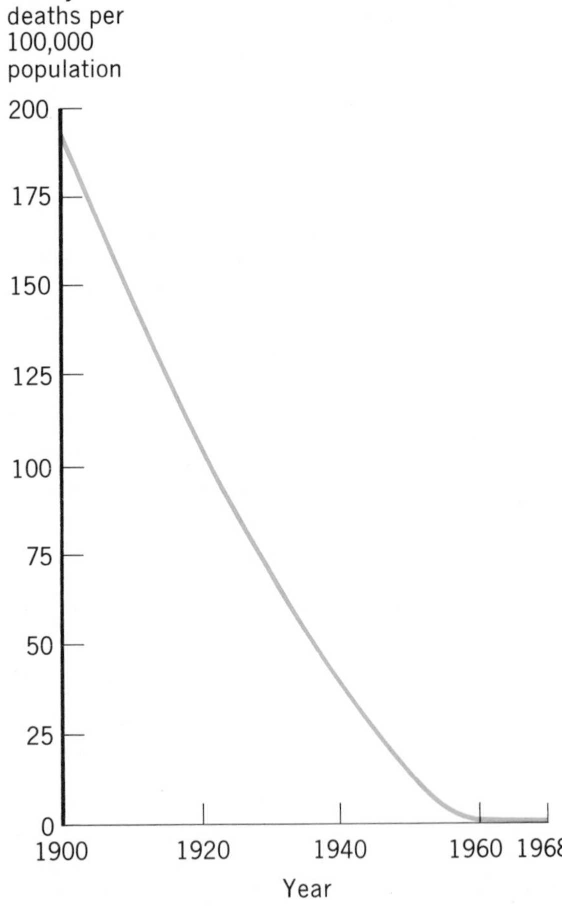

11–2 Many diseases other than tuberculosis have shown a remarkable decline in death rate during the past 25 to 50 (or more) years. The average life expectancy of an infant born today in the United States is seventy years. What do you suppose the corresponding life expectancy was fifty years ago? seventy-five years ago? one hundred years ago?

was even more often fatal than tuberculosis. There was no very useful drug, and only administration of oxygen relieved the patient. Today we no longer need live in such fear of bacterial pneumonia, *or any of the other bacterial diseases on the list.* We know that there are effective countermeasures—effective controls for these diseases.

What Is Disease?

Thus far we have talked about disease as sickness produced in an organism by bacteria (or viruses—see Chapter 9). Many other kinds of organisms besides bacteria and viruses are responsible for infectious diseases. Chapter 1 told us about the infectious disease malaria, caused by *Plasmodium,* a protozoan. Other diseases caused by protozoans are African sleeping sickness and amoebic dysentery. Many other organisms cause infectious diseases. Here we can list such examples as liver flukes, tapeworms, hookworms, and nematodes of plants. All these are wormlike animals.

Fungi cause some of the most important diseases in the world. Smuts and rusts of grain, and late blight of potatoes, are a few that have had a profound effect on the lives of men.

By definition, *disease* includes not only all the infectious diseases of plants and animals, whether caused by bacteria, viruses, molds, protozoa, or other organisms, but any malfunction in an organism, no matter what the cause. With this definition in mind we would have to include as possible causes of disease the consequences of malnutrition, vitamin deficiency, air pollution, chemical poisons, inherited malfunctions, and even defects resulting from injury and imperfections in development. For a complete understanding of diseases, we must also know about the structure, physiology, defense, and regulatory mechanisms of the organism that has the disease.

Naturally, the methods of control of diseases are as diverse as the causes. But we are interested here chiefly in control of diseases caused by bacteria and viruses.

To understand how to control a disease, it is necessary, as pointed out in the case of malaria (Chapter 1), to know what the **pathogen** (PATH·o·jen), or disease-producing organism, is. Koch's postulates are the guide here.

CONTROL OF DISEASE

What happens in an organism after it has been invaded by a pathogen? How does it combat the toxins that may be formed by the virulent pathogen? In higher animals with efficient circulatory systems, intruding pathogenic bacteria are challenged almost immediately.

Host Resistance

The first line of resistance is by cells of the blood stream. These are the **phagocytes** (FAY·go·sites)—certain white blood cells that engulf and destroy the invaders (Figure 11-3). In

11–3 A phagocyte engulfing a chain of bacteria. The circular cells surrounding the phagocyte are red blood cells. The chain of bacteria extends from the phagocyte.

Charles Pfizer & Co., Inc.

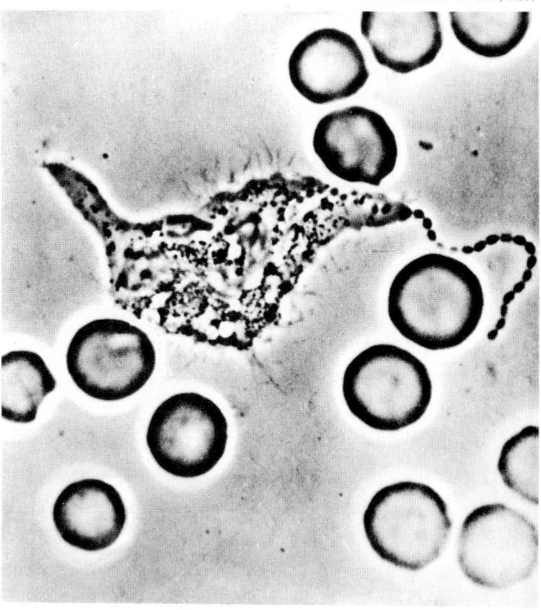

some instances, however, the host may not be able to cope with the rapidly multiplying pathogen. In this event the host may depend on an additional defense—the formation of proteins called **antibodies** (AN·tih·bod·eez). An antibody is produced in the host as a reaction to the introduction of a foreign substance, often a protein, which is called the **antigen** (AN·tih·jen). In this example, the proteins of the bacteria themselves are the antigens. A unique feature of an antibody is its *specificity* for the antigen that stimulated its formation. Thus, in case of typhoid fever, the antigens of typhoid bacilli will cause the host to produce specific antibodies. The latter react with and inactivate the typhoid bacilli proteins with which they come in contact, but do not react with other bacilli—or react more weakly. Antibodies, once formed, may continue to be made for years in the body of the host organism and impart varying degrees of immunity.

Without knowing the reason, peoples in early civilizations recorded the observation that if a tribesman was to become ill with a certain disease and was fortunate enough to recover, from that time on he would be immune to the disease. This same observation was familiar to the English physician Edward Jenner (1749-1823), who was the first to devise a safe and effective means of combating the dreaded virus disease smallpox. If you compare the time at which Jenner lived with the date of the discovery of viruses and the date of proof that viruses can cause disease (1892), you will realize that he knew practically nothing about the cause of smallpox or any other virus disease. Nevertheless, he made two very astute observations. First, he noticed that milkmaids often contracted a mild case of cowpox from the cows infected with cowpox. The cowpox disease did not seriously affect either the cows or the milkmaids. When Jenner examined the histories of the milkmaids, he made the second observation: the milkmaids who had contracted cowpox at some time seldom contracted the far more serious disease, smallpox.

This second observation suggested a daring experiment. Could this be another case of natural immunity, such as had been recorded in the past? Perhaps by injecting a person with a little of the pus from a cowpox lesion, one could give him a mild case of cowpox and spare him the ravages of smallpox. How much it would have helped Jenner, and how many doubts would have been erased from his mind, if he had only known about viruses, antibodies, and antigens.

In spite of his limited information, Jenner proceeded with his bold experiment by **vaccinating** (*vacca*—Latin for "cow") a young boy with pus from a cowpox blister. As anticipated, the boy contracted a mild case of the disease, which soon vanished. Now came the crucial step. Was the boy truly immunized against smallpox? There was only one way Jenner knew of finding out, and that was to inoculate the boy with pus from an active case of smallpox. In spite of what might have happened if he had failed, Jenner continued his experiment. You know the outcome—the boy did *not* contract the dreaded disease. He had indeed become immune. Can you explain what changes Jenner had brought about in the boy to produce immunity?

In Jenner's day it was difficult to persuade people to be vaccinated. They were suspicious of the things that they, as well as the physicians of the time, did not understand. Jenner's success with the boy, however, soon brought many people to his door seeking the new treatment. The number of people who thus benefited from vaccination is incalculable.

Another century was to pass before it was learned *why* vaccination produces immunity. Again we can thank Louis Pasteur for helping to find some of the answers. Today we know that the milkmaids who had contracted cowpox as an occupational hazard acquired **active immunity**—their bodies produced antibodies in reaction to the pathogenic virus of cowpox. Fortunately, the viruses causing cowpox and smallpox were enough alike that the antibodies

The Bettmann Archive, Cartoon by James Gillray

11–4 An eighteenth-century cartoon showing Edward Jenner using his cowpox extract to vaccinate patients against smallpox. The cartoonist seems to have had misgivings about the results of vaccination. The success of Jenner's methods has eliminated such fears.

produced against cowpox were also effective against smallpox. Jenner, in his vaccination experiment, had **artificially induced** active immunity by injecting pus containing cowpox virus (the antigen) into his patients (Figure 11-4).

Since Jenner's time, other methods of preparing antigens to produce immunity have been devised. Perhaps you recently have read about one of these methods in a magazine or newspaper. In the development of methods of immunization against poliomyelitis, Jonas Salk and his colleagues discovered that they could take active polio viruses, kill them with a poison called **formaldehyde** (for·MAL·de·hide), and use the killed viruses as antigens (Figure 11-5). When injected, the antigens still caused the production of polio antibodies that protected the person from poliomyelitis.

Albert Sabin developed a different method. He treated polio viruses to weaken them so that they would not produce the disease. A suspension of living but weakened viruses can then be swallowed, and the person will build antibodies against poliomyelitis.

Yet another method for producing active immunity involves the injection of antigens called **toxoids** (TOK·soidz). Certain diseases, such as diphtheria and tetanus, are due mainly to protein toxins that the bacteria secrete into the host's body. An effective immunization here requires the neutralization of the toxins by antibodies called **antitoxins** (an·tih·TOK·sinz). It is undesirable to inject the active toxin to cause protective antibody production, since the host would then become ill. Toxoids are used instead. Toxoids are produced by treating toxin, collected from laboratory cultures of bacteria, with a chemical substance such as formaldehyde. This treatment destroys the poisonous properties but not the ability of the molecule to cause a person to produce antitoxins. Would you say that this method is more like the Salk or the Sabin method of producing polio vaccine?

Active immunization usually lasts for months or even years. There is, however, a practical drawback to injecting weakened viruses, bacteria, or toxoids to produce antibodies. It usually takes several weeks for the body to build up an effective supply of antibodies. If exposure to a disease has already occurred, it may be too late to start active immunization. In cases such as this, the physician will often rely on measures of **passive immunity.**

Passive immunization depends on the use of antibodies made in another animal. Thus, if antigens are injected into a horse, the horse will produce the specific antibodies. The blood serum of the animal, now containing the antibodies, is known as **antiserum** (an·tih·SEER·um). The antiserum is injected into the person who requires immediate antibody protection. Physicians have supplies of various specific antisera on hand for just such emergencies. For example, horse serum collected from animals immunized with tetanus toxoid may be used to give protection against a potential case of tetanus. The protection is immediate, but is only temporary inasmuch as antibody production by the patient is not involved.

Another kind of protection is provided by a substance found in living cells called **interferon** (in·tur·FEAR·on). This substance is a protein which has the capacity of protecting the organism against nucleic acids other than its own. This is of particular significance in the protection of the individual from the foreign DNA and RNA introduced by viruses and bacteria. It has been suggested that interferon can restrict the proliferation of cancer cells until the development of a new mutant cancer cell that is resistant to interferon.

The National Foundation

11–5 Jonas Salk, the developer of the first polio vaccine. Killed viruses were used as antigens.

Antibiotics

Approximately 75 percent of those who read this sentence have been given some **antibiotic** (an·tih·by·OT·ik) by a physician to help combat certain types of sore throat, bacterial pneumonia, tuberculosis, or some other bacterial disease. Antibiotics have become so important a part of our lives that we should know what they are and how they act. An antibiotic is any biological substance that is produced by an organism and that inhibits or retards the growth of microorganisms.

The effects of antibiotics have been known since about 1500 B.C., when it was observed by Chinese physicians that poultices and dressings containing mold worked very well in curing boils. It took another 3,500 years, however, before anyone understood how antibiotics worked. Near the end of the last century, it was discovered that a blue pigment obtained from a certain pus-forming bacterium had an antibiotic effect against *Staphylococcus aureus,* the common cause of boils. The blue pigment had one serious drawback, however, that prevented its use on internal infections. It was much too toxic for direct injections. This is a major disadvantage of many antibiotics.

An event that was to lead to one of the greatest advances in the history of antibiotics was reported in 1929. At the time, it seemed relatively unimportant that a British microbiologist by the name of Alexander Fleming (1881-1955) should report the antibiotic activity of a blue-green mold in otherwise pure cultures of *Staphylococcus*. As so often happens, the cultures became contaminated with the mold, which was *Penicillium* (pen·eh·SIL·ee·um—Figure 11-6). The mold was perhaps identical with the blue-green molds you have seen growing on spoiled oranges or grapefruit.

A contaminated culture usually ends up by being discarded. But Fleming did not throw this one away. It looked different from the usual contaminated plate because the agar immediately surrounding the mold was almost clear instead of being cloudy with staphylococci (Inquiry 11-2). The appearance of the clear area showed that the growth of *Staphylococcus* had been inhibited by some substance produced by the mold. Fleming isolated the antibiotic substance and named it **penicillin.** Further tests showed that penicillin was not toxic to humans and thus met one of the requirements of a useful antibiotic.

Very little was done to promote the use or production of penicillin until 1938, when two British biochemists started an intensive study to find the range of bacteria affected by penicillin. With their help and the cooperation of American industry, methods were devised within a few years for growth of the mold *Penicillium notatum* on a large scale. This accomplishment proved to be of tremendous value. For at this time we were involved in World War II, during which penicillin was used in great quantities to control infections in wounded soldiers. It has been estimated that without penicillin the death rate during World War II and the Korean War would have been more than tripled because of gas gangrene and other bacterial infections in wounds.

Subsequently, new strains of *Penicillium* with greater capacity for penicillin production have been developed by introducing mutations in the original *P. notatum* stock. Some types of penicillin differ slightly from others, and tests are continually made to evaluate the effectiveness of each new type produced. There are even synthetic varieties of this antibiotic. To this day, penicillin is the most widely used, and among the least toxic, of the multitude of antibiotics now produced (Figure 11-7).

11–6 A colony of the blue-green mold *Penicillium.* Where might you have seen species of *Penicillium* growing? This and other molds produce antibiotics that protect man against disease.

Charles Pfizer & Co., Inc.

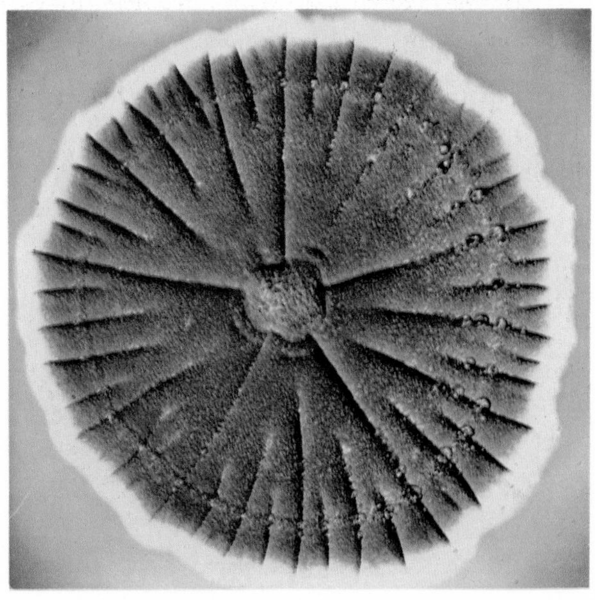

11-7 THE PRODUCTION OF AN ANTIBIOTIC

Courtesy of Eli Lilly & Co.

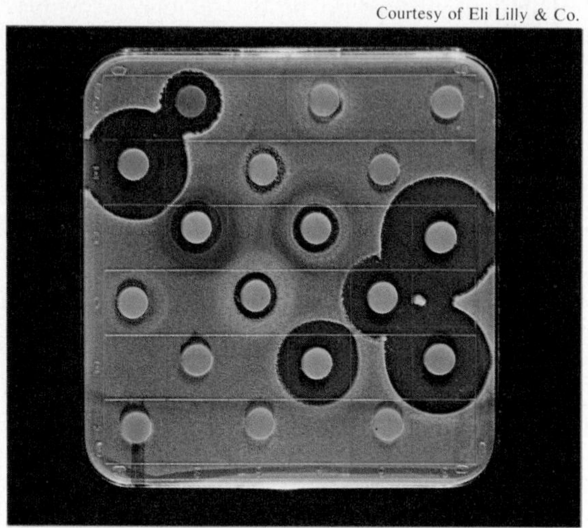

a. Antibiotic activity against specific bacteria is tested with disks impregnated with varying concentrations of different antibiotics. The most effective antibiotics produce clear areas in the bacterial population on the square plate.

Courtesy of Eli Lilly &

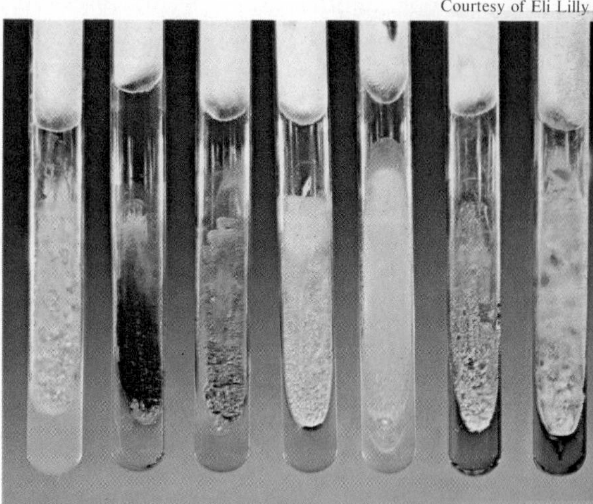

b. The organisms that produced the antibiotics tested in **a** originally were cultured on agar slants in these test tubes. The slants were used to inoculate larger nutrient flasks, until quantities of the antibiotics were available for trial use.

e. The antibiotic is ready. Sterile handling avoids contamination of the bulk product.

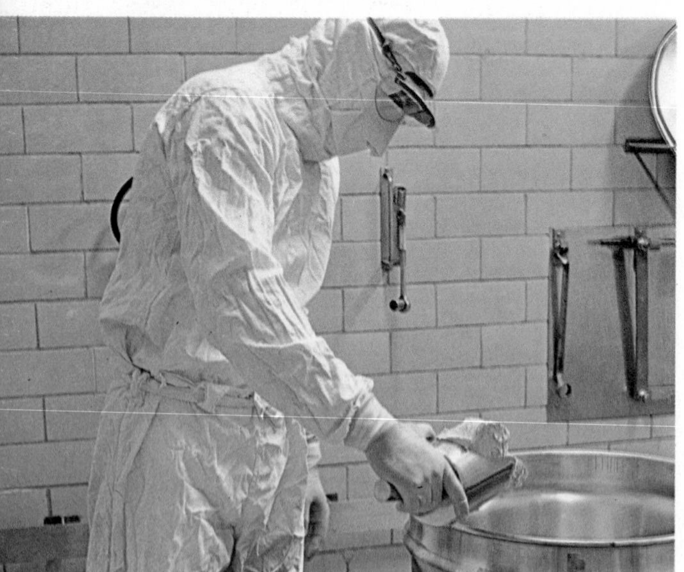

Courtesy of Eli Lilly & Co.

f. Before the antibiotic is packaged in capsules or vials, it is inspected once again.

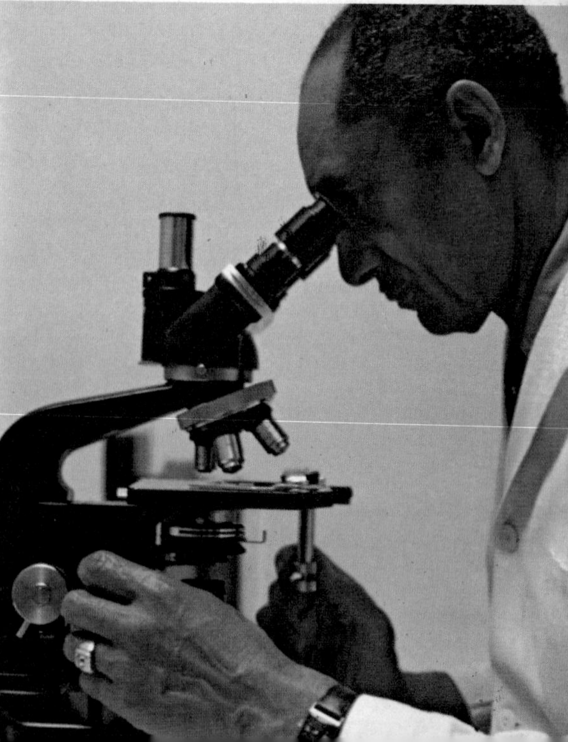

Harbrace Photo

Courtesy of Eli Lilly & Co.

Courtesy of Eli Lilly & Co.

c. The commercial production of an antibiotic that has proved nontoxic to man involves culturing on a large scale. Here a nutrient flask of antibiotic-producing organisms is emptied into a "transfer carrier" used to inoculate a large vat.

d. Several stages later, after a large quantity of the antibiotic has been isolated from the organism that produced it, samples of the antibiotic are tested. Then it is further extracted and purified in the equipment shown here.

g. Even as the product is packed for shipment, some is withheld for re-inspection.

Courtesy of Eli Lilly & Co.

h. In liquid suspension in a hypodermic syringe, the antibiotic goes to work.

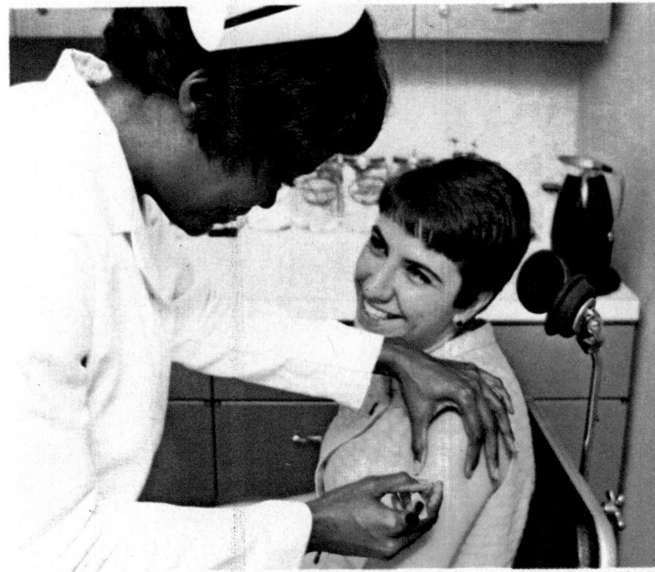

Harbrace Photo

It should be noted that Fleming's discovery was, in a sense, a lucky one. Had he simply discarded the contaminated culture, he might not have discovered penicillin. Others before him had observed that molds seem to inhibit bacterial growth, but Fleming wanted to know why. Many discoveries have been referred to as lucky "chances," but are they really? They are in part, but we might make the observation, as Pasteur did many years ago, that "chance favors the trained mind."

In America, much of the success in discovering new antibiotic-producing organisms can be attributed to Selman Waksman and his co-workers. For many years they studied microorganisms of the soil. They concentrated on organisms called **actinomycetes** (ak·tih·no·MY-seets), a group of threadlike organisms composed of bacteria-like cells. Most of the antibiotics used today, except penicillin, are produced by actinomycetes, many of which were discovered by Waksman and his associates. In 1944, Waksman and his co-workers discovered an antibiotic which we all know, one called **streptomycin** (strep·toe·MY·sin). This they isolated from the actinomycete *Streptomyces griseus* (strep·toe·MY·seez GREE·see·us). Since the discovery of streptomycin, pharmaceutical laboratories and independent investigators have isolated many species of actinomycetes that produce antibiotic substances (Figure 11-7). Today about twenty-five antibiotics derived from molds are commercially produced. Some have their greatest effects against specific bacteria; others show a broad spectrum of action against many bacteria.

In addition to molds and actinomycetes, true bacteria have also been a source of antibiotics. Even higher plants are being studied as a possible source of antibiotics.

There are many good reasons for care in the selection of antibiotics. For instance, the widespread and unwise use of antibiotics may result in a number of undesirable side reactions. The patient may become allergic to the antibiotic and suffer severe reactions when it is used a second or third time. In other instances, some antibiotics, when taken by mouth, may practically sterilize the intestines. When this occurs, beneficial bacteria, which normally produce many of our B vitamins, will be killed, and an acute vitamin shortage may occur in our bodies.

Another reason for careful use of antibiotics is that strains of bacteria highly resistant to a given antibiotic can reproduce and flourish in the absence of competing bacteria the antibiotic has killed. The antibiotic then is useless against the resistant bacteria. Penicillin-resistant staphylococci have developed in many hospitals and occasionally become a major problem. These organisms produce an enzyme, **penicillinase** (pen·ih·SIL·in·ase), which destroys penicillin. Clearly, penicillin is not effective under such circumstances.

Not only are the antibiotics powerful weapons in man's conquest of disease, but some of them are becoming powerful tools for studying important biological problems. For example, streptomycin affects the ribosomes of certain bacteria and prevents their synthesis of normal proteins. Puromycin also prevents the synthesis of normal proteins. Actinomycin combines with DNA in such a way as to prevent the formation of messenger RNA. (You can see how interesting it might be to block the formation of messenger RNA and observe its consequences.) Penicillin has its chief effect on dividing bacterial cells by preventing the formation of new cell walls.

Early in this chapter we mentioned the importance of bacteria as decomposers. Many of the decomposers that play an important role in nature also cause spoilage of foods, and decay of wood, fabrics, and leather. Like pathogenic organisms, the decomposers must be controlled. One such method of control is **pasteurization** (Figure 11-8). Pasteurization requires the use of heat at temperatures high enough to kill nonspore-forming bacteria.

Pasteurization owes its name to Pasteur, who first used it in 1866 to save the French wine industry, as you will read later in this

11-8 PREVENTION OF SPOILAGE

a TEMPERATURE

Canned foods

Sterilization

120° to 126° C, obtained by heating under pressure for 12 to 90 minutes

Milk

Pasteurization

71° C (15 seconds)

62° C (30 minutes)

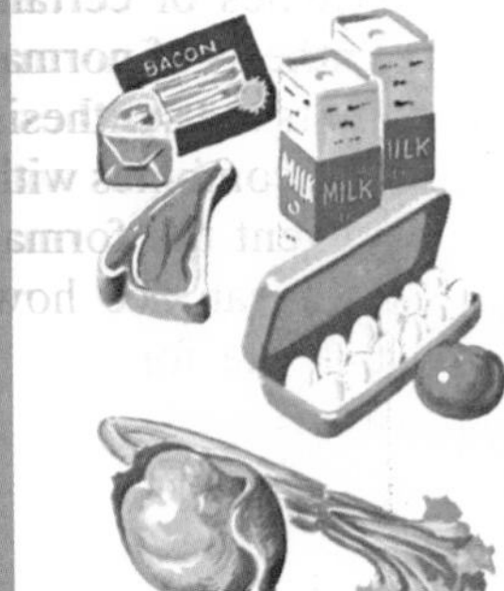

Eggs, milk, vegetables, cheese, and meat

Low temperature storage

10° to 15° C for several days

Meats and vegetables

Freezing

−10° to −18° C for several weeks to several months

b DRYING Water content of foods is reduced to a point at which bacteria cannot grow.

20% or less water

Dried beef

10% or less water

c PRESERVATIVES The pH of foods may be lowered by adding an acid, thus inhibiting growth of microorganisms. The salt or sugar content may be increased so that water in the foods is not available to microorganisms. Chemicals may be added to prevent or retard growth of microorganisms.

Salt and acetic acid

Sugar

Salt

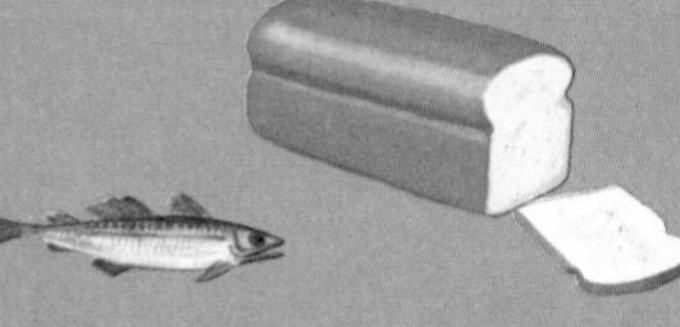

Chemical preservatives

d RADIATION Foods may be exposed to gamma radiation, thereby destroying microorganisms and sterilizing the foods. The Food and Drug Administration now permits commercial irradiation of certain foods and testing of others for wider commercial application of the process.

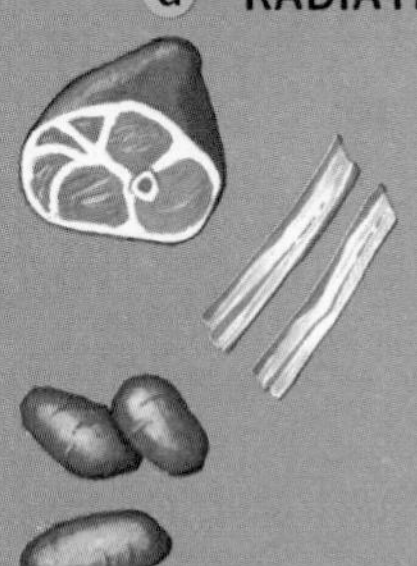

chapter. Today, when we think of pasteurization, we think of milk. When milk is produced under careless conditions and is consumed raw (that is, without pasteurization), it can be dangerous. Pathogens that may grow in raw milk include those which cause typhoid fever, paratyphoid fever, scarlet fever, bovine tuberculosis, and undulant fever.

About 1880, a number of investigators recognized that many children, and often adults as well, were dying of these milk-borne diseases. It was therefore suggested that the milk should be heated, as Pasteur had heated wine, in order to destroy the pathogens. At first, the pasteurization temperatures used were too high and the milk tasted scorched. Furthermore, the cream would not rise properly afterwards. On the other hand, if the milk was heated at too low a temperature the disease-producers were not killed.

After extensive and careful experimentation, using the tough bovine tuberculosis organism as a test organism, proper temperatures for pasteurizing milk were found. They were high enough to kill the tuberculosis bacterium, but not so high as to affect the taste and quality of the milk. Pasteurization kills not only the tuberculosis organism, but other nonspore-forming bacteria as well.

A variety of other methods, or combination of methods, can be used to control bacterial decomposers. Regulation of temperature and pH (see Laboratory Inquiry 6-1) affects the growth of many microorganisms (Laboratory Inquiry 11-3). Other factors that help control growth of these organisms are drying, preservatives, and radiation (Figure 11-8).

BENEFICIAL BACTERIA

Having read the story of bacteria thus far, you will probably conclude that all but those bacteria taking part in decomposition, or those yielding antibiotics, are harmful, and that the world would indeed be a better place without them. We must look again at the other side of the coin and see in what other ways bacteria are beneficial. Some of the ways they help us in our everyday living will surprise you.

Bacteria for Better Health

Has your doctor ever prescribed vitamin capsules for you? Chances are that in addition to the usual collection of vitamins A, C, and D, members of the B complex also are included in the capsules. One member of the B complex is vitamin B_{12} (the cobalt vitamin), which in human beings helps prevent the blood disease **pernicious anemia** (per·NISH·us a·NEE·mee·a).

For many years it has been known that injections of crude liver extracts often help the victims of pernicious anemia. It was not known until recently, however, what substance in the liver is responsible.

In the late 1940's, an American microbiologist, Mary Shorb, studied this problem. She was trying to devise a medium for growing the bacterium *Lactobacillus lactis* (lak·toe·ba-SIL·us). She could supply, in the form of purified chemicals, all but one of the nutrients this organism needed. That extra substance was present in crude beef-liver extract. Was the growth substance for the bacterium the substance that helped victims of pernicious anemia?

Several tons of beef liver were used in an effort to extract the growth factor. After much chemical extraction, a few milligrams of a highly active, pure, red compound were obtained. This compound was not only the missing growth substance Mary Shorb was looking for, but also proved to be one of the factors that can be used to successfully treat pernicious anemia. Thus, by studying the biology of a bacterium, biologists were led to the discovery of a substance of great aid to man—vitamin B_{12}.

The recovery of large amounts of vitamin B_{12} from beef liver is a difficult and costly job. Nevertheless, the vitamin was needed for medical purposes, so it was important to find a better source. Bacteria helped solve the problem.

So far as is known, all bacteria need vitamin B_{12} in their cells. Some species must have B_{12}

added to the medium in which they are grown. Other species can grow in a medium that does not contain B_{12}. How does the second group of species obtain the needed B_{12}? They must have the ability to synthesize it! Investigation soon identified a number of bacteria species that synthesized B_{12} far in excess of their own needs. In an effort to obtain this excess B_{12}, biologists grew these bacteria in huge cultures containing thousands of gallons of media. The vitamin B_{12} obtained is now used not only for treating pernicious anemia patients, but also in commercial vitamin pills. This story of discovery affords an excellent example of one of many ways in which bacteria can serve man.

Did you know that bacteria in your digestive system, especially in the small and large intestines, are important in completing certain digestive processes? They are so important that without them, digestion of foods is incomplete, and you can become ill. This explains why the family physician is reluctant to use penicillin and other antibiotics which will reduce the bacteria in the digestive tract to a dangerous level.

The same protein-digesting enzymes that are so helpful to human digestion may have played an important part in the manufacture of the leather shoes you are wearing. Many of the fabrics in the clothes you wear depend upon bacteria for their manufacture. The coffee you drink in the morning may have had a "bacterial treatment." The Swiss or American cheese in your sandwich was given its flavor and texture by the activity of bacteria.

Fermentation

Earlier in this chapter, and in Chapter 2, the work of Louis Pasteur has been noted. He is famous for his researches discrediting spontaneous generation on the earth today; he saved the silk industry in France by discovering the cause of a disease of silkworms; and he formulated the Germ Theory of Disease, later proved true by Robert Koch.

Much of Pasteur's research, especially that which led him to disprove abiogenesis (see Chapter 2), involved studies of the causes of "sick" wine and beer. The manufacture of wine, a great French enterprise, was faced with ruin in the mid-nineteenth century because of problems in controlling fermentation. In the summer of 1856 a request was made of Pasteur for his help.

The wine makers' problem was simple. As soon as fermentation had been started by the brewers' yeast, substances appeared that turned the wine sour. The substances were not produced by the brewers' yeast, for the damage was caused by lactic acid and acetic acid, neither of which was a fermentation product of the yeast. (Fermentation by brewers' yeast yields alcohol and carbon dioxide.) The problems confronting Pasteur were to discover what caused formation of the acid and how to prevent it.

It did not take Pasteur long to find the cause. Whenever acids were produced in fermenting liquids, he was able to find bacteria. When bacteria were not present, there were no acids, and good wine was produced. A method of control was soon worked out. The bacteria were easily killed—without affecting the flavor of the wine—by exposure to a temperature of 32° C for a period of thirty minutes. Pasteur saved the French wine industry and at the same time introduced the techniques of pasteurization.

Thus far we have said very little about what fermentation really is. Pasteur knew that fermentation resulted in the formation of alcohols and CO_2, or of acids. He knew that it was caused by microorganisms growing in **anaerobic** (an·air·OH·bik) environments, that is, environments in which little or no atmospheric oxygen (O_2) was available (Inquiry 11-4). This was contrary to the requirements of most organisms with which Pasteur was familiar. It had already been demonstrated that most plants and animals were **aerobic** (air·OH·bik)—that is, they required free oxygen for respiration. Some of the details of aerobic respiration (Chapter 6) will be helpful in understanding **anaerobic respiration** (fermentation).

Today we think that anaerobic respiration was the kind of respiration utilized by the first living things that populated the earth. There is good reason for believing that at that time the earth's atmosphere lacked free oxygen (see Chapter 9). Thus, anaerobic respiration, or fermentation, would have been the only way energy could have been released for metabolism.

When compared with aerobic respiration, fermentation is most inefficient. It yields only about 5 percent of the total potential energy from a molecule of glucose ($C_6H_{12}O_6$). Thus, fermentation is an incomplete form of respiration. This is explained by the fact that the glucose molecule is only partially broken down in the process. Most of the total energy remains in the end products of alcohol or acid. In aerobic respiration, by contrast, the breakdown is complete. The intermediate products of pyruvic acid or lactic acid are broken down to the end products of water and carbon dioxide.

Thus, although there are many differences between aerobic respiration and fermentation, both processes release energy from glucose.

Different fermentations produce different by-products, many of which are of economic importance. At the top of the list is the fermentation of fruit juices, malted grains, and molasses by yeasts of various kinds to make wine, beer, and rum. Different strains of yeasts are also used in the baking industry to leaven bread. The carbon dioxide produced during fermentation makes bubbles in the dough and causes the bread to rise, giving it lightness and a desirable texture when it is baked. Yeasts also are an important source of vitamins, especially riboflavin (B_2).

CONCLUDING REMARKS

All too frequently the undesirable effects of bacteria as spoilers and disease producers are the only aspects of these microorganisms that concern us. Actually these harmful effects are more than counterbalanced by the ways in which bacteria benefit us. Nearly all of the benefits have been discovered since the 1860's. This has been indeed a century of discovery. The next century may bring to light other products obtained from microorganisms, perhaps new enzymes, vitamins, or antibiotics to benefit all mankind.

GUIDE QUESTIONS AND PROBLEMS

1. Biologists often classify hypotheses as being either of a "black box" or a "glass box" type. Glass box hypotheses are usually directly verifiable, such as the hypothesis that a certain nerve controls a certain process. Black box hypotheses, on the other hand, are seldom verified directly, but depend on indirect evidence for substantiation. Dalton's work (Chapter 5) on atomic theory is an example of black box hypothesizing. In which of these two categories would the researches of Jenner on smallpox be placed? the work of Koch on anthrax? Why?
2. How does the discovery of penicillin by Alexander Fleming illustrate that accident often plays a role in the advancement of science? What factor might be important in order for a scientist to discover new information by accident?
3. Advances in technology are often correlated with advances in our understanding of biology. Why is this statement true in relation to discoveries of pathogenic bacteria?
4. What explanations can be given for the sharp reduction in the incidence of bacterial diseases in the United States?
5. What is the significance of the fact that antibodies are specific?
6. If a freshwater microorganism is placed in a strong brine solution, what will happen to it? Why? How might this effect of salt be used in preserving food?

RELATED READING

Books

See references for Chapter 10.

Magazines

Gorini, L., "Antibiotics and the Genetic Code," *Scientific American*, Volume 214 (April 1966), page 102.

Isaacs, A., "Interferon," *Scientific American*, Volume 204 (May 1961), page 51.

PART **2b**

PLANTS

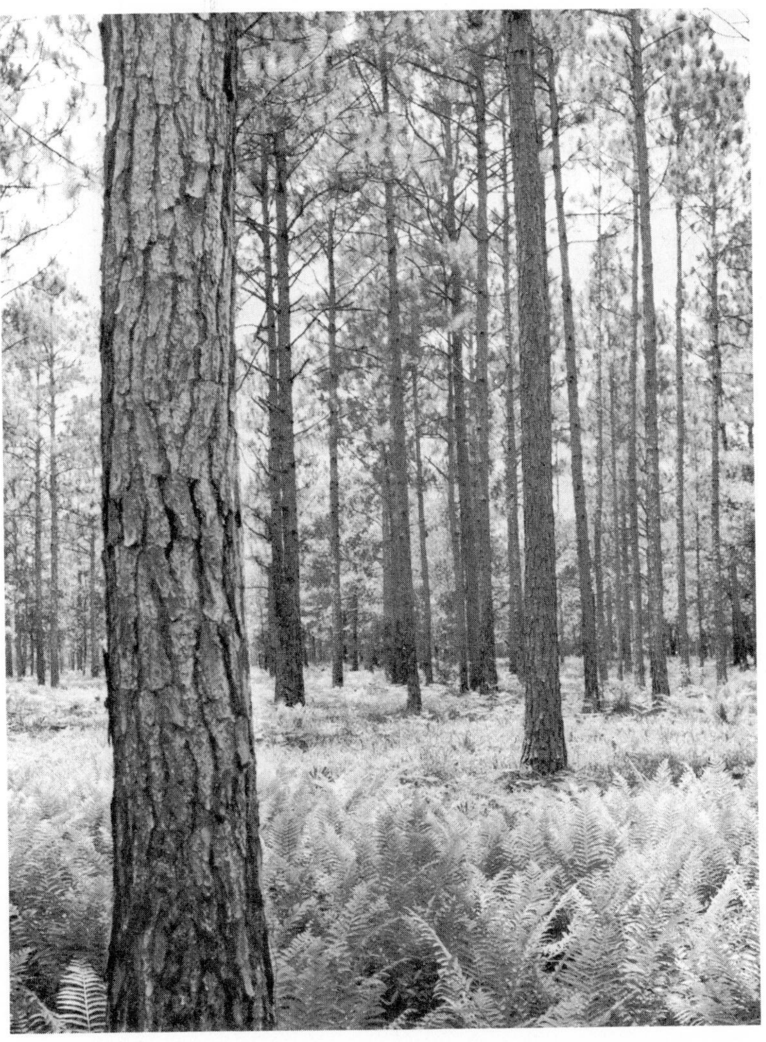

John H. Gerard from National Audubon Society

12

Molds, Yeasts, and Mushrooms

The "Thing"

A common slime mold is of no practical value whatever. You cannot make anything useful out of it, and it does not cause any serious disease. However, as you may have discovered in the laboratory (Inquiry 12-1), a slime mold is a strange and truly wonderful "thing." Its structure and behavior have raised many questions, some of which are still unanswered.

At one stage in their life cycle, some species of slime molds are creeping masses of living substance, having the consistency of unboiled egg white and the color of the yolk (Figure 12-1). The movement of this living thing brings to mind a giant amoeba, for it sends out arms that engulf and digest bacteria from the surface of rotting logs or leaves. This amoeboid stage of the slime mold is called a **plasmodium.** (This same word also is used for the genus of the malaria organism—Chapter 1). In nature, a large plasmodium may cover several square centimeters. It can crawl over grass, creep up the sides of trees, or go almost anywhere where there is food and moisture. It is very much like an object from a science-fiction story. The plasmodium consists of cytoplasm in which are embedded many nuclei, food vacuoles, and undigested food particles. If you look at an active plasmodium through a microscope, you will see the most spectacular exhibition of cytoplasmic streaming you can find anywhere.

The slime mold plasmodium is unusual. Certainly it is not on the borderline between the living and nonliving, like viruses. It is neither a cellular structure divided into many cells,

12–1 a. A portion of the plasmodium of the slime mold *Physarum.* The plasmodium is growing on a nutrient medium of agar. If this were the only part of the organism you could find, how would you classify it? As plant or animal? As unicellular or multicellular? **b.** Fruiting bodies of *Physarum.* The fruiting bodies are shown growing on the surface of rotting wood. How would you discover whether the plasmodium and the fruiting bodies are related? What do the fruiting bodies produce?

a Bob Gilpin, courtesy of Leland Shanor

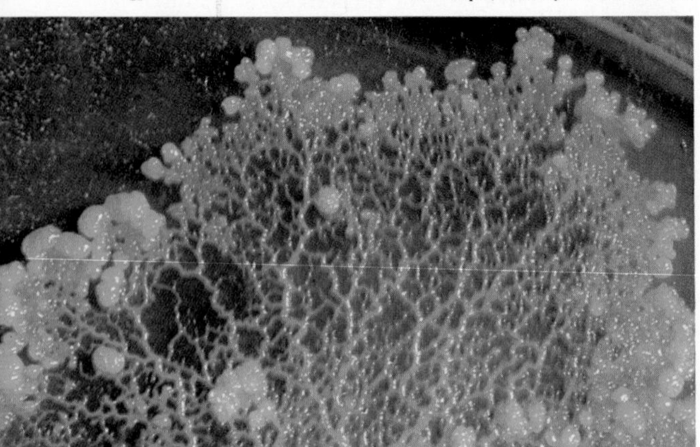

b Constantine J. Alexopoulos

each **uninucleate** (you·nih·NEW·klee·ate—containing a single nucleus), nor is it restricted by a confining cell wall, like a bacterium. Perhaps if we understand how the plasmodium is formed, we can better understand its strange organization—so different from that of any other living thing.

Plasmodia move along the forest floor, onto dead logs and leaves that are bathed in sunlight. In this dry, often warm, environment a miraculous **metamorphosis** (met·a·MOR·fo·sis) takes place. In a matter of hours, the plasmodium changes into clusters of fruiting bodies. Depending on the species, the fruiting bodies (Figure 12-1) look like small golf balls, or feathers, or bird cages, or worms, in a great variety of colors. Part of each fruiting body produces a large number of microscopic, asexual reproductive cells called **spores** (Figure 12-2). Each spore has a single nucleus and a thick, protective wall. A spore may remain inactive for a long time, or it may germinate soon after it has been shed from the fruiting body. Germination of the spore occurs when there is plenty of water and a suitable temperature.

The fruiting stage and the thick-walled spores of the slime mold are very plantlike. *Spores are produced by sexually reproducing plants at some time in their life cycles.* They are very important reproductive cells. When a slime mold spore germinates, it produces one or more tiny cells. Each cell has a pair of flagella that propel it through the film of water that must be present for spore germination. These flagellated cells may function as gametes (sex cells) and fuse in pairs. This is true sexual reproduction, even though the gametes appear to be identical in structure.

Cells resulting from the fusion of gametes become amoeboid and form a new plasmodium that is **multinucleate** (mul·tih·NEW·klee·ate—containing many nuclei). The multinucleate condition can arise by growth of the amoeboid cell and subsequent divisions of the nucleus. It can also result from the fusion of many in-

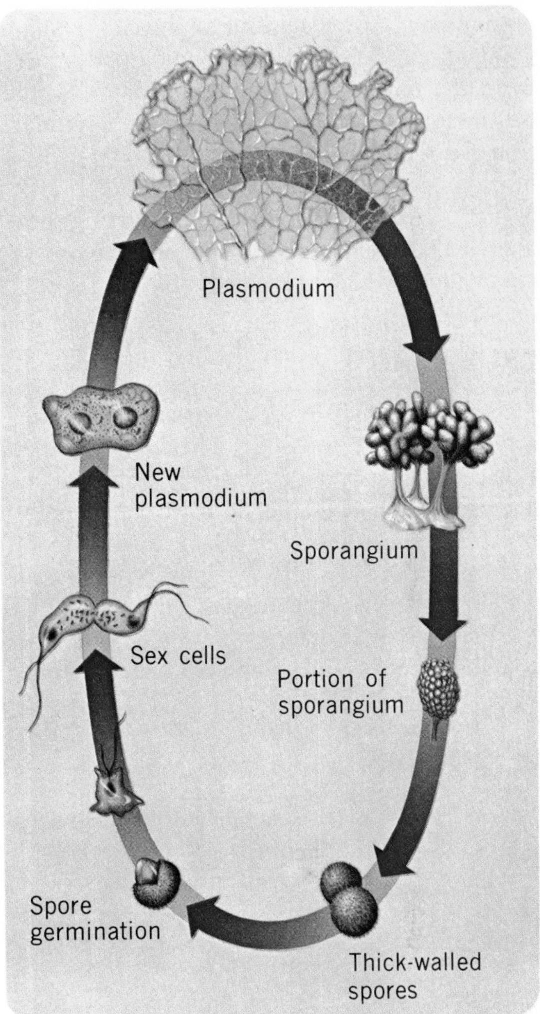

12–2 The life cycle of a slime mold. Which part of the life cycle is best adapted to a dry environment? Which parts of the cycle do you think would require abundant moisture?

dividual amoeboid cells, which thus lose their separate identity. This is a most unusual way for an organism to be formed. How would you interpret this phenomenon according to the cell theory (see Chapter 3)?

Looking back at our description of a slime mold, we can see that it combines characters of animals and plants. If we observed only the plasmodium, we would certainly call a slime mold an animal. If fruiting bodies and spores were the only parts we could see, we would call the organism a plant. Is it plant or animal? Can we really relate this strange organism to other living things? What was its evolutionary origin? We can get some help answering these questions by examining some other more familiar fungi, which are called molds.

TRUE FUNGI

Common names for organisms are often misleading and hard to define. The fluffy mold on a piece of stale bread is certainly not the same thing as a slime mold. Yet both are called **molds.** In its organization, the black bread mold, *Rhizopus nigricans*, (ry·ZOE·pus NY·grih·cans – Figure 12-3) is a true **fungus.** This means that its vegetative structure – the fluffy mass – is composed of slender threads called **hyphae** (HY·fee). All hyphae have distinct cell walls and are branching structures. How does this compare with the vegetative structure (plasmodium) of a slime mold?

Rhizopus is commonly found in the soil with other fungi and bacteria. However, its hyphae may also be found on a piece of bread. Here the hyphae secrete enzymes that digest the starch into soluble compounds. Hyphae then absorb the soluble carbohydrates, which serve as food for the fungus.

Adaptation to a Land Environment

Rhizopus has some structures that adapt it to a dry land environment. The hyphae that absorb water and soluble nutrients also anchor the plant. Large numbers of thick-walled spores are produced in spherical capsules, or **sporangia** (spo·RAN·jee·a), at the ends of upright hyphae (Figure 12-3). From here spores are easily dispersed by air currents and splashing water.

12–3 **a.** A fragment of *Rhizopus* with sporangia. (What type of reproduction is indicated by the spores?) *Rhizopus* is a common contaminant of bread. To combat the organism, bakers put a mold inhibitor in bread dough. **b.** Stages in sexual reproduction of *Rhizopus*. The two mating strains (labeled + and −) look alike but are genetically different.

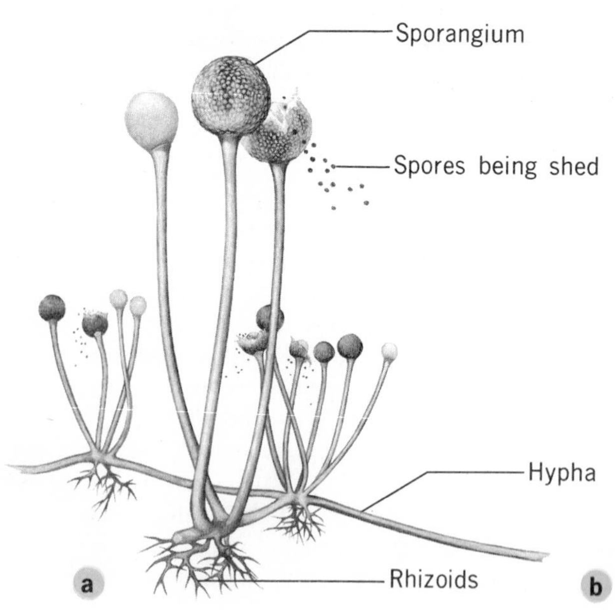

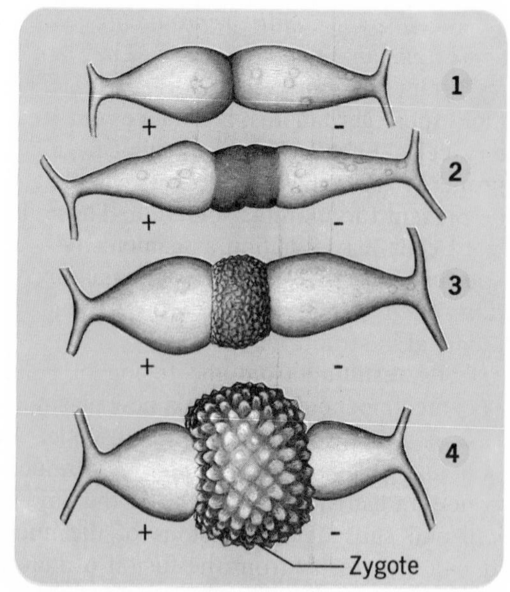

Not only are the spores resistant to drying, but they are produced in tremendous numbers. These features may help you to understand why some molds are so widespread in nature, and why they may contaminate the agar plates used in your laboratory experiments.

Sexual reproduction in *Rhizopus,* as in the majority of true fungi, shows some of the evolutionary changes that adapt it to a terrestrial mode of life. Instead of forming gametes with flagella, as slime molds do, special hyphae fuse with one another (Figure 12-3). Each contributes nuclei and cytoplasm to the **zygote** (ZY·goat), the cell that forms in fertilization by the union of two gametes. In this modification of sexual reproduction, most true fungi (except for some aquatic molds) do not require water (dew, rain, etc.) as a medium for the fusion of their gametes. (Mosses and certain other primitive types of land plants require water for fusion of gametes. The sperms swim to the eggs.)

You will see sexual reproduction of a mold when you mate two strains of *Rhizopus* in the laboratory (Inquiry 12-2). This is an important experiment, because it is the only one in which you will have a chance to see steps in the union of gametes—fertilization—and the formation of a zygote. *Rhizopus* forms a zygote with a very thick wall which, like the thick-walled spores, can withstand drying and other adverse terrestrial conditions.

Are the Fungi Plants?

Earlier we asked the question whether slime molds are plants or animals. We could not give a definite answer. If we asked the same question about *Rhizopus,* it might appear to be answered easily. *Rhizopus,* unlike the slime molds, has no flagellated cells or amoeboid stage to suggest that its ancestors were single-celled (unicellular) animals (Chapter 19). Furthermore, *Rhizopus* has well-developed cell walls and produces spores in sporangia—features that are characteristic of plants. Another feature further relates *Rhizopus* to plants. It was noted long ago that some true fungi—*Rhizopus,* for example—are very similar to certain algae in their structure and method of reproduction (see Figure 12-3). The hyphae of *Rhizopus* lack cross-walls, and in this characteristic they are similar to certain algae. It was also observed that the sexual reproduction of other algae is accomplished by a process similar to sexual reproduction in *Rhizopus* (Inquiry 13-2). Because of these and other similarities, biologists once supposed that the true fungi were evolved from the algae. According to this line of reasoning, fungi were algae that in the process of evolution had lost their ability to carry on photosynthesis—they had become heterotrophic.

Not long after this idea had become widely accepted, an interesting group of primitive fungi was discovered. These were aquatic organisms having some characteristics of true fungi. However, they were not at all like algae. At different points in their life cycles they produced flagellated cells that looked more like **Protozoa** (pro·toe·ZOE·a—unicellular animals) than like the reproductive cells of algae. Further studies of flagellated cells of various true fungi have convinced biologists that the true fungi indeed evolved from protozoans and should be placed in groups quite unrelated to the algae, as shown in the illustrated summary of plant classification at the end of Chapter 14 (pages 276-77).

But what about the slime molds, with their plantlike and animal-like characteristics? The plasmodium and the flagellated cells formed by the slime molds are also very much like protozoans. This, plus their animal-like mode of nutrition and the absence of cell walls in the plasmodium, leaves little doubt that slime molds, like the true fungi, also had their evolutionary beginnings with protozoans. But remember that protozoans live and reproduce in water, while slime molds and true fungi live and reproduce on land, where the environment is relatively dry. The slime molds and true fungi evolved a stage in their life cycles that could withstand drying and other adverse conditions

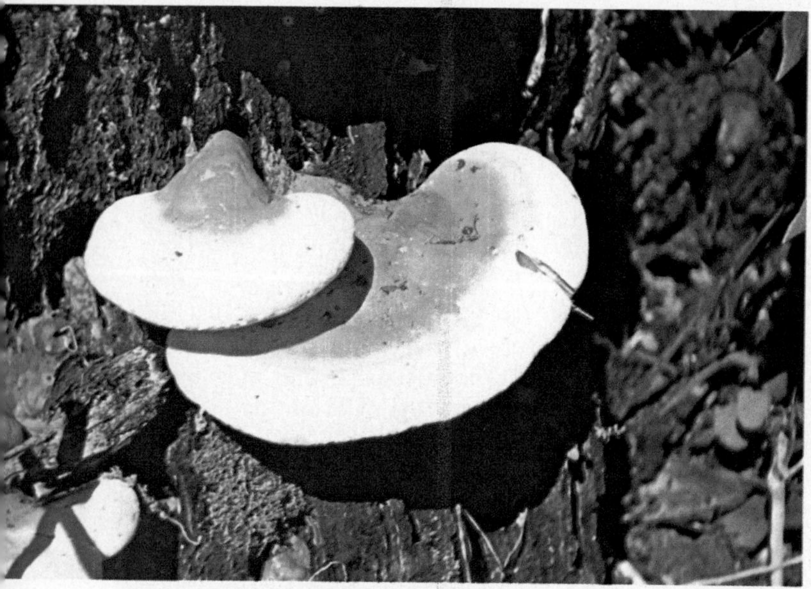

Hugh Spencer

12–4 A bracket fungus on a tree. What you see is the fruiting (spore-producing) structure of the fungus. This fungus and many of its relatives kill or spoil unestimated amounts of lumber and untold numbers of shade trees each year.

of a land environment. This stage is the spore-stage, the plantlike part of the life cycle. Perhaps it is not necessary to decide whether slime molds and true fungi are plants or animals. They are organisms that have evolved from an aquatic environment to become adapted for survival on land. It makes little difference how we classify the characteristics that evolved, as long as we understand what has happened in the evolution of the organism. Now what is your opinion about the classification of a slime mold or a true fungus? Is it animal or plant? Or is it really important which kingdom the fungi are placed in? Perhaps it is more important for us to understand *where* they came from, *how* they have become adapted to their environments, and *why* they are important components of the world we live in.

THE IMPORTANCE OF FUNGI

In many ways bacteria and fungi are similar in their importance to man. Some bacteria and fungi produce useful products from fermentations, while others produce life-saving antibiotics. Most bacteria and fungi are decomposers, and in this respect play an important role in the cycles of nature, as described in Chapter 36. Like some of the bacteria, some of the fungi produce disease. Especially important are the fungus diseases of plants.

Fungi cause tremendous amounts of spoilage that annually costs millions of dollars in loss of foodstuffs, lumber, and leather goods (Figure 12-4). We should not forget the poisonous "toadstools" (from the German *Tod-Stuhl,* meaning "death-stool") that take their toll of human lives each year. At the same time we should remember the delicate flavor mushrooms add to our beefsteak, soups, and a great variety of other dishes.

Not too many years ago, the cultivation of edible mushrooms was a carefully guarded secret. Today they are grown as a crop in many places throughout the world. They are grown in caves, cellars, and especially constructed mushroom-growing houses. The edible portion of a mushroom is really a fruiting body composed of compacted hyphae that arise from hyphae growing in the soil (Figure 12-5). Like the fruiting bodies of other fungi, that of a mushroom produces great numbers of spores from

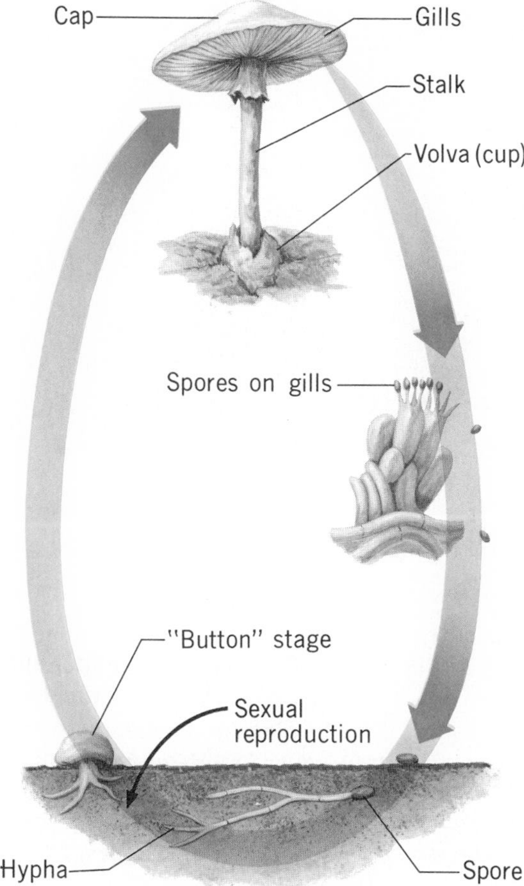

12–5 The life cycle of a club fungus, *Amanita*. How does spore production of a club fungus differ from that of a sac fungus (Figure 12–8)?

thin gills. It has been estimated that one mushroom like those shown in Figure 12-6 or Figure 12-7 produces about 1,800,000,000 spores from its gills (Inquiry 12-2). However, the number of mushrooms that are found in nature remains roughly the same. This means that only a tiny percentage of the spores will ever germinate or ultimately produce new mushroom hyphae in the soil.

Whenever any species produces offspring, in this case the spores, in such tremendous numbers, the chances of survival of the offspring are very, very small. This illustrates an important biological principle—the lower the probability of survival of offspring, the greater the rate of production of offspring. Can you relate this principle to other organisms? (Why would you not expect the reverse to be true?)

Other fungi, known as the sac fungi, also form fruiting bodies that produce spores in tremendous numbers. One of the sac fungi has fruiting structures shaped like little cups (Figure 12-8). These are often brightly colored and look like jewels on the forest floor where they grow. The spores are produced in microscopic sacs on the inner surface of the cup. There are usually eight spores per sac. When the spores are ripe, they are shot from the sac to be distributed by air currents. Spores that land in a favorable habitat will germinate and form new hyphae in the ground. Sooner or later by sexual reproduction between hyphae, a new spore-producing fruiting structure is initiated and the life cycle starts over.

12–6 Edible mushrooms of the genus *Agaricus*. The fruiting bodies are tipped to one side to show the gills of the undersides of the caps. Great numbers of spores are produced and shed by the gills.

Hugh Spencer

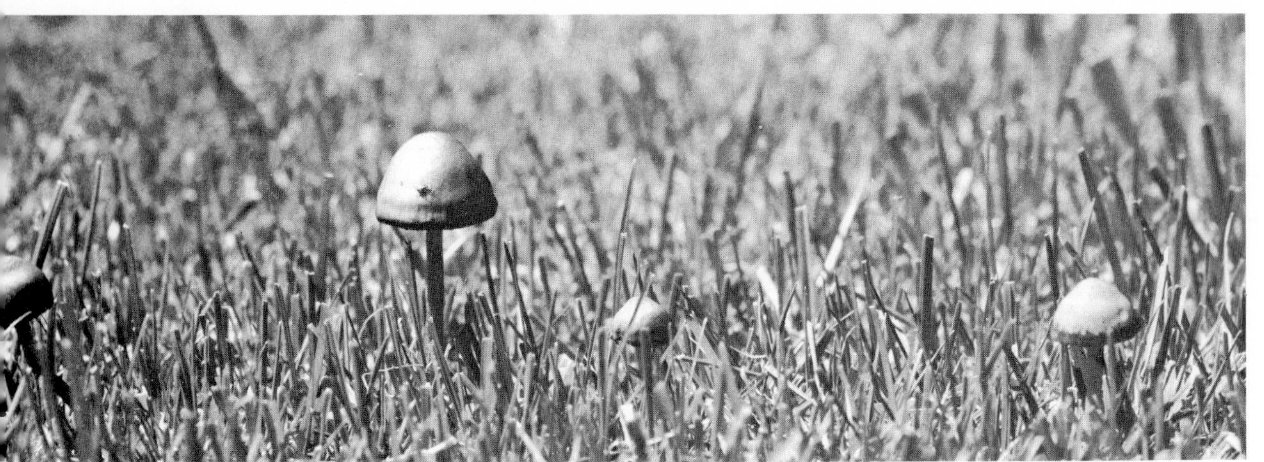

John A. Moore

12–7 A worm's-eye view of mushrooms. The stalks and caps are the parts normally seen, but their stature in lesser forests is lost to us who see them from above.

To Eat or Not to Eat

Some mushrooms (those often called toadstools) contain a poisonous chemical compound called **amanitin** (a·MAN·ih·tin), which may cause respiratory and circulatory failure when eaten. Altogether, approximately seventy species of gill fungi are poisonous to man. The most deadly are those belonging to the genus *Amanita* (am·a·NY·ta—Figure 12-5). *Amanita verna* has a pure white fruiting body. Eating less than one cap from this fungus can prove fatal within one day. It is well named the "death angel." Generally the amanitas and other poisonous mushrooms can be distinguished by a large cup at the base of the stalk (Figure 12-5). However, this may be buried in the ground and not easily detected. There are many old wives' tales about how to distinguish poisonous mushrooms from edible ones. Here are a few of these misconceptions. "A silver spoon will tarnish if put in the pot with poisonous mushrooms that are being cooked"; "The cap of an edible mushroom will peel readily, while that of a toadstool will not"; "If insects or other animals eat a mushroom, it is safe for human consumption." None of these, nor any other general rule, can be used to distinguish edible from poisonous species. The only rule to follow when selecting mushrooms for the table is to divide them into two groups, those produced commercially and purchased at the grocery store, and those that you collect in the field. Unless you intend to have them identified by an expert, dispose of all the mushrooms collected in the field and eat those from the grocery store.

Spoilage and Decay

There are a great many different kinds of fungi responsible for spoilage and decay. Some are wood-rotting fungi, which infect and destroy not only living trees but also railroad ties, fence posts, telephone poles, and all kinds of structural timbers. Probably these fungi are responsible for destroying more wood than all other destructive agencies put together—including fire and man.

This estimate holds true in spite of the preservatives such as creosote, tars, paints, and varnishes that are used in the endless battle to prevent wood decay.

Unfortunately, much of the damage to structural timbers and living trees is done long before there is any visible sign of rotting. Sooner or later, however, a bracket-like fruiting body (Figure 12-4) may appear, which will produce billions of spores. A few of the spores will infect living trees or start fungal rot in railroad ties, telephone poles, fence posts, and the green lumber that is frequently used in building inexpensive homes.

A trip to the basement in search of your leather boots, or the extra leather suitcase or knapsack, may have introduced you to the detrimental effects of blue and green molds some of which may belong to the genus *Penicillium* (Chapter 11). Or perhaps you have had the misfortune of selecting an orange or grapefruit spoiled by one of these molds (Inquiry 12-2). If you have had any of these experiences, you certainly noticed a green powdery substance produced by the fungus on the leather or fruit. This substance is made up of spores formed by *Penicillium* on hyphal branches that look like little brushes (Figure 12-9). The thick walls of these spores are pigmented, and their color accounts for the beautiful greens and blue-greens of these handsome molds. The blue-green mold found in blue and Roquefort cheeses is also produced by species of *Penicillium*. The cheeses get their distinctive flavor from the mold with which the cheese is inoculated. Spores of *Penicillium* are widely distributed and are common contaminants of sterile cultures in the laboratory.

12–8 The life cycle of a sac fungus (the example is a cup fungus). What features of the life cycle are like those of a club fungus (Figure 12–5)? What feature is particularly characteristic of the sac fungi?

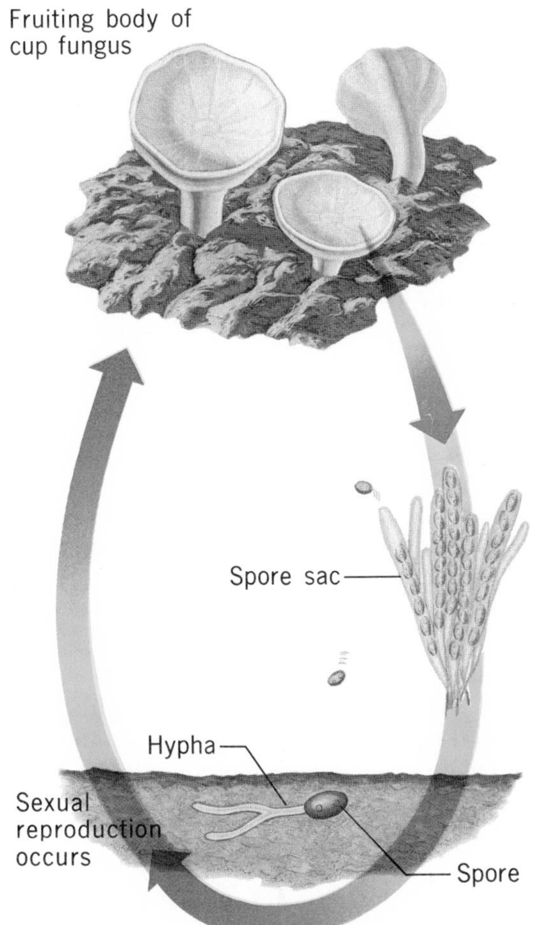

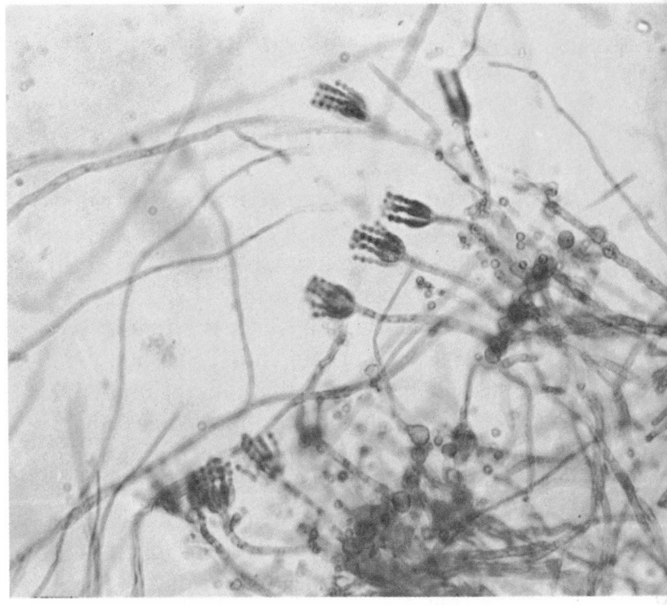

Harbrace Photo

12–9 Brushlike hyphal branches of *Penicillium*. The spores at the tips of branches are enclosed in spore sacs in some species but not others. (500 ×)

Fungi and Disease

We have already discussed the importance of *Penicillium* and other molds in production of antibiotics (pages 222-23). Here we will discuss fungi from the other point of view—as *causes* of disease.

Do you have some Irish ancestors in your family tree? If you do, the chances are very good that they emigrated to the United States during the years following 1845. Up to that time, Ireland was a successful state with a rapidly increasing population that had reached eight million. During this time of rapid expansion, the people of the "misty isles" had become almost totally dependent on one crop as a source of food. This was the "Irish potato," which had been introduced from South America many years earlier. The year 1845 turned out to be a bad one for the "Irish potato" crop. The days during the growing season were cool and damp, and as the young potato vines matured, they became sick and died. At first it was thought that the poor growth of potatoes was the result of the bad weather. It was later demonstrated that a fungus, *Phytophthora infestans* (fy·TOF·tho·ra in·FEST·ans), was causing disease and that the cool, damp days were ideal for its rapid spread.

In the next fifteen years the potato crop failed repeatedly because of the fungus disease. Over a million Irishmen died of starvation and other diseases related to malnutrition. Another million and a half people emigrated to North America. Many settled in the rapidly growing cities of the United States, where they and their descendants have become our tie with Ireland.

The disease of potatoes that scourged Ireland is still with us. In the United States alone, over seven million bushels of potatoes are estimated as lost to this disease annually.

Crop failures resulting from rust and smut diseases of cereals (corn, wheat, rice) have displaced hundreds of millions of humans and caused countless deaths either by starvation or in wars motivated by starvation. In one recent five-year period alone, starvation in one nation took more than 12 million lives. Much of this loss of life can be attributed to loss of crops infected with rusts and smuts.

In the United States, starvation is infrequent, but crop loss is sometimes heavy. It is estimated that wheat rust disease reduces national wheat production by more than 90 million bushels during a normal year! All diseases of field corn result in a loss of 500 million bushels. Of this total, 95 million bushels are lost because of corn smut. Increasing populations and food shortages in many parts of the world make these figures important.

We have not exhausted the list of fungi that cause diseases of plants and animals. Perhaps you live in a community where nearly all of the American elm trees have died within the last few years. The chances are that the elm trees were infected with a fast-working fungus that causes the Dutch elm disease. Fungi also cause other important plant diseases such as apple scab, blights of native trees, and many other diseases. Fungi are also a common cause of disease in animals, including man. Many troublesome skin diseases such as ringworm and athlete's foot are caused by fungi. A fungal infection of the lungs, histoplasmosis, is very prevalent in certain regions of the country.

Yeasts

Common brewers' and bakers' yeasts are different from most true fungi, because they do not form hyphae. These yeasts are unicellular and reproduce asexually by a special kind of cell division called **budding** (Figure 12-10). When a yeast cell buds, it forms a bulge on one side of the cell. A nuclear division occurs in the parent cell, and one of the daughter nuclei moves into the developing bud. As the bud grows, it may separate from the parent cell.

In addition to asexual reproduction by budding, yeasts have a simple sexual cycle—not unlike that of conjugating bacteria.

Yeasts have proved extremely useful as experimental organisms in our quest for knowl-

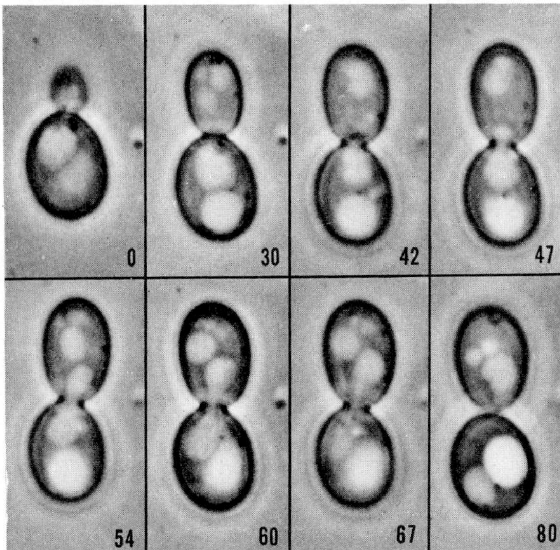

C. F. Robinow

12–10 A sequence of timed photographs of asexual reproduction by budding in brewer's yeast, *Saccharomyces cerevisiae*. The numbers show the intervals in minutes. How does this method of reproduction compare with asexual reproduction in bacteria (see page 205)? How does it compare with cell division in multicellular plants and animals?

edge of outer space. Scientists have been aware of the hazards to man of various kinds of radiation found in outer space. To test the effects of radiation on living organisms prior to man's first flights, rockets were sent aloft carrying living yeast cells. When the yeasts were returned to earth, they were cultured, and the degree of damage to their genetic material was studied.

Another fungus that has been used extensively to help us understand the principles of inheritance is the pink bread mold. Like the cup fungi (Figure 12-8) this mold produces a row of eight spores in a saclike cell (Figure 8-14, page 166). Spores can be isolated individually from the sac, then cultured to analyze their hereditary characteristics. The order of the spores in the sac reflects the events that occur in meiosis, which was discussed in detail in Chapter 7.

CONCLUDING REMARKS–ADAPTATION TO LAND

The evolution of organisms capable of surviving on land is one of the most important of all biological events. The evidence indicates that the fungi, like all other terrestrial organisms, had their beginnings with more primitive, unicellular, aquatic ancestors. These ancestors, like the fungi, were probably heterotrophs and would best be described as protozoans. In the course of adaptation to life on land, certain changes occurred that made it possible for organisms (plants, animals, and fungi) to survive in the dry land environments.

More specifically, in the evolution of the fungi we list these important adaptations:

1. The disappearance of flagellated cells and the evolution of new methods of sexual and asexual reproduction. (Review the life cycle of *Rhizopus*.)
2. The evolution of protective layers around spores and (in some cases) zygotes. The tiny bit of living substance within a spore or zygote provides the only continuity from one organism to the next. The mold or mushroom may die, but survival of the species is assured by the production of these resistant reproductive cells. (Remember the spores of a slime mold, and of *Penicillium* and *Rhizopus*.)
3. The evolution of hyphae with thickened, supporting cell walls. Hyphae are structures that obtain nutrition from the environment, that compose fruiting bodies on which spores are produced and elevated for dispersal, and that–in another modification–are sexual reproductive organs.

Numerous other characters that adapt fungi to a terrestrial existence could be listed. It is time, however, to move on with our story of evolution and see how autotrophic plants succeeded in colonizing the land. Inquiry 13-1 will help you recognize plant features that were important in the evolution of land plants.

John A. Moore

12–11 A biological problem on the end of a log. Can you suggest one or more hypotheses to account for the regular growth of the fungi? If so, what deductions can you make from the hypotheses? What investigations would test the deductions?

GUIDE QUESTIONS AND PROBLEMS

1. How do viruses, bacteria, and slime molds differ in their structure and reproduction? On the basis of your answer, explain which of the three organisms you consider to be the most complex. In what ways are all three organisms alike?
2. Suppose you were sent to collect various fungi for class demonstration. Where would you look for them? How is this correlated with their structure? How do fungi compare in their distribution with that of bacteria? viruses?
3. What is the evidence that the true fungi have evolved from the protozoans rather than from algae?
4. What social, political, and economic consequences have fungal diseases of plants had?
5. What are some of the ways in which true fungi are important to you in your daily activities?
6. What important adaptations occurred in the evolution of the fungi that enabled them to live on land?
7. Figure 12-11 poses a problem of why the growth of fungi on the cut end of a log is ringlike. Suggest an explanation.

RELATED READING

Books

For an authoritative, well-illustrated study of fungi and their importance . . .

Alexopoulos, C. T., *Introductory Mycology*, Second Edition, Wiley, New York, 1962.

Christensen, C. M., *The Molds and Man*, University of Minnesota Press, Minneapolis, Minn., 1961.

For a discussion of the place of the fungi in relation to other plant groups . . .

Bold, H. C., *The Plant Kingdom*, Second Edition, Foundations of Modern Biology Series, Prentice-Hall, Englewood Cliffs, N. J., 1964.

Delevoryas, T., *Plant Diversification*, Modern Biology Series, Holt, Rinehart and Winston, New York, 1966.

Hylander, C. T., *The World of Plant Life*, Second Edition, Macmillan, New York, 1956.

Magazines

Ahmadjian, V., "The Fungi of Lichens," *Scientific American*, Volume 208 (February 1963), page 123.

Rose, A., "Yeasts," *Scientific American*, Volume 202 (February 1960), page 136.

13

The Trend Toward Complexity

How important are green plants in the world of living things? We might answer this question by considering one of the functions unique to green plants—**photosynthesis** (foe·toe·SIN·theh-sis). The vital process of photosynthesis carried on by green plants transforms light energy into the chemical energy which all living things—plants as well as animals—rely on, either directly or indirectly, for their existence.

Has it always been this way? Have there always been green plants on the land, and land animals to eat them? If not, when and where did green plants first appear? Do we have any evidence to give us some idea as to how long photosynthetic organisms have inhabited the earth? If so, what were these organisms like in the distant past? Clearly we must seek the answers to these questions by studying the evolution of photosynthetic plants and their ascendancy in the seas and on the land. (Inquiry 13-1 provides background in plant types and features.) For this study we have to go back in time to search for evidences of ancient plants as recorded in rocks. We must start with the fossil record—the history of life on earth.

Fossil evidence of the first photosynthetic organisms comes from a period of the earth's history called the **Pre-Cambrian** (pre·KAM·bree-an—Figure 13-1). This period embraces about nine tenths of the total age of the earth, starting with the earth's beginning and continuing up to the time of the **Cambrian period.** Since the Cambrian period started, about 600 million years ago, all the evolution of land organisms has occurred.

During the Pre-Cambrian period, tremendous reefs of limestone ($CaCO_3$) were formed. Some of these limestones show a characteristic pattern, as though the limestone had been deposited in concentric layers to form large limestone heads (Figure 13-2), of which the reefs are composed. One such Pre-Cambrian limestone reef in Southern Rhodesia is at least 2.3 billion years old! These unusual limestone deposits have been compared with similar limestone formations produced by some present-day blue-green algae. Could it be that blue-green algae were present in the Pre-Cambrian seas where the reefs were formed? No matter how hard we look, we cannot find conclusive evidence of the remains of algal cells in the ancient limestone.

In 1954 two Americans, S. A. Tyler and E. S. Barghoorn, reported a spectacular discovery. They had found fossilized remains of organisms in rocks of Pre-Cambrian age—at least 1.6 billion years old. These beautifully preserved specimens were discovered in a very hard rock called chert or flint (Figure 13-2). By grinding sections of the rock thin enough to transmit light, Tyler and Barghoorn were able to examine the sections under the compound microscope. These examinations revealed organisms similar to fungal hyphae and spores, and colonies of cells very much like modern blue-green algae! This unique discovery confirmed what had been suspected many years before, that blue-green algae were among the earliest cellular inhabitants of the earth.

Perhaps the most important conclusion to be drawn from this discovery is that both autotrophic and heterotrophic organisms had evolved during the Pre-Cambrian period. Further accumulation of evidence from Pre-Cambrian fossils has led to two additional conclusions: organisms of the Pre-Cambrian period were very primitive in structure, and they lived in water.

13-1 PLANT LIFE ON EARTH — A TIME SCALE

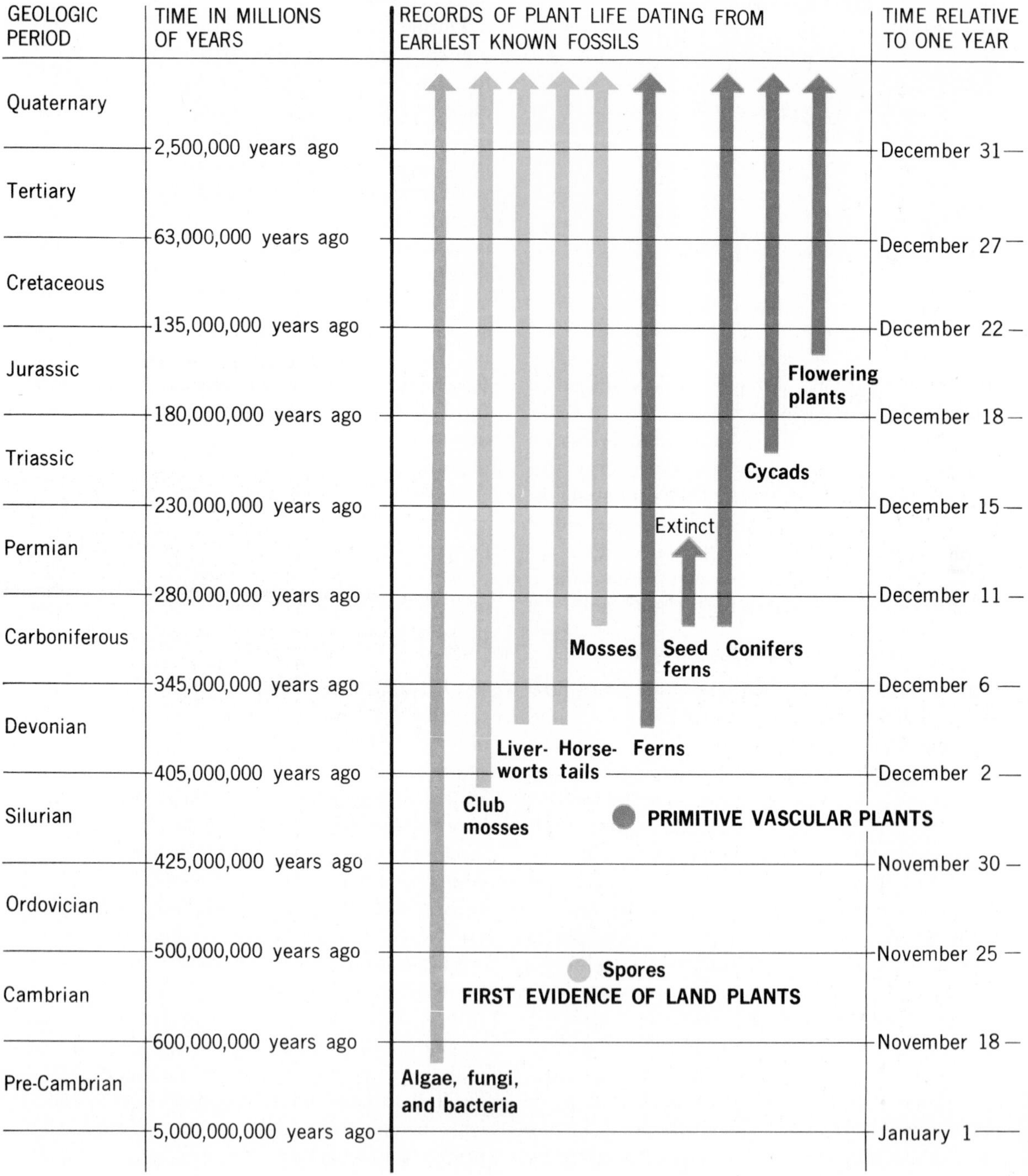

GEOLOGIC PERIOD	TIME IN MILLIONS OF YEARS	TIME RELATIVE TO ONE YEAR
Quaternary	2,500,000 years ago	December 31
Tertiary	63,000,000 years ago	December 27
Cretaceous	135,000,000 years ago	December 22
Jurassic	180,000,000 years ago	December 18
Triassic	230,000,000 years ago	December 15
Permian	280,000,000 years ago	December 11
Carboniferous	345,000,000 years ago	December 6
Devonian	405,000,000 years ago	December 2
Silurian	425,000,000 years ago	November 30
Ordovician	500,000,000 years ago	November 25
Cambrian	600,000,000 years ago	November 18
Pre-Cambrian	5,000,000,000 years ago	January 1

RECORDS OF PLANT LIFE DATING FROM EARLIEST KNOWN FOSSILS

Flowering plants
Cycads
Extinct
Mosses **Seed ferns** **Conifers**
Liver-worts **Horse-tails** **Ferns**
Club mosses
PRIMITIVE VASCULAR PLANTS
Spores
FIRST EVIDENCE OF LAND PLANTS
Algae, fungi, and bacteria

Before we continue the story of plant evolution, let us take a brief glimpse at the Pre-Cambrian landscape. The most obvious difference between the Pre-Cambrian landscape and the one we see today was the total absence of land plants and animals at that time. Clearly sometime between the end of this early period and the present, the land was colonized by living things. All of the evidence at our disposal confirms the hypothesis that land plants and animals evolved from aquatic ancestors. If we accept this hypothesis, as most biologists do, we need to explain how plants and animals living in the seas could possibly become suited to survive in the bleak, desiccating land environment. What kinds of adaptations enabled plants to colonize the land without drying out? What were the primitive land plants like?

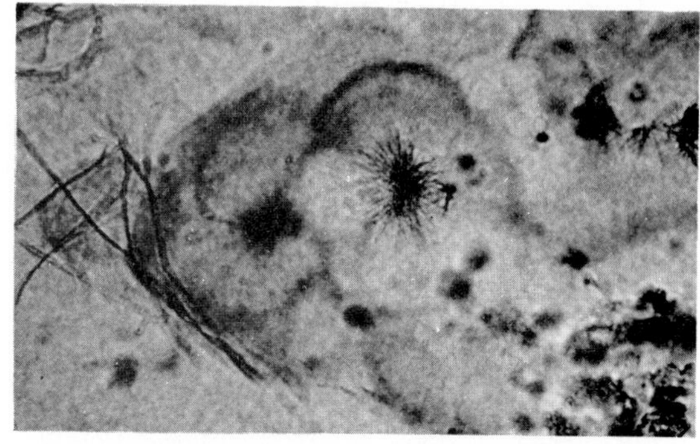

E. S. Barghoorn

13–2 **(Above)** A microscopic view of fossil remains of microorganisms in Pre-Cambrian rock 1.6 billion years old. Note the evidence of algal clusters and hyphae-like filaments. **(Below)** A Pre-Cambrian limestone reef. Biologists believe the concentric layers of limestone were formed by blue-green algae. How does the evidence of the upper photograph help substantiate this hypothesis?

New York State Museum & Science Service

UNICELLULAR TO MULTICELLULAR—THE STORY OF ALGAE

One of the most obvious features of evolutionarily advanced organisms is their multicellular construction. The word *multicellular* literally means "of many cells," but multicellular organisms are more than just organisms with many cells. They are organisms with different kinds of cells, each kind performing specific functions. Thus, multicellular organisms have certain cells modified for movement of materials. There may also be special cells for reproduction, and others with thick walls for support. There is a division of labor among the cells of multicellular organisms.

But where did multicellular organisms come from? Have they always existed? Comparison of the structures of plants, study of the fossil record, and experiments dealing with life's beginnings (Chapter 9) leave little doubt that unicellular organisms were the ancestors of multicellular plants and animals.

Unicellular Origins

The unicellular level of organization should be familiar to you. You have studied unicellular bacteria and yeasts, and you have examined a drop of pond water (Inquiry 1-1), in which you saw a variety of unicellular organisms—plant and animal. Some may have been blue-green in color and arranged in loose packets of cells called colonies. Others, green or colorless, may have been very active, moving in sudden, short jerks or darting across the field of the microscope. Many of the motile forms are propelled by flagella or cilia, while others are amoeboid.

The variety among unicellular types extends to differences in their methods of obtaining food. Many are colorless heterotrophs that

13–3 Some unicellular autotrophs. These microscopic organisms are common inhabitants of aquatic environments. **a.** *Porphyridium*, a red alga, assumes a colonial appearance. **b, c, d.** Diatoms, golden-brown algae, are some of the most numerous unicellular algae in both fresh and salt water. Because the cell walls of these organisms contain silicon, fossil diatoms are very abundant, and are used commercially for insulation and polishing agents. **e.** *Chlamydomonas*, a green alga, although motile, is very plantlike because it has a chloroplast, stores starch, and has a distinct cell wall. It may be very much like the ancestral unicellular organisms from which green plants evolved. **f.** *Gloeocapsa*, a blue-green alga, is one of the most primitive of all autotrophic organisms.

a D. P. Wilson

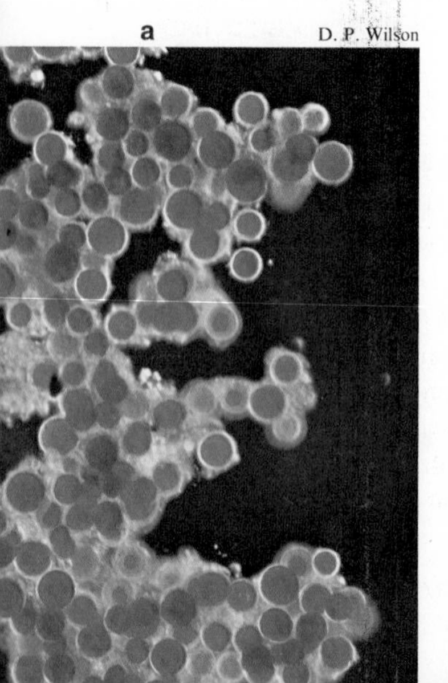

b Eric Gravé

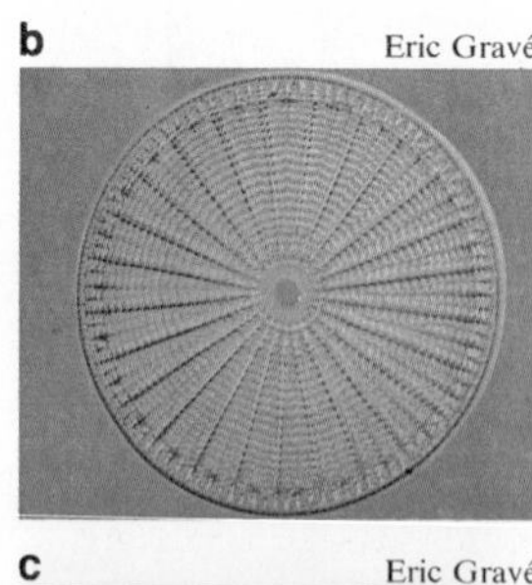

c Eric Gravé

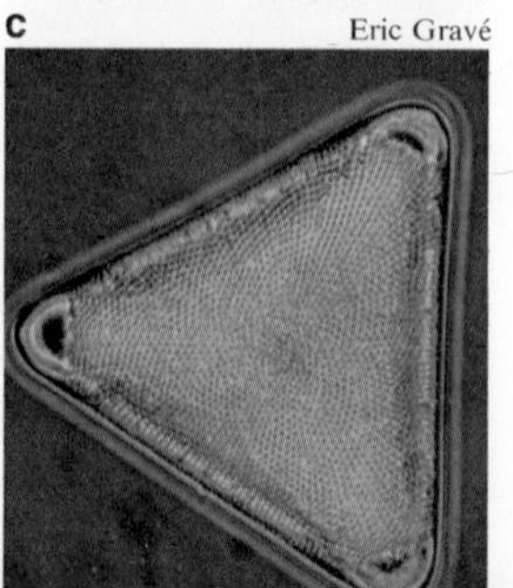

d Eric Gravé

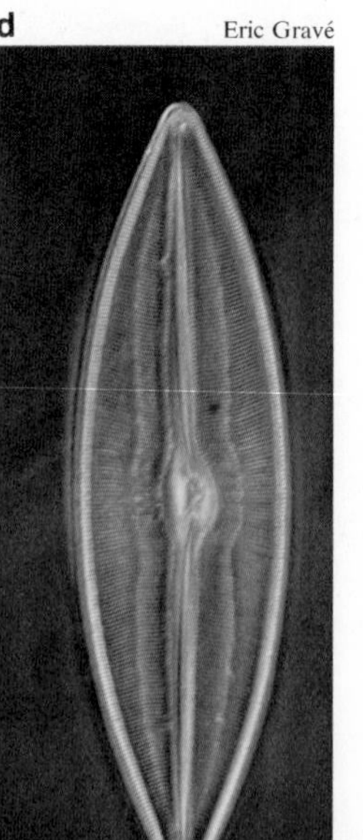

e Harbrace Photo made at E. Leitz, Inc.

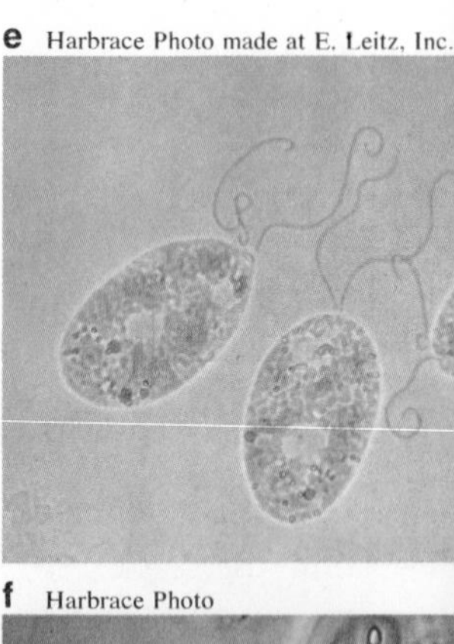

f Harbrace Photo

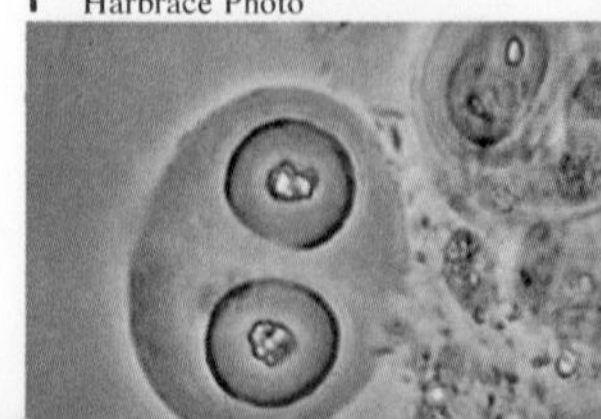

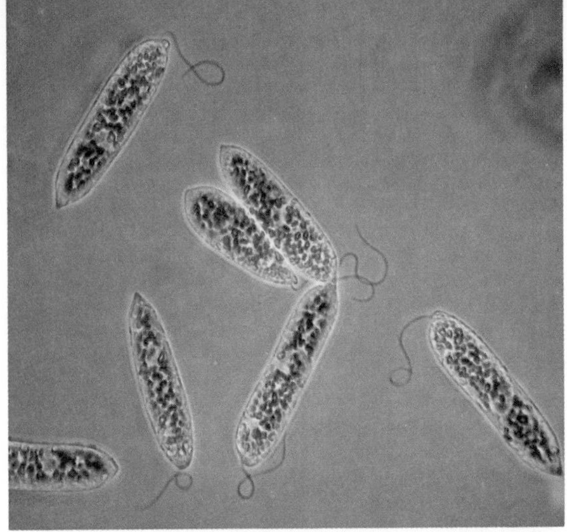

Harbrace Photo

13–4 *Euglena*, a unicellular autotroph, is much like a protozoan (a unicellular animal) except that it has chloroplasts and is photosynthetic.

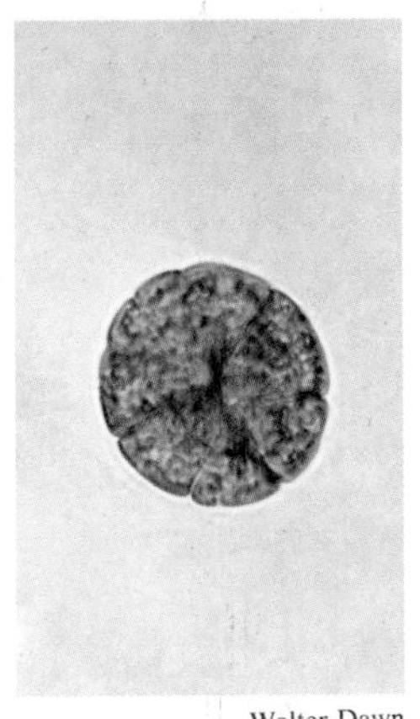

Walter Dawn

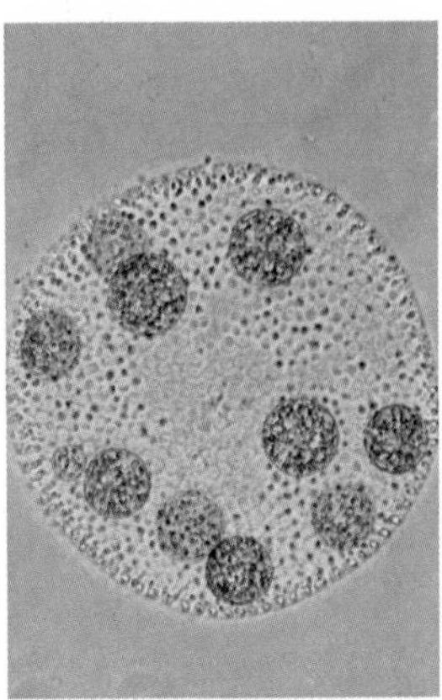

Harbrace Photo

13–5 Two colonial autotrophs. Unlike *Pandorina* **(left)**, *Volvox* **(right)** shows some division of labor; only certain cells are potentially reproductive.

ingest particles of food, including other unicellular organisms, either through an opening at one end of the cell or by engulfing the particles. Not all of the unicellular organisms are colorless, however. Some are brown and others are various shades or green, blue-green, yellow-green or red. All of these are photosynthetic organisms (Figures 13-3, 13-4, and 13-5). They all contain chlorophyll and are autotrophic.

The evidence from the fossil record tells us that blue-green algae were among the early photosynthetic organisms to inhabit the earth. There are, however, many reasons to believe that other unicellular organisms such as *Euglena* (you·GLEE·na) may be more representative of the organisms that were ancestral to multicellular plants and animals. *Euglena* (Figure 13-4) is a flagellated organism with no cell wall. In contrast to the lack of a cell wall, in which it resembles animals, *Euglena* usually has well-defined chloroplasts and stores a carbohydrate only slightly different from the starches of higher plants. It is now known that some of these autotrophs will, under some experimental conditions, lose their chlorophyll. This does not result in their death. They simply become heterotrophs and live by absorbing soluble nutrients. Thus *Euglena,* when treated with the antibiotic streptomycin, or with heat, can be converted from a "plant" into an "animal." A unicellular organism with the potentialities of *Euglena* deserves special attention when we are searching for the kind of organism that might represent the ancestral type from which plants and animals may have evolved at some time in the distant past.

The unicellular autotrophs of greatest interest to us in our study of the evolution of land plants are those with bright green chloroplasts and well-defined cell walls. A common aquatic organism with these characteristics is the green alga *Chlamydomonas* (klam·ih·da·MOE·nas—Figure 13-3e). You will become acquainted with it in Inquiry 13-2. It is obvious that this unicellular organism is like some protozoans in having flagella. Yet when we examine its pigments and stored food we find them identical with those of green land plants. Both the green alga *Chlamydomonas* and green land plants contain two kinds of chlorophyll. These are designated chlorophylls *a* and *b*. Not only are the chlorophyll molecules the same in both types of organisms, but they are present in

Walter Dawn

13-6 *Ulva*, or sea lettuce, is a common green alga of the tidal zone near the shore. Its life cycle is illustrated in Figure 13-8.

similar proportions. The biochemical similarity of the green alga *Chlamydomonas* and the green land plants extends even to their stored food, which is true starch. Because of these and other similarities, *Chlamydomonas* is believed to represent *the general type* of unicellular autotroph from which multicellular green plants may have evolved long ago.

At one stage in its life cycle, *Chlamydomonas* may do a rather unusual thing. The normally motile vegetative cells withdraw their flagella and become attached to some object in the water. They divide to form irregular masses of nonmotile green cells. This stage in the life cycle of *Chlamydomonas* is like an evolutionary signpost. It points to the multicellular organization of nonmotile green plants.

The same tendency of nonmotile green cells to be intimately associated in packets or colonies can be seen in many other organisms (Figure 13-5). In fact, it may be very difficult for a casual observer to distinguish such clusters of cells from true multicellular organisms. To tell the difference between a packet of unicells and a multicellular organism, we must answer this question: is there any division of labor among the cells—or are all the cells alike in being potentially self-sufficient, each one capable of carrying out all of the functions required for survival? If we can find some clear evidence of different kinds of cells, or differences in cell function, then we are looking at a multicellular organism.

Primitive Multicellular Organization

Primitive green plants living in aquatic environments *have* evolved a multicellular organization. One such alga is the common "sea lettuce," or *Ulva,* of our coastal tide pools (Figure 13-6). The bright green sheets that comprise this organism are usually two cells in thickness. Thus only the outer surfaces of the *Ulva* cells are exposed to the aquatic environment. At the base of the plant we find long threadlike cells. These cells are rootlike, in that they anchor the plant to rocks bordering the tide pools. Moreover, these cells are usually colorless, and they are never reproductive. They perform a specific function for the plant; without these anchoring cells, *Ulva* could not survive in the wave-washed tide pools.

Although many steps are missing from our generalized account of the evolution of the multicellular body, it should be clear that the direction has been from unicellular, to colonies of cells, to organisms showing division of labor among cells. (The evolution of a multicellular organization in animals followed basically the same pattern as that which occurred in plants, as we shall see in later chapters.)

The Evolution of Sexual Reproduction

The widespread occurrence of sexual reproduction among plants and animals testifies to its importance (review Chapter 7). We know of only *two* groups in which sexual reproduction has *not* been demonstrated. One of these groups is the blue-green algae. The other is a group of unicellular, flagellated organisms to which *Euglena* belongs.

In each instance of sexual reproduction that we have thus far described—in bacteria, slime mold, and bread mold—the sex cells (gametes) were alike in structure. Sexual reproduction involving the fusion of gametes that are alike in structure is called **isogamy** (i·SOG·a·mee). *Chlamydomonas* has isogamous sexual reproduction (Figure 13-7a). Its gametes are tiny copies of the vegetative cells. This appears to be another evolutionary signpost; gametes probably have evolved from vegetative cells.

In many strains of *Chlamydomonas,* gametic fusion will not occur unless different mating strains are present. The genetically different strains are designated simply (+) and (−). The fusion of *Chlamydomonas* gametes occurs in water. The *zygote* that is formed is thick-walled and can withstand drying and other unfavorable environmental conditions. If the pond or rain barrel in which *Chlamydomonas* is growing should dry up, the chances of survival until more water is available are improved by the resistance of the zygote. Not all algae form thick-walled zygotes, however. Most marine algae, including *Ulva,* produce delicate, thin-walled zygotes. Can you explain why *Chlamydomonas* and the marine algae have structurally different zygotes?

Another sort of sexual reproduction is found in the green alga *Oedogonium* (ee·doe·GO·nee-um). This organism produces two visibly dif-

13–7 Two patterns of sexual reproduction—isogamy and heterogamy. What features of heterogamy indicate that it is a more highly evolved kind of reproduction than isogamy? Of what importance are the thick-walled zygotes to survival?

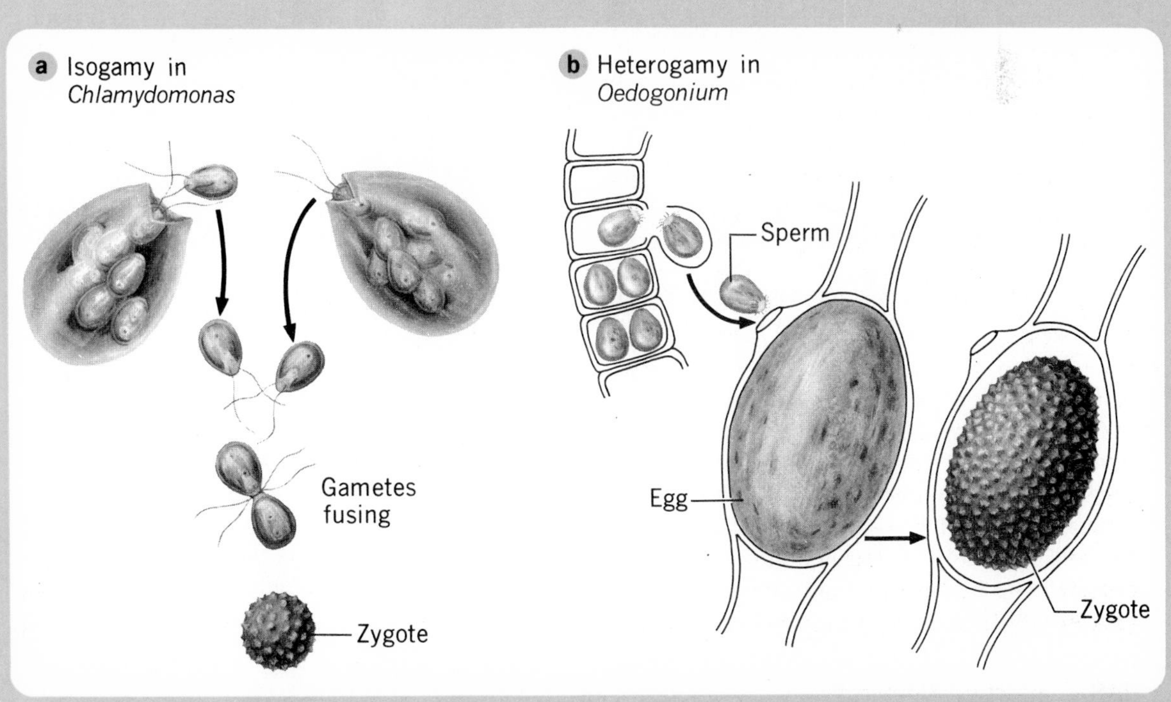

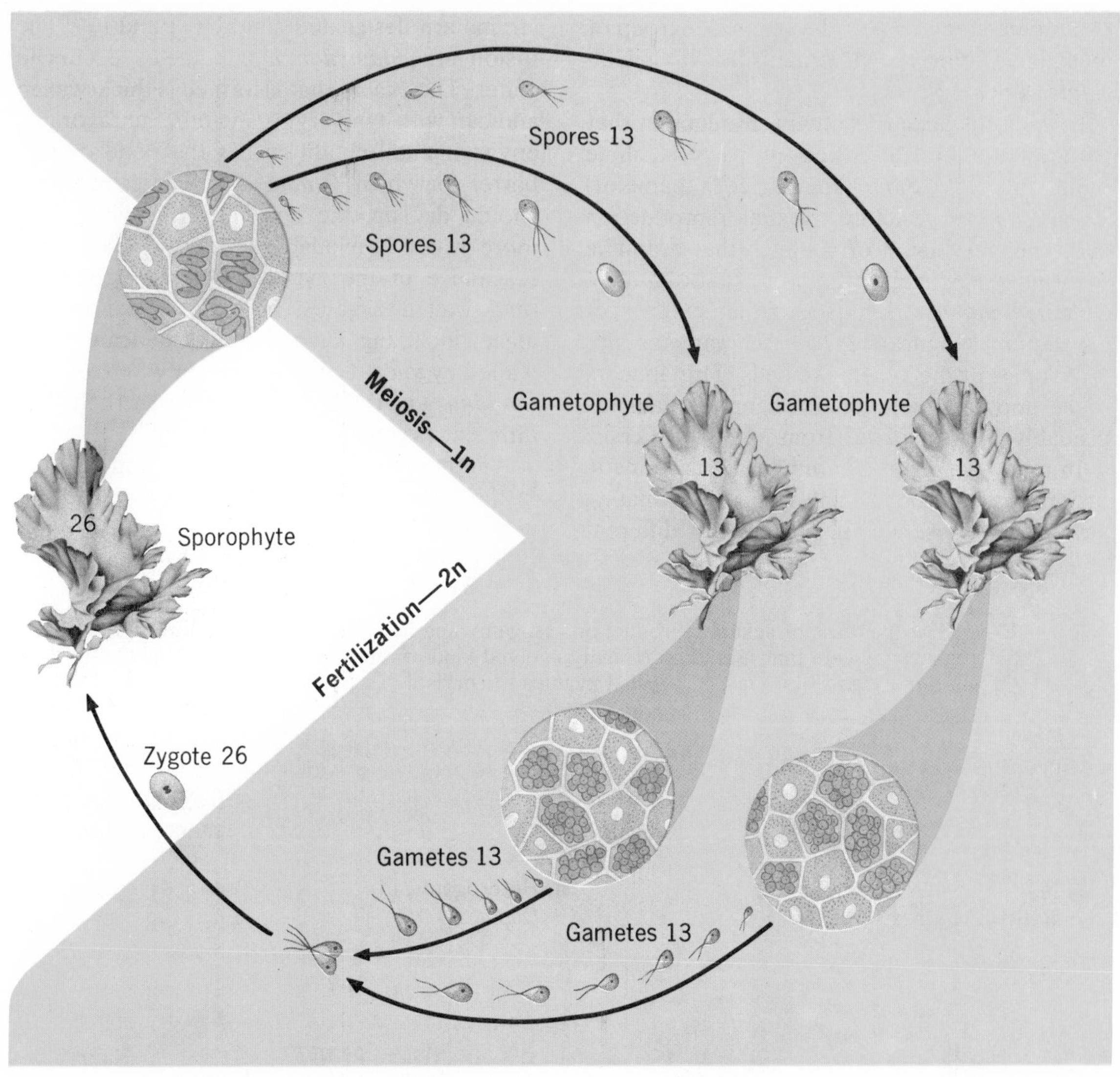

13–8 Alternation of generations of *Ulva*. Note that the gametophytes and sporophytes are alike in their form (isomorphic). How do the two generations differ in chromosome number and in the kinds of reproductive cells that they produce?

ferent kinds of gametes (Figure 13-7b and Inquiry 13-2). It forms small, flagellated sperms and large, nonmotile eggs. The latter are retained in the protective covering of the egg-forming cell. Sexual reproduction such as that occurring in *Oedogonium,* involving the fusion of structurally different gametes, is called **heterogamy** (het·er·OG·a·mee). As an egg of *Oedogonium* develops, it becomes filled with starch grains and other stored food. Prior to fertilization, the cell containing the egg develops a pore on one side. The sperms will enter through this pore to reach the egg. Notice that the egg is *retained* inside the female structure until long after fertilization has occurred. Sooner or later, however, the thick-walled zygote is released into the water.

Heterogamous sexual reproduction, as in *Oedogonium* and many other algae, foreshadows the type of sexual reproduction of green land plants in at least three ways: (1) egg and sperm have been evolved; (2) the egg develops within the protective covering of a female reproductive structure; and (3) a tendency exists for the zygote to be retained in the female reproductive structure. As we will see, all of these characteristics are prerequisites to survival of green plants on land.

Spores

In Chapter 12 we stressed the importance of spore formation in the fungi as a means of asexual reproduction. The algae are also spore-formers. However, their spores are quite different from the thick-walled spores of terrestrial fungi. Usually the spores of algae are thin-walled, and they may have flagella. Both *Chlamydomonas* and *Oedogonium* produce motile, flagellated spores, which are capable of reproducing the vegetative stage of the organism. Compared with the resistant spores of most fungi, the delicate spores of algae would have little chance to survive on dry land. If, as evidence indicates, green land plants evolved from algal ancestors, radical changes in spore structure must have occurred (Chapter 14).

Alternation of Generations

Photosynthesis, the production of spores, the formation of cell walls, and alternation of generations are among the most universal characteristics of plants. There are exceptions, of course. The true fungi are not photosynthetic, and all plants do not have an alternation of generations. But taken together, these features characterize most plants.

Alternation of generations is common among the algae and is more easily understood in their simple life cycles than in the more complicated life cycles of land plants.

Let us examine the life cycle of the marine alga *Ulva* (Figure 13-8). If we bring some specimens of *Ulva* into the laboratory (Inquiry 13-2), we can study them critically. First we take fragments of the living green plants and look at them under the microscope. Not all the cells are the same in structure. Some may be in the process of releasing tiny, motile cells into the water. Almost as soon as these cells are deposited in the surrounding water, they start swimming about independently. If we are very patient, we may see some of these cells pair and fuse with one another to form a single cell. If we remember what occurred in *Chlamydomonas,* we will recognize this as a stage in sexual reproduction, resulting in the formation of a zygote.

Let us isolate all of the zygotes we can find, so that we can see what they will produce. The zygotes of *Ulva*, like those of most other marine plants, start to grow after a very short time. The rate of growth may be a bit slow to watch, but we can observe that the zygote is growing into a new *Ulva* plant. The structure of the new *Ulva* is the same as the structure of the specimens we collected from the tide pool. At this point we might be inclined to conclude our observations, because we seem to be right back where we started in the life cycle.

But no—let us carry our experiment a little farther. Let the new plants mature. Perhaps with more luck and patience we can see what kind of reproductive cells this generation will form. Except for the number of their flagella, the new reproductive cells (Figure 13-8) look very much like gametes, but they do not behave like gametes. No matter how long we look, they reveal no tendency to fuse in pairs. If these are not gametes, what else could they be? Could they be spores such as algae commonly form? If so, they should grow into some kind of vegetative structure. So we will give them the chance by isolating and culturing them as we did the zygotes. Soon the motile cells lose their flagella and begin to divide and grow. They grow into an *Ulva* plant looking exactly like those we obtained from the tide pool and from the zygote.

We must have two generations of plants in this life cycle! Although they look alike, we have found one generation that produces nothing but gametes and one that produces only spores. We have seen that gametes fuse in pairs, and a zygote results. When the zygote grows, it gives rise to the spore-producing plant. The spores that are produced each grow into an *Ulva* plant, which in turn produces more gametes. The cycle is complete. It is a life cycle in which there is an alternation of generations.

We should now try to define "alternation of generations" as it applies to plants. First, an alternation of generations occurs in those plants with *two multicellular stages* (the two *Ulva* plants in our example). One of the generations produces gametes and the other produces spores. A multicellular gamete-producing generation, or **gametophyte** (ga·MEE·toe·fite), alternates with a multicellular spore-producing generation, or **sporophyte** (SPO·ro·fite), in the life cycle of the plant.

Why is alternation of generations important to plants? First we must correlate the life cycle described for *Ulva* with chromosome number. Let us review the life cycle of *Ulva* again. This time we will relate chromosome number to the two generations (Figure 13-8). We will start with the gametes and fertilization.

Each gamete of *Ulva lactuca* has a nucleus containing 13 chromosomes. This is the monoploid, or n number. Two gametes fuse to form a zygote. Each gamete contributes 13 chromosomes to the fusion nucleus of the zygote, thus initiating the diploid, or $2n$ chromosome number of 26. Growth of the zygote is by mitotic divisions, so that each cell of the new *Ulva* plant derived from the zygote is diploid. Certain reproductive cells of this diploid plant (the sporophyte) divide by meiosis (Chapter 7) to form monoploid spores. The monoploid spores, each having the n number of chromosomes (13), grow as a result of mitotic divisions into a new monoploid *Ulva* plant (gametophyte). Some cells of this plant produce monoploid gametes. Now we have returned to the start of the cycle as introduced at the beginning of this paragraph. Read the paragraph again and compare the text with Figure 13-8.

There are several exceptions to this correlation. However, it is a generalization that applies to the majority of plants that show an alternation of generations.

Because of the universal occurrence of alternation of generations in green land plants, and its frequent occurrence among the algae, we can hardly avoid the conclusion that it must be of some advantage. That is, it must be a mechanism that promotes survival. Nevertheless, it is not at all obvious how an alternation of generations does promote survival.

A possible explanation, such as the following, might be offered. In the diploid sporophyte generation, meiosis occurs before the spores are formed. During this process there is a great shuffling of the genes. As a consequence, a great variety of spores with different genetic makeups are produced. Some of the spores will have a genetic makeup that will give them an improved chance of surviving in the particular environment where they occur. Others will have a genetic makeup that is not so good for survival.

The monoploid spores will develop into the monoploid gametophyte generation. The gametophytes with the better genetic makeup for survival in their environment will tend to be the ones that reach maturity. The gametophytes then produce the gametes. There is no meiosis at this time. The gametes are produced by mitotic cell divisions, and so will have exactly the same genetic makeup as the gametophyte. The gametophyte generation, therefore, can be looked upon as a mechanism for transmitting intact groups of genes that have been shown to be superior.

One might ask, therefore, why meiosis is necessary. When we have obtained a genetic makeup that is good for survival in a particular environment, why break it up by meiosis? The answer to this is, at least in part, the fact that the environment is often changing. What is genetically good for survival today may be genetically inadequate tomorrow. None but the simplest of animals or plants in the most stable environments can survive for long if it reproduces without meiosis and genetic recombination. At least, there is no evidence that one ever has.

Thus many plants have evolved a mechanism for taking advantage of the desirable features of two ways of reproduction. The sporophyte generation produces a large variety of spores, which differ in their genetic makeup. The spores grow into the gametophytes, which "try out" the new genetic combinations. The gametophyte generation produces gametes with no further genetic changes. Therefore, the gametophyte generation will reproduce intact the genetic system that has been tried and tested in the environment.

Different kinds of these selected gametes combine. This, of course, brings many more different genetic types into being:

$$n \text{ kinds of sperms} \times n \text{ kinds of eggs} = n^2 \text{ kinds of zygotes}$$

Each zygote so formed develops into a sporophyte, in which genetic variability is once more increased by meiosis preceding spore formation. And that is where we started.

ALGAE AND THE WORLD TODAY

The most obvious organisms are not always the most important, and so it is with the algae. Would you guess that the algae in salt and fresh water together account for 90 percent of the world's photosynthesis? This statistic may give you another partial answer to the question: how are we going to increase our food supply as the population of the world increases? The seas hold a great reserve of food, more of which could be shared by man with the heterotrophs in the sea.

Photosynthetic plants in aquatic environments supply most of the oxygen available to aquatic animals, from protozoans to fish. This explains why we include green plants in an aquarium with our tropical fish. The autotrophic algae are also essential food producers in an aquatic environment. The algae make their food by photosynthesis. Heterotrophic protozoans then utilize the algae as a source of food. Other small animals may ingest the protozoans. Larger animals may eat the smaller ones, and so on up the line to the ocean's largest predators. In harvesting fish from the sea for his own use, man also plays a part in this *food web.* Clearly, without the algae there would be no life in the seas, just as there could be no life on land without green land plants.

The Economic Importance of Algae

You might be surprised at the number of algae that are important in our daily living. For the most part, people living in the United States have an abundance of foods of a great variety, but the 200 million inhabitants of our country represent only a small fragment of the total population of the world. Large numbers of people are found in the countries of China and India. In these and some other countries famine has always been a problem. As a result, almost every possible source of food is utilized. Knowing this, it is not surprising to learn that a wide variety of algae supplies millions of people in the world with one of their staple foods. The algae usually used as food are the kelps (Figure 13-9). Some of these brown algae are among the longest plants in the world! They grow in the seas of northern coastal regions, in the deeper waters beyond the tide zone. Here they may grow to be 60 or more meters in length. Although they contain less available energy—pound for pound—than corn, wheat, rice, and other grains, they are high in mineral content and certain essential elements, such as iodine, potassium, and nitrogen. These elements make brown algae useful as fertilizers as well as food.

Wilson N. Stewart

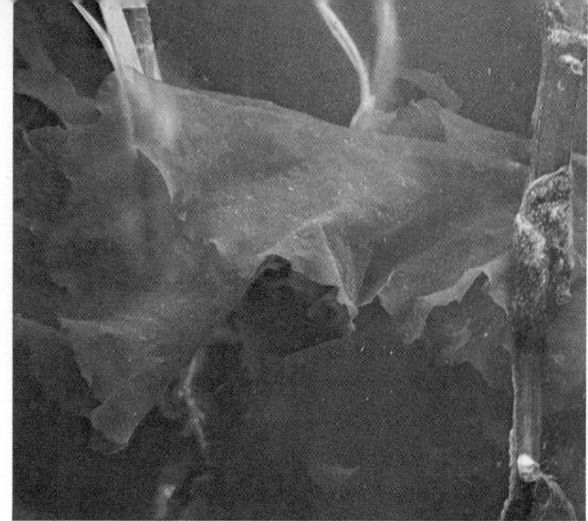

Walter Dawn

13–9 *Postelsia* **(left)** is a brown alga that grows near the tidal zone. Although it has no true stem, leaves, or roots, the form of the plant suggests the appearance of these structures. *Porphyra* **(right)** is a common example of a red alga.

Substances obtained from brown and red algae (Figure 13-9) are widely used. One of these substances is agar, used in the preparation of media for the growth of bacteria and fungi. Another substance is **algin** (AL·jin), used in the manufacture of ice cream to give it a smooth texture, in brushless shaving cream and shampoos as a water-soluble base, and as a substance for taking impressions in making false teeth. Many foods, especially instant pudding, pie fillings, preserves, and candies, make use of these substances derived from marine algae.

Next to bacteria, the **diatoms** (DY·a·tomz—Figure 13-3b, c, and d) are the most abundant organisms in the world. In the seas and oceans they make up the largest part of the **plankton** (PLANK·ton—the floating organisms of a body of water) and are an important source of food for other aquatic organisms.

Most diatoms are unicellular. They have cell walls that are chemically nearly indestructible because the wall is composed in part of silicon dioxide (SiO_2)—the compound used to make glass. We might say that diatoms "live in glass houses." Long ago great deposits of diatom cell walls were formed in the ancient seas. Later these deposits became elevated, and the seas drained. Some deposits of fossil diatoms (diatomaceous earth) are over 3,000 feet thick. The physical properties of the diatomaceous earth are the same as glass and explain why diatomaceous earth is used to insulate boilers and steam pipes, and as an abrasive in metal polishes and certain tooth powders. It is most widely used, however, to filter out foreign particles in the refining of sugar and gasoline. Thus, even the *fossil* algae are of importance to us.

CONCLUDING REMARKS

When considered as a group, the green algae show the following important characteristics in comparison with green land plants:

1. They are biochemically very similar to green land plants in their pigmentation and stored foods.
2. They have evolved a multicellular body plan characteristic of all green land plants.
3. They have evolved heterogamous sexual reproduction—the kind of sexual reproduction common to all green land plants.
4. Many members have evolved alternation of generations, which is a feature of *all green land plants* (as illustrated for mosses and liverworts in Inquiry 14-1).

As a group, then, the green algae may have been ancestral to green land plants.

Thus we have identified the group from which we believe green land plants evolved long ago. We have answered one question: *from what?* We still must answer the questions of *when* and *how* green land plants evolved.

GUIDE QUESTIONS AND PROBLEMS

1. There is little evidence that there have been noticeable evolutionary changes in blue-green algae from the time they appear in the fossil record of the Pre-Cambrian period to the present. They seem to have undergone little evolution. How might this be accounted for?
2. If it were possible to remove the gametophyte generation from the life cycle of a plant and still have the plant reproduce, what might be expected to happen to the rate of evolution of the plant?
3. How can a colony composed of many single cells be distinguished from a true multicellular organism?
4. What effect did the evolution of heterogamy in the green algae have on the colonization of land by green plants?
5. How are the sporophyte and gametophyte generations of *Ulva* similar? How are they different?
6. What is the evidence that the green algae are the most likely ancestors of green land plants?

RELATED READING

Books

For a more complete general account of the algae and their evolution . . .

Chapman, V. I., *The Algae*, St. Martin's Press, New York, 1962.

Gibbs, R., *Botany: An Evolutionary Approach*, McGraw-Hill, New York, 1950.

For a definitive, advanced discussion of the classification of algae . . .

Smith, G. M., *Cryptogamic Botany*, Volume 1, *Algae and Fungi*, McGraw-Hill, New York, 1955.

Magazines

Echlin, P., "The Blue-Green Algae," *Scientific American*, Volume 214 (June 1966), page 74.

14

The Land Turns Green

The land is *our* environment. Many of our characteristics require us to live only on land. For example, like all land animals, we obtain the oxygen we need from the atmosphere. We cannot use oxygen which is dissolved in water. To us, the aquatic environment is hostile. It is an environment that we have learned to respect because we know that we cannot survive in it. Yet many kinds of organisms, from the microscopic diatoms to the largest sharks, are well adapted to live in this environment.

In a way, life for aquatic organisms is an easy life. There is little danger in the seas and oceans of any lack of water, so essential for the growth of all living things. There are abundant carbon-containing compounds in solution that are used by photosynthetic organisms. These organisms, in turn, provide a continual supply of oxygen for *all* the living things in the sea. The temperature in these vast bodies of water does not fluctuate as much as the temperature on land. In short, the aquatic environment of the seas, or any large permanent body of water, is more uniform and better supplied with some of the necessities of life than is the rigorous land environment.

PLANTS BECOME ADAPTED TO LAND

The first evidence that plants had invaded the land from the sea is found in fossils of the Cambrian period (Figure 13-1). These fossils are about half a billion years old. They are nothing more than spores, but these spores have thick walls with markings characteristic of the spores of various land plants. The first more complete land plant fossils are found in rocks approximately 400 to 425 million years old. These earliest preserved plants were **vascular** (VAS·kyou·ler) plants—plants with special conducting cells. (Inquiry 14-2 will help make it clear what conducting cells are.)

What problems faced the green plants of the seas as they evolved features enabling them to live on land? The first great problem was obtaining water. Land plants are not bathed in water but must absorb it from the ground. The second problem was conserving water. Land plants must be constructed to reduce the loss of water to the air. The third problem was the absorption of CO_2 from the atmosphere for photosynthesis.

We can divide green land plants into two distinct groups. One is the group which includes the **mosses** and **liverworts** (Figure 14-1); the other is the group of *vascular plants*. The vascular plants have special conducting tissues called **xylem** (ZY·lem) and **phloem** (FLOH·em). These special tissues are not a characteristic of the mosses and liverworts, which for that reason are often called *nonvascular*.

The Nonvascular Land Plants

The fossil record shows us that plants resembling the liverworts (Figure 14-1 **b** and **c**) were present at least 350 million years ago. Although we know very little about the structure and reproduction of these ancient land plants, we can conclude, by observing the characteristics of their modern counterparts, how adaptation to land was accomplished. We will consider the following adaptive characters exhibited by mosses and liverworts:

1. A compact, multicellular plant body and the ability to conserve water
2. Some modification of photosynthetic tissues for the absorption of carbon dioxide

3. Special structures for the absorption of water
4. Heterogamy, the production of egg and sperm
5. Protection of reproductive cells
6. Formation of embryos
7. Alternation of generations

Of the seven characteristics in this list, the green algae (Chapter 13) show multicellular organization of the plant body, heterogamy, protection of reproductive cells, and alternation of generations. Thus, several features important for land plants had evolved in aquatic ancestors. The evolutionary step from water to land was not as big as might be anticipated.

The Multicellular Plant Body and the Conservation of Water

The plant body, or **thallus** (THAL·us), of all mosses and liverworts is multicellular (Figure 14-2). Does this multicellular organization have any advantages in a land environment? Let us go back to the unicellular vegetative cells of *Chlamydomonas* (Figure 13-3e). A *Chlamydomonas* cell has all of its surface exposed to the aquatic environment where it lives. Thus the whole cell surface of *Chlamydomonas* absorbs water, dissolved carbonates, and other minerals. But what would happen to *Chlamydomonas* in a land environment? All the surfaces of the cell that absorb water and solutes in the aquatic environment would become surfaces of evaporation under terrestrial conditions. Since they would have no way of replacing the water lost as a result of drying, the vegetative cells would soon die.

If such single-celled organisms could not survive when exposed to the air, how can a multicellular organism such as a liverwort live on land? As we look at the cross section of this organism (Figure 14-2), we see that it is many cells thick. Of the hundreds of thousands of cells comprising the thallus, only a small percentage have surfaces directly exposed to the drying effects of the atmosphere.

John A. Moore

John A. Moore

John A. Moore

14–1 **a.** Mosses of the genus *Polytrichum*, growing on a forest floor. **b.** Male liverworts, and **c**, female liverworts of the genus *Marchantia*. These primitive green land plants are frequently found growing on rocks and soil of moist ravines. Can you guess why mosses and liverworts do not grow much larger than shown here?

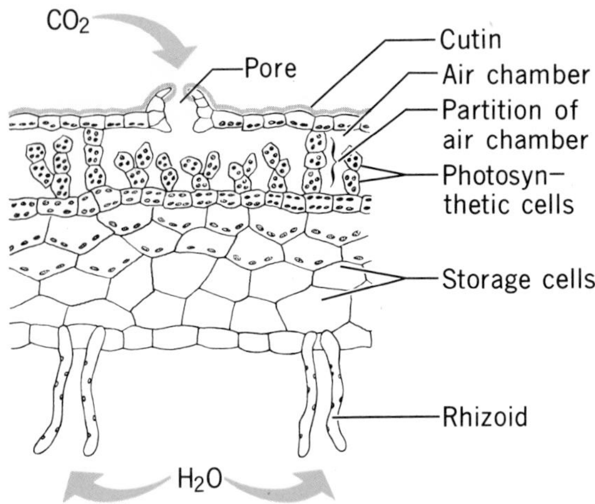

14–2 A drawing of part of a sectioned *Marchantia* thallus. How do the rhizoids and the layer of cutin affect survival of the plant on land?

When compared with *Chlamydomonas,* which has 100 percent of its cell surface exposed, the liverwort has only a small percentage of its total cell surface exposed to the atmosphere. Thus *the relative amount* of cell surface from which evaporation can occur in a multicellular organism is less than in a unicellular one. Further reducing the rate of evaporation from surface cells is the formation of a waxlike substance, **cutin** (KYOO·tin), on the surfaces of some liverworts and mosses. (This same substance is also found covering leaves and some stems of more highly evolved green land plants.)

In spite of these adaptations, some liverworts and mosses that grow on exposed surfaces of rocks and trees become so dry that they are almost brittle. Yet, within a short time after these plants become wet from rain or other water, they turn green again and proceed to carry out their normal life processes.

Absorption of Carbon Dioxide

Ulva and all other algae growing in water can absorb their carbon for photosynthesis directly from the water in the form of dissolved CO_2 and ionized carbonates and bicarbonates. There is an abundant supply of these compounds in the seas and oceans. On land, however, the situation is quite different. Only about 0.03 to 0.04 percent of the atmosphere is CO_2. Green land plants have evolved rather elaborate structures to absorb sufficient quantities of CO_2. We can see an example of a CO_2-absorbing system in the liverwort *Marchantia* (mar·KAN·shih·a—Figure 14-2).

The upper surface of the *Marchantia* thallus has numerous pores. Each pore opens into an air chamber, which is partially filled with branching filaments of photosynthetic cells. The structure of the *Marchantia* thallus is remarkably like that of a leaf of a vascular land plant. The pores allow the inward diffusion of atmospheric gases, including CO_2. The CO_2 is absorbed by the wet surfaces of the photosynthetic cells in the air chambers and diffuses into the cytoplasm. Because of the branching nature of the inner structure of the thallus, the cells present a tremendous amount of surface available for the absorption of CO_2. At the same time, evaporation of water can occur from the wet surfaces of these cells. Thus, while absorbing CO_2 from the atmosphere, the green land plants will lose much-needed water. The evaporating water must be replaced or the *Marchantia* will soon wilt and die.

Absorption of Water

If we look at the underside of a *Marchantia* thallus, we will see water-absorbing structures. *Marchantia,* like other liverworts and mosses, has special structures called **rhizoids** (RY·soidz). These are long, filamentous extensions of the cells of the lower surface of the thallus. They greatly increase the surface for absorption of water from the soil. Rhizoids perform the same functions as the water-absorbing roots and root hairs of vascular plants.

Green land plants require large amounts of water. Most of the water they absorb through rhizoids and roots is lost by evaporation from the photosynthetic organs while CO_2 is being absorbed from the atmosphere.

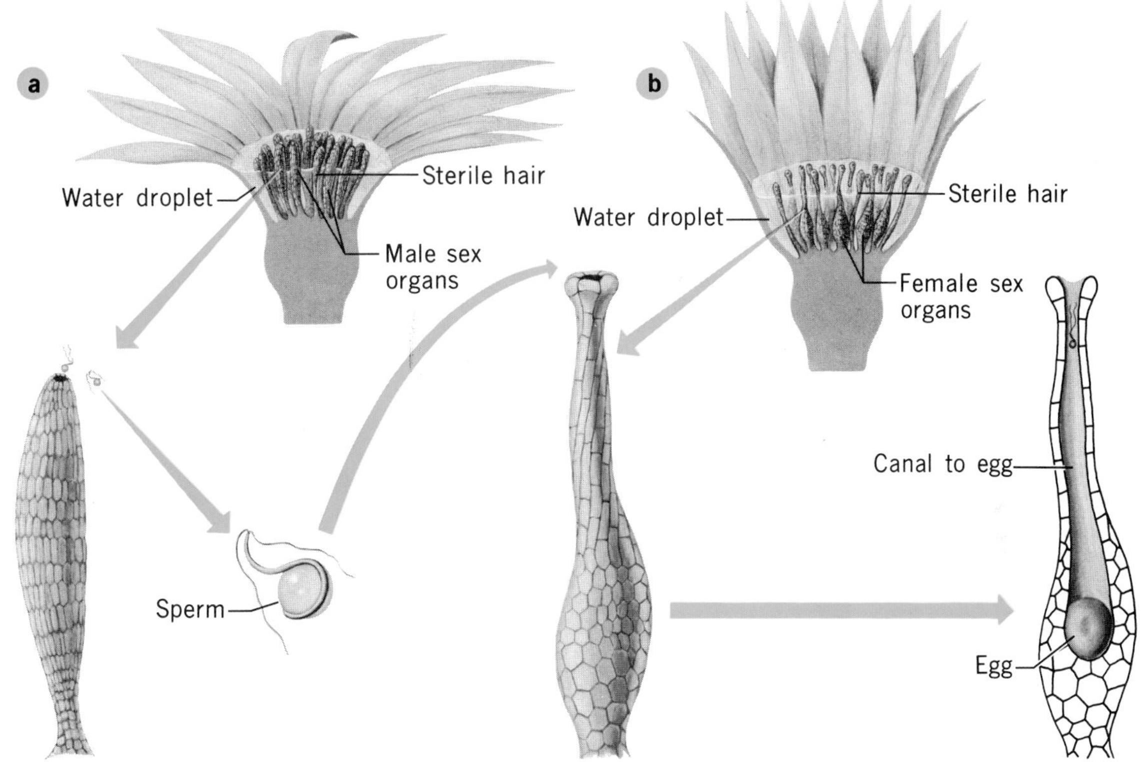

14–3 **a.** A diagram of the sectioned tip of a male moss plant. The saclike male sex organs produce sperms, each of which has two flagella. What environmental substance must be present if the sperms are to travel from the male to the female sex organs and fertilize the eggs? **b.** A diagram of a similarly sectioned tip of a female moss plant. Each of the flask-shaped female organs contains a single egg in the enlarged base.

Heterogamy

The universal occurrence of sexual reproduction (involving eggs and sperms) in green land plants and in animals leaves little doubt that it is the most successful kind of reproduction to evolve. The large, nonmotile egg formed in heterogamy is full of stored food. After fertilization, this stored food is used to nourish the early stages in development of the new offspring. In other kinds of sexual reproduction —for example, isogamy in *Chlamydomonas* —the supply of stored food contributed even by both gametes together is very small. The food required for further development is manufactured by the zygote by photosynthesis.

Protection of Reproductive Cells

Certain algae retain the unfertilized egg in the female reproductive cell. The protection of sperms, eggs, and spores from drying and from mechanical injury is vital to green land plants. Let us see how a moss plant prevents its reproductive cells from drying.

The sex organs of a moss plant are produced at the tip of the green shoot (Figure 14-1 **a**). The shoot consists of an axis on which are radially arranged leaflike parts. Since sexual reproduction is heterogamous, we find two kinds of sex organs, those that produce sperms (Figure 14-3a) and those that produce eggs (Figure 14-3b). Both kinds of sex organs

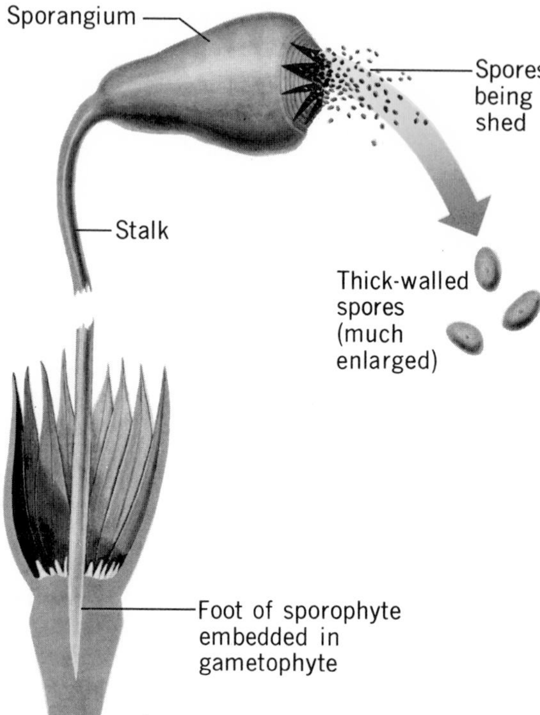

14–4 Which of the moss plant tips of Figure 14–3 is represented by this later stage of development? The stalk of the sporophyte grows from the tip of the gametophyte. After the spores are shed, what prevents them from drying out and dying?

are multicellular. In this respect they differ from their unicellular counterparts in aquatic algae. Most of the cells of the moss sex organs are sterile and form a protective coat around the sperms or eggs. In addition. leaflike structures and sterile hairs produced at the tip of the shoot help to prevent drying of the sex organs.

The spores of this land plant are also well protected from drying. Spores are produced in a multicellular **sporangium** (spo·RAN·jee-um), or spore capsule, at the tip of a naked stalk (Figure 14-4). The capsule has a jacket of sterile cells surrounding the developing spores. As the spores mature in the capsule, each one forms a thick, waterproof layer. This layer completely encloses the tiny bit of fluid cytoplasm and the nucleus in the center of the spore. As the capsule itself matures, it releases the spores to the external environment. Here the spores may survive for several months before germinating to produce new moss plants.

Embryo Formation

In all green land plants the sperm is transported to the egg and unites with it inside the female reproductive structure. In mosses, liverworts, and primitive vascular plants, including ferns, the sperms are flagellated (Figure 14-3a). A film of water is required for the sperm to swim to the egg. A zygote is formed inside the female structure when a sperm fertilizes the egg. An embryo develops from the zygote as it divides, still *inside* the protective coverings of the female reproductive structure. Thus the coverings formed by the female organism protect the growing embryo, as well as the egg and zygote, from drying out and from mechanical injury.

Among green plants, the mosses and liverworts are the first plants that form embryos. Some algae retain the zygote for a short time, *Oedogonium,* for example (Chapter 13). But the subsequent development of the offspring takes place away from the female sex structure. Figure 14-5 contrasts the reproduction in *Oedogonium* and in a moss plant (the female reproductive structure is shown). How does this part of the moss life cycle compare with that of human beings?

Alternation of Generations

The green alga *Ulva* has an alternation of generations in which both the gametophyte and the sporophyte are identical in appearance (Figure 13-8, page 248). Both plants are able to make their own food and thus are capable of an independent existence in the tide pools where they grow.

Although mosses and liverworts also have life cycles with alternating gametophyte and sporophyte generations (you may already have completed Inquiry 14-1), in the moss and liverwort these two generations are quite different in their structure and physiology. We have already discovered that the green shoot of a moss plant produces sex organs and sex cells (Figure 14-3). Thus the green shoot is the mature gametophyte (Figure 14-6). This shoot is autotrophic and is the structure we recognize as a moss plant. If the sporophyte (Figures 14-4 and 14-6) is present, it is attached to the top of the gametophyte. The sporophyte is composed of a **foot** which is embedded in the tissues of the gametophyte, and a **stalk** with a sporangium (spore capsule) on the upper end. The sporophyte bears little or no resemblance to the gametophyte to which it is attached. This evidence indicates that in the evolution and adaptation of aquatic plants to life on land, the gametophyte became the dominant generation. The sporophyte, on the other hand, became partially dependent on the gametophyte

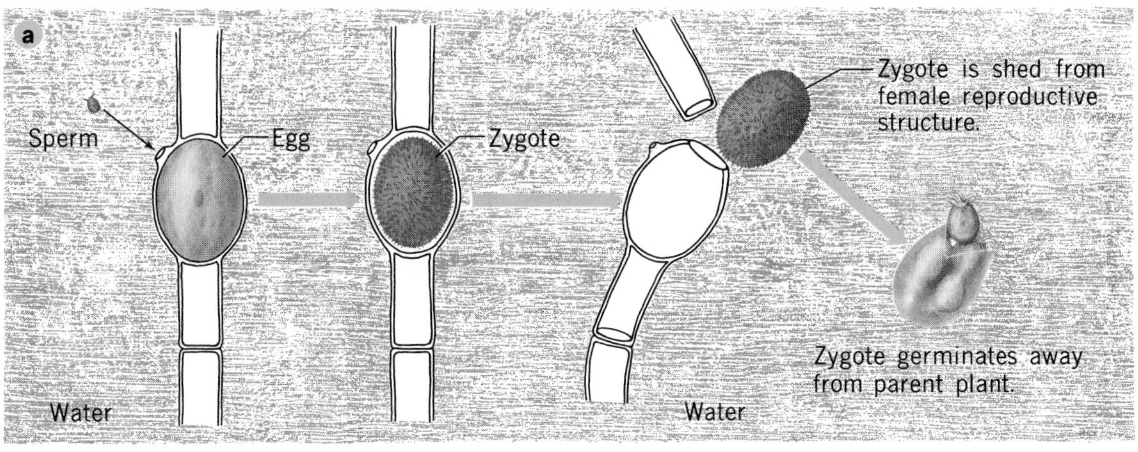

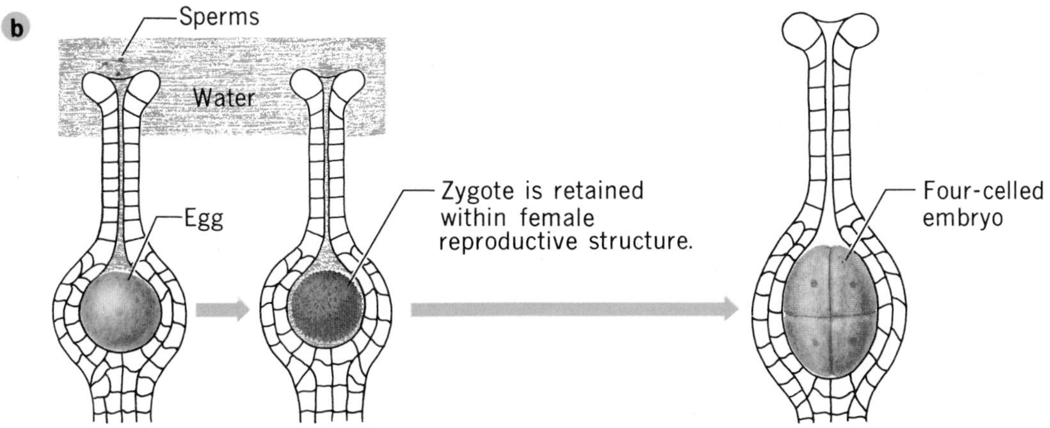

14–5 **a.** Sexual reproduction in the alga *Oedogonium*. The female sex organ is unicellular and affords little protection for the egg. The thick-walled zygote is shed into the surrounding water. **b.** By contrast, the female reproductive structure of a primitive green land plant (a moss in this case) is multicellular and protects the egg from drying out. The zygote is not shed, but is retained within the female structure, where it develops into an embryo. The formation of protected embryos in this manner represented an important step in the evolution of green land plants.

THE LIFE CYCLE OF A MOSS

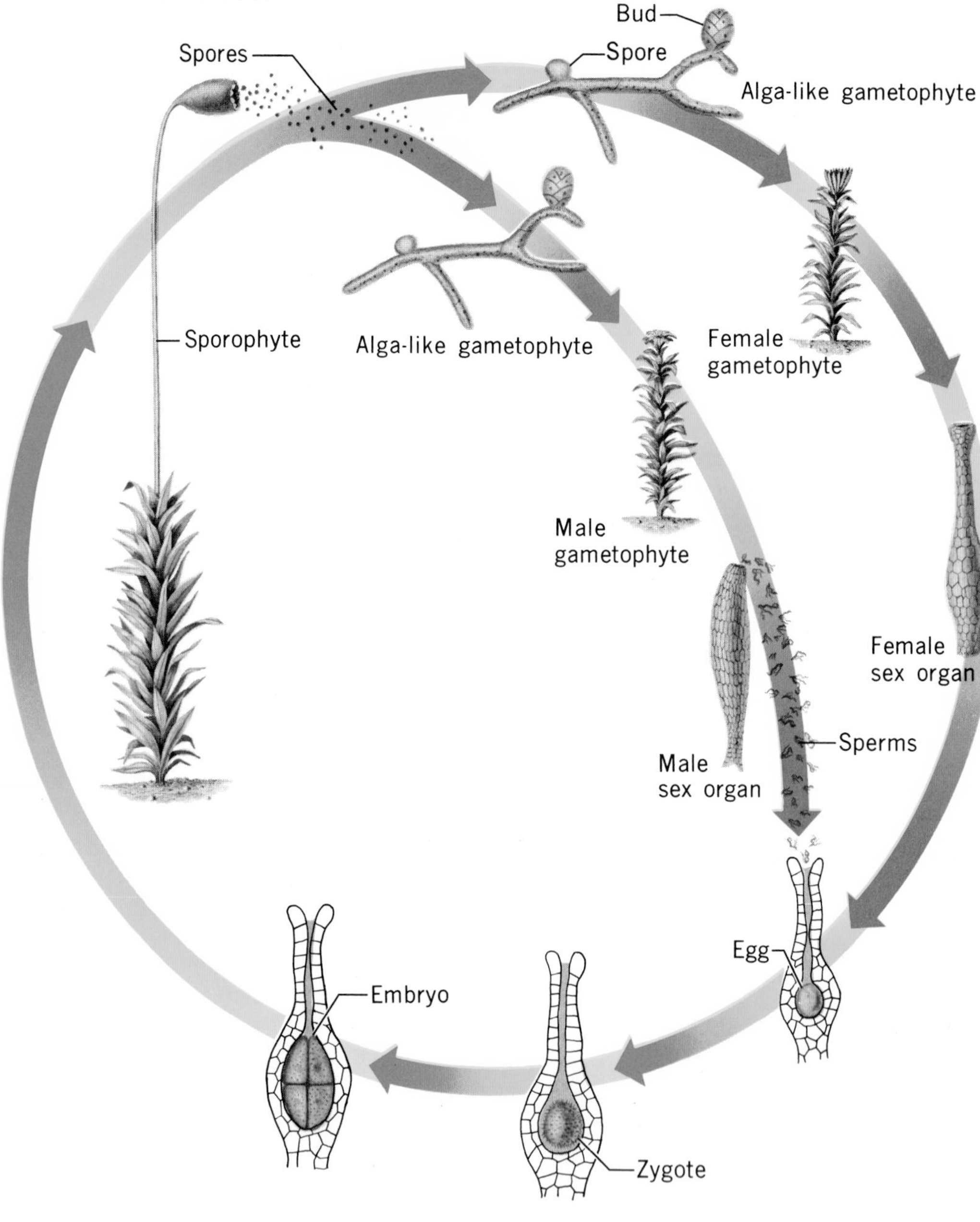

14–6 Compare the life cycle of a moss to that of *Ulva*, a green alga (Figure 13–8). Does an alternation of generations occur in mosses? Which part of the life cycle lasts longer—the gametophyte or the sporophyte stage? Where in the moss life cycle does meiosis occur? Where does fertilization occur? What differences between the moss life cycle and that of *Ulva* may be the result of the land habitat of the moss? What evidence do you see that mosses may have originated from an aquatic ancestor?

and greatly reduced in structure. Even though it has become reduced, the sporophyte still forms large numbers of resistant spores in an elevated sporangium, from which the spores are easily shed and dispersed. When the spores germinate, they produce a gametophyte stage resembling an alga. Later this stage gives rise to the leafy gametophytes which produce gametes, and the cycle is continued (Figure 14-6).

Changes in chromosome number occur at the time of fertilization and meiosis. These changes correspond to those in the life cycle of *Ulva* (Figure 13-8). The fertilized egg represents the first cell of the sporophyte generation, and spores—the products of meiosis—represent the first cells of the gametophyte generation.

Although mosses and liverworts constitute only a very small percentage of all green land plants, a study and comparison of their characteristics and those of more primitive green algae gives us a good picture of the evolutionary steps that were required in the colonization of the land. Some of these steps are peculiar to plants, but many are applicable to the evolution of animals as well. For example, we find that the evolution of primitive animals in the ancient seas likewise resulted in the formation of multicellular organisms that underwent heterogamous sexual reproduction and produced embryos. In their colonization of the land, animals, like plants, evolved structures for support and for prevention of excessive drying. Thus, in their early evolution in the seas and on the land, plants and animals show many parallels.

Evidence from fossils indicates that by the middle of the Devonian period, approximately 370 million years ago, green land plants (both vascular and nonvascular) were well established. Figure 13-1, page 242, indicates the groups of plants that were present at that time. Millions of years passed before plant-eating animals appeared on the lush, green land. Can you explain why green plants had to precede animals in the colonization of land?

LAND PLANTS WITH VASCULAR TISSUE

Xylem and phloem are found in all green land plants other than the mosses and liverworts. These tissues have two functions: conduction and support. Xylem (Figure 14-7b and d) is composed mostly of dead cells whose walls may be perforated, permitting the rapid movement of water. The direction of movement is usually upward from the roots to the leaves. The walls of the dead xylem cells are usually thickened to some extent and help support the parts of the plants above ground.

Phloem tissue is composed of both living and dead cells. Living cells of phloem conduct the soluble foods manufactured by the photosynthetic leaves. Here the direction of conduction is downward toward the stem and roots, where the food is stored. The dead, thick-walled cells of the phloem aid in support. More will be said about the vascular tissues in a later chapter.

We cannot stress the importance of vascular plants too much. They furnish us with the very necessities of life—nearly all of our food, wood for construction of our homes, fibers for clothing, medicines, and fuels such as coal. The trees, shrubs, grasses, roses, ferns, pine trees, corn, wheat, rice—and a multitude of other plants we see every day—are vascular plants. Over two thirds of all the plant species that inhabit the earth belong to this great group. Where did these organisms on which we are so dependent come from? How was it that they, rather than the mosses and liverworts, became so successful on land? When did they first appear? These are the questions we hope to answer in this part of the chapter.

The Primitive Type of Vascular Plant

In searching for the origin of vascular plants, we must turn our attention once again to the green algae and the mosses and liverworts. All of these plants are similar in their photosynthetic pigments and their stored food. Because of these similarities we must consider the al-

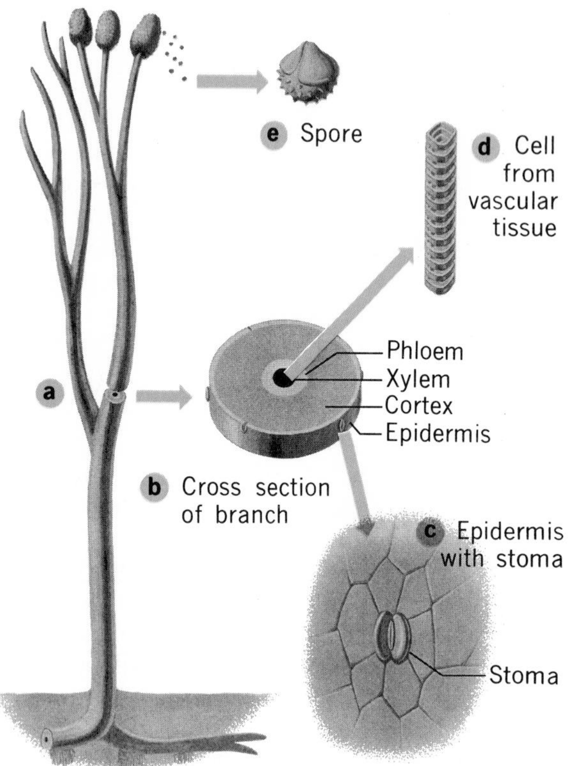

14–7 A reconstruction of the extinct Devonian plant *Rhynia*. **a.** The plant had no leaves or roots. It stood about 30 cm high. Sporangia were produced at the tips of upper branches. **b.** The branches had a core of xylem, with phloem around it. **c.** Evidently the branches carried on photosynthesis, as evidenced by stomata in the epidermis. **d.** The cells of vascular tissue were oblong, and in the case of xylem, hollow. **e.** Thick-walled spores were produced *in fours* in the sporangia—an indication that the spores were produced by meiosis.

ternative possibilities that vascular plants evolved from the group of mosses and liverworts or that they evolved directly from the green algae. Unfortunately the fossil record does not help us settle this point. It does, however, tell us what the primitive type of vascular plant was like. Thus we have a starting point to discuss the origin of vascular plants.

Can you imagine a vascular plant without leaves or roots? This is rather difficult, because we are so used to seeing vascular plants with stems, leaves, and roots. Did vascular plants always have all of these parts? We think not. Again the fossil record provides us with the evidence. Back in the Devonian period (Figure 13-1), which started approximately 400 million years ago, vascular plants had made considerable progress in adapting to life on land. Among the invading plants were some curious species that had no leaves or roots. These plants consisted of a system of branches that forked repeatedly (Figure 14-7a). The two branches above each point of forking were of equal size. One of them could not be called the stem and the other a branch. Some of the branches grew underground where they functioned much like roots, absorbing water and anchoring the plant. Some grew upright and were photosynthetic. How can we know this? The fossils of these plants are so well preserved that the pores, **stomata** (STOE·ma·ta; sing., **stoma**—STOE·ma), for the exchange of gases in photosynthesis are still intact! (Figure 14-7c). It has been possible to cut sections from these fossil plants and use the compound microscope to see what they looked like inside.

In a diagram of such a cross section (Figure 14-7b) of a branch, we can see an outermost layer of cells—the **epidermis** (EP·ih·der·mis)—as well as the entire outer region, or **cortex.** In the center there is a slender strand of vascular tissue composed of thick-walled xylem cells (Figure 14-7d). No doubt this vascular tissue served, as in plants today, for conduction and for support of the upright branches. At the tips of some of these branches we find sporangia containing thick-walled spores (Figure 14-7e) characteristic of land plants. Thus we know that these ancient plants with vascular tissue were sporophytes.

Because these ancient plants are so important to our understanding of the evolution of vascular land plants, let us summarize some of their important characteristics:

1. They had no roots and leaves.
2. They had forked branching systems.

Branches were of equal size above a point of forking.
3. They had a simple, centrally located vascular strand in each branch.
4. They had sporangia at the tips of branches.

We believe that these were the characteristics of the most primitive vascular plants; that from such plants all other vascular plants evolved starting over 400 million years ago.

A living plant that shows many of the primitive characteristics described above is the tropical genus *Psilotum* (sy·LOE·tum) (Figure 14-8). It, too, has leafless green branches that fork. The arrangement of its vascular tissue is simple, like that of its ancient ancestors. Its sporangia, like those of the primitive fossil plants, are borne at the tips of branches.

14–8 *Psilotum*, a primitive vascular plant that grows in the tropics and subtropics. Compare the external features of this plant with the reconstruction of *Rhynia* in Figure 14–7.

Harbrace Photo

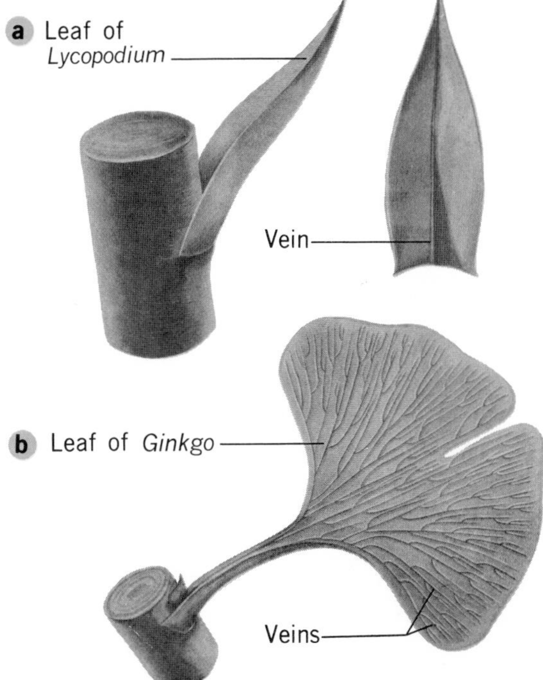

14–9 These leaves illustrate the two principal leaf types among vascular plants: **a,** leaves with a single vein, and **b,** leaves with many veins.

The primitive type of vascular plant we have described provides a logical start for discussing the evolution of (1) the leaf, (2) the root, (3) arrangements of supporting and conducting tissues, and (4) protected sporangia.

Evolution of the Leaf

The leaf is the chief photosynthetic organ of a vascular plant. How did this important organ of plants arise, when none was present in the primitive vascular plants? Before we answer this question, we must distinguish between two basic types of leaves occurring among vascular plants. One kind of leaf is usually quite small, almost scalelike, and has a single bundle of vascular tissue, a **vein,** in it (Figure 14-9a). The

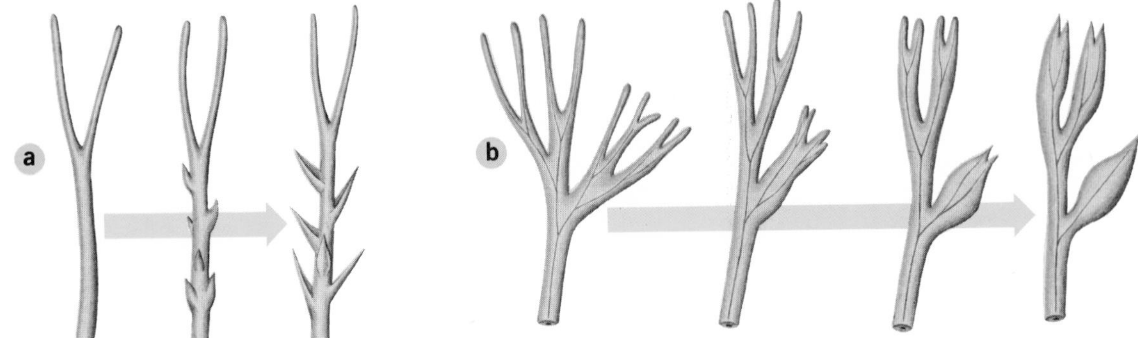

14–10 A diagrammatic summary of two different theories of the evolution of single-veined leaves. Whether leaves emerged from naked branches, as in **a,** or resulted from a reduction of branches, as in **b,** tens or even hundreds of thousands of plant generations must have been required for the evolution to take place.

a John A. Moore **b** John A. Moore **c** John A. Moore

14–11 Two living representatives of primitive vascular plants: **a,** the club moss *Lycopodium*; **b** and **c,** the horsetail *Equisetum.* In *Lycopodium,* the small, scalelike leaves are on radially arranged branches. The candlelike structures at the tips of the branches are cones. The horsetail also has radially arranged branches and leaves. Of the three horsetail branches shown, the one on the left bears whorls of naked photosynthetic branches, and the two on the right have cones at the tips, with tight whorls of scalelike leaves farther down the branches below the cones.

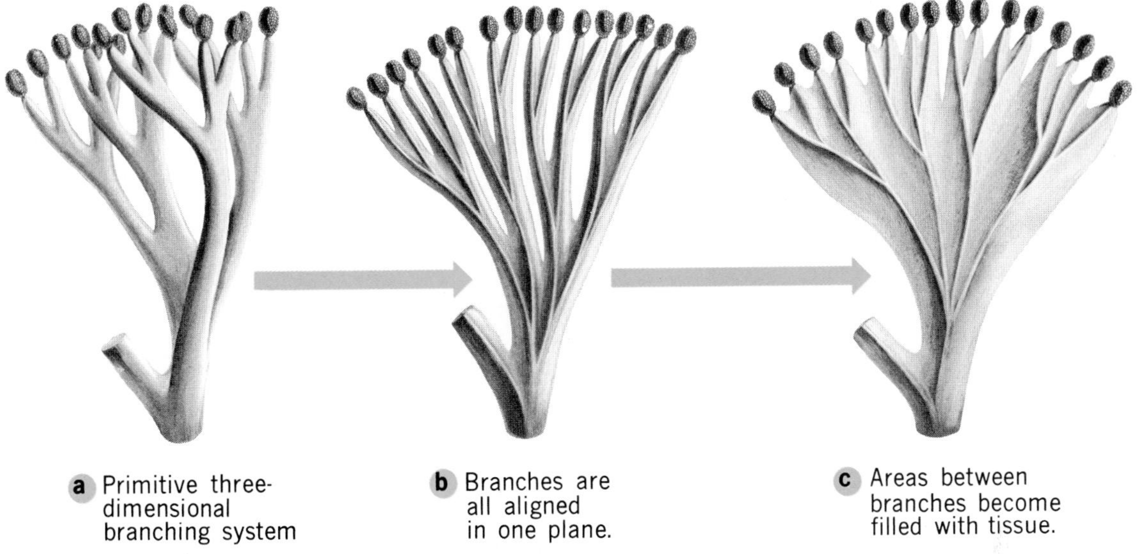
a Primitive three-dimensional branching system
b Branches are all aligned in one plane.
c Areas between branches become filled with tissue.

14–12 The principal steps in the evolution of a many-veined leaf. Much evidence from fossils of ancient vascular plants supports the steps illustrated here. The *Ginkgo* leaf (Figure 14–9b) is a result of this evolutionary process.

other type may be very large, with a conspicuous blade and two or more bundles of vascular tissue entering the blade (Figure 14-9b).

The interpretation of the fossil record does not permit a clear answer as to how the small one-veined leaf evolved. One possibility is that this leaf originated as an outgrowth, lacking vascular tissue, from the naked branches of the primitive plant (Figure 14-10a). With increase in size, vascular tissue was required to supply the leaf with water and to support it. Another possibility is that the single-veined leaf originated by a reduction in size of a part of the leafless branching system of the primitive vascular plant (Figure 14-10b).

In any event, this simple kind of leaf became well established in groups of primitive plants called club mosses and horsetails (Figure 14-11).

The fossilized remains of plants that lived during the Devonian and Carboniferous periods show us how the second type of leaf (many-veined) evolved. When we examine the leaves of these ancient plants, we find that they are nothing more than an evolutionary modification of the forked branching system we saw in the most primitive vascular plant. The first step in the evolution of this leaf type was the restriction of forked branches to a single plane (Figure 14-12). The branching system became flat.

Next in evolution, the space between the bundles and branches of vascular tissue became filled with photosynthetic tissue. The organ, now a leaf, looked superficially like the webbed foot of a duck. The leaves of the majority of vascular plants had their evolutionary origin from a branching system of this kind.

Evolution of the Root

When we say that the primitive type of vascular plant had no leaves or roots, we do not mean that it lacked photosynthetic and water-absorbing organs. Branches above ground were adapted for photosynthesis. The underground parts of the branching system were adapted for the absorption of water. The amount of absorp-

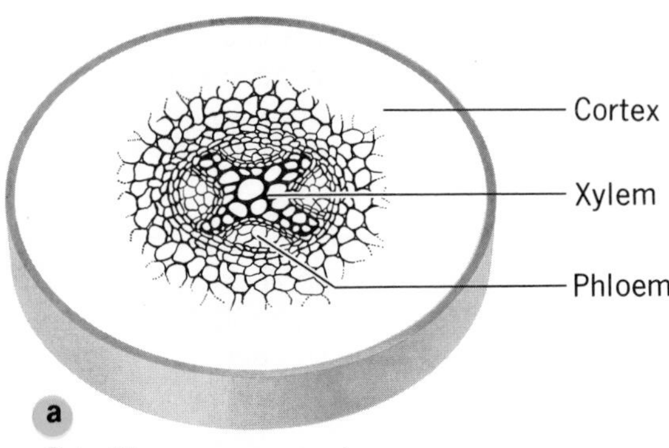

Primitive arrangement of vascular tissue in roots

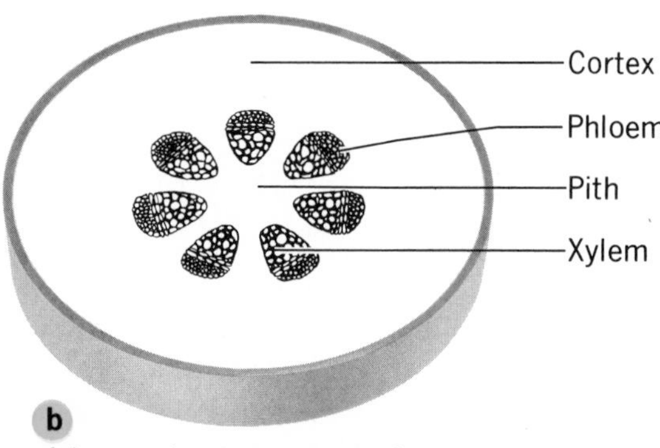

Advanced arrangement of vascular tissue in stems

14–13 Arrangements of vascular tissue in vascular plants. **a.** Roots of most vascular plants, and stems and branches of the more primitive vascular plants, have a central core of xylem, with phloem around it. **b.** Stems of more advanced vascular plants usually have a central pith, surrounded by a ring of vascular tissue (often divided into bundles).

tive surface was greatly increased by many rhizoids that formed on the epidermis. *Functionally* the underground branches of the primitive vascular plants were roots, just as the aboveground parts functioned as leaves. *Structurally,* however, these branches were unlike the roots and leaves of bean plants, ferns, pine trees, and other more highly evolved plants.

One interesting structural similarity between the underground branches of the primitive vascular plants and the roots of more highly evolved vascular plants is the arrangement of the vascular tissue. Both have a central solid rod of xylem tissue (Figure 14-13a). This arrangement of vascular tissue seems to have been retained in the roots of the more complex vascular plants of today.

Support in the Stem

As certain parts of the forked system of the primitive vascular plants were reduced or modified into roots and leaves, other parts became well supplied with vascular tissue.

The engineering principle that a hollow tube of supporting material is stronger than a solid rod composed of the same amount of material apparently was demonstrated in the evolution of the supporting vascular system of the stem of vascular land plants.

In primitive plants not more than 25 centimeters tall, the aboveground branches were supported by a vascular system that consisted of a central solid rod (Figure 14-13a). In larger, more complex vascular plants we find stems supported by one or more rings of vascular tissue. This tissue was often dissected by tissue of the cortex into separate bundles functioning like supporting beams in the stem tissues (Figure 14-13b).

The formation of a supporting tissue called *secondary wood* appeared early in the evolution of vascular plants. We are all familiar with the tough secondary wood in the trunks (stems) of trees. This kind of supporting structure made possible the growth of plants of tremendous size. The largest living things in the world are the giant redwood and sequoia trees of our West Coast. One of these mammoths is 117 meters (385 feet) tall and more than 9 meters in diameter at the base. Nearly all of the bulk of these giant trees is secondary wood. From the standpoint of competition for sunlight and the distribution of spores and seeds, tall plants have proved most successful in the land environment!

The Protection of Sporangia

As we have seen, the primitive type of vascular plant (as represented by the fossil plant *Rhynia* and the present-day *Psilotum*) had sporangia at the tips of upright branches (Figures 14-7a and 14-8). Here the sporangia are well placed for dispersal of their spores. These sporangia are not protected in any way, however. Except in these few primitive vascular plants, and in the equally primitive mosses and liverworts, the sporangia of green land plants are well protected.

Many vascular plants, in addition to the pines and their relatives, form cones. The other cone-forming plants are the club mosses and the horsetails (Figure 14-11). If we dissect the cone of a club moss, we find its sporangia enveloped in a protective covering of leaves (Figure 14-14a), which make up the bulk of the cone. The sporangia of the horsetail cone are produced on little branches. There are several sporangia on each branch and many branches in a cone. Each branch has a flattened end something like the six-sided head of a bolt (Figure 14-14b). The flattened ends of the branches fit together along their sides and form a protective layer over their sporangia, which are completely covered until the spores are mature.

These protected positions of the sporangia have come about through an evolutionary modification of the primitive type of arrangement in vascular plants. There is ample evidence from fossil ferns, for example, to show that, step by step, the sporangia came to lie first at the margins of, and later on the underside of, the leaves.

The Evolution of the Seed

If we look at the plants around us, we notice that they are not predominantly ferns, horsetails, club mosses, or true mosses. Instead they are seed plants (pines and their relatives, and flowering plants). Is there something about seed plants that has made them more successful? Could it be that the seed adapts these vascular

14–14 The protected sporangia of a club moss and a horsetail. **a.** The sporangia in a club moss cone are protected by overlapping leaves. **b.** In a horsetail cone the sporangia are protected by flattened ends of the sporangia-bearing branches.

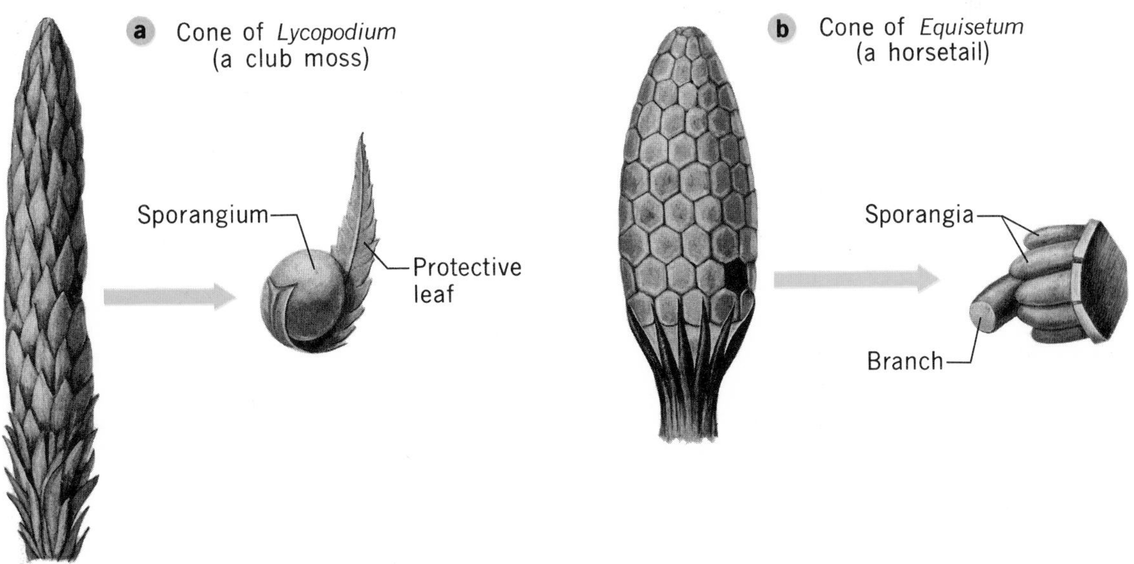

plants to a wider variety of environments? We can hardly avoid this conclusion—but this does not tell us *why* (as Inquiry 14-3 will help to do).

To find an answer, we have to introduce a new idea. All of the green land plants we have described thus far produce only one kind of spore. All spores of a species are nearly identical in size, structure, and function. There are, however, many vascular plants—all of the seed plants, for example—that form *two kinds of spores*. These plants are said to be **heterosporous** (het·er·o·SPOR·us). Generally the spores are of different sizes, and they always have different functions. Instead of growing into gametophytes that are essentially similar in structure, heterosporous plants produce two different gametophytes. One of the two kinds of spores—let us call it the *male spore*—grows into a sperm-forming gametophyte. The other kind, the *female spore*, grows into an egg-forming gametophyte.

The two kinds of spores are formed in two different kinds of sporangia. These, like the sporangia of club mosses, horsetails, and ferns, have become protected as a result of the evolution of various enveloping structures. If we go back in the fossil records to the Carboniferous period (280 to 350 million years ago) we find certain fernlike plants that bore seedlike structures. Each of their sporangia, containing one or more female spores, was nearly surrounded by outgrowths from the sporophyte (Figure 14-15b). These outgrowths appear to have been little branchlike structures, which during evolution have become fused as an envelope, or **integument** (in·TEG·you·ment), around the sporangium (Figure 14-15c).

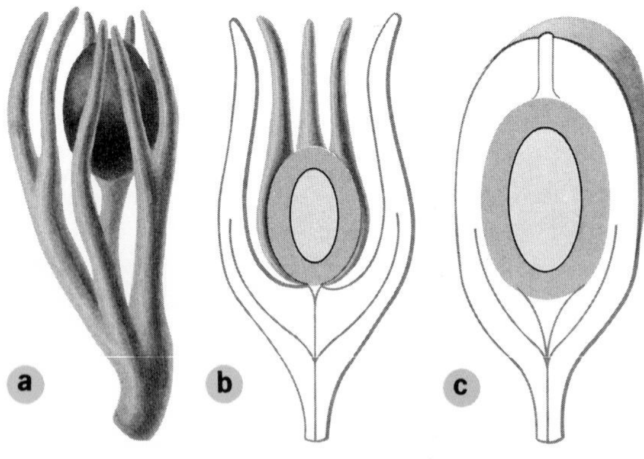

14–15 Steps in seed evolution. Fossil evidence for step **b** suggests hypothetical step **a**. Step **c** shows an integumented seed of a modern plant.

Instead of being shed from the sporangium to fend for themselves, like the spores of all other green land plants, the female spores of seed plants are retained and protected inside the integumented sporangium. The female spore develops into a tiny female gametophyte protected by the integument. Thus, the essential evolutionary steps in the production of this important reproductive structure—the seed—were (1) the introduction of heterospory, (2) the formation of integuments around the sporangium that contains the female spores, and (3) retention of the mature female spores in the sporangium, where the female gametophyte develops.

When we examine an immature seed (an **ovule**—OH·vyool) we find, in addition to the protective covering of integuments, that it contains great quantities of food. Thus the ovule not only protects the female gametophyte from the environment, it also provides food for the new offspring that is produced when the seed matures and germinates. Clearly, seed production is one of the important characters that better adapts vascular plants to their environment and makes them the predominant form of vegetation on our earth.

A Vehicle for Sperms

Of equal importance to the production of seeds was the evolution of **pollen tubes** that transport sperms to eggs. For algae, plenty of water is available as a medium in which their flagellated gametes can move. Primitive land plants also require external water for fertilization, since the sperm cells of these plants still move by swimming. The only way they can reach the large nonmotile egg is through water from rain, dew, or splashings from nearby brooks or waterfalls.

Mosses, liverworts, primitive vascular plants, and ferns, all of which produce flagellated, motile sperms, are consequently somewhat restricted to moist land environments. They grow most abundantly in the tropical rain forests, deep shaded woods, damp ravines, or swamps.

The evolution of pollen tubes parallels the evolution of seeds. The egg produced inside an ovule is very well protected in the sporangium (enclosed by its integuments and other tissues). It is so well protected that a flagellated sperm would not have the slightest chance of ever reaching an egg. This obstacle has been overcome by the development of pollen tubes. Once the pollen grain reaches the cone or flower, it germinates. The germinated **pollen grain** (look ahead to Figure 14-20b) is a tiny male gametophyte. It produces a long pollen tube, which grows to the ovule, and then digests its way through the protecting layers to the enclosed egg. The pollen tube forms a kind of living tunnel (as we will see shortly). Through its cytoplasm the nonflagellated sperms move to the egg.

The emancipation of vascular land plants from the requirement of external water for fertilization adds to our list of the characteristics that adapt seed plants to a wide variety of terrestrial environments. These environments range from the alpine environment of the mountains to the arid conditions of the desert.

The Importance of Flowers

With the evolution of the pollen tube, we might think that the last obstacle in adaptation to land had been overcome. Before we jump to this conclusion, however, let us survey the kinds of plants that have pollen tubes and produce seeds. Because of their abundance, we might suspect that flowering plants are the only plants with these two characteristics. That is not the case. The pines and their relatives—the spruces, firs, and cedars—also have pollen tubes and seeds. Although pines, spruces, and fir trees are abundant in certain parts of the world, they are represented only by about 600 species. That is a very small number when compared with the 275,000 species of flowering plants, which certainly are the most abundant and the most successful vascular plants.

Although flowering plants comprise the largest group of vascular plants, we know very little about their evolutionary origin. Many years ago it was said among botanists that "the origin of the flowering plants is an abominable mystery." Nothing has been added to our information in recent years to change this statement. The fossil record tells us that flowering plants appeared in substantial variety about 130 million years ago, early in the Cretaceous period (Figure 13-1). Almost from the beginning of their record, we find evidence that there were flowering plants with wind-pollinated flowers and with insect-pollinated flowers.

Pollination is the transfer of pollen grains from the **anthers** of the male parts of flowers to the **stigma** of the female flower part (Figure 14-16). Pollination by wind is haphazard. Thus it is not surprising to find that wind-pollinated flowering plants produce very large quantities of pollen and have large, feathery stigmas that strain the pollen from the air. Insect-pollinated flowers, on the other hand, have special

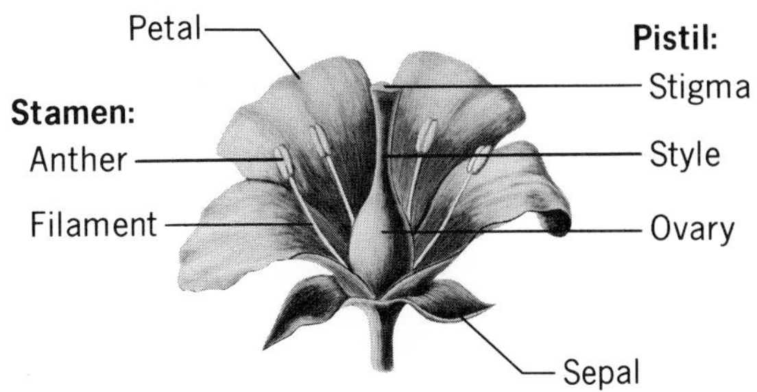

14–16 A diagram of a generalized flower. Some of the outer parts have been removed to show the internal reproductive structures clearly.

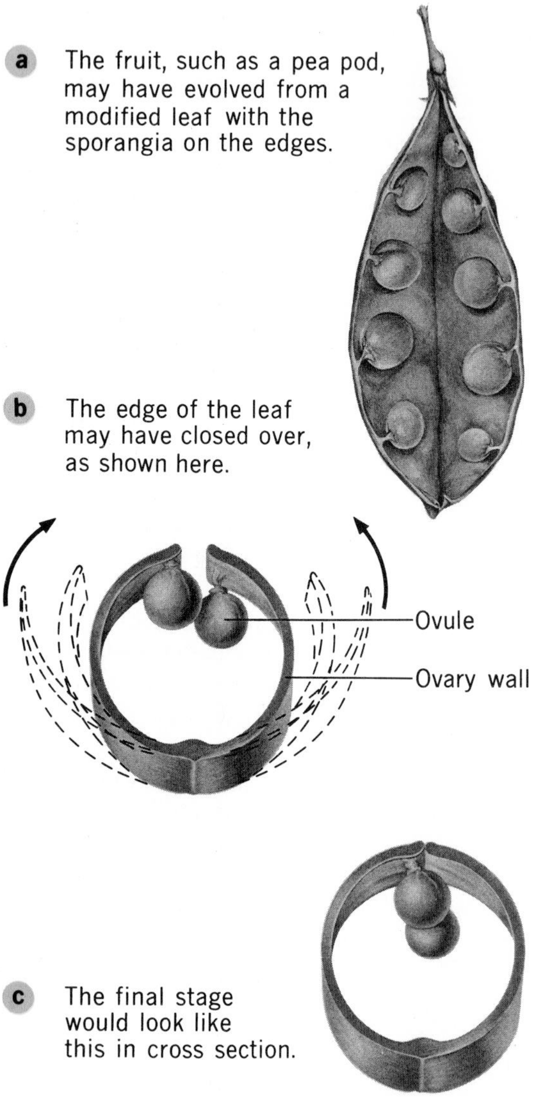

a The fruit, such as a pea pod, may have evolved from a modified leaf with the sporangia on the edges.

b The edge of the leaf may have closed over, as shown here.

Ovule

Ovary wall

c The final stage would look like this in cross section.

14–17 Study of modern vascular plants has suggested a hypothesis for the evolution of a fruit around developing ovules. To date, the fossil record has yielded little evidence.

floral parts that attract insects and insure pollination. The **petals** (Figure 14-16) of insect-pollinated flowers may be brightly colored, and the flowers may produce nectar and aromatic substances that attract bees, butterflies, moths, and many other kinds of insects. At the time an insect visits a flower to collect nectar or pollen, some of the pollen from the anthers is brushed off and sticks to the insect's body. The pollen is then carried to the next flower by the insect.

Many of the different types of flowers represent adaptations that increase the probability that pollination will occur. Unless pollination occurs, seeds will not develop in most flowering plants.

In many plants, **self-pollination**—the transfer of pollen from an anther to the stigma of the *same* flower or another flower on the *same* plant—occurs regularly. Self-pollinated plants with which you may be familiar include the tomato, cotton, bean, and pea.

Much more common than self-pollination is **cross-pollination.** This involves the transfer of pollen from an anther of a flower on one plant to the stigma of a flower on another plant. It is in cross-pollination that insects and wind are most important.

In some species of insect-pollinated flowers, a single species of insect is responsible for the pollination. One of the most remarkable cases of interdependence between plant and insect is the example of the *Yucca* plant and the *Pronuba* (pro·NOO·ba) moth. *Yucca* is a native plant in the arid regions of our Southwest. Self-pollination of flowers in these plants is impossible because the anthers are in a position that isolates them from the stigmas. The flowers open in the evening, and the small white moths, attracted by the fragrance of the flowers, fly to them, and mate within the flower. The female moth then collects pollen from the anthers and rolls it into a ball. She flies to another *Yucca,* bores into the ovary of a flower, and deposits an egg within it. She then goes to the stigma of the same flower and presses part of the ball of pollen she has gathered into a deep chamber in the center of the stigma. This sequence is repeated until several eggs have been laid and the chamber is well stocked with pollen. Some of the seeds that develop later serve as food for the larvae of the moth, which by then have hatched from the eggs laid inside the plant's ovary. Eventually the larvae bore through the wall of the ovary, drop to the ground, and complete their development underground. Of several hundred seeds that form in each ovary, only a few are destroyed by the larvae. Neither moth nor plant is able to complete its life cycle without the other.

This is an extreme example of interdependence. Yet it shows a remarkable example of an evolutionary adaptation between a plant and an animal.

The Protection of Seeds

Perhaps you have observed a squirrel wrestling with a pine cone, biting away the scales of the cone to get at the seeds inside. The scales of the cone form a tough protective envelope around the seeds (Inquiry 14-3), one that squirrels and other rodents find difficult to penetrate. As the cones of most pines mature, the cone scales open outward. When this happens, the mature seeds are exposed and are gradually shed from the cone.

A few pines have cones with exceedingly tough scales. The cone scales may remain closed around the seeds for as much as 75 years before they finally open and release the seeds. If during this time there is a forest fire that heats and scorches these resistant cones, the cones will open in a short time and shed their seeds. This remarkable adaptation insures the seeding of a new crop of pines in the event of a fire, which may kill the parent trees.

In flowering plants the seeds are protected from mechanical injury and other unfavorable environmental conditions by the development of a **fruit.** The fruit is derived from the ovary of the female reproductive part of the flower (Figure 14-16). The ovary completely encloses the ovules, which later become the seeds. We all recognize a watermelon as a fruit that contains seeds. When we eat a slice of watermelon, we eat the pink flesh and throw the green rind away. Both of these parts are protective layers of the fruit that enclose the seeds. Tomatoes, pea pods, and bean pods are also examples of fruits that contain seeds. This may seem a bit strange, because we usually think of peas, beans, and tomatoes as vegetables. Like the watermelon, however, they are true fruits derived from the ovaries of flowers. Other familiar examples of the great variety of fruits produced by flowering plants are oranges, grapefruit, grapes, coconuts and other nuts in their husks, and grains of all kinds.

The fruits of some flowering plants, pea pods, for example (Figure 14-17a), both early in their development and at maturity resemble leaves in form and internal structure. Because of this and other evidence, we think that the protective ovary that develops into the fruit actually evolved from leaves. These were special leaves that had sporangia along the margins. The ovules, as they evolved, contained the sporangia (Figure 14-17b). To produce such a closed structure with the seeds inside, the margins of the reproductive leaf would have to fold until they touched. Finally, fusion, occurring along the line where the folded edges of the modified leaf touched each other, would completely seal in the ovules from the outside and form a fruit.

Fruits have almost every means of dispersal imaginable. The coconut floats from shore to shore and is often carried great distances by ocean currents. The fruit of the cocklebur has hooklike spines, which become tangled in the fur of passing animals. Many fleshy fruits, among them raspberries and mulberries, are eaten by birds. The undigested seeds pass through the bird and fall to earth, perhaps miles from where they were eaten. One novel fruit has long hooks which catch in the nostrils of grazing animals. As the animal tries to dislodge this fruit, the seeds are scattered. The fruits of many plants, such as maple trees and elms, have "wings," which may transport the enclosed seed on the wind for some distance from the parent tree. These examples illustrate that it is not the fruit alone but also the means of dispersal of seed-containing fruits which helps explain the wide and successful distribution of the flowering plants.

Ruth Kirk

14–18 *Nephrolepis*, a fern common in forests of a temperate climate. Large, much-divided leaves such as these are characteristic of the prominent sporophyte generation of many of the ferns.

14–19 An ant's-eye view of a fern gametophyte. The whole structure is less than 15 mm in width. Looking upward from below the plant, we see the bottom surface with hairlike rhizoids extending downward. Just beneath the notch in the plant are the necks of female reproductive structures, glistening in the light. The male reproductive structures occur further behind the notch. (30 ×)

The Lost Gametophyte

Alternation of generations was last discussed when the nature of the gametophyte and sporophyte of a moss plant was explained (Chapter 13). At this stage in the evolution of plant life cycles, the gametophyte was the predominant, photosynthetic structure—the familiar moss plant with its stem and leaves. By contrast, the sporophyte remained partially dependent on the gametophyte—a really inconspicuous part of the moss life history.

In all vascular plants, whether primitive examples or advanced flowering types, the sporophyte is the predominant generation and the gametophyte is subordinate. Thus, when we see grass plants, elm trees, pine trees, ferns, club mosses, or horsetails growing, we are looking at sporophytes. The explanation of the predominance of the sporophyte seems to be that it is the generation in which vascular tissue originated.

Among the primitive vascular plants and ferns (Inquiry 14-2), the gametophyte generation is usually an independent, though incon-

Hugh Spencer

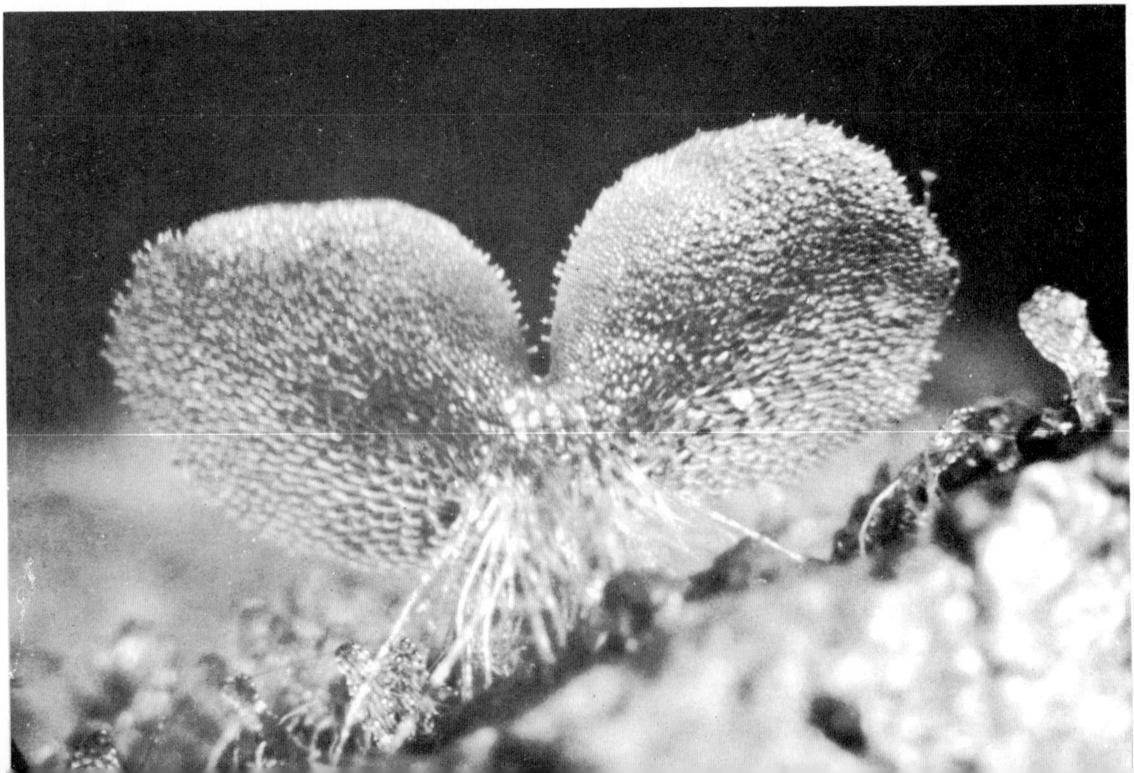

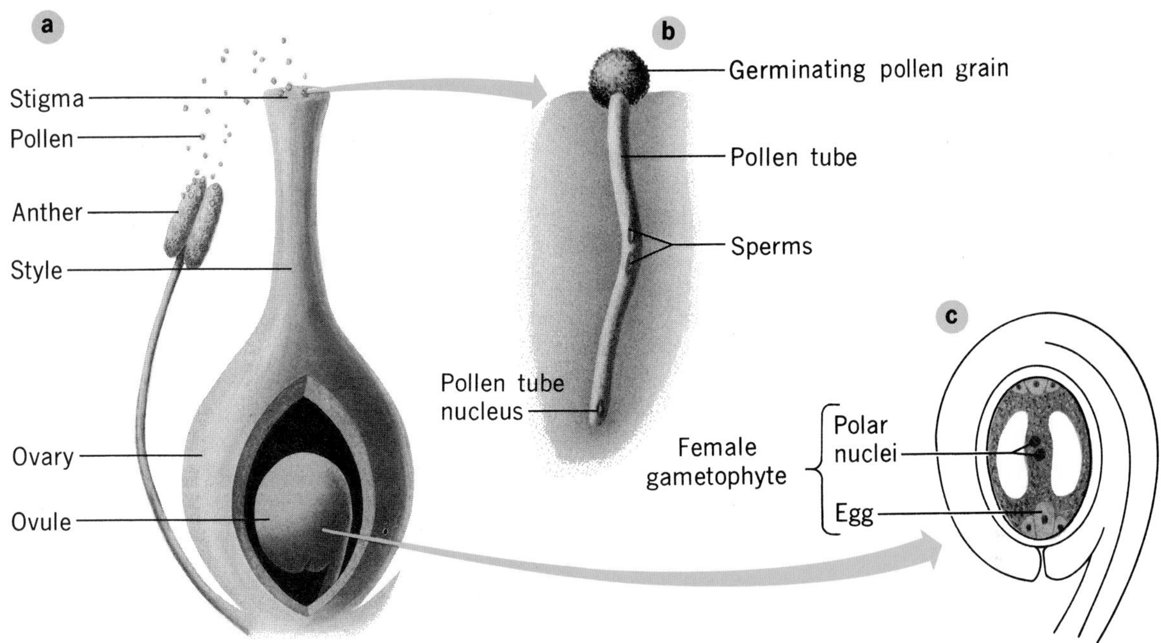

14–20 The gametophyte generation of a flowering plant. **a.** The ovary of the pistil is shown cut open on the near side to reveal the position of the ovule. **b.** A germinating pollen grain is the male gametophyte. Nearly all flowering plants have male gametophytes of the type shown. **c.** Greater variability exists in the structure of the female gametophyte. Nonetheless, 70 to 80 percent of the flowering plants that have been studied have the type of female gametophyte illustrated here (the ovule is shown cut open from top to bottom to reveal the protected gametophyte within).

spicuous, generation. Let us take the fern gametophyte as an example. The fern plants we see in the woods are fern sporophytes (Figure 14-18). Where are the gametophytes? The chances are that many more gametophytes than sporophytes are present, but we do not see the gametophytes because of their small size. You have to get down on your hands and knees and look carefully on the ground to find these tiny, green, heart-shaped structures (much enlarged in Figure 14-19). The largest gametophyte is no bigger than a dime, and usually they are much smaller. These are the structures that produce the sex cells that through fertilization complete the life cycle of the fern plant. Although it is photosynthetic and autotrophic, a simple, nonvascular fern gametophyte can hardly compare with the large, complex fern sporophyte.

Let us see what has happened to the gametophyte in a heterosporous plant. We will use a flowering plant as our example. To see the gametophytes of these plants, we need a microscope and some dissecting equipment. But where are we going to find these gametophytes? The male gametophyte of a flowering plant, you may remember, matures from a pollen grain. The pollen grain is deposited on the surface of the stigma (Figure 14-20a). The stigma supplies food for the growth of the pollen grain into the mature male gametophyte. When the pollen grain germinates, it produces its long pollen tube cell, which grows toward the female gametophyte. The germinating pollen grain also produces two sperms that move through the pollen tube to the female gametophyte. One sperm will fertilize the egg and the other will initiate the formation of the tissue known as the **endosperm** (EN·doe·sperm), which contains the stored food in the seed. Thus, the mature male gametophyte of a flowering plant consists of a pollen tube cell in which one can find two sperms (Figure 14-20b).

What and where is the female gametophyte generation? To find it, we must dissect out an ovule from within the ovary of the flower. Next we must cut through the integuments and the sporangium – the protective layers of the ovule. There in the well-protected recess, completely surrounded by tissue of the sporophyte, is the female gametophyte (Figure 14-20c). A careful examination, using special stains and a microscope, will show us that this female part of the gametophyte generation consists of seven cells (the two polar nuclei eventually fuse; they count as one cell). Only one of the seven cells is an egg. Together, the male and female gametophytes of most flowering plants are composed of only ten structures we can call cells! Is it possible that at some future time in evolution only egg and sperm will be produced and the gametophyte cells will be entirely eliminated? If this happened, we would find that the generalized life cycle of a flowering plant would be essentially similar to our own. Can you explain why?

CONCLUDING REMARKS

As we look back and summarize the changes that have occurred in the evolution of the gametophyte generation of green land plants, we can see two distinct trends. However, before we can understand what these trends are, we must have a starting point. As the illustrated summary of plant evolution on pages 276 and 277 shows, we think that the ancestors of green land plants may have been green algae with a life cycle similar to that of *Ulva*. You will recall that *Ulva* (Figures 13-6 and 13-8) has a life cycle with an alternation of generations. Both its gametophyte and its sporophyte generations are identical in their gross structure. Both are green, photosynthetic plants capable of an independent existence.

When we compare the alternation of generations of this green alga with the alternation of generations of a green land plant, such as a moss or a liverwort, we find that the two generations of the moss or liverwort are *not alike* in structure and nutrition. In the moss, the gametophyte is the predominant, photosynthetic generation, while the sporophyte is small, short in its duration of life, and partially dependent on the gametophyte. What has happened to the sporophyte? We can conclude that in the course of evolution from the algal ancestor, the sporophytes of mosses and liverworts became dependent on the gametophyte for some of their food and all of their water. Under these conditions the sporophyte became a lazy freeloader on the gametophyte. As a result, the sporophyte became reduced or simplified in structure.

Among the vascular plants we see that the sporophyte and the gametophyte are quite different from their counterparts in the mosses and liverworts. The sporophyte generation of vascular plants has become the predominant, complex, photosynthetic generation; the gametophyte has become greatly reduced in size. In ferns the gametophyte, although small, is still a photosynthetic, heart-shaped structure independent of the sporophyte. In seed plants, the gametophyte is reduced even further. It has become completely dependent on the sporophyte. The evolution of the gametophyte and sporophyte in the vascular plants affords us an excellent example of **divergent evolution,** that is, two structures becoming increasingly different as a result of evolutionary changes (Figure 14-21). Thus, the sporophyte has evolved toward complexity, the gametophyte toward simplicity.

This is the end of our story of the evolution of vascular plants, and it ends with the most highly evolved of all plants – the flowering plants. No single characteristic places the flowering plants at the top of the evolutionary ladder. Rather, they are the product of a combination of many characteristics. Some char-

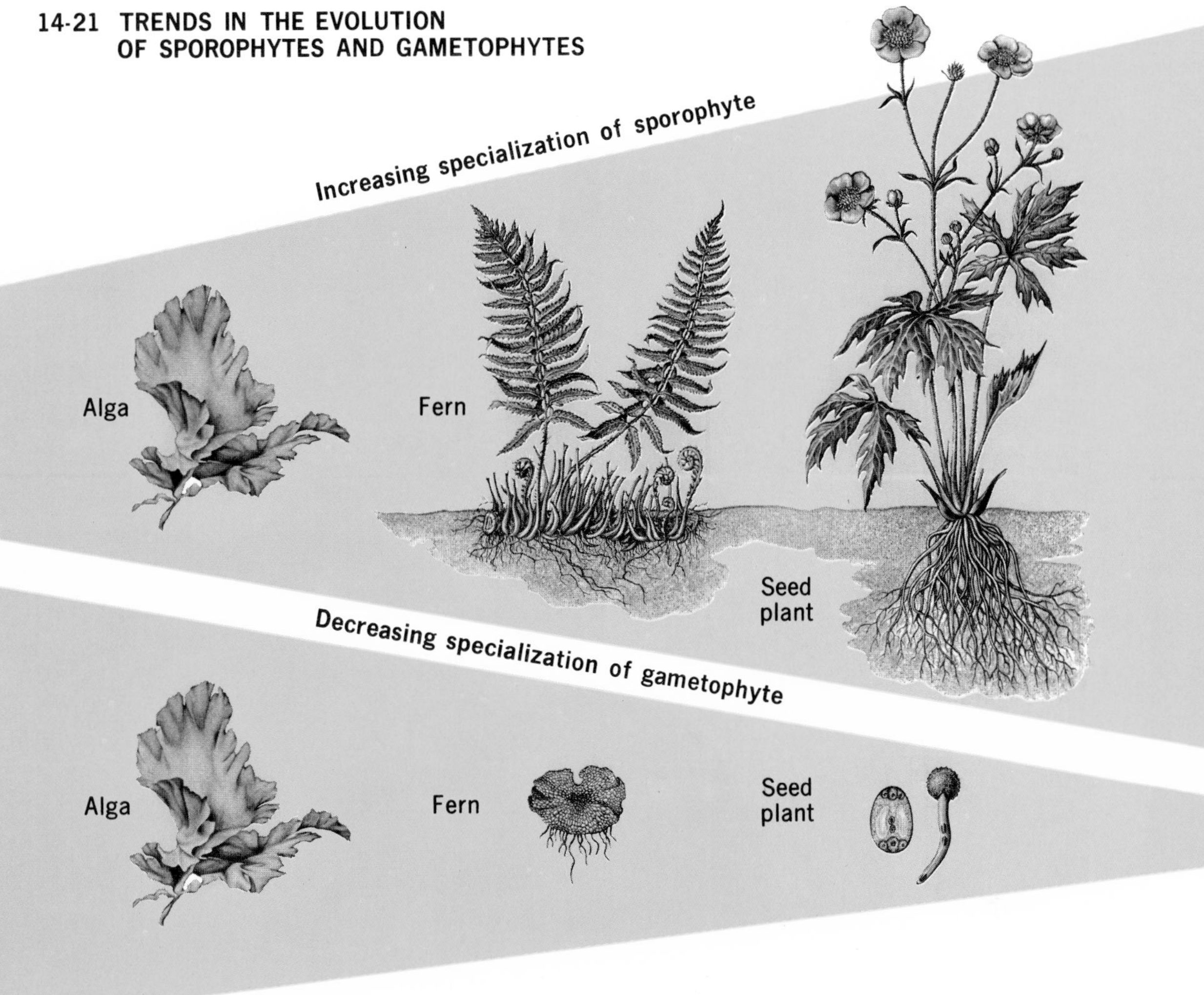

acteristics that have been discussed in this chapter are:

1. The evolution of roots, stems, and leaves
2. The evolution of vascular systems in stems and roots
3. The evolution of protected sporangia, including their enclosure by the seed and fruit
4. The evolution of the pollen tube
5. The evolution of the flower
6. The evolution of the alternation of generations

These characteristics, which include the development of complex vegetative and reproductive structures, did not come about suddenly. They are the result of long periods of successive evolutionary change, beginning with the primitive unicellular ancestors that lived hundreds of millions of years ago.

The illustrated summary of the classification of the green plants and fungi, pages 276-77, is based on the evolutionary relationships that have been described in this and the two preceding chapters.

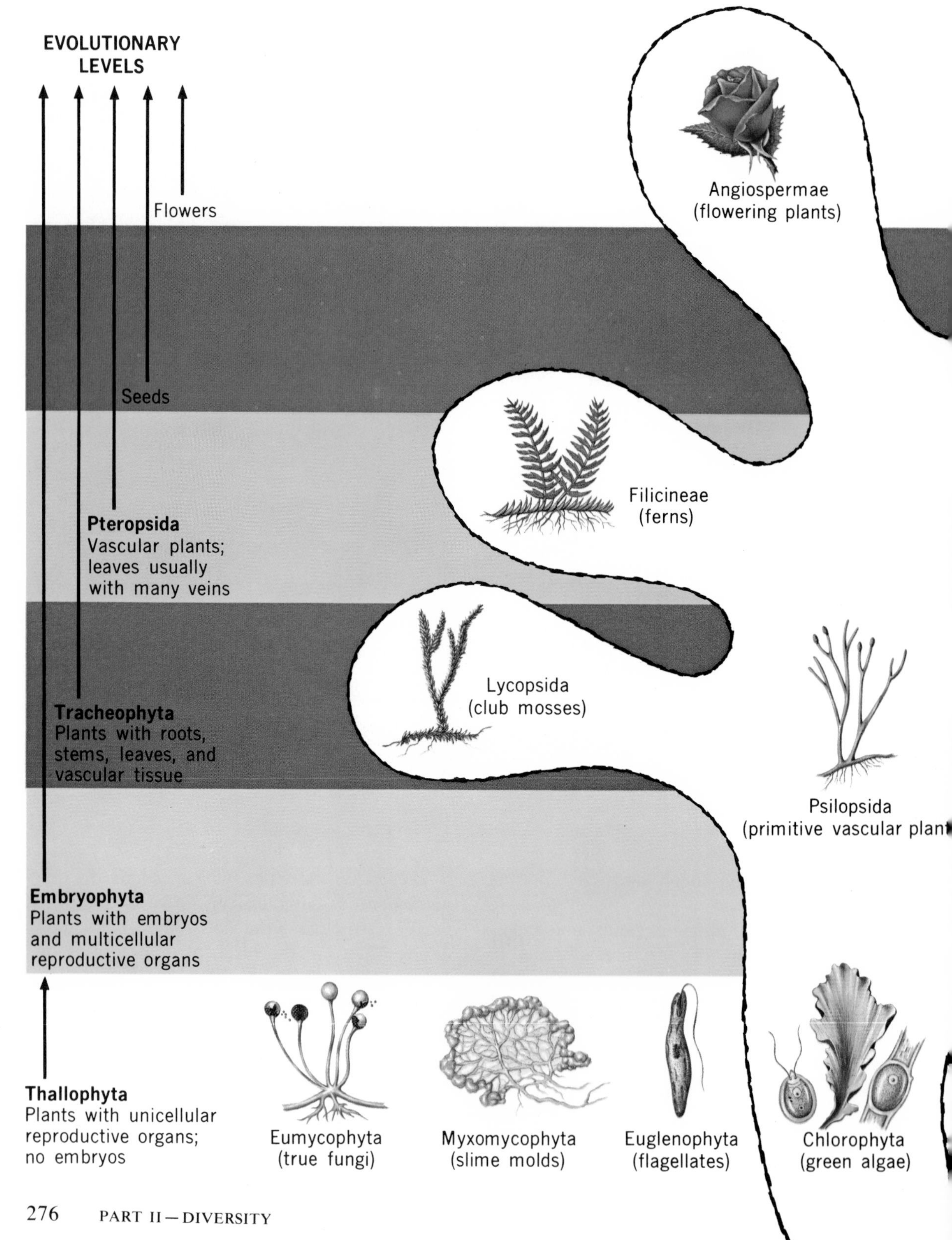
EVOLUTIONARY
LEVELS
Flowers
Seeds
Pteropsida
Vascular plants;
leaves usually
with many veins
Tracheophyta
Plants with roots,
stems, leaves, and
vascular tissue
Embryophyta
Plants with embryos
and multicellular
reproductive organs
Thallophyta
Plants with unicellular
reproductive organs;
no embryos
Angiospermae
(flowering plants)
Filicineae
(ferns)
Lycopsida
(club mosses)
Psilopsida
(primitive vascular plant
Eumycophyta
(true fungi)
Myxomycophyta
(slime molds)
Euglenophyta
(flagellates)
Chlorophyta
(green algae)

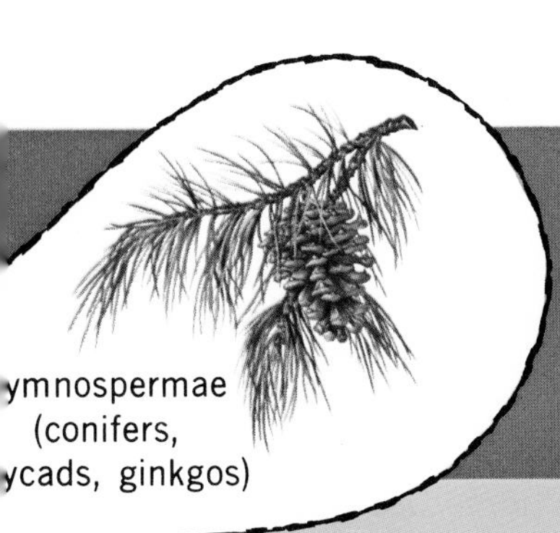

PLANT KINGDOM

Subkingdom - Thallophyta

Phylum	Myxomycophyta
Phylum	Eumycophyta
Phylum	Cyanophyta
Phylum	Rhodophyta
Phylum	Chrysophyta
Phylum	Phaeophyta
Phylum	Euglenophyta
Phylum	Chlorophyta

Subkingdom - Embryophyta

Phylum	Bryophyta
Phylum	Tracheophyta
Subphylum	Psilopsida
Subphylum	Lycopsida
Subphylum	Sphenopsida
Subphylum	Pteropsida
Class	Filicineae
Class	Gymnospermae
Class	Angiospermae

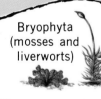

Sphenopsida
(horsetails)

Bryophyta
(mosses and
liverworts)

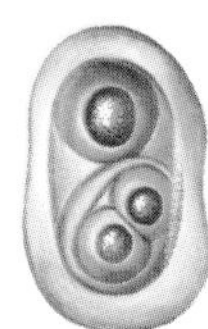

Cyanophyta
(blue-green algae)

Rhodophyta
(red algae)

Chrysophyta
(diatoms)

Phaeophyta
(brown algae)

GUIDE QUESTIONS AND PROBLEMS

1. Liverworts have persisted on land for millions of years, despite a greatly changing physical environment. What structures of the liverwort might have insured this success?
2. List all the ways you can think of in which vascular plants influence your environment and life.
3. Why was it necessary that green plants colonize the land before animals could?
4. What parallel adaptations to the land environment occurred in plants and animals?
5. How does the structure of vascular supporting tissues in primitive vascular plants differ from that in more advanced plants?
6. Biologists believe that heterospory evolved prior to the evolution of seeds. Why?
7. What is the relationship between the evolution of seeds and the evolution of pollen tubes?
8. How might you explain the fact that flowering plants have become the predominant land flora?

RELATED READING

Books

For an interesting, well-illustrated account of plant types . . .

Barnett, L., and editors of Life Magazine, *The World We Live In*, Golden Press, New York, 1955.

For a concise discussion of the evolution of plant groups . . .

Bold, H. C., *The Plant Kingdom*, Second Edition, Foundations of Modern Biology Series, Prentice-Hall, Englewood Cliffs, N. J., 1964.

For a simple discussion of nomenclature . . .

Benton, A. H., and W. E. Werner, *Principles of Field Biology and Ecology*, McGraw-Hill, New York, 1958.

For an advanced discussion of structure in vascular plants . . .

Esau, Katherine, *Plant Anatomy*, Second Edition, Wiley, New York, 1965

15

Photosynthesis — the Link Between Two Worlds

"Therefore, 164 pounds of wood, bark, and root were formed of water only." Do you remember this statement? It was written by J. B. van Helmont (1577–1644) as his conclusion to his famous willow tree experiments (see Chapter 4, pages 56-58). Van Helmont was one of the first to conduct a real experiment in the attempt to solve the mystery of plant nutrition. He was the first to test that old idea that green plants get their food from soil and water. Even though his conclusion was wrong, we can credit van Helmont with starting the inquiry into that link in life's chain we now call photosynthesis.

The link was strengthened by the experiments of Joseph Priestley (1733–1804). A review of Chapter 4, pages 62-64, will help you to recall that it was Priestley who, in 1772, demonstrated the biological importance of atmospheric oxygen and its replenishment by green plants. At about the same time Priestley was conducting his experiments with oxygen, Jan Ingenhousz (ING·en·hous – 1730–1799) found that sunlight was necessary for the production of oxygen by the green parts of plants. The link was strengthened further by Jean Senebier (seh·neh·b'YAY – 1742–1809), who in 1782 discovered that under certain conditions green plants absorb carbon dioxide from the atmosphere. However, Senebier had no idea of the significance of his discovery—that is, the part that carbon dioxide plays in photosynthesis.

In 1804, Nicholas de Saussure (duh·so·suhr – 1767–1845) was able to show experimentally that water, too, is chemically involved in plant nutrition. In a little more than thirty years (between 1772 and 1804), the involvement of the three key factors in photosynthesis—water, carbon dioxide, and sunlight—had been experimentally demonstrated. It was not until the middle of the nineteenth century, however, that biologists were able to fit some of the pieces of the puzzle together. Two discoveries made this possible. One was the demonstration that green plants convert the energy of visible light into chemical energy, which is stored in compounds that the plants manufacture. The second was the identification of a sugar as the principal energy-containing compound produced in the plant's green cells.

The events described above serve as the foundation for our present understanding of the process of photosynthesis. Photosynthesis is a process that provides a link between two worlds—the living and the nonliving. Supplies of carbon dioxide, water, and energy from the sun are obtained from the nonliving world. No foods or fuels for the world of living things exist until green plants absorb and use these supplies to make sugar. We cannot overemphasize the importance of green plants and the part they play in maintaining life! With the exception of a few kinds of bacteria, *green plants are the only organisms that capture the energy in sunlight and use it to synthesize energy-rich compounds. These compounds are the only source of energy available to all the heterotrophic organisms.*

THE LEAF— A PHOTOSYNTHETIC ORGAN

We recognize the photosynthetic parts of plants because they are green. A very casual investigation of the plants that one might find in a garden or greenhouse shows us that different organs of the plants can be green. Their stems and some flower parts may be green.

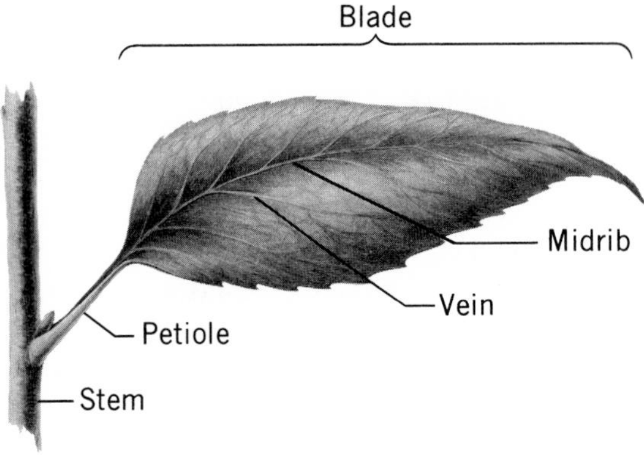

15–1 The external anatomy of a leaf. Of all plant organs, leaves have the greatest variability in form. Some may be several feet long, others reduced to tiny scales. Many have smooth margins, others such marginal irregularities as lobes—or the teeth shown in this drawing. Whatever their differences, however, most leaves are green (or contain chlorophyll in addition to other pigments).

Some tropical plants, such as the vanilla plant and other orchids, have green roots. As you might guess, such roots are not below the ground but are exposed to sunlight. Generally, however, we recognize the green leaves of plants as the chief photosynthetic organs (Inquiries 15-1 and 15-2).

The leaves of many flowering plants—a bean plant, for example—are alike in having two main parts. One is a stalk, or **petiole** (PET·ee-ohl), which attaches the leaf to a branch. The other is the thin, flattened **blade** (Figure 15-1). If you hold the blade of a bean leaf up to a bright light, you will be able to see a network of **veins.** The veins extend from a **midrib,** which is a continuation of the petiole into the blade of the leaf.

Each vein is a complex structure composed of a group of dead tubular xylem cells in the upper part of the vein, and living phloem cells in the lower part of the leaf. The cells of xylem are the pipes through which water moves into the leaves. The phloem cells move the sugars made in photosynthesis from the leaf to the stem and roots where the sugars are converted into starch and stored. A sheath of photosynthetic cells, enveloping the xylem and the phloem, completes the vein's structure.

The Cells of the Leaf

If we were to look only at the outside of a leaf we would certainly get the impression that the only pigment present in the leaf is chlorophyll. Is this true? (Inquiry 15-3.) We would also get the impression that the chlorophyll is more or less evenly distributed through the leaf tissues. A microscopic examination of a thin section through the blade (Figure 15-2) will soon show us that this is not the case. Instead of being evenly dispersed in the cells and tissues, the chlorophyll is concentrated in discrete structures, the **chloroplasts,** within certain cells. Nearly all the chloroplasts are in living cells located in the **spongy** and **palisade** layers of the leaf. These layers are sandwiched between the **upper** and **lower epidermis.** The cells of the layer next to the upper epidermis are vertically elongated and differ in size, shape, and arrangement from those found lower in the leaf. Cells in the layer adjacent to the lower epidermis are less regular in shape, and there are large air spaces between them. Both of these layers are composed of living cells with numerous chloroplasts.

As we look at the distribution of chlorophyll in a leaf, we must be impressed by the fact that most of the living cells of the leaf contain some of this green stuff. Biologists discovered long ago that the green parts of plants had something to do with absorbing light and using its energy in the synthesis of carbohydrates. But how?

Sunlight is complex—a spectrum of light of many wavelengths. Do all portions of this spectrum play a part in photosynthesis? If chlorophyll absorbs light energy, what kind of work does this energy do in photosynthesis? Although we do not know the answers to all of these or the many other questions about photosynthesis, recent advances in this field of study have clarified many of its mysteries.

Light and Photosynthesis

When sunlight—or the comparable light from an ordinary electric light bulb—reaches the surface of a green leaf, several things happen to it. Part of the light is *reflected* from the leaf surface, while some continues through the tissues of the leaf and is said to be *transmitted* light. The light we are most interested in is neither what is reflected nor what is transmitted, but that which is *absorbed* by the green pigments in the leaf. It is this light that provides the energy for photosynthesis.

With the understanding that a beam of light is really composed of a spectrum of light rays having different wavelengths, we can arrange to study that spectrum by passing a light beam through a prism (Figure 15-3, left). The prism separates the beam into bands of colors, deep red at one end of the spectrum and deep violet at the other end. The red light waves are the longest waves of visible light, and they are bent the least when they pass through the prism. The short wavelengths of violet are bent the most. Wavelengths in the violet portion of the spectrum are about 400 millimicrons (mμ) in length, while those at the other end of the spectrum—the red portion—are much longer, about 700 mμ. (You will recall from an earlier part of your work that a millimicron is equal to 1/1,000 of a micron or 1/1,000,000 of a millimeter.)

How can we find out what part of the spectrum is absorbed by the green substance in leaves—the molecules of chlorophyll? First we have to make an extract of chlorophyll. This can be done with such solvents as alcohol, carbon tetrachloride, acetone, and ether, as in Inquiry 15-3. Next we pour the purified extract into a clear glass container with flat, parallel sides and place the container with its contents between a source of white light and a prism (Figure 15-3, right). When we examine the spectrum of light that passes through the prism, we see that certain wavelengths are partly or completely absent, indicating that

15–2 Part of a leaf as it might appear in a cross section under the microscope. The vein near the center is also in cross section. The arrows show the movement of carbon dioxide, oxygen, and water into or out of the leaf. What clues to the relationship of structure and function are evident in the drawing? (What is significant, for example, about the air spaces between many cells in the leaf, and about the openings in the leaf's lower surface?)

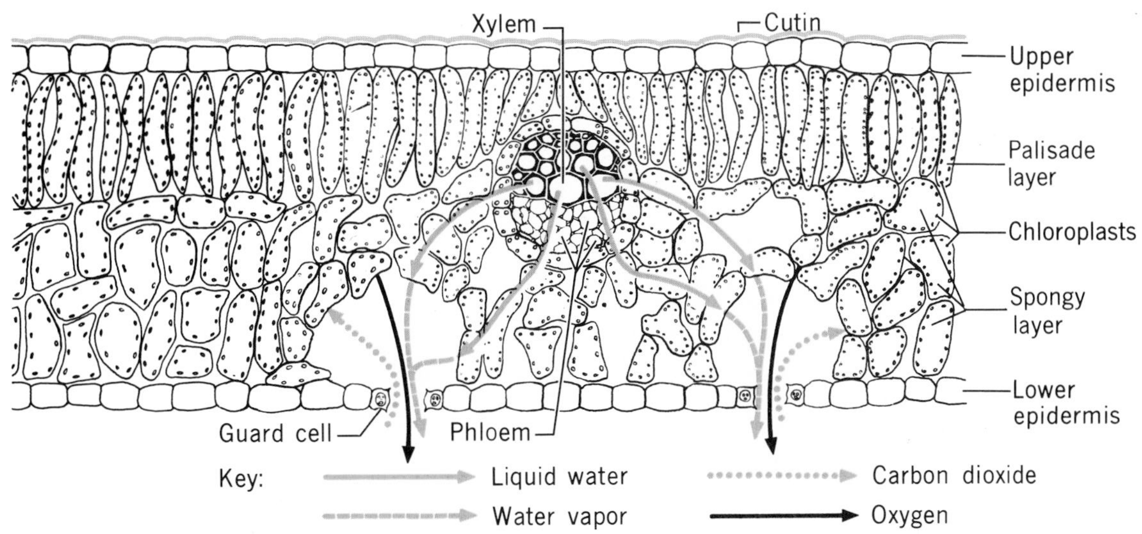

15-3 SELECTIVE ABSORPTION OF LIGHT BY CHLOROPHYLL

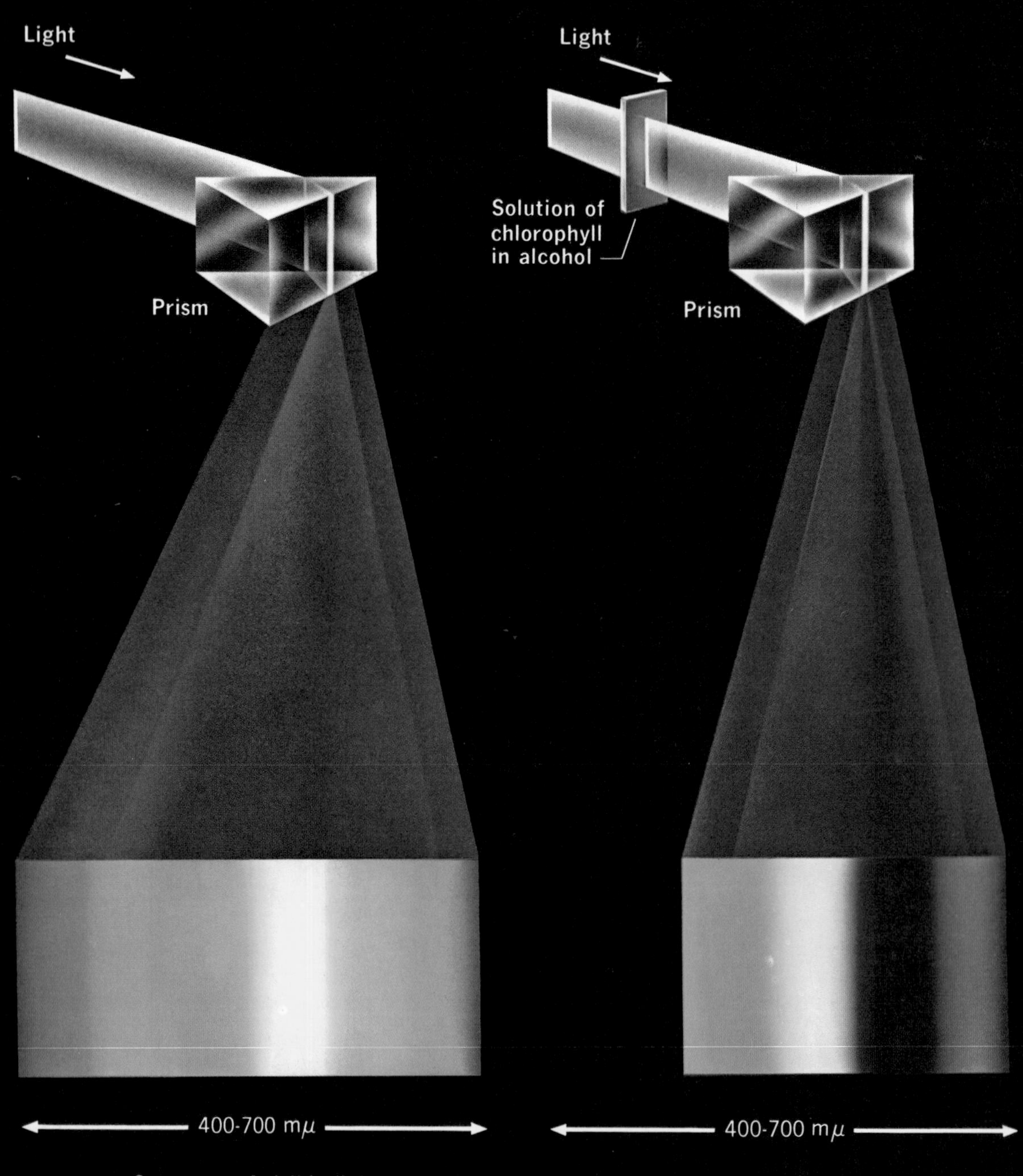

Spectrum of visible light

Spectrum after absorption by chlorophyll

they have been absorbed more or less completely by the chlorophyll solution.

As a result, the original appearance of the spectrum is markedly changed. In regions where chlorophyll is an effective absorber, dark bands will be seen. In regions where little absorption occurs, changes in the spectrum will be slight. If we measure the percentage of light absorbed by the chlorophyll for the wavelengths running from 400 mμ to 700 mμ—that is, for violet, then blue, green, yellow, orange, and finally red light—we can prepare a graph showing the degree of light absorption by the chlorophyll solution (Figure 15-4).

We can now understand the relationship between the chlorophyll in the chloroplasts and the absorption of radiant energy necessary for photosynthesis. Only the light energy *absorbed* in the regions of violet, blue, orange, and red wavelengths can be used for synthesizing energy-rich compounds (Figure 15-3). What do you think happens to the other wavelengths of light—in the green region of the spectrum, for example?

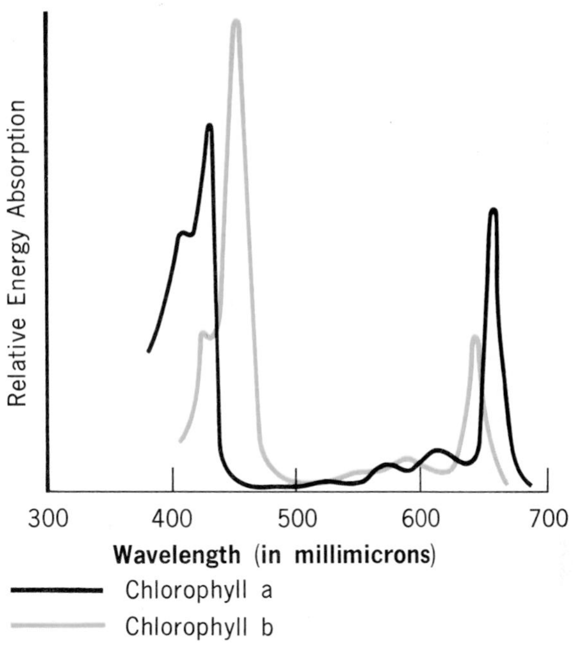

15–4 A graph of the absorption spectra of chlorophylls *a* and *b*, measured for extracts of the pigments in alcohol. Chlorophyll *a* and chlorophyll *b* absorb light of similar wavelengths, chiefly violet, blue, orange, and red. Compare this graph with the absorption spectrum in Figure 15-3.

Chlorophyll and Photosynthesis

What is chlorophyll like? The chemists who first attempted to determine the chemical composition of chlorophyll soon discovered that it was a complex substance consisting of a mixture of closely related substances. Today we know that there are at least six different kinds of chlorophyll—*a, b, c,* and *d* found in photosynthetic plants, and two others found only in photosynthetic bacteria.

Chlorophylls *a* and *b* are both present in most of the green land plants with which we are familiar. Their molecular formulas show that they are made up of five different kinds of atoms:

Chlorophyll *a*: $C_{55}H_{72}O_5N_4Mg$
Chlorophyll *b*: $C_{55}H_{70}O_6N_4Mg$

Each kind of chlorophyll is composed of large molecules containing well over one hundred atoms, but always including four atoms of nitrogen and one of magnesium. Interestingly enough, the chlorophylls are closely related chemically to the pigment of the red protein, hemoglobin, found in our own blood. A striking difference is that one molecule has iron, while the other has magnesium. Although we know that the iron molecule in hemoglobin is required in the transport of oxygen by the blood, we do not know what role magnesium plays in the chlorophyll molecule. How does the plant cell manufacture these complex chlorophyll molecules? Actually, we still know very little about their synthesis. We do know, however, that they are formed inside the chloroplast and are organized in layered, disk-shaped structures called **grana** (GRAY·na—Figure 15-5). Grana can be observed by using the electron microscope (Figure 15-6). Each of the layers, or **lamellae** (la·MEL·ee), of a single

One granum
from chloroplast

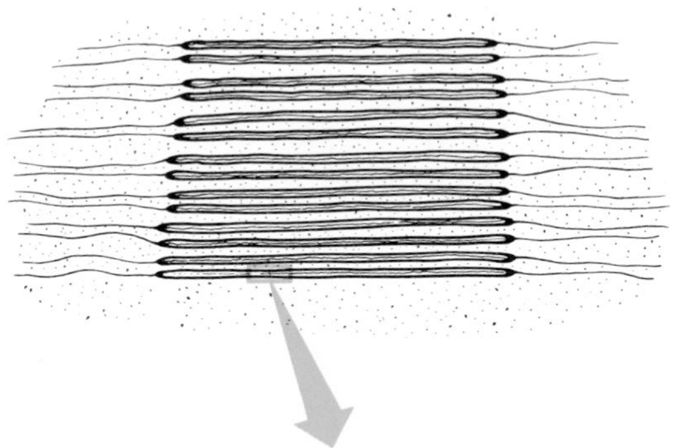

One lamella of the granum

Lipid and chlorophyll
Protein
Inner space
Protein
Lipid and chlorophyll

15–5 A diagram of one hypothesis for the structure of a granum from a chloroplast. A single chloroplast contains many such grana, as an electron micrograph (Figure 15–6) shows. Different investigators have different hypotheses about the disposition of the protein, fatty substances, and chlorophyll in the lamellae (or layers) within a granum.

granum (Figure 15-5) is thought to consist of still smaller layers of protein, fatty substances, chlorophyll, and other pigments.

This special structure of chloroplasts traps light energy and makes it available for bringing about a whole series of reactions, which together constitute photosynthesis (Inquiry 15-4). The raw materials that are utilized are two relatively simple compounds, carbon dioxide (CO_2) and water (H_2O). Our next problem is to find out how the first of these, carbon dioxide, is obtained by the plant from its environment.

Carbon Dioxide and Photosynthesis

Green land plants absorb carbon dioxide from the atmosphere surrounding the leaves and stems (Inquiry 15-5). How much is normally present in an average sample of air? Only about 0.03 to 0.04 percent of carbon dioxide is present in the atmosphere – yet every organic compound green plants manufacture contains carbon atoms. We must keep in mind, however, that green land plants account for only about 10 percent of the total photosynthesis occurring on earth. All of the rest goes on in the seas, oceans, rivers, and lakes, where in addition to dissolved carbon dioxide, large quantities of carbon-containing compounds such as bicarbonates and soluble carbonates are readily available.

In discussing the evolution of land plants (Chapter 14), we explained that the land plants have evolved certain structures for the absorption of carbon dioxide from the atmosphere. Let us see what these structures are, and how they function in a leaf of a green plant. A review of Figure 15-2 will help us.

To absorb carbon dioxide, the green plant must have the wet surfaces of some of its cells exposed to the atmosphere. Within the leaf, these are cells of the spongy and palisade layers. The wet surfaces of these cells are exposed to the atmosphere in the air spaces of the leaf tissues. The carbon dioxide of the atmosphere, coming in contact with the water film that covers the spongy and palisade cells, dissolves in the water and is absorbed. As the carbon dioxide is absorbed from the air spaces by the cells of the leaf, its concentration in the air spaces becomes lower than that present in the outside air. Under these conditions, carbon dioxide in the surrounding atmosphere will diffuse into the air spaces of the leaf.

As air diffuses into the leaf, it passes through stomata (page 262 and Inquiry 15-6) – pores in the epidermal layers. These pores are surrounded by paired guard cells. The size of the pores is regulated by changes in the water content of the guard cells. If stomata are closed by the action of the guard cells, the diffusion of carbon dioxide into the leaf will be halted. Without carbon dioxide, the process of photosynthesis will then cease, even though light energy and all the other factors required may be present. Hence it is important to understand how the guard cells function.

We may start our analysis by recalling that guard cells contain chloroplasts (Figure 15-7). The guard cells are in fact, the only photosynthesizing cells of the epidermis. Like other photosynthetic cells, guard cells absorb carbon dioxide. Some of the carbon dioxide reacts with the water in which it is dissolved to form carbonic acid:

$$H_2O + CO_2 \leftrightarrows \underset{\text{carbonic acid}}{H_2CO_3}$$

In the presence of light energy, carbonic acid in the guard cells is decomposed again into carbon dioxide and water, which are rapidly used in the synthesis of carbohydrates. These carbohydrates are sugars containing phosphate groups. Thus an analysis of the contents of illuminated guard cells reveals that their acid content is low (pH high) and their sugar content is high. Because of the high sugar content (and thus the relatively lower water content) of these cells, water enters them by osmosis from adjacent cells during hours of illumination. Thus they swell up, or become *turgid,* and bend apart like two sausages connected at each end (Figure 15-7). In this way a stoma, or pore, forms between each pair of guard cells. Through this pore, air containing carbon dioxide can pass to the photosynthetic tissues of the leaf.

What do you suppose will happen to the guard cells if we turn off the light or put the plant in the dark? If we analyze the contents

15–6 An electron micrograph of a chloroplast. The structures somewhat like stacked coins are the grana. The "coins" in each granum are the lamellae. (26,000 ×)

L. K. Shumway

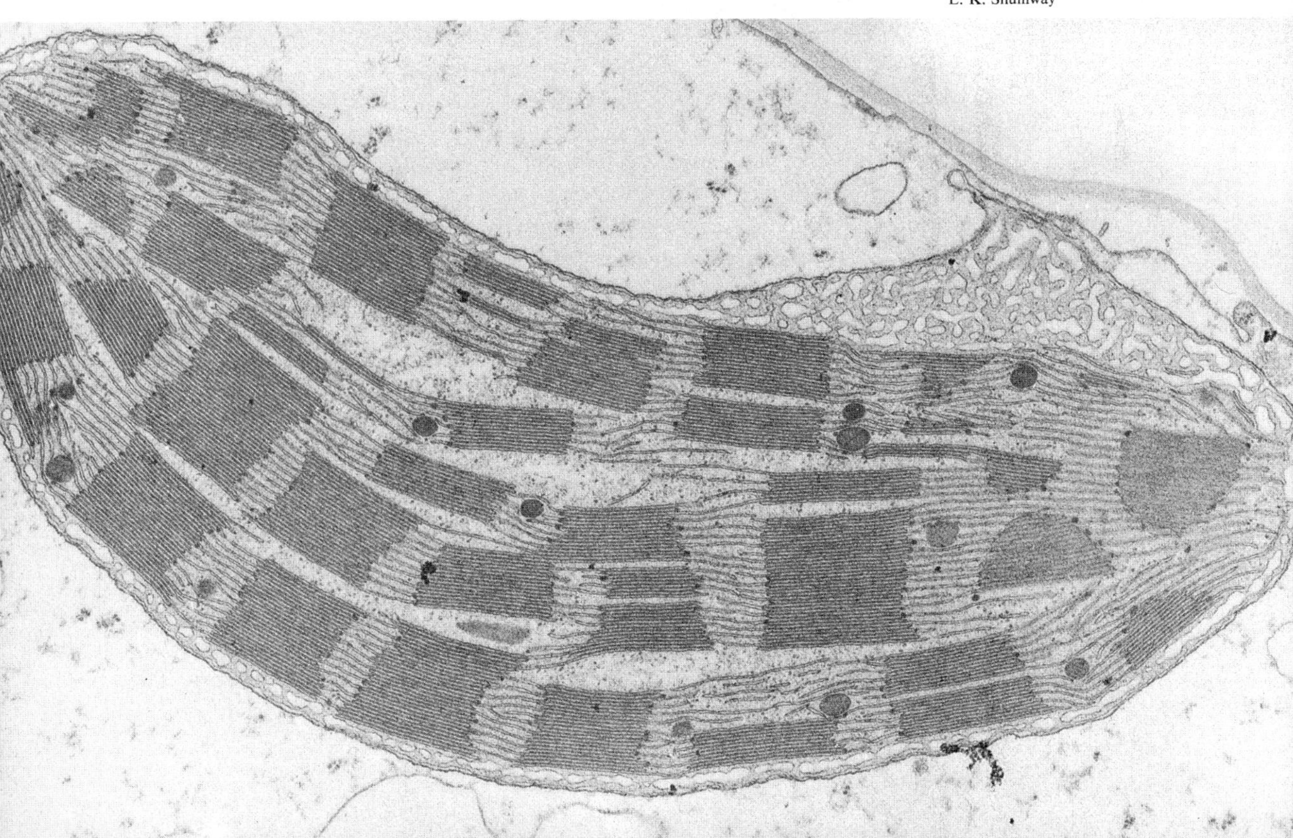

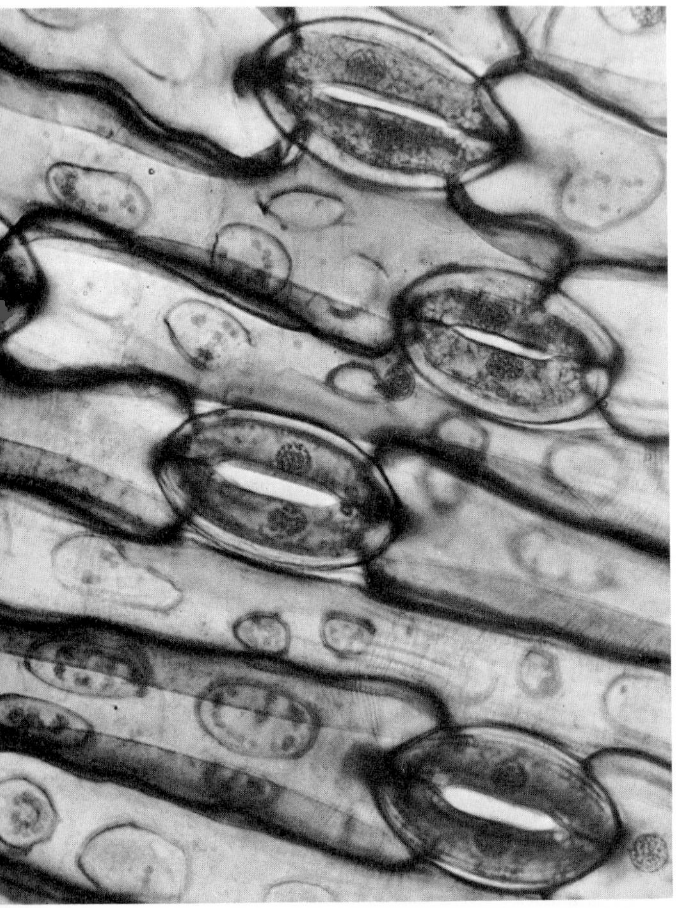

Harold V. Green

15–7 Part of the lower epidermis of a leaf, as seen through a compound microscope. The narrow opening between each pair of guard cells is a stoma. How do the guard cells function in conserving water in the leaf? in obtaining carbon dioxide?

of the guard cells after the plants have been in the dark, we will find that most of the sugar molecules have been removed by respiration or have been converted into insoluble starch. Accompanying this change is an increase in the acidity of the cell contents. Can you explain why? The water balance also changes. As sugar molecules are removed from the guard cells and the relative concentration of water in the guard cells increases, water molecules diffuse out to the epidermal cells. This movement continues until a balance in the concentration of water molecules is established between the two kinds of cells.

As the guard cells lose water, they become less turgid. Their inner walls then move together until the pore between them is closed. The inner walls of the guard cells are thick, and act like straight leaf springs. When the guard cells are turgid, the springlike walls become slightly bent and the stoma opens. With a decrease in turgidity, the walls straighten out and close the pore.

THE BIOCHEMISTRY OF PHOTOSYNTHESIS

We have seen how a green land plant obtains carbon dioxide – one of the four essentials that a plant must have in order to carry on photosynthesis. Now let us see how the plant uses carbon dioxide with the other three essentials – water, light, and chlorophyll. Like respiration, photosynthesis consists of numerous steps, many of which are still not fully known. At the present time there are hundreds of scientists in all parts of the world working to clear up one or another of these areas of uncertainty.

The following general equation for photosynthesis is greatly oversimplified, omitting many of the separate steps that occur. Nevertheless, it is a starting point.

$$6\ CO_2 + 6\ H_2O \xrightarrow[\substack{\text{chlorophyll} \\ \text{(in a living cell)}}]{\text{light energy}} C_6H_{12}O_6 + 6\ O_2$$

This equation indicates that 6 molecules of carbon dioxide and 6 molecules of water would be needed to form every molecule of a carbohydrate (glucose – Figure 15-8), and that in this process 6 molecules of oxygen (which are released) would also be formed. This process by which energy-storing carbohydrates are formed from comparatively low-energy raw materials obviously requires a lot of energy. The energy source is the light that is absorbed by chlorophyll and other plant pigments.

We see in the general equation for photosynthesis that atmospheric oxygen ($6\ O_2$) is produced. This oxygen is important. We believe that it is this oxygen added to the atmosphere that supplies all living things, including the plants that produce it, with the oxygen required for respiration. But where does the oxygen come from? There are two logical possibilities. The oxygen could come from the CO_2 or from the H_2O.

The first step in the solution of this problem came from an unexpected quarter. Photosynthetic bacteria (Chapter 10) had been studied by Cornelis Van Niel to discover how these strange organisms obtained energy for their metabolism. In the process these bacteria release the energy in molecules of H_2S, a smelly gas, by breaking the bonds of the H_2S molecule.

$$2\ H_2S + CO_2 \xrightarrow[\text{chlorophyll}]{\text{light}} \underset{\text{(carbohydrate)}}{(CH_2O)} + H_2O + 2\ S$$

It was noticed that O_2 was not formed in this reaction as it is in photosynthesis carried on by green plants. The product, instead of oxygen, was sulfur. Van Niel recognized that this discovery provided a clue to the origin of the O_2 evolved in green plant photosynthesis. It must be that the compound containing hydrogen atoms (H_2O or H_2S) was split to release energy. In green plant photosynthesis this must be H_2O, not CO_2. But only when supplies of isotopes (see Chapter 5) became available for experimental use could this idea be tested.

Experiments to determine the source of the O_2 released in photosynthesis were designed by Martin Kamen, who made use of an isotope of oxygen, oxygen-18 (O^{18}). To understand what O^{18} is, imagine that we could take from the air a sample of oxygen containing exactly 100,000 atoms. Of these atoms, 99,759 of them will have a mass about 16 times greater than that of a hydrogen atom. To put it another way, their atomic mass will be 16, as compared to a mass value of 1 for the hydrogen atom. Chemists identify this most common kind of oxygen atom as oxygen-16, or O^{16}. Of the remaining oxygen atoms in our sample of 100,000 atoms, 37 will be found to have an atomic mass of 17, and 204 will have a still greater mass, 18 times that of hydrogen. Such "heavier" atoms have additional neutrons present in their nuclei. All isotopes of oxygen have almost identical chemical properties, because they have the same number and arrangement of electrons surrounding their nuclei. But because these isotopes differ in mass, they can be separated and identified by using an instrument called a **mass spectrometer** (spek-TROM·e·ter).

In one of his experiments Kamen supplied a photosynthesizing plant with carbon dioxide in which all of the oxygen of the CO_2 molecules was O^{18}. He found that almost none of the oxygen that the plant released to the atmosphere contained this particular isotope. If, however, he gave the plant *water* molecules in which the oxygen was O^{18}, O^{18} was released to the atmosphere. By using the heavy oxygen isotope, Kamen gave a conclusive answer to our question—the oxygen released in photosynthesis comes from the water that is used, not from the carbon dioxide (Figure 15-9a).

Now that we know the origin of oxygen in photosynthesis, we can go on to a more careful

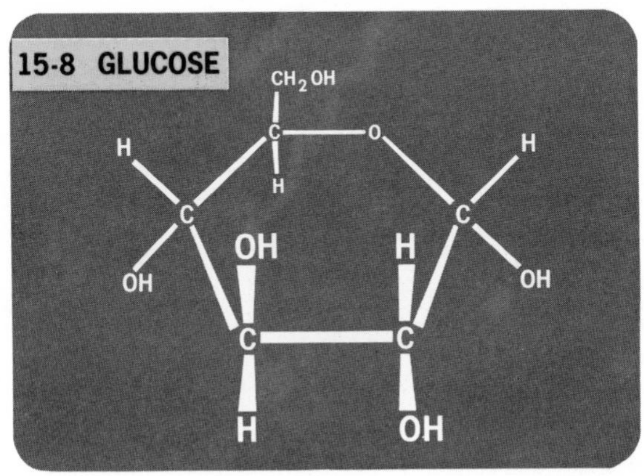

15-8 GLUCOSE

study of how the green plant makes energy-containing glucose molecules. Figure 15-8 shows the chemical structure of a glucose molecule. If you count the carbon atoms, you will find there are six of them. These carbon atoms in the molecule are derived from six carbon dioxide molecules (6 CO_2), one of the raw materials of photosynthesis. Hydrogen atoms are attached either directly (>C< H) or indirectly by bonding to atoms of oxygen (>C< OH). But what is the origin of the hydrogen? Recalling Kamen's experiments confirming Van Niel's hypothesis, we have the answer. The hydrogen must have come from the splitting of water molecules. Count the number of hydrogen atoms in the glucose molecule. You might expect that *six* molecules of water would provide the necessary hydrogen atoms. However, experimental evidence indicates that *twelve* water molecules must be split to provide the hydrogen atoms in glucose. But if 12 H_2O and 6 CO_2 are required for each glucose molecule you might wonder what has happened to all of the extra atoms of hydrogen and oxygen that are not incorporated in the molecule. Although it is difficult to be sure, the extra oxygen and hydrogen atoms probably combine to form water molecules again. They must be removed in some way.

The first steps in photosynthesis, providing hydrogen and electrons (Figure 15-9a), and the putting together of a glucose molecule composed of six carbon, twelve hydrogen, and six oxygen atoms, require considerable energy. If you were asked to tell the origin of the energy, you would say that it was light energy. And this is correct. But there are many other more immediate sources of energy in a cell that also can do the job of synthesis. It is this synthesis—the putting together of the glucose molecule—that we want to talk about next.

15-9 LIGHT REACTION

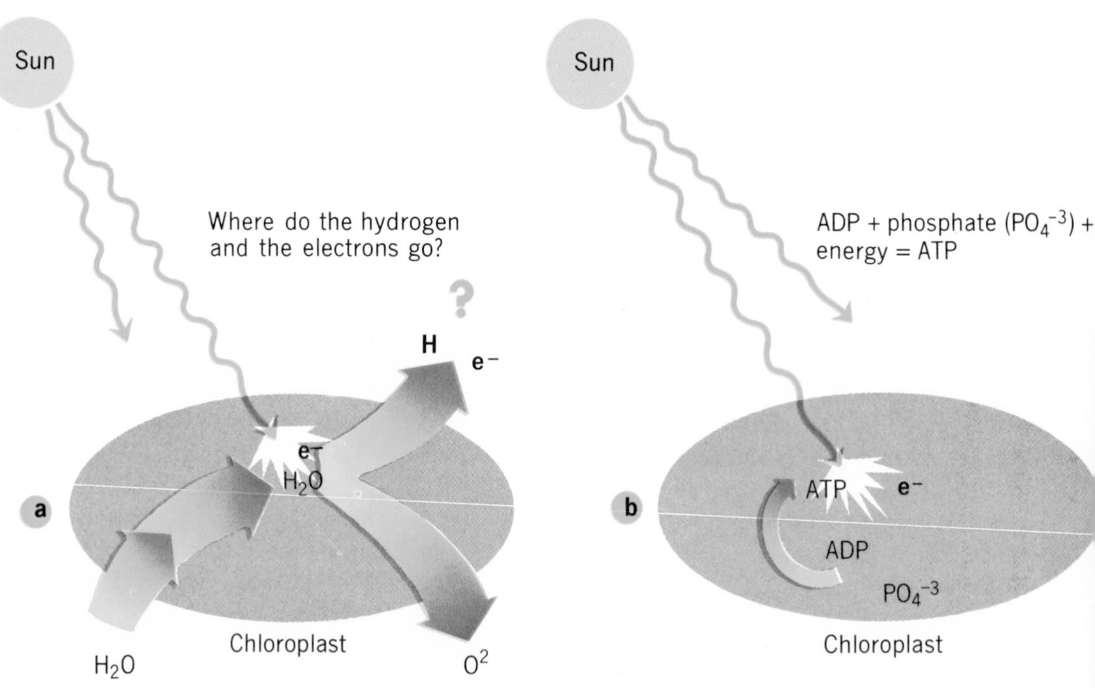

Luckily it is possible to separate some of the steps in glucose synthesis and to investigate them one by one in the laboratory. For example, it has been possible to find out what happens to carbon dioxide in photosynthesis by using radioactive isotopes. Radioactive carbon-14 (C^{14}) can be combined with nonradioactive oxygen to produce carbon-tagged carbon dioxide molecules ($C^{14}O_2$). These, when taken in by the plant, can be detected in very low concentrations by using instruments such as the Geiger-Müller counter.

To use C^{14} for this purpose, the plant is exposed to the radioactive carbon dioxide for controlled periods of time. The period of time may range from less than a second to several minutes. Using sensitive chemical tests, we can then identify the compounds which take part in carbohydrate manufacture from chains of carbon atoms. Much of this work was done by Melvin Calvin and his associates. They found that carbohydrate manufacture in green plants and the enzymes needed for it are not very different from the reactions and enzymes necessary in building carbon compounds in animal cells. At the point where CO_2 enters the photosynthetic process, 5-carbon carbohydrate molecules are already present (Figure 15-10). The carbon atom from the CO_2 joins the 5-carbon compound and a 6-carbon sugar is formed. This 6-carbon product quickly splits into two 3-carbon compounds. It is here that hydrogen and electrons now enter the act. Do you remember where the hydrogen and the electrons came from? If you do not, look at Figure 15-9a once more. The hydrogen and the electrons interact with the 3-carbon compounds and reduce them (see Chapter 6). Other molecules containing carbon appear on the scene. They combine in a series of steps with the reduced 3-carbon compounds and form glucose. In addition to the glucose molecules, 5-carbon carbohydrates are produced that are used to start the cycle all over again. This cycle of events has been named the Calvin cycle. Just as in animal cells, the only thing needed in this cycle, besides starting material and enzymes, is energy. And, as you might guess, only one kind of energy will do for building these carbon chains—the stored chemical energy of ATP. Then where does light fit into the picture? It does not—at this point in photosynthesis. Carbon dioxide can be taken into plant cells and built into carbon chains without light, as long as ATP is available (Figure 15-10). When biologists realized this, they termed these reactions of carbon dioxide uptake, "dark reactions." Of course, in normal plants, dark reactions could take place all of the time, either during the day or the night. They are not dependent on a direct source of light energy.

But where does the cell get the supply of ATP needed in the dark reactions? You may remember from Chapter 6 that ATP can be formed by oxidation of glucose in mitochondria. Could this be the source of ATP for the dark reactions of photosynthesis? Hardly, because if it were, glucose would be broken down and there is net *building*, not *breakdown*, of glucose in photosynthesis.

What other source of energy is available to the cell? You know the answer. It is light energy. An exciting discovery was made a few years ago by Daniel Arnon, studying plant chloroplasts, and Albert W. Frenkel, who was working with pigment-containing structures of photosynthetic bacteria. These pigment-containing structures can absorb light and use its energy to form ATP from ADP and phosphate (Figure 15-9b). These reactions occur even though no carbon dioxide is present so that no carbohydrate can be made! We do not yet know how this ATP is made, although it seems clear that the first step must be absorption of light by photosynthetic pigments. As the pigment molecules absorb light energy, their electrons gain energy. In this way light energy is turned into chemical energy. We do not know how this energy transfer is carried out. It has been suggested that the energy of light "excites" pigment electrons. Excited electrons could be picked up and passed from step to step in an electron transport chain (Chapter 6). This is probably not the same electron transport chain that operates in mitochondria, but it may work in much the same way. According to this hypothesis, as an electron moves from one part of the chain to the next, it leaves some of its energy behind, trapped by the chemical machinery of the chloroplast to build ATP from ADP. As a review, see how many ways you can think of that ATP can be used in the metabolism of a green plant and of an animal.

Perhaps you have wondered what becomes of the electrons that pick up light energy in the first place. If you do ask this question, you will be in good company. Many biologists are eagerly looking for the answer. Some think that a few of the electrons may return to the chlorophyll molecules. Here, when exposed to light again, they will once more gain in energy. Another possibility is that the electrons may be used in reducing the carbon chain compounds formed in the dark reactions. For as we have seen, this is necessary in the formation

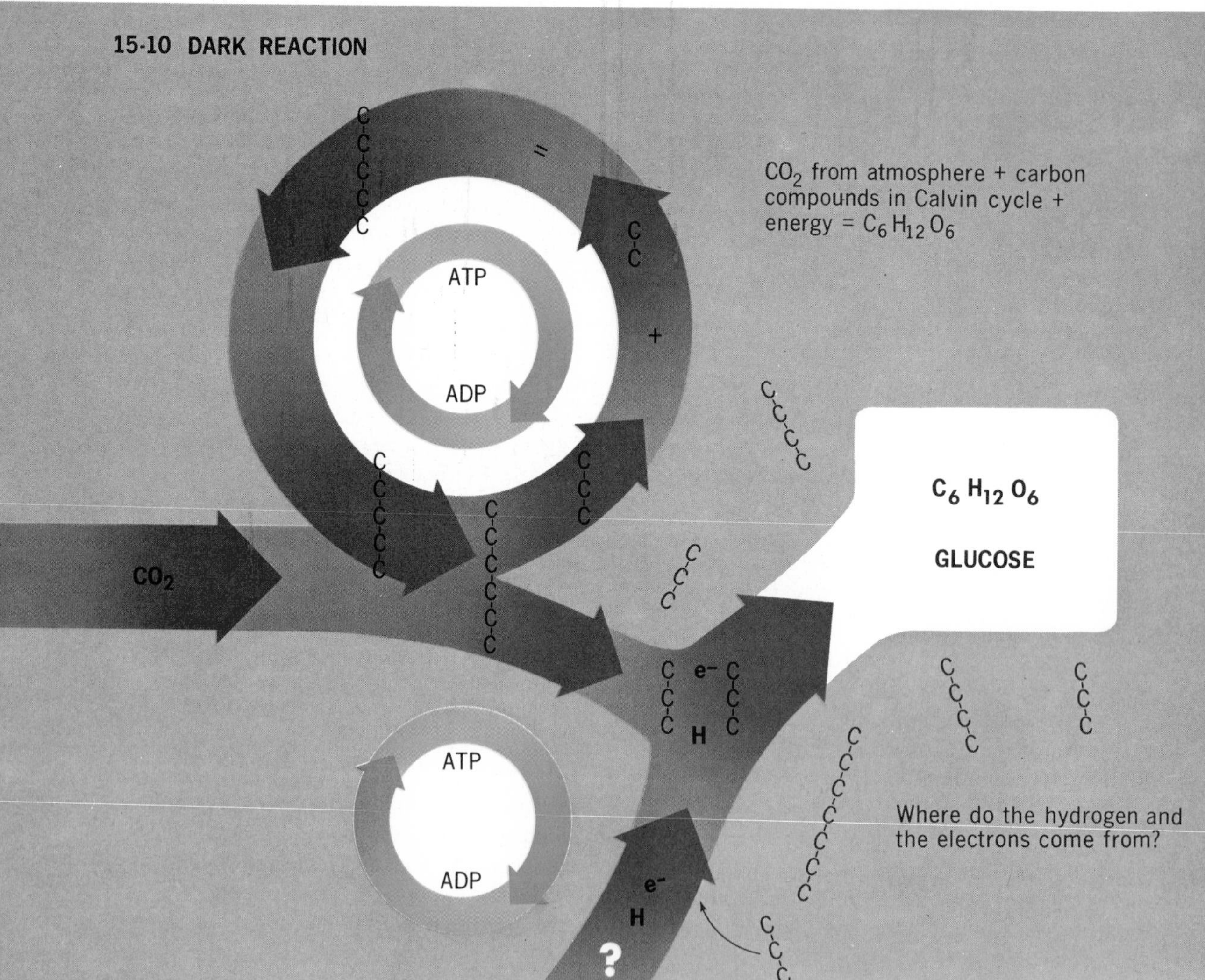

of glucose. It is quite clear, however, that chlorophyll molecules alone cannot be the source of electrons for carbon-chain reduction. These pigments of plant cells do not have enough electrons to spare for this major activity of food production. They must draw electrons from another source. We know that this source must be molecules of water probably split by using the energy of light. Thus, the hydrogen taken from the water must be in the form of hydrogen ions (H^+) and more electrons. We do not know how this happens. One thing is clear, however: the splitting of water molecules is dependent on light. It is a light reaction. Thus, there must be two kinds of light reactions: first, the splitting of water and second, the formation of ATP. These light reactions work together with the dark reactions in photosynthesis.

Summarizing the energy changes and transfers in photosynthesis, we know that light energy can be trapped by pigment molecules in the formation of ATP. Sooner or later this energy is safely stored in the relatively stable molecules of glucose and other carbohydrates that are formed. This is the heart of the photosynthetic process.

We have not forgotten the by-product of photosynthesis—molecular oxygen (O_2). When water molecules are broken down and hydrogen ions and electrons are torn from water, oxygen atoms are left over. Some of these oxygen atoms are built into oxygen molecules and released. But some may remain combined with hydrogen (OH). By combining with one more hydrogen atom, they form water (H-O-H).

We have described some of the experimental evidence which indicates that there are three major kinds of reactions in photosynthesis—carbon chain building, reduction of the carbon chain compounds, and ATP production (Figure 15-11). Perhaps it might sound as if these reactions occur separately in photosynthesis, but this is far from the case. It has taken great experimental effort and ingenuity to separate the processes so that they can be studied independently. In the living, photosynthesizing cell, all the processes take place at once in a beautifully coordinated way and with perfect timing. This coordination must depend in large part on the complex structure of the chloroplast. It explains, too, why, in spite of so much research, we still do not understand this most fundamental of all biological energy transfer processes.

The Amount of Photosynthesis

How much photosynthetic activity is carried on all over the world each year? Here is one estimate that has been made.

$$\underset{\substack{\text{500 billion}\\\text{metric tons}}}{\overset{\text{carbon dioxide}}{6\,CO_2}} + \underset{\substack{\text{410 billion}\\\text{metric tons}}}{\overset{\text{water}}{12\,H_2O}} \longrightarrow$$

$$\underset{\substack{\text{341 billion}\\\text{metric tons}}}{\overset{\text{glucose}}{C_6H_{12}O_6}} + \underset{\substack{\text{205 billion}\\\text{metric tons}}}{\overset{\text{water}}{6\,H_2O}} + \underset{\substack{\text{364 billion}\\\text{metric tons}}}{\overset{\text{oxygen}}{6\,O_2}}$$

The quantities of materials involved are so large that they become almost incomprehensible. Yet each year, only about 1/2,000 of the total available energy received from the sun is captured by plants through photosynthesis. There are, of course, many areas, such as deserts and the tops of high mountains, where lack of water, low temperatures, and other adverse environmental factors permit little or no plant growth. Even plants growing in more favorable regions fix only a relatively small proportion of the energy available. Where, then, does most photosynthesis take place? The answer is indeed surprising—the oceans! Probably 85 percent of all the world's photosynthesis takes place in ocean waters, and another 5 percent in ponds, lakes, and rivers. As much as 90 percent of the total photosynthesis is thus attributable mainly to microscopic, aquatic algae. This estimate becomes more understandable when we remember that about 70 percent of the earth's surface is covered with water. Can you think of any other reasons why an aquatic environment would be more favorable for photosynthesis than land?

15-11 A SUMMARY OF PHOTOSYNTHESIS

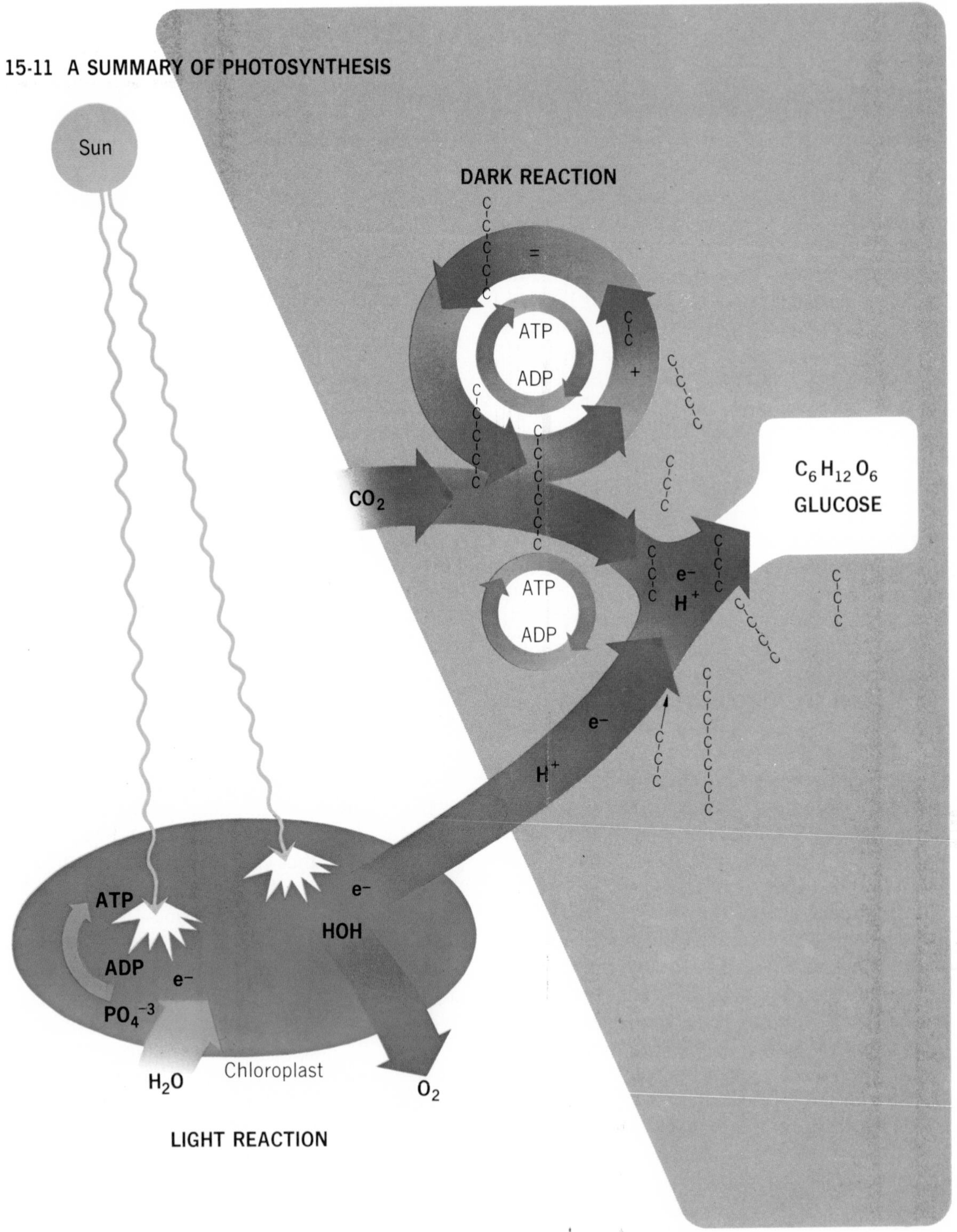

CONCLUDING REMARKS

Before leaving this subject, we should review briefly what happens in photosynthesis and cell energy metabolism. In photosynthesis, light energy is used to *build* organic compounds from carbon dioxide while *splitting* water into hydrogen and oxygen. In cell energy metabolism, electrons and hydrogen ions are *removed* from organic compounds and returned to oxygen to form water. The energy stored in the organic compounds is thus made available for cell activities. You have seen in this chapter and in Chapter 6 that these processes look somewhat like the reverse of one another. Yet they follow very different and complex paths. Although we can summarize them in a few sentences, or in a figure (Figure 15-12), we cannot yet describe them in detail. As in all other animals, our body cells can carry out energy-converting processes which we are only beginning to understand. Plants can carry out all these fundamental processes, and also the whole series involved in trapping light energy.

Much progress has been made in disclosing the secrets of photosynthesis. Yet no one has succeeded in duplicating the process for an extended period of time outside the green cells of living plants. In view of increasing human populations and shortages of food, it is important that scientists find out exactly how photosynthesis works. With this information it may be possible someday to add to the world's food supply by producing carbohydrates synthetically.

This problem is being attacked from many angles by scientists with many different backgrounds. For example:

1. Only certain wavelengths of light are important in photosynthesis, so that we must call on the physicist to help us understand the energy relationships of photosynthesis.
2. We know that carbon dioxide and water are used by plants in the presence of chlorophyll to make glucose. The molecular structure and distribution in the chloroplast of the chlorophylls and other pigments, and of the enzymes and coenzymes, are problems for the biochemist.
3. But how can we be sure about the structure of the chloroplasts unless we see them in finest detail? The efforts of a cytologist, who studies cell structure and who knows how to use an electron microscope, are required.

Thus, the study of a complex process such as photosynthesis requires the combined talents of a great many people.

Although the story is incomplete, many scientists have already fashioned a remarkable story of how green plants manufacture carbohydrates. It is a story of the complementarity of structure and function. The structure is the photosynthetic organ—the leaf of the plant, and its chloroplasts. The leaf is well adapted in its structure to carry out the function of photosynthesis. There are special cells, guard cells, that regulate the exchange of gases between the leaf and the surrounding atmosphere. There are special cells within the leaf that absorb carbon dioxide; these cells also are the ones that contain chloroplasts. The cells with the largest numbers of chloroplasts are oriented in the leaf so as to receive the maximum amount of light. The veins of the leaf are equipped with conducting cells through which water is supplied to the photosynthetic cells, or through which manufactured foods can be moved to other parts of the plant.

How did the leaves of plants become so well adapted to carrying out the function of photosynthesis? We know that the characteristics we find in the leaf of a vascular plant are the result of a long evolution from a primitive kind of vascular plant, which lacked leaves (Chapter 14). Thus, really to understand photosynthesis in plants, we also have to understand the origin and structure of the leaf.

15-12 PHOTOSYNTHESIS AND RESPIRATION

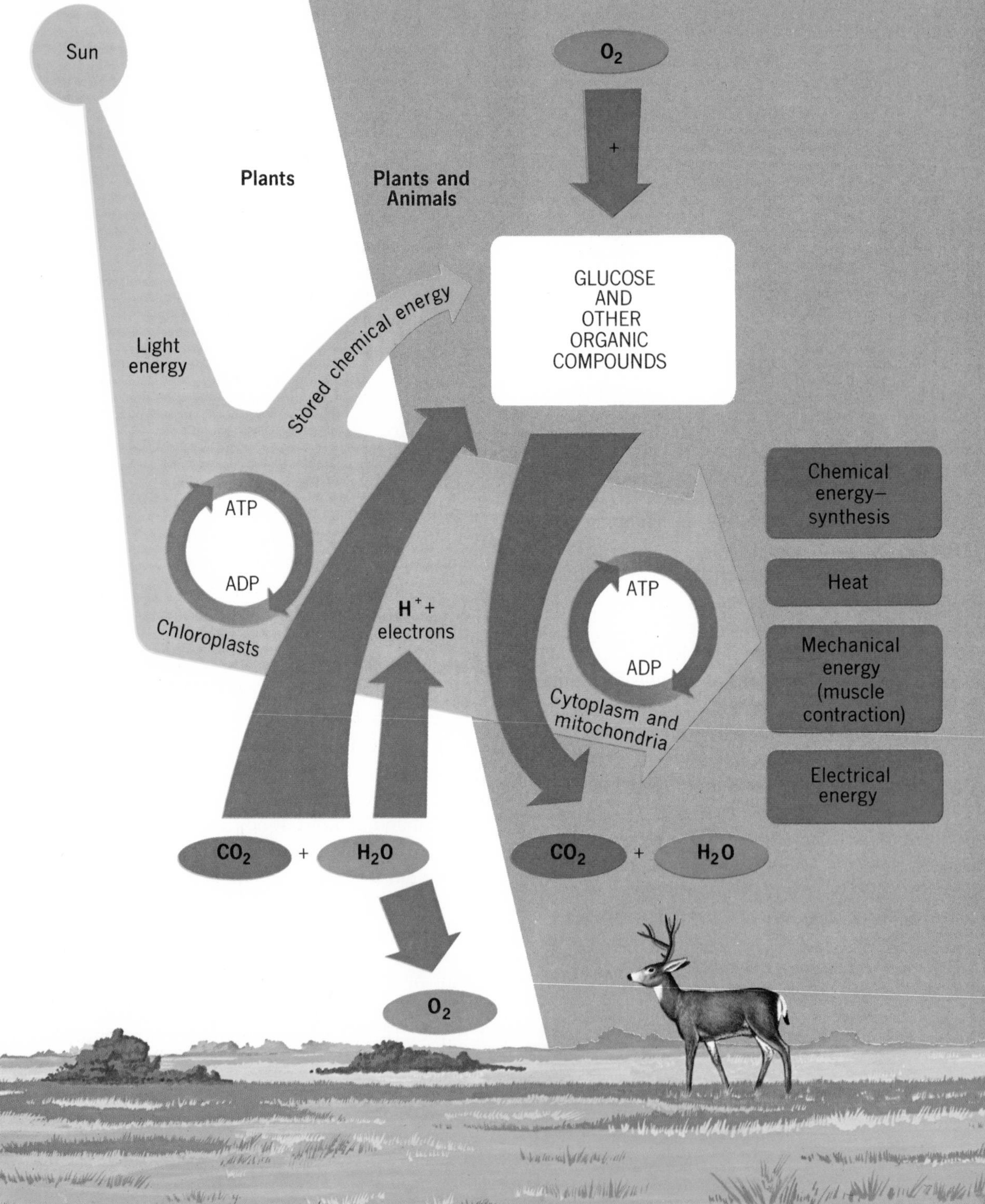

GUIDE QUESTIONS AND PROBLEMS

1. In what way did Van Niel's experiments with photosynthetic bacteria pave the way to our understanding of the light reactions in photosynthesis?
2. What technological advances were necessary before the role of CO_2 in photosynthesis could be understood?
3. What are some of the unsolved problems of photosynthesis? How might the answers help in solving the problem of food production in the world?
4. How are the position of chloroplasts in the leaf, and the general shape of a broad leaf, related to photosynthesis?
5. Describe the utilization of light energy in a chloroplast as we understand it. Where do the light reactions probably occur? Where do the dark reactions occur?
6. When we consider the total energy relationships in living systems, we think of both respiration and photosynthesis. How are these two processes similar? How are they different? How could the rate of photosynthesis be increased? How is a balance achieved between the products of respiration and photosynthesis?
7. How is the leaf structurally adapted to getting the materials needed to carry on photosynthesis and to moving essential manufactured materials to other parts of a plant?
8. The water in small ponds which have great numbers of algae is often depleted of oxygen during certain periods in a 24-hour day, while at other periods the water is saturated with oxygen. What is probably the cause of this fluctuation? When would you expect the CO_2 concentration to be greatest in such ponds? What effect would these fluctuations have on animals living in these ponds?

RELATED READING

Books

For a source of some of the classic papers describing experiments on photosynthesis . . .

Gabriel, M. L., and S. Fogel (editors), *Great Experiments in Biology*, Prentice-Hall, Englewood Cliffs, N. J., 1955.

For a brief, lucid account of plant functions . . .

Galston, A. W., *The Life of the Green Plant*, Second Edition, Foundations of Modern Biology Series, Prentice-Hall, Englewood Cliffs, N. J., 1964.

McElroy, William D., *Cell Physiology and Biochemistry*, Second Edition, Foundations of Modern Biology Series, Prentice-Hall, Englewood Cliffs, N. J., 1964.

For an advanced discussion of photosynthesis . . .

Steward, F. C. (editor), *Plant Physiology*, Academic Press, New York, 1965.

For a source of many plant physiological investigations not requiring elaborate equipment . . .

Machlis, L., and T. G. Torrey, *Plants in Action*, Freeman, San Francisco, 1956.

Magazines

Arnon, D., "The Role of Light in Photosynthesis," *Scientific American*, Volume 203 (November 1960), page 104.

Bassham, J. A., "The Path of Carbon in Photosynthesis," *Scientific American*, Volume 206 (June 1962), page 88.

Gates, D., "Heat Transfer in Plants," *Scientific American*, Volume 213 (December 1965), page 76.

Rabinowitch, E. and Govindjee, "The Role of Chlorophyll in Photosynthesis," *Scientific American*, Volume 213 (July 1965), page 74.

Wald, G., "Life and Light," *Scientific American*, Volume 201 (October 1959), page 92.

16

Stems and Roots — A Study of Complementarity of Structure and Function

Before you read Chapter 15, did you have any idea that a stationary organism such as a tree or a tomato plant could adjust to the changes in its environment? When you read about opening and closing of stomata, you were reading about a mechanism that helps a green land plant to reduce water loss from its leaves at the time when there is no photosynthesis. Without such a mechanism many plants would lose too much water and die. There are many other ways in which the structure of plants is directly related to function. We want to see in what ways there is such a complementarity of structure and function in stems and roots.

THE STEM

The stem of a plant plays two roles of major importance for survival of the plant. First, it provides support for the leaves and other photosynthetic tissues of the shoot. Second, materials are transported in the stem from regions where they are absorbed or produced to other parts of the plant where they are used, stored, or lost.

The Stem Provides Support

First, let us see how the stems of both large and small plants provide the support that makes possible the separation and exposure of leaves to sunlight. What are the forces that this supporting framework must withstand? In the case of land plants they are of two kinds: gravity and wind. How does the stem enable the plant to oppose them successfully?

Actually there are two fairly distinct types of stems. In the first kind, called a **herbaceous** (her·BAY·shus) **stem,** the tissues are relatively soft and easily crushed. Common examples are tomato, geranium, and milkweed. Plants having this kind of stem usually do not become very tall. As in other plants, the cells of their stems have walls that give a little support. However, if they are deprived of water, the stems may wilt, bend, and even collapse entirely. We have seen earlier that the amount of water influences the turgidity of cells in the leaf (Chapter 15). Water also increases cell turgidity and mechanical strength of herbaceous stems.

The second kind of stem, the **woody stem,** derives its mechanical strength from many cells that have stiff, thickened walls. Even when the cells completely dry out, the walls remain strong and maintain their shape. Older woody stems are composed mainly of xylem tissue. This, when sawed into boards, dried, and seasoned, is the wood used for building.

Herbaceous Stems. The shoot of a herbaceous plant is made up of the stem and attached leaves (Figure 16-1). Leaves are attached at different levels along the stem. The points of leaf attachment are called **nodes** (Inquiry 16-1).

Let us examine a cross section of a sunflower stem (Figure 16-2), cut from the midregion between two successive nodes. The basic plan of organization is apparent at a glance. Strands of vascular or conducting tissue run up and down the stem parallel to its axis. These strands are arranged in a circle. They are the **vascular bundles.** Outside the ring of bundles are cells that make up the **cortex** of the stem. Inside the ring of bundles are cells that make up the **pith** region. Cells of pith and cortex are usually thin-walled and living, although thick-walled, dead cells may be found in the outer cortex.

16–1 Part of the shoot of a flowering plant. Besides the growing point at the tip of the shoot, other growing points occur in the angles formed between leaf petioles and the stem.

The outermost region of the stem as seen under higher magnification consists of a single layer of epidermal cells covered with a layer of cutin (Figure 16-2). Guard cells and their associated stomata are also present in the epidermis. Because the outermost *living* cells of the cortex have chloroplasts, the stem is green. Photosynthesis can be carried on in such stems as well as in the leaf.

In a single vascular bundle, we can identify the xylem as a cluster of large, empty cells on the side of the bundle nearest the pith. These thick-walled cells provide support and a means for the conduction of water and soluble materials vertically through the stem. Additional support is provided by thick-walled cells that form a "cap" on each bundle. The xylem and the "caps" form vertical columns, or rods, of supporting tissue arranged in concentric rings in the stem.

Conduction of Materials in Stems

Stems of plants are also adapted to serve as efficient conductors of materials from leaves to roots, and vice versa. What kinds of materials must be transported? In general there are two: (1) water plus dissolved mineral salts, taken in by the roots, and (2) sugars, formed

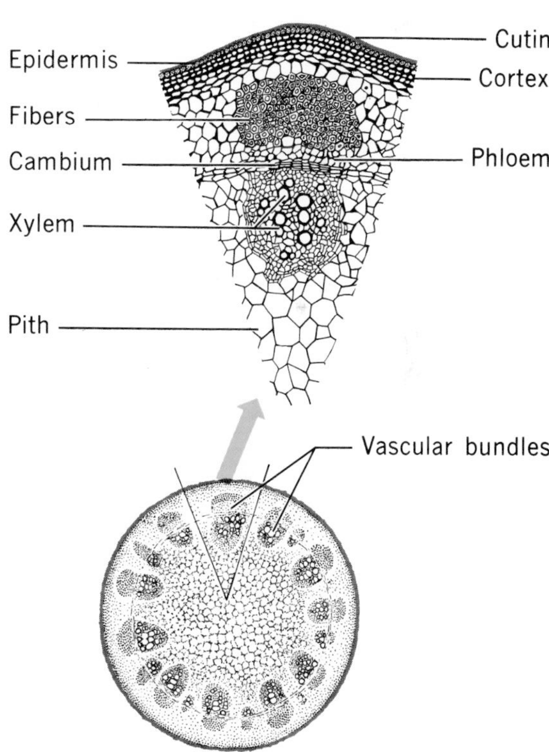

16–2 An internode of a sunflower stem, drawn in cross section. How does the vascular arrangement in a sunflower stem compare with that in a primitive type of stem (Figure 14–13a)?

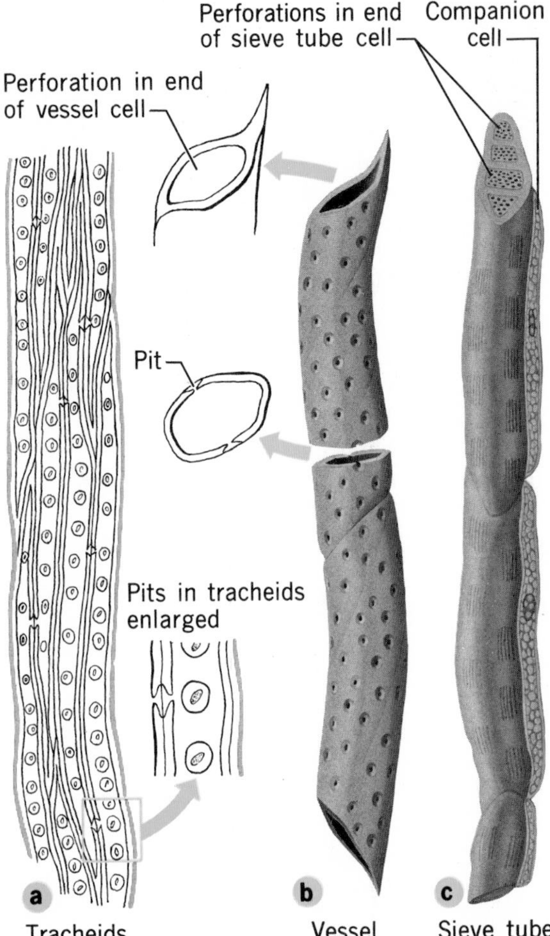

16–3 Some conducting cells of xylem and phloem. **a.** The group of tracheids shown here is in longitudinal section. Conduction in these cells is facilitated by pits in the cell walls. What is another function of tracheids besides conduction? **b.** Two vessel cells are shown from one side. Notice how the cells are situated on top of one another in the makeup of the vessel. What characteristics do vessels and tracheids share? **c.** Conduction in these phloem cells occurs in the sieve tube, probably regulated by the companion cells.

initially in leaves by photosynthesis. Usually the water and salts are transported in an upward direction from the roots, through the stem, and into the leaves. In the summertime, the soluble sugars pass in the reverse direction. Early in the spring, however, food that has been stored in the roots and stem begins to move upward. We say, "The sap is rising," and start to tap the sugar maples.

The structures primarily involved in conducting water and dissolved substances are of two types. They are **tracheids** (TRAY·key·idz) and **vessels.** These two structures, together with strong cells, make up the xylem tissue of a vascular bundle (Figure 16-2). Tracheids are elongated single cells that in the course of their development have formed thickened walls and then died. Figure 16-3a shows in longitudinal section a group of tracheids as they relate to one another in their arrangement.

The contents of tracheid cells eventually disappear, and their cellulose walls become freely permeable to both water and dissolved substances. Thus these substances can readily pass into, through, and out of the tracheids. Thin areas called **pits** occur at many points in the walls of these dead cells. In many cases the pits in two adjoining cells are exactly opposite each other, so that only a thin layer of wall material separates them. Water and dissolved salts can easily pass from one tracheid into another through these thin-walled areas.

The second kind of conducting structure in the xylem, the vessel, is made up of a long line of elongated, thick-walled cells, which are joined end to end. At a late stage in their development, holes are formed by the digesting away of the walls at the ends of the cells. The cell contents, like those of the tracheids, disappear. In this way, the vessels become hollow, elongated pipes running up through the stem, parallel to its axis (Figure 16-3b).

Because water and salts in solution can pass from one end of a vessel to the other without having to pass even through pits, the vessels are much more efficient conducting structures than are tracheids. Both tracheids and vessels form a connected system of conducting channels running from the roots, up through the stem, and out into the veins of the leaves.

The conduction of dissolved sugars from leaf to stem to root takes place principally through long lines of phloem cells, which make up structures called **sieve tubes.** A portion of a sieve tube is shown in Figure 16-3c.

As the sieve tubes develop, a large number of small perforations appear in their end walls. Cytoplasmic connections run through the openings and thus make the cytoplasm continuous from cell to cell. In the final stages of development of a sieve tube, the nuclei in the cells disintegrate. The cytoplasm, however, remains alive as long as the sieve tube continues to function. The cells that make up a sieve tube are in close association with one or more smaller companion cells, which do have nuclei. These companion cells are believed to regulate the activity of adjacent sieve tube cells.

Like the xylem, the sieve tubes of the phloem form an interconnected system which reaches all organs of the plant. Through it, sugars formed in the green tissues are distributed to all the nongreen cells of shoot and root, which are totally dependent upon the sieve tubes for a supply of food.

Located between the xylem and phloem of the sunflower vascular bundle, there is a third kind of tissue, the **cambium** (KAM·bee·um—Figure 16-2). The cambium is made up of a zone of thin-walled cells, which continue to divide during the period when the stem is growing. The outermost cells thus formed by the cambium develop into phloem cells (sieve tubes and companion cells); those formed toward the inside develop into additional tracheids and vessels of the xylem.

Woody Stems. The stems of woody plants grow not only in height but also in diameter from year to year. The trunk, branches, and leaves of a mature maple or oak tree, after fifty years' growth, may weigh many tons. The entire structure may be over 30 meters (100 feet) high and extend out from the trunk for perhaps 12 meters (40 feet) or more. The development of a strong, massive, supporting framework is obviously required for adequate support of such a structure. A diagram of a cross section of a typical woody stem (Figure 16-4a) will show how it is constructed.

If we cut through the trunk of a large tree, at right angles to its axis, the exposed surfaces will be approximately circular in outline. The outermost layer in such a section is the **bark.** It is less compact than the inner parts of the trunk, which are made up of wood. A microscopically thin zone of small cells, the cambium, separates the bark from the wood. Because the cells in this zone are mechanically weak, we can in most cases peel the bark from the wood. The outer region of the wood is light in color. Inside this region of the trunk, there is dark-colored wood. If we smooth the rough, cut surface of the trunk with fine sandpaper, and then apply water to it, we can see that the wood is made up of many successive layers of cells, like a series of concentric rings.

This much we can see with the unaided eye. To learn more, we must examine, with a microscope, thin sections taken from various regions of the trunk. You have already prepared and examined a thin section of cork (Figure 3-7) in the laboratory (Inquiry 3-1), just as Robert Hooke did. In this case you used material obtained from the cork oak, in which very thick layers of bark are formed. The cells of cork have walls that are impregnated with a waterproofing material that forms a barrier which effectively limits water loss from inner tissues of the trunk.

Now let us examine a section that includes tissues from the inner bark, cambium, and the outer regions of the wood (Figure 16-4b). Here many different types of cells can be seen. The wood tissue, or xylem, is made up of cells having strong, resistant walls. Two of these types, tracheids and vessels, have already been described. In addition to these there are large numbers of fibers. These are elongated cells, small in cross section, which have particularly thick walls. These cells contribute greatly to the strength of the wood. Running out from the center of the trunk are radially arranged thin-walled cells serving for storage and transverse conduction. All of these different kinds of cells are formed by divisions of the cells of cambium.

When trees are dormant during the winter or periods of drought, few new cells are formed. When growth resumes in the spring, cells in the cambium begin to divide rapidly, forming the first cells of a new **annual ring.** These cells are larger than those produced later during the summer. This difference in size of cells results in the ringlike pattern that is characteristic of woody stems growing in temperate climates. Annual rings are not as evident in the wood of tropical plants. Can you suggest a reason for this?

In the temperate regions of the world, a new ring of xylem tissue is produced by the cambium during each growing season. By counting the number of rings in the stump of a tree, therefore, we can determine quite accurately the age of the tree at the time it was cut.

Division of cambium cells in a tree trunk proceeds in both directions. The outermost of the dividing cambium cells become transformed into the phloem tissues of the bark, including sieve tubes with companion cells, fibers, and thin-walled cells. Cells in the outer portions divide and give rise to the layers of cork or bark.

What has this examination of the structure of stems shown us? We have seen that most of the tissue composing a woody stem is vascular tissue. In a herbaceous stem the relative amount of vascular tissue may be less, but its importance is not. For it is through the vascular tissues of the stem that leaves are supplied with water—one of the essentials of photosynthesis. This water along with dissolved substances is, in turn, supplied from the roots. Let us now examine this and other relationships between the root and stem.

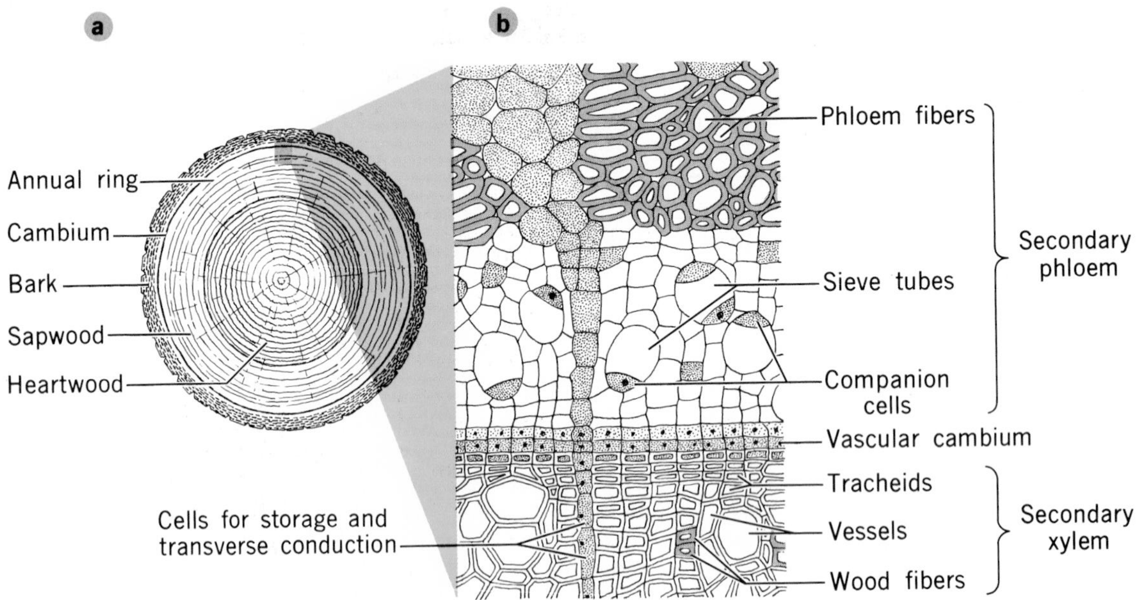

16–4 **a.** A drawing of a cross section through a woody stem. This type of stem is characteristic of oaks, maples, elms, and many other familiar trees. **b.** An enlargement of part of the cross section, showing the relationship between the vascular cambium and the phloem and xylem. What is the origin of the layer of living cells shown on each side of the cambium layer? What will happen to these layers of cells?

THE ROOT

All of us who have ever tried to pull up weeds in a garden, or remove dandelions from a lawn, know that roots anchor plants firmly in the soil. When we look at an uprooted plant, we may see a ball of dirt at its lower end composed of a tough system of roots plus attached soil. This is a **fibrous root system** (Figure 16-5a), typical of grasses, beans, clover, and many other kinds of plants. When we look at the roots of dandelions or carrots, however, we find a single, long, tapering **taproot** (Figure 16-5b), which has only a few small branch roots and very little soil adhering to it. In both cases, most of the root system has remained in the soil. If we had used a stream of water to wash the soil away, the smaller branch roots would have remained attached, and the root system would appear entirely different. A small rye plant (60 cm, or 2 feet, high), with its root system carefully removed from the soil, was found to have about 14 million primary roots and branches with a total length of about 600 kilometers (380 miles). The total surface area of its root system was calculated to be more than 600 square meters (6,500 square feet).

In addition to anchoring the plant, root systems perform two other vital functions. First, they absorb water and soluble nutrient salts from the soil. Second, they provide conducting tissues for distributing these substances to the tissues of the shoot. (Inquiry 16-2 will acquaint you with roots and their functions.)

The principal conducting and strengthening tissues of the root are grouped together at its center to form a rod-shaped core. This core extends throughout the length of the root. If we cut a cross section of a root and examine it under the microscope, this central core of tissue is readily seen (Figure 16-6).

The xylem of this central core has the form of a fluted column, which in cross section may show three to five arms radiating from the center. Vertical strands of phloem tissue are located in concave regions of the flutings. In

a United States Department of Agriculture

b Hugh Spencer

16–5 Two principal types of root systems: **a,** the fibrous root system of a common grass, and **b,** the taproot system of garden beets.

their arrangement, the tissues of the root present quite a different pattern from that found in stems (Figure 16-2). Outside the centrally located xylem and phloem, there is a narrow layer of thin-walled cells, the **pericycle** (PEHR-ih·sy·k'l). The branch roots originate from this tissue. A single layer of cells, the **endodermis** (EN·doe·der·mis) or "inner skin," with walls showing a distinctive pattern of thickening, surrounds the pericycle layer. The remaining tissues of the root consist of a broad zone of large, thin-walled cells making up the cortex. The cortex is bounded on the outside by a single layer of smaller epidermal cells.

If we examine a root tip (Figure 16-7a) from which most of the soil particles have been removed, we can see two other features of roots. The root tip is covered with a layer of loosely attached, dead, or dying cells that form a **root cap.** These cells protect the underlying delicate cells of the root apex from injury as the tip is being forced through the soil by the elongation of cells located immediately behind the tip. As root cap cells are sloughed off, they are replaced by dividing cells of the root tip. A little further back from the tip, many delicate *root hairs* extend out from the surface, giving the tip a fuzzy appearance. From what tissue do the root hairs originate (Inquiry 16-2)?

Absorption of Materials by Roots

The root hairs grow out into the spaces between soil particles. In a typical well-watered soil, each soil particle is surrounded by a thin layer of water containing a variety of dissolved salts. These soluble substances are principally derived from the soil particles and the metabolic processes of other living organisms in the soil.

In soils that are not completely saturated with water, there are many air spaces between the irregularly shaped soil particles. The root hairs with their thin, pliable walls come into direct contact with the soil water and the gases held in spaces between the particles of soil. The thin walls and cytoplasmic membranes of the root hairs are permeable to gases, water,

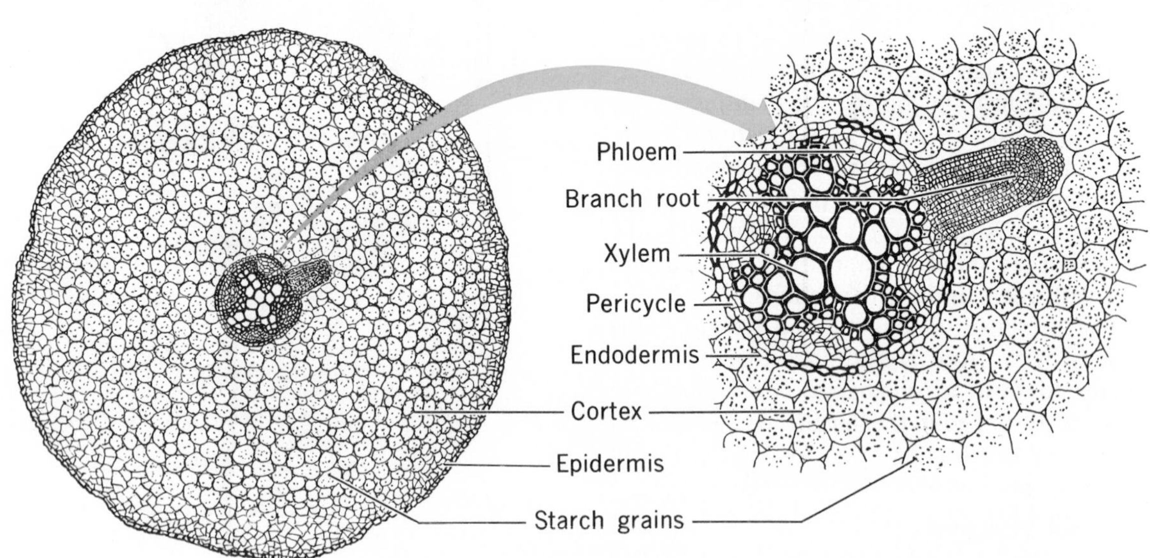

16–6 An enlarged cross section of a buttercup root, with the vascular core and a young branch root further enlarged at the right. Compare this arrangement of tissues with that of the stem in Figure 16–2. On the basis of the vascular structure, which do you think would be the most effective supporting organ—the root or the stem?

and the ions formed from the soluble salts. Oxygen that has diffused into the air spaces from the atmosphere, or has been carried to the root hair in solution in soil water, is readily available. The oxygen diffuses into the root hair, where it may either be used in respiration or be passed on to the living cells deeper inside the root. Because of the respiratory activity in living root cells, the concentration of oxygen is normally higher outside the root than inside; the oxygen therefore continues to diffuse from the surrounding soil into the root cells.

The ions of mineral salts are also taken in and used to form a wide variety of compounds essential for the continuing existence of the plant. Plants, like animals, require compounds that contain a number of different elements in addition to carbon, hydrogen, and oxygen, which are fixed by photosynthesis. As you already have learned, nitrogen is essential for the synthesis of all proteins; sulfur is present in many kinds of proteins. Phosphorus is needed for nucleotides and nucleic acids. Calcium is needed to form the compounds that serve as a cement to hold the cells of the entire plant body together. You will recall, too, that each molecule of chlorophyll requires one atom of magnesium. Iron atoms are not incorporated in chlorophyll itself, but for some reason plants cannot synthesize chlorophyll unless adequate amounts of iron-containing compounds are present. Plants growing in soils deficient in potassium salts may be stunted. Their leaves have yellowed margins and spots of dead tissue.

In addition to the elements mentioned above, traces of other elements must be available. Copper, zinc, boron, manganese, and molybdenum are all necessary for the life of plants. These and other trace elements may serve as necessary components of enzymes or coenzymes without which the plant would die.

Conduction of Materials in Roots

After the ions of essential salts have been absorbed by the root hairs, they diffuse through the living cells of the cortex to the central

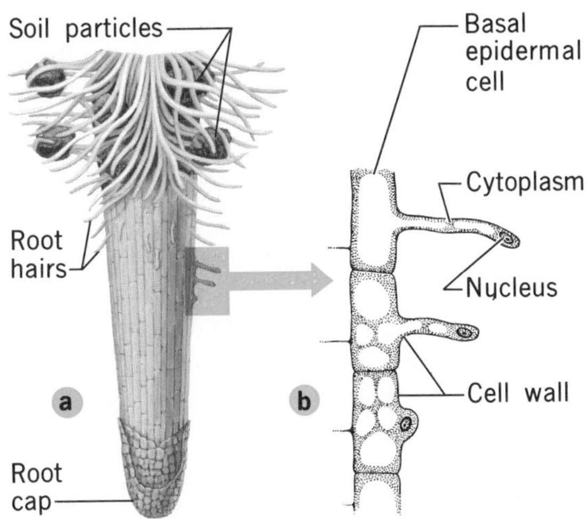

16–7 a. External features of a root. The root cap protects the growing tip from injury. Why is this protection needed? **b.** Root hairs on epidermal cells above the root tip add greatly to the total cell surface directly exposed to soil and water. How does this benefit the plant?

cylinder of conducting tissue. Here, dissolved in water which is being moved from the root up through the shoot, they are finally distributed to all other living tissues of the plant.

As the root absorbs ions in soil water, the concentration of ions inside the root approaches that of the surrounding soil water. When this happens, the rate of uptake of ions may slow down. Once absorbed and transported to the various organs of the plant, some of the ions are quickly incorporated into the structure of organic molecules. Such a synthesis of molecules requires energy from respiration (see Chapter 6), and most plants, like animals, require oxygen for this process. Thus the rate at which ions are taken in by the roots depends upon the amount of oxygen that is available for respiration. Because roots are usually well supplied with oxygen, concentrations of ions many times greater than those present in the soil water may accumulate in the root cells. When this happens, the energy released from rapid respiration in the root cells is used to prevent diffusion of the accumulated ions back into the soil. Just how this energy-requiring mechanism operates is still not clear.

The movement of materials from one part of the plant to another involves forces affecting the entire plant. Associated with an understanding of the mechanisms involved, there are related problems concerned with the storage of various substances that are needed not only for the survival of the individual plant but also for the continuation of the species. Let us consider the mechanisms and the problems.

MOVEMENT AND STORAGE OF MATERIALS

As far as we know, the tallest living tree is a California redwood 118 meters (385 feet) high. The leaves at the top of this tree, and others of similar size, are supplied with water absorbed through millions of root hairs buried in the ground over a hundred meters below. During each growing season, tons of water move into, through, and out of one of these tremendous organisms. Where does the energy come from? By what mechanism is it applied to so enormous a task? Much of the story remains to be learned, but the main outlines can be readily understood (Inquiry 16-3).

Let us start by recalling an experience familiar to all of us. When we go to the corner soda fountain to drink an ice cream soda, we are usually supplied with a straw for the purpose. We suck the liquid up through the straw, and the liquid level in the glass drops.

Now let us try another, less familiar experiment (Figure 16-8a). This time let us place a container of water on the ground next to the wall of the school building. We can, if we wish, add dye to the water to make it more easily visible. We climb up to the roof, almost 14 meters (45 feet) above the ground, and using a long piece of plastic tubing as a straw, we attempt to draw up some of the water. Try as we may, we find that we cannot. Next, we go down the hall to the physics laboratory, borrow a vacuum pump, connect it to the tubing, turn on the pump, and try again. This is also unsuccessful. If our school is located near sea level, we will find that the highest level to which we can draw the liquid is 10.36 meters (34 feet). In Denver, Colorado, where the altitude is approximately 1,520 meters (about one mile) the vacuum pump could raise the water in the tube only about 8.5 meters (28 feet). There are definite limits, therefore, to the height that liquids can be lifted by pumps. How, then, does a tree ten or fifteen times higher than this limit manage to draw up the water it must have to survive?

Why could we not get the water to go any higher in the tube? Why did the water move up the tube in the first place? The answers are not difficult to discover. By removing air in the tube above the water by means of mouth or pump, we created a difference in air pressure. The surface of the liquid in the container was subjected to a higher pressure than that present in the tube. Thus the liquid in the tube rose.

The pressure of the atmosphere at sea level amounts to about 1.033 kilograms per square centimeter (14.7 pounds per square inch). In a plastic tube with a cross section of 1 square centimeter, with air removed at the upper end, air pressure on the surface of the liquid at the lower end will force 1.033 kilograms of water up the tube—a column 10.36 meters high.

Ascent of Water in a Plant

Suppose we try a new experiment (Figure 16-8b). This time we take a leafy shoot and insert the cut end into a piece of rubber tubing. We then connect the other end of the tubing to a slender piece of water-filled glass tubing 14 meters (about 45 feet) long and only a fraction of a millimeter in diameter. We must make certain that there are no leaks in the system. Then, as a last step, we dip the lower end of the tube into a container of boiled water in which some dye has been dissolved. Later we will see why the water must be boiled (Inquiry 16-3).

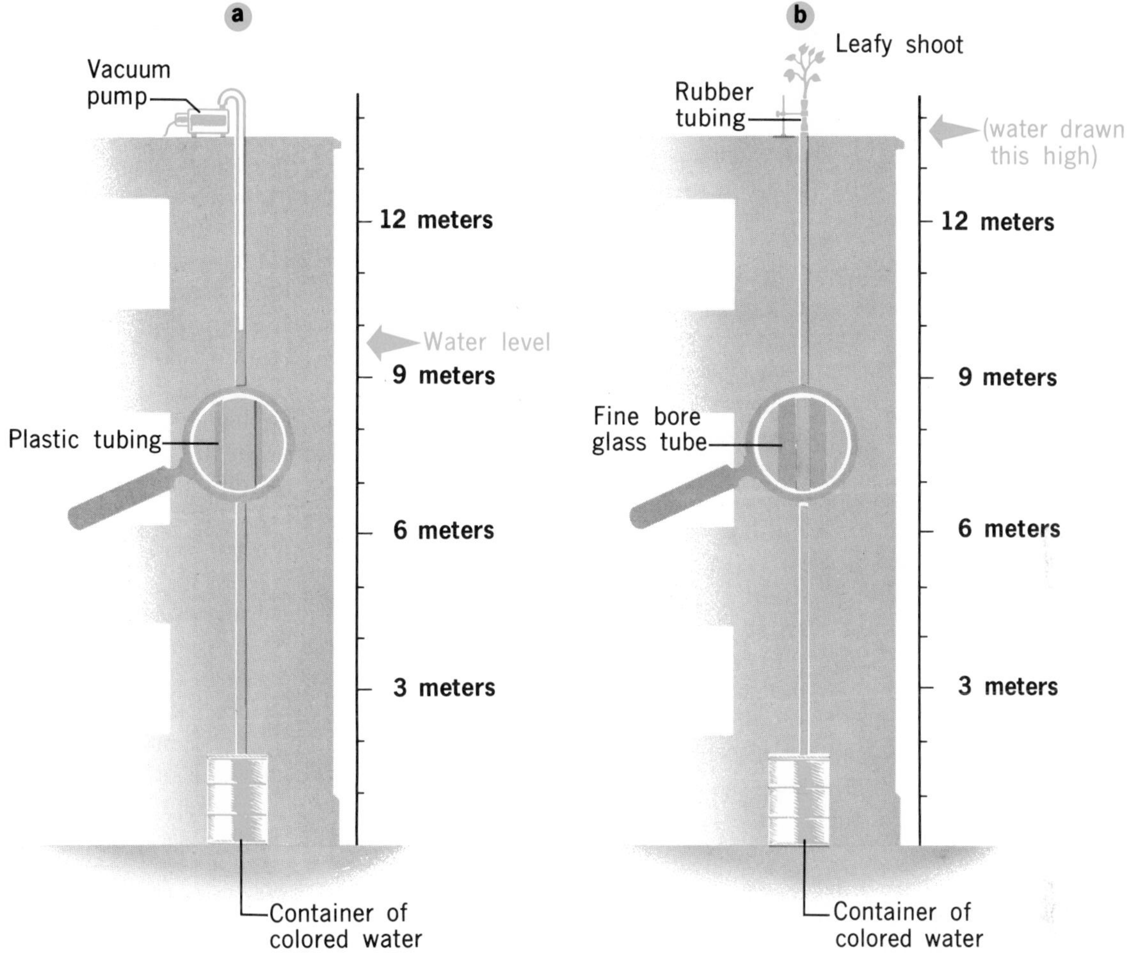

16–8 a. An experiment to test the height to which water in a partial vacuum can be raised by atmospheric pressure. Why will the water not reach the vacuum pump? **b.** Note the modifications in the experimental plan. The pump has been replaced by the shoot of a plant, and the plastic tubing has been replaced by a fine-bore glass tube. How do these modifications affect the experiment and its outcome?

When completed, the apparatus consists of a continuous, connected system filled with water. The system begins with the leaf cells, continues down through the xylem vessels of the veins and branch, to the water in the long, thin glass tube, and ends with the water in the container on the ground. As we watch, the colored water from the container on the ground begins to rise rapidly. It reaches first the 3-, then the 6-, 9-, and finally the 14-meter level, more than 3 meters (10 feet) higher than we could raise the column in our experiment using a vacuum pump. How is this possible?

The answer lies in an unusual property of water, which has a strength similar to that of steel wire *under the following conditions*:

1. The water must be held in a tube (or tubes) of small diameter.

2. The walls of the tube must be made of a material to which the water molecules will adhere.
3. The water under tension must not contain any appreciable amount of dissolved gases, which would come out of solution and form bubbles—causing breaks in the column.

Under these conditions, if water is pulled at the upper end of the column, the pull will be transmitted throughout the column. More water will move in at the bottom as it moves out at the top. Water in columns many times 10 meters in length can thus be moved upward, because it is literally pulled up, rather than being pushed up by atmospheric pressure.

In the living tree, a single column of cells in the network of xylem vessels corresponds to the thin-bore glass tubing of our experiment. The supplies of water in the soil in contact with the root surfaces correspond to the boiled water in the container on the ground. What force supplies the pull at the upper end of the column? Sugars produced by photosynthesizing leaf cells are at a higher level of concentration within these cells than in the rest of the plant. As water evaporates from the cells of the spongy and palisade layers of the leaf and passes out through the stomata, the concentration of soluble materials in the leaf cells increases. When this happens, water moves by osmosis into the leaf cells from the xylem vessels and tracheids of the leaf. As this water moves in, cohesion between water molecules in the leaf cells and those in the xylem tissues makes possible the development of forces that pull water into the root, up the stem, and out into the leaves (Figure 16-9).

Movement of Materials in Phloem

As previously mentioned, energy-rich sugars produced by photosynthesis are moved from the leaf through the sieve tubes of the phloem to other parts of the plant. At the present time there is no generally accepted explanation of the mechanism of such movement. We do know that the movement may be many thousands of times more rapid than could occur by simple diffusion. If the phloem tissues are killed by heat or chemicals, the movement is blocked. Although the direction of movement is usually from the leaf, down the stem, and into the root, movement in the reverse direction is frequently observed. In many cases the direction of movement seems to contradict the laws of diffusion. In sugar beets, for example, the sugars are moved downward for storage in the enlarged roots, where the concentration of sugars is already far higher than in other regions of the plant. For this sugar transport to take place, energy derived from respiration is required. The exact mechanism involved, however, remains unknown.

Energy and the Movement of Materials

What is the source of the energy needed to move tons of water dozens of meters or hundreds of feet against the force of gravity, or to cause sugars to accumulate contrary to the laws of diffusion? The answer should not really surprise you. Directly or indirectly the energy comes from sunlight. The energy-rich substances present in the green leaf cells are all produced by photosynthesis.

Evaporation of water from the tissues of the leaf—the phenomenon bringing about the upward movement of water—requires heat, again representing energy originally absorbed by the leaf in the form of sunlight. The energy released by respiration and used in the transport of sugars in the phloem, if traced back through the biochemical pathways of energy transfer, will ultimately be found to be that originally trapped by light-absorbing chlorophyll molecules. Thus, the energy of the sun is the driving force responsible for the flow of water and of foods throughout the plant.

Storage of Materials

In order to survive, plants must have food and water. It is not surprising to find that many

16-9 WATER MOVEMENT IN A PLANT

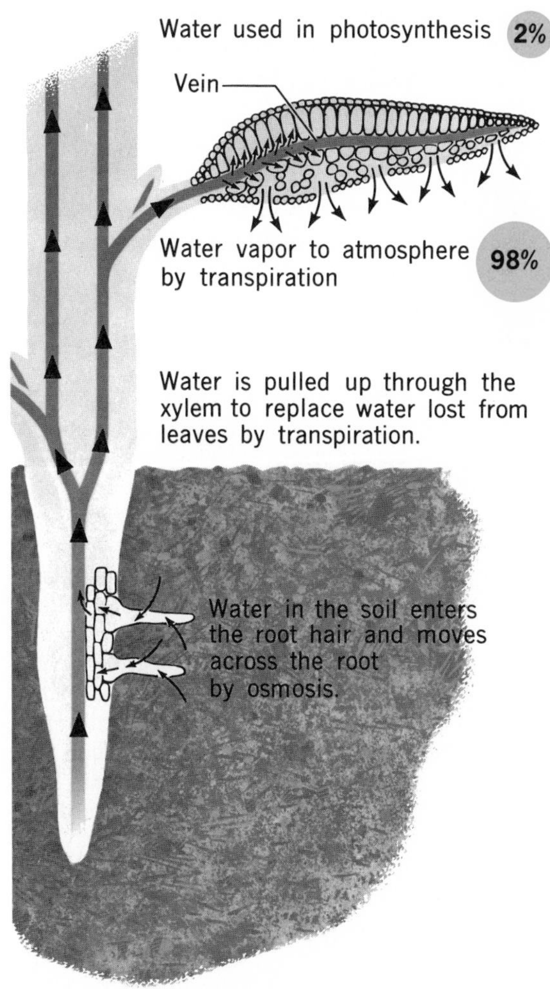
Water used in photosynthesis
2%
Vein
Water vapor to atmosphere by transpiration
98%
Water is pulled up through the xylem to replace water lost from leaves by transpiration.
Water in the soil enters the root hair and moves across the root by osmosis.

plants have specialized structures for storing these vital materials.

In a desert, rain may fall only a few times each year. A cactus plant must, however, have water continuously available if it is to survive, grow, and reproduce. The roots of the cactus extend out from the plant and cover a wide area, only a short distance below the soil surface. Water absorbed by this system is transported back to the main body of the plant, which is actually a very much thickened stem. Most of the volume of the cactus stem is made up of enlarged, thin-walled cells. Water is taken in by these cells and held in their vacuoles. Here it may be stored for long periods and be slowly released as it is needed for photosynthesis.

Foods produced by the plant in excess of what is needed for maintenance, growth, and repair are available for storage. In a corn plant, for example, the food budget can be estimated approximately as follows:

	Percentage of Total Foods Manufactured
Foods used to supply energy	25
Foods used for growth and repair	50
Foods stored	25

Stored foods are accumulated in the form of carbohydrates, proteins, fats, and oils.

In the case of the roots, stems, and leaves, most of the food is stored in the form of carbohydrates. As you are no doubt well aware, Irish, or white, potatoes contain large quantities of starch (a carbohydrate). When you eat onions, you obtain food in the form of another carbohydrate, the sugar sucrose, which is stored in the thickened leaves of this fleshy bulb. Roots in which large amounts of stored sugars or starches are present include sugar beets, sweet potatoes, and turnips.

Proteins, fats, and oils, in addition to carbohydrates, are usually stored in seeds and fruits, the parts of the plant resulting from sexual reproduction. Human beings are so dependent upon these structures for a large proportion of their food that it is possible to classify various civilizations according to their dependence upon particular kinds of cereal grains (wheat, rice, corn, oats, barley), which have served as sources of food for thousands of years. We thus can recognize the rice civilizations of the Far East, the wheat civilizations of the lands bordering on the Mediterranean Sea, and the corn civilizations of the New World.

In these grains, the starches, sugars, proteins, and oils (an oil is simply a form of fat that is liquid at room temperatures) are present in abundance. These foods are thus available to the plant for growth and development of the embryonic parts within the seed. In the next chapter, we will study the events that take place during seed germination and early stages of growth.

CONCLUDING REMARKS

Clearly there is a very intimate interdependence between stem, roots, and leaves in their particular functions. For example, photosynthesis in the leaf would be impossible without roots to absorb the required water and a stem to support the leaves and move the water to them. Conversely, without photosynthesis to manufacture food for development of the plant, there would be no root cells to absorb water and no stem to conduct water to the leaves.

We have learned that stems of plants are well constructed for support, conduction, and storage. Some stems are even photosynthetic. The stem and its branches support the leaves and reproductive structures, giving the leaves maximum exposure to light and carbon dioxide, and giving the reproductive structures elevated positions from which seeds and fruits can be dispersed.

The supporting structures of a stem may be fibers found in the cortex and phloem, or wood cells of various kinds. Some support, especially in herbaceous stems, is derived from the turgidity of living cells. The supporting stems and branches, of course, are anchored in the ground by the roots.

Roots, stems, and leaves are all provided with conducting tissues. These tissues form a continuous system from near the tip of the root to the tip of the uppermost leaf. The principal conducting tissues are xylem and phloem. Tracheids and vessels are dead cells of the xylem that conduct water and soluble minerals, usually upward.

Excess soluble carbohydrate (glucose) manufactured in the leaves is conducted downward through the sieve tubes in the phloem of the leaves, stem, and roots. In the stem and roots the excess food is stored, usually in the living cells of the cortex. Here the sugars are converted into starch as reserve food supplies to be used later by the plant in repair and replacement of old cells, and in development of new cells, including those of reproductive structures such as flowers, seeds, and fruits.

GUIDE QUESTIONS AND PROBLEMS

1. Describe what modifications you would expect to find in the structure of a water lily stem; the stem of a cactus plant.
2. What would happen to the rate of movement of water in a plant on a day that is rainy and cool? on a day so hot and dry that the plant wilts?
3. Why is evolution of vascular cambium considered important to the success of land plants?
4. Why is atmospheric pressure alone not enough to raise water to the tops of tall trees? What other factors help to explain the rise of water?
5. If a branch is girdled (a strip of bark including phloem tissue is removed from around the branch) just below a flower, the flower may produce a fruit larger than usual, but if a girdle is made just above the flower, the flower may wilt and die without producing a fruit. Why?

RELATED READING

Books

See references at the end of Chapter 15.

Magazines

Biddulph, S., and Orlin Biddulph, "The Circulatory System in Plants," *Scientific American*, Volume 200 (February 1959), page 44.

Gates, D., "Heat Transfer in Plants," *Scientific American*, Volume 213 (December 1965), page 76.

Greulach, V. A., "The Rise of Water in Plants," *Scientific American*, Volume 187 (October 1952), page 78.

Zimmermann, M. H., "How Sap Moves in Trees," *Scientific American*, Volume 208 (March 1963), page 132.

17

Reproduction and Development in Flowering Plants

Many kinds of plants and animals are capable of producing offspring by asexual as well as by sexual methods of reproduction. The primary distinction between the two kinds of reproduction is that sexual reproduction involves an alternation of meiosis and a fusion of gametes; asexual reproduction involves no meiosis and no fusion of gametes, but rather the formation of offspring from vegetative organs of the parent organism. Let us consider some examples of asexual reproduction in flowering plants.

ASEXUAL REPRODUCTION

Each spring, when farmers prepare "seed" potatoes for planting, they cut each potato into several pieces. Each piece includes one or more "eyes." The eyes are easy to see on the surface of the potato, since each one lies in a slight depression.

When the pieces of potato are planted, the eyes develop into leafy shoots, drawing upon the water, starch, and other nutrients stored in the piece of potato.

Soon roots appear at the lower end of each shoot, and before long the new plants are well established (Figure 17-1a). From one potato, quite a number of new plants can be propagated in this way.

In the mature banana plant, shoots (or "sword suckers") grow up to the surface of the ground from the underground stem (Figure 17-1b). These can be detached and planted. After a year or more they, too, will have developed into treelike plants bearing a large cluster of fruits.

In pineapple culture in Hawaii, "slips" and "suckers," which are shoots that develop below the fruit-bearing stalk, are similarly used for planting the next season's crop of pineapples.

Branches of *Forsythia* (for·SITH·ee·a) bushes and many other kinds of shrubs may be bent and covered with soil—leaving only the ends of the branches exposed to air and light (Figure 17-1c). Soon roots form on the buried portions of the branches. When these become well established, the branches can be cut from the parent plants, and the new plants will continue to grow independently.

A leaf of *Bryophyllum* (bry·O·FIL·um), the so-called "life plant," has small notches around its edge. Older leaves of this plant may develop small plants, complete with roots, stem, and leaves, at every notch. If the leaves are placed on moist soil in a flowerpot, many of the tiny plants become established. During the early stages of growth they draw upon food and water stored in the thick, fleshy leaf (Figure 17-1d).

All of the examples we have described have two things in common. First, each of a number of single mature plants has produced new plants genetically identical with the parent. Second, the new individuals came from plant parts produced solely by mitosis, cell division, and subsequent cell specialization. There was no meiosis and no fusion of gametes.

This type of asexual reproduction, called **vegetative propagation,** is extensively used in multiplying a wide variety of ornamental and crop plants. It has several advantages. Perhaps the most important one is that the offspring resemble the parent plant exactly, or nearly so. A farmer using a certain variety of seed potatoes finds that the new potatoes that he grows are almost identical to those which were used for seed. If he used seeds produced by potato flowers, his crop would show great variation, although all would be potatoes. Many would be of poor quality, and there would be marked differences in their size, thus reducing the value of the crop. The reasons for this will be clear to you when you have studied genetics (Chapters 29 and 30).

Vegetative propagation is used also for pro-

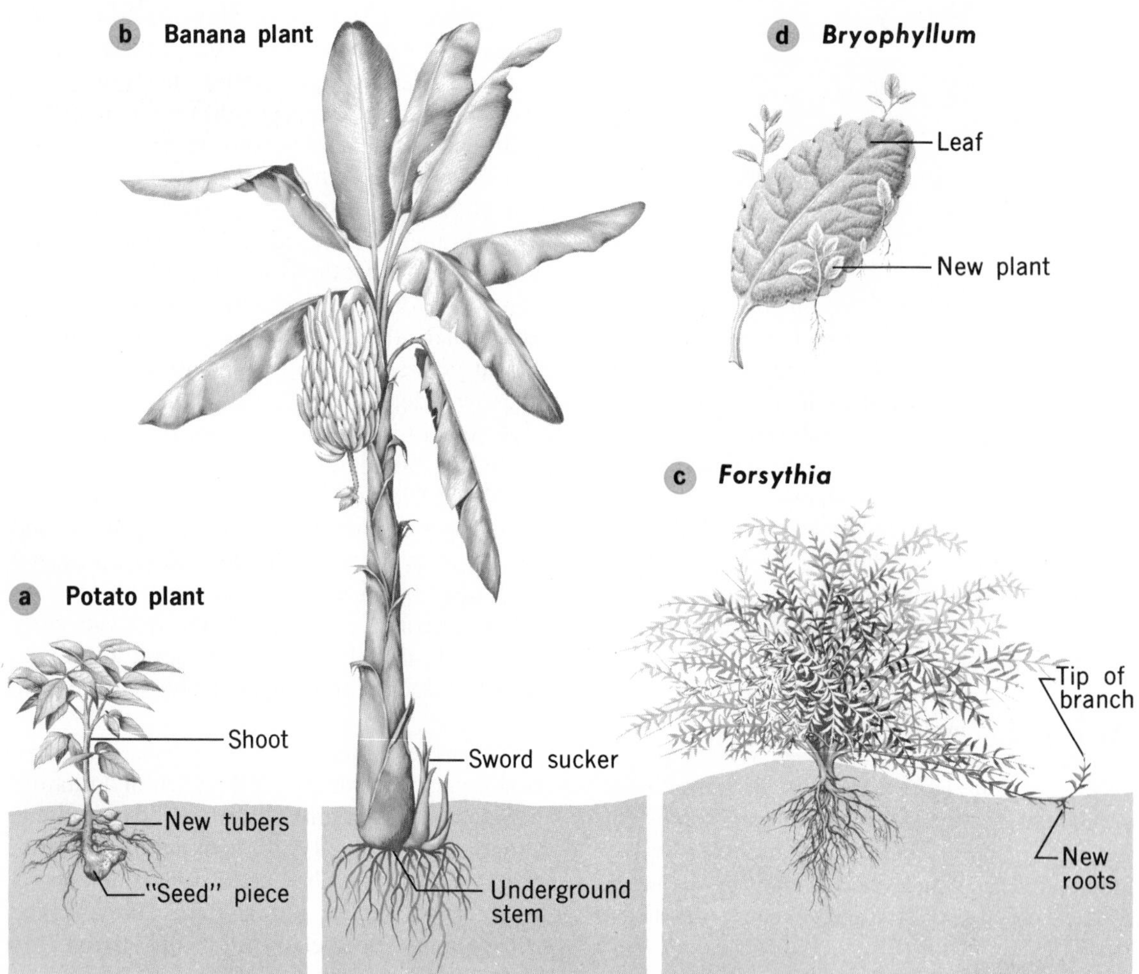

17–1 Asexual reproduction in four flowering plants. **a.** Potato growers prefer to plant pieces of potatoes, rather than seeds, from their good crop of the year before. Can you explain why? **b.** Banana culture is based upon transplanting the "sword suckers" produced at the base of the stem. The seeds of the fruit are useless—nonfunctional—as you can demonstrate by trying to produce new plants from seeds of the next banana you eat. **c.** Many plants like *Forsythia* take root at points where branches are in contact with the soil. Can you name other such plants? **d.** Few people can name another plant like *Bryophyllum*, which produces new plants at notches in its leaves! Until they become established, these tiny plants draw on the food supply of the leaf.

ducing plants that for a variety of reasons are very difficult to grow from seed, or for which the time required to produce seed may be excessive. Some plants, such as bananas, certain kinds of grapes, and navel oranges, either never form fertile seeds or form no seeds at all. These plants must, therefore, be reproduced asexually.

SEXUAL REPRODUCTION

The story of the evolution of sexual reproduction in the Plant Kingdom has been considered in Chapters 13 and 14, where we have emphasized sexual reproduction as it occurs in fungi, algae, and primitive green land plants. Now let us examine the essentials of this process as it takes place in flowering plants.

There are approximately 275,000 species of flowering plants. With few exceptions, all of them give rise to seeds enclosed in fruits. Most of the plants with which you are familiar are flowering plants. Their variety is quite remarkable. They range in size from trees weighing many tons to tiny water plants about the size of a grain of rice. A stunted willow growing in the wastes of the Arctic, a giant cactus in the Arizona desert, an orchid plant perched high up on the branch of a jungle tree—all are flowering plants.

The Structure of a Flower

What is a flower—the characteristic structure possessed by all these plants? Most biologists believe it is a specialized branch or stalk of the plant bearing groups of highly modified leaves at its tip. Variations in floral structure are almost endless. Indeed, it is impossible to speak of a typical flower. We can, however, imagine an idealized or generalized flower, which will illustrate basic features common, in one form or another, to many diverse groups of plants. In such a flower there are four different kinds of structures attached at successively higher levels of the flower stalk (Figure 17-2a). The lower and outermost parts, enclosing other floral parts, are the **sepals** (SEE·p'lz). They are usually green and closely resemble leaves. Attached just above these—and often extending at their upper ends beyond all the other flowering parts—are the **petals,** white or variously colored, and also usually leaflike in shape. Attached above the bases of the petals is a third group of highly modified structures, the **stamens** (STAY·menz), which in most cases hardly resemble leaves at all. Each stamen, a male reproductive structure, consists of a slender elongated stalk, the **filament,** and an expanded lobed structure at its tip, the **anther.** The anthers, as you will recall from Chapter 14, contain sacs in which large numbers of small pollen grains are formed. The uppermost point of attachment at the tip of the flower stalk, and in the center of the flower, is that of the **pistil.** This is the female reproductive structure. It is usually composed of three easily recognizable regions—an expanded tip, the **stigma;** an elongated **style;** and an enlarged base, the **ovary.** Within the ovary are one or more small structures, the **ovules,** which are attached by short stalks to the ovary wall.

How a Flower Functions

Let us trace the series of events beginning with a newly opened flower and ending with the development of mature fruits containing seeds (Inquiry 17-1). Although we have discussed some of the reproductive parts of flowers (see Chapter 14), we have not thus far described the steps in the sexual reproduction of a flowering plant.

An anther, when fully developed, usually consists of two elongated sacs containing pollen grains. As we learned in Chapter 14, these grains develop from uninucleate cells, which are monoploid spores produced by meiosis. As development proceeds, the nucleus in each one of these cells divides to form two daughter nuclei. At this stage in pollen grain formation, the wall of each anther splits, forming openings through which the pollen grains can be shed

THE LIFE CYCLE OF A FLOWERING PLANT

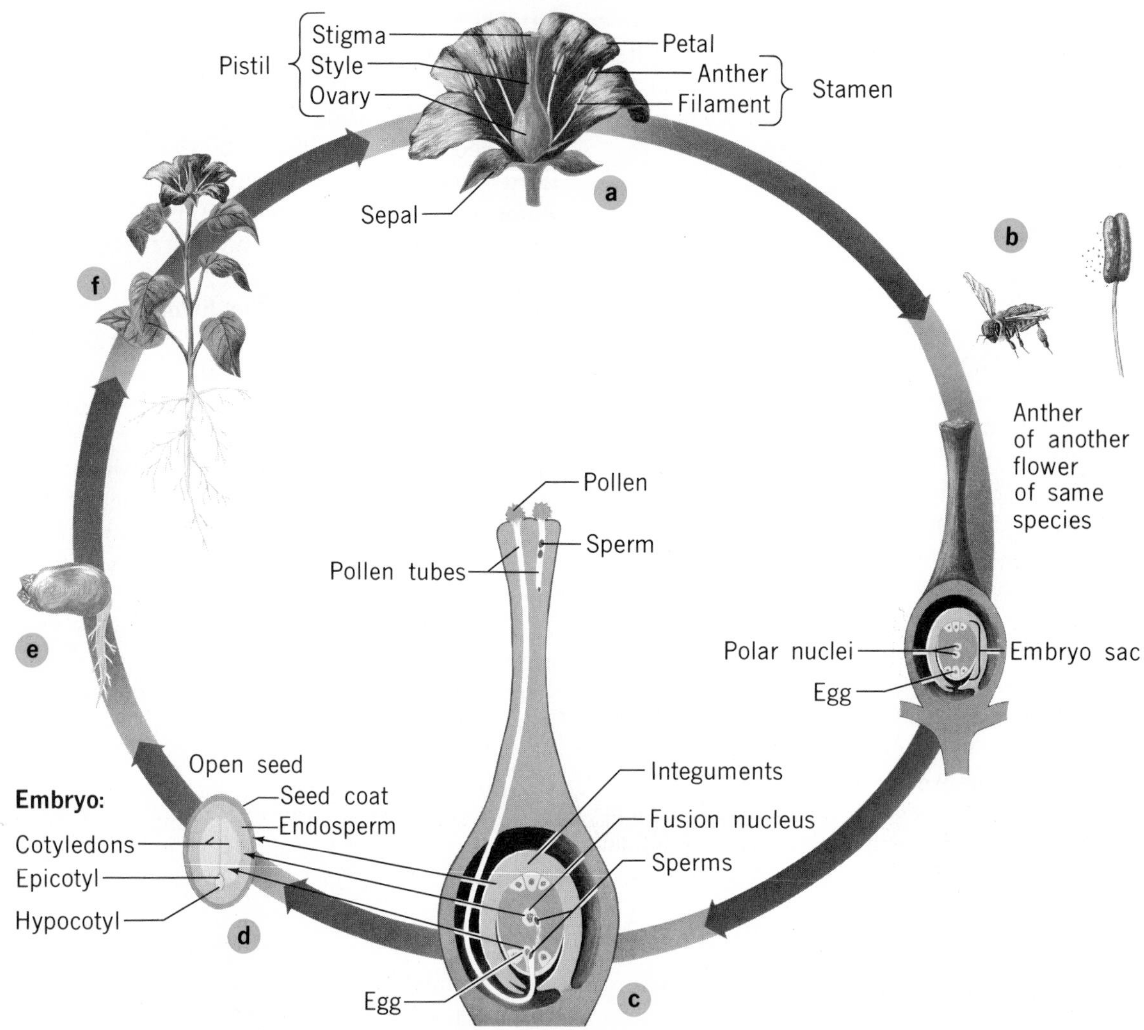

17–2 Shown in sequence for a generalized flowering plant are: **a**, the flower; **b**, pollination by an insect; **c**, the interior of the pistil at the time of fertilization (a pollen tube has grown to the ovule, and double fertilization is about to take place); **d**, the seed (the black arrows indicate that the seed coat is produced by the integuments of the ovule, the endosperm in the seed by the fertilized fusion nucleus, and the embryo by the fertilized egg); **e**, the seedling; and **f**, the mature plant, with flower.

(Figure 17-2b). Pollination is completed when pollen is then transferred to a stigma, by wind, water, or an insect.

Cells on the surface of the stigma secrete a sticky nutrient fluid containing sugars and other substances. As pollen grains germinate on the stigma, each one produces a slender, thin-walled pollen tube (Figure 17-2c). This grows down through the tissues of the stigma, style, and ovary until it reaches the ovule. As the pollen tube develops, the two nuclei of the pollen grain move down into it. One of these nuclei divides again to form two somewhat elongated sperms (Figure 17-2c). The other nucleus is usually located near the tip of the pollen tube, with the two sperms following along behind. The pollen tube, as it reaches the ovule, grows through a small channel leading into the interior of the ovule (Figure 17-2c). What happens then? In order to find out, we must look into the structure of the ovule.

An ovule is an egg-shaped structure attached by a stalk to the inside of the ovary. Depending upon the species of plant involved, an ovary may have one, two, several, or even thousands of ovules. At the center of each ovule is a microscopic **embryo sac** (Figure 17-2b), filled with food and water. The embryo sac, composed of gametophyte cells, is the female gametophyte described in Chapter 14.

The majority of flowering plants have an embryo sac consisting of seven cells, two of which are important to our discussion. One is a large central cell containing two nuclei. These are called the **polar nuclei.** The other cell is the egg. It is located at the end of the embryo sac closest to the opening through which the pollen tube enters (Figure 17-2c).

Soon after the tip of the pollen tube enters the embryo sac, the end of the tube ruptures and releases the two sperms into the sac. One of the two sperms fuses with the egg to form a zygote. The zygote will develop into an embryonic plant within the ovule.

By the time the egg cell has been fertilized, the two polar nuclei have combined to form a single **fusion nucleus** (Figure 17-2c). Now the *second* sperm deposited in the embryo sac by the pollen tube moves to the center of the embryo sac and unites with the fusion nucleus. Fertilization of the fusion nucleus stimulates the formation of a new tissue – the endosperm – in which foods are stored as development of the ovule proceeds.

Union of one sperm with the egg, and the second sperm with the fusion nucleus, is called **double fertilization.** As far as we know, double fertilization occurs only in flowering plants.

After double fertilization, the ovule increases rapidly in size as a result of the formation of endosperm tissue and the development of the new embryo. The embryo consists of one or more **cotyledons** (kot·ih·LEE·dunz), an **epicotyl** (EP·ih·kot'l), and a **hypocotyl** (HY·po·kot'l) (see Figure 17-2d). Both the epicotyl and hypocotyl are parts of a rodlike axis attached to the cotyledons. The cotyledons digest and absorb the endosperm and make the stored food it contains available for the growth of the epicotyl and hypocotyl. The cotyledons of some flowering plants, beans for example, digest, absorb, and store the foods from the endosperm as the ovule is maturing into a seed. As a consequence, the cotyledons become greatly enlarged (full of stored food), as in Figure 17-3a, and the endosperm disappears more or less completely. In many other flowering plants (such as corn or castor bean), the endosperm tissue continues to grow as the ovule matures into a seed. Thus, in a corn grain, most of the seed is endosperm, and the embryo is located at one side (Figure 17-3b).

As an ovule matures into a seed, there are other changes in addition to the formation of an embryo and the accumulation of stored foods. The protective coverings (the integuments and sporangium), which surround the embryo sac, are transformed into a **seed coat.** The seed coats of many seed plants are tough, and they protect the enclosed embryonic plant from injury.

Depending upon the plant species involved, the walls of the fully formed fruit may be dry, resistant structures, or soft and fleshy. The outer covering of the corn grain, for example, is made up of the tough ovary wall fused to the seed coat of the single seed of the grain (Figure 17-3b). Examples of familiar fleshy fruits include the tomato, orange, and peach. In the tomato, the ovary wall and the central tissues

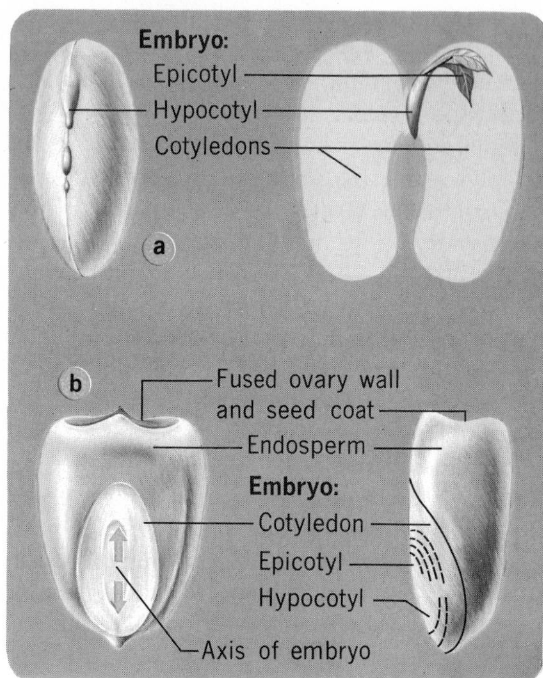

17–3 **a.** A bean seed and its parts. What is the origin of the thin seed coat? the stored food in the cotyledons? the embryo? **b.** A corn grain and its parts. The endosperm (stored food) is not part of the embryo. The corn grain is really a fruit with a seed inside. The seed has a single cotyledon.

to which the seeds are attached are juicy and edible. In the case of the orange—typical of citrus fruits including the lime, lemon, and grapefruit—the outer wall of the fruit becomes leathery. The edible part, the pulp, is made up of juicy multicellular outgrowths of the inner layer of the ovary wall. The cell sap squeezed from these structures is orange juice, a rich source of sugars and vitamin C. In the peach, the inner layers of the ovary wall become transformed into hard stony tissues, the stone. The outer layers by contrast, remain soft and juicy.

Variety Among Flowers

Our account of the structure of a flower and of the events leading to the development of fruits and seeds has been presented in a very general and abbreviated way. There are actually several thousand different types of flowers, many of which would seem to bear only a limited resemblance to the one shown in Figure 17-2a. Many of our common trees—maples, oaks, and hickories—have flowers in which the sepals and petals are either very inconspicuous or have disappeared entirely. In some plants, such as corn, there are *two* kinds of flowers. The flowers that develop in the tassels have stamens but no pistils. Those of the ears, borne lower down on the plant, are just the opposite, with pistils and no stamens.

Corn (maize) is a species of grass. Like all grasses, corn has its flowers modified for wind pollination (see Chapter 14). That is, the flowers do not have the attractive petals and nectar that guide insects to them. Instead, they have large feathery stigmas (the silks) and anthers (in the tassels) that produce abundant pollen. These characteristics help to insure pollination by wind. (Figure 17-4a shows pollen-producing flowers of another wind-pollinated plant.)

All photos by Roche

17–4 Several kinds of flowers. **a.** These flowers have stamens but no pistils. They are the pollen-producing flowers of a shrub closely related to witch hazel. Note the many anthers exposed to air currents. The wind carries the pollen to pistils of other flowers of the plant (or other plants of the species). **b.** These insect-pollinated flowers of the butterfly bush are part of an inflorescence of many small flowers on a single stalk. **c.** The Easter lily is an example of the flower of a *monocotyledonous* plant. Three sepals and three petals all look much alike in the flower. There are six stamens and a three-part compound pistil. **d.** The passion flower is an example of the flower of a *dicotyledonous* plant. Here, too, the sepals and petals (five of each) look much alike in the flower. Five stamens and a compound pistil occupy the center of the flower.

a

b

c

d

17-5 COMPARISON OF DICOTS AND MONOCOTS

Dicot	Monocot
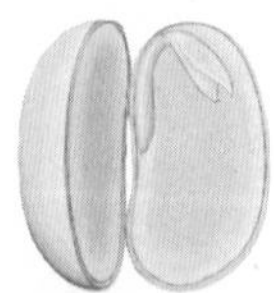 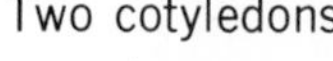 Two cotyledons	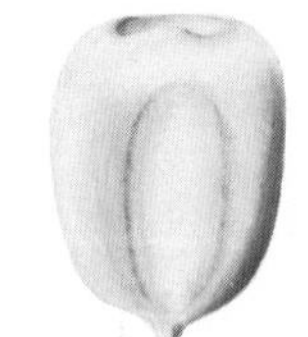 One cotyledon
 Leaves with network of veins	 Leaves with parallel veins
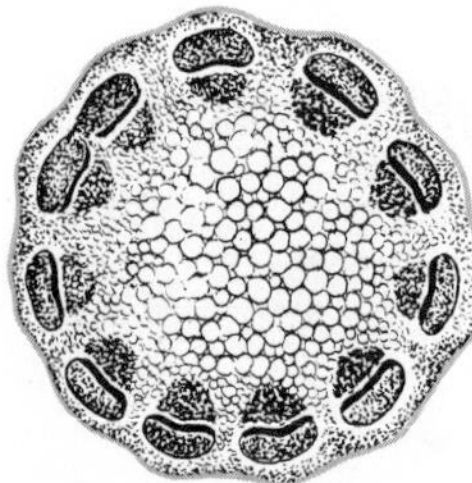 Stems with vascular cambium and with vascular bundles in a ring	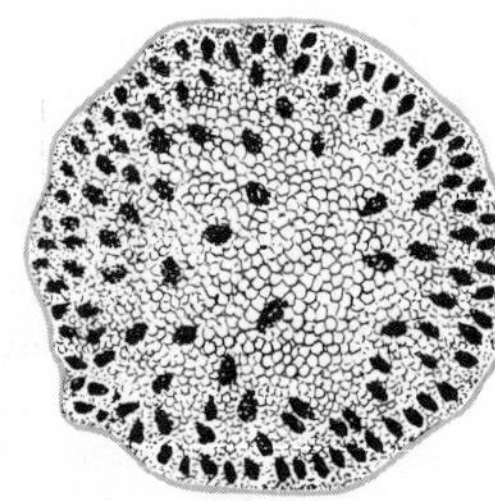 Stems without vascular cambium and with scattered vascular bundles
 Flower parts in 4's or 5's or multiples of 4 or 5	 Flower parts in 3's or multiples of 3

Insects and even birds, especially hummingbirds, are attracted by the showy parts of many flowers. In one species of orchid, the pollen-producing anthers bear a superficial resemblance to the female of a species of bee. Male bees of this species, seeing these reasonable facsimiles, fly to the flower and try to mate with it. In the process the bees pick up pollen from one flower and carry it to another.

The reproductive structures of flowering plants are an aid in their identification and classification (Inquiry 17-2). For example, we find that many flowers resemble a lily or an iris in having their floral parts in three's or multiples of three (Figure 17-4c), and in having a single cotyledon in their seeds. All flowering plants with these characteristics are placed in a group called the **monocotyledons** (mon·o·kot·ih·LEE·dunz). We call them the **monocots** (MON·o·kots) for short.

The majority of flowering plants have their floral parts in two's or five's or some multiple of these numbers (Figure 17-4d). Their seeds have two cotyledons, and for this reason they are called the **dicotyledons** (dy·kot·ih·LEE·dunz) or **dicots** (DY·kots).

A summary of these and other differences between monocots and dicots is presented in Figure 17-5.

DEVELOPMENT

A hundred seeds taken from the cones of a giant California redwood can be held in the palm of your hand. Each, under favorable circumstances, may develop into a tremendous tree—the largest living thing the world has ever known. Each of these small seeds contains a hereditary pattern that, when translated through processes of development, results in a huge plant with hundreds of branches bearing millions of leaves. Extending into the soil from the base of the massive trunk are large woody roots, which branch and rebranch, finally ending in many millions of slender, pointed root tips.

Growth

How does so much growth and development come about? The answer in terms of growth can be stated, in a general way, very simply—but the search for a *complete* answer is the major concern of thousands of biologists working in laboratories all over the world. Let us consider the simple answer to our question by observing what happens when a bean seed germinates (Inquiry 17-3). You can take the opportunity in the laboratory or at home to grow seeds of many kinds of plants. In each case you can see that growth starts with the formation of a slender primary root, which breaks through the seed coat. If we look for the origin of this primary root, we can see that it has been formed by the enlargement and elongation of the hypocotyl of the seed. But why has there been an increase in size? How has *growth* of the root occurred? The answer is twofold.

All of the tissues of the embryo of a bean—the epicotyl, hypocotyl, and cotyledons—are made up of cells. These cells originated by repeated divisions, starting with the first division of the zygote. When the bean seed matured and became dry, the cell divisions ceased. If the seed is supplied with water, however, the cell divisions will begin again. With renewal of cell divisions, we might expect growth to occur—but stop and think for a moment. Does it necessarily follow that if cells divide and increase in number there will be any increase in size?

A cell, by repeated division, may give rise to 2, 4, 8, 16 and even more descendant cells. If each one remains the same size as it was after division, the combined volume of the cells will be equal only to that of the original cell. One brick divided into four smaller ones has not increased in volume.

If, however, each one of the new cells formed by division increases in size, the total volume of the cells resulting from the divisions will necessarily increase. A full-grown bean plant has a volume millions of times greater than that of the original fertilized egg cell from which it was formed. Thus, growth is the result of two processes, *an increase in cell number* accompanied by *an increase in volume of cells.*

Differentiation

Now let us consider a further aspect of development. A mature bean plant is not simply a collection of millions of cells, all like the zygote. Instead it is composed of many different types of cells—tracheids and companion cells, cells of the spongy layers of the leaf, and many more kinds. The increase in cell number and volume during the development of the fertilized egg into the mature plant has been accompanied by **differentiation** (dif·er·en·she-AY·shun)—the production of different *kinds* of cells and tissues.

How did all these cells and tissues differentiate? Each cell was derived from the original fertilized egg by repeated mitosis and cell division; it has the same number and kinds of chromosomes as all other vegetative cells of the plant. Why, then, in one case, is a long, thick-walled tracheid cell formed, and in another a thin-walled cell with green chloroplasts? If, as we believe, the chromosomes direct and control all the activities within cells, how can the same kinds of chromosomes lead to such very different kinds of cells? At the present time the problem remains essentially unsolved, but thousands of research workers are seeking an answer.

Development of the Root

Let us examine the development of a root in the light of what we know about growth and differentiation. Suppose we take a germinating bean and, using India ink, place a series of equally spaced marks along its root (Figure 17-6a). We then place it, root tip down, between layers of moist cotton. After a day or two we again examine it. Changes in the spacing of the ink marks (Figure 17-6b) tell us that most of the increase in length has taken place close to the tip.

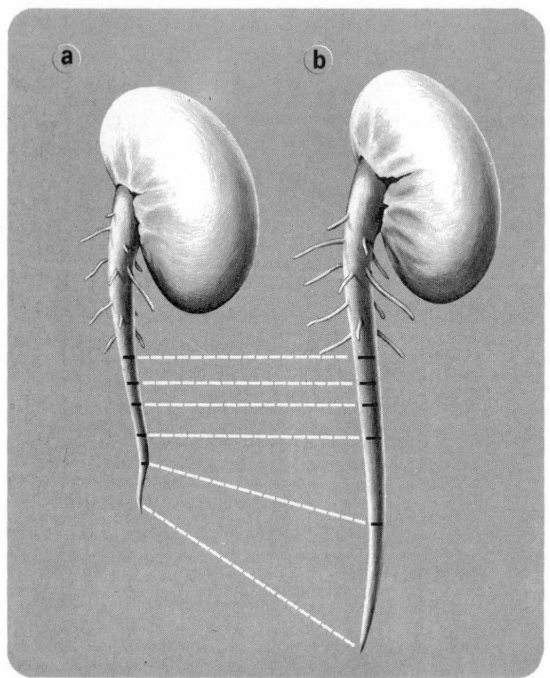

17-6 An experiment on comparative regions of growth in the root of a bean seedling. **a.** India ink marks are placed on the root at equal intervals. **b.** As the root grows, rapid changes appear in the spacing of some of the ink marks. Why do the lines marked near the tip become so much more widely separated than those farther removed from the tip?

If growing roots are examined, three distinct regions can be distinguished (Figure 17-7a). The first of these is covered by the root cap, which protects a group of thin-walled, small cells having relatively large nuclei and small vacuoles. Cells in this region divide rapidly. Immediately above this region is a zone in which the cells are increasing in size, primarily as a result of elongation. In a third region, lying farthest from the root tip, cells are reaching their maximum size and undergoing differentiation into the various cell types of the epidermis, cortex, and central conducting cylinder (see Chapter 16). Thus, as we "read" what we see in the root from the tip upward, we see the processes of cell division, cell enlargement, and cell differentiation producing the tissues that the seedling root will have as a mature root.

Shortly after the primary root becomes well established, branch roots make their appearance from older portions of the primary root. Branch roots originate from cells deep within the primary root (Figure 16-6, page 302).

When a seed germinates, the seedling root system develops rapidly and precedes the growth of the shoot (stem and leaves). From the standpoint of survival, the root system *must* be established first to supply water for growth and to anchor the plant. But what determines that the root system will develop before the shoot? What coordinates this and other events in the growth of a plant? These questions, like others we have raised, remain unanswered for the present.

Development of the Shoot

After the root system of a seedling has become established, the epicotyl of the embryo grows rapidly to form a stem on which leaves and branches are produced. A growing region, basically similar to that at the tip of a root, is found at the tip of the developing stem. In addition to forming cells of the stem, the growing tip forms cells which become differentiated into cells of leaves and branches (Figure 17-7b). Unlike the internally produced branch roots, the branches and leaves of a stem originate from superficial cells of the young shoot. Thus, at its surface, the pattern of organization of a shoot is more complex than that of a root.

All stages of development require large amounts of energy. In the young seedling, prior to the development of photosynthetic structures, energy is derived from food stored in the endosperm or cotyledons of the seed. By the time this energy supply is depleted, the first leaves have usually fully developed, and photosynthesis has commenced. This beautifully coordinated series of events, starting with the germination of a seed and resulting in an independent plant, is shown in Figure 17-2.

During the early stages of development, the shoot and root systems increase mainly in length, by cell elongation. The woody dicot stems and roots increase in diameter (as well as length) during each growing season (see Chapter 16). You may remember that in this sort of growth the cells involved arise by repeated division of a layer of cells called the vascular cambium. This layer produces new xylem tissues on its inner side and new phloem tissues on its outer side. How is the vascular cambium formed? And how is it related to the growing tips of root and shoot?

If we examine under a microscope a cross section through an internode of a young dicot stem, made close to the growing tip, a pattern of development is revealed (Figure 17-8a). Strands of elongated but incompletely differentiated cells are arranged in a circle embedded in tissues of cortex and pith. At this level in the stem, all tissues are *primary tissues* formed by the differentiation of cells that originate from the growing tip of the stem. As development continues, the strands of elongated cells differentiate into vascular tissue. Cells of the outer region of each strand become primary phloem, and inner cells differentiate into primary xylem (Figure 17-8b). Between the primary xylem and phloem of each strand there remains a thin layer of cells that retain their capacity to divide and produce new cells. This layer is the vascular cambium. It gradually extends laterally between the adjacent vascular bundles, until it eventually forms a continuous ring of cambium (Figure 17-8c). Tissues derived from the vascular cambium are called *secondary tissues*. Thus, the layer of new xylem formed just inside the vascular cambium is *secondary xylem,* and the layer of phloem formed just outside the cambium is *secondary phloem*. The accumula-

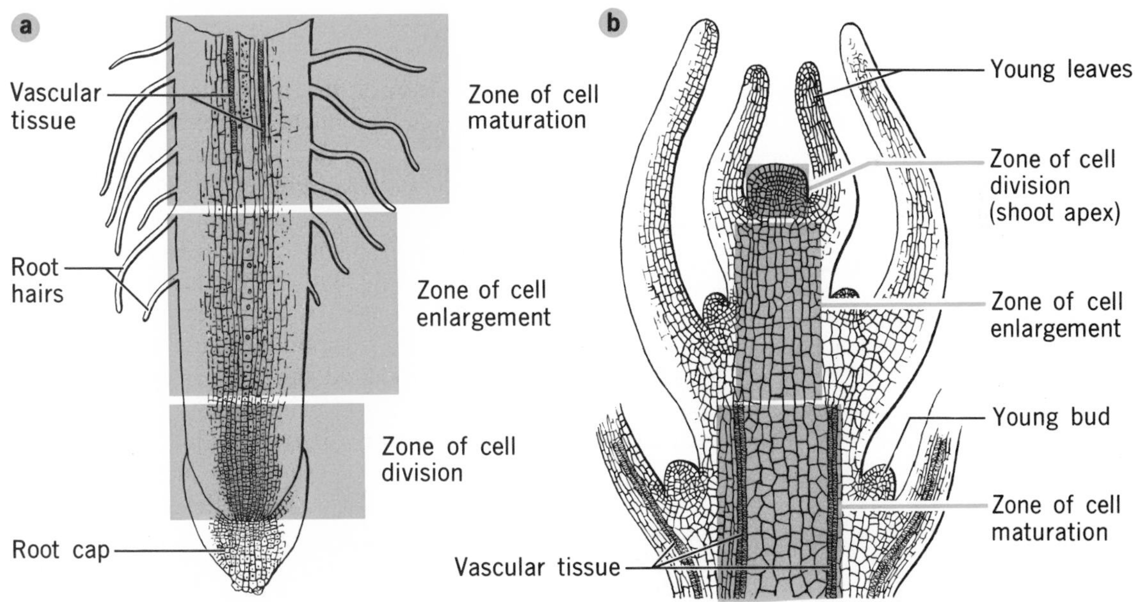

17–7 a. A longitudinal section of a root tip. How well do the zones of growth and differentiation correlate with the changes in spacing of India ink marks on the root of Figure 17–7b? **b.** A longitudinal section of a stem tip. Notice the correspondence between the zones here and in the root at the left. The differentiation of vascular tissue appears to take place independently in the stem and in the young leaves.

tion of secondary tissues, especially the secondary xylem, results in an increase in the diameter of the dicot stem (Figure 17-8d). As stems increase in diameter, cracks appear at the surface through which large quantities of water could escape if it were not for a homeostatic regulation by the stem tissues. Where a crack begins, the tissues of the stem beneath the crack start to divide and produce new secondary tissues. The walls of certain cells of the newly formed tissues contain a waxy, waterproof substance. In this way a kind of living dam

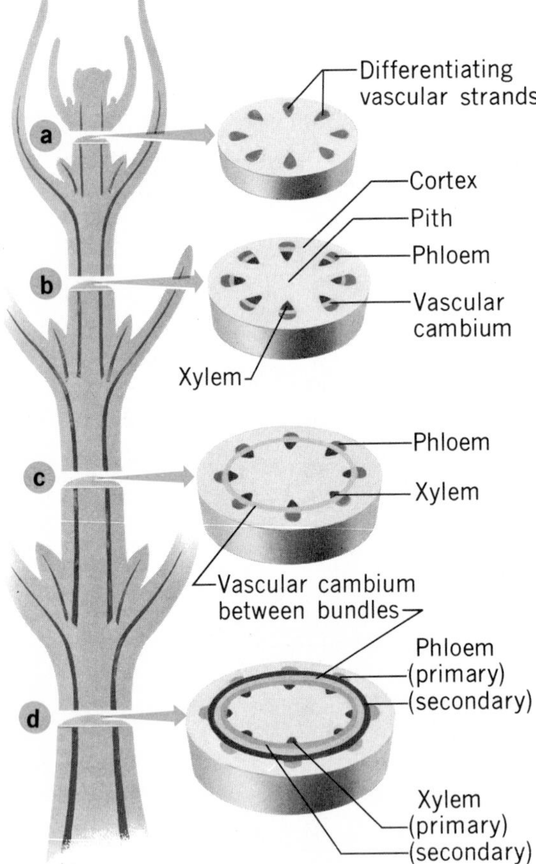

17–8 Part of a stem diagrammed in longitudinal section and in four cross sections. At intervals from the tip, note the increasing complexity as the vascular cambium develops into a complete ring of cells producing secondary xylem and phloem.

is formed that prevents excessive water loss through cracks or other injuries of the stem.

The stems of monocots usually do not have cambium. In these plants all tissues of the root and the shoot are primary tissues, formed from cells produced at the growing tips, or from dividing cells located at the nodes.

Although we have not offered any explanation of factors regulating the development of a plant from a seed, we have shown that the stages in development of a plant are coordinated. If the coordinated events occur where there is plenty of water, oxygen, carbon dioxide, light, and a suitable temperature, then we can expect the plant to grow and finally reproduce. Like all living things, plants adjust to their environment. Thus their leaves may become oriented more favorably to the sunlight, or their roots may grow toward a greater supply of water and salts. If we understand the factors that help plants adjust themselves to their environment, we will have some insight into factors that regulate growth.

Plants Respond to Their Environment

Although you might not expect it because they seem so stationary, rooted to the ground, plants show many different reactions to their environment. The seeds that farmers plant in the ground respond to gravity. They will also respond to light, or the lack of it; to different concentrations of water in the soil; to different concentrations of minerals and nutrients; to rocks and other barriers that hinder root growth. Some plants, such as the sensitive plant *(Mimosa pudica)* react almost instantaneously to the slightest touch applied to their leaves (Figure 17-9). When the reaction of the plant involves a change in direction of growth of one of its parts, the reaction is called a **tropism** (TROH·piz·m). If the reaction is toward the stimulus, the tropism is positive; if away from the stimulus, the tropism is negative.

What makes the plant respond to gravity, light, and other stimuli of the environment? Plants do not have nervous systems that can

Both photos by John A. Moore

17–9 Two photographs of *Mimosa pudica*, the sensitive plant. The photograph on the left shows the plant with leaves extended. The photograph on the right shows the same plant after it was stimulated by being touched.

receive a stimulus as do animals. There must be some other mechanism. To discover what the mechanism is and how it works, with the help of your teacher you will do Inquiry 17-4. This is a different kind of inquiry. All it requires is your ability to reason and make conclusions. Many of these conclusions will be the same ones that Charles and Francis Darwin, Boysen Jensen, and Frits Went, all pioneers in this field of investigation, arrived at in their experiments.

Growth Substances

After many years of experimentation the active substance that brings about the growth responses in plants was isolated. It is called **auxin** (AUK·sin). If you have done Inquiry 17-5, you will know where auxin is produced and how it works in a plant.

Chemical analysis of auxin shows that it is **indole** (IN·dohl) **acetic acid** (IAA).

IAA is of practical importance. It is used to stimulate the formation of roots in cuttings that are difficult to propagate. The IAA is applied in low concentrations to the lower end of the cutting. The auxin stimulates the production of root-forming tissues from the cut surface. By this method it is possible to "root" cuttings of yew, holly, and many other valuable ornamental plants that are otherwise difficult to propagate.

Within the last thirty or so years, a number of different compounds have been discovered which can bring about plant growth. These substances, which are of considerable practical importance, can be synthesized at relatively low cost, and like the naturally occurring IAA, they are effective when used in very low concentrations.

One such compound is **naphthalene** (NAP-tha·leen) **acetic acid** (NAA). It is extensively used to prevent sprouting of potatoes during storage. Whereas untreated potatoes frequently begin to sprout after several months' storage, NAA inhibits development of the eyes, or buds, so that treated potatoes may be kept in good condition for prolonged periods of time—often as long as three years.

Some varieties of apple trees lose a sizable proportion of their developing fruits because of premature development of the separation layer, a zone of thin-walled cells at the base of the stem which attaches each apple to a branch. Fruits that fall from the tree early are bruised as they hit the ground and are of little value. Spraying the trees with NAA avoids most of this loss.

Flowering in pineapples can also be controlled by applying NAA to the growing plants in low concentrations. This treatment causes the plants to produce flowers and fruit several weeks early.

Another group of growth-controlling substances being studied for possible extensive use in agriculture are the **gibberellins** (jib·er-EL·inz). These substances were originally obtained from a fungus that infects rice plants in Japan. The infected plants are taller than normal ones, but they rarely flower or produce seed. It was next discovered that cultures of the fungus growing on artificial media contained substances that stimulate stem elongation in a large number of different plants.

One of the most widely used synthetic compounds is **2,4-dichlorophenoxyacetic** (dy·klo·ro-fee·NOK·see·a·SEE·tic) **acid,** mercifully abbreviated to 2,4-D. This compound, in contrast to the others mentioned above, is employed to kill plants, for it makes their growth wildly abnormal. It is highly poisonous to a wide variety of broad-leaved plants, including many common weeds. Proper concentrations of this substance added to lawns or cornfields will kill unwanted weeds without harming the grasses. 2,4-D is poisonous to animals and human beings when sufficiently concentrated, so that it must be used with care!

Some Other Effects of Light

You have already learned that light energy is trapped in photosynthesis, that it plays a role in the regulation of stomata and water loss in plants, and that it is an important stimulus to which plants react by growth movements. But there is another way that light affects the life of some flowering plants. The men who discovered this effect of light made their discovery quite by accident, as you will see.

In 1920 two investigators, Wightman Garner and Harry Allard, were working with various varieties of tobacco plants, trying to increase productivity of tobacco. One day it was noticed that a single plant, in a field of plants, was quite different from the other varieties in two respects. The new mutant had large leaves and did not flower. The investigators were immediately aware of the importance of this unusual plant. For if they could propagate it, they would be able to improve the productivity of tobacco crops. But how to get it to reproduce? Under field conditions, when the days were warm and long, all of the other tobacco plants flowered profusely. By contrast, the mutant, which they called Maryland Mammoth, showed no signs of flowering. Surely the valuable mutant would be lost for want of seeds. As the growing season came to a close, almost in desperation the investigators moved their plant into the greenhouse to protect it from freezing. Still it showed no signs of reproducing. Finally, to their relief, in the middle of December the plant flowered. It was then allowed to self-pollinate. The seeds thus obtained were planted. You can guess that the offspring behaved the same way as their mutant parent. They would flower only when the days were short, in mid-winter. Could it be that there was a relationship between short days and flowering? To test this hypothesis Garner and Allard put seedlings of the mutants in special chambers where day lengths could be regulated. When day length was shortened artificially to about 9 hours, the plants flowered. This response on the part of the tobacco plant to day length was called **photoperiodism** (Figure 17-10). Since flowering was induced by a short day, Maryland Mammoth plants were called short-day plants. Soon it was discovered that other plants such as chrysanthemums, soybeans, and cocklebурs behaved the same way. Yet another type

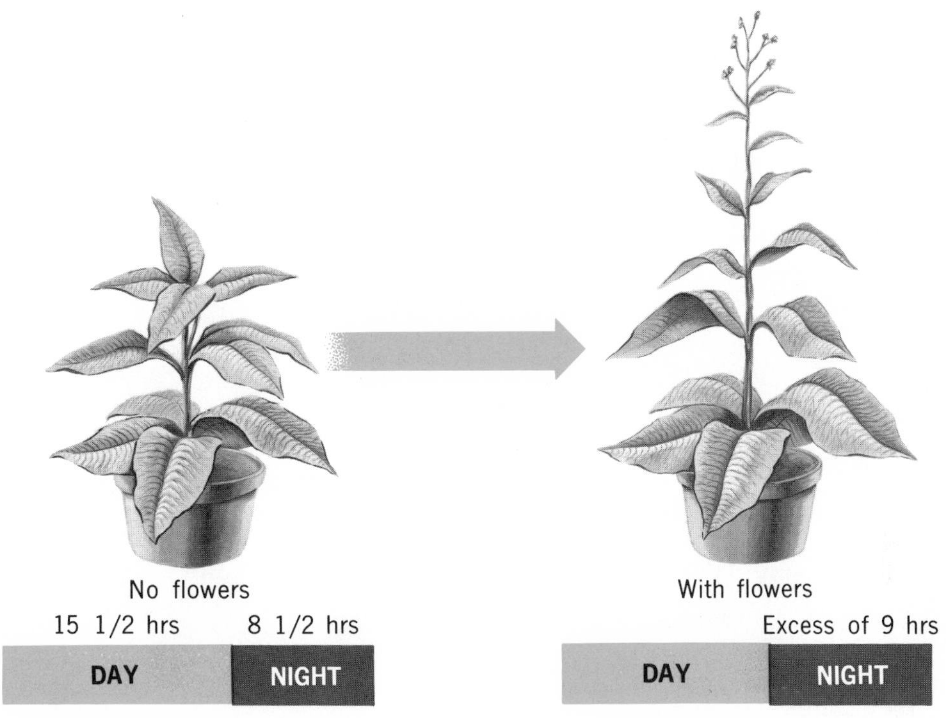

17–10 An experiment illustrating the effect of different photoperiods on the flowering of Maryland Mammoth tobacco.

of reaction was found in spinach and some grains that require a long day for flower initiation. However, in many flowering plants the length of day seems to have little or no effect on the production of flowers.

Subsequent investigations by Garner and Allard of long-day and short-day plants showed that it was not length of daylight that was important in determining the flowering reaction, but the length of the uninterrupted dark period. Thus, a short day plant is really a "long-night" plant that may require more than 9 hours of uninterrupted dark before it will blossom. In many plants, the cocklebur and Maryland Mammoth tobacco to name two, the critical period of dark seems to be just about 9 hours. If the dark period is shortened to 8½ hours, there will be no flowering.

Since the work of Garner and Allard much more has been learned about photoperiodism. Using Maryland Mammoth tobacco, researchers discovered that a single leaf of the plant could be given the short-day treatment and this would initiate flower production at the tip of the plant some distance from the leaf. This experiment illustrated that there was some kind of link between the place where the stimulus (short day) was received and where the response (flower production) takes place.

A more dramatic experiment (Figure 17-11) showed that a plant subjected to a short-day stimulus can transmit the ability to initiate flower development to a plant that has remained in a flowerless condition because it has been exposed to continuous light. This experiment is done by grafting two short-day plants. If a stem girdle (a ring of tissue cut from the stem) interrupts the functions of the phloem in the stem of the plant receiving short days, the transmission of the stimulus to the neighboring grafted plant

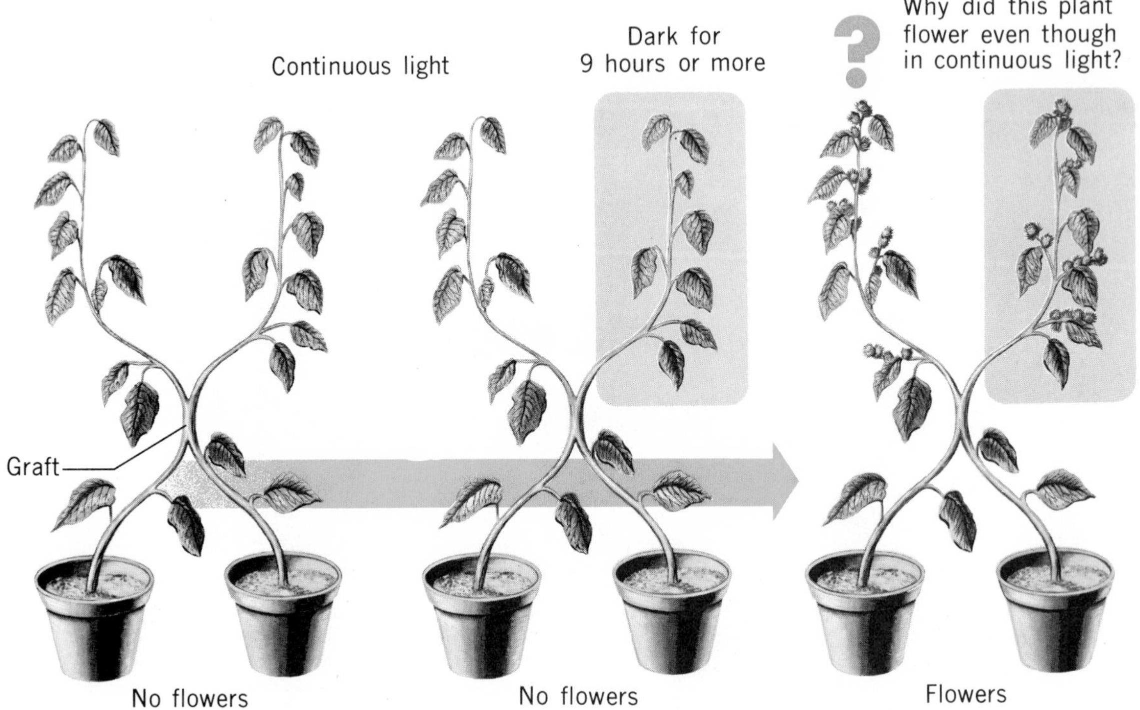

17–11 An experiment illustrating the induction of flowering in Maryland Mammoth tobacco by exposing one branch to short-day conditions.

is prevented (Figure 17-12). These experiments indicate clearly that some substance is formed by the stimulus of short days and transmitted through the phloem to the place where flowering occurs. This substance has been given a name **(florigen)** but to date it has not been identified.

Other experiments show that if the long dark period of a short-day plant is interrupted—if only for a second—by visible light, the plant will not flower as expected (Figure 17-13). A further investigation shows that the kind of light used is important to this unusual behavior. If the flash of light is orange-red with a wave length of 660 mμ, initiation of flowering in the plant will be blocked. If after the treatment with orange-red light the plant is exposed to a flash of far-red light (735 mμ), it will flower just as it would have if its dark period had not been interrupted. What does this unusual behavior indicate about the mechanism of the reception of the light stimulus? One explanation is that there are two special light-receiving pigments, one that receives orange-red light, the other far-red light. These pigments are called **phytochromes** (FITE·O·crohmz). Whether or not flowering will occur depends on the ratio of the phytochromes in the plant. This ratio can be changed in an instant by a flash of orange-red or far-red light.

One of the perplexing problems that has been solved by investigations of photoperiodism is the behavior of seed germination. The germination of seeds of many plants is affected by light. This is well illustrated by seeds of the Grand Rapids variety of lettuce. These seeds will not germinate in the dark. If, however, they are exposed to orange-red light for a moment, then returned to the dark, they will promptly germinate. Further exposure of the seeds to a flash of far-red light will put the seeds back into a dormant stage. This reaction can be reversed again and again depending upon which kind of light the seed has been exposed to.

Today, through the use of our knowledge of phytochromes, florigen, auxin, and other growth substances, we can control the patterns of growth and development of many of our most important food plants and eliminate unwanted plants that compete with them for light, water, and mineral nutrients.

As we have seen, the development of a flowering plant, from the first step of seed germination to the final production of a mature, reproductive organism that produces more seeds, involves many factors and mechanisms about which we know very little. It has been discovered, however, that some growth responses and patterns of development are controlled by auxin, phytochromes, florigen, and other growth-regulating substances. These substances are responsible for the coordinated development of the plant as a whole.

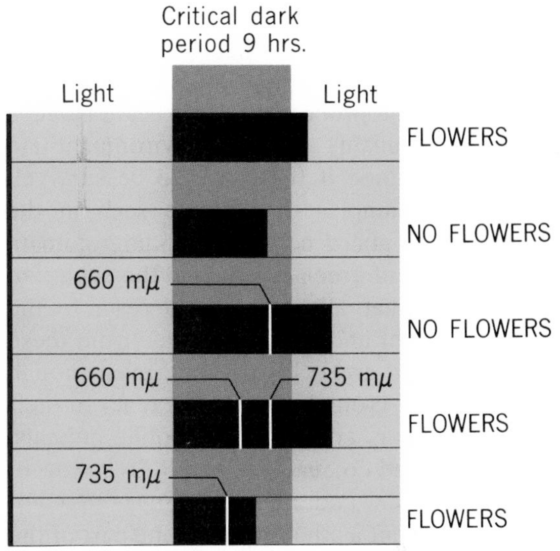

17–13 The effect of the length of photoperiod and of far-red light on flowering of cocklebur plants.

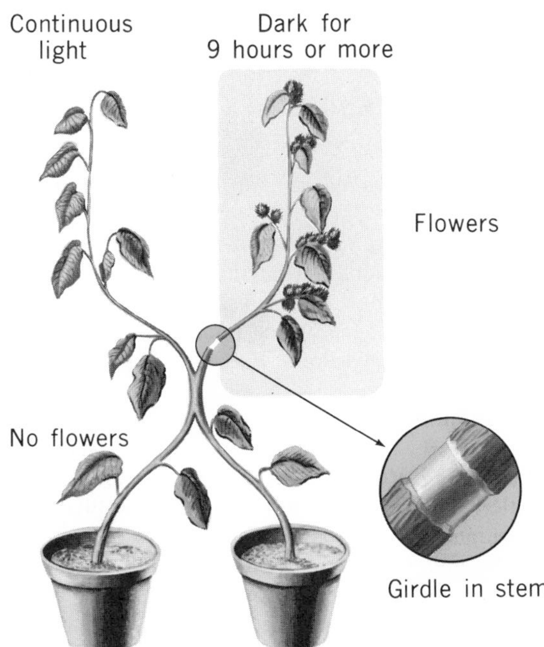

17–12 Grafting experiment between two cocklebur plants. Why is the girdle on the stem of the plant exposed to the long dark period, rather than on the plant exposed to the long light period?

CONCLUDING REMARKS

Before we leave our study of plants, let us look backward, in a very general way, at what we have covered. In Chapters 12 through 17, emphasis has been placed on the structures of flowering plants (their leaves, stems, roots, and flowers) as well as the functions these structures perform. We have discussed the remarkable adaptations of these structures to the special features of the environments in which they perform their functions.

Plants have not always inhabited the land. In the early stages of their evolution they were confined to water. Over long periods of time, they have evolved and become adapted to a wide variety of environments on land as well as in the seas. We have followed their evolution (Chapters 12 through 14), emphasizing only the major steps, from the primitive aquatic ancestors to the most highly evolved land plants—the flowering plants.

As evolution proceeded, the delicate balance between organisms and their environment had to be maintained if there was to be survival. Excellent examples of this are seen in the evolution of guard cells surrounding stomata in the leaves of green plants, and the evolution of systems that allow plants to react to the stimuli of light and gravity. We see from these examples that green land plants, even though rooted in the ground, are able to react to their environment as are the more mobile animals. Plants can, and do, react to stimuli. By means of auxins, florigen, and other substances they are able to transmit a stimulus from one part of the organism to another. Although the mechanisms are different and not as well understood, there is a parallel to be seen in the way plants and animals adjust to their surroundings. All organisms, from the lowliest protozoan to the most complex plant or animal, rely on such mechanisms to survive and to keep them in harmony with their changing environments. These mechanisms provide one more basis for biological study.

GUIDE QUESTIONS AND PROBLEMS

1. How is vegetative reproduction important to plants which reproduce in this way? How is vegetative reproduction important to man in the cultivation of plants he can propagate in this way?
2. In what way has double fertilization played an important role in the evolution of the flowering plants?
3. Which method of fertilization in plants do you think would be most successful in nature over long periods of time, self-pollination or cross-pollination? Explain.
4. How do we explain the coordination of events that occur in the development of the young bean plant?
5. You suspect that a plant's response to a stimulus is controlled by a growth substance. How would you investigate this hypothesis?
6. What are some of the practical uses of auxin and synthetic growth substances in farming and in horticulture?
7. List the ways light affects a green plant.
8. Which large group of plants studied from Chapter 10 through Chapter 17 could disappear from the earth's surface with the least apparent effects? Which other large group could? Explain the reasons for your choices.
9. You have learned that day length is important in regulating the time of flowering in some kinds of plants. Of what importance might the proper timing of flowering be to plants? Flowering in many plants does not seem to be regulated by day length. What other environmental factors might control time of flowering? What experiments can you devise to test your ideas?
10. Fruit production may be reduced in orchards near fields where DDT or other insecticides are used, even though the insecticides may not reach the trees. How might this observation be explained?

RELATED READING

Books

For a more detailed account of plant growth and differentiation . . .

Galston, A. W., *Life of the Green Plant*, Second Edition, Foundations of Modern Biology Series, Prentice-Hall, Englewood Cliffs, N. J., 1964.

Leopold, A. C., *Auxins and Plant Growth*, University of California Press, Berkeley, 1955.

Magazines

Biale, J. B., "The Ripening of Fruit," *Scientific American*, Volume 190 (May 1954), page 40.

Butler, W. C., and R. Downs, "Light and Plant Development," *Scientific American*, Volume 203 (December 1960), page 56.

Naylor, A. W., "The Control of Flowering," *Scientific American*, Volume 186 (May 1952), page 49.

Salisbury, F. B., "Plant Growth Substances," *Scientific American*, Volume 196 (April 1957), page 125.

PART 2c
ANIMALS

Courtesy of the American Museum of Natural History

18

The World of Animals

We can begin a meaningful discussion of the Animal Kingdom now that we have learned about the bacteria, fungi, and green plants without which there would be no animal life. It is the green plants that synthesize the organic compounds necessary for the maintenance and growth of animals. Bacteria and fungi are of great importance, too. As we will explain in Chapter 36, they break down complex structures and compounds in dead organisms, thus freeing chemical substances for use once again by plants (and then by animals). Without this decomposing function of bacteria and fungi, many of the earth's carbon, nitrogen, and other atoms essential for life would gradually be combined in organic compounds of kinds that green plants cannot use or break down.

Thus we and all other animals are here, so to speak, by courtesy of the bacteria, the fungi, and green plants. The plants, our silent companions of the living world, are more important than we may generally think.

ANIMALS IN RELATION TO PLANTS

We learned that plants are found nearly everywhere on earth. This is true also of animals. Wherever it is neither too hot nor too cold, and wherever moisture and the proper chemicals are found, there you can find animals and plants. Most of the surface of the earth—land, water, and air—is inhabited by plants and animals (Figure 18-1).

But there are some spots where we find little life. In the south polar regions, which are covered largely by ice, there is not much life. At the other extreme, although we can find species of both plants and animals that live exposed to the hot noonday sun in Death Valley, their number and variety are quite limited.

The farther we travel from the warm and shallow seas in which we suspect life once originated, or from the warm and moist areas of tropical rain forests, the fewer living forms we find.

In the depths of the oceans, the absence of light makes it difficult for animals and plants to survive. Of course, there can be no green plants there, because darkness makes photosynthesis impossible. Almost no green plants are found in water deeper than 100 meters. Bacteria and fungi, however, have been recorded from the deepest parts of the ocean. The same is true of animals.

Biologists using specially designed ships have explored many parts of the oceans. They have used nets and dredges to collect organisms from various depths as well as from the bottom. An astounding assortment of marine animals has been discovered in this way, and they live in an astounding environment. Here there is no light, save for an occasional flash of a luminous fish, darting around like a firefly of the ocean's depths. Here there are no seasons. At great depths the water is always near freezing, even in the tropics.

Perpetual darkness and perpetual cold—how is life possible there? What is the source of energy? There can be no energy of the sun's rays to be used in synthesizing energy-rich glucose molecules. Yet there are animals that live in these depths, and bacteria that decompose them when they are dead. The animals survive in a strange way. They are, so to speak, garbage feeders. Their food chain begins in the surface waters, where the sun's light permits the growth of algae. The small animals of the

18–1 The environment of life. Evolution has produced species that live almost everywhere on the land and in the oceans. Life is most abundant in the upper 100 meters of the earth's oceans, and on land areas from sea level to an altitude of about 3,000 meters.

surface layers feed on the algae. Larger animals eat the smaller animals. Eventually the animals of the surface layers die. Some are eaten on the spot, but a few drift down into the world of darkness. It is this slow rain of corpses that provides food for the animals of the depths.

Elsewhere, among terrestrial organisms, all are bound in one way or another to the earth's surface. No organisms live solely in the air. Some animals of today, as of the past, such as insects, extinct flying reptiles, bats, and birds, invade the air for varying lengths of time. But these flying animals return to the earth's surface to feed or to rest. No plant lives solely in the air, though seeds and spores are airborne.

Man can escape from his normal environment and travel into outer space or into the depths of the sea only within a strong capsule containing air of nearly the same pressure, temperature, and chemical composition as that to which he is accustomed. He has to take his environment with him.

Some think that man's great success as an animal stems from his ability to use this idea. Cave shelters, fires for warmth, clothes, huts, houses, submarines, and space ships are all used or designed in such a way as to make a small part of the environment more suitable for human existence. You can find ways in which this is true for you wherever you are now.

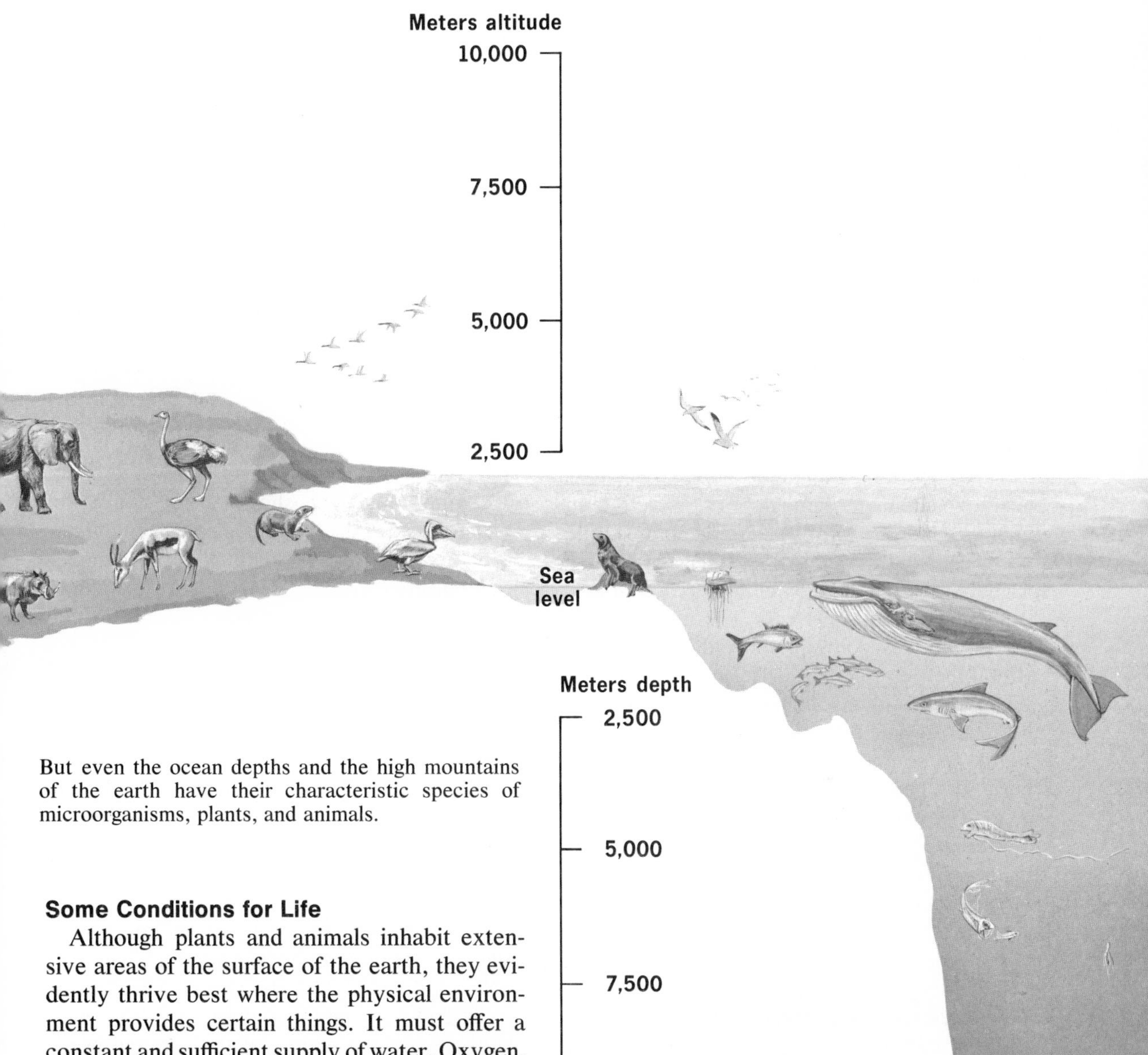

But even the ocean depths and the high mountains of the earth have their characteristic species of microorganisms, plants, and animals.

Some Conditions for Life

Although plants and animals inhabit extensive areas of the surface of the earth, they evidently thrive best where the physical environment provides certain things. It must offer a constant and sufficient supply of water. Oxygen, too, must be plentiful. In addition, plants must have supplies of carbon dioxide and nitrogen compounds in order to manufacture glucose, amino acids, and other organic compounds.

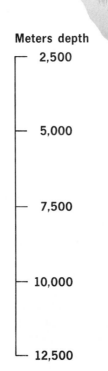

Oxygen and carbon dioxide can be found in the air and dissolved in water. Partly because of this, animals and plants may live either surrounded by air or surrounded by water. In the air, however, they face the problem of losing water. In terrestrial plants and animals the loss of water is controlled in part by the nature of the outer layer of the organism. This layer, of which our own skin is an example, is always partly or completely impermeable to water. Organisms living in water itself avoid this problem. Their outer coverings are often freely permeable to water.

Plants and animals can control the conditions within their cells in ways other than limiting the exchange of water. Yet these control processes can only be carried on successfully in a limited range of environmental conditions. We do not have to go far from the surface of the earth to encounter temperatures that living things cannot endure. Changes in air pressure also are important. In man, if the air pressure is very low, sufficient hemoglobin does not combine with oxygen to allow an adequate supply of oxygen to the body cells. This becomes a problem for individuals climbing mountains. Most persons feel the effects of insufficient oxygen at altitudes above 4,000 meters (13,000–14,000 feet).

Thus, living things can remain alive only if they can obtain the necessary chemical substances as sources of energy and for the synthesis of their living substance. They must have a fairly uniform range of temperature and air pressure. Is there, then, life on planets other than earth? We do not really know, but many scientists believe that the answer is yes. Astronomers tell us that the number of celestial bodies is tremendous. Some of these may be like our earth. If so, perhaps life could have started on one of these remote worlds.

There are numerous kinds of animals and plants occupying the many habitats of the earth's surface. Algae, bacteria, fungi, fishes, whales, seals, shellfish, worms, and many other types of animals are found in the oceans. Trees, mushrooms, mosses, ferns, flowering plants, birds, mammals, salamanders, snakes, insects, spiders, and other organisms occur in the forests. The prairies have numerous grasses and other plants as well as distinctive kinds of animals. Lakes, rivers, and ponds have their own species of animals and plants.

It has been estimated that there are perhaps more than two million species of plants and animals on the earth today. Biologists believe they have a reasonably satisfactory explanation for this diversity. Over the course of time, evolution has given rise to the many species. All are similar in some ways (Figure 18-2), but each has a particular way of life. We have referred to evolution before, and we shall consider it more fully in Chapters 31-32.

How Animals and Plants Are Alike and How They Differ

If animals and plants have evolved from the same ancestors, as biologists believe, it is not surprising that they should have many important features in common. You will encounter problems of distinguishing plants from animals in Laboratory Inquiry 18-1. Figure 18-2 indicates some of their common features in cell structure and cell division.

Numerous processes involved in synthesis of organic molecules and in energy transformation also are similar in plants and animals. The cells of both have many of the same kinds of enzymes. Both transfer the energy from glucose to ATP in similar processes of respiration.

Figure 18-2 also shows how green plants and animals differ in important ways. In addition to the differences illustrated, plants—in contrast to animals—are usually green; some plant cells possess chloroplasts, which are situated in the cytoplasm. The choroplasts contain enzymes and pigments like chlorophyll that help plants absorb the energy of the sun and use it to synthesize glucose. For the green plants are autotrophic and photosynthetic organisms, as you learned in Chapter 15. That is, they can synthesize all their living substances from CO_2, H_2O, and other simple inorganic molecules, by using the energy of sunlight. Animals, on the other hand, are heterotrophic. They require organic molecules for synthesis of their living substance and as energy sources.

18-2 PLANTS AND ANIMALS – LIKE AND UNLIKE

SIMILARITIES	DIFFERENCES	
Plant and animal	**Plant**	**Animal**
Both types of organisms are made of cells, with nuclei, nucleoli, chromosomes, mitochondria, ribosomes, Golgi bodies, enzymes, and cell membranes...	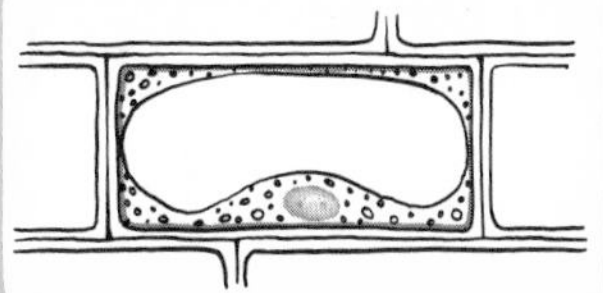 ...but most plant cells have cell walls...	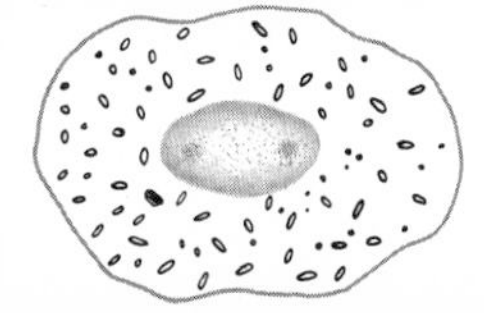 ...while animal cells do not.
Both plants and animals grow by means of cell growth and cell division...	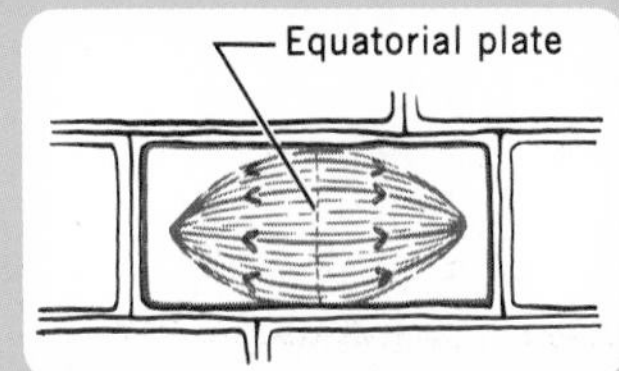 ...but cell division in plants...	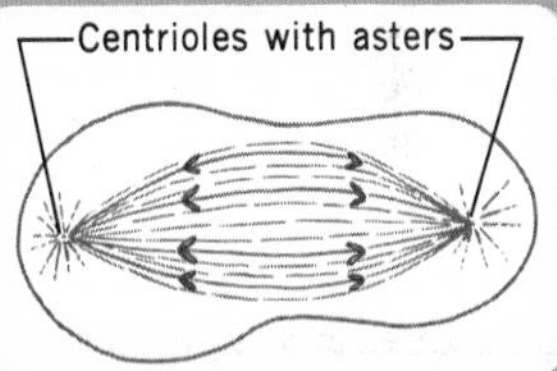 ...is not identical to that in animals.
Both plants and animals require food with carbon, hydrogen, oxygen, nitrogen, and other elements necessary for growth and maintenance...	 ...but plants usually make their food...	 ...while animals take it.
Both plants and animals digest food, excrete wastes, grow, respond to stimuli, and reproduce...	 ...but plants stay in one place as they carry on these life processes...	 ...while animals usually are free to move about their environments.

The Problem of Defining Animals

Now that we have examined similarities and differences between plants and animals, we should attempt to define the term "animal." Let's try: an animal is a living organism that can generally move from place to place and that depends on other organisms for the glucose and the amino acids and other organic molecules that it needs for life. We should add that its cells possess a thin, pliable cell membrane but no stiff outer cell wall and no chloroplasts.

This definition will distinguish between most, but not all, plants and animals. Despite shortcomings, it will suit our purposes.

Problems of Being an Animal

When we compared plants and animals, we said that animals are heterotrophic creatures. What does that mean? In a broad sense, they are parasites among living organisms. They must be food gatherers. Only in this way can they obtain the food substances they need and make these substances available as molecules or ions to all of their cells. Let us determine what kinds of molecules and ions are required, and how they are brought into animal cells.

Animals cannot, as green plants do, make their carbohydrates and fats from carbon dioxide (CO_2) and water (H_2O) alone; they must have organic molecules such as glucose and fats. They also cannot combine CO_2, H_2O, and nitrogen-containing salts to make proteins; they must take in amino acids. Similarly, to synthesize nucleic acids, animal cells must have both amino acids and simple sugars. In maintaining cell organization and in these various syntheses, vitamins, mineral substances, and water are also required.

The water and mineral substances (ions of calcium, phosphorus, sodium, and so on) are usually available to animals in the nonliving environment. On the other hand, simple sugars, fats, amino acids, and vitamins are not ordinarily available from the nonliving environment. They are formed only by living cells, and even here they are rarely available as such—that is, in "free" form—but combined in much larger molecules. The meat you eat, for example, contains only traces of *free* amino acids. Nearly all of the amino acids in the meat are chemically bonded to one another to form the proteins characteristic of the animal from which the meat came. Most of these proteins would be useless as such to your cells. Similarly, there is almost no free glucose in most foods. Instead, glucose occurs combined in large carbohydrate molecules.

Somehow, then, animal cells must obtain and break down the complex proteins, carbohydrates, and other molecules formed by plant cells or the cells of other animals to get the foodstuffs that are essential to animal maintenance and growth. And here is a further complication. With few exceptions, large molecules like proteins and carbohydrates are too big to cross cell membranes.

What a problem it is to be an animal!

Variations in the Animal Way

The difficulties we have noted are overcome by the cells of different animals in one of two ways (Figure 18-3).

1. If the large molecules can be taken into the cells by some means, they may be broken down chemically within the cells.
2. If the large molecules can be broken down into smaller molecules outside of the cells, the small molecules can diffuse into the cells or be taken in by active transport (Chapter 6, page 113).

Both of these processes of breakdown of large molecules are called *digestion*. The first is called **intracellular digestion** because it occurs inside cells. The second is called **extracellular digestion** because it occurs outside of cells.

Different species of animals may use one method, or the other, or even both. In man, both intracellular and extracellular digestion take place in the digestive tract.

Once the smaller molecules are inside a cell, they can be used either to synthesize more of

18-3 INTRACELLULAR vs. EXTRACELLULAR DIGESTION

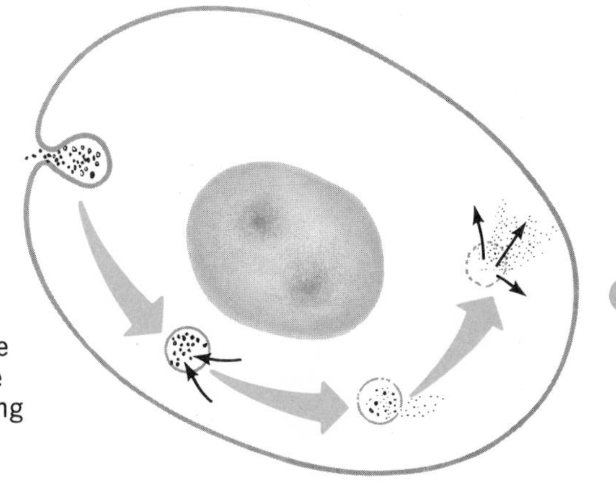
Intracellular
a Food is taken into the cell.
b The cytoplasm secretes digestive enzymes into the vacuole containing the food.
c The enzymes change large molecules to smaller ones.
d Small molecules enter the cytoplasm from the vacuole.

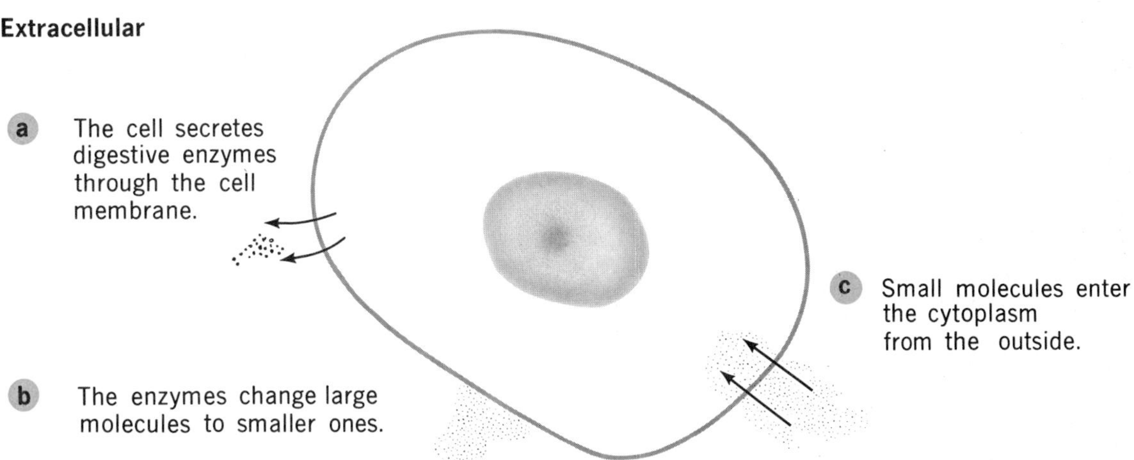
Extracellular
a The cell secretes digestive enzymes through the cell membrane.
b The enzymes change large molecules to smaller ones.
c Small molecules enter the cytoplasm from the outside.

the living material of the cell or to liberate energy. We saw in Chapter 5 and Chapter 6 that synthesis proceeds in a complex process involving ATP and similar energy-transfer compounds. We can summarize the reactions that transfer energy by this equation:

$$\underset{\text{glucose}}{C_6H_{12}O_6} + \underset{\text{oxygen}}{6\ O_2} \longrightarrow \underset{\text{carbon dioxide}}{6\ CO_2} + \underset{\text{water}}{6\ H_2O} + \underset{\text{(in ATP)}}{\text{energy}}$$

As a result of this complex process, oxygen is used in the cell, and carbon dioxide and water are produced. The oxidation of fats also requires oxygen and produces carbon dioxide and water. When proteins are oxidized, carbon dioxide and water are again produced. However, protein molecules also contain nitrogen. The nitrogen leaves the cell in a nitrogen-containing molecule such as urea. Thus, the total

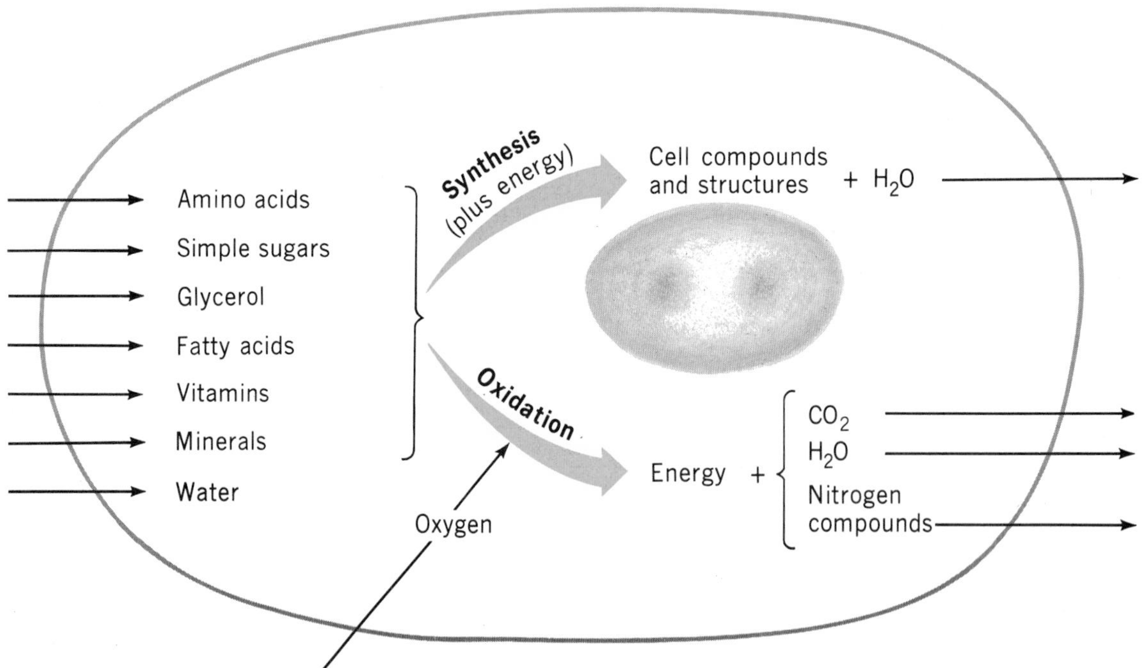

18–4 A summary of metabolism in an animal cell. All animal cells require similar substances, utilize them in similar ways, and eliminate similar waste products.

movement of substances into animal cells and out can be summarized as in Figure 18-4.

All cells in all animals have these same basic problems of obtaining the molecules they require and eliminating those in excess. The kinds of substances differ somewhat in detail from one animal to another. And even a moment's reflection will show you that different animals must have different ways of handling their problems of exchange with the environment.

Recall the microscopic animals that Leeuwenhoek saw when he examined drops of water with his crude microscope (Chapter 2, page 28). Some of these were protozoans, that is, single-celled animals. The cell membrane is in immediate contact with the surrounding environment—the primary source of the chemical substances required by the cells. Such are the conditions existing for single-celled animals.

Another set of conditions exists for many-celled animals. There are no living cells of your body exposed to the environment—apart from those of the **mucous** (MEW·kus) **membranes** lining the eyeballs and the respiratory and digestive passages. Except for these cells, which produce protective fluids to counter environmental hazards, the outer portion of your body consists of dead skin cells. Hair and nails are made by cells, but they are not living cells themselves. Your *living* cells are generally far removed from the food and oxygen of your environment. Yet each of your living cells must have these supplies, as with the protozoan.

Certain other many-celled animals have a layer of living cells covering their bodies. Even in these organisms, however, most of the body cells are within the body, remote from the primary source of food and oxygen.

Our study of animals will be an exploration of the many ways in which different animals solve the problem of keeping their cells, and hence themselves, alive. Our first examples will be two kinds of single-celled animals, or protozoans, ***Amoeba*** (uh·MEE·buh) and ***Paramecium*** (pair·uh·MEE·see·um). We will describe *Amoeba* in this chapter, and you will be able to study *Paramecium* for yourself in the laboratory (Inquiries 18-2 to 18-6). As you compare these two kinds of animals, you can get some insight into problems of living in one cell.

AMOEBA—THE ANIMAL WAY OF LIFE IN ONE CELL

If you search in almost any pond, you are likely to find the protozoan *Amoeba*. This animal is so small that it can just be seen with the unaided eye. We should qualify this statement, however; some species of *Amoeba* are larger or smaller than others, so that the length of the mature individual may be as little as 200 microns or as much as 600 microns, depending upon the species.

There are many kinds of *Amoeba* found all over the world, not only in fresh water ponds and lakes, but also in sea water and moist earth, and living as parasites in the bodies of larger animals. We will describe one particular kind of fresh water *Amoeba*—***Amoeba proteus*** (PRO-tee·us)—shown in Figure 18-5. The body form is irregular. Even more surprisingly, if you watch this *Amoeba* under the microscope, you can see that its form changes from time to time. Perhaps it rests quietly for a while, then

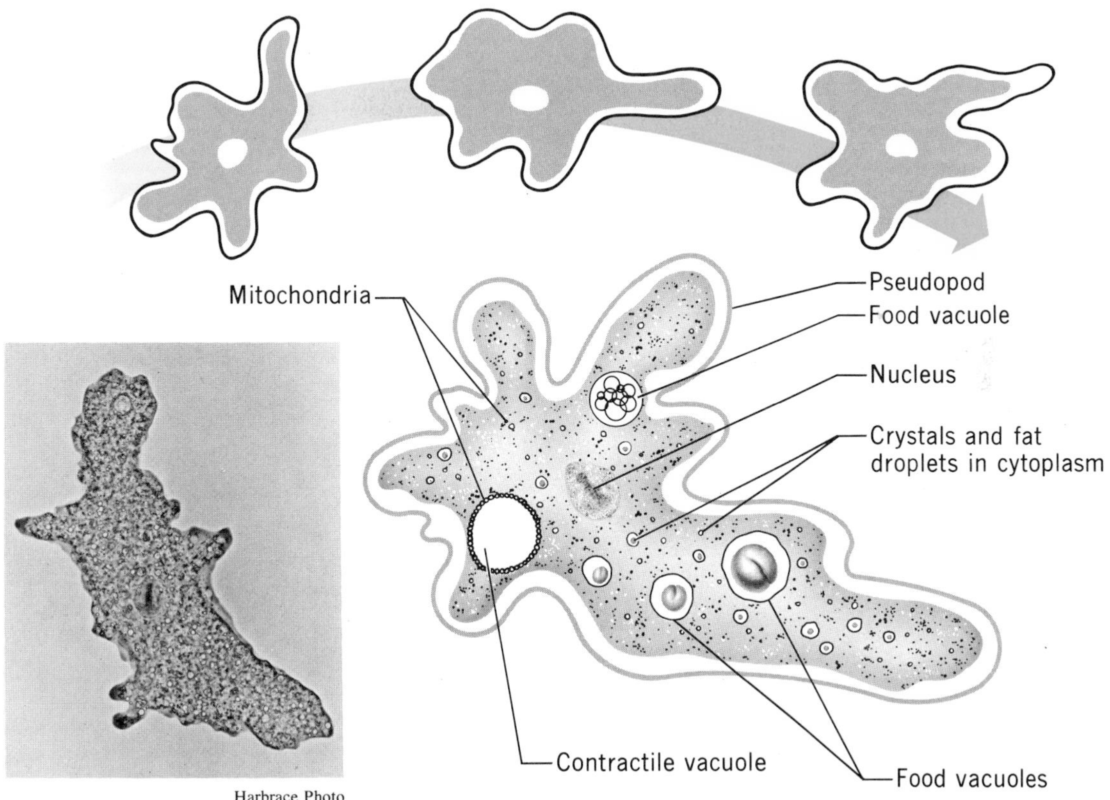

18–5 *Amoeba proteus*, a protozoan you will study in this chapter and compare with another, *Paramecium caudatum* (Figure 18–6), which you will investigate in the laboratory. *Amoeba* has no fixed form. It changes shape and moves in any direction.

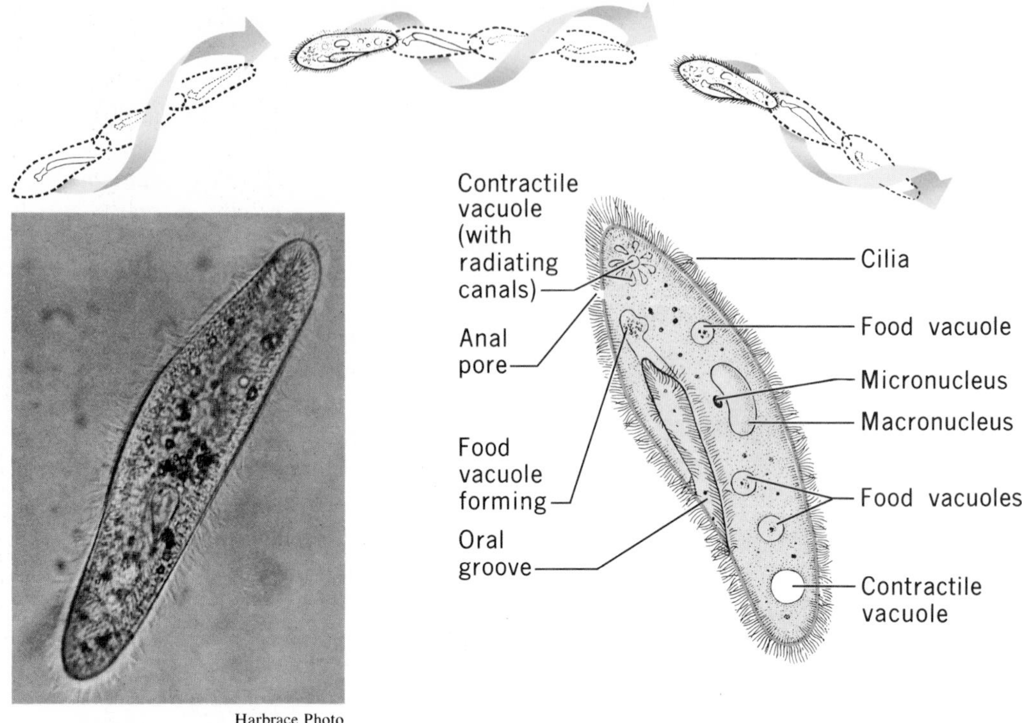

18–6 *Paramecium caudatum*, the protozoan of your laboratory studies. The photograph was taken through a compound microscope, as was the photograph of *Amoeba* in Figure 18–5. *Paramecium* has an anterior end and a characteristic swimming motion. Study the diagram of swimming movements, then identify the anterior end in each larger view.

part of the cell begins to bulge out, almost like a rather shapeless arm or leg. With the formation of this "arm" or **pseudopod** (SUE·doe·pod), the whole mass of the animal may move. The pseudopod can be drawn back into the animal's body, and new pseudopods formed. Meantime, inside the cell the cytoplasm is flowing around the nucleus. Close to the cell membrane the cytoplasm is more rigid. Probably formation of pseudopods depends on interactions between the rigid and flowing parts of the cytoplasm. This process requires cell energy, and is of the greatest importance since it gives the animal its ability to move and to feed. At the time when this book is being written, we do not yet know how this curious type of movement, called **amoeboid** (uh·MEE·boyd) **movement,** takes place. It will be interesting for you to compare form and movement in this *Amoeba* with form and movement in the beautifully structured little animal, *Paramecium* (Figure 18-6 and Laboratory Inquiries 18-2 to 18-6).

Feeding

Amoeba feeds on many kinds of tiny organisms that live with it in ponds and puddles. It is quite easy to see how this happens if you watch a living *Amoeba.* It may be sitting quietly on submerged wood or pond weed, then a *Paramecium* swims along and settles for a moment against the *Amoeba's* cell membrane. Almost instantly the *Amoeba's* cytoplasm begins to move out around the *Paramecium,* surrounding it with pseudopods. Unless the *Paramecium* starts swimming vigorously, it may be trapped in a cup-shaped mass of *Amoeba* cytoplasm. Soon the *Amoeba* flows all around the *Paramecium*, which is now inside a **food vacuole.** As the *Amoeba* moves about, it can take in many other kinds of food materials. Small plant cells, animals, and even bits of nonliving things are enclosed in food vacuoles in the cell in this way. But as we examine this feeding process closely, it becomes clear that *Amoeba* has not solved all its problems by taking food into its food vacuoles. The inside of the vacuole is surrounded by a membrane. What is *inside* the vacuole is still *outside* the cytoplasm of the *Amoeba*.

Digestion and Transport

As you continue to watch a single food vacuole, you will see several things happen. The vacuole is moved around in the cytoplasm and changes in form. First it may grow smaller, then larger, and the material inside it loses its clear-cut shape and color (Figure 18-7). You might guess that the material is changing chemically, and this is exactly what we think is happening. Apparently enzymes and substances that change the hydrogen ion concentration enter the vacuole from the cytoplasm and begin to break down the big molecules in the food. Then the smaller molecules that are formed, like glucose and amino acids, cross the food vacuole membrane into the cytoplasm. We do not yet know how enzymes enter the food vacuoles, nor how food materials leave them, but processes of diffusion and active transport must be involved.

While all of this is happening, the food vacuoles are moved about to all parts of the

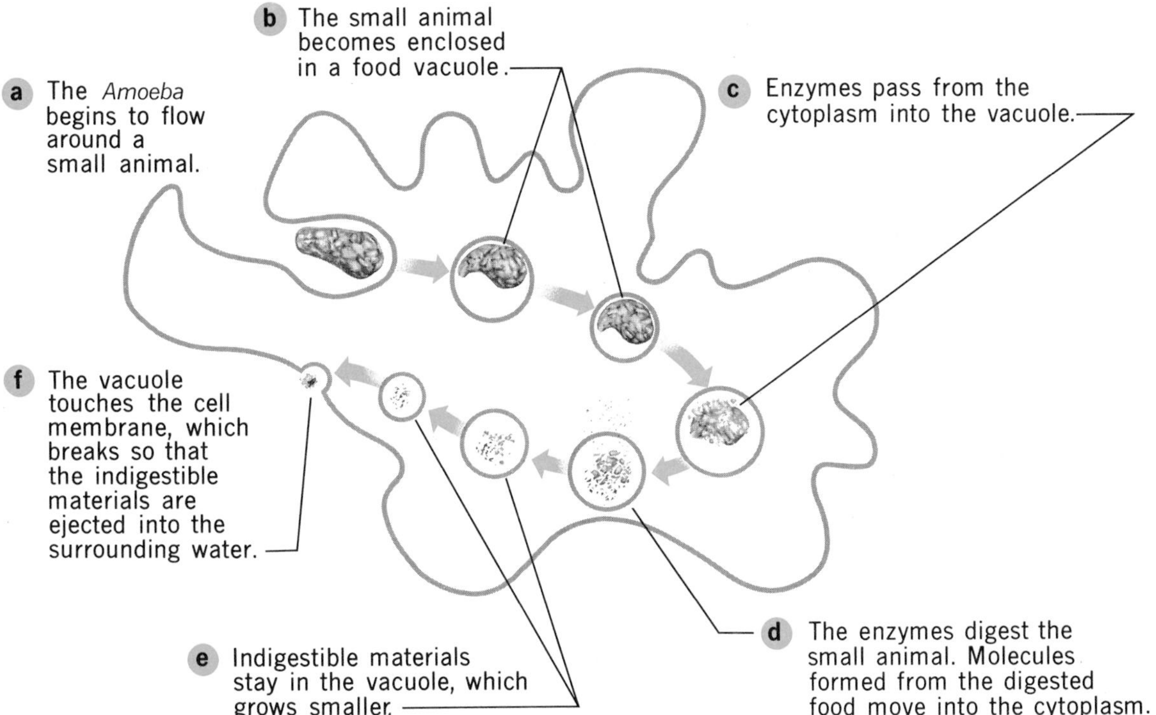

a The *Amoeba* begins to flow around a small animal.
b The small animal becomes enclosed in a food vacuole.
c Enzymes pass from the cytoplasm into the vacuole.
d The enzymes digest the small animal. Molecules formed from the digested food move into the cytoplasm.
e Indigestible materials stay in the vacuole, which grows smaller.
f The vacuole touches the cell membrane, which breaks so that the indigestible materials are ejected into the surrounding water.

18–7 Feeding and digestion in *Amoeba proteus*. These changes occur during the 12 to 24 hours following the formation of a single vacuole. An *Amoeba* may contain as many as 50 food vacuoles at once, each with food in different stages of digestion.

cell. In this way, digested foods are transported wherever they may be used. As you can see, food transport is quite simple in this one-celled organism.

Gradually the food vacuole becomes smaller and smaller in size as food materials leave it. Some indigestible materials remain, however. The food vacuole moves to the outside of the cytoplasm until it touches the cell membrane. Suddenly the membrane opens and the indigestible contents of the vacuole burst out into the surrounding water. Then the cell membrane quickly closes up, and the *Amoeba* moves off on its way.

Assimilation

The use of the products of digestion in synthesis of cellular structures is known as **assimilation** (uh·sim·ih·LAY·sh'n).

The movement of food vacuoles, plus the passage of small molecules across the food vacuole walls, supplies amino acids, sugars, and other food molecules to all parts of the cytoplasm. Within the confines of its single cell, *Amoeba* builds its living substance from the amino acids, simple sugars, and other substances that enter the cytoplasm. Its fats can be synthesized from molecules formed during the breakdown of carbohydrates.

Nucleic acids are synthesized from amino acids and simple sugars. The proteins, carbohydrates, fats, and nucleic acids synthesized by these one-celled animals differ from those of *Paramecium* and other organisms that an *Amoeba* eats. For example, *Paramecium* proteins are digested to amino acids and then used to synthesize "*Amoeba*-type" proteins. Highly specific nucleic acids (the hereditary basis for the animal being *Amoeba*) are synthesized from substances that a few hours before were highly specific for *Paramecium.*

Energy-releasing Reactions

The synthesis of structural needs such as proteins and nucleic acids in *Amoeba* is an energy-consuming process. To obtain the required energy, the animal oxidizes glucose and other organic molecules. The chemical energy released is used to synthesize ATP from ADP (see Chapter 6, pages 115-22). The energy of ATP is then used for all the energy-requiring activities of the cell. This is a very complicated process. In *Amoeba,* many of the reactions of oxidation occur in the mitochondria, as they do in other animals and plants; these reactions require oxygen, which is obtained from solution in the pond water (Figure 18-8) in which the *Amoeba* lives. The cell membrane is freely permeable to oxygen, which enters by simple diffusion.

Getting Rid of Wastes

As you may remember from page 120, carbon dioxide and water are formed when carbohydrates, fats, and proteins are broken down in reactions supplying energy to the cell. In the case of the oxidation of proteins, there is always at least one other product—one containing nitrogen. In *Amoeba proteus,* the chief nitrogenous product is ammonia (NH_3).

What becomes of the compounds formed in oxidation? Water is always needed in the cell, but if more is formed by respiration than can be used, the excess water is a waste product. Animal cells also can use small amounts of carbon dioxide, but most of what is formed during respiration is more than can be used. The excess carbon dioxide is a waste product, like excess water. Similarly, ammonia can be used in only small amounts—in fact, it is very poisonous to cells when present in large concentration. Thus, *Amoeba* must get rid of wastes if it is to survive.

This process of getting rid of the waste products formed by the biochemical reactions occurring within the body is known as **excretion** (ex·KREE·sh'n). *Amoeba* has no special structure for getting rid of two of the excretory products, namely, carbon dioxide and ammonia. It needs none, for these wastes simply diffuse from the cell into the surrounding pond water (Figure 18-9).

John A. Moore

18–8 A typical habitat of *Amoeba*. From the water of the pond, the animal takes food and oxygen; into the water go the indigestible remains of food and the wastes generated by the busy operations of living. This one pond probably contains billions of single-celled animals—more than the human population of the entire earth.

Diffusion in *Amoeba* is very effective, since these organisms are so small. And being small, they have a relatively large surface compared to their volume. That is, every part of *Amoeba* is close to the outside. Diffusion, aided by the fact that the cytoplasm of *Amoeba* is in constant motion, is sufficient to allow carbon dioxide and ammonia to pass from the cell to the surrounding water. Getting rid of excess water, however, is a special problem.

Amoeba and Water: an Example of Homeostasis

Amoeba proteus not only produces water as a waste product, but it lives surrounded by water. Its living substance contains more molecules of water than of anything else. Getting enough water is not a problem, but getting rid of *excess* water is. There is just too much water!

The cell membrane of *Amoeba* is freely permeable to water, but not to many of the substances in the cytoplasm. So far as relative concentration is concerned, the cytoplasm of *Amoeba* has less water than the surrounding pond (which will be more than 99.5 percent water). With a greater concentration of water on the outside than on the inside, and with a permeable membrane between, the result is inevitable. The net movement of water is from the pond into the cytoplasm. Water constantly enters the body of *Amoeba* more rapidly than it moves out. We have considered this process of water entry by osmosis in Chapter 6 and

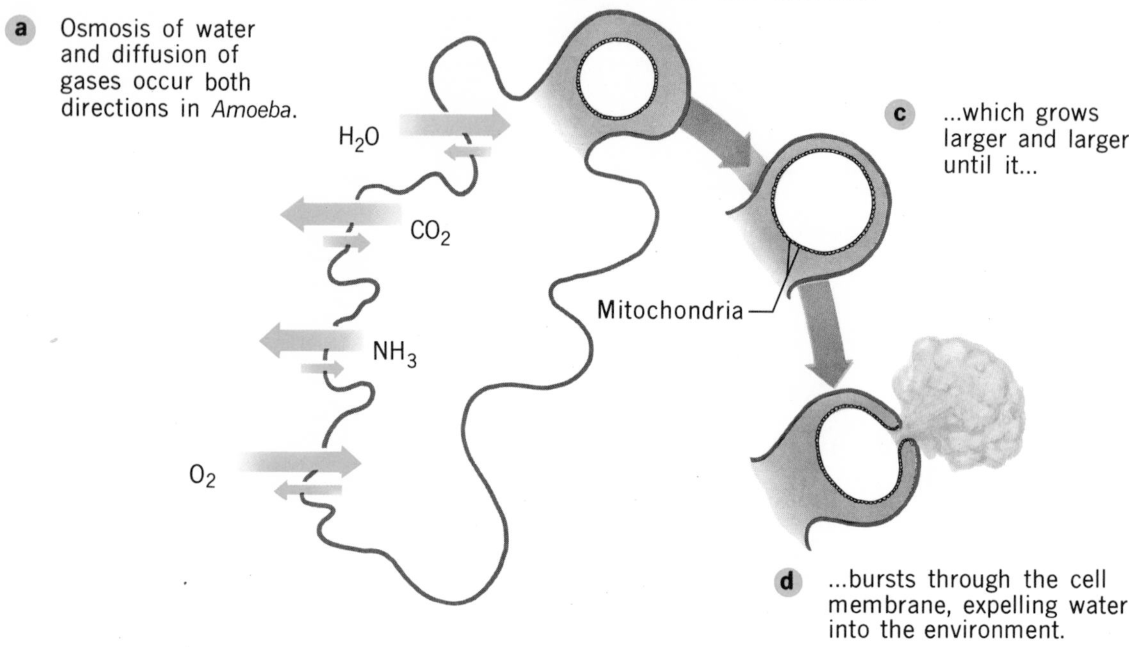
b Excess water entering the Amoeba by osmosis is passed from the cytoplasm into the contractile vacuole...
a Osmosis of water and diffusion of gases occur both directions in Amoeba.
H_2O
CO_2
NH_3
O_2
c ...which grows larger and larger until it...
Mitochondria
d ...bursts through the cell membrane, expelling water into the environment.

18–9 Like all other animals, *Amoeba proteus* has problems of exchanging substances between the inside of the cell and the outside environment. Oxygen, carbon dioxide, and ammonia move by diffusion; water movement occurs by osmosis and the activity of the contractile vacuole. The net exchanges are indicated by the heavier arrows.

Laboratory Inquiry 6-4. If no other processes were involved, the body of the *Amoeba* would swell and, in a short time, burst.

To survive, *Amoeba* must be able to bail itself out! It does this by means of a structure known as a **contractile** (kon·TRAK·til) **vacuole** (Figure 18-9).

This is only one of the many illustrations of a great principle in biology termed **homeostasis** (hoh·me·o·STAY·sis)—the capacity of living things to maintain constant or nearly constant internal conditions.

Notice that the homeostasis in this case involves the transfer of water from a region of lower concentration (the cell) to a region of higher concentration (the pond). Energy must be provided for this to be done. The energy for the activities of the contractile vacuole comes, as you might guess, from ATP. This was recognized when it was discovered that an *Amoeba* swells up and may die when it is poisoned with compounds that interfere with the activity of enzymes in forming ATP. Biologists do not yet understand how the contractile vacuole fills, nor how it empties. We also do not understand how energy is supplied for this important process of "bailing out the cell." So far, almost the only clue we have in this problem is an observation made with high powered microscopes. Numerous mitochondria are closely packed around the contractile vacuole of an *Amoeba* (Figure 18-9). As you may remember from Chapter 6, mitochondria are the structures that form most of the cell's ATP.

Coordination and Behavior

Amoeba has no nervous system—it is, after all, unicellular in organization. Nevertheless, its behavior is coordinated: it can clearly make appropriate responses to stimuli in its environment. When an *Amoeba* bumps into an obstruction, it can back away by changing the direction in which it forms pseudopods. Or, instead, it can flow around an object small enough for the *Amoeba* to take it into a food vacuole. These different ways of reacting involve coordinated movements. There is much uncertainty, however, as to just how coordination occurs.

Amoeba clearly can avoid harmful areas in its environment, such as a place where the pond water is too acid. Where it goes, it seems to find its food both by accidental contact and by some sort of chemical sense. An *Amoeba* responds to light, too, often becoming less active when exposed to strong light. As far as we know now, its movements are based on trial and error, and it has little if any capacity to learn—that is, to modify its behavior in the light of experience.

Reproduction

Amoeba reproduces asexually. Asexual reproduction is by cell division, with an animal dividing nearly in half to produce two individuals. The internal events involve division of the nucelus by mitosis and distribution of about half the cytoplasm to each daughter cell (Figure 18-10). To each daughter cell, too, go special cytoplasmic structures like the mitochondria. The one contractile vacuole of the original cell disappears before cell division, but a contractile vacuole appears in each daughter cell within a few minutes of the time when the daughter becomes independent of its sister cell. This whole process, by which one *Amoeba* turns into two, takes place in about half an hour at a temperature around 20° C. It raises some questions about the life of an individual *Amoeba* because, as you can see, an *Amoeba* reproducing in this way disappears as an individual. Would you say that the parent *Amoeba* had died? Hardly, since each of its halves continues to live as a daughter *Amoeba*. Thus, unless killed by some accident, an *Amoeba* never dies, although it does cease to exist.

It is interesting to compare this pattern of life with the pattern seen in animals that reproduce sexually, like some kinds of *Paramecium* and all people.

When *Amoeba* reproduces *asexually,* both new individuals possess sets of chromosomes identical with those of the parent individual. In other words, the daughter individuals will be identical insofar as their heredity is concerned. Whatever life the parent was fit for, the offspring will be fit for. Whatever conditions the parent could not endure will be unendurable for the offspring, too.

On the other hand, in the case of animals which reproduce sexually, each new individual is to some degree different from either parent. It receives a monoploid nucleus from each one. If the hereditary elements, the genes, are at all different in the two lines of ancestry that are brought together in the mating, then the combination of genes will be a new one. Sexual mating, in other words, introduces *variety* into the hereditary constitution of new individuals. Thus, different patterns of reproduction have a most important relation to the long-range history of living organisms. We will discuss these problems in much more detail in Chapter 32.

The *Amoeba* Population and Its Community

The animal way of life includes the place of the individual in the population and the community of which it is a part. Our treatment of *Amoeba* would not be balanced if we considered only the life of an individual. If the conditions for life are favorable, individuals multiply and soon form a population of large numbers. The number in any given environment depends upon several factors, such as the time since the population began to grow, the amount of food, the available space, and the presence or absence

18-10 REPRODUCTION IN *AMOEBA*

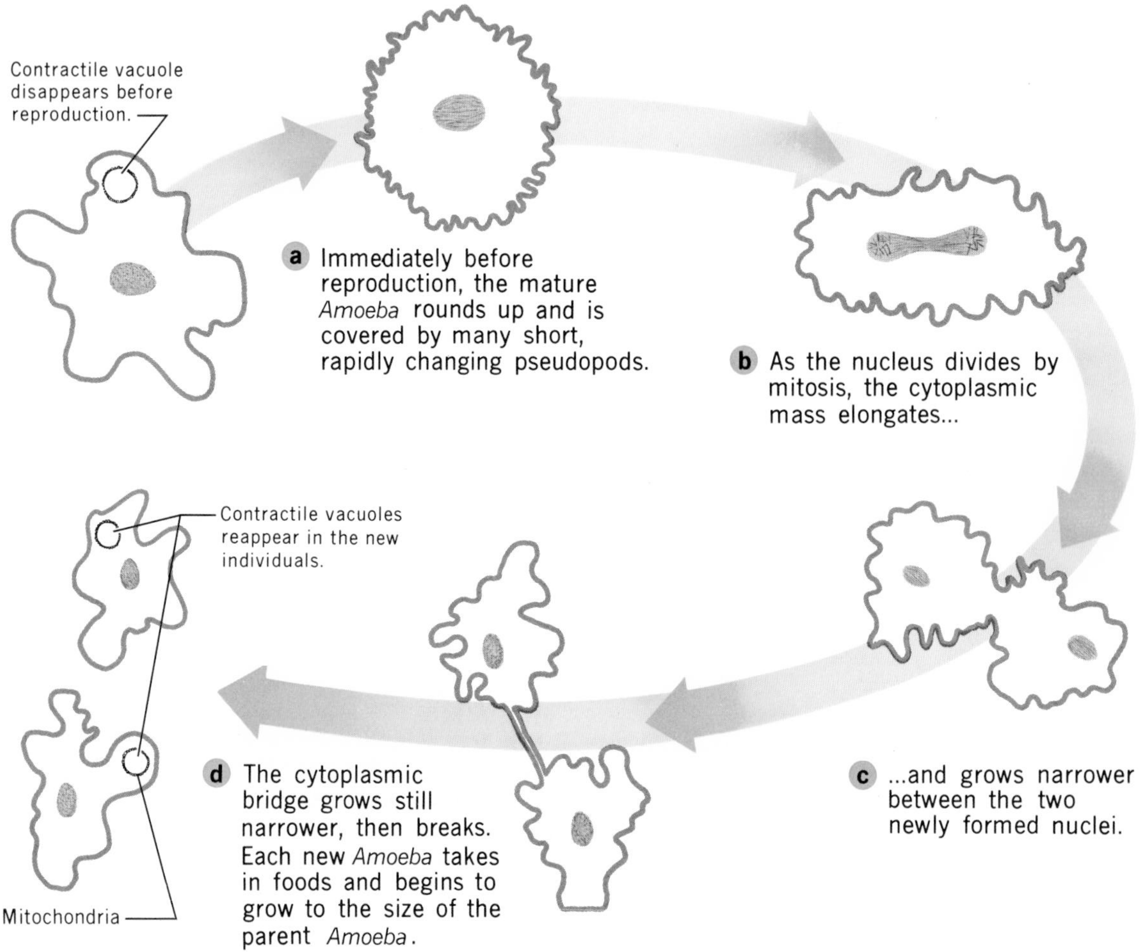
Contractile vacuole disappears before reproduction.
a Immediately before reproduction, the mature Amoeba rounds up and is covered by many short, rapidly changing pseudopods.
b As the nucleus divides by mitosis, the cytoplasmic mass elongates...
c ...and grows narrower between the two newly formed nuclei.
Contractile vacuoles reappear in the new individuals.
d The cytoplasmic bridge grows still narrower, then breaks. Each new Amoeba takes in foods and begins to grow to the size of the parent Amoeba.
Mitochondria

of predatory creatures that eat *Amoeba*. Studies of the growth of *Amoeba* populations in the laboratory illustrate some interesting general principles about population increase. Whether one studies yeast cells, bacteria, fruit flies, mice, or men, the same relationships appear.

Suppose we start with a single *Amoeba* in a culture vessel with plenty of food. It divides to make two, the two make four, the four make eight, and so on. In a few days there will very likely be more than one hundred individuals (Figure 18-11). At first the growth is rapid, until the population becomes crowded in its living space. Then the rate of increase becomes less and less, until finally there is no increase in numbers. We say that the population, in this stage of its history, has reached a maximum. Thereafter one of several things may happen. If the food supply is continually replenished (but not increased), the population may remain at a constant size. If the food supply diminishes, the population will decrease. Under certain conditions the population size will fluctuate.

To illustrate this, let us turn to a population of *Paramecium,* the organism on which your laboratory study is based. The graph of population growth of *Amoeba* in Figure 18-11 could represent the growth of a *Paramecium* colony, too, with some change in the details of timing. The food of *Paramecium* is itself most likely to be some form of living organism. Suppose we plan to feed our *Paramecium* culture on a pure culture of growing yeast cells, which are themselves growing in a sugar solution. We may begin by establishing the yeast population in the sugar solution. It will grow, showing a pattern like the one illustrated in Figure 18-11. Probably the yeast cells will reach a maximum number, depending on the food supply. When the first *Paramecium* is introduced into this environment, it will multiply rapidly. But as the *Paramecium* population increases and eats the yeast cells, the growth of the yeast population will be checked. As the yeast population declines until it reaches a minimum, the *Paramecium* population will begin to starve. The individuals first stop multiplying and then diminish in number. When very few are left, the yeast cells will multiply faster than the *Paramecium* population and soon reach a maximum number

18-11 GROWTH OF A LABORATORY POPULATION OF *AMOEBA*

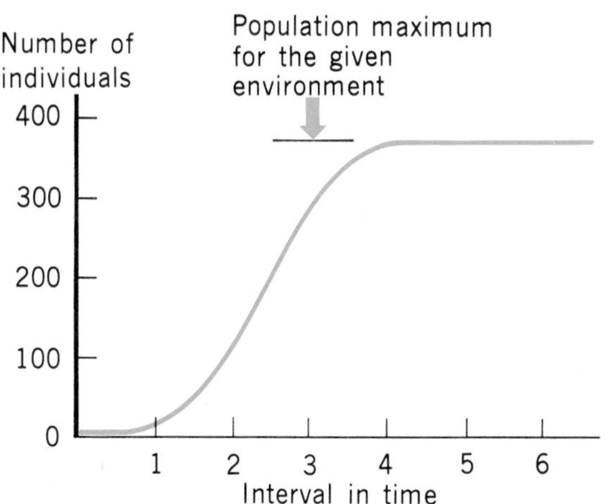

18-12 FLUCTUATIONS IN POPULATIONS OF *AMOEBA* AND *PARAMECIUM*

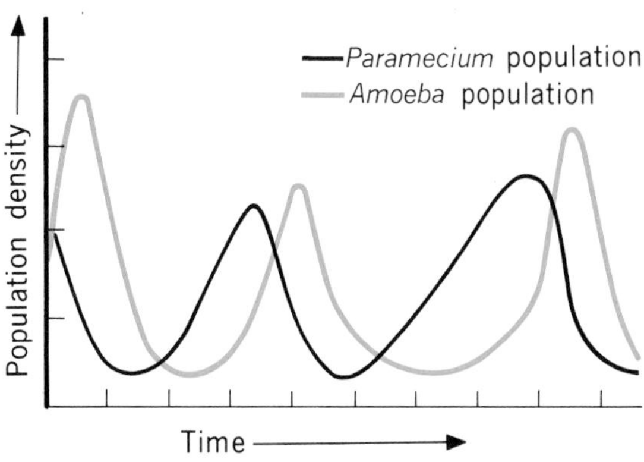

again. But this encouragement to the *Paramecium* population to multiply sets the cycle in motion again.

The same phenomenon occurs with a *Paramecium* population that is being preyed upon by *Amoeba.* The two populations fluctuate in an interlocked rhythm (Figure 18-12). Now try to figure out how yeast, *Paramecium,* and *Amoeba* populations will all oscillate in rhythm.

Another sort of relationship occurs when two similar species of *Amoeba* occupy the same environment. Competition for food results between them, and the faster-reproducing species gains the advantage. Soon the population of the slower-reproducing species diminishes, and may die out, while the faster-reproducing species flourishes.

The natural environment of *Amoeba* is a variable and impermanent one. Little pools of water containing organic matter afford a temporary spot for bacteria to grow. Soon the *Amoeba* population increases in numbers, and then predatory animals that eat *Amoeba* may appear. Or bacteria and fungi may start growing on the population of *Amoeba.* Where do these parasites and predators come from? The pool may quickly dry up; and even ponds freeze in winter. Where does the *Amoeba* population disappear to, along with the organisms they eat and are eaten by? Like most other microorganisms, *Amoeba* can form **cysts** (SISTS) or spores. The individuals become inactive; there are changes in their structure; finally they are encased in tough-walled, drought-resistant capsules. Tiny living organisms, in cyst or spore form, can endure great extremes of heat and cold and drought, adverse pH, low oxygen concentration, and a variety of other environmental conditions that would make active life impossible for them. This remarkable process explains in part why *Amoeba*, which seems so small and defenseless, has survived for countless generations.

CONCLUDING REMARKS

Amoeba has served to show us how one kind of animal lives. It has the same general problems as do all animals. To survive, it must—

Procure food composed of proteins, carbohydrates, fats, vitamins, and inorganic substances.
Digest food, that is, break it down into smaller molecules such as amino acids and simple sugars.
Transport the molecules of digested food into the body, and through all parts of the body.
Assimilate the molecules of digested food to form structures of the cell.
Respire, or transfer some of the energy in the molecules of digested food to ATP and similar molecules that store energy.
Exchange gases with the environment—absorb oxygen and expel carbon dioxide.
Excrete wastes, including excess water and nitrogen compounds.
Coordinate behavior in obtaining food, avoiding enemies, and avoiding situations in the environment that are harmful.
Reproduce, that is, produce offspring like the parents.
Grow and *develop*.
Defend itself against unfavorable conditions.

Amoeba does all of this within the confines of a single cell. But is it truly a single cell? Let us consider this question.

If we wish to decide whether or not *Amoeba* is a cell, we must first decide on an acceptable definition of a cell. In the morphological sense, we might say that a cell is a structure containing a nucleus, cytoplasm with a variety of particles such as mitochondria, Golgi bodies, ribosomes, and centrioles, and an enclosing cell membrane. In a general sense, *Amoeba* fits this definition. It resembles in many ways the single cells of our own bodies. In fact, it is very similar to some human blood cells, which look like *Amoeba*, move about by amoeboid movement, take materials into food vacuoles, and generally behave in their way of living very much like *Amoeba proteus*.

In other ways, *Amoeba* also resembles our *entire* body. That is, both we and *Amoeba proteus* are *organisms* that must obtain food, digest it, respond to stimuli, reproduce, grow, and so on. Without doubt, we must admit that *Amoeba* is an organism. It carries on an independent life in marked contrast to the dependent existence of each of our body cells. Looking at *Amoeba* in this way, we might say that it is an organism whose body is not divided into cells (it could not be, of course, if it consisted of only one cell!).

So *Amoeba* can be thought of either as a single cell that carries out all of the basic functions of an organism, or as an organism whose body is not divided into cells. In short, cell and organism are one in *Amoeba,* and in most other protozoans.

GUIDE QUESTIONS AND PROBLEMS

1. What environmental factors limit the distribution of plants and animals on earth? In what ways does each factor limit distribution?
2. What would be the consequences to animal life if biological decomposers no longer carried out their activities?
3. Why must animals digest proteins, large carbohydrate molecules, and complex fat molecules before these food materials can be used?
4. How can you account for the observation, graphically displayed in Figure 18-12, that changes in

one population of organisms may be dependent upon changes in a population of another species?
5. Consider the following situation. A biologist observed that an *Amoeba* living in a pond had a contractile vacuole that emptied four times every minute. The same *Amoeba*, in 1 percent salt solution, shrank and the biologist could see no contractile vacuole. When placed in water without salts of any kind, the *Amoeba* became swollen and the contractile vacuole emptied ten times every minute. How would you explain these observations?
6. Why do animals need protein in their diet?
7. If the food vacuoles in *Amoeba* are serving as food digestion chambers, what types of digestive enzymes would you expect to find in them? Why might pH changes (changes in hydrogen ion concentration) take place in the food vacuoles during the course of the digestion?
8. In what ways are an *Amoeba's* energy-releasing reactions similar to ours?
9. How is it that *Paramecium*-type proteins and fats can be converted to *Amoeba*-type proteins and fats, even though the molecules involved are complex and in many cases very different from one animal to the other?

RELATED READING

Books

For handsomely illustrated introductions to the world of animals . . .

Buchsbaum, Ralph, *Animals Without Backbones*, Second Edition, University of Chicago Press, Chicago, 1948.

Buchsbaum, Ralph, and Lorus J. Milne, *The Lower Animals: Living Invertebrates of the World*, Doubleday, New York, 1960 (revised printings 1962 and 1964).

von Frisch, Karl, *Biology*, Harper and Row, New York, 1964.

Magazines

Allen, Robert D., "Amoeboid Movement," *Scientific American*, Volume 206 (February 1962), page 112.

19

The Diversity Among Animals — Variations on a Theme

It has been estimated that nearly two million species of animals now live on the earth. They range in complexity from relatively simple single-celled *Amoeba proteus* to large, complex, book-writing *Homo sapiens* (HO·mo SAY·pih-enz). Some live in the sea, some on land; some walk, others fly, and still others are as stationary as the flowering plants.

Each has its own way of life. *Amoeba* has one way—that of a particular kind of animal that lives in ponds. There are many other ways of life in the Animal Kingdom—that of an earthworm, fly, shark, sparrow, and man—to name just a few. Each species of animal alive today has its own way of doing things—securing food, avoiding enemies and unfavorable environments, finding a place to live, and reproducing its kind.

When we realize that there are so many species of animals, it becomes clear that no one can learn about the way of life of each. Even if it were possible or desirable to do so, it would be unnecessary for this reason: although each species has its own way of living, these ways of living are not equally different. For example, a bullfrog and a green frog are different species, yet their ways of life have many features in common. Both spend most of their lives along the edges of ponds and lakes. Both eat insects. They digest their food, breathe, excrete, and reproduce in almost identical ways. Their nuclei contain the same number of chromosomes. They respond in similar ways to heat or cold and enemies such as snakes or man. Thus if one knows about the life of a bullfrog, much of the knowledge would also apply to the green frog. And, as a matter of fact, it would apply to most kinds of frogs.

CLASSIFICATION

We might say, therefore, that there is a "frog way of life"—just as in more detail there is a "green frog way of life" and a "bullfrog way of life." That is, there are groups of animals that do similar things in similar ways. Biological classification is a recognition of this—it is the arrangement of living organisms into groups of similar species. There are many different groupings beginning with *species* and ending with *kingdom*. Thus, you and all other human beings belong to the species *Homo sapiens*. In addition, you and all other animals belong to the group **Kingdom Animalia** (an·ih·MAY·lih·a).

Species

A system for classifying organisms has developed gradually over the past 300 years. It was not until the late seventeenth century that an Englishman, John Ray (1627–1705), developed a clear concept of species. To him a species consisted of offspring of similar parents. The concept has been modified since the time of Ray. We now look upon a species as a group of individuals that can breed with one another. At the same time individuals of one species do not usually breed with individuals of other species *in nature*. We must emphasize the "in nature" because many species can crossbreed under artificial conditions even though they do not under natural conditions. Figure 19-1 shows a handsome example.

It was left to the eighteenth-century Swedish biologist Carolus Linnaeus (CARE·oh·lus lih-NEE·us) to establish the rules that are used for naming organisms. Linnaeus gave every species that he knew a name of two words. Hence his system is known as **binomial nomenclature** (by-NOHM·ih·al NOHM·en·klay·tyoor). The first word of the species name is the name of the **genus** (pl., **genera**) to which it belongs. The second name is the so-called descriptive or trivial name. Both words are Latin or Latinized Greek (later systematists have not always used classical words in naming organisms). The genus and descriptive name together constitute the species name of the organism concerned. For example, the large group of cats was given the generic (genus) name *Felis* (FEE·lis). A particular group of cats was given the trivial name *leo.* These words together, *Felis leo,* are used for the lion, one species of cat. The scientific name of the common house cat is *Felis domesticus* (doh·MES·tih·kus); of the tiger, *Felis tigris* (TI·gris). All are cats, but each is a different species of cat.

Linnaeus listed 4,236 species of animals in his *Systema Naturae* of 1758. The total today is almost a million known species. We are sure there are just as many, and possibly more, that have not been named.

To ensure that no two groups of animals get the same specific name, a very elaborate system has been set up for classifying animals. There is even an international court of biologists that will decide any disputed cases of naming that occasionally occur.

Utah Zoological Society

19–1 The liger's mother is a tiger and its father a lion. Individuals of different species rarely crossbreed in nature, but in captivity similar species of animals and plants can often be crossed experimentally. This liger was born in a zoo.

19-2 EXAMPLES OF ANIMAL CLASSIFICATION

Common Name	Species Name
Man	*Homo sapiens*
Lion	*Felis leo*
House cat	*Felis domesticus*
Tiger	*Felis tigris*
Dog	*Canis familiaris*
Gopher	*Thomomys bottae*
Gopher	*Spermophilus tridecimlineatus*
American robin	*Turdus migratorius*
European robin	*Erithacus rubecula*
Gopher turtle	*Gopherus polyphemus*
Green frog	*Rana clamitans*
Bullfrog	*Rana catesbeiana*
Paramecium	*Paramecium caudatum*

The Need for Binomial Nomenclature

Many students question the need of giving animals scientific names based on Latin. Why does a robin, for example, require a scientific name? As an indication of the need, the "robin" in England is a very different species from the "robin" of North America. Which one do you mean by "robin"?

Let us take another example. The word "gopher" is known to people in many parts of the United States. In California a gopher is a small burrowing rodent. Its scientific name is *Thomomys bottae* (THOH·mo·mis BOT·ee). In the Midwest a gopher is a 13-lined ground squirrel—the lines are on its back—whose scientific name is *Spermophilus tridecimlineatus* (sper·MOF·ih·lus try·des·im·lin·e·AY·tus). In Florida a gopher is not a rodent at all, but a kind of turtle, or tortoise, whose scientific name is *Gopherus polyphemus* (GO·fer·us pol·ih·FEE·mus). Thus, the word *gopher* is ambiguous.

Can you imagine the confusion that would result if a biologist from California, one from Iowa, and one from Florida got together and the topic of "gophers" was brought up?

A scientific name has the advantage of standing for a single kind of animal, plant, or microorganism throughout the world. It reveals in a small way what great advantages a universal language would confer.

The Classification of Species

The group *species* is the starting point for classification. Sometimes smaller groups, *subspecies,* are recognized, but these will not concern us until we discuss evolution. There are many larger groups: genus, family, order, class, phylum, and kingdom. These groups are suc-

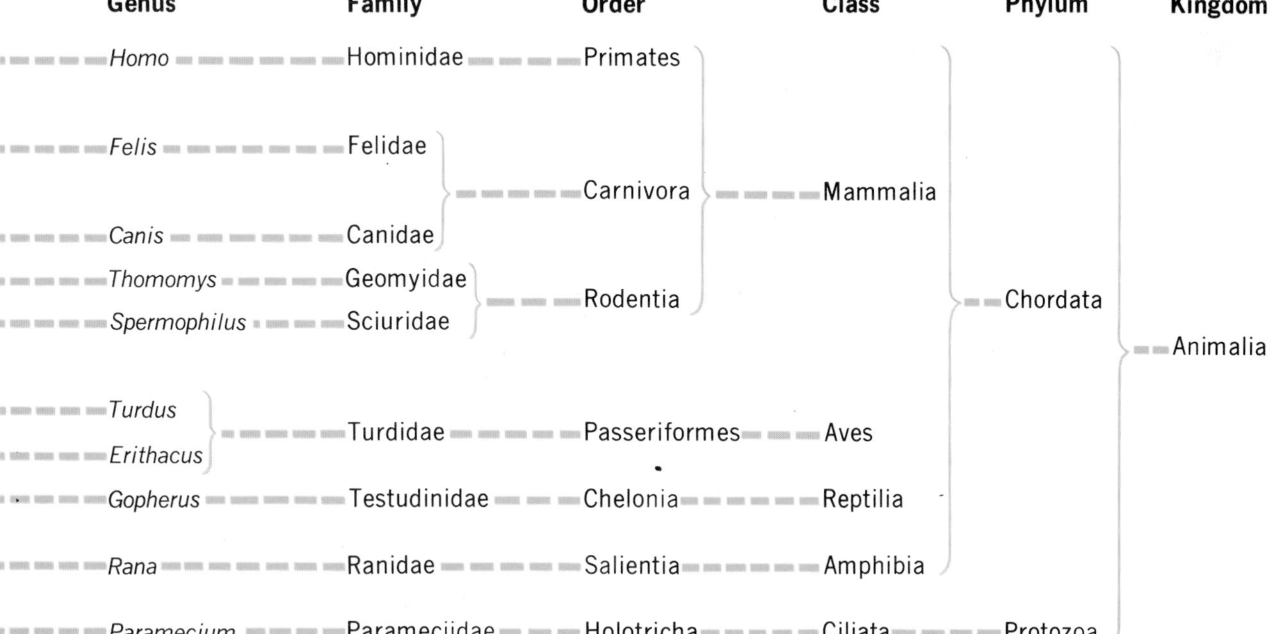

cessively more inclusive. The relation of the various groups is shown in Figure 19-2, which shows the classification of the species we have been discussing.

Let us begin with the first seven species. We belong to the genus *Homo* and to more inclusive groups: (1) the family **Hominidae** (hoh·MIN·ih·dee), which includes, in addition to *Homo,* extinct men *not* of the genus *Homo,* and (2) the order **Primates** (pry·MAY·teez), which includes also the lemurs, monkeys, and apes. The three cats—lion, house cat, and tiger—belong to the genus *Felis.* In general we can think of a **genus** as a group of closely related species. The three cats also belong to the family **Felidae** (FEE·lih·dee). Generally a **family** includes related genera (in the table, this is shown only in the case of the two genera of robins). The dog, on the other hand, belongs to a different genus, *Canis* (KAY·nis), which also includes the wolves and coyotes, and to a different family, **Canidae** (KAN·ih·dee). The dogs and cats, however, do resemble one another in many ways. You will agree that they look more similar to one another than to a man or a horse. On the basis of their resemblances, the families Felidae and Canidae are put in a common order, **Carnivora** (kar·NIV·o·ra). Generally an **order** includes related families.

In a similar way, two of the "gophers" (excluding the tortoise) are not enough alike to be included in the same genus, or even in the same family, but they are alike enough to be put in a still more inclusive group, the order **Rodentia** (ro·DEN·she·a).

The first seven species, different enough to be put in three orders, are yet alike in many ways. All are covered with hair, they nurse their young with milk, and their red blood cells are without nuclei. Because of these and other resemblances they are combined in a still more inclusive group, Class **Mammalia** (ma·MAY-lih·a). A **class,** therefore, is composed of related orders.

What is the relation of these first seven species, which we classify as Mammalia, to the other species in the list? A close study would show that all, with the exception of *Paramecium,* have certain points of resemblance. For example, all have a backbone. Their internal organs are also alike in many ways. All have gills, or structures like gills, in their embryonic stages. These general resemblances are sufficient for us to recognize a still more inclusive group, Phylum **Chordata** (kor·DAY·ta). A **phylum,** then, includes similar classes.

Paramecium, which you have studied intensively in the laboratory, is so different from the other species listed that it, together with other single-celled animals, is placed in Phylum Protozoa. *Amoeba proteus* is another protozoan.

Finally, the Chordata, the Protozoa, and the many other animal phyla not represented in Figure 19-2 are grouped together as the Animal Kingdom. The Animal Kingdom and the Plant Kingdom are all-inclusive for our purposes. Some biologists, however, prefer to put viruses, bacteria, unicellular plants, and unicellular animals in a third kingdom, the **Protista** (pro·TISS·ta).

Biologists have classified all of the known animals and plants in the way just described. Their system of classification not only shows how organisms are related to one another, but it also conveys much information about the organisms themselves. This can be brought out by analogy. Suppose you are told that object X belongs to a group "vehicles." Even if you have never seen this particular X you would be able to make some very general predictions about its structure and function. It would probably have wheels or runners, be used for carrying objects or people, and so on. If you were then told that X belongs to a more specific group "vehicles with internal combustion engines," you could make more specific predictions. It would probably have spark plugs and pistons and use a fuel derived from petroleum. If you were told that X is an "automobile" you would be able to make still more specific predictions. Finally, if you were told that X is a "Ford automobile" you would know a great deal more about it. The group, Ford, might be thought to correspond to the group, genus, in biological classification. The many kinds of Fords would correspond to the various biological species within a genus.

Biological classification, then, is a useful and important way of systematizing biological knowledge. Just as the word "automobile" carries certain connotations, so does the word "Mammalia." When a biologist is told that Y is a mammal, he immediately knows a great deal about its structure and way of life. Not only will he know that Y has hair, nurses its young, and has no nuclei in its red blood cells, but a host of other things as well.

Homology, the Major Basis of Classification

We might well ask what criteria are used to classify animals into groups. Briefly, the animals placed in a particular group all have many fundamental similarities in their structure. It is not always easy to recognize these basic similarities. At first sight, the flipper of a whale, the wing of a bat, and the arm of a man do not seem to have much in common. The first is used for swimming, the second for flying, and the third, with its hand, for grasping. Yet if one examines their internal structure—the bones and muscles—it can be seen that the three are very much alike (Figure 19-3). The flipper, wing, and arm are all built on the same pattern. During the course of evolution, each has been modified from the basic pattern to serve a particular, and usually highly specialized, function.

The flipper, wing, and arm are believed to resemble one another because they originated

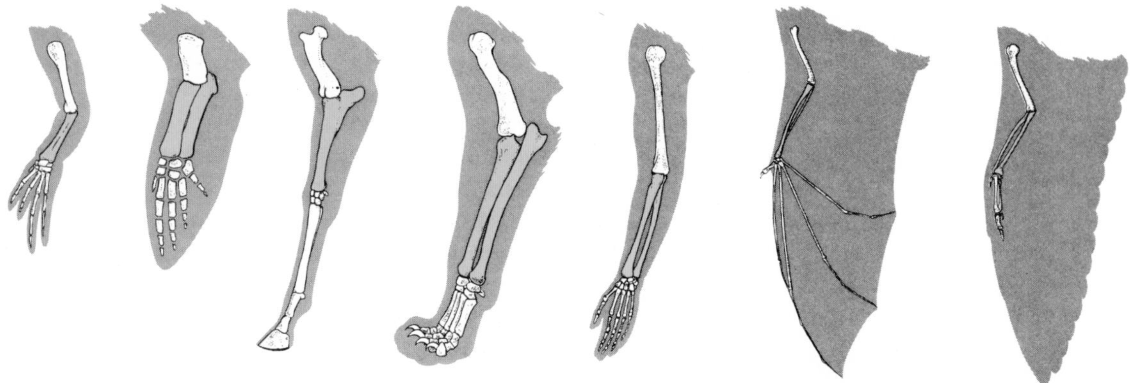

19–3 Homologous bones in the forelimbs of seven vertebrates—from left to right, the foreleg of a frog, the flipper of a whale, the forelegs of a horse and of a lion, the arm of a man, and the wings of a bat and of a bird. In addition to the set of bones shown in color, can you find other bones that are homologous? The skeletons of these and other vertebrates have many homologous bones throughout the body.

from the same structure in a common ancestor, and thus were once controlled by the same genes. Structures that are similar because of their common origin are said to be **homologous** (ho·MOL·o·gus). It is principally the homologous structures that one considers in grouping animals in a classification scheme.

Figure 19-3 should not be misconstrued to mean that homology refers to gross structures alone. Nowadays cellular structures, especially chromosome number and type, are considered, too. Then there are physiological homologies, and even biochemical homologies. Structure and function are always closely related. You should not be surprised, therefore, that homologous structures may carry on homologous functions. We should also expect details of cell physiology in related organisms to have many similarities. For example, all of the vertebrates synthesize insulin. This is interpreted to mean that the remote ancestors of the vertebrates evolved the insulin-secreting mechanism. This has been transmitted to the descendants as a homologous biochemical process that takes place in homologous cells. The insulins are too much alike to be accounted for independently of one another, as coincidences.

Analogy

There is another type of similarity between the structures of different animals. For example, the leg of an insect and the leg of a cat are both *legs*, used for walking. Also, the wing of a fly and the wing of a bat are both *wings*, used for flying. A careful study of the two legs would reveal that they are constructed on totally different plans. The leg of the cat has the bones of the skeleton in the center of the leg. These are covered by muscles. The insect leg is the reverse: the muscles are *inside* and the skeleton is a hard case surrounding them.

A careful study of the bat's wing and the fly's wing would show that the two wings are likewise built on totally different patterns.

Therefore, the legs of the insect and the legs of the cat are not homologous. Neither are the wings of a fly homologous with the wings of a bat. Moreover, from fossil records we know that there was no common structure in an ancestor of both insect and cat that evolved one way into the cat's leg and another way into the insect's leg.

The legs of a cat and of an insect do have a superficial resemblance. Both are long appendages that are used for walking. We speak of

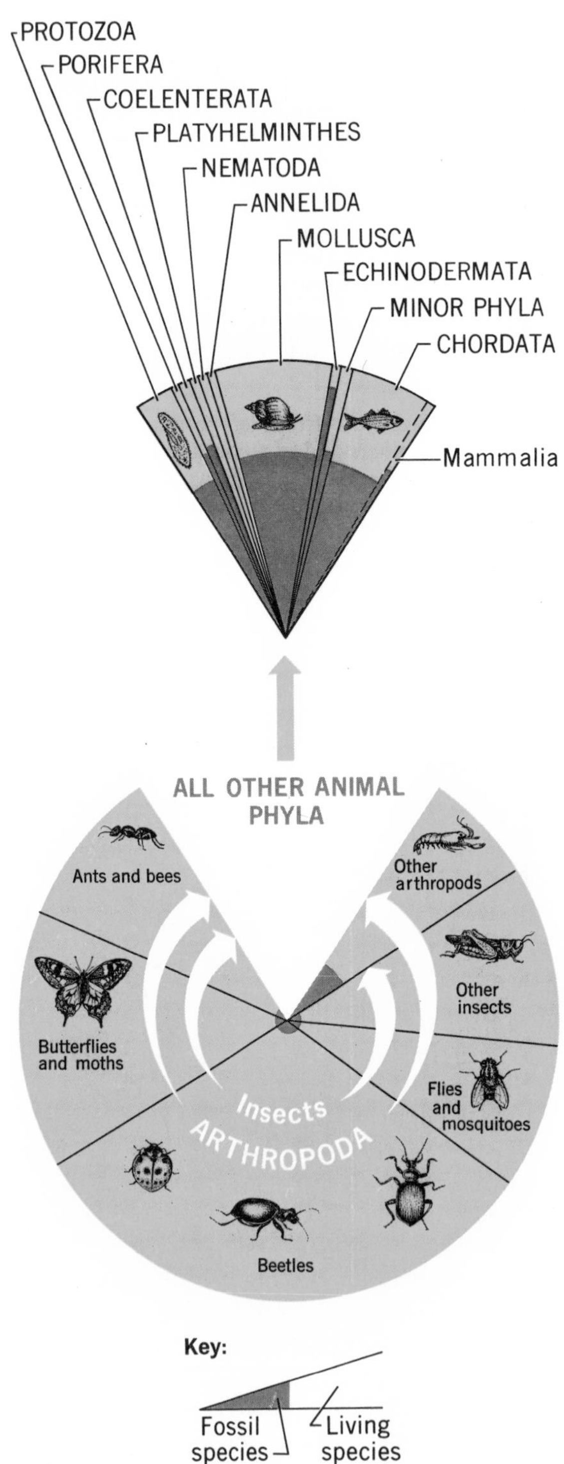

Redrawn after Muller and Campbell, *Systematic Zoology*, 3:168–70

structures having a superficial resemblance and serving roughly the same function as being **analogous** (a·NAL·o·gus).

Evolution has a role in the origin of both homologous and analogous structures. Homologous structures have an evolutionary origin in the same structure of a common ancestor. During the course of time the homologous structures of different animals evolve in different ways—and the result is the flipper of a whale, the wing of a bat, and the arm of man. Thus, one structure is modified into several.

The formation of analogous structures is just the opposite. In this case evolution begins with two different structures; as they evolve, they come to resemble one another.

A BRIEF SURVEY OF ANIMAL PHYLA

We are now at the point where we can identify the fundamental basis of the similarity of organisms included in the same group: the different species of a particular genus or family or order or larger group resemble one another because they have been derived from the same ancestral source. The homology may be of organs or organ systems, or it may be less evident initially but equally striking after careful study—a homology of physiological processes. Usually it is both. Thus, on the basis of evidence, every species in Phylum Chordata is believed to have evolved from a common ancestor. The same is true of all species in the class Mammalia or the genus *Felis*.

We will make no attempt to survey in detail the classification of the Animal Kingdom. Nevertheless, it is important that you have a

19–4 A visual comparison of the relative numbers of species in each of ten principal animal phyla. How does your impression of this graph compare with other impressions you may have of relative biological success among the animal phyla?

general understanding of the kinds of living things that are called animals and of their general relationships. The most convenient way to achieve this is to study briefly the more important phyla.

There are dozens of animal phyla. Some consist only of animals that now are extinct—they were experiments that worked for a time and then ended. Other phyla contain only a few, and often exceedingly rare, species. The ten major phyla briefly described here contain nearly all living animals (Figure 19-4). Once this survey has been made we will discuss what is known of the evolution of the major phyla of the Animal Kingdom. The phyla are listed roughly in the order of their structural and functional complexities, beginning with the least complex. There is a brief description and diagram for each. You should also consult Chapter 39 (pages 776-819) for illustrations of animals belonging to these and other phyla. But best of all, you should become familiar with animal diversity from your observations in the laboratory. Inquiry 19-1 is a good way to start.

Phylum Protozoa

The protozoan body typically is composed of a single cell. Some species, however, form colonies; that is, the individuals consist of groups of cells. A number move by pseudopods (*Amoeba*, Figure 18-5, page 337), others by cilia (*Paramecium*, Figure 18-6, page 338), or flagella, and still others have no structures specialized for locomotion *(Plasmodium)*. Protozoans occur in fresh water, oceans, moist earth, and as parasites of many animals and plants. Figure 19-5 illustrates several protozoans, one of which you have studied before.

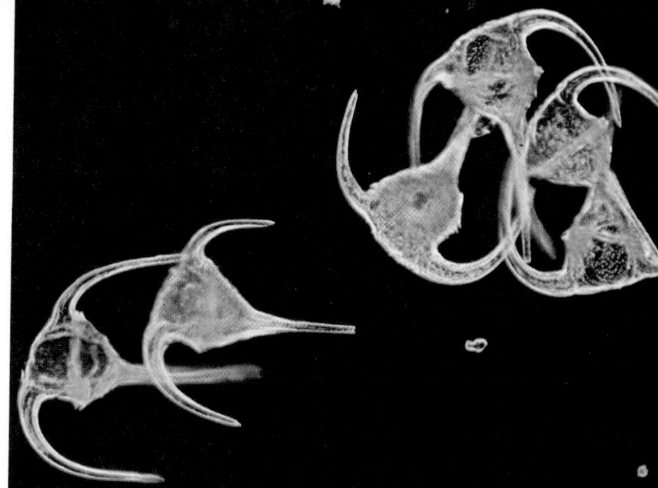

D. P. Wilson

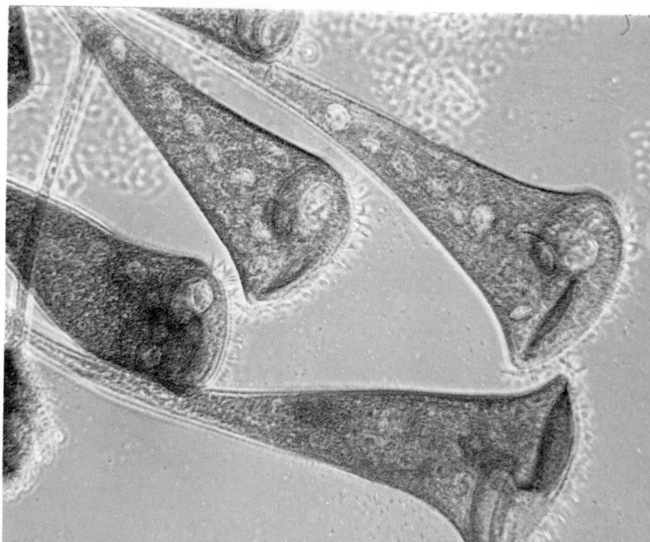

Eric Gravé
Harbrace Photo

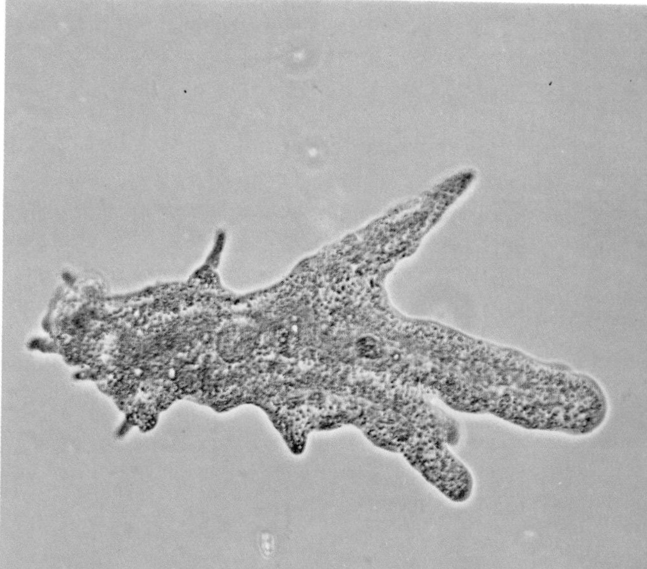

19–5 Phylum Protozoa. At the top is a cluster of *Ceratium* (seh·RAYSH·ee·um); in the center are several *Stentor* (STEN·tor); at the bottom is a single *Amoeba*. *Ceratium* is a marine organism; *Stentor* and *Amoeba* live in fresh water. If you wish to examine a larger group of protozoans at this time, turn to page 776 of Chapter 39.

D. P. Wilson

D. P. Wilson

D. P. Wilson

19–6 Phylum Porifera. The two larger organisms in the **left** photograph, the lumpish one at the **top right,** and the flattened one on the **bottom right** are all marine sponges. In which can you see the pores for the exit of water? Inside the body, water is constantly circulated; food organisms are taken from the circulating water. (See also page 777.)

The last chapter introduced you to the protozoan way of life. We have here the simplest of all animals. The Animal and Plant Kingdoms meet in the Protozoa and the Algae (pages 276-77). There is a complete series that covers the range from species that are clearly animals, through those that have features of both kingdoms, to species that are clearly green plants. To many biologists this suggests that the Protozoa evolved from the green algae.

Phylum Porifera

The **Porifera** (po·RIF·er·a) are the sponges. Several are pictured in Figure 19-6. Sponges are composed of many cells, like animals of all phyla except the Protozoa. The cells, however, are not very highly specialized. There are no true organs. There is a single cavity (or many cavities) inside the body. The cells lining these cavities have flagella. The beating of the flagella creates a current of water that flows through the body. A sponge lives on small animals and plants that are brought to it in this current of water.

Until recently, we had always assumed that sponges were without nerves. Now there is some evidence, as yet not convincing, that sponges may have nerve cells.

The bath sponge has a skeleton of fibers. This skeleton is the "sponge" formerly widely used in kitchens and bathrooms (most "sponges" used today are synthetic). Some sponges have a skeleton of hard spicules.

The sponges are strange animals indeed. Most live in the oceans, but a few live in fresh water. The adults are stationary, spending their lives attached to rocks, wharf pilings, the bottom mud, or other solid objects. They seem almost lifeless, but they can react to many stimuli, though very slowly. They have no true organs and little interdependence of the cells. This relative lack of organization can be demonstrated by a dramatic experiment. It is possible to squeeze the body of a sponge through a fine cloth that breaks the body into individual cells or small groups of cells. The individual cells can then clump together and grow into a new adult.

Phylum Coelenterata

The **coelenterates** (se·LEN·ter·ates) are more complex than the sponges. Several coelenterates are shown in Figure 19-7. The body wall consists of two main layers of cells, an inner layer and an outer layer. There usually is a jelly-like layer between, and this may contain cells that enter from the inner or outer layers. There is a digestive cavity with a single opening, which is often surrounded by tentacles. Stinging cells are characteristic of the coelenterates. Many species have an alternation of generations. One generation reproduces by sexual means and the other by asexual means. Both generations are diploid, in contrast with many of the plants that have an alternation of generations. Often the two generations consist of one free-living and one attached stage.

If you have ever visited the seacoast, you may have seen coelenterates. Jellyfish, sea anemones, corals, and sea fans all belong to this phylum. Some species consist of free-living individuals, while others are colonial (sea fans, for example).

Some coelenterates, such as *Hydra* (Figure 19-8) are found in fresh water. *Hydra* will be one of the animal types that we will use in our discussion of functions in the chapters to come, so we should mention something about it here.

A *Hydra* is about 5 mm in length. Frequently these animals are found on water plants in ponds and streams. The body of a *Hydra* looks much like a tall vase with a narrow opening at the top. The body wall, corresponding to the walls of the vase, is fairly thin. It encloses a central cavity, the digestive cavity. There is a single opening, the mouth, leading into the digestive cavity. This opening also serves as an exit for undigested remnants of the food. A circle of tentacles surrounds the mouth.

There is no right or left side to the body, anymore than a tall, round vase has a right or left side. The body could be cut across, and the exposed surface would resemble a doughnut. Such a body arrangement is known as **radial symmetry** (RAY·dih·al SIM·e·trih).

A *Hydra* attaches itself to some object, such as a water plant, with the basal end of its body. It can move, though very slowly, from place to place. Generally it stays in one position waiting for food to come to it. It feeds on other small animals in the pond water; it captures them with its tentacles. The outer layer of cells on the tentacles, and other parts of the body as well, contain stinging cells. These, too, aid *Hydra* in capturing food.

Hydra consists essentially of two layers of cells. These little animals have no circulatory system, no respiratory system, and no excretory system. Nerves extend all over their bodies, but there is no concentration of them that could be called a brain. The characteristics of *Hydra* are generally those of other coelenterates, with some variation, so that we can describe the

D. P. Wilson

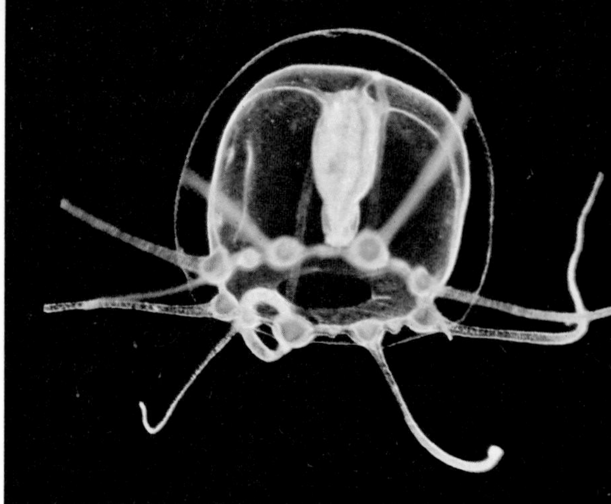

William H. Amos

D. P. Wilson

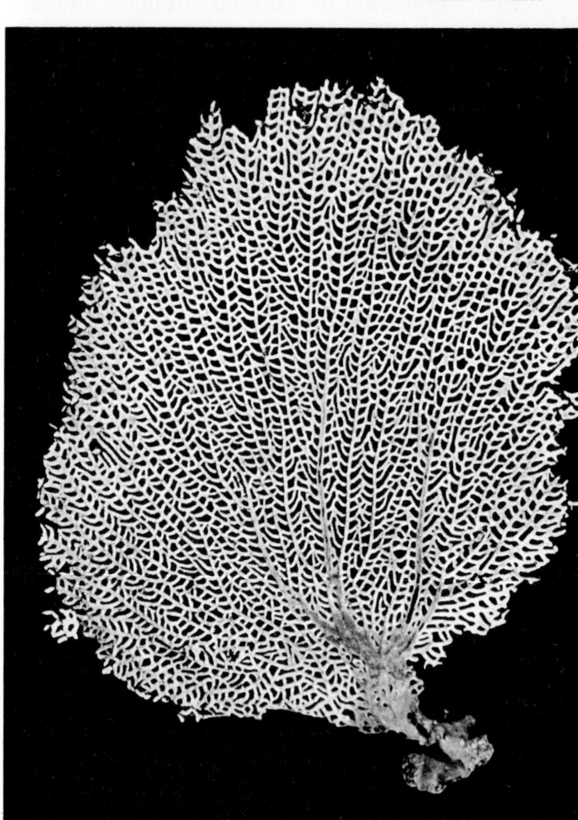

Carolina Biological Supply House

19–7 Phylum Coelenterata. **(Upper left)** A freshwater *Hydra*, one of the animals you will study further in later chapters. The other three kinds of coelenterates shown here live in the ocean: **(upper right)** a jellyfish; **(lower left)** a group of sea anemones; **(lower right)** the skeleton of a sea fan. In life, the sea fan is a colonial organism whose skeleton is covered with thousands of tiny individuals, each somewhat like a *Hydra*. (Another group of coelenterates is shown on pages 778-79 of Chapter 29.)

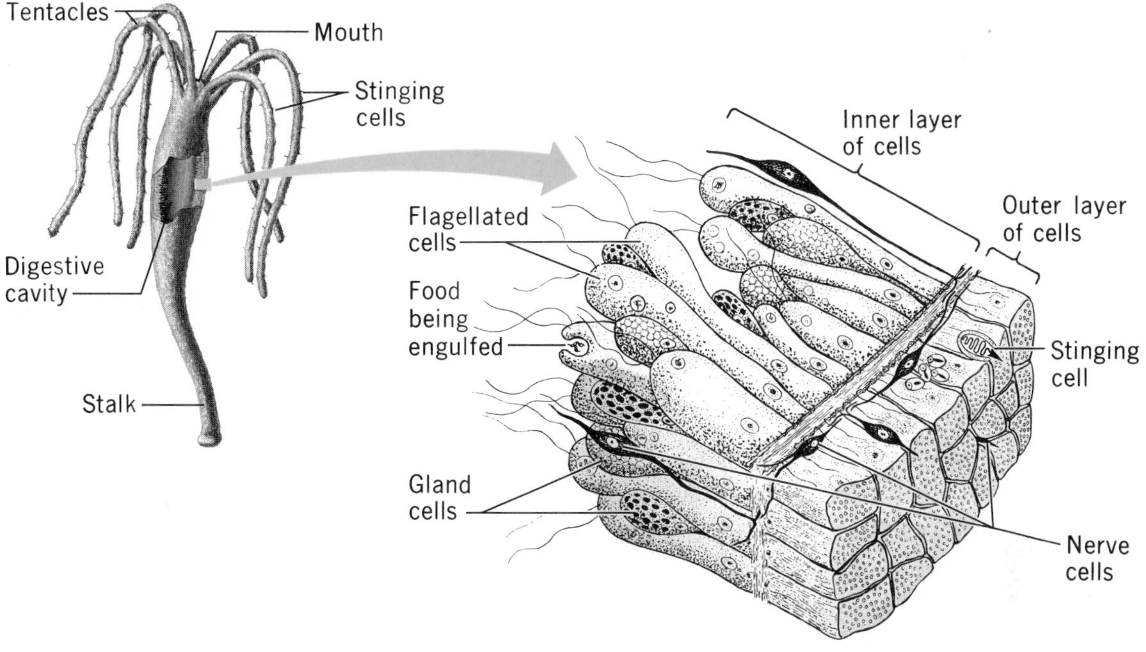

19–8 The body plan of *Hydra*. The interior of the body is a single, central cavity, as shown in the drawing at the left, where part of the body wall has been cut away. Food enters the cavity through the mouth, which is the only body opening and serves also as an exit for undigested remnants of the food. The drawing at the right shows a section of the body wall enlarged. The outer layer of cells is primarily for protection; it includes stinging cells that shoot out barbs into food or foe. The inner layer of cells is primarily digestive in function. The gland cells of the inner layer are enzyme-secreting cells; many other of the inner cells engulf and digest food particles from partly digested organisms the *Hydra* has captured and taken into its central cavity.

coelenterates as relatively uncomplicated animals by comparison with other phyla we will consider.

In some species of *Hydra*, male and female reproductive organs occur in the same individual. In most species, however, there are separate males and females.

Phylum Platyhelminthes

The name **Platyhelminthes** (plat·ih·hell·MIN-these) can be translated as "flat worm." Nearly all are small worms with flattened bodies (Figure 19-9). In contrast to a body with only two main layers, as in the coelenterates, the platyhelminths have three body layers. In this respect they resemble almost all higher animals. In general the outer layer forms the skin and nervous system, the inner layer the digestive system, and the middle layer everything else. There is a digestive cavity with a single opening. Excretory structures are present. The nerves are localized slightly and there is the beginning of a brain. In contrast to the coelenterates, the flatworms have a right and left side to the body. We speak of this as **bilateral** (by-LAT·eral) **symmetry.** The many species occur in fresh and salt water, in moist habitats on land, and as parasites in other animals.

Among the parasitic platyhelminths, the tapeworms, liver flukes, and blood flukes may cause

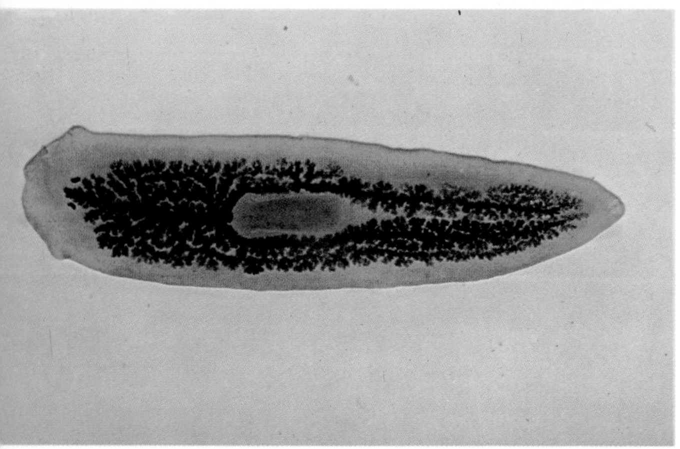

Russ Kinne from Photo Researchers

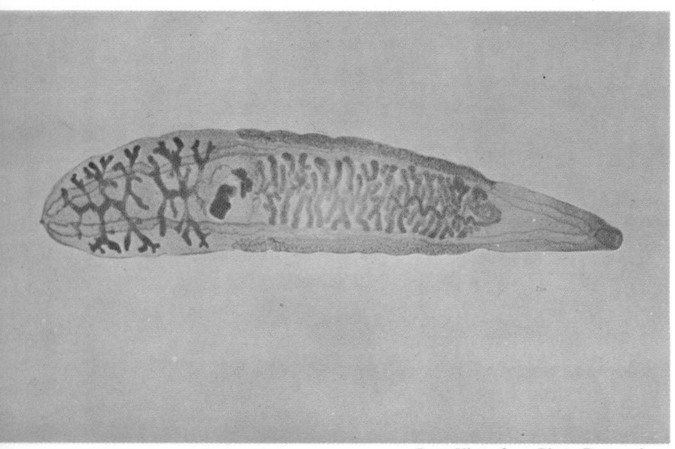

Russ Kinne from Photo Researchers

Russ Kinne from Photo Researchers

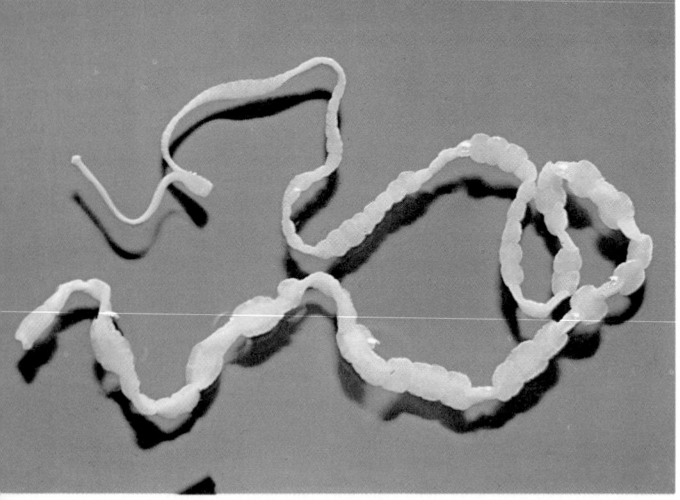

diseases of man. These parasites are usually more common in the tropics than in the temperate zones.

One group of flatworms, the planarians (Figure 19-9, top view, and Figure 19-10), will be used in discussions of functions in the chapters to come. Planarians are generally about 10 mm in length. They live in freshwater ponds and streams, frequently occurring on the undersides of rocks and dead leaves.

Planarians move about freely. The outer cells on the undersides of their bodies have tiny, hairlike structures, cilia, like those of *Paramecium* (Inquiry 18-2). The cilia beat in unison and move the animal over surfaces of rocks and leaves, in a film of mucus that the flatworm secretes from cells on the lower side of its body. Planarians have muscles that enable them to change direction.

Planarians feed on small animals that live in the ponds, and on the bodies of dead and decaying animals.

Much of the body space is taken up by a branching digestive system. This digestive system has a single opening, as in *Hydra*. There is a simple excretory system, but no respiratory or circulatory systems. In the head end there are two concentrations of nerve cells that can be called brains. Above these brains are two dark eyespots, sensitive to light. The eyespots represent a very primitive type of eye. When one end of an animal contains a brain and generally prominent sensory structures, we call this end the head or the **anterior** (an·TIHR·ee·er) end of the animal.

Planarians have male and female reproductive organs. All planarians and some species of

19–9 Phylum Platyhelminthes. Three flatworms, two of which are parasites, are shown here. At the **top** is a stained specimen of a free-living planarian. Below it **(middle)** is a stained specimen of a Chinese liver fluke, a parasite of man and other mammals. At the **bottom** is a tapeworm of dogs; its smaller end is the anterior end. For illustrations of other flatworms, see page 780 of Chapter 39.

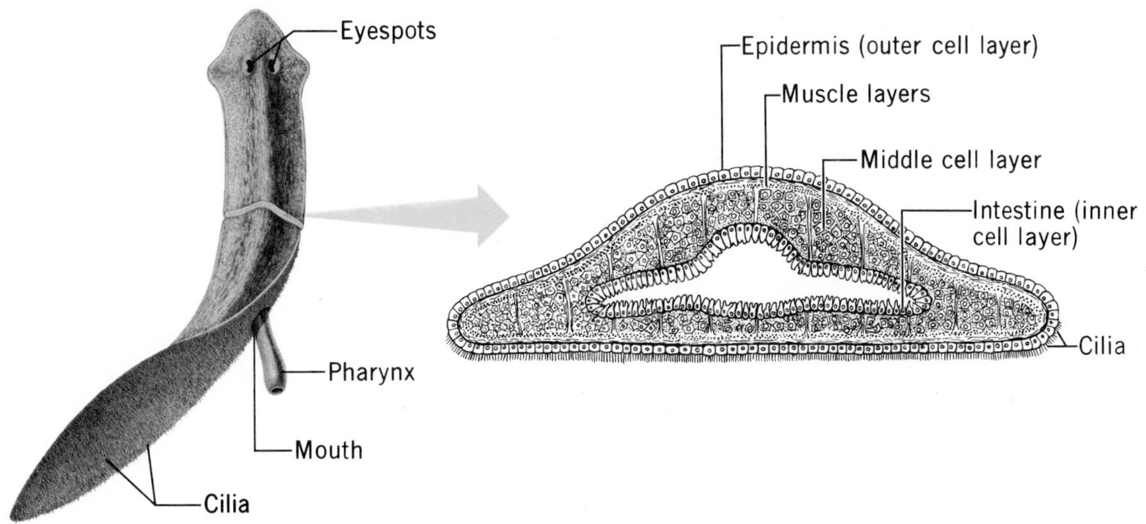

19–10 A diagram of a planarian. At the left is an entire individual, with its pharynx extended as in feeding. (At other times, the pharynx is withdrawn into the body.) At the right is a cross section of the body. Three main layers of cells can be seen. Planarians of this general type are common inhabitants of many ponds and streams. A small chunk of raw liver will often attract them by the dozens.

Hydra are **hermaphroditic** (her·maf·ro·DIT·ik)—that is, a single individual produces both eggs and sperms.

Phylum Nematoda

Phylum **Nematoda** (nem·a·TOH·da) is also composed of wormlike species. These species, however, have cylindrical rather than flattened bodies (Figure 19-11). Usually the body is sharply pointed at each end. One end is definitely anterior. This is usually difficult to tell externally since there are, for example, no special sense organs such as eyes, and no clearly marked head. One of the body differences in comparison with the previous phyla is an alimentary canal. This is a tube for digestion that has an entrance at the mouth and an exit at the anus. A space between the alimentary canal and the body wall gives the nematodes a "tube within a tube" type of structure. There are excretory organs but no specialized organs of circulation or respiration.

Some species are found in freshwater habitats, some in the oceans, and tremendous numbers in the soil (where they may cause diseases of plants, including man's food plants). Many nematodes are parasites of animals.

Among the nematode parasites of man are hookworms and pinworms. Another is *Trichinella* (trik·ih·NEL·a), which causes the disease **trichinosis** (trik·ih·NOH·sis), acquired by eating undercooked pork containing the worms. In tropical regions **filaria** (fi·LAY·rih·a) **worms** live in the blood and cause a disease called **filariasis** (fil·a·RY·a·sis).

The life cycle of *Trichinella* illustrates its parasitic relation to man. The trouble begins when a person eats poorly cooked pork that contains the larvae of *Trichinella*. When the pork is digested in the man's alimentary canal, the larvae are liberated. They quickly mature and reproduce. A few adults can produce thousands of *Trichinella* embryos. These embryos bore their way through the walls of the man's

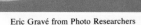

Eric Gravé from Photo Researchers

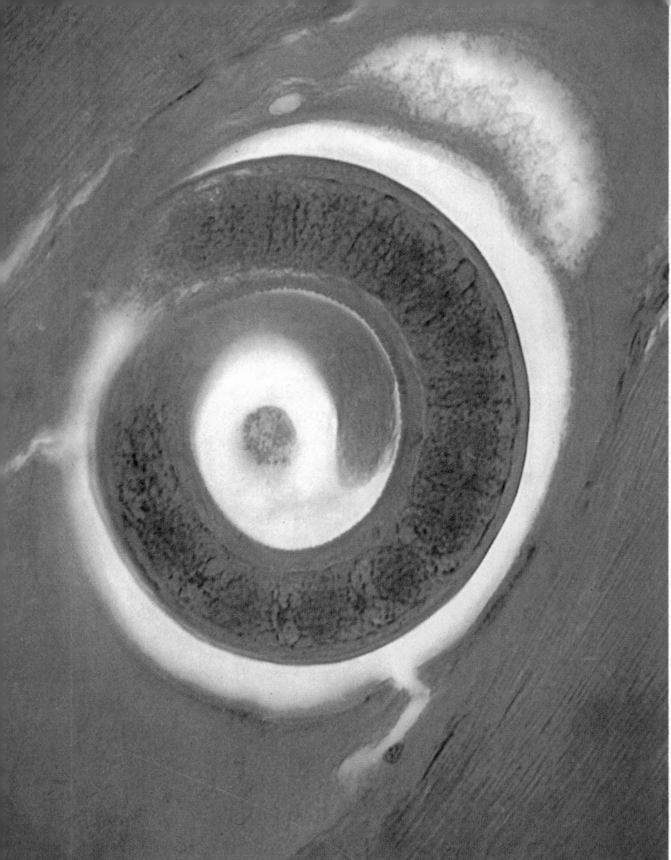

Harbrace Photo

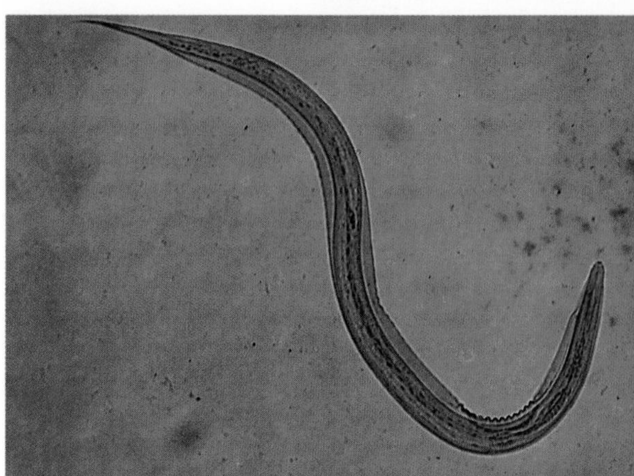

Walter Dawn

19–11 Phylum Nematoda. Many round worms are free-living, but these are parasites of man. *Trichinella* adults **(upper right)** live in the intestine. They produce larvae that spend most of their lives encysted in muscles **(left).** A hookworm is shown at the **lower right.** Other nematodes are illustrated on page 780.

intestine and enter the blood stream. They eventually leave the blood and bore their way into muscles (Figure 19-11, left). Here they encyst and become inactive. They remain in this state unless they happen to be eaten by another animal—which does not happen often these days! Normally these larvae would die with their host, or sooner, and the cycle would be broken. Yet *Trichinella* persists as a common parasite of man. Can you suggest why?

Phylum Annelida

Most of the "worms" with which you are familiar belong to Phylum **Annelida** (a·NEL·ih-da); they are commonly called **annelids** (AN·eh-lidz). The earthworm (Figure 19-12) is a common example. Other species (Figure 19-13) are abundant in the oceans, especially along coasts. Compared to the phyla already considered, annelid worms show much more specialization of body structure. You will be able to observe many of the differences between annelid worms and nematode worms as you undertake Laboratory Inquiry 19-2. The annelids have a circulatory system, which was not present in lower forms. All of their other organ systems, such as the excretory and nervous systems, are more complex in organization. The body is segmented—that is, divided into similar sections. If you have ever looked at an earthworm closely, you will have noticed that the body seems to have lines across it. These are the divisions between the segments.

The earthworm will be one of the forms that we will discuss frequently in the next few chapters. Earthworms may be 20 cm or even more in length. They live in burrows in moist, rich soil. Earthworms feed on decaying matter in the soil. In order to obtain their food they pass large amounts of soil through their digestive systems. The undigested parts are the "castings," which you may have seen near an earthworm's burrow. This churning of the soil has benefits for plants and man. The soil becomes mixed and is made less compact. The earthworm is acting as a living plow.

Earthworms die quickly if they are in a dry place. You have probably noticed what happens to them after a rain. As their burrows are flooded, the worms come out. They crawl about on the ground. When the rains are over and the ground begins to dry, the worms begin to dry up too. Their skins are permeable and cannot prevent loss of water.

An earthworm is far more complex than a planarian. It has a digestive system with two openings, a mouth and an anus. It also has well-developed circulatory, excretory, and nervous systems. It is hermaphroditic—that is, it has male *and* female reproductive organs. In fact, it has all systems found in man except breathing and skeletal systems.

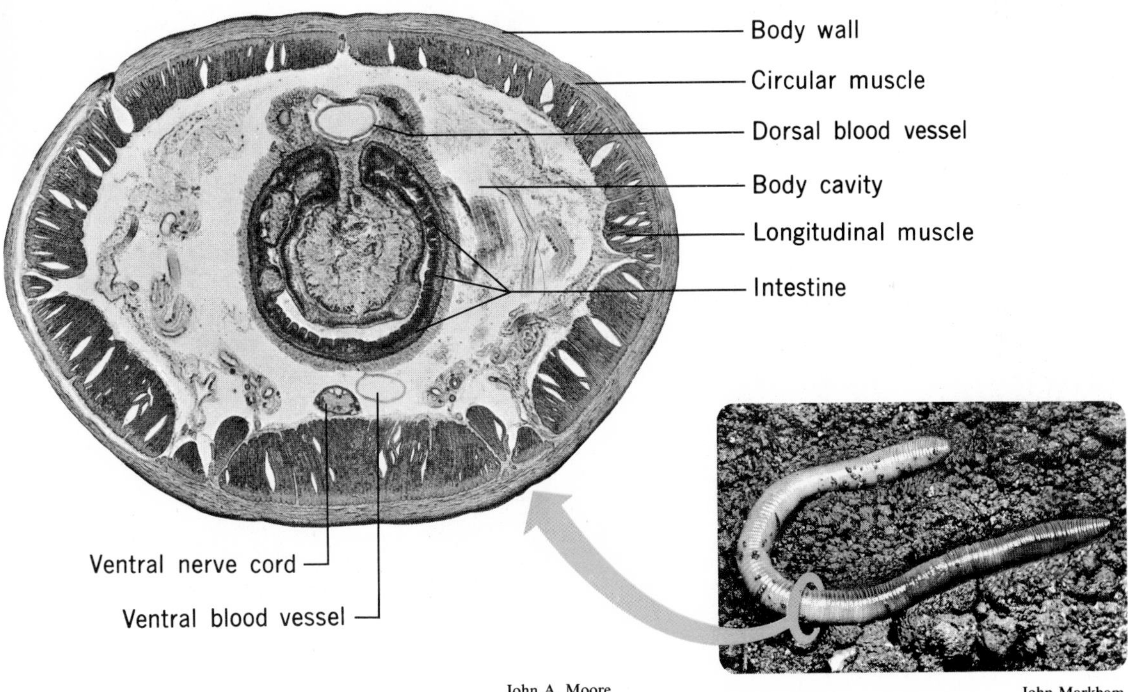

John A. Moore

John Markham

19–12 An earthworm and a cross section of its body. Outwardly, earthworms may not appear more complex than *Hydra* (Figure 19–8) or planarians (Figure 19–10). In fact, identifying the anterior end of an earthworm is much more difficult than in planarians. (In the photograph, the anterior end is at the extreme right.) Yet the cross section of the earthworm's body shows considerably more complexity than in *Hydra* or planarians. Notice the well-developed muscles, the blood vessels, the nerve cord, the large body cavity, and the different types of cells in the intestinal wall.

Walter Dawn

Walter Dawn

Walter Dawn

D. P. Wilson

19–13 Phylum Annelida. The earthworm (**upper left** and Figure 19–12) lives in moist soil. Most leeches (stained specimen, **upper right**) live in fresh water. They are parasites of vertebrates, living on the blood they suck from the bodies of their victims. The living annelids in the lower two photographs are from the ocean—a sand worm **(lower left)** and a tube worm **(lower right).** Neither is a parasite. For other annelids, see page 781.

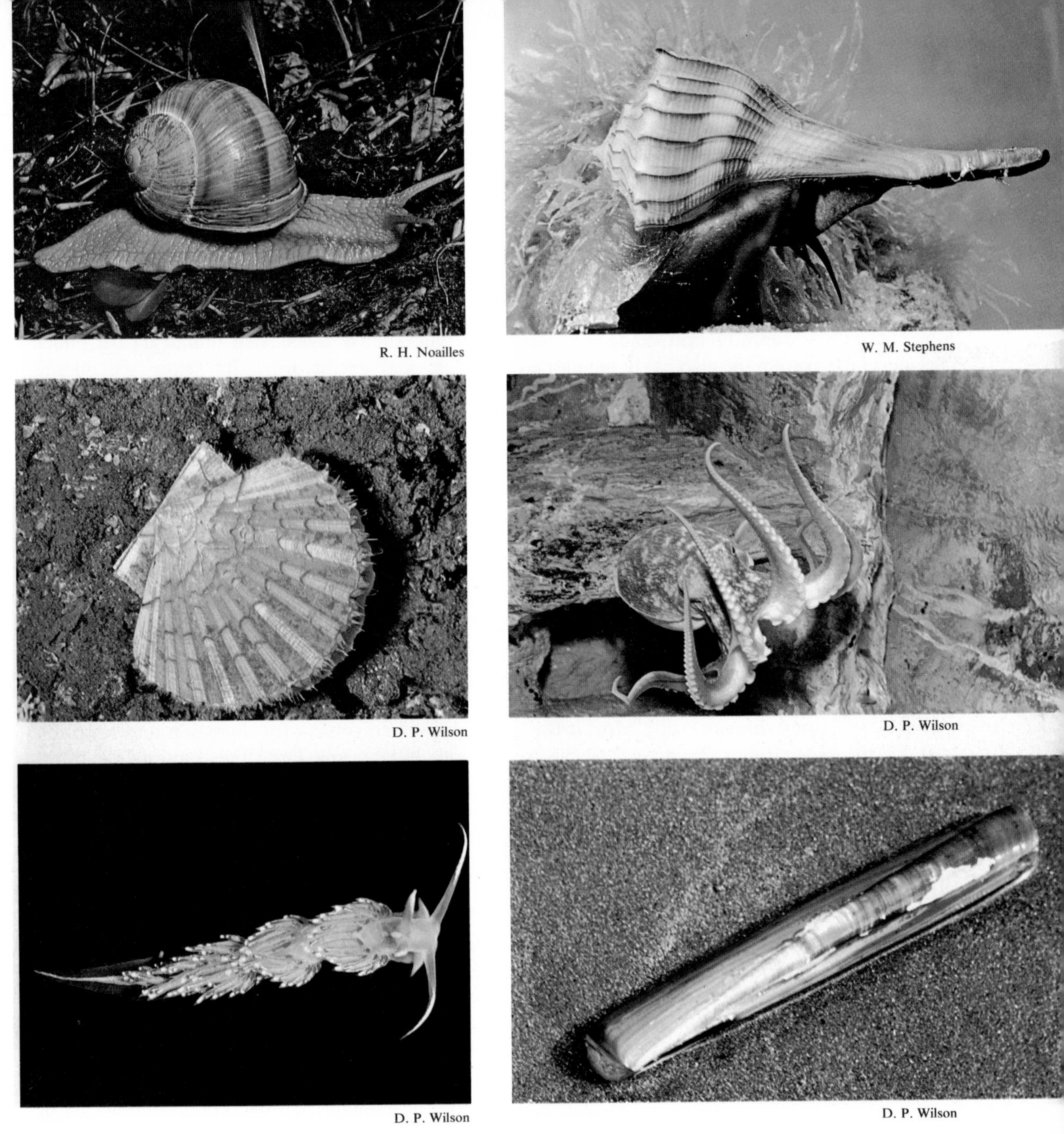

19–14 Phylum Mollusca. All but one of the mollusks shown here live in the ocean. The exception is the land snail at the **upper left.** At the **upper right** is a whelk; at the **middle left** a scallop; opposite the scallop **(middle right)** is an octopus; at the **lower left** is a **nudibranch** (NUDE·ih·brank); and at the **lower right** is a razor clam. For other photographs of mollusks, see pages 784-85 of Chapter 39.

Phylum Mollusca

Snails, slugs, clams, oysters, octopuses, and squids belong to Phylum **Mollusca** (mo·LUSS-ka). Several of these animals are shown in Figure 19-14. The bodies of most **mollusks** (MOL·usks) are covered by shells. In spite of the rather shapeless forms of the soft parts of many species, the body is highly organized, with complex systems for digestion, respiration, circulation, reproduction, and excretion. The nervous system is also well developed, especially in active forms like the squids.

The mollusks are the first group of animals in our survey that serve as food for man. The sea supplies clams, oysters, mussels, squid, and octopus. Some snails that live on land are regarded as a great delicacy.

Phylum Arthropoda

The **Arthropoda** (ar·THROP·o·da) have segmented bodies (Figure 19-15), as was the case with the annelid worms. There is a skeleton—on the outside of the body—which is rich in the chemical substance **chitin** (KY·tin). Most **arthropods** (AR·thro·podz) have appendages; these are jointed (as are ours). Arthropods occupy all the major habitats: land, air, sea, and fresh water.

More species of animals belong to Phylum Arthropoda than to any other phylum (Figure 19-4). In fact, most of the living creatures that one comes in contact with are arthropods. Possibly a more impressive fact is this: there are more species of beetles alone than there are species of all the nonarthropod animals in the world. Laboratory Inquiry 19-3 introduces you to this important phylum.

In addition to beetles, the grasshoppers, butterflies, and all other insects are arthropods. So are the lobsters, shrimps, spiders, scorpions, centipedes, millipedes, ticks, mites, and crabs.

One of the organisms we will study further in succeeding chapters is the grasshopper (Figure 19-15, lower right). A grasshopper is generally more complex than the earthworm in all of its body parts. The major advances in organization that it shows, however, are a breathing system and well-developed sense organs such as eyes. Also, unlike *Hydra*, planarians, and earthworms, its sexes are distinct. That is, male and female reproductive organs do not occur in the same individual.

Phylum Echinodermata

The various species of sea star, sea urchins, sea cucumbers, and sea lilies belong to Phylum **Echinodermata** (e·ky·no·DER·ma·ta). Sometimes the body is shaped like a biscuit or a disk. More frequently, however, there is a central disk from which arms radiate. In fact, the **echinoderms** (e·KY·no·dermz) are generally radial in their symmetry (Figure 19-16). There are specialized organs for digestion and reproduction, but by and large these animals exhibit a rather low degree of organization. There are usually no specialized organ systems for respiration or excretion. The nervous system is also poorly developed—there is no brain. There is only a poorly organized circulatory system. The echinoderms are the only major animal phylum that is exclusively marine.

Possibly you wonder why we place the echinoderms near the top of our list of phyla when they seem to be comparatively simple in structure and physiology. Their true place in terms of complexity would probably be slightly below the annelid worms. The echinoderms are

19–15 (Facing page) Phylum Arthropoda. The majority of animals on land, in the air, and in water are arthropods. This phylum alone accounts for most of the known animal species. Shown here are two horseshoe crabs **(upper left),** a shrimp **(upper right),** a scorpion **(middle left),** a centipede **(middle right),** a butterfly **(lower left),** and a grasshopper **(lower right).** The horseshoe crabs and the shrimp are marine; the others live on land. A larger group of arthropods is shown on pages 786-91.

Walter Dawn

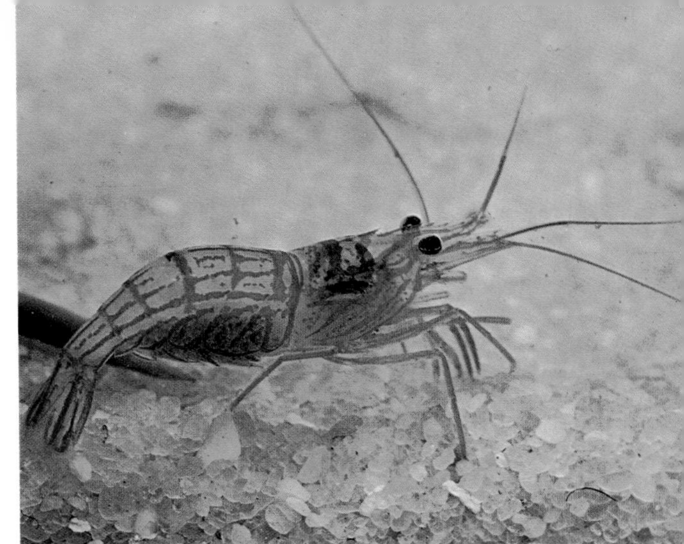

W. M. Stephens

Russ Kinne from Photo Researchers

Walter Dawn

Dade Thornton from National Audubon Society

Carolina Biological Supply House

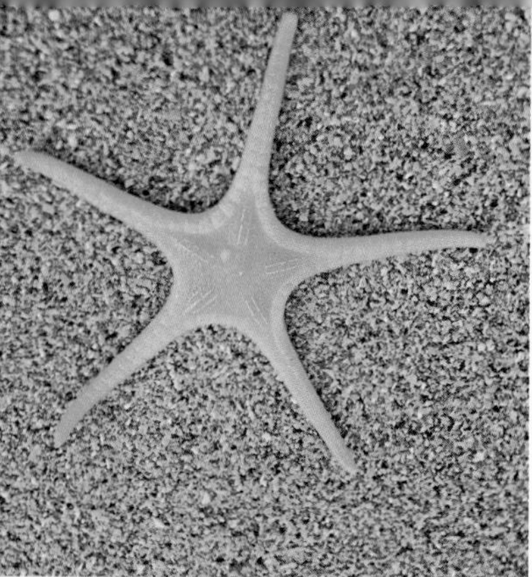

John A. Moore

John A. Moore

John A. Moore

19–16 Phylum Echinodermata. The echinoderms are the only major phylum of exclusively marine animals. Frequently the body has five axes through its center. Can you see evidence for this in all three photographs? The brightly colored specimen is a sea star. The other two photographs show the same individual—a sea urchin—from the dorsal and ventral sides. Page 792 of Chapter 39 shows other kinds of echinoderms.

placed here for another reason. Of all the major phyla, they seem to be the closest to the **chordates** (KOR·dates) our phylum and the next to be discussed. They are not really very close at all, but the echinoderms are the only other animals that seem to be related to the chordates. The two groups share some features of early development and some biochemical peculiarities. The evidence, which is far from conclusive, is that the chordates and the echinoderms may have had a common ancestor long ago in Pre-Cambrian times.

Phylum Chordata

Here we are! Our own species, *Homo sapiens*, and all other mammals, birds, snakes, lizards, turtles, salamanders, frogs, toads, and fishes, belong to this phylum (Figure 19-17).

19–17 Phylum Chordata. Below is *Amphioxus*, a tiny marine chordate showing the three characteristics of the phylum. Its topmost structure is a **dorsal nerve tube,** which appears light gray in the photograph and is identifiable by the many black pigment spots at its base. Beneath the nerve tube is the **notochord,** a darker rod extending from the anterior end to the tip of the tail. The prominent **gill slits** take up most of the anterior third of the body. Other chordates are on the facing page: a fish, a tree frog, an alligator, an owl, and a chimpanzee with its child. For additional chordates, see pages 793-819.

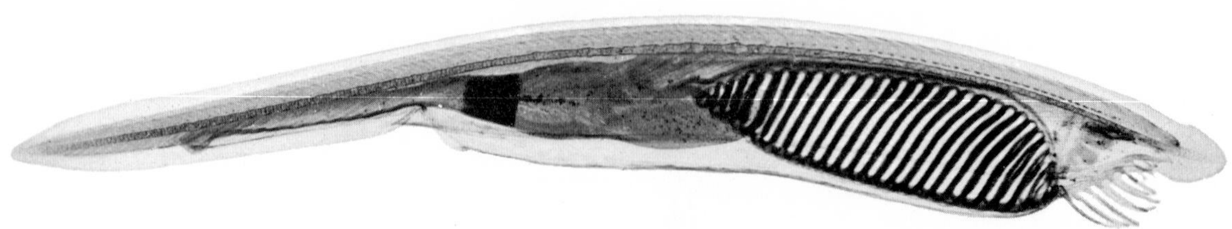

John A. Moore

Walter Dawn

Leonard Rue III

John H. Gerard from National Audubon Society

John A. Moore

E. Cruller from Freelance Photographers Guild

The various organ systems in chordates generally reach a higher degree of complexity than in animals of any other phylum. The nervous system is more highly developed. Our bodies are bilateral. The skeleton is on the inside of the body (in contrast to the skeletons of arthropods).

The three most distinctive features of the chordates are a **notochord** (NO·toh·cord), **dorsal nerve tube**, and paired slits in the **pharynx** (FAIR·inks). You are a chordate, but the chances are none of these structures is familiar to you. The notochord is usually a structure found only in the embryo. It is a long rod that extends down the back. The dorsal nerve tube is modified as the brain and spinal cord in man. The paired slits in the pharynx are associated with the gills in fish and are involved in respiration. There are only traces of these pouches in our bodies. All but a few chordates are also **vertebrates**; that is, they have a vertebral column or backbone. The vertebral column replaces the embryonic notochord. Both are supporting structures.

Laboratory Inquiry 19-4 helps introduce you to this phylum. There, as you study the frog, you should reflect on the significance of the fact that so many of the structures of the frog's body are also present in yours.

INTERRELATIONSHIPS OF THE ANIMAL PHYLA

In our earlier survey of the plants we found great differences in the complexity of their structure. There were simple plants, such as the single-celled algae, and progressively more complex forms such as mosses, ferns, and flowering plants. The evidence from fossils strongly supports the hypothesis that the complex forms evolved from the simpler forms. The order of appearance and the interrelationships for major types of plants are believed to be as shown in Figure 19-18.

In our survey of the major animal phyla we have also learned of vast differences in complexity. There are some protozoans that do not differ greatly from single-celled green algae. Other animals are somewhat more complex: for example, the sponges and coelenterates. Still more complex are the platyhelminths and the nematodes. The echinoderms and the annelids continue the trend toward increasing complexity. Finally, the mollusks, arthropods, and chordates are the most complex of all.

Is there evidence that the animal phyla have evolved from one another as the plant phyla have? Biologists believe so, but they are far from agreed on the exact interrelations. One hypothesis for the relationships is shown below:

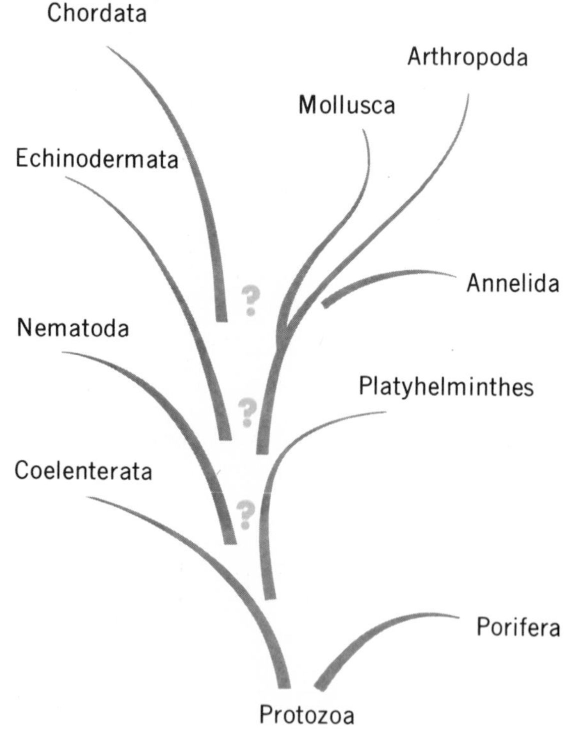

But why all the question marks? Why are we uncertain about the evolution of the major groups of animals, yet fairly certain about the evolution of plants? The reason for our ignorance, at least, is known!

You should recall from Chapter 9 that we learn most about the evolution of organisms from the study of fossils—fossils preserved in the sedimentary rocks of the earth's crust. Recall also that the oldest sedimentary rocks with abundant fossils are found in the Cambrian Period (Chapter 13). Older rocks have been so altered that very few useful fossils are present. One can trace the past history of organisms by their fossils most readily in the interval between the Cambrian and the present. At the beginning of the Cambrian Period there were only a few plants—algae, fungi, and bacteria. *All the other major types appeared later* (Figure 19-18). Therefore it is possible to discover fossils of the higher plants and to learn about their interrelationships.

The situation is very different for animals. Essentially all the major groups of animals, except the chordates, are known from fossils in the Cambrian rocks—some even from Pre-Cambrian times. This means that they must have evolved long before the times for which a good fossil record exists (Figure 19-19). Thus, their evolutionary interrelationships remain unknown to us.

The single exception, the chordates, is a happy one for us since this is *our* group. Their evolution is well recorded in the sedimentary rocks. Furthermore, chordates usually have hard structures, such as bones and teeth, that fossilize well. You should not be surprised, therefore, that we know more about the evolution of the chordates than about the evolution of any other phylum of animals.

Let us now reconstruct briefly the history of animals during the past 600 million years. We can add the highlights of plant evolution that we learned about in Chapters 13 and 14.

LIFE IN THE PALEOZOIC

A few fossil animals are known from Pre-Cambrian rocks. Perhaps some day more will be found. Discoveries of the past twenty years in South Australia make us more hopeful (Figure 19-20). New parts of the world must be explored for fossils of early animal life.

The invertebrates that were fossilized during the Cambrian were those with skeletons. Possibly it was not until this time that most of the invertebrates had evolved skeletons. The fossil protozoans, for example, are not like *Amoeba, Paramecium,* or *Euglena*; rather, they are species with shells or internal skeletons. You probably think of sponges as soft and perishable animals. Yet many sponges have an internal skeleton of hard spicules. Some of these are preserved in the Cambrian rocks.

As far as we know, all of the Cambrian animals and plants lived in the seas. The land masses must have presented a desolate appearance: no plants or animals—just the inorganic substance of the earth's crust.

But the seas were full of life (Figure 19-21). On the ocean floor were sponges, coelenterates, and **brachiopods** (BRAY·kih·o·podz—shelled animals with a superficial resemblance to mollusks but belonging to a separate phylum). But there were more active animals as well. Dominating the scene were large arthropods, the **trilobites** (TRY·lo·bites—Figures 19-21 and 19-22). Some were 30 cm in length. They swam and crawled with their many legs along the ocean floor.

Trilobites were exceedingly abundant in the Cambrian but became extinct by the end of the **Paleozoic** (pay·le·o·ZOH·ik) era. Trilobites were, like all groups of animals and plants, an experiment in evolution. This experiment, a great success for over 300 million years, came to an end. Why? We can only guess.

As millions of years rolled by, new kinds of animals and plants evolved. In the seas of the **Ordovician** (or·doh·VISH·an) and **Silurian** (sih-LUR·ee·an) periods, great reefs were built by corals and algae. Along these reefs lived brachiopods, trilobites, mollusks, and other animals. The **nautiloids** (NAW·tih·loidz) were especially common; these mollusks were the ancestors of today's squids and octopuses.

The **eurypterids** (yoo·RIP·ter·idz—Figure 19-23) were among the more spectacular ani-

19-18 PLANT LIFE ON EARTH – A time scale with evolutionary relationships

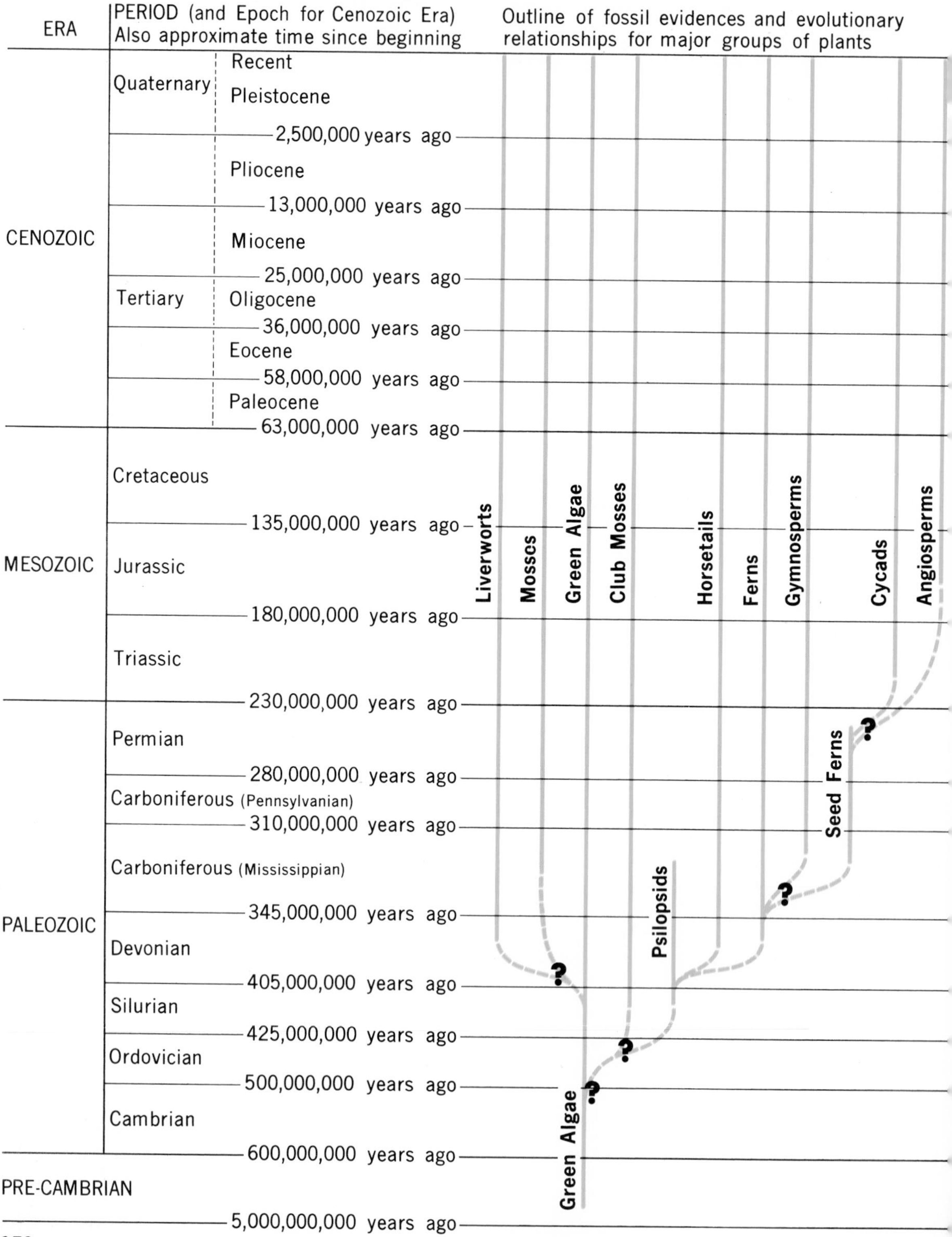
ERA
PERIOD (and Epoch for Cenozoic Era) Also approximate time since beginning
Outline of fossil evidences and evolutionary relationships for major groups of plants
CENOZOIC
Quaternary
Recent
Pleistocene
2,500,000 years ago
Pliocene
13,000,000 years ago
Miocene
25,000,000 years ago
Tertiary
Oligocene
36,000,000 years ago
Eocene
58,000,000 years ago
Paleocene
63,000,000 years ago
MESOZOIC
Cretaceous
135,000,000 years ago
Jurassic
180,000,000 years ago
Triassic
230,000,000 years ago
PALEOZOIC
Permian
280,000,000 years ago
Carboniferous (Pennsylvanian)
310,000,000 years ago
Carboniferous (Mississippian)
345,000,000 years ago
Devonian
405,000,000 years ago
Silurian
425,000,000 years ago
Ordovician
500,000,000 years ago
Cambrian
600,000,000 years ago
PRE-CAMBRIAN
5,000,000,000 years ago
Liverworts
Mosses
Green Algae
Club Mosses
Horsetails
Ferns
Gymnosperms
Cycads
Angiosperms
Seed Ferns
Psilopsids
Green Algae
?
?
?
?
?

19-19 ANIMAL LIFE ON EARTH – A time scale indicating earliest fossil evidence for major phyla

Outline indicating periods in which the major phyla of animals occur

Protozoans, Porifera, Coelenterates, Platyhelminthes, Nematodes, Annelids, Brachiopods, Mollusks, Arthropods, Echinoderms, Chordates

PERIOD (and Epoch for Cenozoic Era) Also approximate time since beginning		ERA
Recent	Quaternary	CENOZOIC
Pleistocene		
2,500,000 years ago		
Pliocene	Tertiary	
13,000,000 years ago		
Miocene		
25,000,000 years ago		
Oligocene		
36,000,000 years ago		
Eocene		
58,000,000 years ago		
Paleocene		
63,000,000 years ago		
	Cretaceous	MESOZOIC
135,000,000 years ago		
	Jurassic	
180,000,000 years ago		
	Triassic	
230,000,000 years ago		
	Permian	PALEOZOIC
280,000,000 years ago		
	Carboniferous (Pennsylvanian)	
310,000,000 years ago		
	Carboniferous (Mississippian)	
345,000,000 years ago		
	Devonian	
405,000,000 years ago		
	Silurian	
425,000,000 years ago		
	Ordovician	
500,000,000 years ago		
	Cambrian	
600,000,000 years ago		
		PRE-CAMBRIAN
5,000,000,000 years ago		

? ? ? ? ? ? ? ? ? ?

Evolutionary origins and relationships obscured in Pre-Cambrian rock

M. F. Glassner

M. F. Glassner

19–20 Two of the oldest known animal fossils, more than 600 million years old. They were found in Pre-Cambrian rocks in South Australia. The one at the left has been tentatively identified as a type of marine worm; the one at the right, as a jellyfish.

mals of the Ordovician and Silurian periods. They were gigantic predatory arthropods, some of them three meters in length.

Plants Invade the Land

An event of major importance occurred fairly early in the Paleozoic, near the end of the Cambrian period. Green plants invaded land (see Chapter 14). An entirely new environment, with great possibilities for both plant and animal evolution, was opened up. Green plants seem not to have evolved above the algal stage of complexity as long as they remained in the sea. Once they invaded land, however, they evolved into the tremendous diversity of types characteristic of our landscape.

19–21 A model of life in a Cambrian sea. At the left, a jellyfish (a coelenterate) floats in front of an alga. Beneath the jellyfish, at the extreme bottom of the photograph, are two brachiopods. Standing at the right of the brachiopods is a sea cucumber (an echinoderm), and alongside it is an annelid worm the size of the sea cucumber. The next large organism to the right is a trilobite (an arthropod), and above it is another arthropod. Other organisms include sponges, more algae, and worms.

American Museum of Natural History

American Museum of Natural History

19–22 Fossil trilobites. Several of these once-abundant arthropods also appear in the model of Cambrian life in Figure 19–21. The trilobites flourished in the oceans for 300 million years.

Green land plants evolved in two principal directions. One group remained small and developed the ability to colonize almost-bare rock surface. In this situation, moisture is abundant at some seasons, but soil and available mineral matter are scanty. This first group gave rise to the mosses and liverworts. The second group evolved an ever-increasing amount of conducting and supporting tissue, and true leaves. These plant lines evolved into the ferns and all other higher plants—the trees, shrubs, and herbaceous flowering plants.

The invasion of land by green plants was an event of enormous importance for animals. Being heterotrophic (page 203), animals require complex organic compounds as food. The animals of the Cambrian seas depended directly or indirectly on the algae for their food. Since there were no green plants on land at this time, there would have been no source of food on land for animals. The invasion of land by green plants was, therefore, an evolutionary step that had to be taken before animals could also invade the land and become established.

19–23 A model of life in a Silurian sea. Two large eurypterids (arthropods) dominate the scene. A third is almost hidden beneath an outcropping of the sea bottom (lower right). Snails (mollusks) and clusters of Silurian plants also can be seen.

N.Y. State Museum and Science Service

American Museum of Natural History

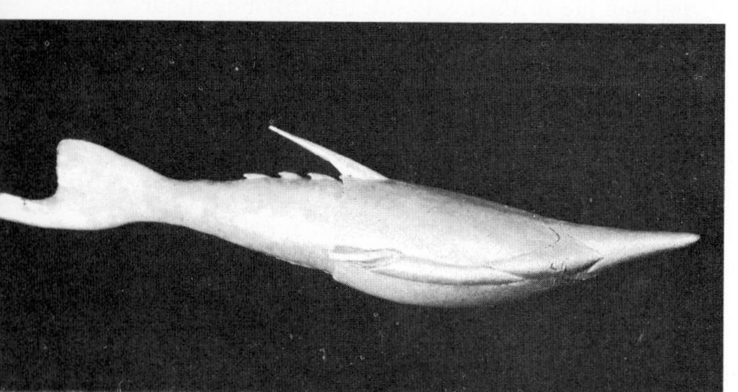

American Museum of Natural History

19–24 (Above) A model of early fish in a Devonian sea. At the bottom center, and in the second photograph **(left),** are models of ostracoderms, early jawless fish. Also shown in the larger photograph, at the left and right of the ostracoderms, are several species of more advanced fish, with jaws and paired fins. What was the significance of paired fins in these early fish to the evolution of land-inhabiting vertebrates?

The Beginnings of the Chordates

There are a few fossils from Ordovician rocks that, from our point of view, are extremely interesting. They do not look like much—just fragments of bones and scales. Why are they so exciting? They are the earliest fossil chordates—the first known examples of our own phylum. During the Silurian and **Devonian** (de·VOH·nee·an) periods they became abundant.

These early chordates (Figure 19-24) are primitive fish, called **ostracoderms** (OS·TRAK-oh·dermz). In some, the body was covered by bony plates and scales. The ostracoderms had a primitive vertebral column, so they were vertebrates as well as chordates. Some of the ostracoderms were bottom feeders. They sucked mud containing food material into their mouths. There are no ostracoderms living today, but the lamprey and hagfish are fairly closely related to them.

Perhaps the most interesting thing about the ostracoderms is their lack of jaws and paired fins. Jaws are present in all higher chordates, where they are important in capturing and grinding food. The ostracoderms sucked in their food.

Even without being told what they are, you might have classified the ostracoderms seen in Figure 19-24 as fish. In other words, you would have put them in our own phylum and not in any other. But what did they evolve from? Ostracoderms did not just "happen." They must have evolved from more primitive ancestors. Part of the answer must lie buried somewhere in the Cambrian rocks. Some biologists believe that the chordates evolved from very primitive echinodermlike invertebrates.

In the Devonian period there were also more advanced fish with jaws (Figure 19-24). Some of these had paired fins. Paired fins are important in the higher fish as an aid to swimming. In the course of evolution, paired fins evolved into the paired legs of chordates that live on land (amphibians, reptiles, birds, and mammals). The paired fins of fish, then, are homologous (page 353) to the arms and legs of the higher chordates. The Devonian fish with paired fins were the ancestors of still more advanced fish and of the higher vertebrates.

The Amphibians

Fossil evidence from the later part of the Devonian period indicates that large populations of fish belonging to a group known as the "lobe-fins" were already living in shallow, fresh water. There is every reason to suppose that some of these animals crawled from pool to pool and then, spending more time on the land, gave rise to the terrestrial populations that we recognize as **Amphibia** (am·FIB·ih·a).

The amphibians (Figure 19-25), were the first chordates to come out on land. Many structural and physiological changes were necessary for life on land. The paired fins evolved into legs. Gills could no longer be used in respiration. Lungs, which were already present in the lobe-finned fish, became the chief structures in which oxygen and carbon dioxide are exchanged between the environment and the blood.

The earliest amphibians known from the Devonian still looked like, and presumably behaved much like, fish (Figure 19-25). Animals of this sort probably wandered upon the land for tens of millions of years before the definitely terrestrial types of the later Paleozoic evolved. All living amphibians are much modified from their Devonian ancestors, yet they retain many features that show how the transition from water to land was made. The modern forms are by no means a precariously existing remnant, but are quite numerous and successful. However, they do not succeed in maintaining themselves in any great variety of habitats. Broadly speaking, they are unable to survive for very long unless they are close to water, where they lay their eggs and where the young develop. This restricts the range of amphibian habitats.

Other Invaders of the Land

The amphibians were not the first animals to invade the land. In the previous period, the Silurian, some scorpions left the water. Neither scorpions nor amphibians, nor any other animals for that matter, could live on land for long unless green plants were there. As we have already seen, green plants had invaded dry land by the time of the Silurian period and to some extent even earlier.

Land plants were not very common in the Silurian, or even early in the Devonian. By the end of the Devonian, however, there were forests. The plants in these forests were not like those in our forests today. The Devonian trees were actually giant species of club mosses

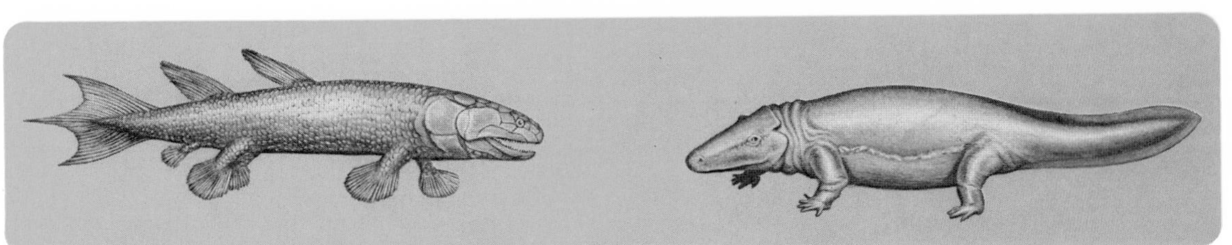

19–25 A lobe-finned fish **(left)** and a primitive amphibian **(right).** In the late Devonian, some of the lobe-finned fish may have crawled out on land and moved from pool to pool in an amphibious manner. They were ancestral to the amphibians.

and horsetails (Figure 14-11, page 264) and tree ferns (Figure 19-26).

There was even a more spectacular development of land plants in the **Carboniferous** (kar-bon·IF·er·us) period, 345 to 280 million years ago—commonly subdivided into the Mississippian (early) and Pennsylvanian (late) periods. This is the time in geological history when the great coal deposits were formed, as the name "Carboniferous" implies. Coal, which is so important economically, is found in many parts of the world. Coal beds are the fossilized remnants of plants that grew in swamps. The world in those days was largely tropical and subtropical, even in areas where it is now very cold, such as Greenland and Antarctica. The forests were jungles of lush vegetation (Figure 19-27). Sometimes the trees were more than 30 meters high—yet they were not the trees we know. Most were related to club mosses.

These spectacular examples of evolution among the plants were rivaled by those of animals. Ancestral dragonflies (Figure 19-27) with wing spans of 50 to 75 cm, giant cockroaches, and other primitive insects lived in the Carboniferous forests. Many species of amphibians lived in the swamps.

The Rise of the Reptiles

During the Carboniferous period, one group of amphibians evolved into reptiles. This was a momentous change.

The amphibians never really conquered *dry* land. The adults often were forced to stay near water. This is true of modern amphibians as well. In addition, the embryonic stages are nearly always found in water. If not, they occur in wet earth or wet vegetation. Reptiles, on the other hand, have an outer skin that is much less permeable to water. They can live in very dry places; as you may know, reptiles are often abundant in desert regions. In addition, reptiles usually lay eggs on land. With a protective outer skin and an egg that could

19–26 These tree ferns, growing in New Zealand, are similar to those of the Carboniferous period. Today tree ferns are found in the wet tropics and in moist, temperate areas of Australia and New Zealand.

G. R. Roberts

Field Museum of Natural History

19–27 A reconstruction of a forest of the Carboniferous period. The trees were relatives of today's club mosses, ferns, and gymnosperms. Note the giant ancestral dragonfly **(right center).** Can you find two other insects that are shown?

develop on land, the reptiles were set to rule the living world for some 200 million years.

The warm seas of the late Paleozoic had a rich variety of invertebrates as well as vertebrates. Corals, brachiopods, mollusks, and echinoderms were abundant.

As the Paleozoic era drew to a close, the environment began to change. Some parts of the world that had been warm now became increasingly cold. Shallow seas were restricted by the emergence of land masses. Great mountain chains were pushed upward. Our own Appalachian Mountains are the remains of a mighty upheaval that occurred at this time.

This was a period of crisis for marine invertebrates. Many forms became extinct—though we can only guess the reasons. Their rates of mutation and recombination were presumably not sufficient for the evolution of populations capable of living competitively under the new conditions.

On land, however, the story was different. The uplifted lands of the **Permian** (PER·mee·an) period held an increased variety of environments. No longer were the continents low and covered with monotonous jungles. There were hills and lowlands, swamps and deserts, and varied climates. This variety of habitats offered many new opportunities to animals that could take advantage of them. Such animals were the reptiles, until then of small size and hardly more than competitors on an equal footing with the numerous amphibians that had dominated the Carboniferous swamps (Figure 19-28). The reptiles had a great advantage because they laid their eggs on land, far away from swamps and streams. Consequently, there was an expansion of reptiles during the Permian period. As Permian history ran its course, the reptiles became increasingly dominant, the amphibians increasingly reduced. The Age of Reptiles had begun.

19–28 A scene in Texas during the Permian period. In the foreground and the right background are two large amphibians (*Eryops*—EAR·ee·ops). In the center background are two primitive reptiles (*Dimetrodon*—dy·ME·tro·don), with large sail-like structures extending above their backs. The function of these structures remains unknown.

LIFE IN THE MESOZOIC

With the dawn of the **Mesozoic** (mes·o·ZOH-ik) era, there was a new outburst of reptilian evolution. This can be correlated with the increase of land areas and consequent increase in ecological opportunity for land animals. Many new kinds of reptiles evolved. These varied from small species to the giants among the dinosaurs (Figure 19-29). Some became flying reptiles, others evolved into aquatic forms. Some were carnivorous; others were herbivorous. Some lived on dry land; others lived primarily in swamps. From a study of Figure 19-29 could you guess the habitat and way of life of each of the dinosaurs shown?

The plant world was also changing. The earlier forests of club mosses, horsetails, and ferns were now overshadowed by forests of **cycads** (SY·kads—Figure 19-30), **ginkgos** (GING·koes), and **conifers** (KON·ih·ferz—evergreen plants). Representatives of these three groups are still living, especially conifers such as pines, firs, and spruce.

Reptilian Experiments: The Birds and Mammals

During the middle period of the Mesozoic, known as the **Jurassic** (ju·RAS·ik), one group of reptiles gave rise to the birds. The first birds had feathers, for the most part, instead of scales (Figures 19-30 and 19-31), but in many ways they were still basically reptilian. They had teeth, a long bony tail, and claws on several digits of each wing. No modern bird has teeth. All have a very short bony tail, with tail feathers set in like a fan. Only one living species of bird has retained claws on its wings.

In the early days of the Mesozoic, the reptiles also gave rise to another class of chordates, the mammals. For nearly 100 million years, the mammals were small, scarce, and apparently not important in the Mesozoic way of life. Their day came later.

The Decline and Fall of the Mighty Reptiles

In late **Cretaceous** (kre·TAY·shus) times, barely 100 million years ago, the dinosaurs reached their evolutionary peak. Many new groups, each adapted to a different way of life,

19–29 Mesozoic reptiles (not drawn to scale). One was a flying reptile (*Pteranodon*); two were swimmers (*Elasmosaurus* and *Ophthalmosaurus*). The rest lived on land.

19–30 A Jurassic scene in Europe. The dinosaur is *Allosaurus* (al·oh·SAUR·us). One living and one dead ancestral bird, *Archaeopteryx* (ar·key·OP·teh·rix), are seen. Among the Jurassic plants are the cycads at the left and right foreground.

developed, giving the reptiles a variety never previously attained. Then, while seemingly at the height of their development, these mighty reptiles became extinct. The reason is one of the puzzles of paleontology. Numerous theories have been advanced; not one has been generally accepted.

The extinction of the characteristic reptiles of the Mesozoic points up an important principle: extinction of species can be important in evolution. Extinction weeds out the old, and so makes way for the new. Most of the land habitats of the Mesozoic seem to have been occupied by the reptiles. When these reptiles became extinct, the inconspicuous group mentioned before—the mammals—could then exploit the land. Of course, the change was not sudden. Millions of years were involved.

THE CENOZOIC—AGE OF MAMMALS

The last part of the Mesozoic and the first part of the **Cenozoic** (see·no·ZOH·ik) were periods of mountain-making. All of the great mountain systems of the present—the Rockies, the Andes, and the Himalayas—were formed. The uplift of these huge mountain chains greatly affected the environment and, therefore, the evolution of Cenozoic animals and plants. High mountains modify the wind patterns and, hence, the amount of rainfall reaching different regions of the earth. Thus, mountains can influence the formation of forests or of deserts.

The mammals took over where once the reptiles had ruled. The first part of the Cenozoic witnessed an explosive evolution of the mammals. All of the major groups that we know today were present. There were also many mammals that evolved and then became extinct (Figure 19-32). Some of the newly evolved mammals were superficially like the reptiles they replaced. The porpoise, for example, resembles some of the extinct aquatic reptiles in body shape and fish-eating habits (Figure 19-29). This similarity of form and way of life in different groups of organisms is an example of **convergent evolution.**

Mammals arose from a different reptilian stock than the one from which birds were derived. Both birds and the mammals, which escaped the destructive forces that caused the extinction of the Mesozoic reptiles, have two things in common. First, they have a far more

American Museum of Natural History

19–31 The oldest known fossil bird, *Archaeopteryx.* It lived in the Jurassic period. A drawing of the bird is included in Figure 19–30.

19–32 An Eocene (early Cenozoic) group of mammals. The large mammal on the right is *Uintatherium* (YU·in·ta·THIR·ee·um). At the left in the foreground is a primitive carnivore, *Mesonyx* (MEZ·o·nix). Behind the *Mesonyx* is an early horse, *Hyracotherium* (HY·rak·o·THIR·ee·um).

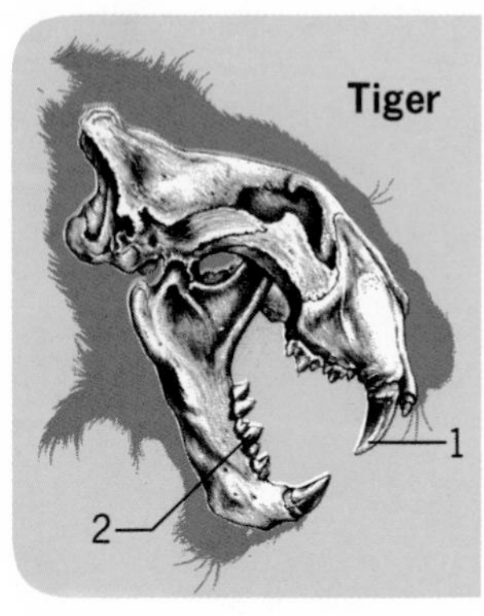

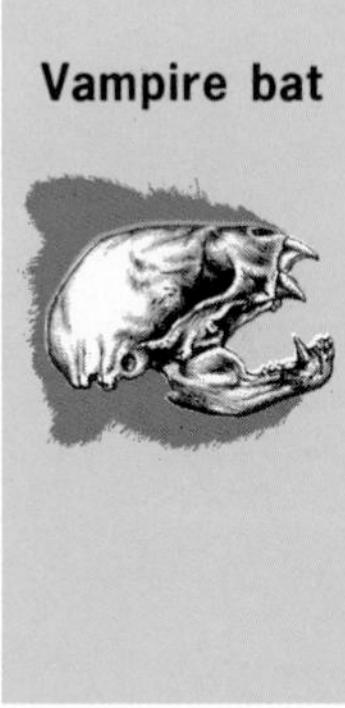

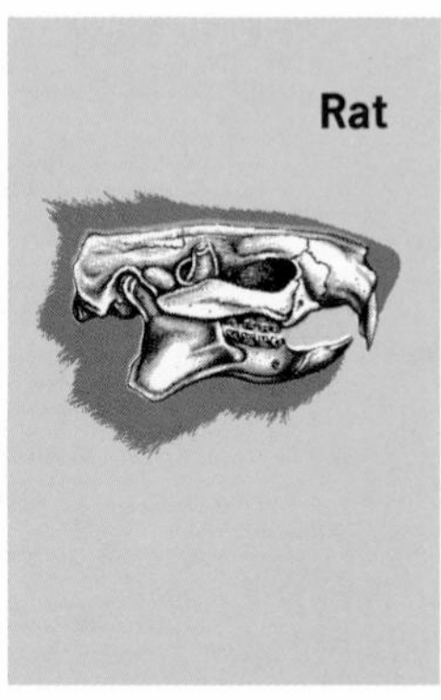

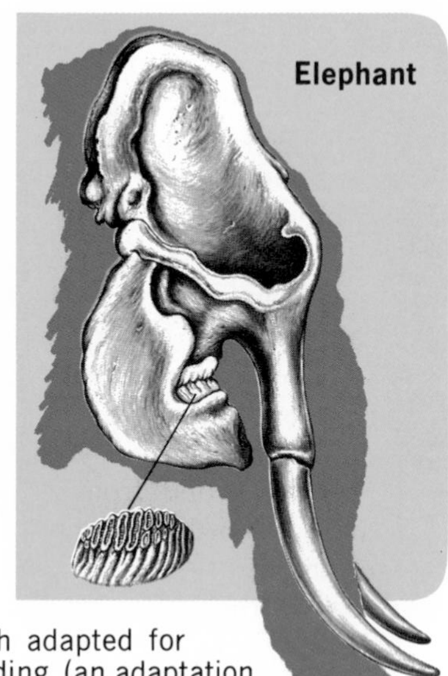

19–33 Examples of specialization in mammalian teeth. There are many patterns other than the four shown; for example, can you think of an animal that is not classified as a herbivore but that has some of its numerous teeth adapted for grinding?

effective protection against changes of environmental temperature than is found in any reptile; and second, they usually care for their eggs and their young.

Mammals maintain a constant body temperature, independently of the environment, partly by means of the insulation offered by *hair*. Most female mammals *retain their eggs in the body,* where embryonic development takes place; thus, they usually bring forth living young. They care for the young after birth and feed them with milk secreted by the *mammary glands*. The teeth of the different mammals are specialized for specific diets (Figure 19-33).

The mammals of today are divided into three main groups: the egg-laying mammals, the pouched mammals, and the **placental** (pla·SEN·tul) mammals. The last are the more highly developed and include most of the mammals of the world, including man.

Two mammals that suckle their young but also lay eggs (you will learn more about them in Chapter 26) have survived to this day. These are the duckbill **platypus** (PLAT·ih·pus—Figure 26-5, page 480) and the **echidna** (e·KID·na), which live in Australia and on some of the nearby islands. They are the survivors of what was probably a much larger number and variety of small egg-laying mammals.

Pouched mammals are very widely diversified in the Australian region. They also occur in the New World. Examples are the kangaroos of Australia and the opossums of the New World. In these forms, the young are born very early in their development and find their way into a pouch on the female's belly. Here they are nourished with milk and complete their development, as you will study in Chapter 26.

The placental mammals, the third group, are characterized by the presence of a **placenta** (pla·SEN·ta), an organ for nourishing the young within the body of the female parent. Nearly all familiar mammals (except those native to the Australian region) are placental mammals.

Ten million years ago the mammals were not strikingly different from many alive today. Figure 19-34 shows some that lived in North America during the **Pliocene** (PLY·O·seen). The forerunners of man lived during the Cenozoic; we will devote a later chapter to them.

The Rise of the Angiosperms

The changes during the late Mesozoic and early Cenozoic, which were so important for the evolution of animals, were equally important for the evolution of plants (Chapter 14). The earliest angiosperms (flowering plants)

19–34 Some Pliocene (late Cenozoic) mammals. How many remind you of closely related mammals that live on the earth today? Several of these species of animals became extinct only within the past 10,000 years; some were hunted by early man.

appeared late in the Mesozoic. They probably lived in mountainous regions, while the conifers and cycadlike plants dominated the plains. The angiosperms did not become the dominant terrestrial plants until the Cenozoic.

The environmental change that gave the flowering plants their first advantage over gymnosperms (the pines and their relatives) was probably associated with the rise of new kinds of animals. Flowering plants are superior to gymnosperms chiefly in their better solutions to the problems of cross-fertilization, seed dispersal, and establishment of seedlings. Insects and birds are much more efficient agents for transporting pollen than are wind and water. Birds and small mammals are the only means by which large seeds such as acorns and nuts, which contain a generous food supply for the young seedling, are transported for long distances. The extensive spread of angiosperm trees was probably brought about largely by these animals and by the retreat of inland seas.

The fossil record of insects at this time is very imperfect, but there is some evidence that the bee family was actively evolving. Butterflies also appeared on the scene. These insects were taking over the role of pollinating flowers from the more primitive beetles, which are the pollinators of the most primitive flowering plants even today. Beetles, bees, butterflies, birds, and early mammals must have had a strong selective influence in the evolution of the families and genera (plural of genus) of flowering plants. By the end of the age of dinosaurs, about 70 million years ago, the plants were essentially like those of modern times.

CONCLUDING REMARKS

The approximately two million species of living animals can be classified according to a scheme that is based on their relationships. The major groups in which they are arranged are the phyla. It is believed that all the animals in a single phylum evolved from a common ancestor. Little is known, however, of the interrelationships among the various phyla. Presumably most of the phyla evolved in Pre-Cambrian times and have not left adequate fossils. The chordates appeared later, and we know the main outlines of their evolution.

The main fossil record begins in Cambrian rocks about 600 million years old. From that time until today, there is a continuous record of the evolution of life (Figures 19-18 and 19-19).

At the beginning of the Paleozoic era, the first great time division of the fossil record, life was confined to the sea. Plants were simple, but there were many kinds of invertebrates. Early in the Paleozoic, plants and invertebrates emigrated to the land. At about this same time the first fishlike vertebrates arose. By the middle of the Paleozoic, the fish had evolved along several different lines, leading to the major groups of modern fish. At this time one group of fish ventured onto land, and in so doing evolved the amphibian way of life. The amphibians in turn rapidly evolved, becoming the dominant land animals during the age when great coal forests blanketed the land. At the end of the Paleozoic, the continents were further uplifted and environments became varied. The reptiles, which had evolved from amphibian ancestors, became the dominant land animals.

With the beginning of the Mesozoic era the reptiles became quite numerous and varied, both on the land and in the sea. The dinosaurs arose and became the rulers of the land for more than 100 million years. Some reptiles flew through the air, which they shared with primitive birds. Toward the end of the Mesozoic, the dinosaurs and many other reptiles became extinct. The great extinction of reptiles occurred when the modern mountain systems were being formed.

The Cenozoic era, the last great division in the history of life, was marked by the continued uplift of mountains and the cooling of climates. At the beginning of the Cenozoic, there was a great multiplication of mammals, which had first appeared during the time of the dinosaurs. About the middle of the Cenozoic, the modern groups of mammals evolved.

There is tremendous variety today in the Animal Kingdom. Yet Paramecium, *Hydra*, planarians, earthworms, grasshoppers, and man are all faced with similar problems—problems once shared by animals that are extinct. Each animal must obtain food, digest it, transport the digested products throughout the body, respire, excrete, reproduce, act in a coordinated way, and so on. Now, problem by problem and chapter by chapter, let us see how these problems are solved.

GUIDE QUESTIONS AND PROBLEMS

1. List and describe the divisions of the biological classification system in order of increasingly inclusive groups.
2. What is the basis for the biological classification system developed by Carolus Linnaeus? Why is a classification system needed?
3. What are the problems of placing—or of *not* placing—the viruses, bacteria, and other unicellular organisms into one kingdom separate from plants and animals?
4. Contrast the use of homologous and analogous structures as a basis for classification in an evolutionary sense.
5. Although biologists believe that the animal phyla have evolved from one another as the plant phyla have, they are unable to substantiate this evolution as readily as they can with plants. Why?
6. Which group of vertebrates made the first really effective transition to dry land? What were the successful features of this group's evolution? What effect did this have on subsequent animal colonization of land areas?
7. Why do we not expect to find fossil evidence of land animals in rock strata older than those containing the first evidence of land plants?
8. What effect may extinction of a species have in the evolutionary process? How may convergent evolution offset the effect?
9. One biologist recently suggested that if and when complex life forms are discovered elsewhere in the universe, they will be found to have left and right sides and head ends. What would you say if asked to defend or criticize this statement?
10. Reptiles of one legless species outwardly look more like earthworms than like other reptiles. Why aren't they classified as belonging to Phylum Annelida? How is this similarity of appearance between two distantly related animals accounted for?

RELATED READING

Books

For brief introductions to animal types . . .

Zim, Herbert, S., *et al*, in Golden Nature Series (paperbacks), Golden Press, New York: *Birds* (1949), *Fish* (1959), *Insects* (1951), *Mammals* (1955), *Reptiles and Amphibians* (1953), *Seashores* (1955).

For more elaborate, beautifully illustrated guides to animal life . . .

Buchsbaum, Ralph, and Lorus J. Milne, *The Lower Animals: Living Invertebrates of the World*, Doubleday, New York, 1960 (revised printings, 1962 and 1964).

Klots, A., and Elsie Klots, *Living Insects of the World*, Doubleday, New York, 1959 (revised printing, 1965).

Herald, E. S., *Living Fishes of the World*, Doubleday, New York, 1961.

Cochran, Doris M., *Living Amphibians of the World*, Doubleday, New York, 1958.

Schmidt, K. P., and R. F. Inger, *Living Reptiles of the World*, Doubleday, New York, 1957 (revised printing, 1962).

Gilliard, E., *Living Birds of the World*, Doubleday, New York, 1958.

Sanderson, I., *Living Mammals of the World*, Doubleday, New York, 1955 (revised printing, 1966).

For standard texts and handbooks . . .

Buchsbaum, Ralph, *Animals Without Backbones*, University of Chicago Press, Chicago, 1948. Nicely illustrated college text.

Collins, H. H., *Complete Field Guide to American Wildlife*, Harper and Row, New York, 1959. Over 2000 illustrations.

Moore, John A., *Principles of Zoology*, Oxford University Press, 1957. Emphasis on interrelationships and principles.

Simpson, George Gaylord, and William S. Beck, *Life: An Introduction to Biology*, Second Edition, Harcourt, Brace & World, New York, 1965. Comprehensive and detailed.

20

Digestion in Multicellular Animals

The animal way of life involves great dependence upon the environment. We have seen that *Amoeba* depends on its environment for food and oxygen. The environment also is a place for it to dump its wastes—carbon dioxide, water, nitrogen compounds such as ammonia, and the indigestible contents of food vacuoles.

For *Amoeba* these problems are simplified to some extent because its body is very small—a single cell. Every part of this cell is close to the environment on which it depends (Figure 20-1a).

Similar Requirements Among Animals

All animal cells have similar requirements, although these requirements differ in detail. Animals must have a supply of water, amino acids (pages 93-95), simple sugars, **fatty acids** (products of fat digestion), vitamins, oxygen, and many other organic and inorganic substances. They must be able to dispose of their waste products, principally carbon dioxide, water, and nitrogen compounds such as ammonia, urea (page 89), or uric acid.

Most species of animals have bodies of many cells. This introduces a greatly different consideration. Whereas every part of *Amoeba* is close to the outside, most cells of multicellular animals are far from the outside environment (Figure 20-1 b). A cell deep inside a large animal cannot capture and ingest food particles as *Amoeba* does. If it dumps its wastes, they are dumped not into the surrounding environment but among the other cells that also are producing wastes. The interior cells, therefore, are unable to obtain the substances they require directly from the environment and unable to dispose of their wastes directly into it.

Animals overcome in two ways the problems associated with size and many cells.

First, *division of labor* characterizes the cells. The single cell of *Amoeba* does everything—captures and digests food, obtains oxygen, disposes of wastes, moves, and reproduces. In animals composed of many cells, evolution has introduced specialization. Different groups of specialized cells capture food, digest it, obtain oxygen, get rid of wastes, move, provide support, carry on reproduction, receive stimuli, and coordinate the various activities of the whole organism.

Second, the multicellular animals have *systems for transport* within the body. These transport systems carry food and other materials to each cell and remove waste substances from it.

In both these respects, multicellular animals resemble multicellular plants, which solved the same problems in the same general ways. As you will recall, plants have also undergone differentiation of their cells and a division of labor (see Chapters 13 and 17). They, too, have evolved transport systems (Chapter 16).

No matter how specialized a cell becomes, it still has the same basic requirements for staying alive. Yet as a cell becomes specialized, it becomes increasingly less able to provide for all its own needs. It becomes more and more dependent on its fellow cells.

Let us consider a human muscle cell. It is *highly* specialized, its function being to contract. When it contracts it may move, but that is about all it can do. The muscle cell depends on cells of the digestive tract for its supply of digested food materials. It depends on cells of the lungs for oxygen from the environment. It depends on cells of the kidneys and the lungs for ultimately casting out most of its waste

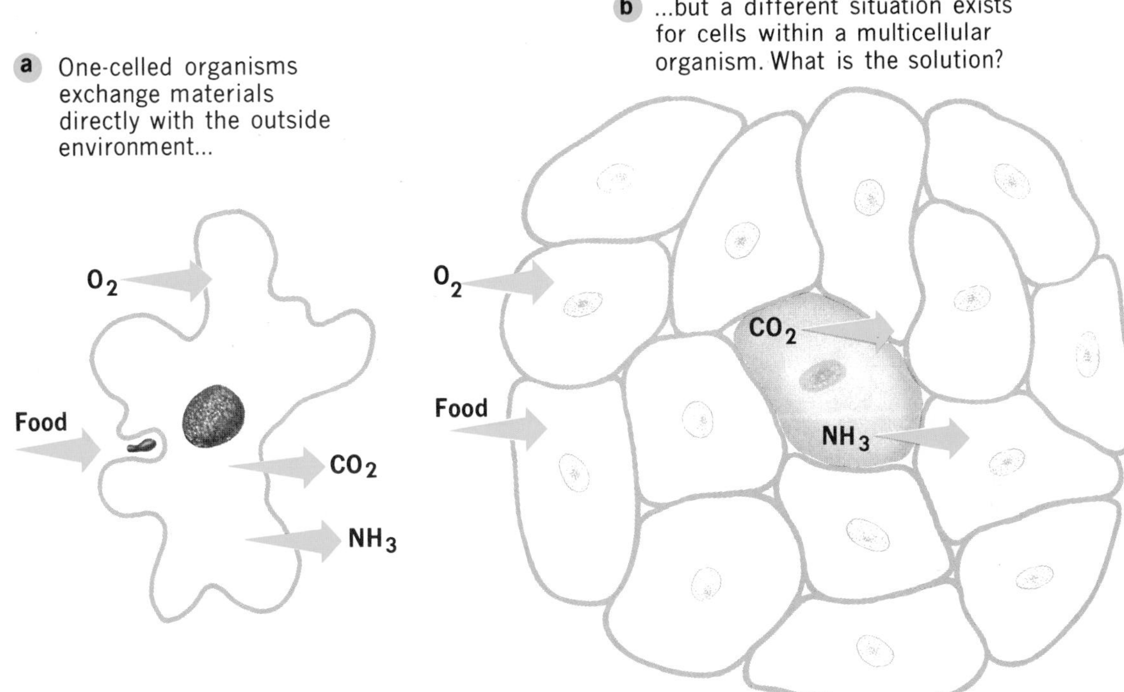
a One-celled organisms exchange materials directly with the outside environment...
b ...but a different situation exists for cells within a multicellular organism. What is the solution?
O_2
Food
CO_2
NH_3
O_2
Food
CO_2
NH_3

products. It depends on cells forming the vessels of the circulatory system for carrying digested food substances and oxygen to it and for removing its waste products from its immediate vicinity. It depends on cells of the nervous system, in part, to coordinate all these complex activities, including its own contraction.

Every cell in the body, in its own specialized way, contributes to the functioning of the whole. Conversely, we can think of the whole body as functioning to keep every individual cell alive. This is not two ideas, but one.

The organization of a human community is somewhat like the organization of a complex animal. Farmers raise the food, carpenters build the houses, physicians strive to maintain health, railroad men and truckers transport what we need, and the community government attempts to regulate all these activities. The individual depends upon the community, and the community depends upon the individual. The more specialized the members of the community, the more dependent they become on all their fellow specialists. Life in our society today furnishes many examples.

This chapter is the first of several that will deal with cell specialization. The specialty to be considered here, in animals selected from several phyla, is digestion.

PROBLEMS AND METHODS OF DIGESTION

The substances that animal cells require, such as oxygen, water, inorganic salts, amino acids, simple sugars, vitamins, and fatty acids, can pass across cell membranes and enter the cells of all animals.

Oxygen, water, and inorganic salts are usually readily available in the environment. The molecules and ions are all in a form that can enter cells and be used. All that is required is that the oxygen and inorganic salts become dissolved in the watery film of body fluid on cell surfaces. Then they will diffuse through the cell membranes, or be moved into the cells by special processes of active transport (Chapter 6, page 113).

Amino acids, simple sugars, vitamins, and fatty acids, as such, are rare in the natural environment. Organisms almost never have these substances *directly* available to them. In nature, all but the vitamins (and sometimes these, too) are usually parts of much larger molecules—like proteins, starch, and fats. Generally these larger organic molecules cannot pass across cell membranes. *Amoeba* solves this problem by taking these larger molecules, which are present in its food, into its food vacuoles. However, for most multicellular animals, a sufficient rate of supply to the cells depends upon *extracellular digestion* (page 334). Large organic molecules must be changed to kinds that can cross cell membranes.

Why is it that so few proteins and other large molecules can pass through the cell membrane? The answer is entirely logical, in terms of evolution. Since the cell is made largely of proteins, RNA, and DNA, and since it stores large molecules of carbohydrates and fats, it could not survive if these essential components escaped from it. Therefore the cell must have evolved—a very long time ago—a differentially permeable membrane *that would keep essential things in.* Consequently, only the smaller molecules could be permitted to move back and forth.

Digesting converts large organic molecules, which are found in foods, into small organic molecules that can easily pass across cell membranes. Not only must the molecules be small, but they must be of certain specific types. Thus the proteins must be broken down into amino acids, not into other types of molecules.

Amino acids, simple sugars, and fatty acids are a biochemical "common currency" in living creatures. These small organic molecules are used by each species to synthesize its own specific cellular structures. Man eats beef. The beef protein is digested to amino acids. These amino acids are used to synthesize human proteins. No matter how much beef you eat, your proteins will never be beef proteins.

Digestive changes from large to small molecules are, of course, chemical changes. All these changes are controlled by enzymes (pages 106-08).

Apart from varying dependence on intracellular digestion, other general features of digestion are the same in *Amoeba, Hydra*, planarians, earthworms, and man. This is another example of the fact that all animals face the same problems and solve them in much the same way.

Amoeba takes food into its food vacuoles. This food cannot be absorbed until it is converted to amino acids, simple sugars, and other small molecules. Enzymes are secreted by the cytoplasm into the food vacuoles. Slowly the food is digested, and the products are absorbed and assimilated.

Digestion in *Hydra*

Small aquatic animals are paralyzed by the stinging cells and caught by the **tentacles** (TEN-ta·k'lz) of *Hydra*. The tentacles slowly move the food to the mouth. The food is then pushed into the digestive cavity (Figure 20-2). The cells that line the digestive cavity secrete enzymes into this cavity, much as substances are secreted by certain cells of man and other animals (Figure 20-3). The enzymes begin the digestion of the large molecules that are in the body of the prey.

This is only a small part of the digestive process in *Hydra*. Most digestion takes place *not* in the digestive cavity but inside body cells, in the manner of *Amoeba*. As the body of the prey is broken down into smaller and smaller chunks in the digestive cavity, some of these tiny chunks are taken into the cells lining the digestive cavity. When a chunk of food is adjacent to the cell, the cell membrane bulges out and encloses it. In this way the food becomes enclosed in a vacuole within the cell. The big organic molecules in this food vacuole are no more useful to the cell than when they were still in the body of the prey. They must still be broken down. Enzymes inside the cells bring these changes about. Outside, in the digestive cavity, the same changes are going on with the remainder of the prey.

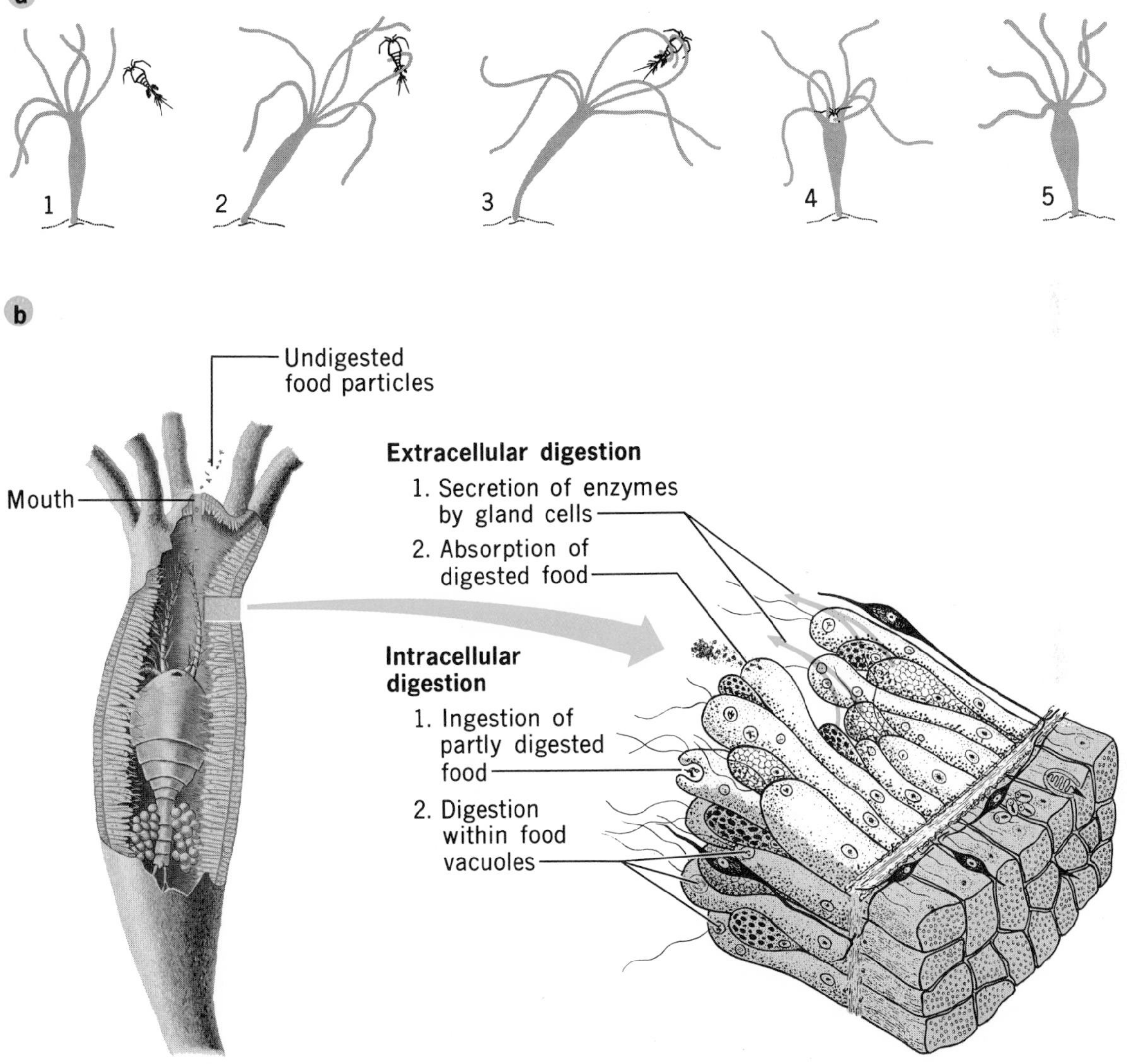

20–2 Food-getting and digestion in *Hydra*. **a.** In this sequence, *Hydra* is capturing and ingesting a smaller freshwater animal. **b.** The food organism, now within the digestive cavity, is attacked by enzymes secreted by gland cells. The enlargement at the right indicates that digestion is both extracellular and intracellular.

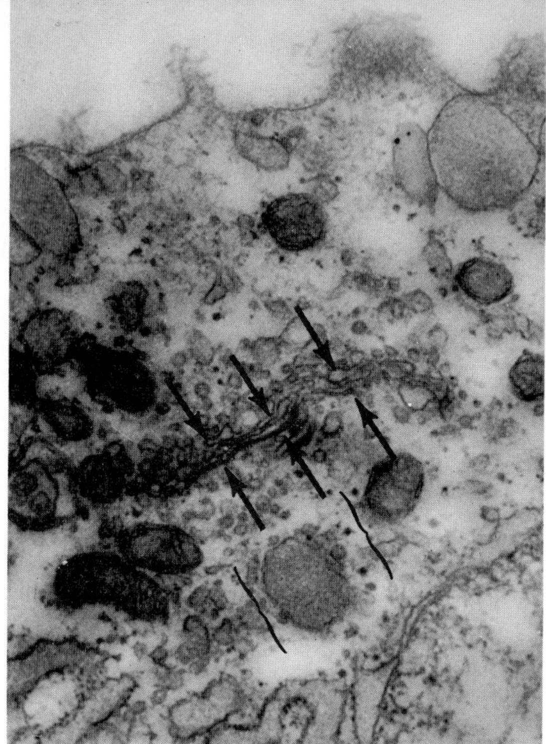

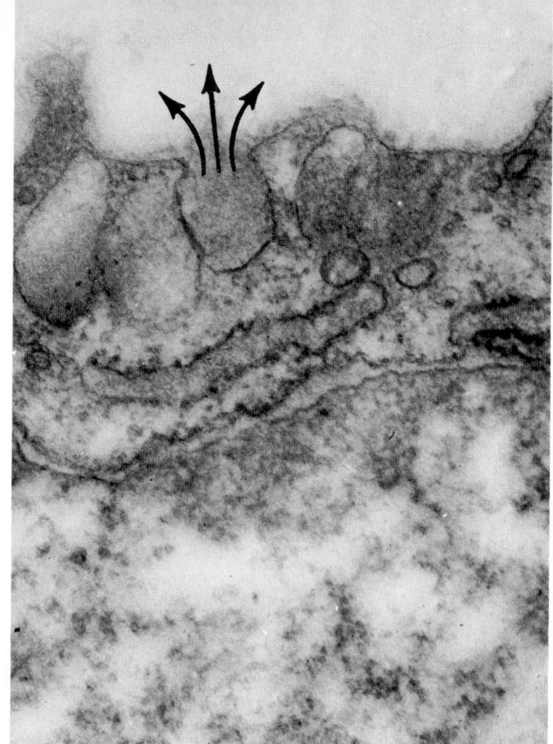

Both photos by Lee D. Peachey

20–3 Evidence of secretion, photographed with the electron microscope. At the left is part of a cell from the wall of the urinary bladder of a toad. Two rows of arrows identify the Golgi bodies, where materials synthesized in the cytoplasm are concentrated for secretion. Within the brackets in the same photograph is a secretion droplet formed by fusion of smaller secretion vesicles. (Other tiny secretion vesicles can be seen dimly between the Golgi bodies and the larger droplet.) At slightly higher magnification, in the photograph at the right, a secretion droplet empties its contents outside the cell, into the bladder. (Magnifications: 30,000 × and 60,000 ×)

Digestion in *Hydra* is thus both extracellular and intracellular. It occurs in the digestive cavity and within the cells, converting the prey to amino acids, fatty acids, vitamins, and other organic substances, as well as some inorganic ones. Those products of digestion formed in the digestive cavity are absorbed by the cells lining the cavity. The small organic molecules are used for energy and for the synthesis of the living substance of *Hydra*.

There are wastes as well as useful substances. Any undigested material from the body of the prey is ejected from the digestive cavity. Since there is only one opening in the digestive cavity it serves *Hydra* as both a mouth and an anus (Figure 20-2).

Digestion in a Planarian

A planarian, like *Hydra,* has a saclike digestive cavity. There is only a single opening, which must, therefore, serve both as a mouth and an anus. In the planarian the opening is a tubelike projection on the underside of the body, almost midway between the anterior and posterior ends (Figure 20-4).

A planarian can capture small, living, aquatic animals, but most of its food seems to consist of the bodies of dead aquatic animals. Digestion is not very different from that in *Hydra,* so there is no need to describe it in detail. Some digestion occurs in the digestive cavity. In addition, the cells lining the digestive cavity engulf and digest small particles of food.

Digestion in the Earthworm

Compared to *Hydra* and planarians, the digestive system of earthworms is much more highly specialized. Instead of being a sac with a single opening, the digestive system of the earthworm is a tube with two openings—a mouth at one end (Figure 20-5), an anus at the other.

There is one important advantage of the tube type of digestive system over the sac type. In the sac type, food enters a single cavity, where it is digested. Any undigested remains go out through the same opening through which food entered. In the tube type of digestive system, food passes in one direction only. The food enters at the mouth and passes along the tube to the anus. Thus, with a one-way digestive tube, *it becomes possible for different parts of the tube to do different jobs in succession.* An assembly line *division of labor* can occur along the way.

We can illustrate this by examining the parts of the digestive tube of the earthworm. The first section of the earthworm's digestive tract, the **pharynx** (FAIR·inks), has strong muscular walls. It pumps the soil, containing decaying organic matter (the earthworm's food), into the **esophagus** (e·SOF·a·gus), which continues to push the ingested material along. Next, the digestive tract widens out. This is the **crop,** a place for the temporary storage of material. The next section, the **gizzard,** has heavy muscular walls. Here the material is ground and broken into small particles. The last and longest section of the digestive tract is the intestine. The cells that form the walls of the intestine secrete enzymes that work on the food in the cavity of the intestine. End products of this digestion are absorbed by the cells that line the intestine. Undigested material is pushed along through the intestine and out through the anus.

A similar, one-way, tubular digestive system is found in most groups of complex animals. The grasshopper (Figure 20-6) and man have digestive systems of this general type. There is consequently little need to discuss the digestive tract of the grasshopper or man as far as *general principles* are concerned. We must, however, say something about the digestive *process* and how it occurs in our own bodies, and in so doing we will need to be familiar with the layout of the digestive tract and the functions of the different organs it includes.

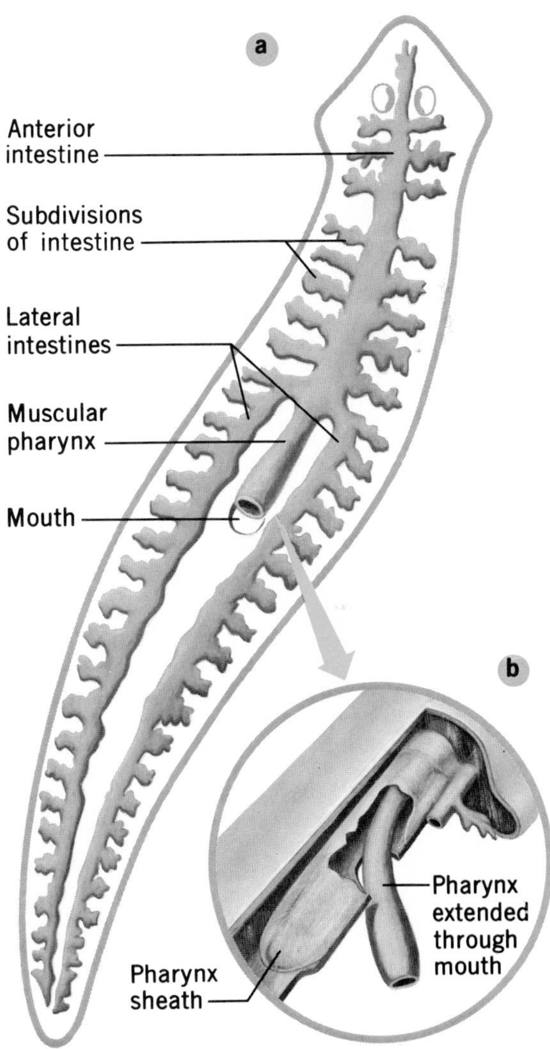

20–4 The digestive system of a planarian. Like that of *Hydra*, it has a single opening. The planarian swims to its food, however; it does not wait, as *Hydra* does, for food to come to it.

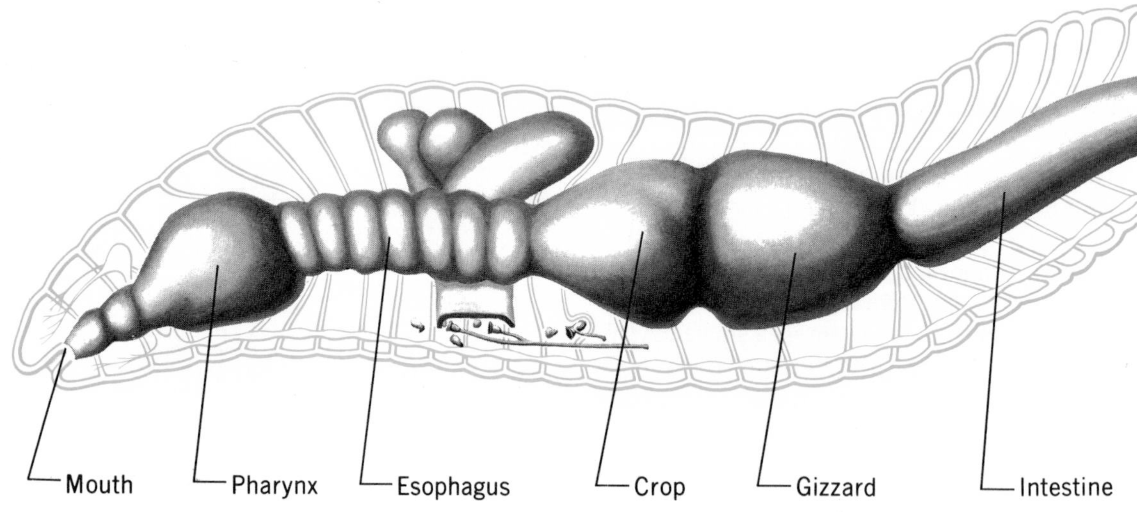

20–5 The digestive system of an earthworm. Traffic is one way, with division of labor among the organs along the route from the mouth to the anus. What specific function is associated with each of the organs shown in the digestive tract?

DIGESTION IN MAN

The digestive system in man consists of a long tube that extends from the mouth to the anus (Figure 20-7). The main sections, in the direction of the passage of food, are the oral cavity, esophagus, stomach, small intestine, large intestine, and rectum. In addition there are many glands, the most obvious being the three pairs of salivary glands, the pancreas, and the liver. The salivary glands and the pancreas secrete juices that contain enzymes. The liver secretes bile, which also aids digestion but does not contain enzymes.

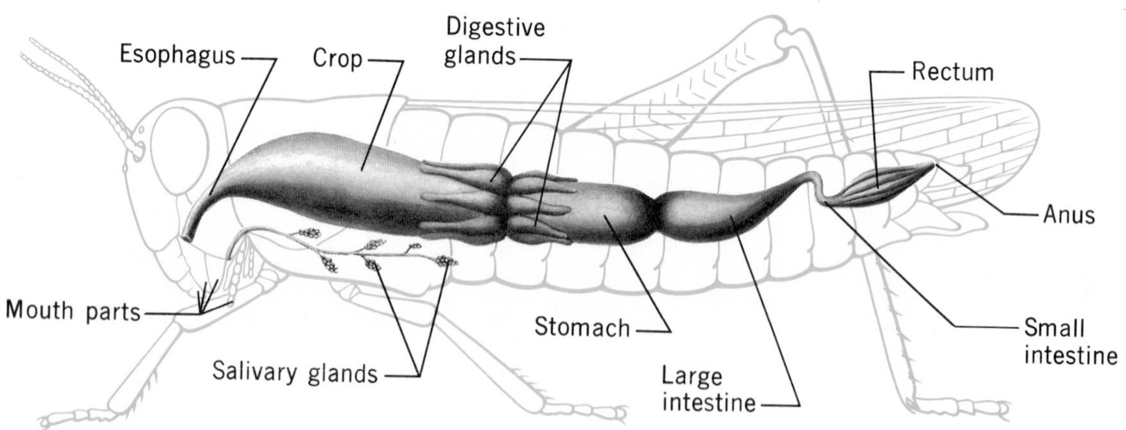

20–6 The digestive system of a grasshopper. As in the earthworm, traffic is one way, with a succession of specialized functions performed by the organs between the mouth and the anus. How do these digestive organs relate to man's?

20-7 THE DIGESTIVE SYSTEM IN MAN

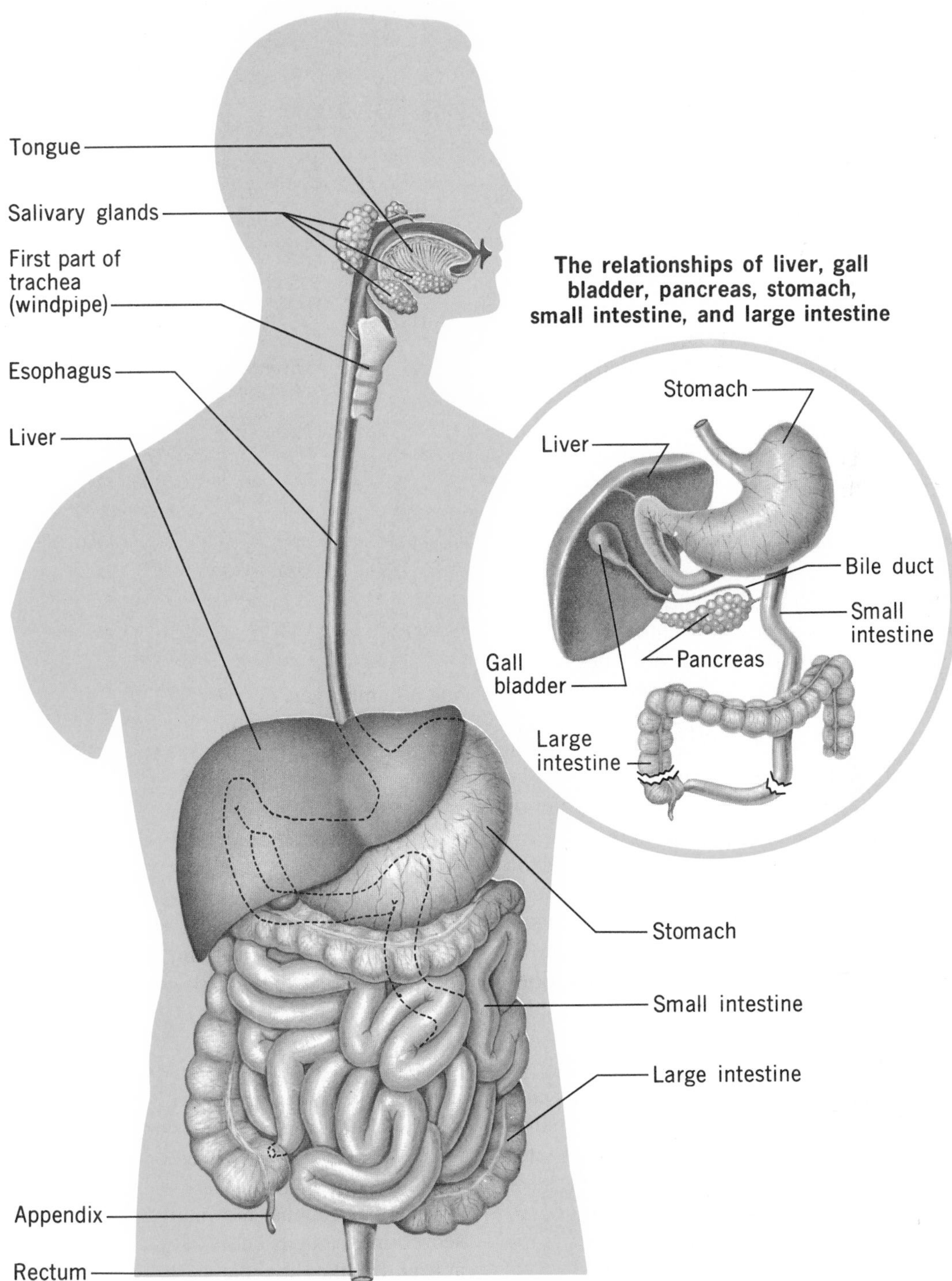
Tongue
Salivary glands
First part of trachea (windpipe)
Esophagus
Liver
Appendix
Rectum
Stomach
Small intestine
Large intestine
The relationships of liver, gall bladder, pancreas, stomach, small intestine, and large intestine
Stomach
Liver
Bile duct
Small intestine
Pancreas
Gall bladder
Large intestine

We can explain digestion in man by describing how a hamburger on a bun, for example, is converted to small molecules like amino acids, simple sugars, fatty acids, vitamins, salts, and water.

Digestion in the Oral Cavity

There are several specific functions of the oral cavity. Food selection is one of them. When food enters the oral cavity it is tasted, smelled, and felt. If the taste or smell of the hamburger suggests that it is old, we reject it. If the teeth or tongue detect hard objects, such as pieces of bone or dirt, we also reject the hamburger. The oral cavity is aided in selecting food by the senses of smell and sight.

A second function of the oral cavity is the grinding of food into small particles. This is useful first because the esophagus can pass only relatively small pieces. (You can bite off a much bigger piece of hamburger than you can swallow whole.) Also, food is easier to digest when it is in small particles. Enzymes must be in contact with the food molecules they digest. In a solid mass of food, the enzymes would penetrate slowly from the exposed surface inward and only gradually would convert the food to small molecules. With food in small particles, there is much more surface for the enzymes to attack and much less solid interior to penetrate.

The third and fourth major functions of the oral cavity are the digestion and lubrication accomplished by saliva. Under the tongue, behind the jaw, and in front of the ear are the salivary glands, which pour their secretions through tubes, or ducts, into the oral cavity (Figure 20-7). Saliva has two main functions. First, it adds water and **mucus** (MEW·kus) to the food. (Mucus is a secretion of cells and glands that serves to moisten and protect them.) The water dissolves some substances. Water and mucus act as a lubricant and ease the passage of food through the esophagus. Second, saliva contains an enzyme that begins the conversion of starch to smaller molecules.

Within the oral cavity, therefore, the food is selected, ground, lubricated, and its digestion begun. The food is then swallowed and passed into the esophagus, which conveys it quickly to the stomach.

This quick conveyance is achieved by a process called **peristalsis** (pair·ih·STAHL·sis—Figure 20-8). This is a pattern of contraction of the muscular wall of the esophagus. An area of the muscle wall contracts, and almost immediately contraction of the wall just beyond begins. Then even further along, the wall starts contracting, while relaxation starts in the area which contracted first. It almost seems as if a *wave* of contraction passes along the wall. In this way, peristalsis starting just behind the mass of food squeezes the food along the esophagus. The wave of peristalsis can sweep from the throat to the stomach. These peristaltic waves are responsible for moving food not only through the esophagus but also through the entire alimentary canal. To demonstrate peristalsis in your esophagus, and to show that it is not gravity alone that makes the food go down, you might try chewing and swallowing a hamburger, or even drinking water, while hanging from a horizontal bar.

Digestion in the Stomach

Considerably more digestion occurs in the stomach than in the oral cavity. Cells lining the stomach secrete gastric juice, which contains an enzyme, **pepsin,** and hydrochloric acid. The hydrochloric acid controls the pH (see Laboratory Inquiry 6-1) at the level suitable for the protein-digesting work of the pepsin. You will study digestion of this sort in the laboratory (Inquiry 20-1).

An interesting problem is raised here. Gastric juice is a powerful protein-digesting fluid. Why doesn't it digest the stomach itself, which is mostly protein? The answer is not fully known. Certainly one factor is that cells lining the stomach secrete mucus. Normally the thick, sticky secretion of mucus coats the inside of the stomach and makes it difficult for the gastric juice

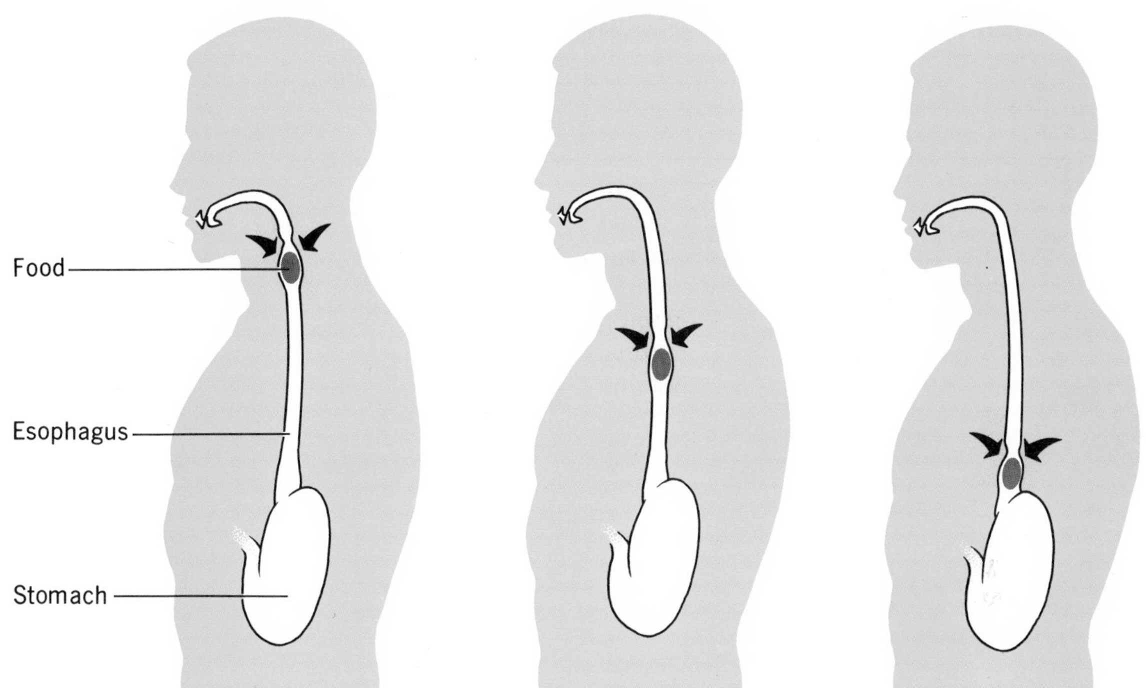

20–8 Movement of food through the alimentary canal. A wave of constriction of the esophageal wall forces the food through the esophagus and into the stomach. The same process of peristalsis carries material through the small and large intestines.

to attack the stomach wall cells (including the cells that produce the gastric juice!)

Unhappily, the protective mechanisms do not always work. The stomach does digest itself at times—a small portion of the lining may be eaten away. The result is an ulcer. If the ulcer is small in size and properly treated, it will heal. Large ulcers may have to be removed by surgery.

The chemical work of the stomach is facilitated by its muscular activity. Its walls contract and relax, and these movements help to mix the gastric juice and the food, thus helping enzymatic digestion.

But our story of digestion in the stomach is not complete. What causes gastric juice to be secreted? Let us return to our hamburger and bun. If we bite off a piece of the hamburger and bun, chew it, and then swallow it, there will be some gastric juice ready for the food by the time it reaches the stomach. How is the stomach able to prepare for the arrival of food? Sometimes even the sight or thought of tempting food—like a hamburger, if you are hungry—is associated with increased gastric secretion. When food is in the oral cavity, the nerves in the cheeks and tongue are stimulated. These carry messages—in the form of nerve impulses—to the brain. From the brain these messages pass to nerves that extend to the wall of the stomach, where they stimulate the gastric glands. As a consequence, there is some gastric juice in the stomach when the food arrives.

When food touches the lining of the stomach, more gastric juice is secreted. If you eat only a bun, which has little protein in it, the stomach does not secrete much gastric juice. On the other hand, the meat you eat results in a need for abundant gastric juice—and there is an abundant secretion of it in response.

The way in which proteins stimulate secretion of gastric juice is elaborate. The gastric juice that is on hand when food reaches the stomach begins the digestion of any proteins that may be present. The huge protein molecules are broken down to smaller molecules. These smaller molecules have a specific stimulating effect on some of the cells lining the stomach. They stimulate these cells to secrete a substance called **gastrin.** Gastrin enters the blood system and is distributed to all parts of the body, including the stomach. Here it has the specific effect of stimulating the cells of the stomach to secrete more gastric juice.

The economy of this mechanism is obvious. If there is protein in the stomach's contents, a large amount of gastric juice is secreted. If only fats and carbohydrates are present, there will be no gastrin and little increased secretion of gastric juice.

Gastrin is a **hormone** (HOR·mohn). As such, it belongs to a class of complex organic molecules that have the following characteristics: first, hormones are secreted by cells; second, they are carried by the circulatory system; third, they have very specific effects on other cells—often in different parts of the body than where they are secreted.

Gastric juice, then, is secreted in response to various types of stimuli: first, in response to messages (nerve impulses) from the brain, evoked by various stimuli including the presence of food in the mouth; second, in response to similar messages evoked by the stimulus of food in contact with the stomach wall; third, in response to the products of protein digestion, which cause a liberation of gastrin that in turn stimulates the secretion of more gastric juice. These are only a few of the major factors regulating gastric secretion, which is closely controlled in relation to events occurring all along the digestive tract.

What have we accomplished so far? Our hamburger and bun have been chewed into small bits by the teeth. The starch-digesting enzyme of saliva has begun the conversion of starch from the bun into smaller molecules. Digestion of proteins in the meat has begun in the stomach but cannot be completed there. The contractions of the stomach walls mix the food with digestive enzymes and also help break the food into smaller particles. By the time the food is ready to leave the stomach it is a souplike mixture, thanks to partial digestion and to the water from saliva and gastric juice.

An Aside on Alexis St. Martin's Stomach

For a great many years the interior of the human body was a puzzle to investigators. Air and food went in and waste products came out. The beating of the heart could be detected. At times strange noises, gurglings, and rumblings could be heard from within.

Observations of this sort told little regarding what occurs within the body of a living individual. The only direct way of finding out what happens would be to open the body and look. The difficulties with *this* approach are rather obvious.

Major surgery was uncommon, because it was nearly always fatal, until late in the nineteenth century. Direct observations of the functioning of the parts of the body, therefore, were exceedingly rare until recently. Only as a result of the strangest of circumstances could one see inside a living human body. But this was the opportunity that came to William Beaumont (1785–1853), a physician in the United States Army.

In 1822 in Michigan, a badly wounded man, Alexis St. Martin, was brought to Beaumont. The accidental discharge of a shotgun had blown a large hole in St. Martin's left side. Parts of the ribs, muscles, and wall of the stomach had been shot away. Beaumont patched up his patient as well as he could, but the wound never closed properly. The wall of the stomach healed by growing to the skin and muscles of the body wall. As a result, there was a permanent hole in the left side of the

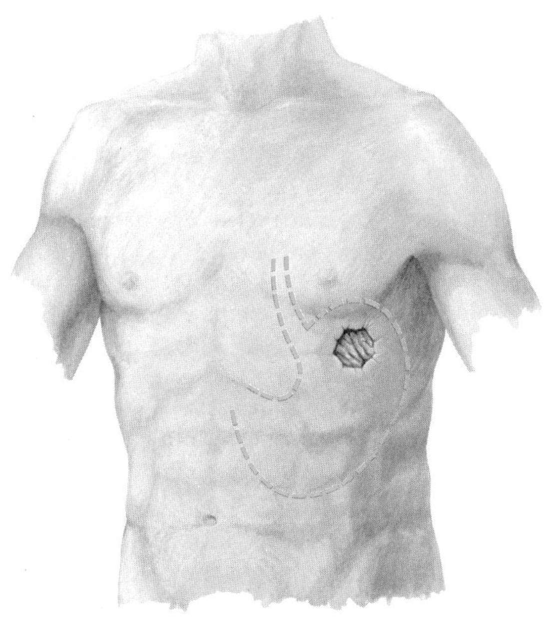

20–9 A diagram of Alexis St. Martin's shotgun wound. The stomach wall and the body wall grew together around the edges of the wound, leaving a permanent "window" through which digestion could be observed in the stomach.

body that led to the interior of the stomach (Figure 20-9). Bandages had to be kept over the hole to prevent food from falling out.

Beaumont realized that he had a wonderful opportunity to study the function of the stomach. Alexis St. Martin cooperated, and the interior of his stomach was studied for eleven years.

Beaumont made many observations. He observed that the stomach secreted a fluid, gastric juice. He put gastric juice on meat and found that the meat was digested. He observed that the stomach moved and churned when food was in it. These and many other observations helped to lay the basis for our understanding of the stomach in man.

As a result of Beaumont's investigation, later research could be undertaken on a much more intelligent basis. Gradually more and more was learned of stomach functioning, and gastric juice was analyzed to discover its chemical nature and activity. Eventually, the facts as we know them today emerged. Nevertheless, there is still much to be learned about the physiology of the stomach.

Digestion in the Small Intestine

Food is a souplike mixture when it leaves the stomach and enters the small intestine. Within the intestinal cavity the food is mixed with three secretions: pancreatic juice, intestinal juice, and bile. These are the secretions that complete almost all the processes of digestion. (There is evidence, however, that some substances are taken up by intestinal cells for digestion just at the cell membrane, or even inside the cells—processes that may remind you of intracellular digestion in *Amoeba* and *Hydra*.)

The secretions that flow into the intestine contain salts that adjust the pH of the digestive tract contents back towards the neutral point. This is important, for the enzymes that work here function best at neutral pH—in contrast to the stomach enzymes, which function best at acid pH.

Pancreatic juice is secreted by the pancreas (Figure 20-10), a large gland in the abdominal cavity just below the stomach. The juice reaches the intestine through small ducts that connect the pancreas to the first portion of the small intestine.

Pancreatic juice contains enzymes that act on the three main classes of food. One of its enzymes is similar to the enzyme in saliva. It acts on starch and converts it to sugar. Another enzyme acts to break down fats. Pancreatic juice also contains several enzymes that act in specific ways on proteins and their partly digested products, changing them into smaller molecules.

Intestinal juice is secreted by the cells of the inner lining of the small intestine. This, too, contains different sorts of enzymes, each active on one of the major kinds of food. Just as in other cases, intestinal enzymes are quite specific in relation to the substrates they react with (Chapter 6, pages 106-08). Thus, a wide range of enzymes is necessary to carry out all the complex chemistry of digestion.

Bile, secreted by the liver, contains no enzymes, but it has an important role in the digestion of fats. Fats are insoluble in water and, therefore, are not easily attacked by digestive enzymes, which must be dissolved in water to act. Bile contains substances, the bile salts, that emulsify fats, breaking them up into small globules. This increases the surface area of the fats and speeds up enzyme action.

20–10 A photograph of a microscopic section of human pancreas. The two light areas are groups of islet cells, which secrete insulin into the capillaries. Other pancreatic cells secrete pancreatic juice.

William Windle

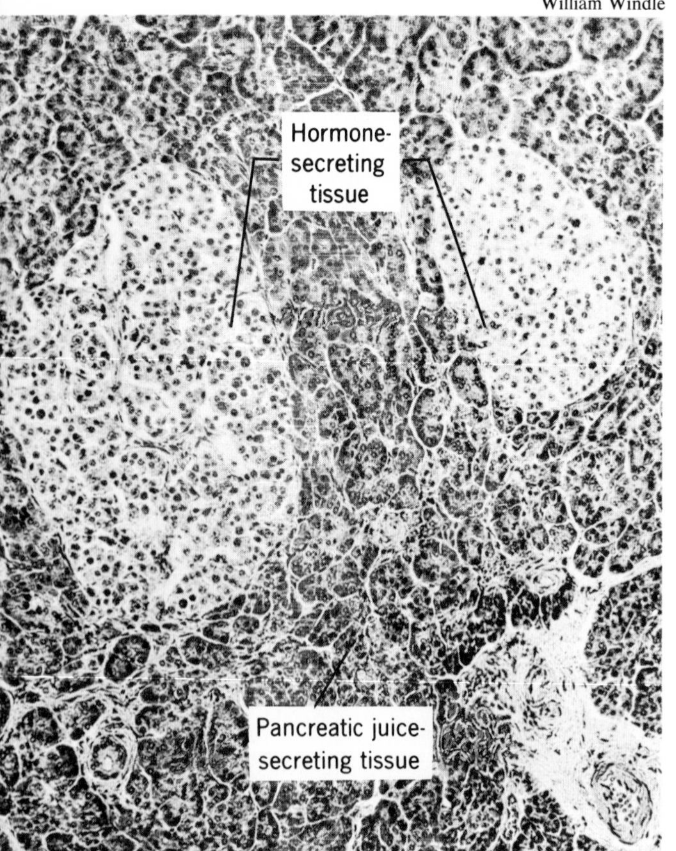

Absorption in the Small Intestine

The end products of digestion enter the body through cells of the small intestine. The surfaces of cells that face the cavity of the intestine absorb the food. The food is then moved across these cells to the opposite surface by diffusion and active transport across the cell membranes. Then it enters one of two transport systems. The amino acids, simple sugars, some vitamins, salts, and most of the water are transferred to the blood stream. Fats and some other vitamins go into other, less familiar transport vessels called the **lymphatics** (lim·FAT·iks), which you will read about in Chapter 21.

This process of absorption takes time, and the volume of food to be absorbed and transported is considerable. If the interior of the intestinal wall were a smooth cylinder, there would be relatively few cell surfaces to do the work of absorption. Hence absorption would be very slow—too slow, indeed, to serve the needs of a large body such as man's. A very simple expedient solves this problem. The inner surface of the intestine is wrinkled into thousands of small "fingers," called **villi** (VIL·i—Figure 20-11), which project into the intestinal cavity, thus vastly increasing the available surface.

Absorption in the Large Intestine

Where the small intestine enters the large intestine there is a blind sac, and off this is a little fingerlike projection called the **appendix** (Figure 20-7). Sometimes food becomes trapped in its cavity and an infection results—called **appendicitis.** In such cases it may be necessary to remove the appendix.

The material that passes from the small intestine to the large intestine contains a large amount of water and dissolved salts. One of the main functions of the large intestine is to extract most of the salts, accompanied by water, and return them to the blood stream. The body periodically rejects the remaining water and solid matter. These rejected materials are the feces. A large part, but not all, of the fecal

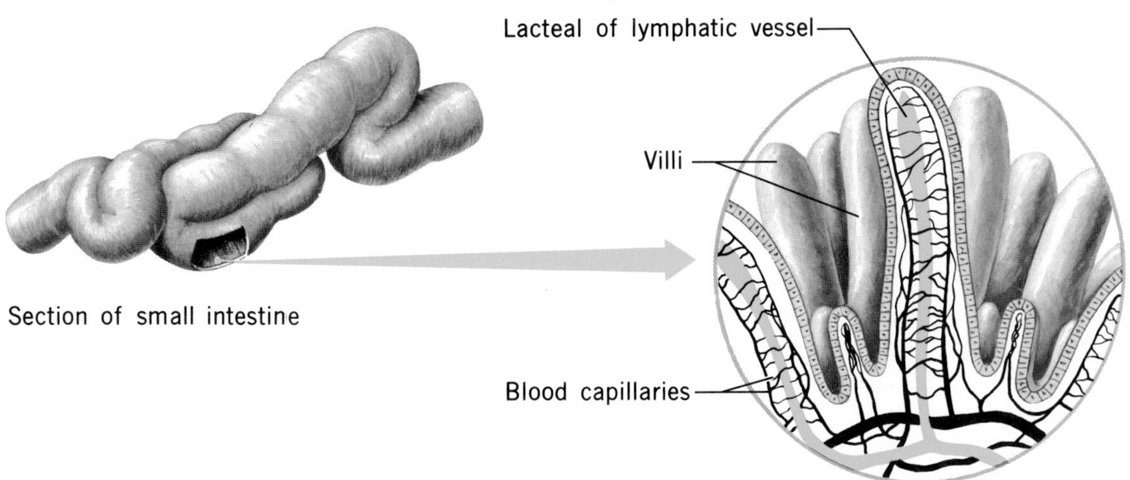

20–11 A drawing of part of the small intestine, with a section enlarged to show the villi of the inner wall. Each villus contains a branch (lacteal) of a lymph vessel and a network of blood capillaries. What is the function of the lacteal? of the capillaries?

material consists of undigested food. A considerable proportion consists of bacteria and worn-out cells sloughed off from the walls of the digestive tract. These cells need not concern us, but the bacteria do, for they modify functions that take place in the large intestine. One of their favorable effects is serving as a source of useful substances for our own bodies: they synthesize some of the vitamins necessary for our normal body function. These may be absorbed into the blood stream.

An Aside on Secretin

In our brief coverage of digestion in man, we indicated what happens in each organ of the alimentary canal. Only for the secretion of gastric juice, however, did we explain what causes the secretion to occur. We could have carried the question of *cause* to other organs as well. For example, when food enters the small intestine, the pancreas secretes pancreatic juice. The pancreatic juice flows along the pancreatic duct and into the small intestine. Here it helps to digest the food, as we have learned.

The pancreas does not secrete all the time, however. In fact, there is almost no secretion unless food (or acid, such as acid gastric secretion) is in the small intestine. This is obviously an economical arrangement. But what is the control?

The answer came in 1902 from the work of two English physiologists, Bayliss and Starling. At the time they did their experiments, it was well known that nerve impulses can stimulate glands to secrete. This can be shown for the pancreas as well. If the nerves to the pancreas are stimulated, pancreatic juice is secreted. Could nerve stimulation be the explanation for the increase in pancreatic juice flow when food enters the intestine?

A reasonable hypothesis might be this: acid food, or acid alone, stimulates the nerves in the small intestine. These nerves carry messages to the brain. Connections are made in the brain, and other nerves carry the message to the pancreas: "Secrete!" All of the data are accounted for, but is the hypothesis correct? Let us try to check it in the usual way.

We first assume our hypothesis to be true. If it is true, certain deductions follow. One of the most obvious is this: if the nerves to the pancreas are cut, and if we place acid in the small intestine, there should be no secretion of pancreatic juice. Bayliss and Starling carried out this experiment. They cut the nerves to the pancreas and then put acid in the small intestine. When this was done, *the pancreas secreted pancreatic juice.* Clearly the hypothesis is inadequate. There must be some mechanism, quite apart from nerves, that causes the pancreas to secrete.

After much experimentation they discovered the explanation. They ground up the lining of the small intestine and extracted it with a weak acid. The acid in the extract was neutralized, then the extract was injected into the blood vessels of an experimental animal. The result was a voluminous secretion of pancreatic juice.

Their extract, therefore, contained a substance that stimulated the pancreas to secrete. They named the substance **secretin** (se·KREE-tin). This was the first real proof of the existence of chemical substances secreted by one class of cells but controlling the activity of other cells. Such substances, as we have already discussed in the case of gastrin, are known as hormones.

The cells of the small intestine secrete the hormone secretin. In man and other animals that have a circulatory system, hormones are carried throughout the body in the blood. When secretin is liberated by the cells of the intestine, therefore, it is carried all over the body by the circulatory system. Hormones have specific effects. Secretin specifically affects the pancreas. (It stimulates secretion by the liver, too, but has no other important function—as far as we know—except this control of digestive glands.)

There are some organs that secrete hormones as well as other substances. Thus, the pancreas itself has two types of secretions (Figure 20-10). One is the digestive juice known as pancreatic juice. The other is the hormone insulin, which we will discuss in Chapter 24.

Those examples of control of digestive glands by hormones and nerves are only a few that we could give in describing the digestive processes in man. Research has shown that all phases of this complex activity—digestion, movement of materials along the tract, secretion, and absorption—are controlled by and coordinated with one another. Nerves, hormones, and the activity of the digestive tract cells themselves play important parts in this control. The net result is the smooth, efficient operation of the food supply system on which human life depends.

CONCLUDING REMARKS—DIGESTION

The large protein molecules of a hamburger and a bun are digested into successively smaller molecules by the protein-digesting enzymes in gastric juice, pancreatic juice, and intestinal juice. The end products of these chemical reactions are *amino acids.* The starch of the bun is acted on by starch-digesting enzymes of saliva, pancreatic juice, and intestinal juice. The fats in the hamburger and the bun are digested—by enzymes of pancreatic juice and intestinal juice—into fatty acids and some other compounds.

At the end of digestion, therefore, our hamburger and bun have been reduced to a soup of small molecules in the cavity of the small intestine. We began with a tremendous number of different sorts of molecules. At the end we have comparatively few: about twenty different kinds of amino acids; a few kinds of simple sugars; fatty acids; water; dissolved salts; and smaller amounts of special compounds including vitamins, of great importance to the life of cells.

These end products of digestion have three features in common: they are small molecules that can pass across cell membranes by diffusion or active transport; they are molecules that cells can use for energy; and they are the kinds of molecules that the cell can use to make its own specific structure. This last point should be stressed. The proteins of the hamburger were beef proteins. They were digested to about twenty different kinds of amino acids. The structure of each type of amino acid is the same whether it comes from beef, lamb, pork, or beans. The amino acids enter the cells of our own bodies and are built into the proteins characteristic of man.

GUIDE QUESTIONS AND PROBLEMS

1. Describe the status of animals with regard to green plants, for sources of nutrients needed by the two groups.
2. What is the advantage, if any, to chewing food rather than swallowing it whole?
3. Suppose you were unable to secrete saliva. How would this affect your ability to consume food?
4. Why is the action of bile in fat digestion not considered an enzymatic action?
5. Why is it that a person can get along without his stomach? Would a person with his stomach removed be able to get along without a small intestine? A large intestine?
6. What specialized features of your small intestine account for the efficient absorption of digested foodstuffs?
7. How is it possible for a giraffe, drinking water with his head down, to move the water upward to his stomach?
8. Carbon dioxide, water, ammonia, and indigestible foodstuffs may all be thought of as waste products. Some biologists, however, hesitate to call them wastes. What arguments would you propose that they use in supporting this view?
9. Termites live on a diet of wood as long as a large population of a certain ciliated protozoan exists in their digestive tracts. Without these protozoans, a termite literally starves to death. What kind of relationship between the termite and the protozoan would explain this?
10. After major surgery, patients are sometimes "fed through the veins" during the early period of recovery. The food is placed directly into the blood in veins; it receives no treatment in the digestive system. What must be the nature of the food so used?

RELATED READING

Books

For Beaumont's original observations on human digestion . . .

Beaumont, W., *Experiments and Observations on the Gastric Juice and the Physiology of Digestion* (1833), Dover, New York, 1958 (paperback).

For other comparative studies of digestion in numerous animals . . .

Buchsbaum, Ralph, *Animals Without Backbones*, Second Edition, University of Chicago Press, Chicago, 1948.

Keeton, William T., *Biological Science*, W. W. Norton, New York, 1967. (Chapter 5, pages 176–99).

For a concise account of animal physiology, including digestion . . .

Schmidt-Nielsen, K., *Animal Physiology*, Second Edition, Prentice-Hall, Englewood Cliffs, N. J., 1964 (paperback).

BSCS Pamphlet

Hungate, R. E., *Cellulose in Animal Nutrition* (Pamphlet 22), D. C. Heath and Co., Boston, 1965.

21

Transportation Within Multicellular Animals

The processes of digestion make available molecules like amino acids, glucose, and fatty acids. Our next topic is to explore how these molecules, together with vitamins, salts, and water, are transported to where they are used.

One way molecules move is by diffusion (pages 91 and 112). The molecules and ions of substances dissolved in body fluid or a cell's cytoplasm are never at rest. They bombard and are bombarded by other particles, chiefly water molecules of the fluid or the cytoplasm itself. All this motion results in diffusion; the dissolved substances are spread around.

The unfailing restlessness of all these molecules and ions is not enough, however. Animals require additional means for transporting essential materials. Diffusion alone cannot supply the need, for it takes much time for materials in solution to diffuse even a few inches.

NEEDS AND METHODS OF TRANSPORTATION

Suppose we were to enlarge one specimen of *Amoeba* to the size of a man. Let us then place some molecules of glucose or amino acids at one end of our gigantic *Amoeba*. How long would it take some of these molecules to reach the other end *by diffusion alone*?

Diffusion of dissolved substances is so slow a process that it could take at least a year for molecules to diffuse the length of our man-sized *Amoeba*. With only diffusion to distribute materials, the giant *Amoeba* would die almost immediately. Some more effective means of transporting materials from one part of the body to another would be required if the animal was to survive. Even a normal-sized *Amoeba* could not be as active as it is if it relied solely upon diffusion to transport materials throughout its one-celled body. We have already seen that the cytoplasm circulates and that food vacuoles move about, helping to distribute materials.

As a generalization, we can say that no animal or animal cell large enough to be seen by the unaided eye can rely solely upon diffusion as a means of transporting molecules.

Transportation Within *Hydra*

A *Hydra* is, of course, large enough to be seen. In fact, the body may be half a millimeter in diameter. Yet it has no specialized transportation system. How can this be?

Very little of the half-millimeter diameter of the body is occupied by cells (Figure 21-1). Most of the interior of *Hydra* is its digestive cavity. The surrounding body wall itself has only two main layers of cells. Therefore, nearly every cell is adjacent either to the outside pond water or to the water in the digestive cavity.

The amino acids, fatty acids, and other compounds are made available in the digestive cavity, and absorbed by the cells lining this cavity. Additional amino acids and fats are made available by digestion within these cells themselves. Some of the molecules resulting from digestion diffuse from this inner cell layer to the cells of the outer layer. The cells of the outer layer, therefore, depend entirely on the inner cells for their organic food substances.

There is a second aspect of transportation in *Hydra*. Some of the cells lining the digestive cavity have long, hairlike flagella. The beating of these flagella stirs up the contents of the digestive cavity. In this way, food particles as well as digested food molecules are brought into contact with the cells lining the cavity.

Transportation Within a Planarian

A planarian seems to be near the maximum size and complexity that animals can attain without a general transport system. Animals larger and more active do have circulatory systems.

A planarian shows many adjustments to the absence of a general transport system. For one thing, the body is greatly flattened, as shown in Figures 19-10 and 20-4. Actually, the body is considerably more flattened than either drawing shows; both drawings have been made in a way to show the internal structure more clearly. Because the body is so flat, every cell is close to the outside, and hence in a position to absorb oxygen and to eliminate carbon dioxide.

The distribution of digested food materials is taken care of largely by the digestive sac itself, which occupies much of the interior. No part of the body is far from some branch of the digestive sac.

A planarian does have one special transport system. All over the body there are tiny tubes that arise in specialized cells and carry liquid wastes to the outside. These are parts of the excretory system, and they will be discussed in Chapter 23.

Transportation Within the Earthworm

The segmented worms are the least complex animals to possess a general system for transporting materials throughout the body. They have a circulatory system.

The circulatory system of the earthworm is similar in its basic structure to that of man and many other complex animals. It consists of a series of tubes, the blood vessels, which contain a fluid, the blood. Some of the blood vessels have walls that pulsate, and this moves the blood. Blood vessels reach every part of the body—hence every cell in the earthworm is adjacent to or at least very near a blood vessel.

The essential features of a circulatory system are shown in Figure 21-2, where a few of the blood vessels of the earthworm are drawn in a diagrammatic way.

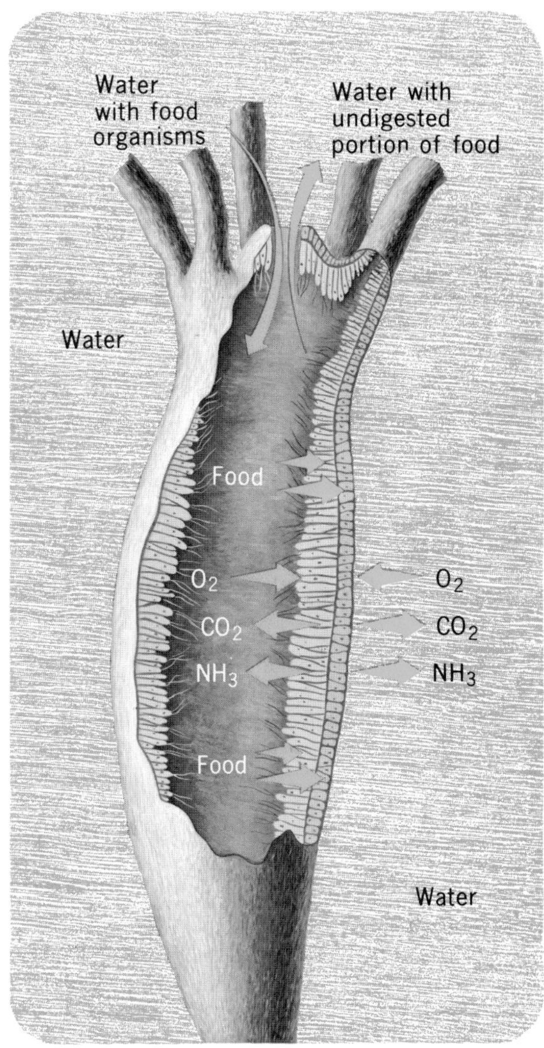

21–1 The movement of water, food, oxygen, and wastes in *Hydra*, which lives without a specialized transport system. How is this possible?

In the anterior part of the worm are blood vessels known as **lateral hearts.** Five of these are found on each side. These vessels pulsate and pump the blood toward the lower side of the worm. The lower ends of the lateral hearts join a blood vessel, the **ventral vessel,** that runs along just below the digestive tract. The ventral vessel carries blood from the hearts to-

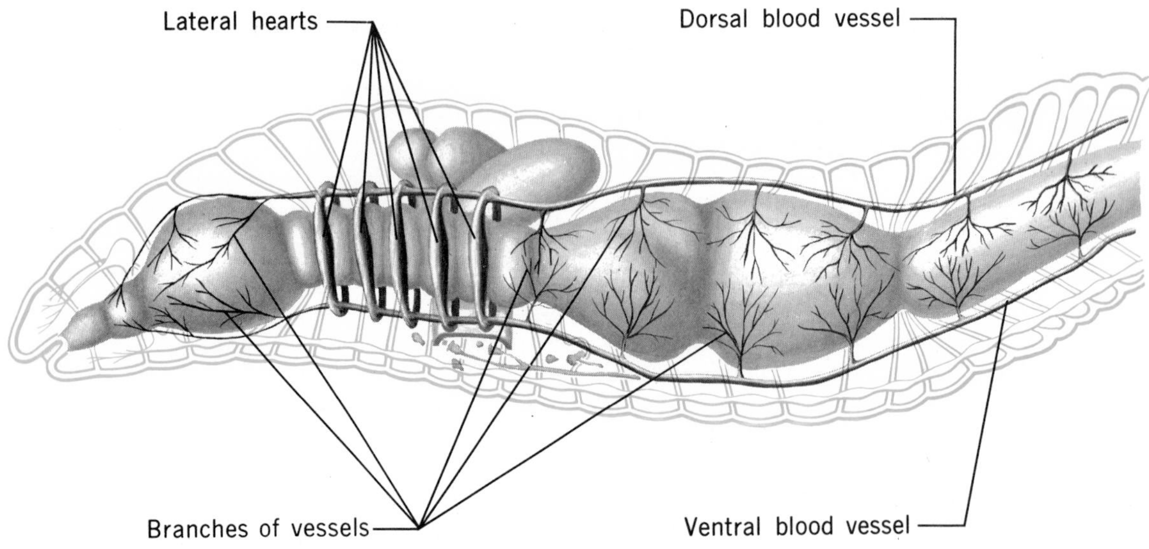

21–2 The circulatory system of an earthworm. Blood is circulated to and from the cells throughout the body in a series of tubes, the blood vessels. In the skin, the blood picks up oxygen and loses carbon dioxide. In the intestine, digested foods enter the blood and are delivered to body cells everywhere. Wastes from the body cells are transported by the blood to the excretory organs—and in the case of carbon dioxide, to the skin. Can you suggest why the earthworm would need a more specialized system of transportation than is found in *Hydra* (Figure 21–1)?

ward the anterior and posterior ends of the worm. Many small vessels branch off the ventral vessel. These go to all parts of the body. (The ones that go to the digestive tract are indicated in the diagram.) Each small vessel branches into even smaller vessels as it enters the tissues. Eventually the smaller vessels branch into **capillaries.**

Capillaries are exceedingly small; in fact, they are microscopic in size. They are also so numerous that every cell is next to—or very near—a capillary. The branches of the ventral vessels that enter the walls of the digestive tract break up into innumerable capillaries. These capillaries have very thin walls, and diffusion across these walls occurs quite rapidly. The end products of digestion, such as amino acids and glucose, enter the cells lining the intestine, then enter the capillaries. Once in the blood stream, these end products of digestion are distributed to all parts of the body.

The capillaries play a unique role in the circulatory system. Only these vessels have walls thin enough for molecules to diffuse across readily. Consequently, all the important exchanges that occur between blood and the environment, or between blood and cells, occur in capillaries. This is true for all animals with a blood circulation system.

The capillaries of the intestinal wall join one another and eventually form larger vessels. These carry blood to a vessel, the **dorsal vessel,** that runs along the top of the digestive tract. The dorsal vessel is contractile. It helps force the blood forward to the lateral hearts where it is pumped again into the ventral vessel and redistributed to the body.

The blood of the earthworm is a circulating fluid that always remains enclosed in tubes—the blood vessels. This type of circulatory system is known as a **closed circulatory system** and is the kind of circulatory system we have.

Transportation Within the Grasshopper

The grasshopper has two main systems for transporting materials – one for gases and the other for foods and nitrogenous waste products.

Gases are transported in a series of tubes known as **tracheal** (TRAY·kee·al) tubes. These open to the outside of the body (Figure 21-3). From these openings the tracheal tubes extend to the interior of the body. They branch repeatedly, and the branches reach every part of the body. (The tracheal tubes will be discussed again in the next chapter when we consider respiration.)

The grasshopper's second transporting system is a blood system. This consists of a fluid that moves throughout the body carrying digested food materials and waste products, as is the case in the earthworm. However, the blood system of the grasshopper is built on quite a different plan from the closed circulatory system of the earthworm.

The grasshopper has an **open circulatory system.** That is, its blood is not always enclosed in tubes; much of the time it flows in large spaces among the tissues in the body.

The grasshopper has a small heart located in the upper portion of its body (Figure 21-3). The heart pumps blood out toward the head in a single vessel. This vessel ends in the head region, where the blood flows out of the vessel and into the spaces among the body tissues. The blood moves back through the cavities of the body, bathing the body tissues as it goes. Eventually the blood returns to the heart to be pumped forward once again.

In the laboratory, you will have an opportunity to study the activities of the heart in an invertebrate animal (Inquiry 21-1).

TRANSPORTATION WITHIN MAN

In man there is a single coordinated system for transport of fluids. This is the blood circulatory system and the **lymphatic** (lim·FAT·ic) system associated with it. There is no special transport system for gases, as these are moved

21–3 The circulatory and respiratory systems of a grasshopper. In grasshoppers and other insects, tracheal tubes, rather than the blood system, carry oxygen to the body cells and carbon dioxide from these cells to the outside of the body. The circulatory system is simpler than in the earthworm or in man. A heart and a single blood vessel carry blood forward from the heart; elsewhere the blood circulates through spaces between body organs. Is this system less efficient than the circulatory systems of the earthworm and of man? Before reaching a decision, consider the abundance of insects on the earth today, as you first noted on page 354 (Figure 19–4).

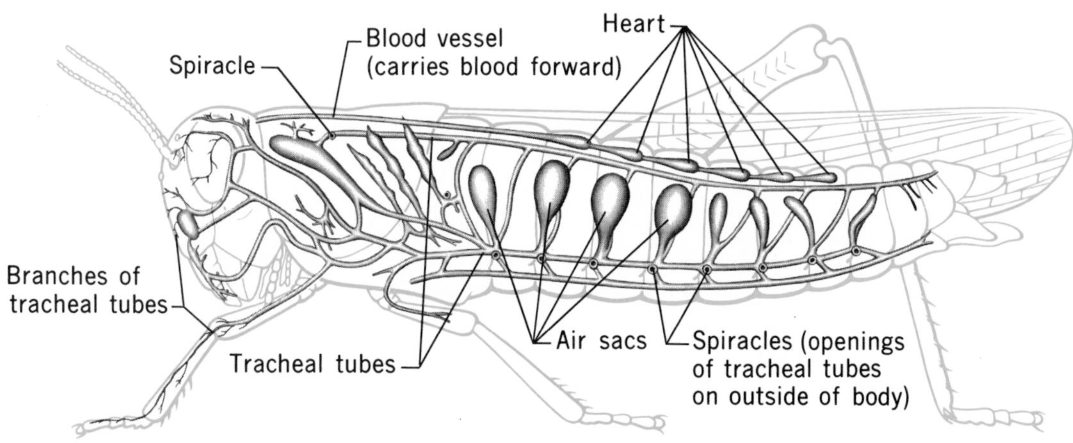

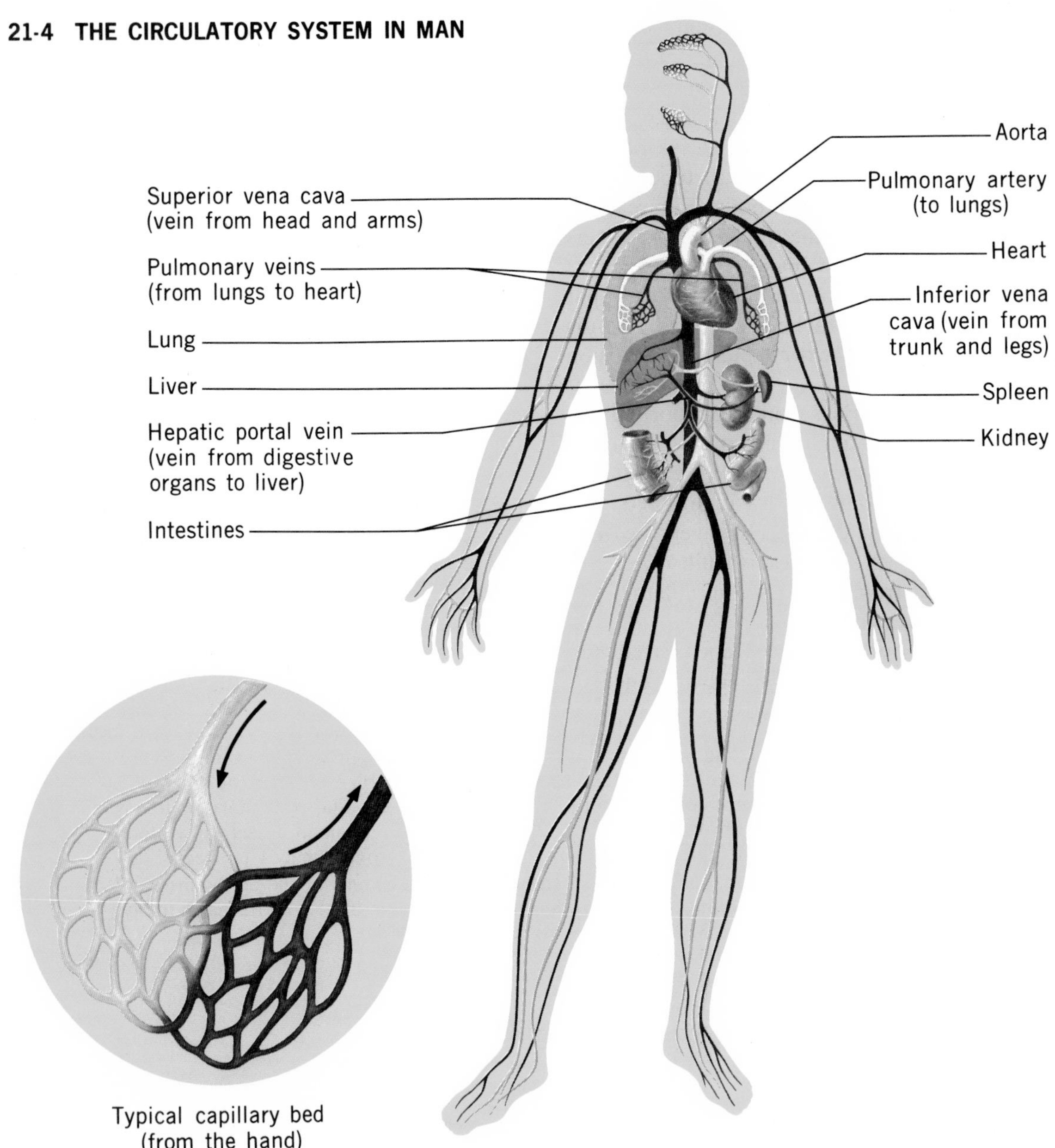

Typical capillary bed
(from the hand)

about dissolved or combined in the body fluids. The human transport system is of the closed type, as in the earthworm. It functions the same general way as in the earthworm.

Of course, there are many differences. A single portion of man's circulatory system, the heart, serves as a pump. In the earthworm the five pairs of lateral hearts, the dorsal vessel, and probably some other vessels, all contract and pump the blood.

In the earthworm, the major blood vessels are not usually differentiated as "arteries" or "veins." In man a distinction is made. **Arteries** carry blood away from the heart. They branch repeatedly and end in capillaries. **Veins** carry blood from the capillaries toward the heart.

The main pathways of circulation in the human body are shown in Figure 21-4. Let us go over some of them, beginning with the artery leading from the left side of the heart, the **aorta** (ay·OR·ta). The aorta is the chief distributing vessel of the body. Smaller arteries branch from the aorta and carry blood to capillaries of the head, arms, liver, stomach, intestines, kidneys, legs, and other organs.

The capillaries connect with tiny veins, which join to form larger veins. The veins carrying blood back from the head and arms join to form the **superior vena cava** (VEE·na KAY·va). Blood from the posterior part of the body is carried toward the heart by the **inferior vena cava.**

The superior vena cava and the inferior vena cava both carry blood to the **right atrium** (AY·trih·um), one of the four chambers of the heart. Blood next passes into the **right ventricle.** The right ventricle and the **left ventricle** are the main pumping portions of the heart.

The right ventricle contracts and forces blood into the **pulmonary** (PUL·mo·nehr·ee) **artery.** The pulmonary artery divides and carries blood to the capillaries of each lung, where, as we will see in the chapter on respiration, oxygen enters blood and carbon dioxide leaves it. Next the blood passes in the **pulmonary veins** to the **left atrium** and then to the left ventricle. The left ventricle contracts and forces blood into the aorta. This is where we began the story of circulation.

The human heart is a double pump. The left ventricle pumps blood to all parts of the body except the lungs. This blood supplies the cells with digested food substances and oxygen. It also collects carbon dioxide and nitrogenous wastes. Then this blood returns to the right side of the heart and is pumped to the lungs. Thus the blood must pass through lung capillaries, gaining oxygen and losing carbon dioxide, before it is pumped around the body once again.

The blood always flows through the chambers of the heart in one direction. The direction of flow is controlled by valves (Figure 21-5). There are valves between the right atrium and right ventricle as well as between the left atrium and left ventricle. When the ventricles begin to contract, these valves close the openings into the atria. As a result, the blood passes into the pulmonary artery and into the aorta, not back into the atria.

There are also valves in the base of the aorta and the pulmonary artery. After the ventricles have contracted and forced the blood into the aorta and the pulmonary artery, the ventricles relax. If there were nothing to hold the blood in the aorta and the pulmonary artery, it would flow back into the relaxed ventricles. However, the valves at the base of the aorta and the pulmonary artery close and prevent backflow.

An individual's heart is about the size of his fist. This muscular organ must continue to contract as long as life continues. Its activity is staggering; during a normal lifetime, it contracts three billion times or more. Often it carries on its work even following the damage of a "heart attack." Such malfunctions are of numerous types, one of the more common of which is illustrated in Figure 21-6.

Arteries, Veins, and Capillaries

Arteries carry blood away from the heart to the capillaries, which supply food and oxygen to the body cells. Veins carry blood from the capillaries back to the heart.

The blood leaving the ventricles and entering the aorta and the pulmonary artery is under considerable pressure; it moves rapidly. The pressure is maintained by the repeated contractions of the ventricles, which force more blood into the two major arteries. It is also maintained by the elastic nature of the walls of these arteries, which are stretched by the outward flow of blood with each heartbeat and then gradually contract between heartbeats.

The pressure is sufficient to send the blood through branching arteries, through capillaries, and start it through veins back to the heart.

If one compares the artery leading to a particular body organ with the vein that receives the blood from the organ, two main differences will be apparent. The artery has a smaller bore and a thicker wall than the vein. The thicker-walled artery must withstand greater blood pressures than the vein. Furthermore, the artery's elasticity helps change the *pulsing* flow of blood as it leaves the heart into the *steadier*

21–5 The human heart and its pumping cycle. **a.** The parts of the heart are shown in longitudinal section. What is the function of the four valves? **b.** The heart is really two pumps in one: the right atrium and the right ventricle are one pump, and the left atrium and the left ventricle are the other. Blood from the lungs does not mix in the heart with blood from the rest of the body.

a The human heart

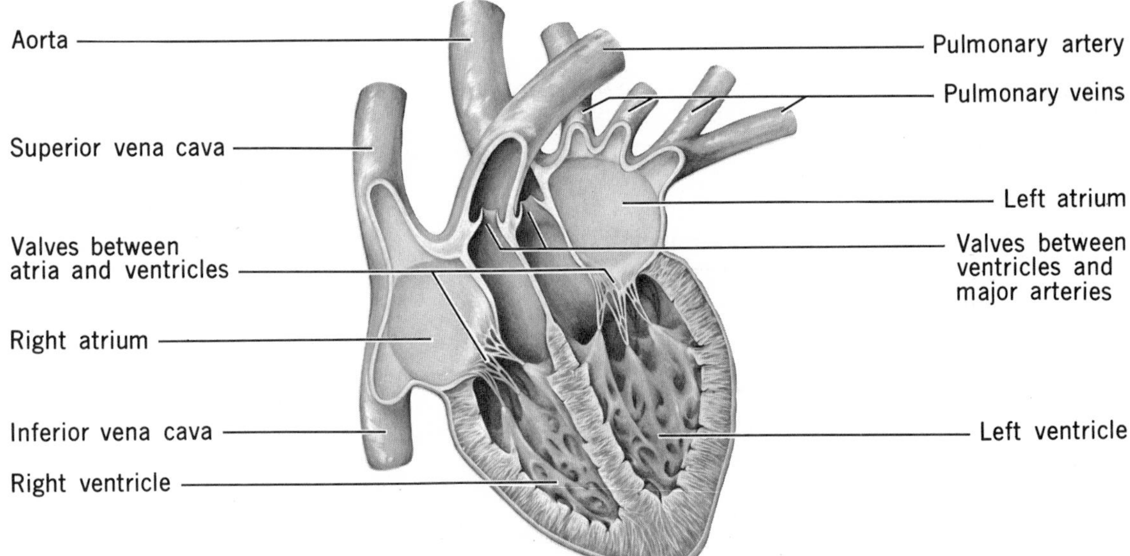

b The pumping cycle of the heart

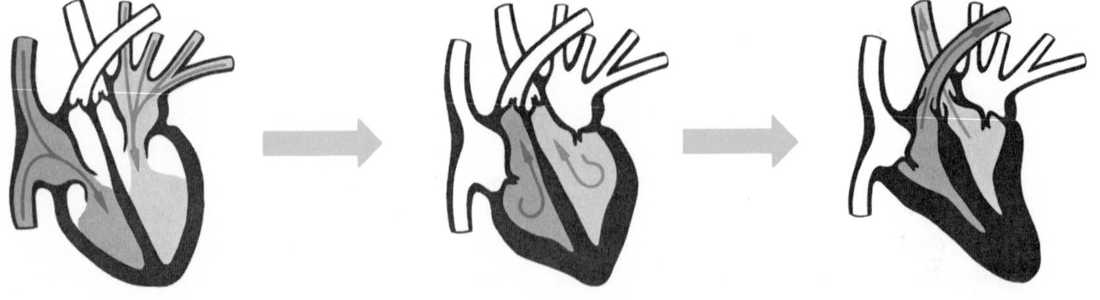

21-6 THE MECHANISM OF A "HEART ATTACK" (CORONARY THROMBOSIS) AND POSSIBILITIES FOR RECOVERY

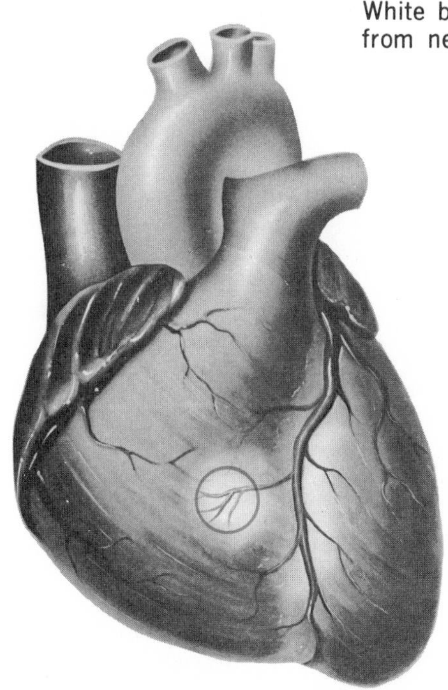

The heart's own system of blood vessels supplies the muscular walls of this powerful pump with food and oxygen. Sometimes trouble develops in a branch of one of the blood vessels (see circled area). Blood flow may be blocked, and then the muscles are damaged by failure of their supply of oxygen and foods. If the damage is too great, the heart ceases to function and the person dies. But if the "heart attack" is not too severe, the wall of the heart may heal up with scar tissue. Heart disease is a major cause of death in the United States today.

White blood cells from nearby vessels

Clot

5 days

a When a coronary artery supplying a segment of heart muscle is blocked by a clot, the muscle fibers disintegrate. If the damaged region is small, repair processes start. White blood cells invade the site and ingest the dead tissue.

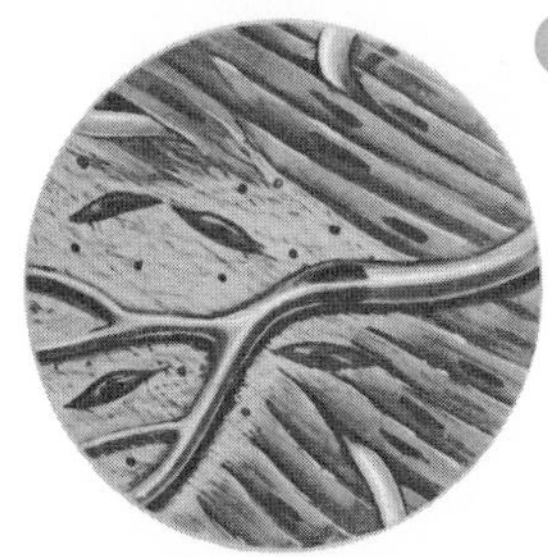

6 weeks

b Another type of cell —spindle-shaped— also invades the damaged area. These cells begin producing strong, connective tissue scar fibers.

12 weeks

c By the end of three months, a nearly complete scar is formed. As the scar tissue contracts, intact muscle edges are brought closer together. Muscle function is not restored to the area with scar tissue.

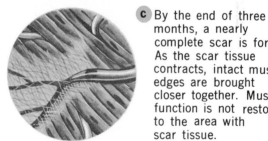

flow seen in the smaller arteries. The smaller size of the branch arteries does not indicate a lower capacity, for the *total* cross-sectional area (which is related to the volume of blood that can be carried) is greater for the branch arteries than for the main arteries, and greater for the capillaries than for the branch arteries.

Capillaries are the most numerous blood vessels in the body (Figure 21-7). Cells are always close to a capillary. It is through the capillaries that the actual exchange takes place between blood and the individual cells (Figure

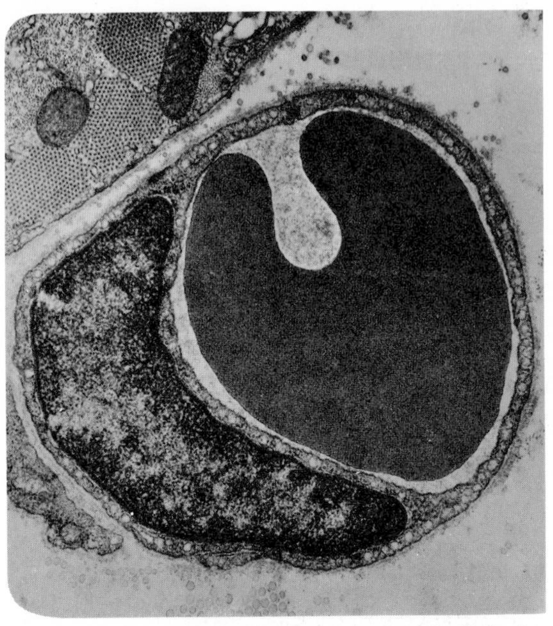

Lee D. Peachey

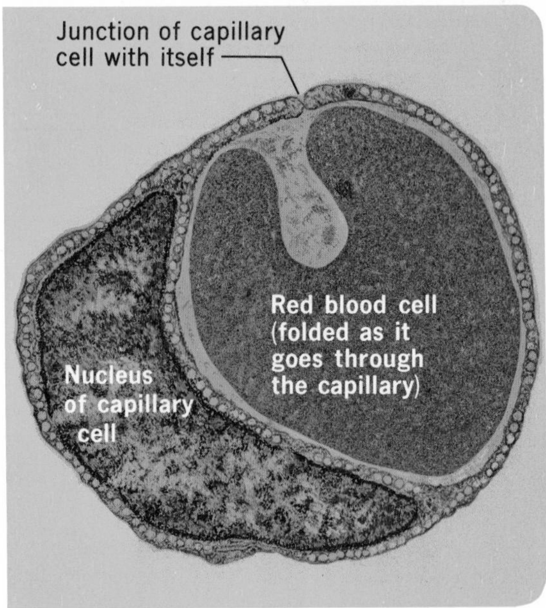

21–7 A photomicrograph and a drawing of a cross section through a capillary. Notice the red blood cell; its shape as it is pushed through the capillary by pressure behind it shows just how small most capillaries are. The entire circumference of the capillary in this photograph is made up of one cell that forms a junction with itself. The nucleus of the capillary cell is on the left in each view. (20,000 ×)

21-8). Thus, we can say that all the rest of the circulatory system functions just to supply blood to the capillaries. You will find it of great interest to observe capillaries of living organisms in the laboratory (Inquiry 21-2). Blood flow through the capillaries is regulated by tiny muscles in the walls of the arteries that open into each branching bed of capillaries. It is thus possible to control the amount of blood reaching any organ at any given time. During strenuous exercise, such as running or swimming, a great deal of blood is in the capillaries and other small vessels of the muscular system, and very little is in the capillaries of the digestive system. (Does this suggest to you the reason why you are told not to swim or indulge in excessive exercise immediately after a meal?)

Capillaries immediately under the skin contain more blood when the body is warm and thus serve to radiate heat away from the body through the skin. Conversely, when outside temperatures are low and the body is in danger of losing too much heat, these small vessels are partially shut off and contain far less blood. This is a good example of how the transport system takes part in a homeostatic mechanism. In many ways it functions to maintain constancy of conditions within the body—in this case constancy of body temperature.

Blood flows from the capillaries into small veins, and from these into larger and larger veins toward the heart. The major veins have valves that serve to keep the blood from flowing backward, away from the heart. The flow in veins is dependent on many other factors, too, including the position of the body with respect to gravity, body muscle movements, and breathing. People sometimes faint when they stand still too long, as then the blood is not returned through veins fast enough to maintain the steady flow needed by the brain. This matter of blood flow is one of the reasons why exercise can be so healthful for the human body.

Not only does the transport system play a part in regulating body conditions, but it, too, is under the most precise control. We have mentioned that during exercise, after eating, or when the body is hot or cold, there are changes in blood flow to different organs—muscles, digestive system, and skin. But this is not a case of *all* the blood rushing to a particular active organ. Control systems operate to maintain a fairly steady blood flow to important organs like the brain and the heart itself, in spite of great changes in the pattern of blood flow. This is fortunate indeed, for even a brief interference in the blood flow to these organs may result in disaster. We know this from studying disease conditions in which the control breaks down, or the transport system itself is damaged. No doubt you are familiar with the consequences of disturbance of blood flow to the brain—in severe cases we call this a **stroke.** Serious disturbance of flow to the muscular walls of the heart is familiar to you as a "heart attack" (Figure 21-6). The rate of the heart's contraction may change drastically, and so may the amount of blood driven out of the heart with each contraction. Blood vessels in one region of the body may increase in volume, and vessels in another decrease, but these events take place in patterns closely regulated by hormones and nerves.

Blood

The circulatory fluid within the blood vessels is a complex substance. It consists of a fluid portion, the **plasma** (about 55 percent of the volume), and various cells and cell products (about 45 percent of the volume).

The plasma is principally water with a large number of inorganic and organic substances dissolved in it. There are, for example, several types of blood proteins. These help to maintain the osmotic pressure of the blood. They also have important special functions, such as helping the blood to clot. Some of the blood proteins are hormones. The antibodies that help the body combat disease organisms also are blood proteins.

The plasma also contains the products of digestion—amino acids, simple sugars, fats, and other supplies used by cells. Nitrogenous waste substances, such as urea, and some of the carbon dioxide produced by cells are also found in the plasma. We could go on for a long time with this list of dissolved substances in human blood plasma—hundreds have been discovered. Yet

21–8 A diagram of the exchange of materials at a capillary. As blood enters the capillary at relatively high pressure, water and dissolved substances from the blood move out at (1) by filtration through the membrane. Plasma protein molecules and blood cells mostly stay inside the capillaries. At (2) water reenters the capillary by osmosis, where blood pressure inside the vessel has fallen and plasma protein concentration is relatively high. Carbon dioxide diffuses from tissue cells into the capillary (3), and oxygen diffuses from blood cells into the tissue cells (4). Amino acids, glucose molecules, and waste substances like urea also move across the capillary wall by diffusion. Which arrows might represent the movements of these substances? Some of the tissue fluid enters the lymph capillaries instead of blood capillaries (8).

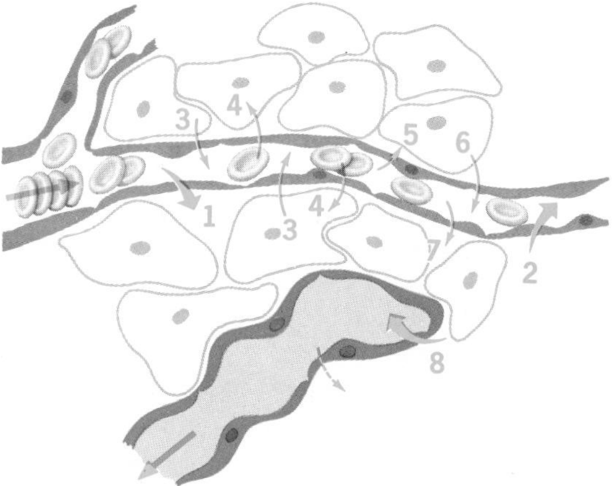

we are far from being able to give a complete chemical picture of this remarkable fluid. Its functions are probably nearly as many as the substances it contains. One of these functions is very obvious—plasma provides a means of movement all over the body of the blood cells, which we will describe next.

Three sorts of cells or cell-like bodies—red blood cells, white blood cells, and platelets—are found in blood (Figure 21-9). The most numerous are the red blood cells. Each cubic millimeter of blood contains about five million of them. In the adult, the red blood cells are produced in bone marrow—special tissue in the centers of some bones. During the formation of the cells, the nucleus is cast out of each cell. Red blood cells contain large amounts of hemoglobin (pages 168-69), a protein of great importance for carrying oxygen and to a lesser extent for carrying carbon dioxide. More will be said about red blood cells when we discuss respiration.

21–9 A stained smear of human blood, as seen under the compound microscope. The numerous pale, rounded structures with lighter centers are red blood cells. The two larger cells with dark nuclei are white blood cells. Small, irregularly shaped platelets are the remaining objects.

F. W. Maynard

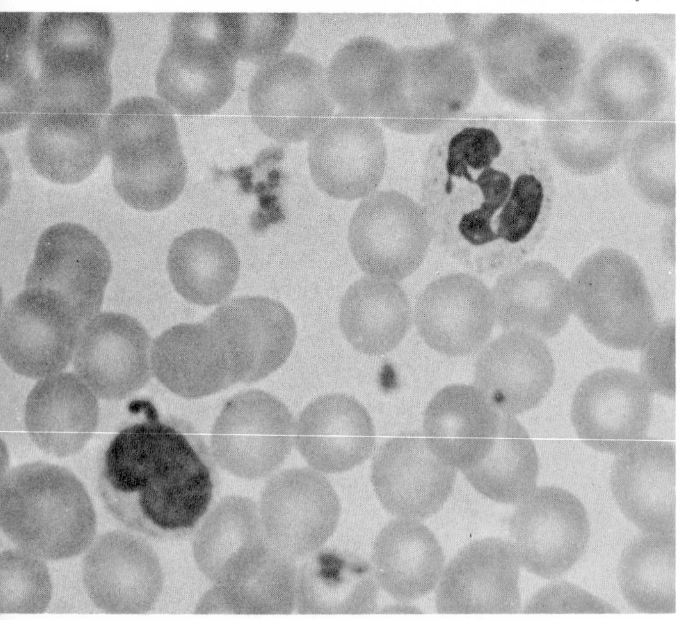

White blood cells, of which there are several kinds, are produced in bone marrow, lymph nodes (page 415), and in the spleen. A cubic millimeter of blood usually contains 7,000 to 8,000 of them. All have a nucleus. The chief function of white blood cells is to protect the body against bacteria (Figure 11-3, page 217). Some of these cells can actually engulf bacteria; they push their cell membrane around the bacteria. The bacteria are then used as food by the cells. (This behavior may remind you of the manner in which *Amoeba* and the cells of *Hydra* feed.) Other white blood cells form antibodies.

In an infection, such as pneumonia, the white blood cells greatly increase in number. They help to combat the disease, by forming antibodies and by destroying the bacteria. The pus that forms in an infected wound is largely an accumulation of white blood cells that have died fighting bacteria.

The platelets are much smaller than either red blood cells or white blood cells. They play a key role in the clotting of blood, the process which tends to stop blood from flowing out of damaged blood vessels.

Throughout this account of blood, has it surprised you that this fluid is a mixture of so many different substances, cells, and cell parts? Many studies have shown that there is remarkable constancy of blood composition—both within one person throughout his lifetime, and in comparing one person with another. This in itself may suggest to you an important aspect of the physiology of the blood—its composition is very closely controlled. Hormones, nerves, and the activities of many organs take part in this control. In Chapter 23 we will describe one of the control systems—the kidneys—in some detail.

The Lymphatic System

Some of the fluid of blood is constantly passing through the capillary walls and entering the spaces between the cells (Figure 21-8). The walls of the capillaries prevent most of the blood cells and some of the proteins of the plasma from leaving the blood stream. (Some white blood cells leave the capillaries by forcing their way out between the cells that make up the capillary walls.) Except for these components, the composition of tissue fluid is much the same as blood.

Tissue fluid bathes the cells and then returns to the blood capillaries, or along irregular channels known as lymph vessels to the veins (Figure 21-10). Fluid traveling in lymph vessels is called *lymph.* It flows through these vessels for much the same reasons that blood flows through veins. For lymph flow, too, depends on muscle contractions, breathing movements, and the pressure of valves in lymph vessels.

Located along the lymph vessels are lymph nodes, which filter harmful substances and bacteria from the lymph. These lymph nodes are found at various places in the body, such as around the major organs, in the limbs, and in the neck. During infections the lymph nodes may swell as they remove bacteria and other particles from the lymph.

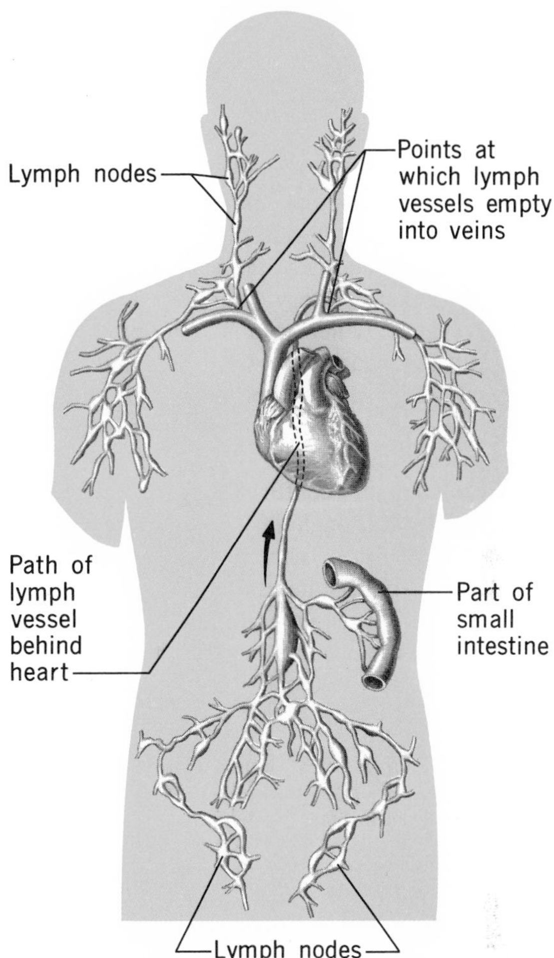

21–10 The lymph system in man. Fluid escapes from the capillaries and enters spaces between body cells. Materials are exchanged with the cells, and some of the fluid (lymph) then enters tiny branches of lymph vessels. Traffic here is one way—leading through lymph nodes back toward the heart. Most of the lymph re-enters the blood at a point on the large vein leading from the left arm toward the heart. Some lymph enters the corresponding vein on the body's right side.

An Aside on William Harvey

It seems safe to say that man's written intellectual history goes back at least 5,000 years. During the first 4,700 of these years a most elementary fact about blood—namely, that it circulates—was unknown or unproved. (Early Chinese physicians related the pulse to a movement of the blood.) This is not surprising, for if you think of your own body, you will see that it is almost impossible to guess what is happening inside it. You can feel your heart beat, and you know that it goes faster or slower depending on your activities. You can also feel your pulses, and see and feel that your skin is sometimes pale and cold, sometimes hot and red. Do these observations give you any clues as to what is happening to the blood and its distribution within your body?

The fact that blood circulates was demonstrated by William Harvey (1578–1657) and Marcello Malpighi (mal·PEE·gee—1628–1694) in the seventeenth century. In order to understand their achievement, we must know some of the theories (or were they only hypotheses?) about blood that were held in the sixteenth and early seventeenth centuries.

Aristotle believed blood to be produced in the liver. From there, according to belief, it flowed to the heart and then out in the veins to all parts of the body. Yes, veins—not arteries. In Aristotle's day it was believed that arteries contained air. The very term "artery" is based on this belief. Artery is derived from the Greek *arteria,* which means "windpipe."

About 500 years after Aristotle's time, Galen (A.D. 130–200), a Greek physician and author of important books on medicine, found that arteries contain blood.

In the sixteenth century people believed that blood moved, though in a slow and irregular way. Generally it was believed that blood flowed out from the heart and back in the same vessel. There was no understanding that the heart is a pump.

21–11 William Harvey demonstrating part of his theory of blood circulation. By referring to Figure 21–12, you can understand what he was attempting to do. Was Harvey's theory correct? In what way was his evidence short of proof?

Harvey (Figure 21-11) *almost* proved that blood circulates. He studied the hearts of pigs, dogs, snakes, frogs, fish, chick embryos, and even of such invertebrate animals as mollusks and water fleas. In many instances he examined the heart and blood vessels of living animals. As a result of his observations, Harvey came to realize that the heart is a pump. He believed that blood circulates; that is, the heart pumps it into arteries, the arteries then carry the blood to the organs, and the veins carry it back to the heart. Harvey would have found our Figure 21-4 a good representation of his views. Why, then, is the statement made that "Harvey *almost* proved that blood circulates"?

There is an important distinction. Harvey *believed* that blood circulates; he did not *prove* it. This he realized. He knew that blood is carried to a given organ by an artery and brought back to the heart by veins. He did not know how the blood manages to get from the arteries to veins. He could see that the arteries branch and become smaller and smaller. He also knew that small veins join to become larger and larger. A connection between the ends of the tiny arteries and the beginnings of the veins must exist, but he could not find it because he did not have the instrument to do so—a microscope.

Malpighi did. If one examines with a microscope a small portion of the lung or urinary bladder of a living frog, the tiny capillary connections between arteries and veins can be seen (see also Laboratory Inquiry 21-2). Malpighi saw that blood flows through the small arteries, into the even smaller capillaries, and then into the veins. Harvey's theory of the *circulation of blood* had been demonstrated beyond a reasonable doubt.

Harvey's work was one of the intellectual triumphs of man. That being the case, you may wish to repeat one of the experiments that led to his theory of circulation. It had previously been discovered that there are valves in the veins. Harvey realized that the valves made it possible for the blood in veins to move in one direction only – there could be no ebb and flow. Try for yourself the experiment illustrated in Figure 21-12.

CONCLUDING REMARKS

Some system of transporting materials throughout the body is present in all the more highly developed animals. Even the earthworm has a complicated circulatory system with distributing and collecting vessels, capillaries, and specialized vessels that pump the blood. No animals that are large in size and active in movement are without a transportation system. In some animals, such as the earthworm and man, the blood remains in the arteries, veins, and capillaries. These animals are said to have a *closed circulatory system*. Other animals, such as the grasshopper, have a different arrangement. The blood leaves the arteries and enters large cavities and bathes the organs. The blood continues through these cavities until it reaches the heart. This arrangement is known as an *open circulatory system*.

The circulatory system of man transports chemical substances throughout the body. Everything that the individual cells must receive and eliminate is moved by blood and lymph, the fluids of the circulatory system. The blood is pumped by the ventricles of the heart through the arteries – the distributing vessels of the blood system. Next the blood enters the capillaries, and it is here that exchanges are made with the cells. Some of the plasma, minus most of its blood proteins, leaves the capillaries and passes into the spaces around the cells as tissue fluid. The blood that remains in the capillaries continues into the veins. Tissue fluids re-enter capillaries, or enter lymph vessels and eventually return to large veins near the heart. Finally, blood and lymph enter the heart from the veins.

Other sorts of transporting systems are found in planarians (for transporting water and nitrogenous wastes) and in grasshoppers (for transporting gases – see Figure 21-3). In animals in general, as in man, movement of

William Harvey, from Linda Hall Library

21–12 You can duplicate Harvey's demonstration (Figure 21–11) by following these directions (in his own words): "Let an arm be tied above the elbow as (A, A, Figure 1). In the course of the veins, certain large knots or elevations (B, C, D, E, F) will be perceived . . .; these are all formed by valves. If you press the blood [through] . . . a valve, from H to O (Figure 2), you will see no [new] influx of blood [from below, leading to the valve] . . .; yet will the vessel continue sufficiently distended above that valve (O, G). If you now apply a finger of the other hand upon the distended part of the vein above the valve O (Figure 3), and press downwards, you will find that you cannot force the blood through or beyond the valve. If you press at one part in the course of a vein with the point of a finger (L, Figure 4), and then with another finger streak the blood upwards beyond the next valve (N), you will perceive that this portion of the vein continues empty (L, N). That blood in the veins therefore proceeds from inferior to superior parts of the heart appears most obviously."

fluids through the transport systems is closely correlated with the needs of the body cells for supply of materials and removal of wastes.

GUIDE QUESTIONS AND PROBLEMS

1. The more cells animals have, the more dependent they are upon some type of specialized transport system. Why is this?
2. How does the transportation of materials in large land plants compare with transportation of materials in large land animals?
3. In animals with closed circulatory systems the total cross-sectional area of the capillaries is greater than that of the arteries or the veins. What is the significance of this to the animals?
4. Valves in veins of the legs sometimes fail to stop backflow of blood. What could be the consequences of this failure to a person?
5. What is the relationship between blood plasma and lymph?
6. Veins, arteries, and capillaries differ in structure. What are these differences and how are they related to the functions of each kind of vessel?
7. **Atherosclerosis** (ATH·er·o·skla·RO·sis) is a condition also called "hardening of the arteries," resulting among other effects in reduced elasticity of the arteries. What circulatory problems might arise from this effect on the vessels?
8. How is the nature of an organism's transportation system related to the environment in which it lives? its activity? its size?
9. If you were told that a certain animal has no special transport system, what deductions could you make about the animal without additional data?
10. In human infants at birth, the wall between the two atria of the heart sometimes fails to close completely. Compare this condition with a heart having only one atrium and one ventricle. What is the consequence of mixing blood from the lungs and from the rest of the body, in the heart? Why do you suppose the afflicted babies are called "blue babies"?

RELATED READING

Books

For original accounts of early discoveries of the circulatory functions in animals . . .

Graubard, Mark, *Circulation and Respiration: The Evolution of an Idea*, Ideas in Science Series, Harcourt, Brace & World, New York, 1964 (cloth or paperback). A compact book with original accounts of discoveries by Aristotle, Leeuwenhoek, Harvey, Malpighi, Hooke, and a number of others whose names are associated with the history of knowledge about circulation and respiration. Included in the latter part of the book are seventeenth-century "warnings" about the mixed advantages and dangers of blood transfusions, as reported in *Philosophical Transactions*, the journal of the Royal Society of London.

For further information on circulation in invertebrate animals . . .

Buchsbaum, Ralph, *Animals Without Backbones,* University of Chicago Press, 1948.

Barnes, R. D., *Invertebrate Zoology,* Saunders, Philadelphia, 1964.

For discussions of circulation in vertebrate animals . . .

Romer, Alfred S., *The Vertebrate Body,* Third Edition, Saunders, Philadelphia, 1962.

Best, Charles H., and N. B. Taylor, *The Human Body: Its Anatomy and Physiology,* Fourth Edition, Holt, Rinehart and Winston, New York, 1963.

Jacob, Stanley W., and Clarice A. Francone, *Structure and Function in Man,* Saunders, Philadelphia, 1965.

Simpson, George G., and William S. Beck, *Life: An Introduction to Biology,* Second Edition, Harcourt, Brace & World, New York, 1965.

Magazines

Adolph, E. F., "The Heart's Pacemaker," *Scientific American,* Volume 216 (March 1967), page 32.

De Bakey, M. E., and L. H. Engel, "Blood Vessel Surgery," *Scientific American,* Volume 204 (April 1961), page 88.

22

Respiration in Multicellular Animals

With a few exceptions, including some microorganisms, living cells require oxygen. Without it, the cells of animals, fungi, most species of bacteria, and green plants could not use the energy of glucose to make ATP. You may recall from Chapter 6 and other sections of this book that we can summarize the many reactions involved in making the energy of the glucose molecules available by writing:

$$\underset{\text{glucose}}{C_6H_{12}O_6} + \underset{\text{oxygen}}{6\ O_2} \rightarrow \underset{\text{carbon dioxide}}{6\ CO_2} + \underset{\text{water}}{6\ H_2O} + \text{energy}$$

Thus, two gases are involved. Oxygen is used and carbon dioxide is produced. Although small amounts of carbon dioxide are used in animal cells, so much is produced in the processes of metabolism that most of it is a waste product. Respiring cells must therefore have some means not only of obtaining oxygen but of getting rid of excess carbon dioxide.

METHODS OF RESPIRATION

Respiration is the sum of all the processes involved in the equation given in the introduction above. Respiration includes not only the processes occurring within a cell as described in Chapter 6, but *all* the events concerned with getting oxygen to the cell and disposing of carbon dioxide. Thus you can see that *breathing* and respiration are not the same thing.

Respiration in *Amoeba* is relatively simple (Chapter 18, page 342). Oxygen molecules in pond water diffuse across the cell membrane and into the cytoplasm. Diffusion and the movements of the cytoplasm carry the oxygen to the mitochondria (pages 114 and 116). Here the oxygen is combined with hydrogen to form water. The carbon dioxide molecules move in the reverse direction. Diffusion and movements of the cytoplasm carry the carbon dioxide molecules to the cell membrane. They diffuse across the cell membrane and into the surrounding pond water. *Amoeba* swims on, leaving its wastes behind.

The supply of oxygen for animals that live on land is in the air that surrounds them. The supply of oxygen for aquatic animals is dissolved in the water. The source of supply in both instances is the oxygen produced by photosynthetic plants.

Oxygen and carbon dioxide molecules cross living cell membranes readily. They can do this when living membranes are moist; they cannot easily cross dry membranes. Frogs are able to respire through their skin, which is moist. Animals with dry skin have the problem of obtaining oxygen and disposing of carbon dioxide in other ways. Even the frog has its problem, too, for its body is too large to be supplied with oxygen solely (or even largely) through the skin. The solution is roughly the same for all these animals. Thin, moist membranes, with large surface area, which are effective for respiration, are formed as the linings of lungs, tracheal tubes, and gills.

Respiration in *Hydra* and a Planarian

Neither *Hydra* nor a planarian has organs specialized solely for respiration. As we have learned before, both have their cells in thin layers. Both live in water. Oxygen diffuses into their bodies across the membranes of the outermost cells. In the case of *Hydra*, oxygen also diffuses from the water in the digestive cavity into the adjacent cells. Carbon dioxide leaves *Hydra* and planarians by simple diffusion.

22-1 RESPIRATION IN THE EARTHWORM

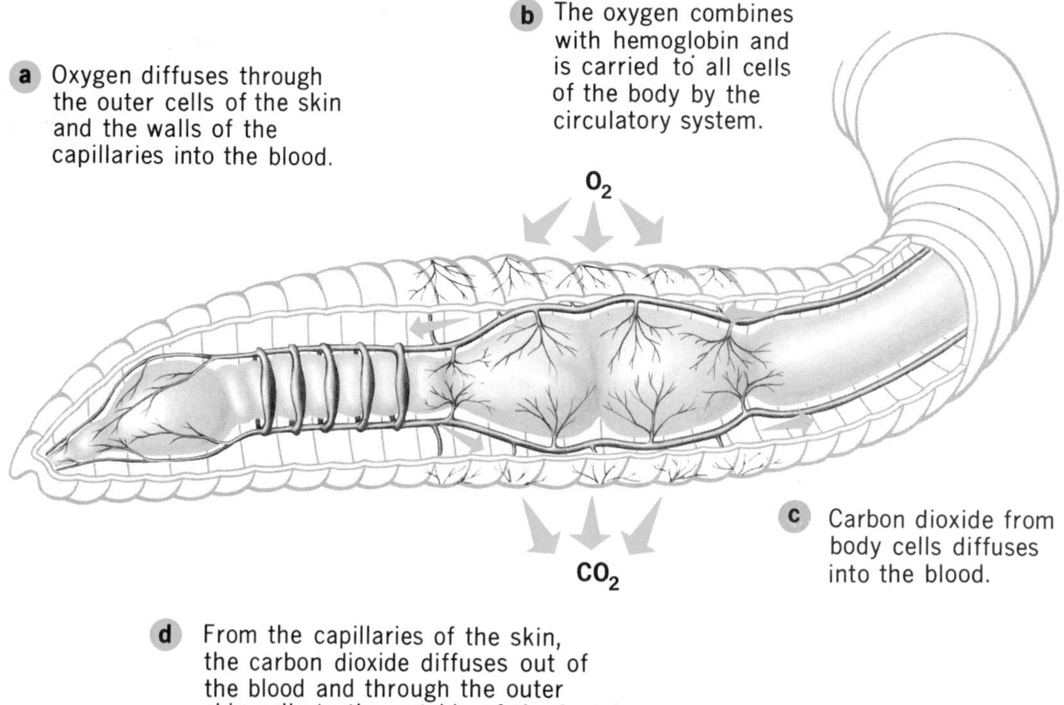

a Oxygen diffuses through the outer cells of the skin and the walls of the capillaries into the blood.
b The oxygen combines with hemoglobin and is carried to all cells of the body by the circulatory system.
O_2
CO_2
c Carbon dioxide from body cells diffuses into the blood.
d From the capillaries of the skin, the carbon dioxide diffuses out of the blood and through the outer skin cells to the outside of the body.

Respiration in the Earthworm

The earthworm has a moist skin. Oxygen diffuses across the outermost cells. Carbon dioxide leaves by diffusing out from the same cells. In these respects earthworms resemble *Hydra* and planarians.

If the earthworm relied only on diffusion to supply its cells with oxygen and to remove the carbon dioxide, it would have been extinct long ago. Or, rather, it never could have existed at all. Its body is too big. The oxygen that diffuses in would move too slowly to be used by any except the outermost layers of cells. Most of the earthworm's cells are deeper within the body. These cells in the interior would die from lack of oxygen.

Blood forms the necessary link between the inner cells and the outside environment. In the last chapter we learned that the earthworm has a circulatory system. The blood in the circulatory system transports oxygen to the cells and carries carbon dioxide away (Figure 22-1). The skin is richly supplied with capillaries. Oxygen diffuses across the outer cells of the skin and the walls of the capillaries into the blood. The blood then moves around the body, carrying oxygen to all the cells. Carbon dioxide is carried away.

The cells of active animals require large amounts of oxygen and produce large amounts of excess carbon dioxide. If they depended on the amount of oxygen and carbon dioxide that can be carried dissolved in the water of blood, they could never be very active or very large.

In the course of evolution, animals have evolved ways of carrying large amounts of oxygen and carbon dioxide in blood. They do this by combining oxygen and carbon dioxide with some molecule in the blood. One such molecule is hemoglobin. Both the earthworm and man use hemoglobin to carry oxygen. (The actual details will be discussed in the section of this chapter on respiration in man.)

The advantages of a blood system containing hemoglobin can be understood from the following data. About 5 ml of oxygen can dissolve in a liter of water (at room temperature). The same amount of blood from the earthworm, which has hemoglobin in solution, can hold about 65 ml of oxygen. Man has an even better arrangement, with large amounts of hemoglobin in his red blood cells. A liter of his blood will hold 250 ml of oxygen. Thus, earthworm blood can carry about 13 times as much oxygen as can water. Human blood can carry about 50 times as much as water.

Respiration in the Grasshopper

It is possible that the ancestors of the grasshopper and of other arthropods had a circulatory system with hemoglobin (since arthropod ancestors are believed to have been annelid-like). As the primitive arthropods evolved, however, blood became increasingly less important for land-dwelling arthropods in the transport of oxygen and carbon dioxide. Some insect larvae have hemoglobin in their blood, but apart from these, the blood of insects lacks hemoglobin. Their blood, therefore, is unimportant for carrying respiratory gases. Then how do they manage?

The insects have evolved quite a different way of carrying oxygen and carbon dioxide to and from their cells. They have tracheal tubes (Figure 21-3, page 407).

The grasshopper has ten pairs of openings on the sides of its body. These lead to a series of tracheal tubes that extend throughout the body.

The grasshopper pumps air through these tubes by contracting and expanding its abdomen. When the abdomen expands, the front four pairs of holes are open. Air enters these holes. Then, as the abdomen contracts, the front holes close and the hind six pairs of holes open. This forces the air through the tubes and eventually out of the body. The tracheal tubes branch repeatedly and reach all parts of the body. The inner ends contain a fluid. The oxygen dissolves in the fluid and then diffuses into the cells. Carbon dioxide moves in the reverse direction—also by diffusion and the movement of the air through the tracheal tubes.

RESPIRATION IN MAN

Man faces the same general problems of obtaining oxygen and getting rid of carbon dioxide as do all other large and complex animals. He must have moist and thin respiratory membranes across which gaseous exchanges with the environment can occur. In addition, he must have some means of transporting oxygen and carbon dioxide to and from the cells.

The respiratory membranes through which exchange of gases with the environment occurs are the linings of the lungs. The linings are much folded, and so their total surface is enormous. If flattened out, they would cover an area of about 93 square meters (1,000 square feet). How does this compare with the area of the floor of your biology classroom?

The transport of oxygen and carbon dioxide between lungs and body cells is taken care of by the circulatory system. The lining of the lungs is richly supplied with capillaries. In some parts of the lungs, moreover, the capillary walls themselves form the lining of the lungs. Thus, blood is as close to air as possible. Diffusion of the respiratory gases between lungs and circulatory system occurs readily.

The lungs are closed sacs that connect to the outside by way of the **trachea** (TRAY·kee-uh) and the nostrils or mouth (Figure 22-2). Diffusion alone is not enough to keep the air in the lungs "pure." It is necessary to pump air constantly into and out of the lungs.

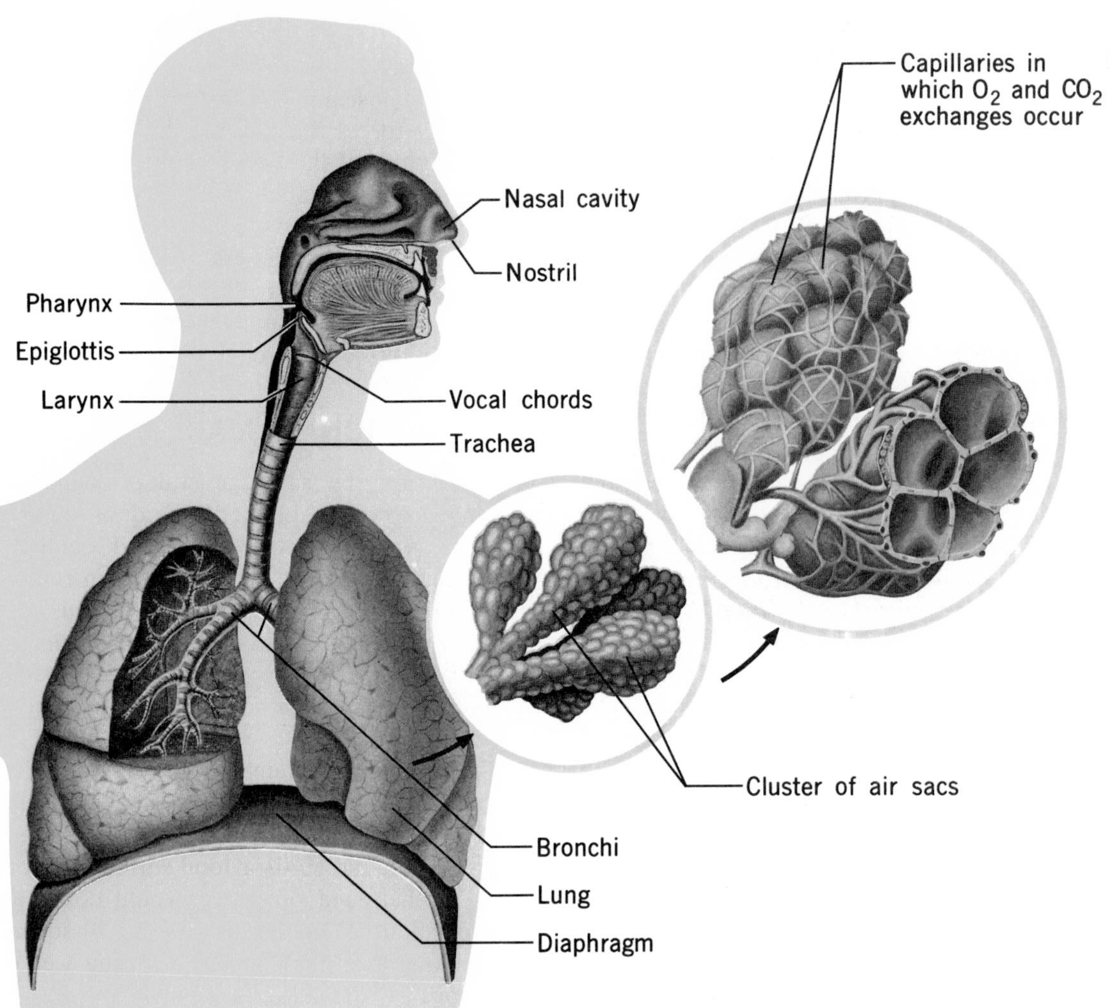

22–2 The respiratory system of man. Part of the right lung has been cut away to expose the branching system of bronchial tubes. A portion of the left lung has been enlarged to show first, the air sacs, and second, their relation to the capillaries.

Breathing

The events concerned with pumping air in and out of the lungs are called breathing.

The structures directly concerned with channeling air into contact with capillaries containing blood are the nostrils, nasal cavity, pharynx, **larynx** (LAIR·inks), trachea, **bronchi** (BRONG·ky), and lungs (Figure 22–2). Air enters the body through the nostrils (or, instead, the mouth) and passes into the nasal cavity. Here it is filtered. The moist surfaces of the lining of the nasal cavity, and the hairs growing from its sides, remove some of the tiny particles of dirt in the air. In addition, as the inhaled air passes through the nasal cavity, its temperature is brought close to that of the body, and it takes up water vapor so that it becomes more moist than before.

From the nasal cavity the air goes into the pharynx. There is a tricky problem here. At the back of the pharynx there are two passageways, one to the lungs and one to the stomach. It is important that air go in one and food in the other. It is also important that food *does not* enter the tube to the lungs, and it is desirable for air not to go to the stomach. The traffic is kept properly channeled by a flaplike valve, the **epiglottis** (ep·ih·GLOT·iss), that protects the tube to the lungs. This valve is partly closed when we swallow; it deflects food down to the stomach and keeps it out of the trachea—the route to the lungs. The epiglottis opens more widely when we take a breath, and air enters the lungs (Figure 22-3). This is not quite the full story—nervous regulation is important in guiding food and air movements, too. Try to make breathing and swallowing movements at the same time—can you do this?

The passageway to the lungs goes first through the larynx. This stiff box contains our vocal cords. When air passes out of the lungs and over the vocal cords, it causes them to vibrate. This produces sounds—the basis of our speech and song.

The larynx is at the upper end of the trachea. You can feel both larynx and trachea by press-

22–3 Events in the throat associated with breathing **(a)** and swallowing **(b).** The commonly held belief that the epiglottis closes downward upon the larynx when food is swallowed is not quite true. The closure is probably never complete; the degree of closure is determined partly by the backward movement of the tongue during swallowing (which forces the epiglottis into a more or less horizontal position) and partly by the upward movement of the larynx (which brings it up under the epiglottis). Food does not enter the partly open larynx and obstruct breathing primarily because the epiglottis diverts the food mass to one side of the opening and safely down the esophagus.

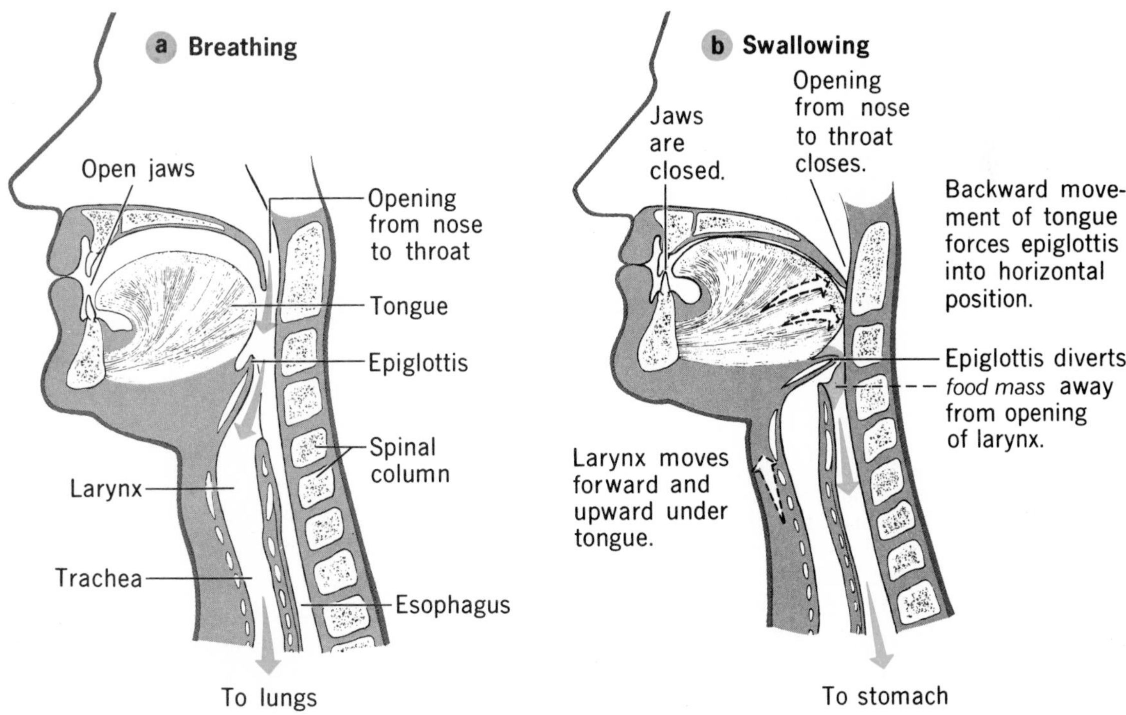

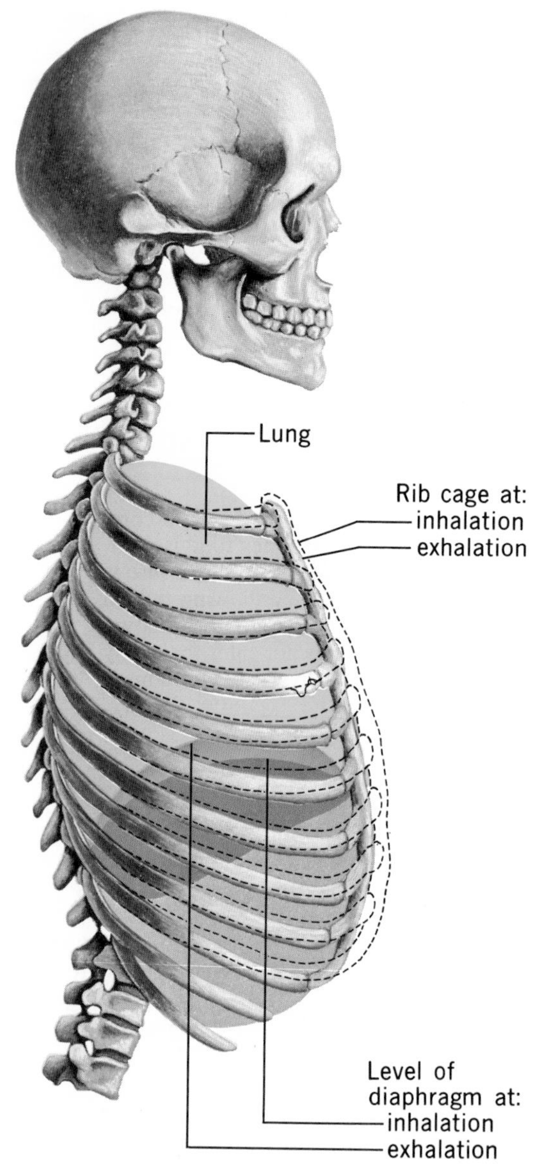

22–4 Movements of the chest wall and the diaphragm during inhalation and exhalation. The two positions of the rib cage and the two of the diaphragm as shown represent the degree of movement characteristic of moderately deep breathing. During periods of rest or of quiet activity, only the rib cage may move as much as indicated here; the diaphragm would contract to this extent only occasionally. Thus, the type of breathing used most of the time by most people is chiefly "rib breathing."

ing gently on your throat. At its lower end the trachea divides into two bronchi—one leading to each lung.

The lungs seem spongy in structure. Their interior is divided into millions of small chambers, thus tremendously increasing the moist surface available for transfer of gases between air and blood.

Breathing is the process of inhaling and exhaling. The lungs themselves neither draw in air nor push it out. Instead, the chest wall and the **diaphragm** (DY·a·fram) act as a large pump in moving air into and out of the lungs (Figure 22-4).

The chest wall is made up of the ribs, their muscles, and the skin. The ribs are attached at an angle to the spine (if you run your finger along one rib, you will notice that it extends downward from the spine). When we inhale, the chest wall moves up and out. This increases the volume of the chest cavity.

The diaphragm is a sheet of muscle that extends across the body cavity. It may be imagined as the "floor" if you think of the chest cavity as a "room." When the diaphragm is relaxed, it is in the shape of a dome—with the convex side of the dome extending into the chest cavity. When the diaphragm contracts it flattens out a bit. That is, the dome moves downward. As a result, the volume of the chest cavity is still further increased.

There are two ways, therefore, for the volume of the chest cavity to increase: by elevation and outward movement of the chest wall, and by flattening of the diaphragm. When the volume of the chest cavity is increased, its internal pressure decreases and the air from the outside rushes into the lungs. This is **inspiration** (inhalation).

Then the reverse occurs. The chest wall is lowered and moves inward, and the diaphragm relaxes and assumes its dome shape. These changes increase the pressure on the lungs; their elastic tissue contracts and squeezes the air out through the nose to the external atmosphere. This is **expiration** (exhalation).

Of all the basic activities of the body, breathing is one of the most familiar. Indeed, people commonly associate breathing with the existence of life itself, for a mammal that is breathing normally is obviously alive, no matter how unresponsive in other ways. And people often recognize death of such an animal by the stopping of all its respiratory movements. Though we have explained the mechanics of breathing movements of the chest in some detail, we have said nothing about their *timing*. This is because there is no need to point out to you that breathing movements are regular and rhythmic, yet always extremely sensitive to changes in body activity. You must have noticed that your own breathing is slow and shallow when you are at rest, and deeper and faster when you exercise hard. Indeed, patterns of breathing show a great range, for they are coordinated with moment-by-moment needs of the body for supply of oxygen and removal of carbon dioxide. You can establish this relationship in Laboratory Inquiry 22-1. There you will have an opportunity to study breathing patterns more closely under varying conditions. But can any of these observations tell you *how* the rhythmic activities of breathing occur? Do the muscle contractions result from nerve stimulation, or from cyclic changes in the muscles themselves? These questions can only be answered by direct observations and experiments. It has been found that all movements of breathing stop at once when the nerves leading from the brain to the respiratory muscles are cut. This and other evidence has been put together to give a picture of how breathing movements occur. From the brain, messages travel in waves to activate the muscles. But what is the origin of the rhythmic activity of the brain on which these respiratory movements depend? And how does the brain activity change from moment to moment in such a way that breathing is controlled precisely in relation to body activities? Here we encounter another example of homeostasis—in this case, the regulation of breathing in relation to the body cells' needs for supply of oxygen and removal of carbon dioxide. Experiments have given us much information about control of respiration, but we cannot describe it to you until you have learned more about the organization of the coordinating systems themselves—nervous and hormonal. We ask you to remember the questions raised in this chapter—and others that may occur to you as you work in the laboratory—and look for ways of answering these questions in Chapter 24.

The Transportation of Oxygen

Air contains about 21 percent oxygen. When brought into the cavity of the lungs, the air is in close contact with the capillaries in the lung membranes. Oxygen molecules pass from the lung cavity across the capillary walls and into the blood (Figure 22-2). Here they combine with hemoglobin in the red blood cells.

Hemoglobin, being a protein, is a very large molecule. In spite of its size and complexity, it has been studied so carefully that we know the structure of few protein molecules better. It consists of four **peptide** (PEP·tide) chains—which are chains of amino acids (Chapter 5, page 94, and Chapter 8, page 171 and Figure 8-17)—loosely bound together, two chains of one sort and two of another. Each of these four chains is folded into a coiled structure very similar to the myoglobin molecule (Figure 5-7, page 96). Each chain bears a **heme** (HEEM) group, a complex molecular structure similar to that of chlorophyll, but carrying in its center an iron, instead of a magnesium, atom.

When oxygen combines with hemoglobin it attaches to the iron atoms. A molecule of oxygen, O_2, combines with each of the four iron atoms in a hemoglobin molecule. The combination of oxygen and hemoglobin is called **oxyhemoglobin** (ok·sih·HEE·mo·glow·b'n). We can express the reaction as:

$$Hb + O_2 \rightarrow HbO_2$$

(The symbols Hb and HbO_2 are abbreviations for hemoglobin and oxyhemoglobin. They are

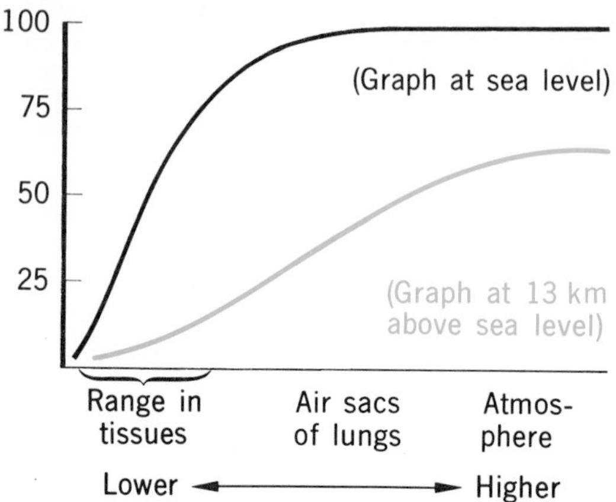

22–5 Differences in oxygen concentration in the atmosphere and in the lungs and other body tissues, at sea level and at 13 kilometers above sea level. The difference in amount of oxygen combined with hemoglobin in blood in the lungs and blood in the tissues is an indication that the blood releases oxygen in the tissues (where the relative oxygen concentration is always low—why?). At high altitudes, such as 13 km shown here, the concentration of oxygen in the atmosphere is so low that even in the lungs the hemoglobin molecules combine with only about half as much oxygen as at sea level.

not true chemical symbols. Any given hemoglobin molecule can actually combine with 4 O_2 molecules, as we mentioned above.)

There are some important things to learn about this reaction between hemoglobin and oxygen. One is that the reaction can be reversed very easily:

$$HbO_2 \rightleftharpoons Hb + O_2$$

Not only can hemoglobin combine with oxygen, but oxyhemoglobin can break up into hemoglobin and oxygen.

Another important feature of the reaction is its dependence on the *concentration* of oxygen. If hemoglobin is exposed to air at sea level, nearly every molecule combines with oxygen to form oxyhemoglobin (Figure 22-5). At a height of 13 km (about 8 miles) above sea level, the concentration of oxygen is much lower—about one fifth as great as at sea level. Under these conditions only about half as many molecules of oxygen as at sea level are combined with hemoglobin to form oxyhemoglobin. This is important, because blood cannot carry enough oxygen to the tissues if hemoglobin is combined with so relatively few oxygen molecules. In fact, human life is impossible at such an altitude without a supplementary supply of oxygen. Provision for such a supply is built into modern aircraft, which have pressurized cabins that maintain an enriched air supply.

Air next to the lung membranes in our lungs is not the same as the surrounding air. When we are at rest, or exercising moderately, our breathing exchanges only a small portion of the air in the lungs. The concentration of oxygen in the lung cavity is about two thirds of that in fresh air. Nevertheless, this is sufficient for about 95 percent of the hemoglobin molecules to form oxyhemoglobin.

In the capillaries of the tissues, the red blood cells meet a very different environment. The tissue cells are continually using oxygen; hence, the concentration of oxygen is quite low in them. It might be only one third of that in the lungs. When the concentration of oxygen is so low, only about half of the heme groups in hemoglobin can be in the form HbO_2. The other half are in the form Hb. This means that as the blood reaches these tissues, about half the HbO_2 units break down and form Hb and O_2. The oxygen enters the cells.

To summarize, the hemoglobin molecule forms a loose compound, oxyhemoglobin, with oxygen molecules when there is a great amount of oxygen available, as in the lungs. The oxyhemoglobin gives up its oxygen when the circulating blood brings it to an area poor in oxygen, as in the tissues of the body.

The Transportion of Carbon Dioxide

In the reactions that occur within cells in our bodies, an excess of carbon dioxide is produced. The excess carbon dioxide diffuses into the capillaries. Carbon dioxide is carried in blood in several forms: some is combined with hemoglobin; some is combined with compounds other than hemoglobin; some is not combined with another compound but is carried as carbon dioxide; but most is carried as the bicarbonate ion.

The formation of the bicarbonate ion occurs in the following way. First, carbonic acid is formed by combination of water and carbon dioxide. This important reaction is carried out rapidly because of the presence of a specific enzyme in the red blood cells.

$$CO_2 + H_2O \xrightarrow{\text{enzyme}} H_2CO_3$$

The carbonic acid then ionizes to form hydrogen ions and bicarbonate ions:

$$H_2CO_3 \rightarrow H^+ + HCO_3^-$$

When blood leaves the capillary beds in the tissues of the body, therefore, the carbon dioxide is mostly in the form of HCO_3^-.

In the capillaries of the lungs the reverse reactions occur:

$$HCO_3^- + H^+ \rightarrow H_2CO_3 \xrightarrow{\text{enzyme}} H_2O + CO_2$$

Carbon dioxide passes out of the capillaries, by diffusion, into the cavity of the lungs, from which it is exhaled.

The blood, therefore, serves as a carrier of the respiratory gases, oxygen and carbon dioxide. The mechanisms involved are noteworthy in that those occurring in the capillaries of the lungs are the exact opposite of those occurring in the capillaries of other tissues. This is a most economical situation, because the hemoglobin and the water are not used up. Thus, the hemoglobin molecules of the body's millions of red blood cells can be used over and over again in the transport of oxygen and carbon dioxide.

CONCLUDING REMARKS

Before we discuss the next organ system of the animal body, we should pause and take stock. What have we learned so far?

Reactions are constantly going on in the cells of animals. Some of the most important involve the oxidation of organic compounds and exchange of energy. The chief end products of these reactions are carbon dioxide and water. There must be mechanisms to provide a constant supply of the things being used and to dispose of those being produced. We can review these mechanisms in terms of the important organic compound, glucose. Complete oxidation of this molecule requires a supply of oxygen in the cells of most animals. And we have already learned how the digestive system supplies the glucose, which then is transported to all cells either by diffusion or by the circulatory system.

In some animals, such as *Amoeba, Hydra,* and planarians, oxygen is supplied by diffusion. In other animals the combined efforts of the respiratory and circulatory systems make oxygen available to the cells. A special pattern for gas exchange, seen in some animals including the grasshopper, is a tracheal system.

There is no problem with the products of a reaction if they can be used by the cell. If they cannot be used, or are overabundant, they must be removed. Consider the case of carbon dioxide and water. A small amount of carbon dioxide is used in animal cells, but so much more is produced than is needed that most is a waste product. In *Hydra* and planarians, the carbon dioxide diffuses out. In earthworms and man, a combination of diffusion from cells and processes carried out by the circulatory and respiratory systems eliminates the excess carbon dioxide. Grasshoppers dispose of the carbon dioxide diffusing from their cells via the tracheal tubes.

Water is usually not present in excess in man and other animals that live on land. In our own case, water is constantly lost by evaporation from the moist lining of our lungs and in perspiration—so it must be replaced. Water is also necessary to us for removal of wastes by the kidneys. Insects, too, use the water produced in their cells.

In planarians and *Hydra*, water tends constantly to enter the body, and it must be removed to keep the water content balanced.

The mechanisms described so far account in a general way for what happens, not only to glucose, but to all carbohydrates and fats. They contain carbon, hydrogen, and oxygen, and the end products of their oxidation are carbon dioxide and water. The proteins represent a special situation because they contain nitrogen as well as carbon, hydrogen, and oxygen. The nitrogen presents a special problem—one handled by the *excretory system*. We will consider the function of the excretory system in the next chapter.

GUIDE QUESTIONS AND PROBLEMS

1. Most respiratory surfaces have what properties in common?
2. How do body systems used for fluid and gas transport in insects, and in animals such as earthworms and men, indicate that evolution from ocean life to life on land took place more than once among the animals of long ago?
3. The blood of earthworms and of men contains hemoglobin. Yet an earthworm's blood can carry only one fourth as much oxygen as an equal volume of your blood. Account for the difference.
4. The same exertion at sea level and at 12,000 feet above sea level produces different breathing rates and different degrees of fatigue. What factors are operating to cause the differences?
5. How is blood able to take on oxygen in the lungs and release it to the tissue cells?
6. Distinguish between cellular respiration and pulmonary respiration in man.
7. A vital biological principle is that animals preserve an internal balance, within narrow limits, by regulation of intake and loss of substances. How is this principle illustrated in respiration processes in animals?
8. Aquatic mammals breathe with lungs, as you do. What special adaptations might they have which permit them to remain underwater for longer periods of time than you can remain underwater?

RELATED READING

Books

For original accounts of early discoveries about pulmonary respiration . . .

Graubard, Mark, *Circulation and Respiration: The Evolution of an Idea,* Ideas in Science Series, Harcourt, Brace & World, New York, 1964.

For further information on the body systems involved in respiration in invertebrate animals . . .

Buchsbaum, Ralph, *Animals Without Backbones,* University of Chicago Press, 1948.

Barnes, R. D., *Invertebrate Zoology,* Saunders, Philadelphia, 1964.

For a broader coverage of pulmonary and cellular respiration in man . . .

Best, Charles H., and N. B. Taylor, *The Human Body: Its Anatomy and Physiology,* Fourth Edition, Holt, Rinehart and Winston, New York, 1963.

Dejours, P., *Respiration,* Oxford University Press, New York, 1966 (paperback).

Hughes, G. M., *Comparative Physiology of Vertebrate Respiration,* Harvard University Press, Cambridge, Massachusetts, 1963.

Magazines

Comroe, Julius H. Jr., "The Lung," *Scientific American,* Volume 214 (February 1966), page 57.

Scholander, P. F., "The Master Switch of Life," *Scientific American,* Volume 209 (December 1963), page 92.

23

Excretion and Homeostasis in Multicellular Animals

More kinds of chemical reactions go on in every animal cell than in the largest of chemical factories. Many of these reactions build the cell's own "factories" and other structures. Chromosomes, mitochondria, ribosomes, contractile vacuoles, cell membranes, and all other cell structures are constructed by chemical reactions within the cell.

Other chemical reactions that occur within cells produce substances or transfer energy that the cell uses to remain alive. As you know, energy is made available when glucose and other organic compounds are oxidized in processes necessary to the life of the cell. However, molecules of carbon dioxide and water are also formed. For the most part, the cell has little chemical use for carbon dioxide, and except in certain animals, produces water in surplus. Thus the carbon dioxide and water are waste products. At the same time that they are formed, some of the energy transferred in the many reactions is also changed to "waste" form as heat. In this chapter, we will describe problems of disposal of waste chemicals and energy and see how some different animals solve the problems. The animals will again be *Amoeba, Hydra*, a planarian, an earthworm, a grasshopper, and man.

METHODS OF EXCRETION OF CHEMICAL COMPOUNDS

Considering the tremendous numbers of reactions that occur in cells, it is surprising that so few of the molecules produced are waste products. Chief among these are carbon dioxide, water, and nitrogen-containing compounds (such as ammonia, urea, and uric acid). The removal of these, as well as any other substances unneeded in the cell's activities, is **excretion** (ex·KREE·shun).

In Chapter 20 you learned how *Amoeba* excretes excess chemical substances. The carbon dioxide and ammonia formed in metabolism diffuse out of the cell. Water is more of a problem. The cell obtains some as a consequence of oxidation. Much more is constantly diffusing in from the surrounding pond. The surplus water is removed by the contractile vacuoles.

Excretion in *Hydra*

Hydra has no structures specialized for excretion. Carbon dioxide and the principal nitrogen-containing waste, ammonia, leave the cells by diffusion. Nearly every cell is either adjacent to the outside pond water or to the digestive cavity, so that there is a ready place to pass the wastes.

Hydra is a freshwater organism. Its cells have a lower concentration of water than does the surrounding pond. The cells of *Hydra*, therefore, face the same problem *Amoeba* does. Water constantly enters the animal faster than it diffuses out. The mechanism by which the surplus water is removed is not fully known, although it must be quite complex and require the expenditure of energy.

Excretion in the Planarian

In flatworms the excretion of carbon dioxide and much of the chief nitrogen-containing waste, ammonia, is simply a matter of diffusion. To an extent both gases dissolve in and form other products with water, and they are carried away in the water of the environment.

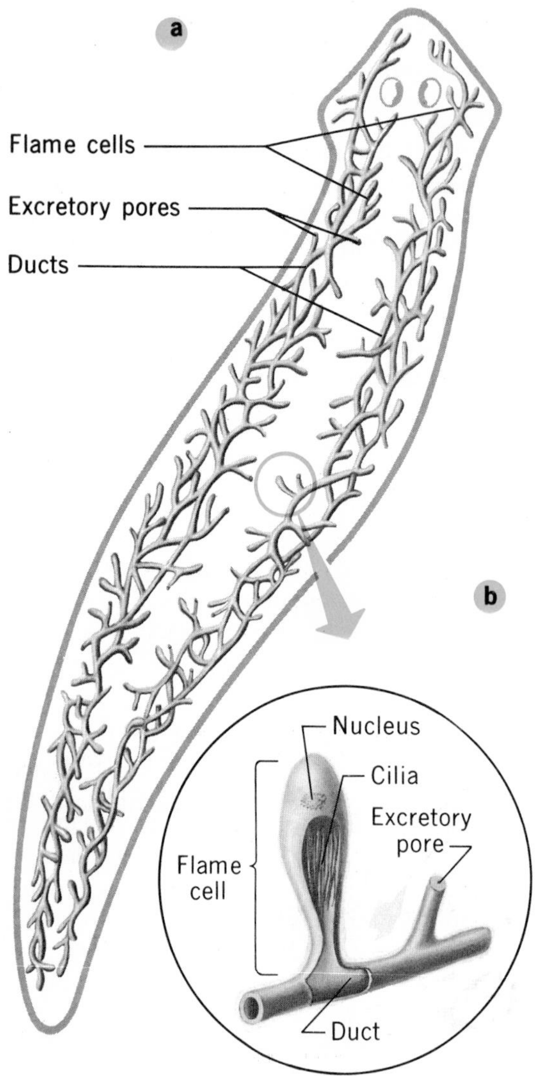

23–1 The excretory system of a planarian. A flame cell and an excretory pore are shown enlarged. The wastes and excess water removed by flame cells are eliminated through the pores in the body wall.

A planarian, however, does have an excretory system. This consists of a series of branching tubes, or ducts. The outer ends of the tubes end in **flame cells** (Figure 23-1). Each flame cell contains a space that connects with an excretory duct. A tuft of cilia projects into the space within the cell. In a living animal, the movement of the cilia reminded the early observers of a flickering candle flame—hence the name "flame cell."

Planarians must cope with the same problem that faces *Amoeba* and *Hydra*. Water constantly diffuses into the cells and must be removed. Probably this is accomplished largely by the excretory system. We do not yet know *how* it is done, although some evidence suggests that it may be through activities of the flame cells.

Excretion in the Earthworm

Once again, in earthworms, our understanding of excretion is most incomplete. The earthworm has a circulatory system that carries blood to the body surface. This is the chief route for the removal of carbon dioxide, which diffuses through surface cells.

The earthworm has excretory tubes (Figure 23-2), two for nearly every segment of the body. The inner end of each tube is in the body cavity. The body cavity contains a fluid, and within this fluid many waste substances collect—among them ammonia and urea, the chief nitrogen-containing wastes formed by the earthworm. These and other waste materials are removed by the excretory tubes, which have openings encircled with cilia. The cilia propel fluid into each excretory tube. Contractions of the muscular wall of the excretory tube then force the fluid *through* it to the outside of the body.

Excretion in the Grasshopper

The grasshopper disposes of its carbon dioxide through the tracheal tubes (Chapter 22, page 421, and Figure 21-3, page 407). For other waste products of cell metabolism, it has a specialized excretory system. This is made up of long, fine tubes often called **Malpighian** (mal·PIG·ih·an) **tubules** (Figure 23-3). (They were discovered by Malpighi, who, you may recall, made many contributions to biological science.) One end of each tube opens into the digestive canal. The other end floats freely in

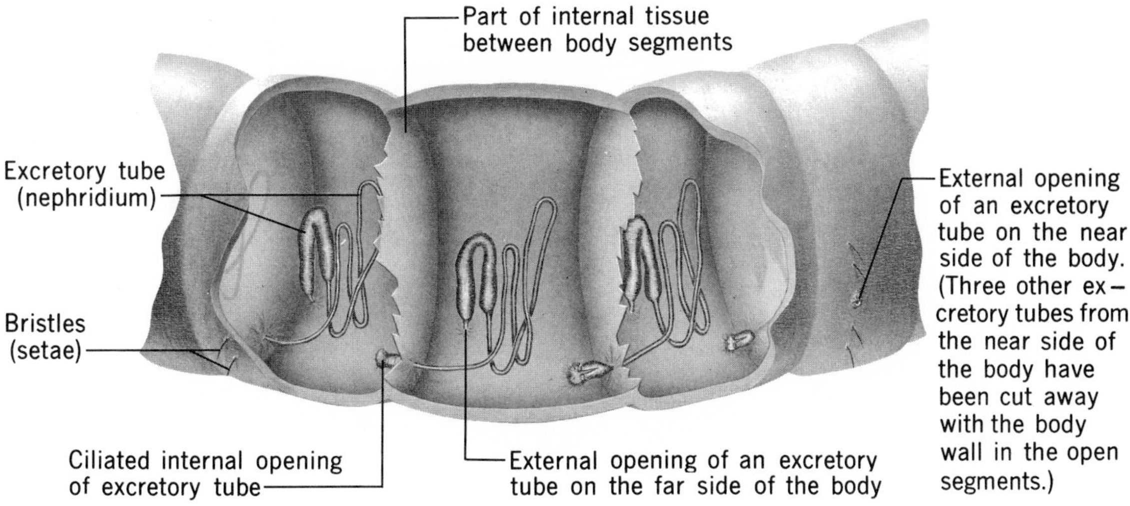

23–2 Excretory tubes in the earthworm. The near side of the body, including the alimentary canal and the circulatory system, is cut away. Most of the segments of the body have a pair of excretory tubes, one on either side. Each excretory tube has its origin in one body segment and its external opening in the body wall of the next segment to the rear.

the large blood cavities. These excretory tubes extract waste products from the blood and pass them into the digestive canal. Eventually the wastes are eliminated through the anus.

The chief nitrogen-containing waste formed by the grasshopper is uric acid. The formation of uric acid rather than ammonia or urea is one of the grasshopper's evolutionary adaptations

23–3 The excretory system of a grasshopper. The Malpighian tubules are the excretory organs. They remove nitrogen-containing wastes from blood in the cavities between body organs. The wastes are dumped into the alimentary canal and eliminated through the anus. In what other functions besides excretion have you found the grasshopper's solution to problems of living different from that of man?

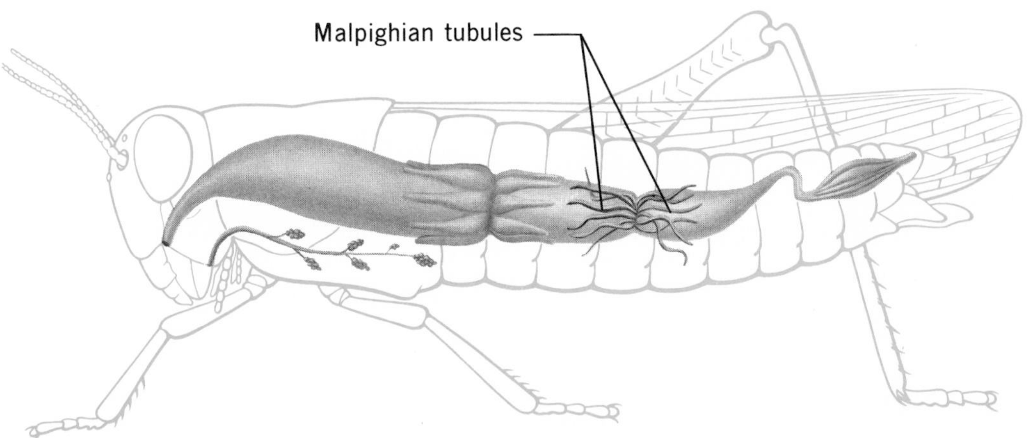

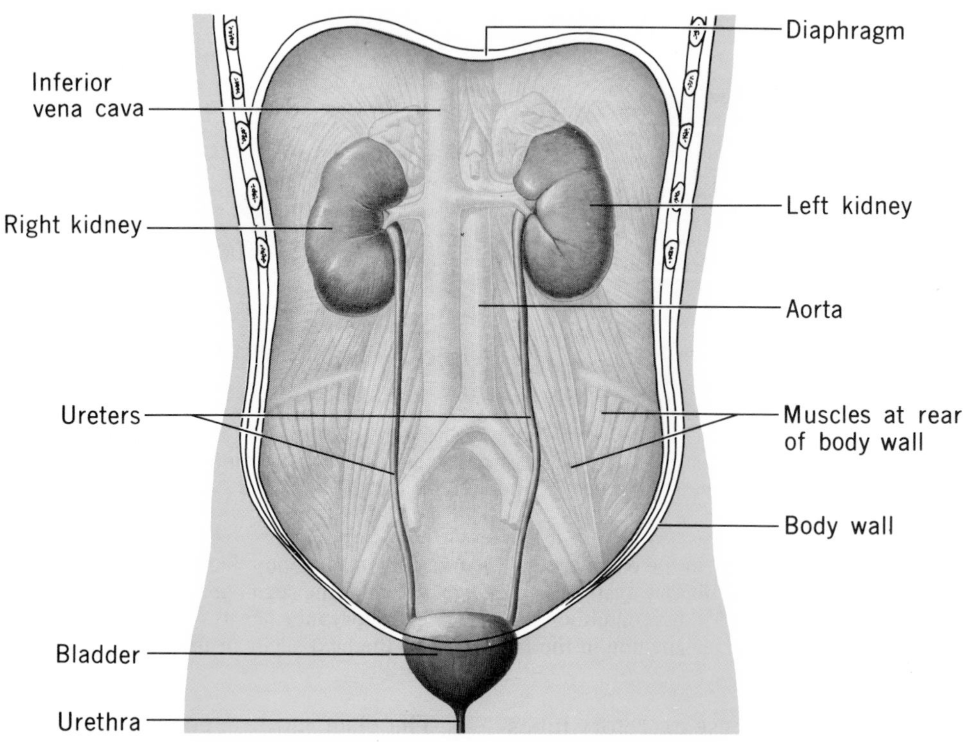

23–4 The excretory system of man. The chief excretory organs are the kidneys, which remove wastes from the blood stream. Other parts of the system – the ureters, the bladder, and the urethra – eliminate the excreted wastes from the body. Excretion takes place also in the lungs and in the liver. (The structures on the upper end of the kidneys are the adrenal glands. They are not parts of the excretory system.)

for life on land. Uric acid can be formed from protein sources by some rather complex reactions. By comparison, ammonia and urea are formed more easily from similar starting materials, raising a question of what advantage an animal like a grasshopper derives from excreting uric acid as its chief nitrogen waste. The answer is that uric acid is almost completely harmless to cells and can be excreted with very little water. In fact, the grasshopper deposits solid uric acid crystals in the cavities of its excretory tubes. These crystals then pass into the digestive tract and out with the undigested food materials.

The grasshopper's excretion of uric acid is in sharp contrast to the situation in animals that excrete ammonia or urea as their major nitrogen-containing waste. Ammonia is very poisonous to cells. If the ammonia concentration in the blood of a rabbit, for example, reaches as much as one part in 20,000, the rabbit dies. Ammonia can be the chief nitrogenous waste product only if there is plenty of water available to wash the wastes away. Thus, *Amoeba, Hydra,* and planarians can excrete ammonia along with lots of water.

Urea can be formed from ammonia. It is also somewhat harmful to cells, though less so than ammonia. Urea can easily be excreted by animals that have an adequate water supply for this purpose, or special body mechanisms that save water. Man excretes urea – along with so much water that the urea concentration is kept low. We use at least a liter of water each day to carry away the urea our cells produce.

Returning to the grasshopper, we can say that uric acid excretion permits this animal to survive under conditions where enough water is not available for "water-costly" processes of excreting nitrogen as ammonia or urea.

EXCRETION IN MAN

In man, as in grasshoppers, excess molecules are removed from the body along two major paths. Carbon dioxide is excreted through the lungs, as explained in Chapter 22, pages 422-24. Almost all other substances present in excess in body fluids are removed by the **kidneys** and excretory structures associated with them (Figure 23-4). There are two kidneys, one located on each side of the spine and just above the hipbone. A duct, the **ureter** (yoo·REE·ter), extends from each kidney to the **bladder.** The bladder opens to the body surface through the **urethra** (yoo·REE·thra). It is through the urethra that the final product of kidney function, urine, flows to the outside.

As in planarians, earthworms, and grasshoppers, the basic structures of the excretory system in man are series of tubes. But there are incredible numbers of these tubes, or **nephrons** (NEFF·ronz).

Each kidney is composed of about a million tiny nephrons (Figure 23-5a and b) that do the work of removing waste materials from the blood. Each nephron is long and coiled (Figure 23-5b). One end opens into a duct that collects

23–5 A kidney in longitudinal section, with an enlargement of a single nephron. What substances are transferred from the blood to the cup-shaped cavity at the closed end of the nephron? What transfers between the blood and the nephron take place farther along the way in the nephron tubule, and how do they affect what is excreted?

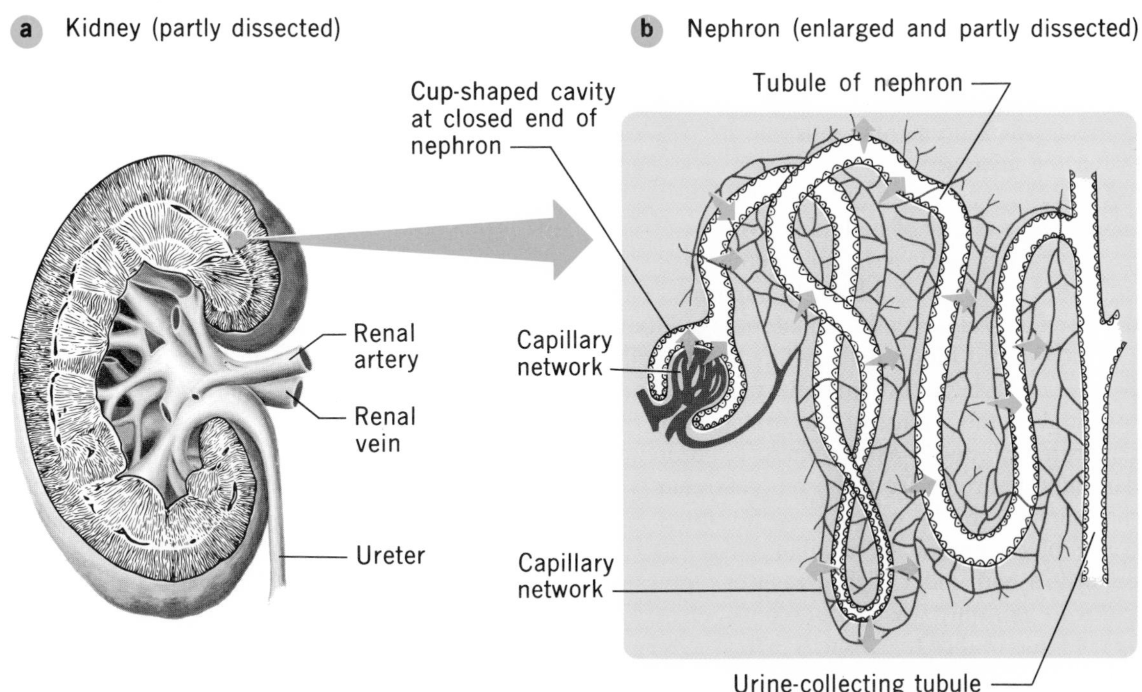

urine. The other end is closed, but spread out and fitted tightly over a mass of capillaries. There are many other capillaries, too, surrounding each tubule along its twisting path to the collecting duct (Figure 23-5b).

As you might guess from the complicated structure of the kidney and the microscopic size of the individual nephrons, it has taken years of work to find out even the general outline of kidney activity in man and other mammals. But so much research has been done to explain this important function that we understand it today perhaps better than we do the simpler excretory processes of *Hydra* or planarians. Biologists have studied the relationship between the composition and rate of flow of blood and of urine under many conditions. Important data have been collected for 30 years by a very difficult method—tiny glass tubes are stuck into various parts of individual nephrons in anesthetized experimental animals. Through these glass tubes, fluid can be withdrawn and analyzed chemically, showing how the fluid changes in composition as it flows along the nephron. You can imagine some of the problems in using these methods when you realize that the steps of handling the glass tubes, collecting fluid, and, often, making the chemical measurements, must be carried out under the microscope.

By now, we have a great deal of evidence that there is a flow of materials from the blood in the capillaries *across* the membranes and into the closed end of each nephron. This fluid contains almost all the materials of blood, except the red blood cells, white blood cells, platelets, and large protein molecules. In short, the fluid in the cavity of the first part of the nephron is blood plasma minus its proteins. The fluid is driven from the blood stream into the nephron by a process of filtration, because blood enters the capillary mass at the nephron's end under high pressure. Naturally there are not only wastes but many substances of vital importance to cells in this fluid. Glucose is one of these substances.

As the fluid moves along the cavity of the nephron, the cells of the nephron remove glucose and other substances that are useful. These substances are extracted and passed *back* into the blood stream. But the traffic is not one-way. The nephron cells take up other substances which diffuse from the blood in the capillaries around the tubules (Figure 23-5b). These substances are then passed into the cavity of the nephron. Thus, two-way traffic of molecules occurs across the nephron wall—*from* the tubules into the blood capillaries, and *from* the blood capillaries into the tubules.

It is especially interesting that the glucose and many other important substances continue to be reabsorbed from the nephron and restored to the blood long after their concentrations in the blood are higher than in the tubule. Obviously, simple diffusion cannot account for this. Here is another example of *active transport* (see Chapter 6, page 113), which involves expenditure of energy. Thus, the transfer of glucose from the fluid in the nephron cavity into the blood continues until, under normal circumstances, virtually *none* is left in the tubule. Other substances that are similarly removed from the tubule and restored to the blood include amino acids, fatty acids, vitamins, and hormones. A similar process applies to salts needed by the body. Water moves from the tubule back into the blood stream in association with these salts, glucose, and other substances. In the lower part of the nephron, so much water may be reabsorbed that the concentration of the dissolved substances in the urine left in the tubule is higher than in the blood. Certain waste substances, such as urea and uric acid, are greatly concentrated in this fluid in the tubule. It has been estimated that a significant part of the total expenditure of energy by the body is used in carrying on the *many* transport processes which take place in the kidney.

We can summarize all these processes by saying that blood under high pressure flows into the capillaries in the kidneys, and from this blood, fluid is filtered into the nephrons.

Nephron cells reabsorb from the filtered fluid substances that are of use to the body. Other substances are not taken up, and still others are moved from the blood into the tubule, so that they flow along the nephron and eventually out of the body in the urine. Thus, the nephron cells are constantly acting to sort out and keep valuable molecules, and to discard useless, harmful, or excess molecules. No wonder one biologist, Homer W. Smith, has written of the kidneys as "the master chemists" of the body fluids!

The function of the kidneys is remarkably stable, and they are protected by their position deep within the body. Nevertheless, even here they may be injured mechanically by rough exercise or blows falling on the body wall. Diseases may attack the kidneys, too, and doctors often examine the composition of the urine as a clue to how these important organs are functioning. The chemical compounds in urine also can reveal information about the condition of the body cells in general.

There are few better examples, in all physiology, of the regulation of the internal environment—the homeostatic control, within narrow limits, of certain states of the body—than that carried out by the kidneys. (You will investigate an aspect of this control in frogs, in Laboratory Inquiry 23-1.) Kidney activity varies, depending on body needs, for the kidneys are themselves closely controlled by hormones and other factors. Thus, if you drink a large amount of water, it will pass across the lining of the alimentary canal and enter the blood. The excess water will be removed rapidly by the nephrons. Similarly, if a large amount of salt is eaten, this also enters the blood, and the excess is removed by the nephrons. The accuracy of both those adjustments depends on hormonal regulation.

The nephrons have a vital role in maintaining the constancy of blood. They are assisted by the lungs—which remove carbon dioxide—and by a few other organs that play a minor part in excretion, including the liver.

PROBLEMS OF HEAT PRODUCTION

In addition to chemical waste materials, heat is constantly formed in living processes. In a way, this heat is also a "waste product" of metabolism, and animals must get rid of it in one way or another. For if the heat stayed in the cells, their temperature could rise without check. Can you think of some very unfavorable effects this might have on a living organism?

In small animals like *Amoeba, Hydra,* and planarians, heat is lost easily through the body surface by radiation or conduction to the surrounding water. Bigger animals may have much more trouble getting rid of excess heat, since they have such a large cell mass as compared with the body surface. Some of the methods animals use to remove heat are already familiar to you, since they are your methods, too. Blood circulation plays a major part, by carrying heat from inside the body to the skin. There the heat is lost by conduction or radiation to the environment, and by the evaporation of sweat as you perspire. Patterns of blood flow and sweating change with changes in body heat production. Have you observed this with your own activities?

In birds and many mammals, the lungs and mouth play a part in heat removal, too, and the body covering of feathers, fur, or clothing (in man) is adjusted with changing demands for heat loss. Thus, somewhat as in the case of the kidneys, the organs that remove heat from the body are closely controlled. Heat can also be saved, or produced in greater amounts by increased activity of body cells. This is because heat can be a useful asset to the body in birds and mammals, which regulate their body temperature so that it does not vary with varying environmental temperature. We know that other animals, too, like reptiles and insects, sometimes control reactions in their bodies by special ways of adjusting heat production. Thus, homeostatic control of the internal environment is complicated and far-reaching, involving not only chemical compounds but also energy balance.

CONCLUDING REMARKS—THE MAINTENANCE OF A CONSTANT ENVIRONMENT

The life of a multicellular individual depends on the life of its cells. We learned earlier that the various activities of multicellular animals can be thought of as ways of keeping the cells alive. The organism as a whole obtains food and oxygen. But these are used by individual cells (Figure 23-6). The organism also removes the cell wastes—or the cells will die.

As we progress from simple to complex animals, there is a trend toward the specialization of groups of cells to serve specific functions. For example, *Hydra* has no excretory system; planarians and earthworms have simple excretory systems; the human excretory system is very complex.

As cells become more specialized, they lose some of their abilities to perform a variety of functions. A cell lining the digestive cavity of *Hydra* can capture food particles, digest them, absorb oxygen, and eliminate carbon dioxide, ammonia, and excess heat. It can even contract like a muscle, though in a rather feeble way. It can divide by mitosis. It can do everything that *Amoeba* does except move away independently of other cells.

In complex animals with a closed blood system, such as man, we can make more specific this notion of the whole organism functioning to keep the individual cells alive. The substances that must be supplied to and removed from cells are carried in the blood. Therefore, we can say that the various organ systems function in ways that tend to keep the composition of blood nearly constant.

In man, the blood must be kept remarkably constant. If the concentration of oxygen is only slightly below normal, the individual becomes unconscious. As another example, we may note that there is only a trace of calcium ions

23-6 A SUMMARY OF CIRCULATION, RESPIRATION, DIGESTION, AND EXCRETION

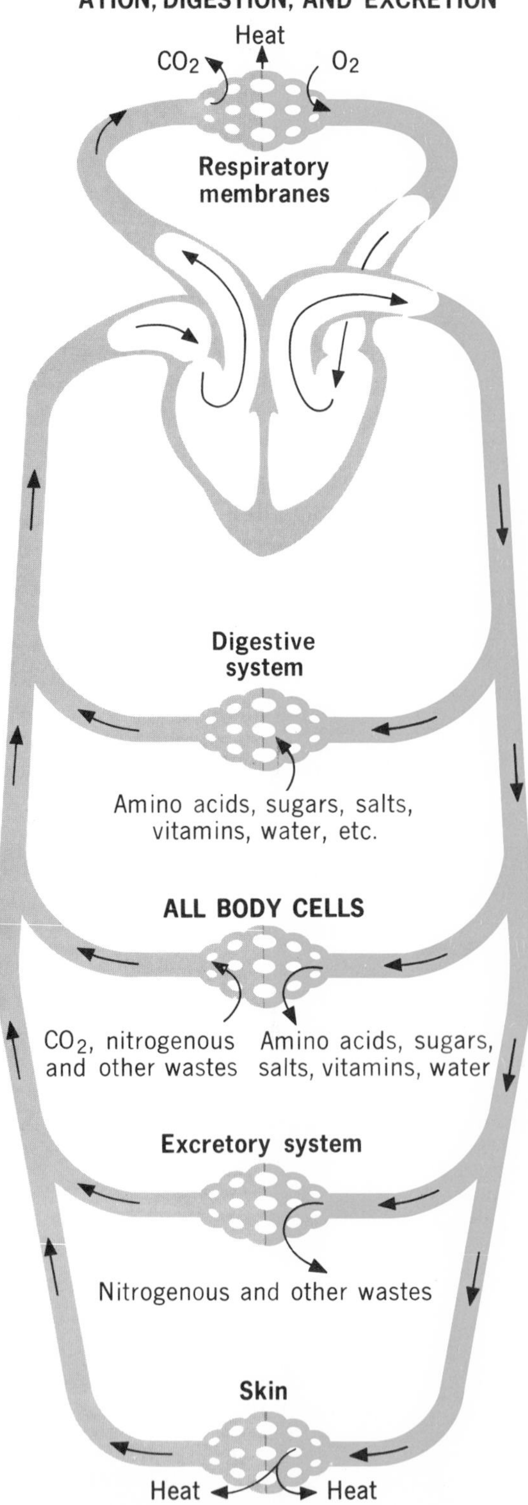

(Ca^{++}) in blood plasma—the concentration is about 10 mg per 100 ml of plasma. If the concentration drops to about 5 mg, the individual goes into convulsions and dies.

The blood supplies glucose to cells. The normal concentration of glucose is about 70 mg per 100 ml of blood. If the concentration drops to 30 mg, convulsions and death are the result. If the level rises to 120 mg and remains there, it is very likely that the individual has the disease diabetes.

Temperature regulation is also critical. If the blood temperature varies by 6° C above or below normal, the change may be fatal.

Figure 23-6 shows in a general way how the blood is kept constant. Various groups of specialized cells, such as those of the digestive, respiratory, and excretory systems, add to and remove chemical substances from the blood. Heat exchange is regulated as well. You may regard this figure as a summary of the material covered in Chapters 20-23. All systems function in maintaining the constancy of blood, and hence the life of cells.

There is one important thing missing in Figure 23-6. There is no provision for coordinating all the activities. Yet we have mentioned control as a necessary part of the functioning of each of the systems shown. Any physiological enterprise as complex as a multicellular animal requires coordination. Such an animal possesses two interrelated means of coordination—nerves and hormones—which we will discuss in the next chapter.

GUIDE QUESTIONS AND PROBLEMS

1. In what ways do the circulatory and respiratory systems play a part in excretion?
2. Numerous different excretory structures have evolved in invertebrate animals. How are they basically alike? How do they contribute to homeostasis?
3. What general relationships exist between the environment an animal lives in and its method of excreting nitrogenous wastes?
4. What conclusions can you draw about an animal that excretes its nitrogenous wastes in the form of ammonia?
5. During physical exercise your body's heat production increases. What homeostatic mechanisms are involved in dissipating the excess heat? How do these mechanisms function?
6. When your body's heat loss is excessive, homeostatic mechanisms cause heat production to be increased and heat loss to be decreased. What are some of these homeostatic mechanisms and how do they function?
7. The closed end of a healthy nephron allows most of the materials of the blood except proteins and blood cells to enter the cavity of the nephron. How does the body recover the essential sugars, amino acids, vitamins, minerals, and so forth, that are filtered through the nephron?
8. In this and preceding chapters you have learned how *vital* homeostasis is in the maintenance of life in animals. With this idea in mind, can you suggest why blood analysis and urine analysis are valuable tools to a medical doctor?

RELATED READING

Books

For more information on the excretory systems of animals . . .

Buchsbaum, Ralph, *Animals Without Backbones,* University of Chicago Press, Chicago, 1948.

Romer, Alfred S., *The Vertebrate Body,* Third Edition, Saunders, Philadelphia, 1962.

Storer, Tracy I., and Robert L. Usinger, *General Zoology,* Fourth Edition, McGraw-Hill, New York, 1965.

Magazines

Benziger, T. H., "The Human Thermostat," *Scientific American,* Volume 204 (January 1961), page 134.

Merrill, J. P., "The Artificial Kidney," *Scientific American*, Volume 205 (July 1961), page 56.

BSCS Pamphlets

Mayer, William V., *Hibernation,* D. C. Heath and Company, Boston, 1964 (Pamphlet No. 19).

Overmire, T. G., *Homeostatic Regulation,* D. C. Heath and Company, Boston, 1963 (Pamphlet No. 9).

24

Coordination in Multicellular Animals

In multicellular animals there is division of labor among cells. Some groups of cells are specialized in securing food, others in digesting it, some in excreting wastes, others in respiring. An important consequence of specialization is that, as a cell becomes more specialized, it also becomes more dependent.

The Need for Coordination

In an animal composed of many different kinds of specialized cells, each kind has comparatively specific functions but is incapable of independent existence. Another consequence of specialization, therefore, is that coordinating mechanisms are required. No organism could consist of so many specialized cell types with each type carrying on its activities independently. Organisms are *organized,* and part of the organization consists of coordination.

Organization and coordination have to do with conditions not only internal but external—for organisms are not independent of the world in which they live. They must be able to change their activities in relation to the outside world. Cells deep inside an animal often must respond to something which happens far away from them. An example of this was mentioned in Chapter 20—how stomach cells change their rate of secretion of gastric juice when food is taken into the mouth—or even when the eyes see food in the external environment.

Three conditions are necessary to coordination: (1) some part or parts of the organism must act as the coordinator; (2) information must pass from the other parts of the organism to the coordinator, and from the external environment to the coordinator; and (3) information must pass from the coordinator to the other parts of the organism.

BREATHING—AN EXAMPLE OF COORDINATION

As an example of coordination, consider the parts of the human body that are involved in removing carbon dioxide produced by the cells. We have already learned what the principal parts are. The lungs provide the moist membranes where blood containing carbon dioxide comes in contact with the atmosphere. The diaphragm and the mucles of the ribs change the size of the chest cavity, making possible the movement of air into and out of the lungs. Blood carries carbon dioxide to the lungs from all cells of the body.

Everything seems to be accounted for—but it is not. The *independent* functioning of these parts could not maintain the activity of removing carbon dioxide, so necessary for life. We have not yet accounted for coordination. Let us see why. At this moment you are probably breathing at a rate of about fourteen times a minute and are taking shallow breaths. This rate and depth of breathing are sufficient to remove the carbon dioxide formed by your cells in your body's resting state. Now let us suppose that you begin a game of tennis or walk upstairs rapidly. Under these conditions your muscle cells become much more active. ATP changes to ADP, and energy is transferred. Glucose is oxidized, changing the ADP back to ATP. Much more carbon dioxide is produced in your muscle cells than when you are at rest.

From your past experience and your observations in Laboratory Inquiry 22-1, you can describe what happens as the rate of carbon dioxide formation increases. Your rate and depth of breathing greatly increase. More carbon dioxide passes from the blood capillaries across the lung membranes. Furthermore, the heart beats faster and the blood is forced around the body more rapidly. The result of these various changes is that carbon dioxide is removed more rapidly from the muscle cells.

That is fine; when carbon dioxide is produced faster, it is removed faster. But what is responsible for this ideal solution of the problem? Before we can try to answer this question, we must look at some more experimental data.

Measurements of the concentration of carbon dioxide in the blood show that it increases somewhat during exercise. But it does not go nearly as high as we might expect from the great increase in carbon dioxide production in muscles. We can explain this in terms of the increased breathing that you observed directly. Increased breathing speeds the removal of carbon dioxide from the blood. A related conclusion from many other experiments is that whenever the concentration of carbon dioxide in the blood rises, breathing always tends to increase. This is true no matter what the cause of increased carbon dioxide concentration in the blood—whether increased cell activity (as in our example), or slowed removal of carbon dioxide by the lungs, or an upset in normal cell metabolism. Moreover, breathing is *decreased* if the blood concentration of carbon dioxide *decreases* below normal levels. Consider these observations carefully and see how they lead to a hypothesis: *breathing is directly controlled so that carbon dioxide concentration in the blood tends to remain near a constant value.*

But still we have not solved the problem of *how* breathing is regulated to control carbon dioxide concentration in blood. Any mechanism for maintaining the constancy of carbon dioxide in the blood can operate only if there is accurate information about the concentration of carbon dioxide at a given time. There must be some way of knowing if there is too much, too little, or the proper amount—at all times. Two main questions are raised by these considerations. The first: what is the mechanism for rhythmic breathing movements? The second: how are breathing movements controlled by blood carbon dioxide concentration?

What Is the Mechanism for Rhythmic Breathing Movements?

As yet, we can only answer the first question in part. Experiments have shown that there are many cells in the part of the brain called the **medulla** (meh·DUL·a—Figure 24-1) that are con-

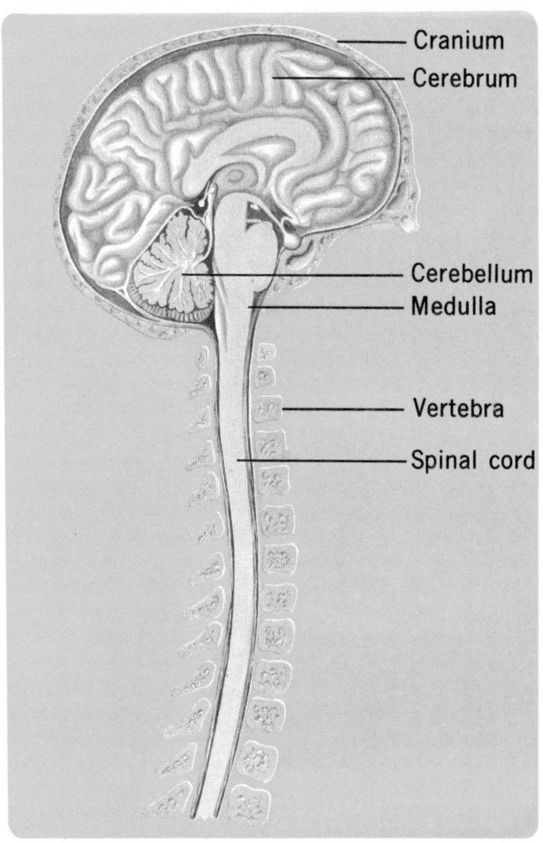

24–1 The central nervous system of man. The brain and spinal cord have been sectioned (compare with Figure 24-7). The medulla, in which the breathing center is located, is one part of the brain. Some nerves originate directly from the brain, but most originate from the spinal cord, which has nerve pathways leading to and from the brain.

nected by nerves with the breathing muscles. Activity of these cells in the medulla results in a flow of messages along the nerves to the muscles. When these muscles are stimulated, breathing movements occur. (Do you remember from Chapter 22 some experimental evidence supporting this statement?) Quite reasonably, the group of cells in the medulla from which the messages flow can be termed a *breathing center*. Thus, we know the location of the cells controlling the breathing pattern. We do not understand, however, what happens in the breathing center and in other parts of the brain to cause the nerve messages to go out to the breathing muscles in rhythmic bursts. Why is there not simply a continuous flow of messages from the center? Though we cannot answer this question, we can easily see why it is necessary that this pattern exist. It allows for both inward and outward breathing movements, and thus for the exchange of air by the lungs.

How Are Breathing Movements Controlled by Blood Carbon Dioxide Concentration?

Knowledge of the existence of the breathing center in the medulla has led to an important discovery. The cells in the center are themselves extremely sensitive to carbon dioxide concentration! Their pattern of activity changes as the blood concentration of carbon dioxide changes. Thus, when cells anywhere in the body produce extra carbon dioxide, they can affect the activity of the breathing center indirectly by changing the concentration of carbon dioxide in the blood. As the pattern of activity in the breathing center changes, the rate and depth of breathing movements increases. And this results in a decrease of carbon dioxide in the blood. Thus, through the coordination of blood flow and breathing, the problem of too much carbon dioxide in the body is quickly solved.

This is not the full story of this control, for there are specialized nerve endings located in arteries, with connections also to the breathing center. These can detect changes in blood concentration of both carbon dioxide *and* oxygen. These, too, take part in controlling the activity of the breathing center, adjusting it in relation to the cells' demands for oxygen, as well as their needs for removal of carbon dioxide. Many other kinds of nerve messages affect the rate and depth of breathing—messages about the degree of filling of the lungs with air, for instance, and messages about the mechanical stretching and movement of the body muscles. Can you control your breathing at will, even while all these other coordinating mechanisms are operating? Even as you sit at your desk, you can easily plan and carry out some experiments designed to answer, in part, this interesting question.

As you can see, problems of coordination are complicated and fascinating. And there is even more to this story than we have told so far, as we will point out at the end of this chapter. Let us put all of our information from this case together: cells in your body function normally only if the capillaries near them contain blood with a sufficiently high concentration of oxygen and a sufficiently low concentration of carbon dioxide. These are not really two separate problems, for the process of breathing that maintains the concentration of oxygen at a high level also maintains the concentration of carbon dioxide at a low level. The rate and depth of breathing must be coordinated.

Coordination involves, first, information passing from the parts to the coordinator. There must consequently be a change in coordinator activity which affects the parts of the body that respond. In our example, blood carries information to the coordinator (breathing center) about its concentration of carbon dioxide. If the concentration is too high, information passes from the coordinator to the parts (diaphragm and rib muscles) that results in greater activity of the parts—a quicker rhythm and an increase of muscle contraction. Breathing becomes more rapid and deeper; more carbon dioxide diffuses from the lung capillaries, and thus its amount is reduced in the blood; more oxygen is taken in, and thus its amount is increased in the blood. The information is carried from the coordinator to the parts by nerves.

Conversely, if the concentration of carbon dioxide is below the normal range, the coordinator responds to this information by controlling a decrease in the rate and depth of breathing.

As a consequence of coordination, the activities of the lungs, blood, diaphragm, and rib muscles are so regulated and interrelated that the concentrations of oxygen and carbon dioxide in the vicinity of the cells of your body remain nearly constant. It is a beautiful example of homeostasis. Homeostasis would be impossible if each part acted in an independent and unregulated way.

The example of coordination just given is not only for you but for many multicellular animals. *All* organisms are coordinated in some way. This is true even of the single-celled forms such as *Amoeba*. An individual *Amoeba* responds to changes in temperature, to changes in concentrations of various chemicals, and to electric currents. The response usually involves movement. The movement, in turn, depends on the coordinated motions of the pseudopods.

In most multicellular organisms, there are two distinct, though related, systems of coordination: the **nervous system** and the **endocrine** (EN·doe·krin) **system.** Although these two coordinating systems work together and in many ways are not separate, for convenience we will study them one at a time.

NERVOUS SYSTEMS

Before we discuss the nervous systems of specific animals, we need some general understanding of how animals receive stimuli and respond to them. Even in the simpler multicellular animals we can recognize three main types of structures related to stimuli and responses. Each has a specific function in relation to the others. The three structures are **receptors, neurons** (NYOO·ronz), and **effectors.**

Receptors may be neurons themselves, or they may be organs that are specialized for detecting stimuli. We have many receptors, including those for touch, taste, smell, temperature, light, and sound. You can study the function of some of these receptors in Laboratory Inquiry 24-1.

The unit of structure and function in the nervous system is the neuron (Figure 24-2), which is a single cell. *Nerves* are bundles of neurons (although in some of the simpler multicellular animals, such as *Hydra,* individual neurons rather than nerves are the common structure). Neurons are often very long. Some of the longest neurons in the human body reach from the fingers or toes to the spinal cord.

The neurons are specialized for transmitting **nerve impulses.** A nerve impulse is a wave of changes traveling along the cell membrane, involving chemical reactions and movements of ions. Usually it begins at one end of the neuron and travels rapidly to the other. In some neurons of man, the nerve impulse moves with a speed of approximately 100 meters per second. In other neurons both in man and in many of the lower animals, the speed is much less.

Generally, several neurons or more are involved in any behavioral activity. One neuron carries an impulse along its length. When the impulse reaches the end of the first neuron, it stimulates the next neuron. The gap between the end of one neuron and the beginning of another is called the **synapse** (SIN·aps – Figure 24-2).

In those animals that have **central nervous systems** – with concentrations of neurons that amount to a brain at some point in the body – it is convenient to recognize different classes of neurons. **Sensory neurons** (Figure 24-2, left) carry impulses from receptors to the central nervous system (Figure 24-1). **Motor neurons** (Figure 24-2, right) carry impulses from the central nervous system to effectors. The central nervous system itself is built up of many neurons which we term **associative neurons** (in

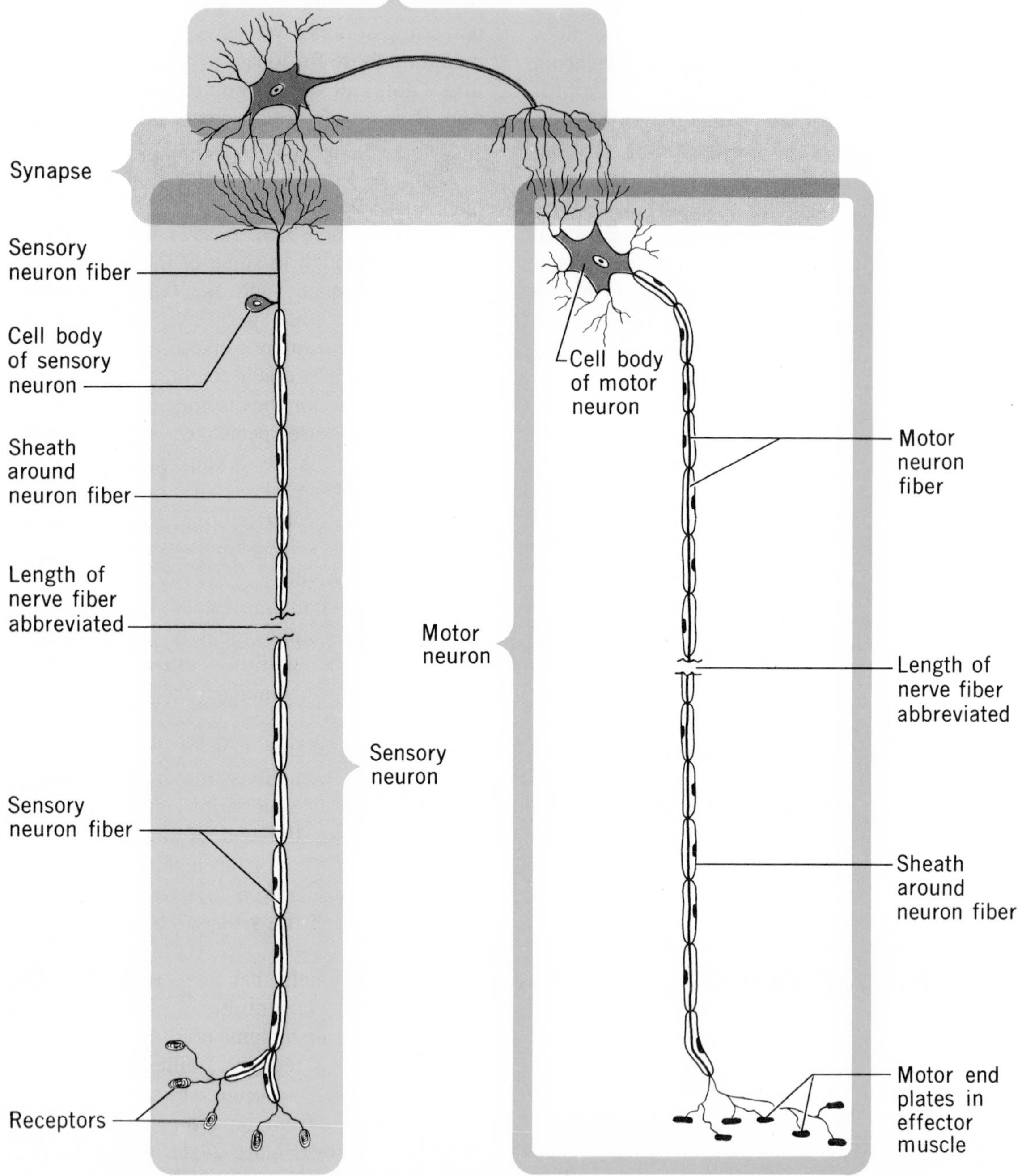

24–2 Three types of neurons in man – an associative neuron **(top),** a sensory neuron **(left),** and a motor neuron **(right).** Can you suggest a plausible pathway for a nerve impulse along these neurons? In which direction would it travel? As a check upon your suggestion, relate these three neurons to the events occurring in Figure 24–3.

man, the spinal cord and brain contain many millions of associative neurons). Associative neurons have many branching processes connecting them with other neurons, and they have a most important part to play in nerve function—the integration of sensory and motor neuron function, involving coordination of sensory impulses to lead to motor impulses and action by appropriate effectors.

Effectors are the structures that respond when they are stimulated by nerve impulses. In the more complex animals, the principal effectors are *muscles* and *glands*. Muscles respond by contracting; glands respond by secreting (Figure 20-3, page 392).

The way in which receptors, neurons, and effectors are all involved can be understood from the following. Let us pretend that you are walking without shoes and you step on a sharp rock. You feel pain and rapidly lift your foot (Figure 24-3). What really happens in the nervous system to account for these events?

The skin of the foot contains many receptors. Some are stimulated by strong pressure. Others (actually naked nerve endings) respond to any intense stimulation; these are associated with pain. When you step on the sharp rock, the receptors are stimulated.

The receptors, in turn, initiate nerve impulses in the neurons. Neurons extend from

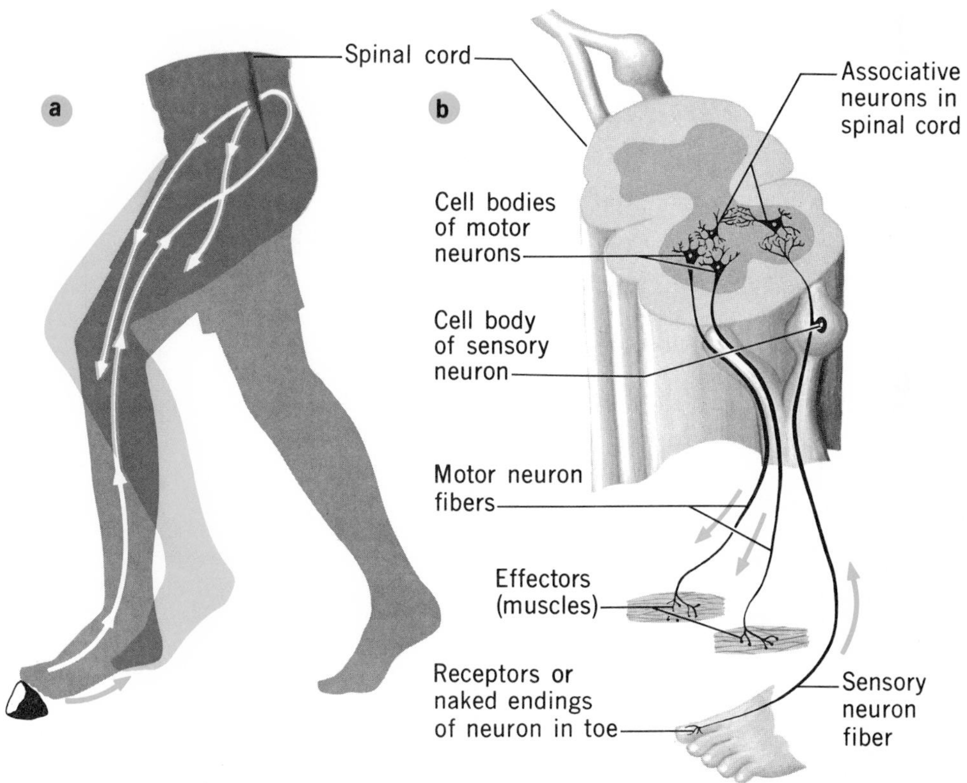

24–3 A reflex arc, initiated by stepping upon a sharp rock. Impulses travel along sensory neurons to the spinal cord, where associative neurons are stimulated. The impulses are "switched" to other neurons—among them motor neurons that stimulate leg muscles to contract and move the foot away from the rock. Nor is this all (although in a sense it is for the initial reflex arc). The story continues in Figure 24–4.

a Impulses coming in from an injured toe not only result in reflex movement (Figure 24-3), but also travel up nerve pathways to the brain.

b Associative neurons in the brain are activated. Impulses may pass from the brain to many parts of the body, leading to voluntary movement.

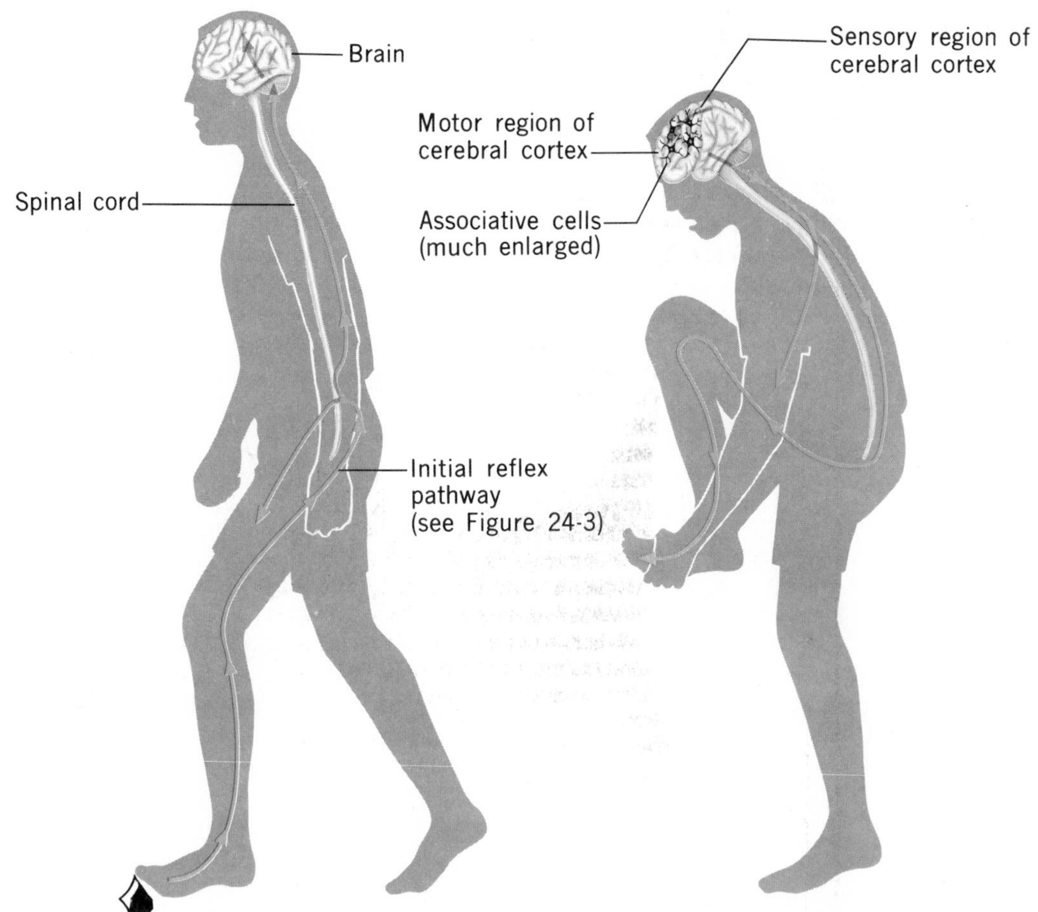

24–4 Yes, it hurts. Not only do the associative neurons in Figure 24–3 transmit nerve impulses to the motor neurons, but also to neurons that extend up the spinal cord and into the brain. It is then that you feel pain and decide what to do next.

these receptors up the leg to the spinal cord, where they end. Their endings are in close association with the ends of other neurons. Some of these other neurons extend up the spinal cord to the brain. Others extend to the muscles of the leg. Thus, there are two major routes that the nerve impulses can take. Some go back over other neurons to the muscles of the leg and cause these muscles to contract, which moves the foot from the stone. This relatively simple pathway, shown in Figure 24-3, is termed a **reflex arc.** Other nerve impulses

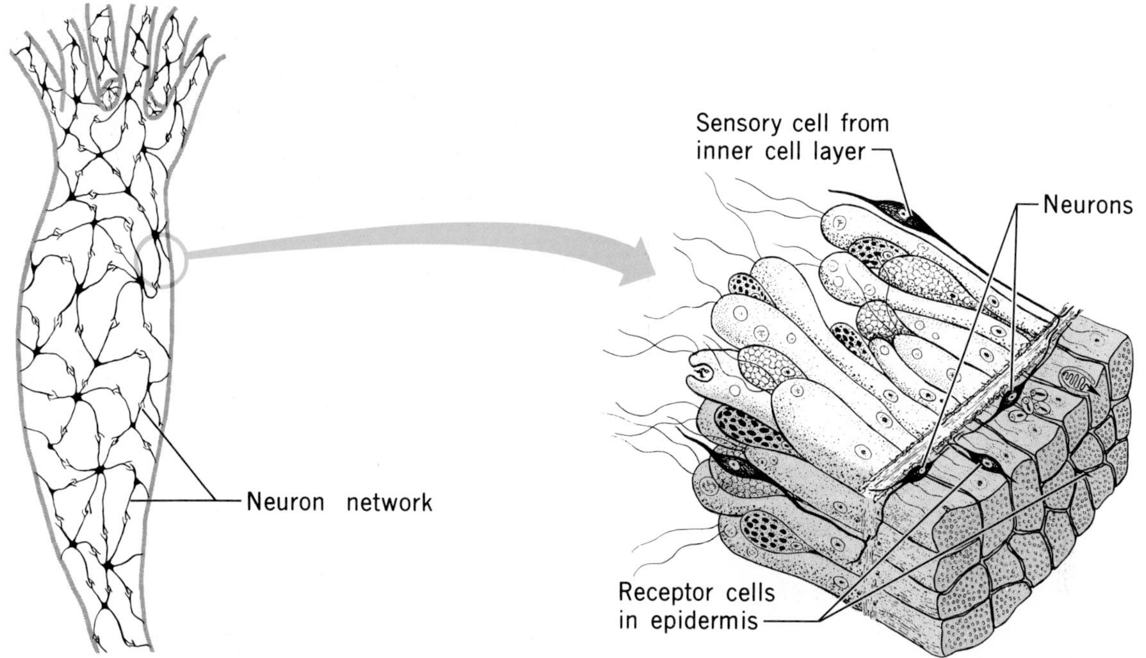

24–5 The nervous system of *Hydra*. A network of neurons extends throughout the body, but there is no brain. The relationship of neurons to other specialized cells is indicated in the enlarged drawing of a portion of the inner and outer cell layers.

travel along the neurons to the brain. When the impulses reach the brain, you become aware of what has occurred. It is not until this time that you feel pain in the toe or the foot. You probably have moved your foot by reflex action by the time the brain takes control of the situation. Perhaps you decide to hold the injured foot with your hands (Figure 24-4). For you to do this, your brain must send nerve impulses along the neurons of the spinal cord and out to the appropriate muscles.

The muscles are the effectors in this example. When stimulated by nerve impulses, they contract, and movement occurs—in this case away from the stone.

The Nervous System of *Hydra*

To maintain comparisons of several animals as in earlier chapters, we will describe the nervous system of *Hydra*, then of a planarian, and then man. Although our introduction has been in terms of your own nervous system, there is much to be developed, so much that we will omit discussion of the nervous systems of the earthworm and the grasshopper.

As you can see from Figure 24-5 the nervous system of *Hydra* looks like a net of threads that extends throughout the animal. This net-like structure is made up of neurons, with synapses between them. Since each neuron has synapses with another or with several others, it is possible for communication to occur from any point in the animal to any other point. In *Hydra* there is no definite pattern that messages follow. The nerve impulses can move in all directions, depending on where the stimulation begins.

How does this nerve net function in *Hydra*? Primarily, it seems, for local contractions. That is, if one area of the organism receives a stimulus, impulses in a neuron will cause the local cells to contract. *Hydra* has no specialized muscle cells, but most of the cells of the inner and outer cell layers of the animal can contract. With a strong stimulus the impulses may spread to other neurons, and the whole organism may react.

Hydra receives certain information about its environment from another kind of receptor cell. These are special cells that are very sensitive to stimuli such as chemical substances or pressure. The receptor cells can stimulate the neurons, which then carry nerve impulses to all parts of the body. Although *Hydra* does have receptor cells, neurons, and contractile cells, the movements it can make are very limited. It can bend and shorten its body and move its tentacles. There is nothing resembling a brain or any other center of nervous coordination.

The Nervous System of a Planarian

Planarians have the beginnings of a central nervous system, that is, a concentration of neurons in some part of the body. There is a concentration of neurons in the head region that can be called a brain (Figure 24-6). There are also two main longitudinal *nerves*—bundles of neurons.

Also in the head end of a planarian is a concentration of receptor cells connected directly to the brain. These receptor cells are sensitive to light, pressure, touch, and chemical stimuli. The central nervous system contains neurons that transfer impulses from the receptor cells to the motor neurons, which lead to the muscles.

Removal of the brain of a planarian reduces its ability to move. The action of the cilia is not disturbed, but the muscular movement necessary for crawling is completely stopped. This seems to indicate that the muscular movements of planarians are controlled by the brain. We know very little about nervous control in planarians, however, so we must wait for further research to answer questions about it.

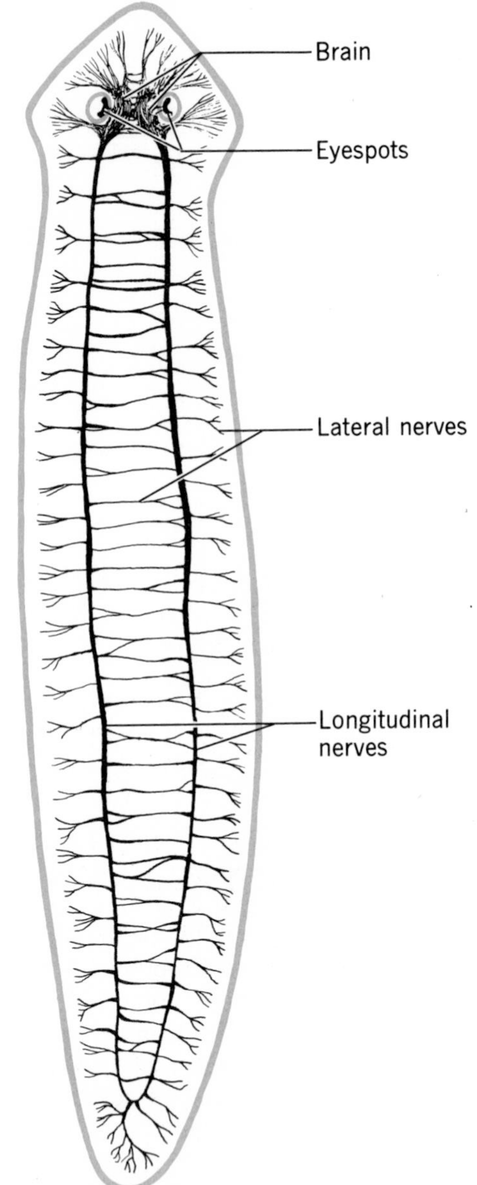

24–6 A diagram of the nervous system of a planarian. At the anterior end is what might be called a brain. Connected to the brain are receptor cells—those of the eyespots, which are sensitive to light, and other types of receptor cells that are sensitive to touch, to pressure, and to chemical stimuli. Of what types of cells would you expect the longitudinal and lateral nerves to consist? Where would the animal's effectors be found?

THE NERVOUS SYSTEM OF MAN

The brain of man is a triumph of evolution. Man alone can convey intricate thoughts to other members of his species by means of language. Man alone can preserve his understanding of himself and the world about him in written records. Man alone is skilled in making and using special tools. Man alone can transmit adequately the knowledge he gains to succeeding generations. All of these remarkable abilities are dependent on the human brain.

In spite of the unique intelligence of man, his nervous system is essentially like that of other mammals. Even the most primitive of vertebrates have receptors, neurons, brains, and effectors with the same general pattern as ours. As you know, too, even *Hydra* has the rudimentary beginnings of a nervous system, with receptor cells, neurons, and effector cells.

Receptors in Man

Information about the external world is received through receptors—the sense organs. Each sense organ is specialized to receive a specific type of stimulus. Our ears are stimulated by air vibrations, our eyes by electromagnetic radiation of specific wavelengths, our taste buds and organs of smell by chemical substances.

Any one type of sense organ receives only a small portion of possible stimuli. The eyes are stimulated by electromagnetic radiation that varies from the short-wave violet to the long-wave red. These wavelengths are only a small portion of the total range of wavelengths that actually occur in the world around us. The waves shorter than violet, the ultraviolet for example, do not stimulate our eyes in such a way that we see. There are also waves that are longer than red—the infrared and radio waves. We know of their existence only when we use special instruments to detect them.

Have you ever thought of the ceaseless activity that is going on around you and is *undetected* by your sense organs? Imagine that you go into a closet and close the door. Let us also suppose that the door and the walls shut out all air vibrations that you could detect with your ears, and all electromagnetic radiation lying between the short-wave violet and long-wave red. You stand in the closet seeing nothing and hearing nothing, so you might feel shut off from the environment. Are you really isolated from the environment? No, for if you carried a powerful radio into the closet you would find the closet full of messages. Hundreds or thousands (depending on the excellence of your equipment) of broadcasting stations throughout the world would be transmitting electromagnetic radiation that is undetected by your sense organs, yet detected, amplified, and converted into sound by the radio. A television set would reveal other sorts of messages. Other instruments would show that even inside the closet you are constantly bombarded by cosmic rays.

Clearly, our eyes and ears tell us very little about the many events going on around us. We are blind and deaf and without other sensory responses to *most* changes in the environment.

Sensory Neurons

When you stepped on that sharp rock earlier in the chapter, neurons carried impulses from your foot to your spinal cord. Recall that these and other neurons that carry impulses to the brain and spinal cord are *sensory* neurons. They carry impulses from the ears, eyes, taste buds, nose, skin, and also from all the internal parts of the body. You are aware of some of these messages but not all. Even with your eyes closed, you know the position of your arms—whether they are outstretched or at your sides. You know because sensory neurons associated with muscles are constantly carrying impulses to the brain, informing it about the position and degree of contraction of the muscles.

There are other sensory neurons that function without your awareness, bringing to your brain or spinal cord messages from the heart, liver, digestive tube, blood vessels, kidneys, and other internal organs. These impulses are necessary for coordination and all normal functioning of digestion, respiration, circulation, and excretion. You have learned about some of these nerve impulses already, like those that inform the breathing centers about the carbon dioxide and oxygen concentrations in the blood. Are you ever aware of these messages traveling in your own nerves to your brain?

The Brain and the Spinal Cord

The brain and spinal cord are the coordinating centers of the nervous system. Their functional units are associative neurons. Sometimes the brain and spinal cord are compared to the central switchboard of a telephone system. The comparison is apt in some ways, but the brain operates on a much higher level than a switchboard. The brain can make judgments and direct. A switchboard merely connects.

All of the impulses that reach the brain over the sensory neurons are patterns of electrochemical changes in neuron membranes. They do not differ in any important ways whether they come from the eyes, the ears, or any other receptors. Neurons can be stimulated to carry impulses by being touched in an appropriate way. If you were to touch a neuron connected with the eye you would have the sensation of light. If you were to touch a neuron from the ear you would have the sensation of sound. If it were possible to attach the receptor cells of your ear to the nerve leading from your eye to the brain, and you "listened" to a Beethoven symphony, you would have the sensation of seeing—not hearing.

You can convince yourself that some of this is true by the following experiment. Move your eyes so that you are looking upward and to the left. Close your lids. Now tap with your finger on the outer side of the right upper eyelid. Usually you will see a flash of light. There was no light, of course, but you stimulated the neurons of the eye by the tap with your finger. The brain interprets all impulses coming over these neurons as "light."

Since nerve impulses do not differ in important ways, why do we normally see light with our eyes, and not with our ears? Experiments have shown that there are two reasons for this. In the first place, each sense organ is much more sensitive to its normal stimulus than to any other. For instance, a very faint light will stimulate the eye, but any other kind of stimulus has to be quite strong in order to affect the eye at all. And even a very strong flash of light is too weak to affect the ears. A second, very important factor which determines our sensations is the pattern of attachment of nerves in the brain. Thus, the sensory neurons from each type of sense organ connect with special places in the brain (Figure 24-7). The neurons from the eye, for example, connect with the **cerebrum** (SAYR·e·brum) in specific regions for vision and eye-adjustment.

The brain not only receives impulses, but also sends impulses out. In this way it controls the responses that you make.

The Motor Neurons

The motor neurons carry impulses from the brain and spinal cord to the effectors in all parts of the body. The impulses, once again, are all about the same in all motor neurons.

The Effectors

We are now nearing the end of the story of how an organism is coordinated within itself and with its environment. The stimulus is received by a sense organ; it is transmitted as a train of nonspecific nerve impulses along the sensory neurons to the brain; the brain analyzes the impulses (we have no sure knowledge of what this involves); the brain then sends messages (again, nerve impulses) by way of the motor neurons to the parts of the body that respond—the muscles and glands.

Our responses are generally due to contraction by muscles or secretion by glands, and in our use of these effectors we are somewhat like *Hydra* and planarians. But we also have cerebral activity that does not involve muscles

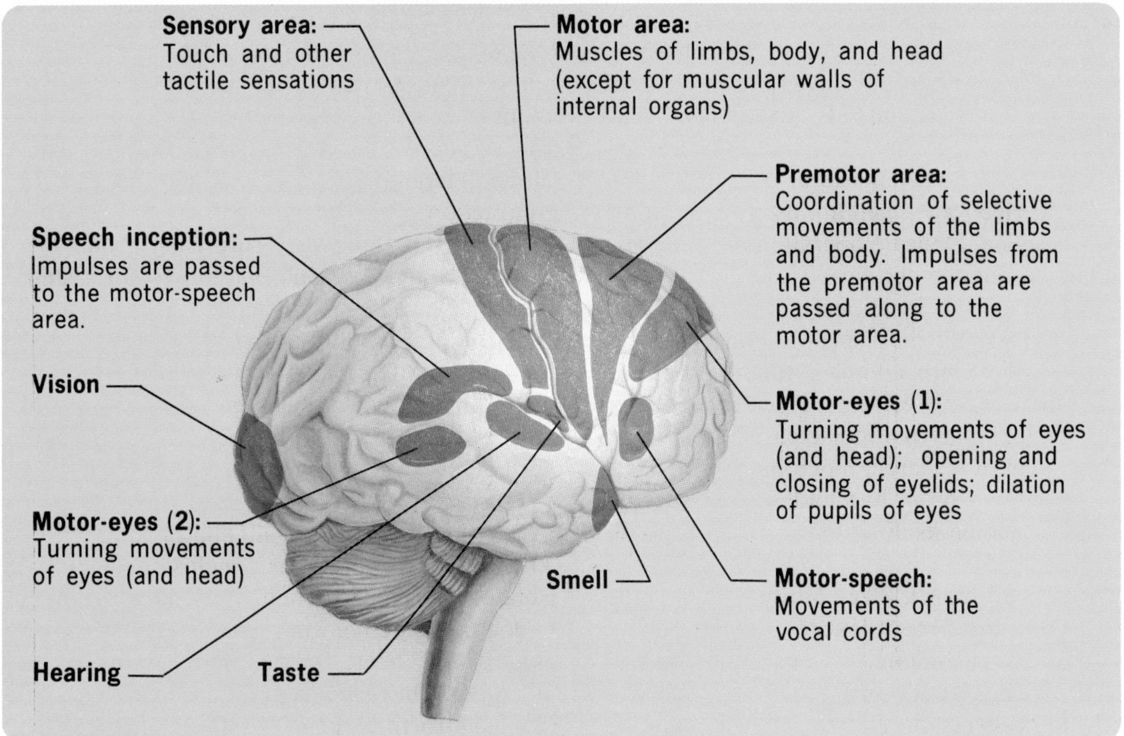

24–7 Some functional areas of the human cerebrum. What do you suppose would happen if you could stimulate one of these specialized areas directly? Regions not labeled with specific functions seem to have the most complex functions of all—thinking, planning, associating, directing, learning, remembering, and other remarkable things that collectively characterize man's unique intelligence and behavior.

or glands. Thus, an enormous amount of activity is always going on in our association neurons. Part of this involves thoughts that we often do not translate into body activity.

Conscious and Unconscious Activity

Some of the examples of the functioning nervous system that we have given are for activities we are aware of and to which we can consciously respond. In addition to these, there is a whole group of activities that are controlled by the brain without our conscious participation.

We discussed one such example at the beginning of this chapter. During exercise our cells use increased amounts of glucose and oxygen and produce more carbon dioxide. The body as a whole responds by increasing the rate and depth of breathing. There is also an increase in the speed of movement of the blood. This results from change in the pattern of nerve impulses which control heart beat and the size of the blood vessels. All these things occur without conscious effort on our part—no thinking is involved. Wouldn't life be difficult if we had to think about each of these things before doing them?

Much is known about the physiology of the nervous system, but we have almost no understanding of the functions of the brain responsible for such complex things as memory, thinking, joy, sadness, and the like. There are specific parts of the brain which seem to be concerned with sleep, rage, simple pleasure, and sexual feelings. They have been discovered in experiments on animals, using needlelike electrodes, which can be pushed into an animal's brain without damage or pain to the animal. The electrodes then are used to stimulate a given region. Delicate operations on the brain of man to remove certain diseased parts have also revealed the locations of centers of certain activities. But in respect to consciousness itself, or the more complex functions of the brain, there is little clear evidence that specific brain regions play particular parts. In spite of a great deal of research, much more is needed, for the human brain has had limited success in understanding itself so far.

An Aside on Nerve Physiology—Loewi and the Frog's Heart

Scientists are among the most inquisitive of human beings—but they are rarely satisfied with the answers they obtain. It was quite an accomplishment to discover the basis of nervous control of muscle and gland activity—the receptors, neurons, and effectors are stimulated successively. But this knowledge only raised more questions.

A nerve impulse travels down a motor neuron to an effector—say a muscle. The muscle contracts. What causes the muscle to contract? Is it the message that we call the nerve impulse?

Perhaps we could look at the junction between the neuron and muscle with a microscope and obtain some hint. If we did look, we would see that the neuron ends with tiny branches adjacent to a specialized area of the muscle cell (Figure 24-8). That is all we would find out.

As is so often the case in science, the answer to one question may come from trying to answer an entirely different question. This was certainly the case in one important experiment that helps us understand how neurons function.

The heart of a frog beats in a rhythmic fashion like all other vertebrate hearts. It has been known for a long time that nerves extend from the central nervous system to the heart. One of the nerves is the **vagus** (VAY·gus). When nerve impulses pass from the brain along the vagus nerve, the heart beats more slowly. Nerve impulses passing along another nerve, the accelerator nerve, speed up the rate of contraction of the heart.

There is nothing very surprising about this, but the next bit of information *is* surprising: the frog's heart can be removed from the body and it will continue to beat. If properly cared for—that is, kept moist with a solution containing inorganic salts and glucose—it will live and beat for days. Of course, since its nerves are cut, there can be no control by the brain.

The frog's heart, then, must have its own internal mechanism that stimulates contraction. There is no escaping this conclusion, since the isolated heart can continue to beat. Clever biological detective work revealed that a special area in the heart, named the **pacemaker,** is involved. The pacemaker sends out rhythmic impulses to the rest of the heart, causing the heart muscles to contract. What, then, is the function of the nerves to the heart?

In 1921, the German biologist Otto Loewi carried out an important experiment with far-reaching results in the study of nerve function. The experiment itself is not hard to understand. Loewi removed the hearts, with their attached vagus nerves, from two frogs. Each heart was maintained carefully in a suitable solution, so that it continued to beat. Next, Loewi stimulated the vagus nerve of one of the hearts, and watched this heart slow down and stop. Then he removed some fluid from this heart and placed it in the other heart which had been beating normally. Almost at once, this second heart stopped just as if Loewi had stimulated its vagus nerve! You can easily see what sort of hypothesis would be needed to explain these results—there must be a chemical substance released by the heart when its vagus nerve is stimulated. This chemical substance can be transferred to another heart, and inhibits it just as vagus stimulation would.

Loewi called the hypothetical chemical substance "vagus-material." Many later experiments confirmed this hypothesis. "Vagus-material" was identified as an organic compound, **acetylcholine** (a·see·til·KOHL·een). Acetylcholine, made in the laboratory, slows the heart just as "vagus-substance" and vagus stimulation do. And at the nerve endings in the hearts of frogs (and all other vertebrates) are specific enzymes which both form acetylcholine and break it down rapidly. (What would happen to a frog if the acetylcholine released during vagus stimulation stayed around unchanged?)

What about the accelerator nerve to the heart? It *in*creases the rate of the heart's contraction. Its action, too, was found to be associated with a chemical substance, **adrenaline** (ad·REN·al·in). Adrenaline stimulates the pacemaker, causing it to send out impulses more rapidly.

Later, acetylcholine and adrenaline were found to be associated with the function of

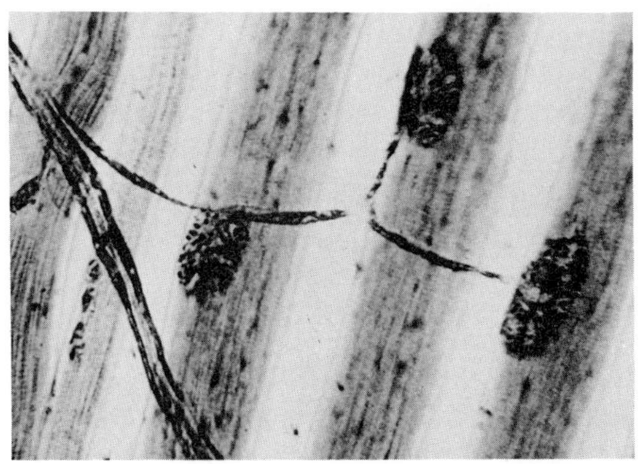

Clay-Adams, Inc.

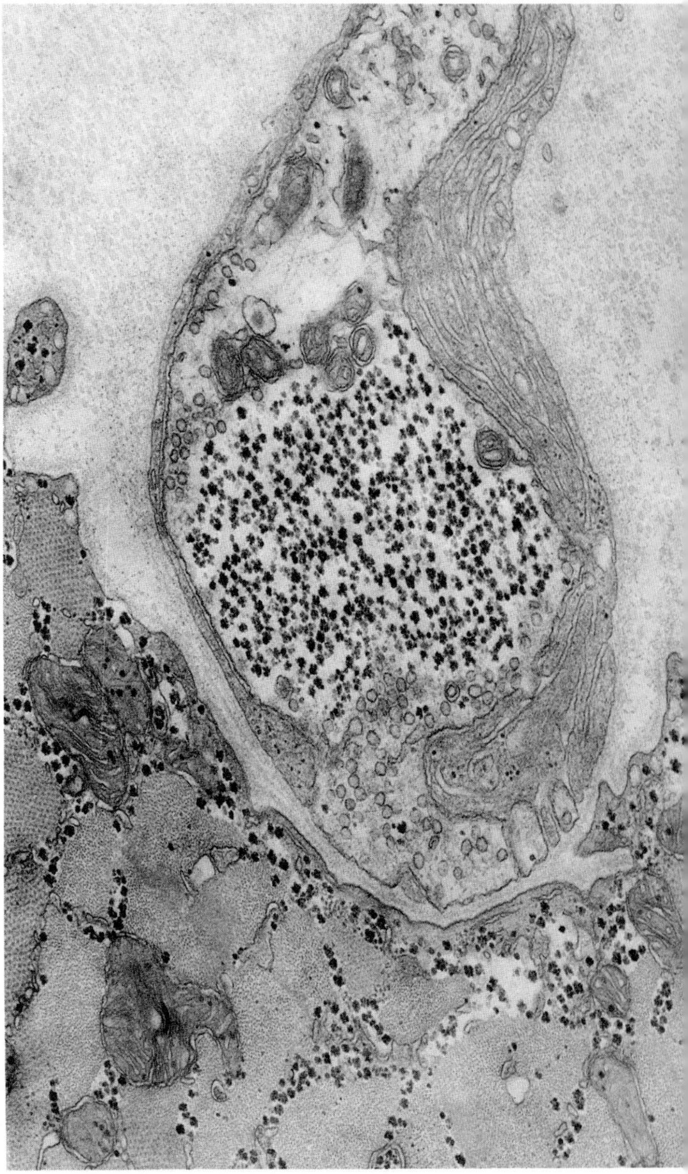

Lee D. Peachey

24–8 Two photomicrographs of motor-end plates in skeletal muscle. The one at the left was taken under a compound microscope. (1,000 ×) It shows how the neuron terminates in tiny branches with enlarged motor-end plates, in or adjacent to specialized areas of the muscle cells. The photograph at the right was taken through an electron microscope. (31,500 ×) It shows a single axon of a neuron descending from the top and ending in a bulb-shaped motor-end plate full of darkly stained particles of **glycogen** (GLY·ko·jen), an energy source (see Chapter 25). At the bottom of the righthand photograph is a small portion of a single muscle cell in cross section. Compare it with the muscle tissue in the righthand photograph of Figure 25–8, page 465.

many other nerves as well. They play a part in nerve stimulation of muscle and gland cells in the digestive system and in many other parts of the body. Acetylcholine seems to be involved often in the stimulation of one neuron by another across the synapse. We do not yet know exactly how these chemical "transmitter" substances function, but many biologists believe that they are actually formed in the neuron and moved across the cell membrane to stimulate the next neuron, and from the last neuron in line to the effector. Other chemical "transmitter" substances have been discovered which seem to be similar to acetylcholine and adrenaline in function, but different in detailed chemical structure. Still others are believed to exist and to play parts, for instance, in the complex nerve activity of the brain. There are many exciting and puzzling problems still unsolved in this area of chemical substances and the parts they play in nerve function. It seems probable, among other things, that drugs and poisons—like LSD and some narcotics—may exert their dangerous effects on the central nervous system by disturbing the normal metabolic release, action, and breakdown of transmitter substances in the brain.

Loewi and his frog hearts started us on a fascinating trail which probably will lead us to many important answers—even about the workings of our own minds!

ENDOCRINE SYSTEMS

Loewi's observations and those of others have broken down the distinction that was formerly made between the nervous system and the endocrine system. It was thought that the nervous system worked because of neurons and the electrochemical messages they carry. The endocrine system worked by secreting chemical substances, the hormones. The nervous system was the fast worker—nerve impulses traveled as much as 100 meters a second. Hormones circulated less rapidly in the blood. There seemed little in common.

These neat distinctions vanished when it was discovered that nervous control of the effectors (muscles and glands) is so closely related to acetylcholine or adrenaline. The latter is identical to the hormone adrenaline, secreted by the adrenal gland. This is not too surprising, for the part of the adrenal gland that secretes adrenaline is just a modified group of neurons.

Thus, in controlling body functions, the nervous system and the endocrine system function in somewhat similar ways. It still remains true that nerve responses tend to be faster and more limited in range than endocrine control, but even this generalization is not true in every case. As a matter of fact, there is little point in looking for big differences between nervous and endocrine control, for both take part, in close cooperation, in regulating almost all the processes in higher animals. We will return to this point later.

Endocrine Glands of Man

The principal structures that secrete hormones in the human body will now be listed to give you an idea of the variety of hormones and their effects (Figure 24-9).

The **thyroid** (THY·roid) **gland** is in the throat. It secretes **thyroxin** (thy·ROK·sin), which regulates the general rate of the body's metabolism.

The **parathyroid** (par·a·THY·roid) **glands** are embedded in the thyroid gland. Their hormone controls body use of calcium.

The **adrenal** (a·DREE·nul) **cortex** is the outer part of the **adrenal gland** which is located on top of each kidney. It secretes several hormones, one of which is **cortisone** (KOR·tih·sohn). These hormones influence the use and balance of salts and carbohydrates in the body.

The **adrenal medulla** is in the central portion of each adrenal gland. It secretes adrenaline and a related substance, noradrenaline. These play a part in regulating blood circulation and carbohydrate metabolism, and many biologists believe that the adrenal medulla helps the body meet emergency situations.

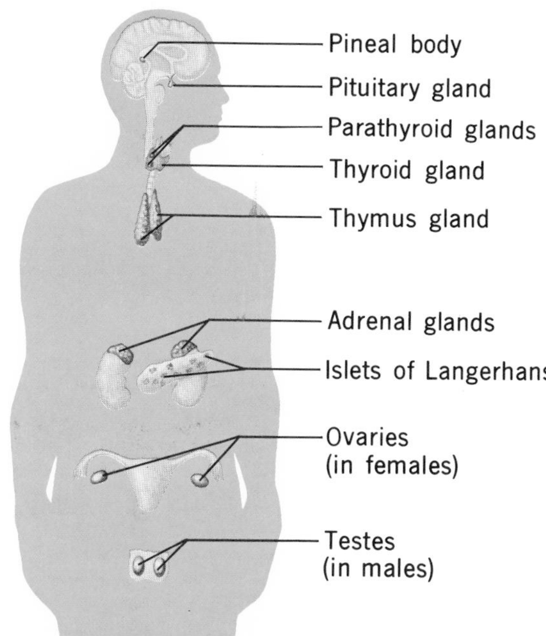

24–9 Some of the endocrine glands of the body. The stomach and part of the small intestine are also endocrine structures, as well as digestive organs. All of the structures labeled, except the thymus and the pineal body, can be associated with known hormones. Some biologists suspect that they have endocrine functions (in addition to a known association of the thymus with antibodies).

The **islets of Langerhans** (I·lets [of] LAHNG-er·hahns), which are located in the pancreas, secrete two hormones—**insulin** (IN·suh·lin) and **glucagon** (GLEWK·a·gon). These hormones have important roles in controlling the way glucose and some other organic compounds are used in the body. The familiar disease **diabetes mellitus** (dy·a·BEE·teez meh·LY·tus) may be a result of abnormal functioning of the islets of Langerhans.

The **pituitary** (pih·TOO·ih·tehr·ee) secretes a number of hormones in close association with cells of the brain, and under the brain's control. Some of these hormones have effects on other endocrine glands. Thus, the pituitary secretes a hormone that controls the secretion of thyroxin by the thyroid gland. Other pituitary hormones control the rate of bone growth, the secretion of milk by the mammary glands, the development of the **ovaries** (OH·va·reez) and **testes** (TES·teez), the activity of the adrenal cortex, the removal of water from the nephrons of the kidney, and the contraction of the muscles of the uterus. In each of these cases, the rate of secretion of the specific pituitary hormone is itself closely controlled. What is the basis of this control? We do not know in all cases, but some mechanisms have been analyzed by careful and ingenious experiments. A good example is the control of the thyroid-stimulating hormone. The pituitary cells which release this hormone do so in response to stimulation from brain cells. This stimulation itself depends on the level of thyroxin in the blood. The *more* thyroxin, the *less* thyroid-stimulating hormone is released. If the blood thyroxin level *drops, more* thyroid-stimulating hormone pours out of the pituitary cells. Such an arrangement, in which a *controlling mechanism* is itself *controlled* by the product of the reaction it is *controlling,* is called a **feedback mechanism.** In this case, since *increase* of the controlled product *decreases* the rate of operation of the mechanism, the feedback is *negative feedback.* For some years, human engineers have known and used the principle of negative feedback—such a system may regulate your school's heating system, for instance. But long before engineers thought of such systems, feedback had been developed as part of sensitive and effective controlling devices for endocrine regulation. You may recognize feedback as an important part of the patterns of regulation in homeostasis.

The **testes** are the male reproductive glands. In addition to producing sperms, they secrete **testosterone** (tes·TOS·ter·ohn). After fetal life, testosterone is first secreted in appreciable amounts at the time of puberty. It influences the events involved in the maturing of the male. The hormone will be discussed in Chapter 26.

The ovaries of the female secrete several hormones that influence the maturing of the female and are necessary for the prenatal development of the human infant. The ovarian hormones will be discussed in Chapter 26.

Remember, too, the production of secretin, gastrin, and other hormones by parts of the digestive system (pages 398 and 401-02). The *stomach* and first portion of the *small intestine* are endocrine structures to be added to the list. Hormones are known to be important substances for controlling biological processes in many kinds of animals. Most of the early knowledge of endocrine function was restricted to man and other vertebrates, but in recent years hormones have been found in insects and many other animals. Plants, too, have hormones that are important in controlling their growth, as you learned in Laboratory Inquiry 17-5.

An example of the way hormones work will be given now. It involves the body's use of glucose. In Chapter 26 we will supply additional examples by describing the way hormones are involved in human reproduction.

Diabetes Mellitus

The blood of man contains only a trace of glucose—about 0.07 to 0.12 percent. This trace, however, is vital for the life of all the cells. Earlier we learned that if the amount drops to about 0.03 percent, convulsions and death will result. In the disease diabetes mellitus, the concentration of glucose in the blood may reach a level above 0.14 percent. Unless the rising blood sugar level is controlled, the disease becomes very serious and death may result. The control of glucose concentration, then, is a problem of great importance.

Diabetes mellitus has been recognized as a specific disease since the days of the Romans. The very name reveals two features of the disease. *Diabetes* comes from two Greek words meaning "to go through." *Mellitus* is the Latin word for "honey." In diabetes mellitus, "the honey goes through"—that is, the patient passes a large amount of urine containing sugar.

Although knowledge about some aspects of this disease goes back far, we can begin in 1889 with two German physiologists, Von Mering (phone·MAY·ring) and Minkowski (min·KOW·skih). They were using dogs to study the function of the pancreas.

One way to study the effect of an organ is to remove it. It was not anticipated that this would be too serious in the case of the pancreas. Although this gland secretes pancreatic juice, it was thought that the enzymes in gastric juice and intestinal juice would enable the dogs to digest their food.

This prediction was incorrect. When the pancreas was removed, all the dogs died. Von Mering and Minkowski made another observation in these experiments which might at first seem trivial: ants were attracted to the kennels where the dogs that had no pancreases were kept; there was no gathering of ants in the kennels of the dogs not operated upon.

Great discoveries in science often result from chance observations of this sort. Most scientists probably would not have noticed the ants. After all, the experiment was on dogs, not ants. Even if they had noticed the ants, it is unlikely that they would have thought much about their presence.

Yet this was the key—why were ants so much more numerous in the kennels with the experimental animals? Were they everywhere in these kennels? As a matter of fact, they were not. The ants went to the places where the dogs had urinated. On the other hand, ants were not attracted to the urine of the normal dogs.

There must be something strange about the urine of dogs without pancreases. Chemical analysis showed this to be so: the urine contained a large amount of glucose. The glucose had attracted the ants.

It was also noticed that the experimental dogs passed much more urine than did the normal dogs—more urine, *and* glucose in this urine. Von Mering and Minkowski then realized what had happened: their dogs without pancreases had diabetes mellitus!

A pancreas was necessary, therefore, to keep a dog from developing diabetes mellitus. We spoke earlier of scientists as persons never satisfied with one answer. Now that they knew the pancreas was necessary to prevent diabetes, they wanted to know more: is all or only some part of the pancreas necessary?

The pancreas is composed of two main types of cells. One type, by far the more abundant, was thought to secrete pancreatic juice. The other consists of little clusters of cells—the islets (or islands) of Langerhans (Figure 24-9; also Figure 20-10, page 400). No one knew their function, so they were named for their discoverer.

When it was found that the pancreas was important in preventing diabetes, the next step was obvious. What would the pancreas look like in human patients who had died of diabetes? When the pancreases of these patients were examined, it was found that the cells that secrete pancreatic juice were normal. On the other hand, the cells of the islets of Langerhans were definitely abnormal. This observation suggested that some abnormality of the islet cells might be the cause of diabetes.

The islet cells are not connected to the pancreatic ducts. Their only contact with the rest of the body is by way of the blood stream. A likely hypothesis, then, was the following: the islet cells secrete a hormone that regulates the amount of glucose in the blood. This hypothetical hormone was given the name *insuline*—the insulin we know today. (Its name is derived from the Latin word for islands, referring to the islets of Langerhans.)

The next step was to try to isolate the hormone. Many investigators tried to do it. They ground up the pancreases of cows, sheep, and other mammals, and made extracts. All early attempts failed. We now know why. Insulin is a protein. When a whole pancreas is ground, the material liberated contains the enzymes of pancreatic juice. Some of these enzymes can digest proteins, and so digest the hormone!

The problem of how to obtain insulin was solved in 1922 by a Canadian physician, F. G. Banting, and his assistant, C. H. Best. They succeeded where others had failed, because they were able to put two and two together, so to speak. Twenty years earlier another physiologist, Ssobolew (so·bo·lev), had been working on the pancreas. He observed that if he tied off the pancreatic ducts, the pancreas would begin to degenerate. After a time all enzyme-secreting cells would degenerate, while islet cells remained normal.

Banting knew of Ssobolew's work and realized it was a solution to his problem. He would tie off the ducts and wait for the enzyme-secreting cells to degenerate. Then he would extract the pancreases without fear that the hypothetical hormone would be destroyed by enzymes.

The experiment succeeded. Banting obtained an extract that would maintain life in dogs from which he had removed the pancreas.

The extract was soon tried on humans. The first subject was so ill from diabetes that life was nearly gone. But he recovered! The experiments on a few dogs have saved the lives of thousands of human beings.

The hormone insulin promotes the body's use of glucose and thus lowers its concentration in blood. Insulin does not *cure* diabetes. Diabetes can be caused by many sorts of hormone disturbance, but even when it is due simply to failure of function of the islets of Langerhans, it can only be treated, not cured, by insulin. A cure could be made only if it were possible to return the cells of the islets of Langerhans to a normal state. There is no known way to do this. But a diabetic person can control the level of glucose in his blood by receiving definite amounts of insulin at regular times.

For many years biologists thought that this was the full story of the islets of Langerhans. But quite recently a startling discovery was made—those islets also secrete the hormone glucagon, which has effects almost the opposite of insulin's effects. Glucagon tends to raise the blood sugar, while insulin lowers it. Glucagon and insulin, then, may take part in the beautifully adjusted homeostatic pattern for controlling the body's use of carbohydrates.

Other hormones are also involved in this homeostatic mechanism. For example, adrenaline increases glucose level. Cortisone, from the adrenal cortex, and a hormone from the pituitary likewise increase the amount of glucose in the blood. Can you suggest why so many hormones control glucose concentration?

Clearly the control of the concentration of glucose in the blood stream is a complex affair. Glucose is taken up rapidly from the blood stream by body cells, and is added to the blood stream by the intestine and liver. Always, in normal conditions, its level is closely controlled. Part of the control comes from the balanced secretion of insulin, glucagon, adrenaline, cortisone, and a pituitary hormone.

Nerves and Endocrine Hormones

At the beginning of this chapter we gave an example of coordination – the control by nerves of breathing patterns in relation to the carbon dioxide concentration in the blood. We did not mention hormone control, yet in the living organism endocrine glands and neurons operate in close cooperation to regulate every living function. In the case of breathing, the general level of metabolism of glucose by the muscle cells involved in breathing movements is dependent, as we have just explained, on many hormones – hormones of the thyroid, adrenal cortex and medulla, pancreas, and pituitary. The parathyroid glands, in regulating calcium balance, play a part in adjusting the level of activity of nerves and muscles, including the nerves and muscles involved in breathing. Even the hormones of the testes and ovaries can be involved, though somewhat less directly. These hormones affect patterns of behavior (as we will mention again in Chapter 35), and in this way influence what an organism does – in this instance its breathing activities.

We could almost end our description of nerve and hormone function at this point, with the picture of beautifully integrated control of all body processes. Unfortunately, this is not quite the full story – for homeostatic controls can break down. We have suggested this already in our account of diabetes mellitus. Diseases like poliomyelitis can destroy nerves and nerve coordination. Many types of endocrine disturbance in addition to diabetes are also known. You can almost guess what symptoms might be seen in animals with abnormal endocrine function, on the basis of your knowledge of the glands' normal functions. Thus, since you know that a pituitary hormone regulates the growth of bone and body size, you can understand the striking effects of removal of the pituitary gland in a young mammal like a rat or mouse; the animal's growth is checked so that it becomes a dwarf. Disturbances in metabolism result from thyroid disease in mammals, and in most vertebrates an upset of calcium balance and nerve excitability can result from damage to the parathyroid glands. We could give other examples but these illustrate our point. Only when nerves and endocrine glands are operating normally, and stresses applied to the organism are not too great, are the delicately balanced bodily states achieved on which healthy life depends.

CONCLUDING REMARKS – COORDINATION

Coordination, as we have seen, involves receiving information and doing something about it. The information may be of many sorts: the words you are now reading, the odor of a skunk, the hot air near a flame, the noise of an automobile horn, the concentration of carbon dioxide in the blood, the presence of acid food in the first portion of the small intestine, a nerve impulse, or glucose in the blood. These various sorts of information (or stimuli) can lead to a variety of responses: a feeling of pleasure that you have nearly finished reading the chapter, holding your nose, moving from the flame, turning to look at the automobile, breathing more rapidly, release of secretin, contraction of a muscle, or release of insulin.

In multicellular animals, there is nearly always a division of labor among structures that detect, transmit, coordinate, and respond to information. Detection is generally done by some part of the nervous system or a sense organ. Transmission is by way of neurons (with their nerve impulses) or the blood (with hormones). Coordination usually occurs in the central nervous system. Body response is through action of effectors.

The ultimate result of coordination is survival—by maintaining the normal homeostatic conditions for the life of cells and by responding to the environment in such a way as to make further homeostatic control more probable. But there are patterns of stimulation and response that cannot be explained in the simple terms used in this chapter. When we consider such complex aspects of coordination and reaction as all the behavior we observe in man and in many other animals, we find ourselves asking a whole new series of questions. Answers to some of these questions can be looked for in Chapter 35.

GUIDE QUESTIONS AND PROBLEMS

1. In what way can the nervous system of a planarian be considered more highly organized than the nervous system of a *Hydra*?
2. What basic function do *receptors* have? How is this function related to the fact that most animals have a head end? What relationship exists between the kinds of receptors an animal has and where it lives?
3. How does regulation of carbon dioxide and oxygen content in your blood illustrate the concept of homeostasis?
4. How does the respiratory center in the human brain control rate and depth of breathing?
5. What evidence supports the idea that nerve cell impulses stimulate other nerve cells, muscles, and glands by chemical means?
6. What functional differences are there among sensory, motor, and associative neurons?
7. Suppose you have just placed your finger on a hot stove. Describe the events that would follow and relate them to your nervous system.
8. If the nature of a nerve impulse is similar in all nerve fibers, how can you account for the fact that light and sound result in such distinctly different sensations in our brains?
9. Suppose you wanted to know more about the function of a particular gland suspected to be an endocrine gland. What might you do in an investigation into its function?
10. Eating a lot of candy can cause temporary increase in blood glucose concentration. What control mechanisms bring the blood glucose concentration back within its normal range (about 0.07 percent)?

RELATED READING

Books

For further information about nervous systems in animals . . .

Asimov, Isaac, *The Human Brain,* Houghton Mifflin, Boston, 1964.

Barnes, R. D., *Invertebrate Zoology,* Saunders, Philadelphia, 1964.

Romer, Alfred S., *The Vertebrate Body,* Third Edition, Saunders, Philadelphia, 1962.

For the role of the endocrines in body regulation and development . . .

Turner, C. D., *General Endocrinology,* Fourth Edition, Saunders, Philadelphia, 1966.

Magazines

Baker, Peter F., "The Nerve Axon," *Scientific American,* Volume 214 (March 1966), page 74.

Benziger, T. H., "The Human Thermostat," *Scientific American,* Volume 204 (January 1961), page 134.

Eccles, Sir John, "The Synapse," *Scientific American,* Volume 212 (January 1965), page 56.

Fender, Derek, H., "Control Mechanisms of the Eye," *Scientific American,* Volume 211 (July 1964), page 24.

Held, R., "Plasticity in Sensory Motor Systems," *Scientific American,* Volume 213 (November 1965), page 84.

BSCS Pamphlets

Overmire, T. G., *Homeostatic Regulation,* D. C. Heath and Company, Boston, 1963 (BSCS Pamphlet No. 9).

Suckling, E. E., *Bioelectricity,* D. C. Heath and Company, Boston, 1962 (BSCS Pamphlet No. 4).

25

Animal Support and Locomotion

Animals have two major ways to solve the problem of getting food. The way of most animals is to go where the food is. This requires a means of locomotion. The second way is to depend upon food that comes to the animal. An animal that lives attached to a surface and feeds in this way is called a **sessile** (SES·il) animal (Figure 25-1).

Most sessile animals live in the shallow areas of seas where microscopic plants and animals are abundant. Some of these sessile animals, such as sponges and sea squirts, feed by passing water through their bodies and filtering out the tiny animals and plants. Other sessile forms, such as corals and sea anemones, capture food organisms by using specialized tentacles. *Hydra* feeds in this manner (Figure 20-2, page 391). In either case, a sessile existence depends upon a constant, abundant food supply in the vicinity of the animal.

Most animals are not sessile, but move from one place to another in search of food, as we have mentioned. Animals capable of such locomotion are said to be **motile** (MOH·til).

Locomotion in animals is accomplished in a variety of ways (Figure 25-2). Horses browse from place to place on the grasslands, standing on long legs that can be alternately flexed and extended. To escape becoming the food of animals of prey, they can cover swiftly the great distances of flat grassland. Porpoises and fishes move swiftly through the water by undulations of the body and vigorous action of the tail. Birds, bats, and bees fly by means of wings, which push against air. Snakes crawl on their bellies. Monkeys, squirrels, and opossums climb trees.

D. P. Wilson

25–1 Sea anemones – sessile animals with radial symmetry. *Hydra* (Figures 19–7 and 19–8) also is an example. Other radially symmetrical animals that are not sessile, but motile, include jellyfish and sea stars (Figures 19–7 and 19–16). Sea stars could also be classified as bilaterally symmetrical since part of their water-circulating system is not centered. All radially symmetrical animals are aquatic.

The Body Form of Animals

If you were to survey all the animals that move on the surface of the earth, you would find that most of them have similar body plans. Perhaps the most significant feature of motile animals is that one end generally moves forward first. This is the head. Heads explore the environment: they contain sense organs and the main nerve centers, or brain. The sense organs receive information from the environment and pass it to the brain. The brain then controls what kind of response will be made.

An animal that possesses a head always has two similar sides. That is, an imaginary line drawn down the center of the organism from head to tail divides the animal into two similar halves (Figure 25-2). An animal with this kind of body plan shows bilateral symmetry (as you learned in Chapter 19).

Some kinds of animals, such as the corals, jellyfish, or adult sea stars, do not have a head and a tail end and are not bilaterally symmetrical. These animals have bodies arranged like a wheel, around a single central point. All sides of their bodies seem to be equally sensitive. The hub or center of the circular body has an opening, the mouth, through which the food passes. You read in Chapter 19 that ani-

25–2 Four motile and bilaterally symmetrical vertebrates. The ray **(below)** swims. The duck **(below right)** and the chaffinch **(right)** fly. The field mouse **(right)** depends on its legs. All accomplish their locomotion in the same way—by muscles contracting and moving the bones of the skeleton.

Marcel Cognac

D. P. Wilson

Eric Hosking

mals with this pattern of body construction show radial symmetry (Figure 25-1).

Some radially symmetrical animals, such as corals and sea anemones, are sessile. Others, such as jellyfish, move about slowly.

METHODS OF ANIMAL LOCOMOTION

Animals with bilateral symmetry and others with radial symmetry have existed in the seas for more than 500 million years. But the bilateral body plan has played a more prominent role in evolution than has the radial body plan. Only the animals with bilateral symmetry have invaded the land. Even in the seas, most of the animals that can move rapidly are bilateral.

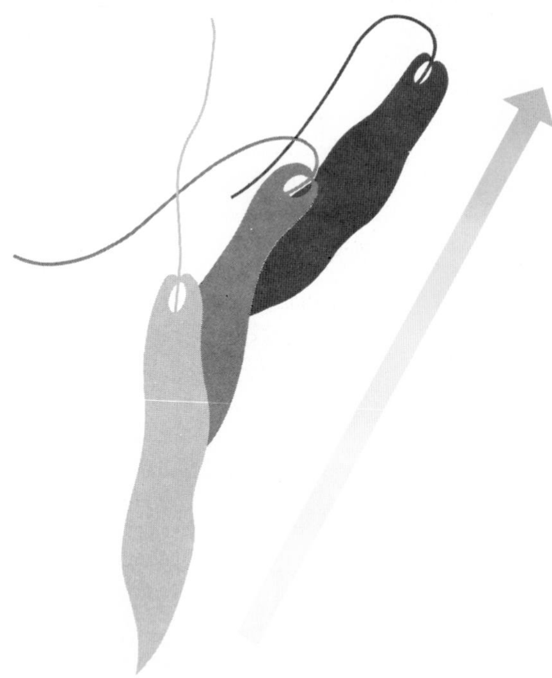

25–3 Locomotion in *Euglena*. As the flagellum is whipped backward, the organism moves forward. Yet as the flagellum is moved forward the organism does not move backward. Can you suggest why? (Recall your arm movements when you are swimming. Possibly this will help you with your answer.)

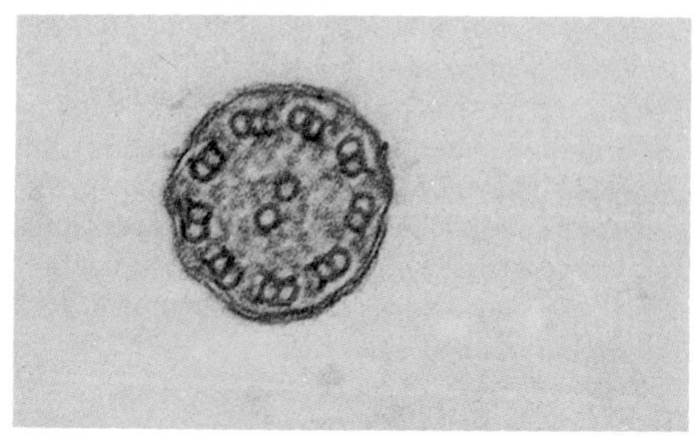

Delbert Philpott

25–4 An electron micrograph of a cross section through a cilium of *Paramecium*. Cilia have this structure from *Paramecium* to man. (100,000 ×)

Locomotion in the Protozoa

Many biologists believe that the first protozoans to evolve were flagellated forms. That is, they moved themselves through the primordial seas by whipping their flagella against the water (Figure 25-3).

Other protozoans are adapted to crawling. One of these, for example, is *Amoeba proteus*, which moves about by using pseudopodia (Chapter 18). This kind of locomotion results from a flowing movement. That is, the cytoplasm moves into the gradually extending pseudopodia. We do not yet understand how this movement is carried out, nor how the energy needed for it is supplied.

Still other kinds of protozoa, such as *Paramecium,* swim through the water by the beating of hundreds of small cilia. You have observed this ciliary movement in the laboratory. The cilia are short, delicate, threadlike structures stretching out from the cell membrane (look again at the *Paramecium* in Figure 18-6, page 338). Although it is impossible for you to see with the light microscope whether cilia have any internal structure, the electron microscope has revealed a characteristic pattern in almost all cilia. Some features of this pattern are shown in Figure 25-4, a cross section of one of the cilia of a *Paramecium.* You can see the small dark structures rather like figure 8's inside the mem-

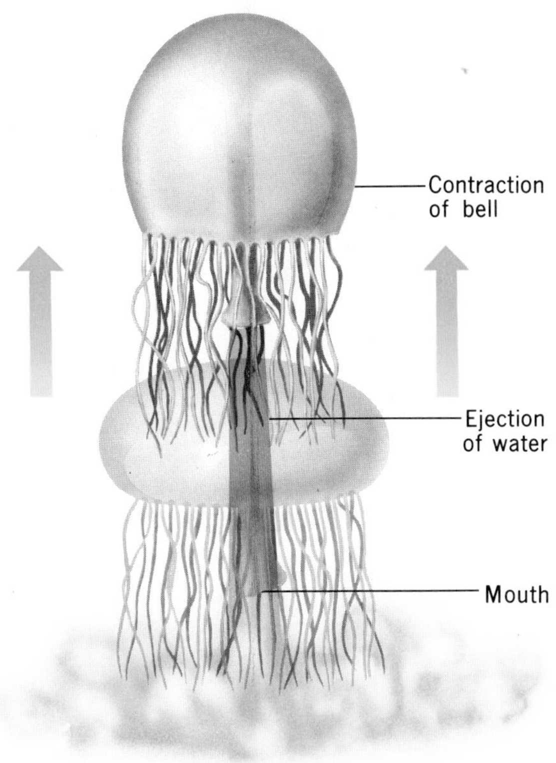

25-5 Another type of locomotion. Any jellyfish can demonstrate the principle of jet propulsion.

brane of the cilium. Each "figure 8" represents cross sections of two tiny rods running the length of the cilium. Though we do not understand the exact significance of this structure, it must be very basic to ciliary function, for it is found in cilia of many organisms—both simple and complex, and both plants and animals. Cilia function not only to move a whole organism (as in *Paramecium* and planarians), but also objects and fluids over membranes in respiratory, digestive, excretory, and reproductive systems in many animals. Ciliated membranes in your respiratory passages move foreign particles that enter in the air you breathe, passing them upward to the throat.

Bending, or perhaps shortening, of the tiny rods of cilia could cause the characteristic movements they make. This is one of the common explanations for how ciliary movement may take place. As for the energy supply needed for the movement, it was an exciting discovery to find that cilia contain enzyme molecules that can break down ATP. Poisons that stop ATP formation in the cell stop ciliary action. But even these discoveries do not give us all the information we need in order to understand how cilia function. If ATP is formed inside the cell, how is it or its stored energy transferred out to the cilia where energy is needed? And *how* do the enzymes in cilia break ATP down? Perhaps the most difficult question of all is this: how are all the movements of the thousands of cilia coordinated so that the movements (of an organism, or of something being moved along a ciliated membrane) occur in definite directions? Much more research must be done before we can answer these questions.

In summary, there are three main ways by which protozoans move: with flagella, with pseudopodia, and with cilia. In all these movements of single-celled organisms, coordination plays an important part.

Locomotion in Multicellular Animals

Within a multicellular animal, the cells, tissues, and organs work together to move the animal. One type of locomotion is demonstrated by the radially symmetrical jellyfish (Figure 25-5). This animal moves by a kind of jet propulsion. You could imagine it to be like the opening and closing of an umbrella under water. When the umbrella is closing, water is forced out. This pushes the jellyfish through the sea. Thus, although the jellyfish floats largely at the mercy of wind and wave, it has some control over its movement.

The sea stars and sea cucumbers, which are echinoderms, have another interesting pattern of locomotion (Figure 25-6). If you examine carefully the surface on which the mouth of a sea star opens, you will see that each arm has a groove extending from the mouth to the tip. In this groove there are hundreds of soft tube feet. The sea star uses its tube feet to hold

D. P. Wilson

25–6 Mealtime in a marine aquarium. The sea stars' meal will be scallops, and the chase will be brief, since an imbalance in means of locomotion favors the sea stars.

objects or to walk. Each individual tube foot acts as a suction cup and is under muscular control. The tube feet are extended by water being pumped into them. Contraction of muscles in the tube feet shortens them. The tube feet can also be moved laterally. The animal moves by extending its tube feet, fixing them by suction to a firm support, then shortening the tube feet. As they shorten, they drag the body forward.

A planarian moves along on underwater surfaces with a kind of gliding locomotion. This movement is accomplished by cilia on the lower surface of the animal. It is supplemented by muscular contractions of the body.

The gliding locomotion of the planarian can be contrasted with the accordionlike motion of the earthworm. The earthworm first becomes long and thin. Then little bristles, which are on the lower side of the body, dig into the soil and hold the front end steady while the tail end is pulled forward. The bristles of the rear end then serve as anchors as the front end is extended. This accordion type of locomotion is familiar if you have watched earthworms.

Skeletons and Locomotion

The multicellular animals discussed thus far are incapable of rapid locomotion. We can get a clue to one of the major reasons why the earthworm, for example, cannot move rapidly, by comparing its structure with that of a grasshopper or a rabbit.

The earthworm, using muscles and bristles, moves itself slowly. The grasshopper and the rabbit are capable of much more rapid motion (Figure 25-7). Both of them have appendages (legs) that are moved by muscles. The appendages act as levers; the muscles move the levers. Levers work only if stiff, and the bones of the rabbit's skeleton possess this necessary mechanical property. The grasshopper also has a skeleton that makes its legs stiff.

The rabbit has an internal skeleton, or **endoskeleton.** The grasshopper has an external skeleton, or **exoskeleton.**

Skeletal Muscle

There are several kinds of muscles in the human body. You already know something of their functions, for they include the **cardiac muscle** of the heart and the **smooth muscle** of the blood vessels, digestive tract, and many other organs. Cardiac muscle and smooth muscle are entirely independent of voluntary control. You cannot voluntarily make your heart beat faster, or slow down peristalsis in your small intestine. Cardiac and smooth muscles generally are controlled, at least in part, by hormone and neuron activity entirely out of the range of consciousness (Chapter 24, page 449). You will have an opportunity to study the function of these muscles in the laboratory (Laboratory Inquiry 25-1).

There is another type of muscle, **skeletal muscle,** which is usually associated with the

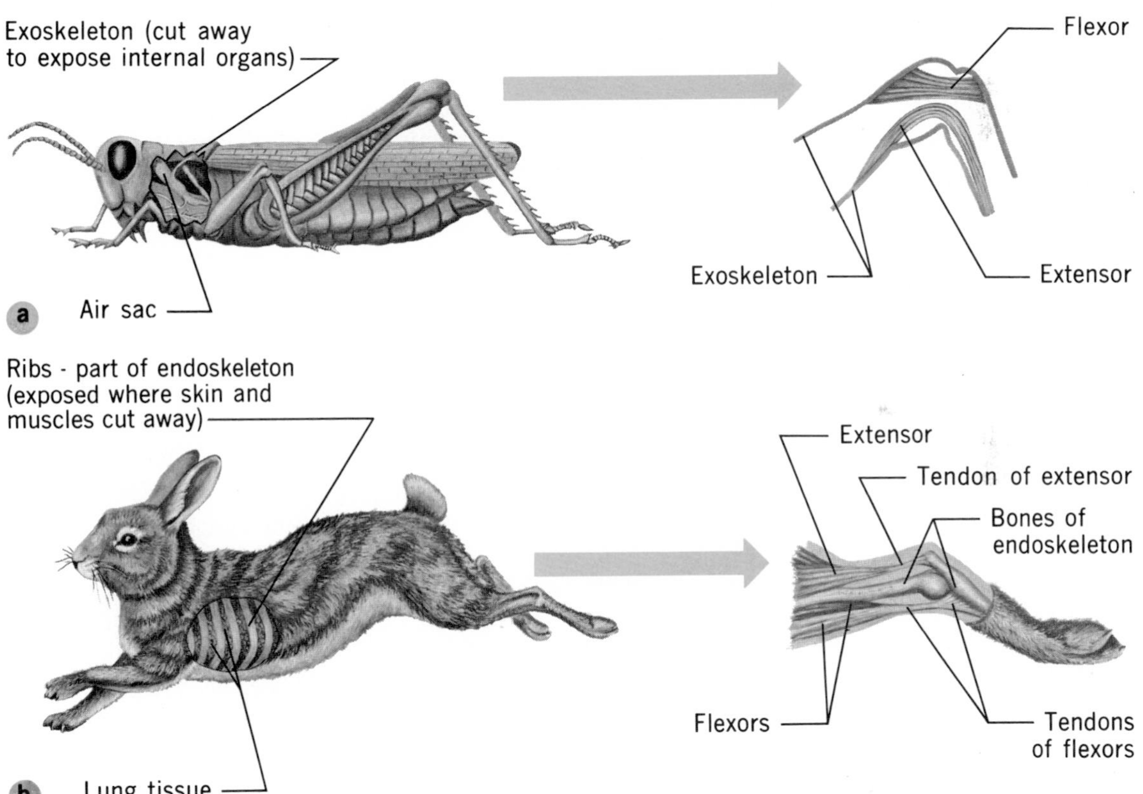

25–7 The relationship of locomotion, support, and protection of vital structures in an insect and in a mammal. The insect has an exoskeleton, the mammal an endoskeleton. Locomotion for both animals is basically the same. One end or tendon of a muscle is attached to one bone or skeletal part, and the other end or tendon to a different bone or part. Contraction of the muscle then produces skeletal movement. How does a skeleton serve a role in protection as well as in locomotion and support?

movements of bones (Laboratory Inquiry 25-2). The action of skeletal muscles is under conscious control, so we say that they are voluntary muscles. Generally these muscles do not contract at all unless they receive impulses from the central nervous system.

Many skeletal muscles work in pairs. That is, one muscle pulls a bone in one direction, and the companion muscle pulls the bone in the opposite direction. This arrangement of skeletal muscles is known as **antagonism** (an-TAG·o·niz'm). A muscle's action is antagonistic, so to speak, to that of its companion muscle. Most of the skeletal muscles are arranged in such antagonistic pairs. A good example is the combination of a **flexor** muscle and an **extensor** muscle. A flexor bends a joint, while an extensor straightens it out again. The knee movement used in walking involves such a flexor-extensor antagonism. Raising and lowering the foot, as in standing alternately on tiptoe and on the sole of the foot, is much the same. What are other examples?

Figure 25-7 shows a diagram of part of an insect limb and part of a vertebrate limb. Notice how the muscles must be attached to endoskeletons and exoskeletons. Also notice that each muscle requires an antagonistic muscle in order to function effectively.

Contractility

Contractility, the ability to contract, is a fundamental characteristic of living substance. So far as we know, it is essential to all kinds of movements except growth and cytoplasmic streaming. It looks very simple, but the simpler it looks the harder it is to explain. What is it that keeps the filaments of the blue-green alga *Oscillatoria* and some of its relatives ceaselessly waving in perfectly still water? What makes a flagellum or a cilium move so vigorously and so rhythmically? When we watch an *Amoeba* pull itself in here and protrude its pseudopodia there, how does it do this? Are these simple forms of motion related to the contraction of an animal's muscles? As we have mentioned before, these questions are still being studied and cannot be answered as yet with certainty.

Much of what we know about contractility comes at present from studies of vertebrate muscle cells, especially those that form the skeletal muscles, also called **striated** (STRY-ayt·ed) muscles. Striated means striped, and this term is used because each skeletal muscle cell, when examined under the microscope, shows numerous cross bands of alternating dark and light stripes. When the muscle cell contracts, the pattern of cross bands shifts. By a combination of observations with the electron microscope (Figure 25-8 left), and the methods of the biochemist, the meaning of these shifts in the appearance of the cell when it contracts has been revealed.

A muscle cell is a long fiber containing a great many smaller **fibrils.** Nuclei (the cell has many) lie in an outer layer just inside the cell membrane, while many mitochondria lie among the fibrils. Each fibril consists largely of special contractile proteins, the two most abundant ones being **myosin** (MY·o·sin) and **actin.** In a cross section of a cell's fibrils seen under the electron microscope (Figure 25-8 right), one observes bundles that represent the fibrils, and within each bundle, dark spots that represent many **filaments** running lengthwise along the fibril. The filaments are of two sizes, the thicker ones being about 10 millimicrons in diameter, and the thinner ones about 5 millimicrons in diameter. They are arranged in a very regular hexagonal pattern, six thin filaments surrounding each thick one (see inset, Figure 25-8 right). It has recently been shown that the thick filaments are myosin filaments and the thin ones are actin.

The cross bands in striated muscle change in width when the muscle cells contract. Certain thin cross bands, known as **Z lines,** get closer together in all the contracting fibrils within a cell. But the filaments of myosin and of actin, we now believe, do not contract—at least not in the sense that each gets shorter. What kind of model can we devise that will explain these observations? A clever hypothesis was suggested by the English biologists H. Huxley, A. F. Huxley, and their associates. The actin and myosin filaments could slide over each other. This is possible since the actin filaments are attached to the Z lines by one end, and the myosin filaments lie free at each end, in between the Z lines (this arrangement is shown in Figure 25-9).

The energy for the contraction apparently comes from ATP that is stored in the muscle cell. Again, we do not know exactly how this

25–8 A striated muscle of the arm, with one of its fibers or muscle cells **(lower center)** enlarged and sectioned at both ends. Fibrils from cells similar to those in the arm muscle are shown in the electron micrographs **(left** and **right).** The lefthand micrograph shows parts of four fibrils in longitudinal section. The Z lines are the narrow, dark cross-lines in the lighter areas. Regions where actin and myosin fibers overlap (Figure 25–9) are the broader, dark areas. In the righthand micrograph, the fibrils are in cross section; the inset drawing compares sizes of actin (small) and myosin (large) filaments.

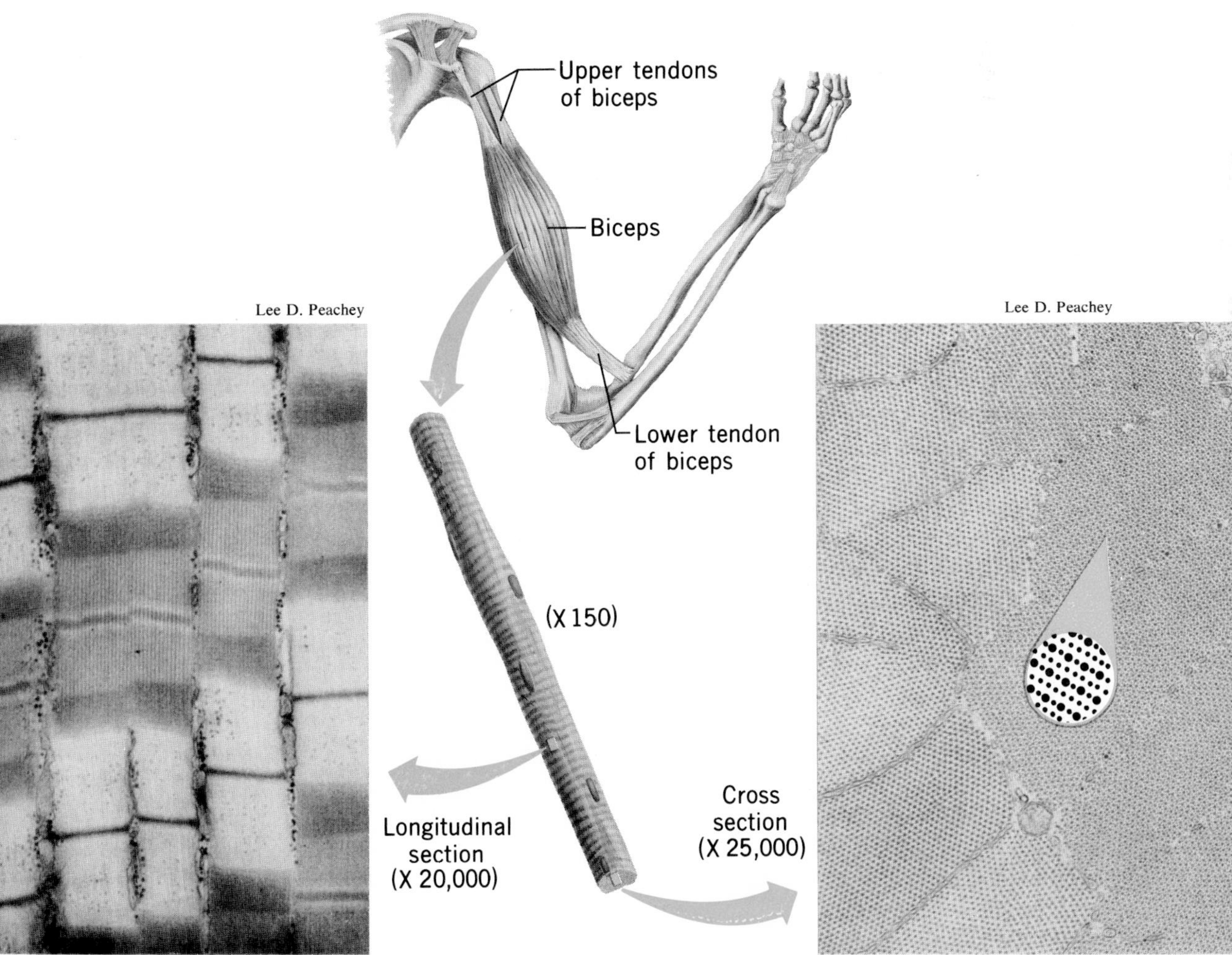

happens, although we do have some important clues. As in the case of cilia, the muscle proteins can act as enzymes, and some can break down ATP. These proteins can be isolated from muscle cells and formed into artificial threads. In these conditions, the threads can both act as enzymes and change their shape, shortening as they break down ATP! When a nerve impulse passes along a motor neuron to its terminal, ionic and other chemical changes take place at the cell membrane. Recent experiments suggest strongly that the muscle cell's special endoplasmic reticulum (Chapter 6) carries the stimulus deep into all parts of the large muscle cell. The traveling stimulus leads to a sudden activation of the enzymes that act on ATP. The ATP is converted to ADP. Thus, the stored chemical energy of ATP is changed to mechanical energy as the actin and myosin filaments of each fibril in the cell slide past each other, and the fibrils shorten. The muscle cell as a whole contracts, and work is done on the masses that are attached by tough, inelastic tendons to the ends of the muscle (Figure 25-7).

It is very interesting, and perhaps it will surprise you, that the contraction of each muscle cell is "all-or-none." If it contracts at all, then *all* of its fibrils participate – no halfhearted action here! The reason a *muscle* can contract to varying degrees is because it has thousands of muscle cells; the contraction of the muscle as a whole may involve dozens or many hundreds of cells.

A muscle cell's recovery from contraction is a complicated business, since the reserve supply of ATP must be replaced from the ADP formed when the contraction occurred. This process of forming ATP from ADP, you may recall, requires the breakdown of glucose through many steps, and the flow of electrons along the electron transport chain of the mitochondria until they combine with free oxygen. But in a big muscle cell the necessary oxygen can hardly be supplied fast enough to meet the mitochondria's demands. To supply additional oxygen to a muscle requires *time*.

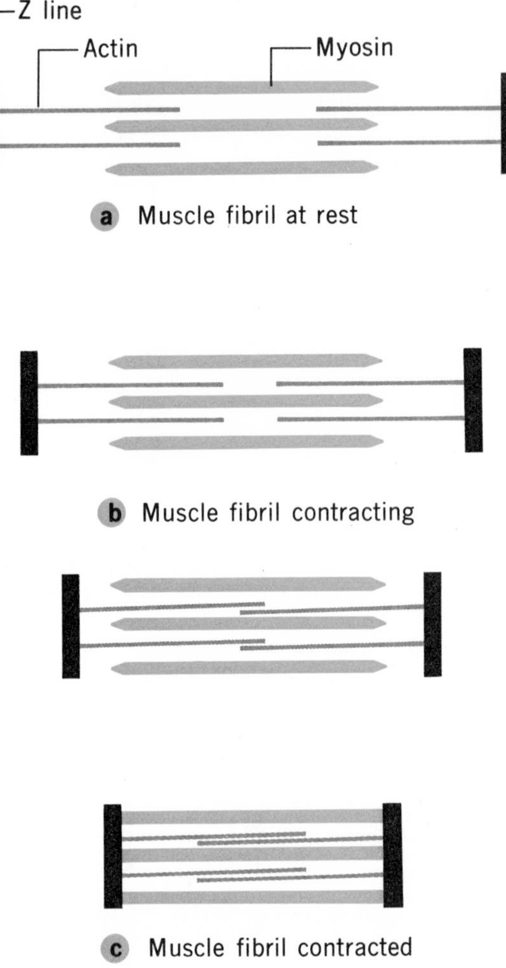

25–9 A leading hypothesis of how a muscle fibril contracts. Energy is supplied by ATP. Do some contractions stop at stage **b** (either of the middle two views)? Or do all proceed to stage **c**? If all contractions are "all the way," how can you explain varying degrees of muscle activity?

Have you ever noticed that when you exercise vigorously – say by running quickly up a flight of steps – you do not begin to breathe deeply or to pant until a considerable time after the effort is begun? You can actually run up an "oxygen debt" in your muscles before the relatively slow mechanisms that speed up your rate of breathing begin to operate. How is this kind of sustained muscle activity possible?

Essentially what happens is as follows. In the muscle cell there is another kind of energy-storing compound, known as **creatine** (KREE-a·teen) **phosphate.** Creatine phosphate will donate some of its energy to ADP in a reaction that goes like this:

$$\text{Creatine P} + \text{ADP} \xrightarrow{\text{enzyme}} \text{ATP} + \text{Creatine}$$

In this way, creatine phosphate can act as an energy reserve, working to keep up the muscle's supply of ATP. But obviously, as ATP is built, creatine phosphate is broken down. The muscle cell will then be short of creatine phosphate. The supply of that reserve energy-storing substance must also be replaced. Glucose is brought to the muscle cell, during its rest and recovery periods, by the blood. The glucose is converted into **glycogen** (GLY·ko·jen—sometimes called "animal starch") and stored. When the muscle cell has contracted and is recovering, glycogen is reconverted into glucose and the glucose is broken down to yield some of its energy. This process goes only part of the way along the complicated path to carbon dioxide and water. It stops at a point where some oxidation has occurred, but oxygen has not been involved. The oxidative steps produce a small amount of ATP, sufficient to replenish the supply of creatine phosphate and ATP used up. Another major product of the reactions is a 3-carbon compound, **lactic** (LAK·tik) **acid.**

It has often been supposed that muscle fatigue is produced by the accumulation of lactic acid. We really do not know all the factors involved in fatigue, but in any case lactic acid is harmful to the cell and must be eliminated. Lactic acid, oxidized in a series of steps, supplies electrons for the transport chain in the mitochondria, whereby an abundance of ATP is generated. As this oxidation of lactic acid occurs during rest, the muscle cell's "oxygen debt" is "paid." This explains in part something you may have noticed about yourself (Laboratory Inquiry 22-1)—that you continue to breathe deeply and fast for some time after you have ended a period of vigorous exercise.

In 1922 Otto Meyerhof (MY·er·hof) of Germany and A. V. Hill of Great Britain shared a Nobel prize for their magnificent work on muscle contraction and muscle physiology. One of the important and very surprising discoveries Meyerhof had made was that only about one fifth of the lactic acid produced during muscle contraction is actually oxidized to carbon dioxide and water. What happens to the rest of it? A beautiful arrangement of nature, truly, for it turns out that the energy released from the fraction of the lactic acid that is oxidized is used to "push" the remaining four fifths "uphill" to re-form glycogen and replenish the store of that substance in the muscle.

This remarkable story of the contraction and recovery mechanisms of striated muscle once again offers an example of the homeostatic capacity of living systems. It seems likely that similar mechanisms, if not so refined, are operating in the contraction and recovery of smooth, involuntary muscle cells. Indeed, this story may point to the fundamental nature of all contractility, for glucose, ATP, and proteins similar to myosin and actin almost undoubtedly play a universal role in organisms from *Amoeba* to man.

EXOSKELETONS AND ENDOSKELETONS

Exoskeletons (Figure 25-7a) are composed of either inorganic or organic substances, or both, secreted by the cell (in protozoans) or by specialized cells (in multicellular animals).

In many cases exoskeletons are very rigid and heavy. They restrict an animal's movements to the extent that the animal must lead a very slow-moving life (clams, snails) or even a sessile life (corals). One group of animals, however, has attained a very successful solution to the difficulty posed by the rigidity and weight of an exoskeleton. These animals, the arthropods, are completely encased in a very light substance known as chitin. In addition, their exoskeletons, instead of being formed of just one piece (as in snails) or even two pieces (as in clams, oysters, scallops), are divided into several distinct sections. Thus, the arthropods have combined relative ease of motion with a protective outer covering. No doubt this is a factor in the biological success of this group. But, successful as this type of exoskeleton seems to be, it presents at least one great disadvantage – if the animal is to grow at all, it must rid itself of its restricting armor. Arthropods do this by molting. As they grow they periodically shed their skeletons and grow larger ones. This loss of the shell is a difficult and often dangerous business. While the animals are "in between" old and new shells, they can easily be attacked by other organisms.

"Soft-shelled" crabs are those caught just after molting. They have cast off their former tough exoskeletons, and the new ones have not yet hardened. Among insects, molting occurs only in the immature stages. An adult beetle, for example, has reached its maximum size.

A different and highly successful approach to the problem of support is the development of an endoskeleton.

The largest of animals, both living and extinct, have been those with endoskeletons. The blue whale, the elephant, and the extinct giant reptiles are good examples. A rigid framework sheathed in layers of muscle, in addition to providing a means of locomotion, is apparently a good design for supporting and for holding an animal together. This framework is built up of solid structures – bones – connected by joints to form a solid yet movable skeleton. The hardness of bone results from its chemical composition – in a close network of fibrils, ions of calcium and phosphate and other salts are built into a precise arrangement resembling, in some ways, certain kinds of stone.

In addition to the skeleton's role in locomotion and support, it serves also to protect parts of the animal. An internal skeleton, such as we have, may protect some of the internal organs (Figure 25-7b). For example, heavy bone protects such important structures as the brain, the internal ears, and parts of the eyes. The backbone encloses the spinal cord. The ribs protect the lungs and heart.

The bony skeleton of vertebrates, in contrast to the inert exoskeleton of insects, contains living tissue. Thus, bones contain bone cells, which form the fibers and deposit the minerals that make up the bone. Experiments with radioactive isotopes have shown that calcium, phosphate, sodium, and other bone materials are constantly moving into and out of the skeleton. This in-out exchange is not always in balance, for when the body is at complete rest for too long, and in certain diseases, more of the minerals are lost than are replaced. When exercise begins again, or disease is cured, the bone minerals are built up to normal levels again. Bone, like all other body structures, is under close homeostatic control by hormones and other factors.

Evolution, Internal Skeletons, and Locomotion

The fossil record gives a clear and fairly detailed picture of the development of the skeleton in various groups of vertebrates. The earliest vertebrates were fish, in which several adaptations for swimming are to be seen. The jawless fish, which are the oldest vertebrates found in the rocks, were animals that swam by undulating their bodies. Usually there were no paired fins of the sort characteristic of most living species of fish. The body moved by alternating waves, or ripples, of muscle contractions passing along the muscles on either side of the animal. This caused the body to undulate from side to side. These undulations were transmitted through the back part of the body and the tail as a series of backward pushes against the dense water. This is the primary type of locomotion among vertebrates.

This type of locomotion, with many variations, is the most efficient way of getting through the water, and is retained in a great majority of fish. For such swimming animals it is generally advantageous that the vertebral column, the "backbone," be quite flexible. This can be seen in fish whose vertebrae commonly lack articulations or processes for locking the individual bones together (Figure 25-10).

The lobe-finned fish, a group of early fish, differed from the other fish of their time in that (among other things) their paired fins were supported by a series of bones arranged in a particular way. A single long bone was at the base of each fin, and its attached, or **proximal** (PROX-ih·m'l), end joined and rotated on the bones of the shoulder girdle, or of the hip girdle. At the other end of this bone, the **distal** (DISS·t'l) end, were two more rather long bones, side by side. And at the distal end of these two bones were several bones, all side by side. Here was the beginning of the skeleton of the **tetrapod** (TET-ra·pod) or four-legged vertebrate's limb: a single bone in the upper part of the leg (or arm), the two lower bones of the leg (or arm), and the several bones of the feet (or hands).

Lobe-finned fish were the ancestors of the four-legged amphibians. As the amphibians evolved, they faced the problem of gravity, heretofore of little consequence to the water-living vertebrates. At an early stage in amphibian evolution, the vertebrae became rather complex, linked together by interlocking articulations (see Figure 25-10). Thus the backbone became a strong, but reasonably flexible, girder that supported the weight of the body.

With the land-living vertebrates the basic method of locomotion has been that of walking on all four legs (Figure 25-11). In the early amphibians the legs sprawled out from the body, so that the animal probably dragged itself over the ground. This type of locomotion also characterized the first reptiles. Most of

VERTEBRAE AND BODY SUPPORT

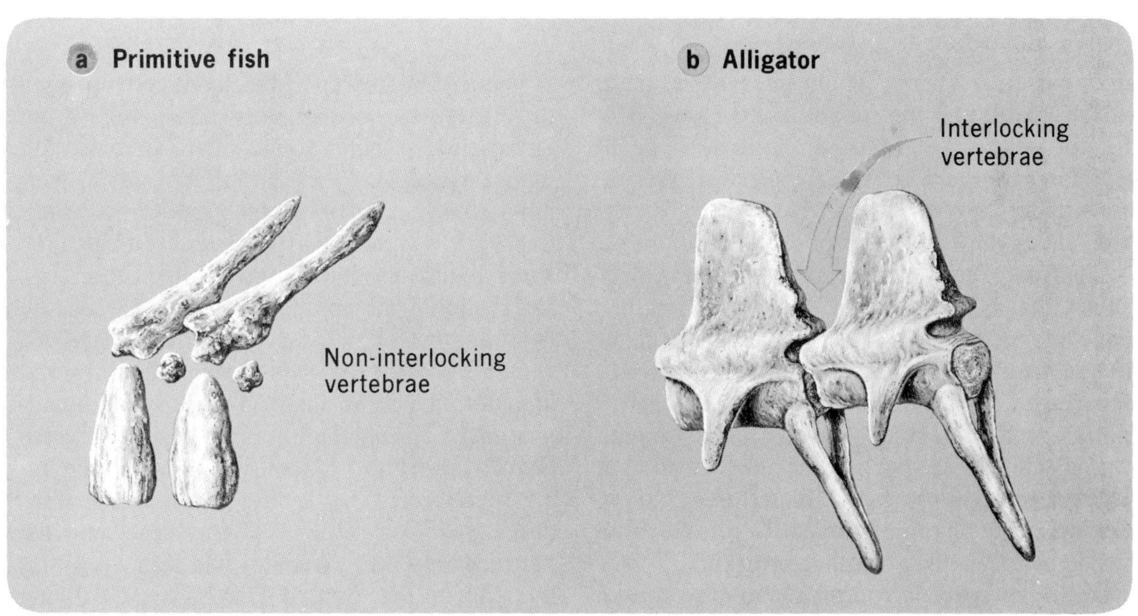

25–10 What is the most noticeable difference between these two patterns of vertebrae? In what way is pattern **a** not adequate for a land-inhabiting vertebrate? How does pattern **b** restrict the movements of the animals in which it is found?

THE EVOLUTION OF BODY SUPPORT IN LAND VERTEBRATES

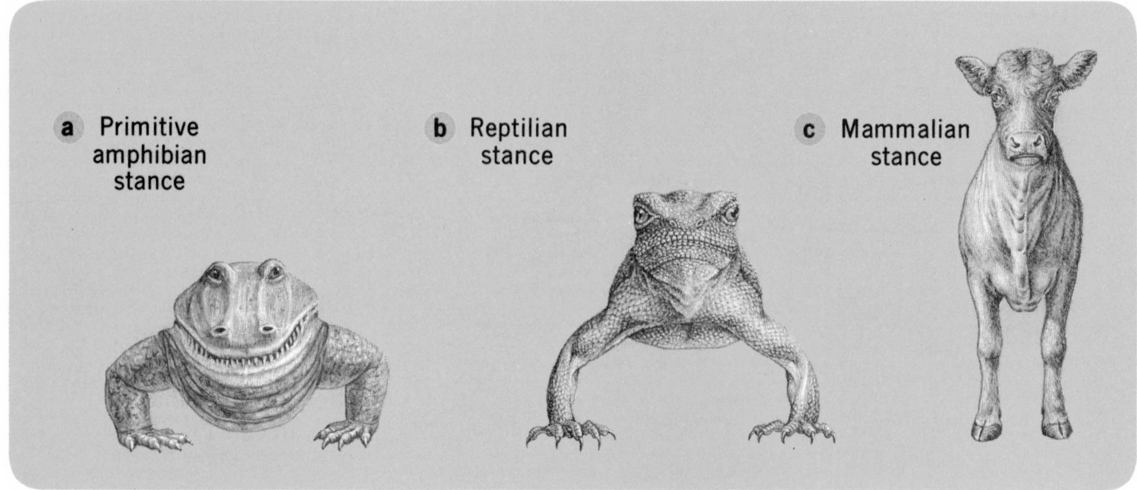

25–11 **a.** The legs of the first land-inhabiting vertebrates projected laterally from the body and then down. **b.** The reptiles are about intermediate, while in mammals, **c,** the legs project straight down. Which is the most efficient way of supporting the body? To find out, try a test. Place your knees on the floor, lean forward, and support your body by holding your arms at the angles shown in **a, b,** and **c.** Use the second hand on a watch to determine how long you can maintain each position.

their muscular energy would have been spent just in holding up the weight of the trunk, if it did not rest on the ground. In an early stage in reptilian evolution, however, there were trends toward bringing the feet in beneath the body and raising the body clear of the ground.

This more efficient method of walking and running has been characteristic of most reptiles since the beginning of the Age of Dinosaurs, and of nearly all mammals. As a specialized departure from the four-footed means of locomotion, many reptiles and mammals have, through the ages, become bipedal—walking, running, or hopping on their hind limbs. Such a method of locomotion commonly releases the forelimbs for feeding or other activity.

One very special type of locomotion found among most of the primates—the monkeys and apes—is **brachiation** (bray·kih·AY·sh'n). By this method, a primate can swing through the trees by using its grasping hands and long arms.

Many animals that climb trees are too small to brachiate; consequently they jump from branch to branch. Some small animals that jump through the trees flatten the body as they jump, thus making of themselves a sort of primitive glider. It is but a short and obvious step from this adaptation to one in which there is a large gliding membrane, usually between the front and hind legs, as in the flying squirrels.

Of course, the ultimate development in aerial locomotion is true flight. This evolved simultaneously during the Jurassic period of earth history, about 175 million years ago, in the flying reptiles and in the first birds, which were descended from reptiles. With these animals, the forelimbs were transformed into wings. At the end of the Age of Dinosaurs, the flying reptiles became extinct, but the birds continued and became highly varied.

One should not suppose any of these advantages in locomotion were purposefully acquired. As we will see in Chapters 31 and 32, mutation and genetic recombination—and the differences they produce—are sufficient to account for all adaptations of living beings, through the more successful reproduction of some hereditary types, and the less successful reproduction of others.

GUIDE QUESTIONS AND PROBLEMS

1. Structure often helps us understand function and vice versa. How does the microscopic structure of skeletal muscle help us understand the function of the muscle cells?
2. How are creatine phosphate and ATP related in muscle physiology?
3. The contraction of skeletal muscle liberates heat. How is the heat produced?
4. What are the chemical events that lead to accumulation of lactic acid during contraction of skeletal muscles? What becomes of the lactic acid produced?
5. What is thought to be the relationship among actin, myosin, and ATP in skeletal muscle contraction?
6. Is bone living tissue? Explain.
7. In what ways are exoskeletons and endoskeletons similar in function?
8. What clues to function are revealed by a close examination of various features of the human skeleton:
   a. its size and shape?
   b. the rigidity of connections between some bones (as in the top of the skull)?
   c. the lack of rigidity in joints between other bones (as in the arm and leg)?
   d. the shape of certain bone assemblies (as the rib cage and the skull cap)?

RELATED READING

Books

For illustrated accounts of the fascinating variety of ways animals move . . .

Buchsbaum, Ralph, *Animals Without Backbones,* University of Chicago Press, 1948.

Gray, J., *How Animals Move*, Revised Edition, Cambridge University Press, 1959.

For more on animal skeletons and muscular systems . . .

Storer, Tracy I., and Robert L. Usinger, *General Zoology,* Fourth Edition, McGraw-Hill, New York, 1965.

Young, J. Z., *The Life of Vertebrates,* Second Edition, Oxford University Press, 1962.

Magazines

Allen, R. D., "Amoeboid Motion," *Scientific American,* Volume 206 (February 1962), page 112.

Hildebrand, Milton, "How Animals Run," *Scientific American,* Volume 202 (May 1960), page 148.

Huxley, H. E., "The Mechanism of Muscular Contraction," *Scientific American,* Volume 213 (December 1965), page 18.

Satir, Peter, "Cilia," *Scientific American,* Volume 204 (February 1961), page 108.

BSCS Pamphlets

DuBrul, E. L., *Biomechanics of the Body,* D. C. Heath and Company, Boston, 1965 (BSCS Pamphlet No. 5).

26

Reproduction in Animals

In one respect reproduction differs from all other functions in living things. It is not necessary for the well-being of the individual. Any one of the reproductive organs—even the whole system—can be removed, and yet the individual may continue in good health. Yet if the reproductive systems in *all* members of a species were suddenly to stop functioning, the species would be doomed. These existing individuals would live out their life spans and die, and the species would die with them.

In some species of animals, reproduction is carried out for the species by only a very few of its members in every generation. Bees are an example. Only the queen bee of the hive produces eggs. A few individuals of the hive are fertile males, which produce sperms. The vast majority of hive members are sterile females, called workers, that have no part in reproducing new members of the species, although they do take care of the developing young.

PATTERNS OF REPRODUCTION

Many ways of reproduction have arisen independently in the evolution of the invertebrates and vertebrates. There are two main patterns: sexual reproduction and asexual reproduction.

Sexual reproduction is any method of producing new individuals that involves a fusion of nuclei from different sources, either from different individuals or from different organs in the same individual. There are three common patterns:

1. The fusion of the nucleus of an ovum, produced by a female, with the nucleus of a sperm, produced by a male (man and most other familiar species)
2. The fusion of the nucleus of an ovum produced by a hermaphroditic (Chapter 19, pages 360–61) animal, with the nucleus of a sperm produced by (a) the same hermaphroditic individual (as in the tapeworm) or by (b) another hermaphroditic individual of the same species (as in earthworms).
3. The fusion of nuclei produced by individuals of different mating types *(Paramecium)*

Whatever the method of fertilization, there must also always be meiosis. Meiosis and fertilization alternate in the life cycle. In animals meiosis characteristically comes just before fertilization, during the formation of the reproductive cells.

Asexual reproduction is any method of producing new individuals that does not involve the fusion of the nuclei of two cells, and does not involve meiosis.

We will consider the two main patterns of reproduction, beginning with asexual.

Asexual Reproduction

In the Protozoa, mitosis followed by cell division is a simple type of asexual reproduction. In *Amoeba* and *Paramecium* a parent cell gives rise to two daughter cells (Figure 26-1). In *Amoeba* this is the only type of reproduction known to occur, but in *Paramecium* there is sexual reproduction as well (Figure 26-1).

Recall that a slightly different type of asexual reproduction in a protozoan occurs in the malarial parasite, *Plasmodium* (Figures 1-5 and 1-8, pages 7 and 11). After the parasite enters a red blood cell of its human victim, it divides by mitosis, producing a total of a dozen or more new individuals.

26-1 EXAMPLES OF NORMAL WAYS OF REPRODUCTION

Organism	Asexual reproduction	Sexual reproduction
Amoeba	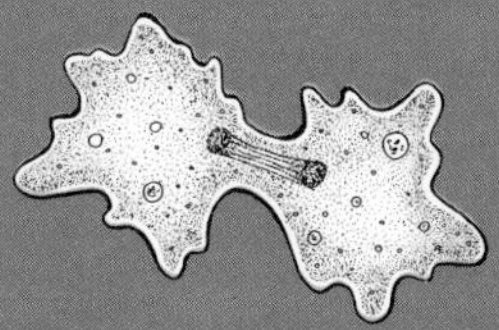 Mitosis and cell division	None
Paramecium	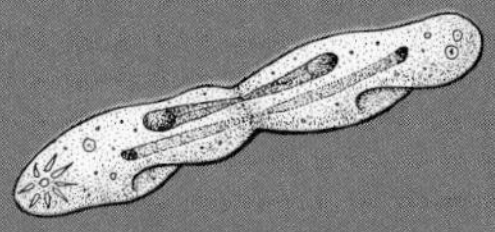 Mitosis and cell division	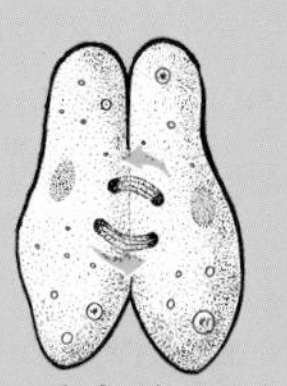 Conjugation and fusion of micronuclei
Hydra	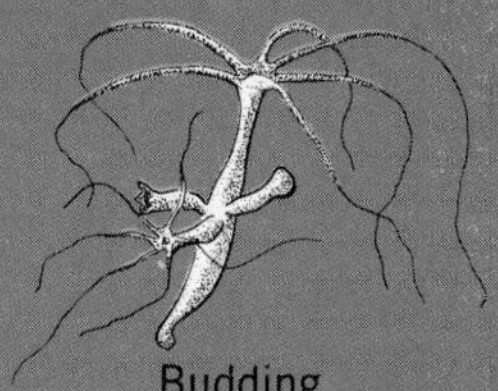 Budding	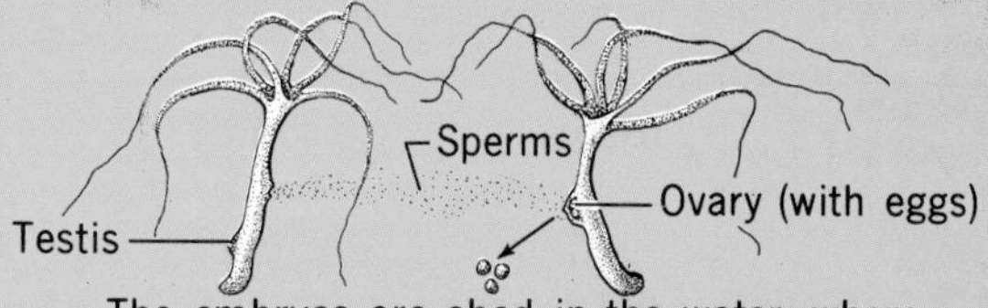 Sperms; Testis; Ovary (with eggs). The embryos are shed in the water, where they develop into new individuals.
Tapeworm	None	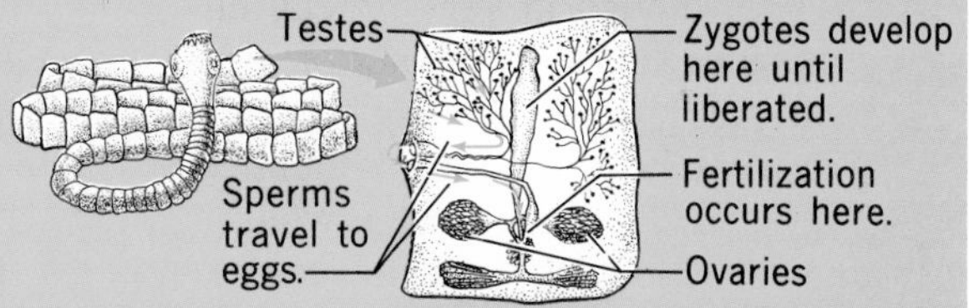 Testes; Zygotes develop here until liberated.; Sperms travel to eggs.; Fertilization occurs here.; Ovaries. Internal self-fertilization
Earthworm	None	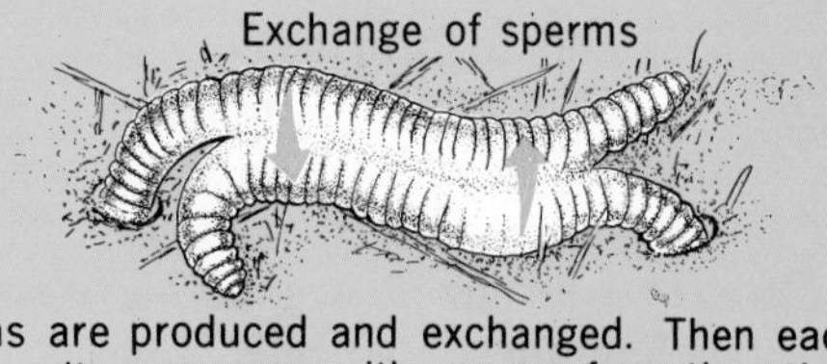 Exchange of sperms. Sperms are produced and exchanged. Then each worm fertilizes its own eggs with sperms from the other worm.
Man	None (For special case of identical twins, see text)	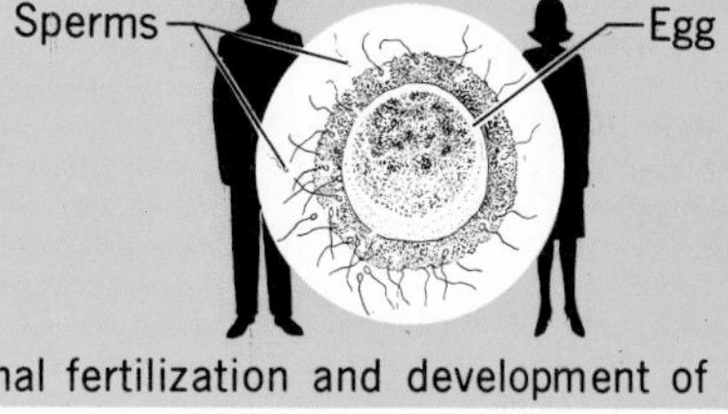 Sperms; Egg. Internal fertilization and development of offspring

Budding is a type of asexual reproduction in which a new animal is produced as a bud, or outgrowth, on an older animal. The process is somewhat like branching in plants. The bud eventually breaks off and becomes a new individual. You may have observed this process of budding in your laboratory study of *Hydra*. You will remember that in this coelenterate some cells form an outgrowth from the body of the animal, and the outgrowth eventually separates as a new individual (Figure 26-1). Similar reproduction occurs in other coelenterates.

Many flatworms reproduce asexually by constricting into two halves, each of which becomes a new individual. Among the annelid worms there are groups living in fresh water that regularly reproduce by dividing into two pieces. The anterior piece regenerates a new posterior part and the posterior piece regenerates a new anterior part. This is somewhat like the division of a protozoan, but on a multicellular scale.

While asexual reproduction does occur in animals, most species do not depend exclusively on asexual methods. Asexual reproduction occurs even in man, though in very special circumstances, namely, in the formation of identical twins from one zygote.

The exact details of the formation of identical twins are unknown for man. From what is known of early development in other species, a highly probable hypothesis can be constructed. In normal human development the fertilized egg divides repeatedly to form the embryo and finally the adult. All of the cells remain a part of the same individual. Identical twins may be thought of as resulting from an error in normal development. The fertilized egg divides into two cells. Somehow these two cells come apart, and then each continues *separately* to undergo division and eventually produce an embryo and later an adult. It is possible that the separation of the embryo into two parts may come about somewhat later than the two-cell stage. Whenever the separation does occur, the development of identical twins is asexual reproduction because the two individuals are formed from one zygote by an asexual process. The process is essentially the same as asexual reproduction in *Paramecium* and *Amoeba*—cell division. Identical triplets, quadruplets, and quintuplets, such as Canada's celebrated Dionne quintuplets, form in a similar way.

Parthenogenesis (par·thuh·no·JEN·uh·sis) is yet another type of asexual reproduction. Generally, the egg develops without meiosis and fertilization ever occurring. The offspring are diploid. Parthenogenesis may occur in species that also show sexual reproduction. In addition there are some animals known as rotifers in which all reproduction is parthenogenetic. There are no males known in these species.

There is a type of parthenogenesis in which meiosis does occur, and the egg (monoploid) can develop whether fertilized or not. The monoploid offspring develop into males, the diploid offspring into females. This strange kind of reproduction occurs in bees, ants, and wasps and their insect relatives. Here one finds asexual and sexual reproduction going on almost simultaneously.

Sexual Reproduction

In the great majority of animals, as in sexually reproducing plants, we recognize two kinds of individuals that produce sex cells, or gametes. The males produce sperms, the females produce **ova** (O·vuh—or eggs). Reproduction depends upon the union of a sperm and an ovum to form the cell from which a new individual develops. This is sexual reproduction, the most common pattern of reproduction in the Animal Kingdom.

Most of the animals that reproduce sexually (other than some protozoans and sponges) have specialized organs, the **gonads** (GO·nadz), for the production of gametes. Gonads are of two types: ovaries, which form ova, and testes (singular, testis), which form sperms.

The gametes from the two sexes of a species are quite different. The ovum is usually spherical or oval and is immotile (Figure 26-2). Ova of

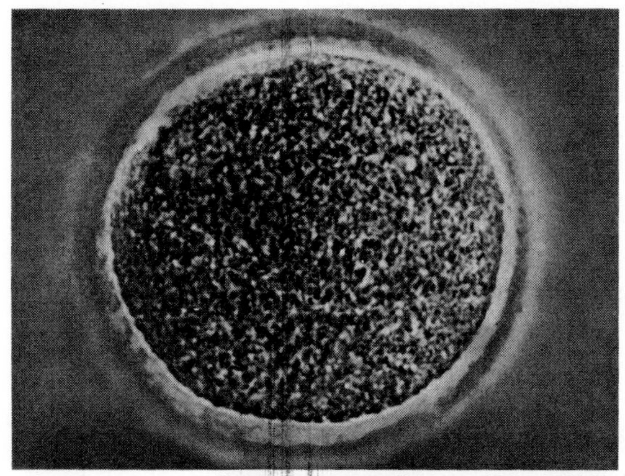

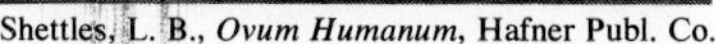

Shettles, L. B., *Ovum Humanum*, Hafner Publ. Co.

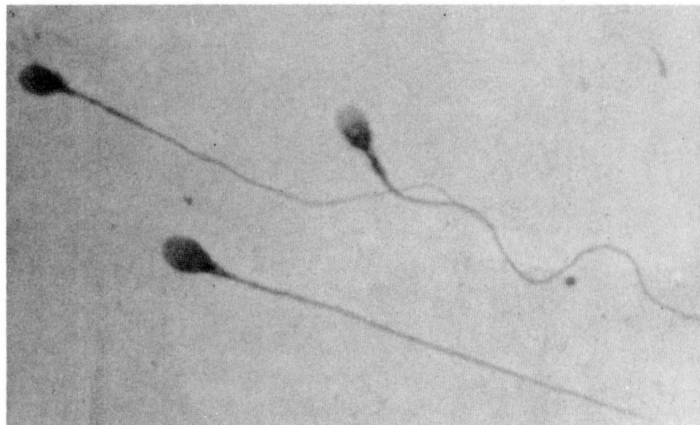

Harbrace Photo

26–2 A human ovum **(left)** and three sperms **(right),** as seen under the compound microscope. The sperms have been enlarged several times more than the egg. (At the same scale the egg would fill this page.) Of what significance is the egg's larger size?

different species carry varying amounts of yolk, which nourishes the newly developing individual. The largest single cells in the world are the ova (the yolks) of birds' or reptiles' eggs.

Sperms are generally very small and motile. They usually have a single flagellum, a long whiplike tail (Figure 26-2). The movement of a sperm is made possible by the beating of its flagellum.

The great advantage of sexual reproduction is the *variation* in individuals that it produces – a variation that serves as the raw material of evolution. In asexual reproduction, there are no gametes. In sexual reproduction, each parent produces a variety of gametes. These gametes differ in the kinds of hereditary units, or genes, that they contain. When ova and sperms combine at fertilization, many different variations in offspring subsequently develop. Those offspring with variations best suiting them to survive and reproduce do so. Sexual reproduction is consequently of enormous importance in evolution, which helps explain why this type of reproduction is so common among living organisms.

In many species belonging to various phyla, the same individual possesses both ovaries and testes. Examples are planarians and earthworms. Animals with both ovaries and testes in the same individual are called hermaphrodites, as you recall from Chapter 19, pages 360–61. Even among vertebrates, hermaphroditic *individuals* occasionally occur; hermaphroditic *species*, however, are rare among vertebrates.

There are two main patterns of reproduction in hermaphrodites. First, two hermaphroditic individuals may mate and exchange sperms, as in earthworms. Second, a sperm and ovum of the same individual may unite and produce a zygote. The tapeworm (one of the flatworms, and a parasite of man and other chordates) provides an example of this pattern of reproduction (Figure 26-1).

In most hermaphroditic species, the great advantage of sexual reproduction – the shuffling and recombining of genes – is maintained. There is some shuffling and recombining of genes even when ova and sperms of the same individual unite. There is more when two hermaphroditic individuals mate and exchange sperms.

In most animals there are two sexes – male and female. The difference between male and female is genetic (the evidence will be presented in Chapter 30). Male and female are de-

David W. Corson from A. Devaney, N.Y.

Lightfoot from National Audubon Society

Philip Gendreau

Grant Heilman

Philip Gendreau

fined on the basis of the type of gamete they produce—sperms by a male, ova by a female. The presence of testes or ovaries, therefore, can be said to be a *primary sex characteristic.*

In many species there are other differences between male and female. These are known as the *secondary sex characteristics* (Figure 26-3). Frequently the secondary sex characteristics develop in response to hormones produced by the testes or ovaries. You will investigate the effects of such a hormone upon developing chicks in Laboratory Inquiry 26-1.

To summarize, the ways in which animals reproduce are varied. Basically, *the function is the same in all—reproduction ensures the continuance of the species; and sexual reproduction ensures a variety of genetic types in the population, the variety upon which evolution depends.*

External Fertilization

The ovum, with its food supply for the new organism, does not have any device for locomotion. The sperm can move, but its swimming motion requires a liquid in which it can travel from where it is liberated to the location of the egg. For animals that live in water, this usually presents no special problem. In some species, ova and sperms may simply be shed into the surrounding water.

But there may be another problem. Gametes have no way of nourishing themselves. Hence, they cannot exist long when shed from the parent animal. Furthermore, sperm cells cannot travel far. So if there is to be any reasonable chance of a sperm finding an ovum, both must be shed at approximately the same time and place. Individuals of some aquatic species do just this; they shed their sperms and ova *into the water* at the same time and same place. We know that there are many mechanisms by which this simultaneous spawning is accomplished, but we are far from fully understanding how they operate.

Internal Fertilization

Internal fertilization, a method characteristic of many species, further insures the meeting of sperm and ovum. The male places sperms within the tube that the ova must traverse in their journey from the ovaries to the outside of the body. This method of internal fertilization takes place even among animals living in the water. Many crustaceans have it; so do some fish, such as dogfish, a type of shark.

For land animals, internal fertilization is nearly always a necessity. Sperms are quickly killed by drying. Since terrestrial animals are all motile, they need not depend on films of dew or rain to transport sperms from male to female, as some land plants do (see Chapter 14); hence internal fertilization is the rule.

Internal fertilization does not solve all the problems of efficient transport of sperms to ova, however. There is still a problem of timing. In most cases, the tiny sperms, which lack any quantity of stored food to support their active swimming, live only a short time. Furthermore, ova can be fertilized only when they reach a proper stage of development and are released from the ovaries.

In many insects this timing problem is solved by storage of the sperms. Once the sperms are deposited within the reproductive system of the female, they are maintained in a special pouch and released as the ova are laid. In bees, for example, sperms may be stored for several years. In many mammals, the timing problem is solved by means of a complex control system of hormones. We shall turn to this problem very soon.

26–3 (Facing page) Secondary sex characteristics in three species of vertebrates. Of the two white leghorns at the far left, which is the hen and which is the rooster? In the right-hand photographs, note that the male lion has a mane and the female does not, and that the antlers of a buck distinguish him from a doe.

PATTERNS FOR NOURISHING AND PROTECTING THE EMBRYO

Fertilization is only one part of reproduction. Once this is achieved, there is still the problem of nourishing the developing embryo, providing a suitable environment for it, and protecting it against danger. There are many ways whereby fertilization is achieved and care for the developing young is provided. We will describe a few of the important ones.

Insurance by Numbers

With many animals, continuation of the species is assured mainly by reliance on numbers. For example, a single codfish can produce five million ova! Many are eaten or otherwise destroyed, but even the survival of a small percentage of the total is enough to maintain the species. Generally the number of ova produced by each female of any species is correlated with the average chance of a single offspring developing to maturity. This is not accident or coincidence, but the result of evolution, by which species evolve and survive if well adapted.

There are many other variations and additional safeguards. In the first place, the ova of many living organisms are supplied with stored food, which nourishes the developing young until they are able to feed. In many cases a proper temperature is assured by the fact that production and fertilization of the ova occur at a definite season of the year. In other cases, such as that of birds, few eggs may be laid, but each developing offspring is warmed and protected by a parent, or parents, both before and after hatching.

Protective Coats for the Embryo

Amphibians, such as frogs, generally lay their eggs in water. Each ovum is surrounded by layers of jelly that afford some degree of protection for the developing embryo. The ovum contains enough stored food for the early development of the embryo. Oxygen diffuses in from the surrounding pond; wastes diffuse out and are carried away by the pond water.

Animals belonging to the next class of vertebrates, the reptiles, lay eggs on land, although many of them, as adults, live in water. The reptiles were the first vertebrates to lay their eggs on land. Of interest to us now are the changes in egg structure that made possible life on land. You are familiar with two necessary structures in the hen's egg – a porous shell, and just inside it, a tough but thin shell membrane.

The outer shell and membrane are not the only protective structures of the land egg evolved by reptiles and birds. As you study an early chick embryo in Laboratory Inquiry 27-2 you are likely to notice first that the embryonic digestive tract swells, about midway along its length, into a large sac. This is the **yolk sac,** a membrane filled with stored food (Figure 26-4). Just how much food there may be you can judge from the yolk of the hen's egg you ate for breakfast.

If you look closely you will find another membrane that extends from the embryo's body wall and encloses the entire embryo within a sac. This sac, called the **amnion** (AM-nih·on), is filled with fluid. So you see, even though the adult animal lays its eggs on land, the young are supplied with adequate food, and the development of the embryo takes place in a fluid environment.

The **allantois** (a·LAN·toh·is), the third membrane, is an outgrowth from the digestive tract of the embryo and becomes a large saclike structure, well supplied with blood vessels. The outer portion of the allantois joins with the fourth embryonic membrane, the **chorion** (KOH-rih·on). The chorion completely encloses the embryo and all other membranes. It lies very close to the egg shell, which is porous and readily permits gases to diffuse through it. The allantois, fused in part with the chorion, acts as a respiratory organ for the embryo. Its blood vessels allow for the exchange of oxygen and carbon dioxide with the atmosphere. (What

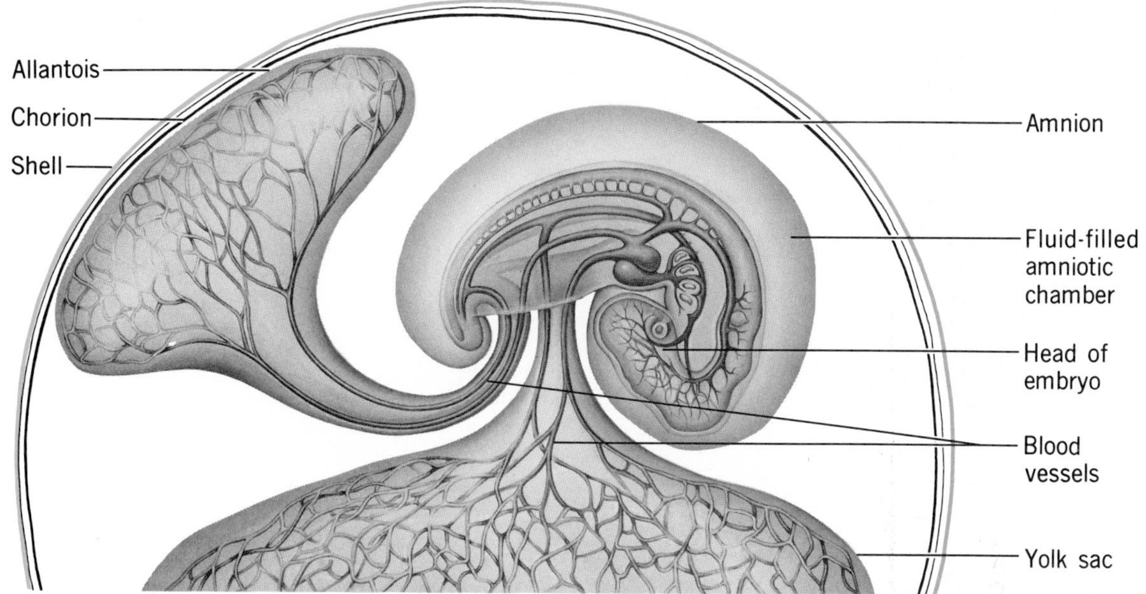

Redrawn from Patten, *Foundations in Embryology*

26–4 A developing chick embryo. The embryo is enclosed in fluid within one membrane – the amnion. The food supply, along with its associated blood vessels leading to the embryo, is enclosed within another membrane – the yolk sac. Oxygen-carbon dioxide exchange takes place in still other blood vessels enclosed by a third membrane – the allantois. All these membranes and their separate enclosures are located within a fourth membrane – the chorion. There is also a shell membrane inside the shell. The porous shell – the outermost structure – accommodates oxygen-carbon dioxide exchange with the atmosphere, as the membranes within the shell also do.

do you suppose would happen to the embryo if you coated the eggshell with wax?) In addition, the allantois serves as a storage tank, because nitrogenous wastes are deposited here – outside the body of the embryo. The arrangement is like that of a house with a remote septic tank.

In summary, reptiles and birds have evolved reproductive systems that make it possible for them to lay their eggs on land. The egg usually has a firm shell that keeps the embryo from being crushed and that protects it from drying out. In addition, there are embryonic membranes that protect, aid in respiration, provide a liquid environment, serve in storing nitrogenous wastes, and aid in the nourishment of the embryo throughout its development.

Protection by Internal Development

In some animals with internal fertilization, the embryo develops within the body of the female. You will recognize this as true for man and most other mammals, and we will consider these shortly – but first we must account for a variation in this reproductive pattern in certain other vertebrates.

The fertilized eggs of some animals in which internal development of offspring occurs develop in isolation within their membranes, *using their own stored food supply*. Eventually the offspring reach a stage at which they can fend for themselves; then they are born. We find this kind of protection – internal development, but *without* food being supplied by the mother – in some sharks and reptiles.

26-5 REPRODUCTION IN THE PLATYPUS AND THE OPOSSUM

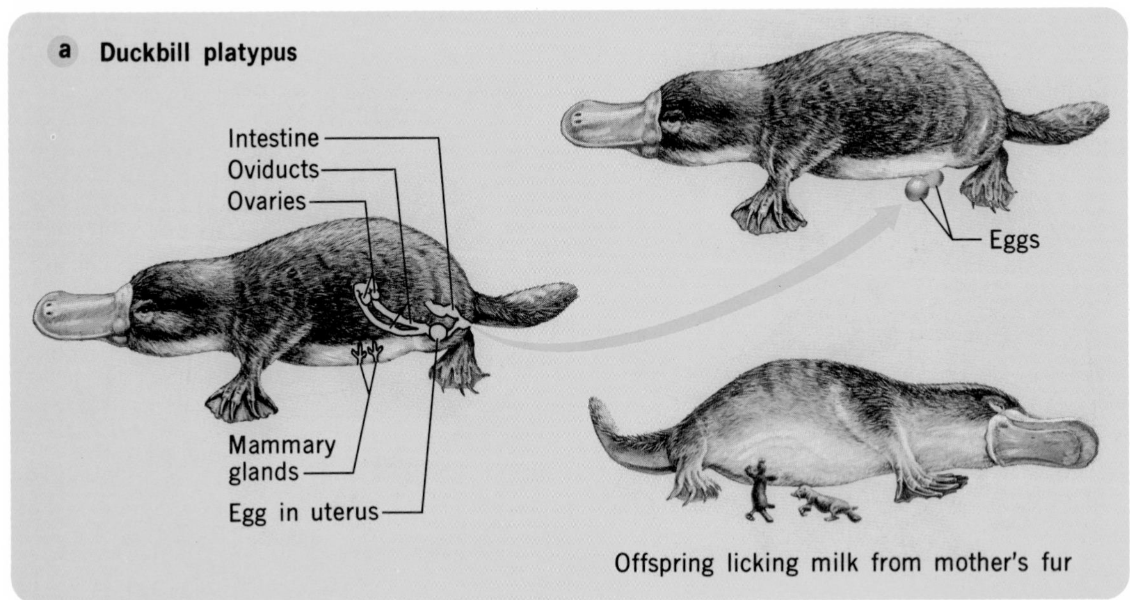

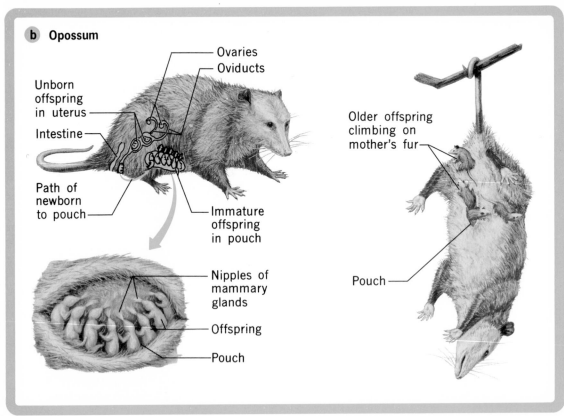

b Opossum

Ovaries

Oviducts

Unborn offspring in uterus

Intestine

Path of newborn to pouch

Immature offspring in pouch

Nipples of mammary glands

Offspring

Pouch

Older offspring climbing on mother's fur

Pouch

Food from the Female—the Egg-laying Mammals

The mammals, our own group of animals, make an important new contribution to the feeding of the young—the secretion of milk. Mammals have also elaborated in various ways the family system of care for the offspring. In other respects mammals, for the most part, rely on a combination of methods evolved by more primitive vertebrates.

The duckbill platypus (Figure 26-5a) is a member of the most primitive group of living mammals. It produces an egg very much like the egg of a reptile. The egg is not laid immediately after it is formed. Instead, it is retained for a time in the body of the female. Then it is laid in a nest and hatched.

Once the embryos hatch, the female secretes milk from glands on her belly, and the young lick it off the fur. The glands that secrete milk, which nourishes the newborn mammals, are called **mammary glands.** Mammary glands are characteristic of the chordate class Mammalia.

Food from the Female—the Pouched Mammals

The American opossum, and the many pouched mammals of Australia, belong to another group of primitive mammals, the pouched mammals. They have evolved a unique pattern of caring for the young (Figure 26-5b). Their small eggs have but little yolk—enough to provide for the development of only very small and immature individuals. Early development occurs within the body of the female. Then the tiny, almost helpless infants emerge from the female's body. They crawl up the female's belly and slip into the pouch, from which this group of mammals gets its name. Here the infants are sheltered and kept warm; also, they find food, for the female's mammary glands open here in the pouch. Each infant opossum, or the baby kangaroo, slips a nipple into its mouth and lives on the female's milk as it continues its development.

Maximum Care of the Embryo—the Placental Mammals

No animals go farther than the placental mammals in the care and protection of their young. Fertilization is internal, and the early development of the young occurs in the female's body (Figure 26-6). The female supplies the embryo with oxygen and food while it is within her body, and she disposes of the embryo's metabolic wastes by means of her own kidneys and lungs. We will see how special tissues, which form the placenta (Chapter 19, page 384), make possible these exchanges of oxygen, food, and wastes between the embryo and the female. After birth the young individual is nourished by the female's milk.

REPRODUCTION OF A PLACENTAL MAMMAL—MAN

We will study human reproduction as an example of reproduction in the placental mammals. We shall see how development with regard to protection of the offspring reaches its peak with the internal development, birth, and later care and feeding of the young. The process begins, as with other animals that reproduce sexually, with the sperms of the male and ovum (egg) of the female.

In the male human the two testes are located in an outpocketing of the body wall called the **scrotum** (SKROH·tum). The male reproductive cells, the sperms, are produced in very large numbers (hundreds of millions) in a series of small, highly coiled tubes in each of the two testes. Most other parts of the male reproductive system (Figure 26-7) are essential for the transport of the sperm cells.

The development of the male reproductive organs is regulated by the male sex hormones. Usually during early teens the voice of the male becomes lower in pitch, and hair grows on his face. These events are controlled by the male sex hormones, which are secreted by the testes. The production of sperms by the testes has begun when these events occur.

The two ovaries, where ova are formed, are located deep in the female's body (Figure 26-8; also Figure 24-9, page 453). The ova develop in tiny cellular structures called **follicles,** which at first look like cellular bubbles (Figure 26-8). As a follicle grows, it develops a cavity filled with fluid. Each follicle contains a single ovum. When an ovum is mature, the follicle ruptures at the surface of the ovary and the tiny ovum (almost the size of a period in newsprint) is flushed out. This release of the egg or ovum is called **ovulation** (oh·vyoo·LAY·shun). Generally the ovum enters the widened funnel of an **oviduct** (OH·vih·dukt), a tube that extends from the neighborhood of an ovary to the muscular, thick-walled **uterus** (YOO·ter·us). Fertilization occurs as the ovum passes through the oviduct; thus begins a new life, with the union of a sperm with the ovum, or egg.

As the egg passes from the oviduct to the uterus, we encounter one of the most marvelous control mechanisms that man and other mammals possess: the uterus at the time of fertilization is beautifully adapted to receiving the developing embryo, providing it with food, and disposing of its wastes. A few days prior to this time, the uterus was in no such condition. Then it was small, its tissues were thin, and its supply of blood vessels was poor. Now that the fertilized egg, or zygote, is about to enter, the uterus is much larger. Its inner wall is thick, soft, and moist with fluid; its blood supply is greatly increased. It is, so to speak, just waiting for an embryonic occupant.

26–6 Internal development of the young in a placental mammal. The blood vessels of the mother and of the embryo are in close association in the placenta—they are separated only by capillary walls. Food and oxygen diffuse from the mother's blood into the embryo's blood. The embryo's wastes pass into the mother's blood stream.

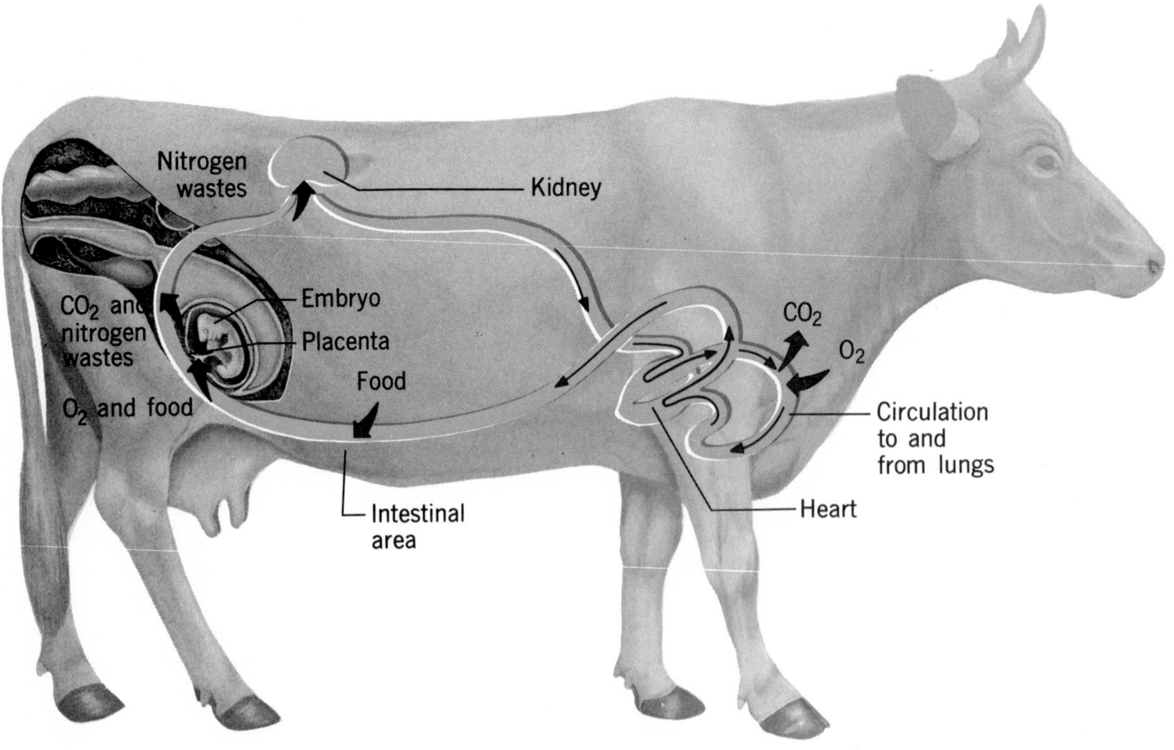

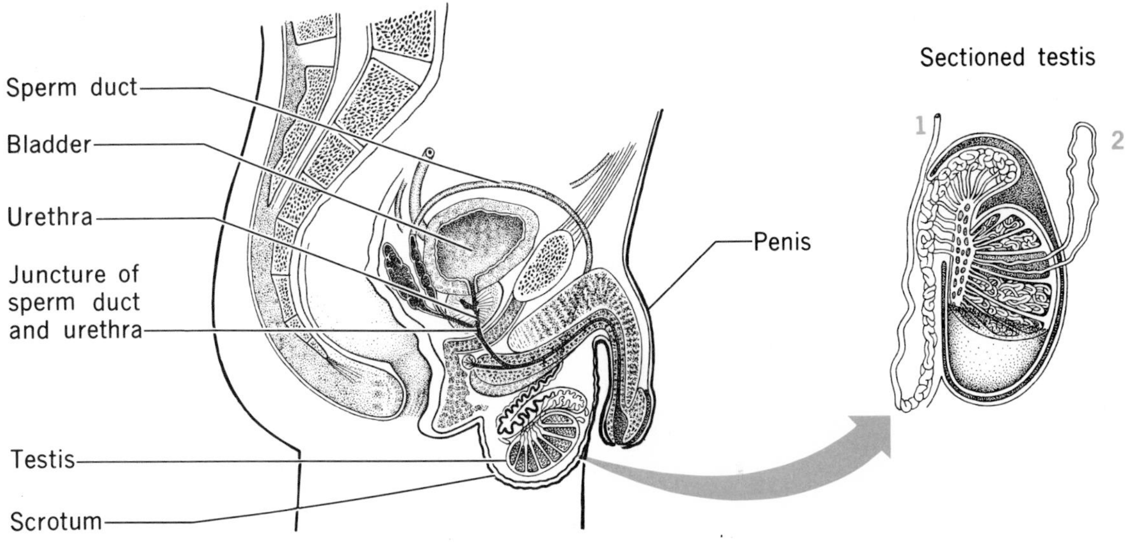

26–7 A schematic view of the reproductive system of a human male, viewed as if cut along a midline between the left and right sides of the body. To the right is an enlargement of a sectioned testis, showing at **1** the sperm duct and at **2** one of the numerous sperm-producing tubes, uncoiled and extended from its normal position.

Shortly we shall return to this transformation and see something of how it occurs and how it is timed for the arrival of the fertilized ovum. But now let us see what the transformation does for the developing embryo.

The human fertilized ovum undergoes mitosis and cell division as it moves down the oviduct and finally attaches to the soft tissues of the uterus. Once attached, the embryo sinks into the soft inner uterine wall. Then certain cells of the embryo develop into the four membranes (similar to those of the bird's or reptile's egg) that help to nourish, protect, and support it.

The chorion, the outer membrane surrounding the embryo and all its other membranes, is the first to form. During the development of the embryo, tiny fingerlike projections grow from the surface of the chorion into the soft tissues of the uterus. Gradually, small pools of rapidly moving blood form around these fingerlike projections in the uterine wall. These tissues of the chorion and the adjacent part of the uterine tissue make up the placenta.

Under normal conditions there is never a direct blood flow between mother and young. The blood systems of the two are separated by thin membranes made up of cells that allow an exchange, by diffusion, of oxygen, carbon dioxide, nutrients, and waste materials.

Another embryonic membrane, the amnion, grows around the embryo itself. The cavity within the amnion becomes filled with fluid. The embryo develops in this fluid-filled cavity, which keeps it moist and protects it from minor mechanical injury. In man, as in reptiles and birds, a yolk sac develops, even though in man it does not contain yolk.

The last of the four membranes to form is the allantois, which originates from the digestive canal of the embryo. Together with the chorion, the allantois helps form the placenta.

The edges of the amniotic folds come together around the stalks of the allantois and

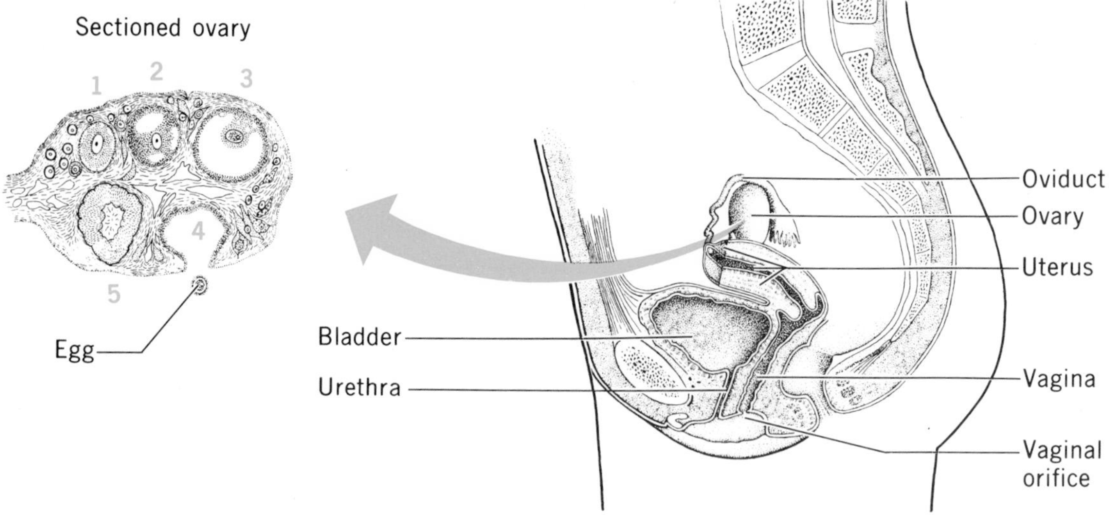

26–8 A schematic view of the reproductive system of a human female. The uterus has been cut along its length and at an angle across the top, revealing the entrance of one oviduct. To the left is a composite view of events that take place (not all at the same time) in an ovary. The egg is forming at **1,** growing in **2** and **3,** and it leaves the ovary at **4.** In **5,** the empty follicle forms a corpus luteum.

yolk sac and form a tube, which leads from the embryo to the placenta. This tube is called the **umbilical cord.** It contains the very important blood vessels that connect the embryo with the placenta, and contains, in addition, the remnants of the yolk sac and allantois.

Thus the embryo (three isolated stages are shown in Figure 26-9) develops until it is ready to be born. Pregnancy lasts, on the average, 9 months, or 280 days, in the human female. The average length of pregnancy varies by species: it is 63 days for the domestic cat and dog, 330 days for the horse, 280 days for the cow, and 20-22 days for the rat and mouse.

BIRTH

As pregnancy progresses, the **fetus,** which is the name we give an embryo after it has taken on a characteristic form, grows and the uterus increases in diameter. Usually, at about the ninth month after fertilization, near the end of human pregnancy, the head is turned down toward the opening of the uterus. At birth the head usually comes out first (Figure 26-10). Sometimes the feet come first; this makes the delivery more difficult.

We still do not understand how the childbirth mechanism, or labor, is triggered. This is a complex problem. Childbirth begins when the muscle layers of the uterus start to contract and relax—these actions are felt as labor pains. At first, muscular activity of the uterus is just strong enough to move the baby slowly toward the **vagina** (va·JY·na), the outer canal of the female reproductive tract. Generally, at this stage, the sac (amnion) around the baby breaks, and its fluid contents are released. This is a good sign that labor is well on its way.

Then the contractions of the muscles become stronger and more frequent, and the baby is pushed through the vagina and into the outer world. The umbilical cord (containing blood vessels), leading from the baby to the placenta, is tied off and cut by the doctor. (The small piece of cord remaining attached to the baby shrivels and falls off within a few days. The navel marks the place where it once entered the body.) After the birth of the baby, the muscular contractions of the uterus continue until they push out the tissues of the placenta, which are commonly called the "afterbirth."

During the last part of pregnancy, a watery lymphlike fluid called **colostrum** (ko·LOS·trum) accumulates in the mammary glands, which have gradually been enlarging and undergoing a transformation. For the first few days after the baby is born, the mammary glands secrete only colostrum. Following this, milk is secreted.

Each mammary gland of the human female is composed of sixteen to twenty-five lobes. Each lobe is connected to the nipple by a duct. The duct, as it travels back to the individual lobes, becomes highly branched. When the gland is not secreting milk, it consists mostly of an extensive duct system and cells filled with fat.

A characteristic change occurs during pregnancy. The duct system becomes even more highly branched. At the end of each tiny branch lie cells that secrete milk.

If the newborn baby does not feed from the mammary glands of its mother, they soon stop secreting and return to normal size. After childbirth, and when milk secretion has stopped, the female reproductive cycle (see next topic) begins again. However, ovulation, fertilization, and new pregnancy sometimes start during the period of milk secretion.

26–9 Human embryos at three stages of development (the surrounding embryonic membranes have been removed). From left to right are a four-week, a six-week, and an eight-week embryo. The first body organ to fulfill its function is the heart (the dark bean-shaped structure on the chest region of the four-week embryo). Well before the end of the first month of development it begins circulating the blood. By eight weeks of development, the eyes, ears, mouth, ribs, fingers, and toes are evident.

Chester F. Reather, FBPA, Carnegie Inst. of Washington

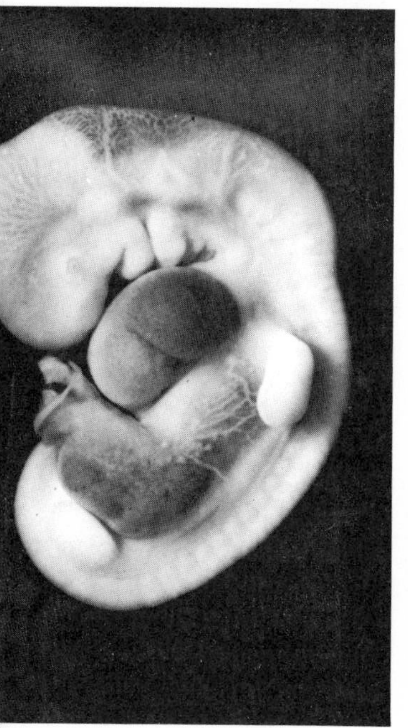

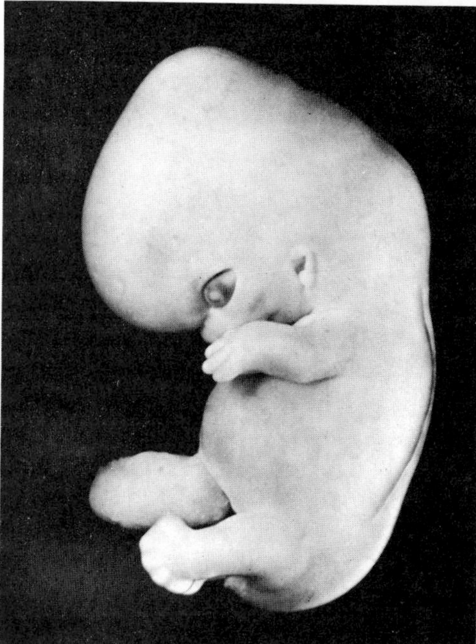

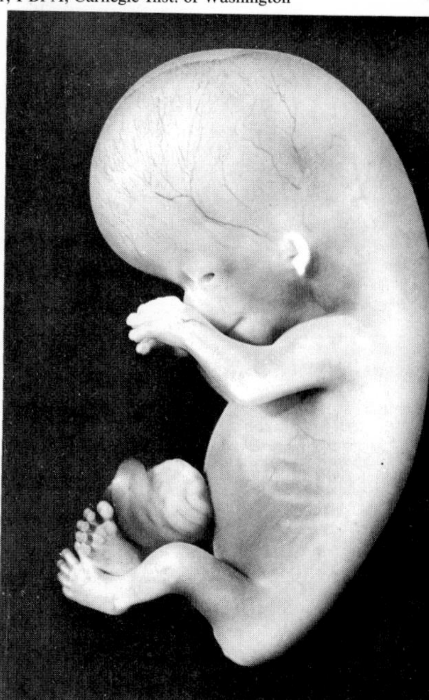

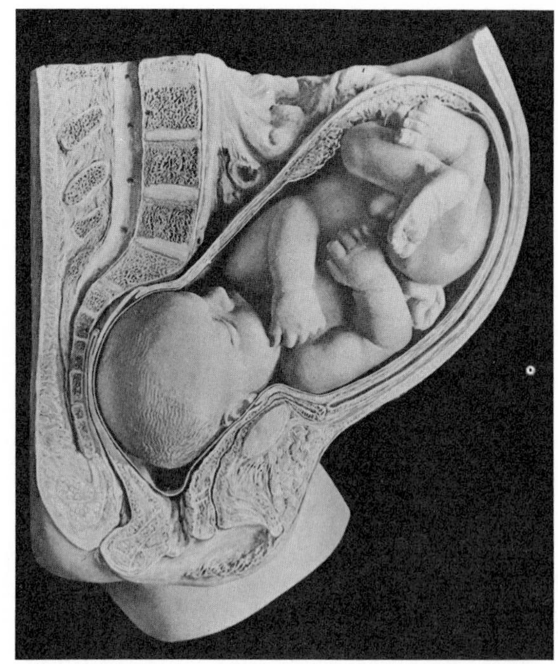

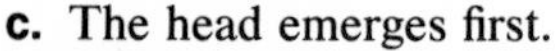

26–10 Childbirth.

a. Position before birth.

b. Birth is beginning.

c. The head emerges first.

d. It won't be long now.

Courtesy of *Birth Atlas*, published by Maternity Center Assoc., New York

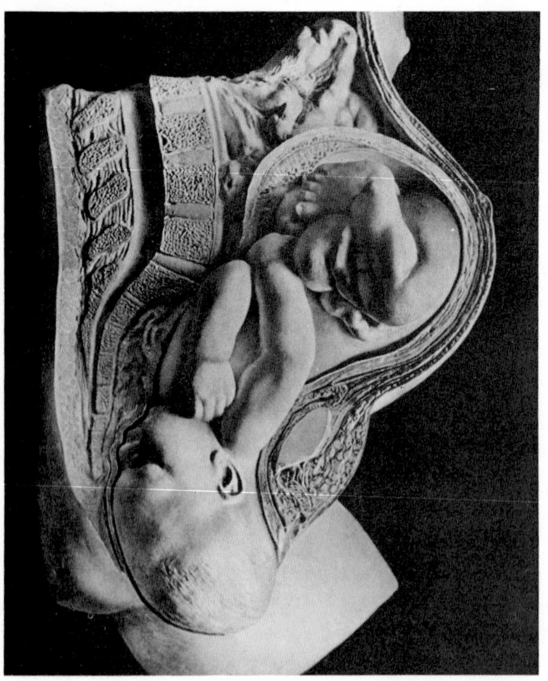

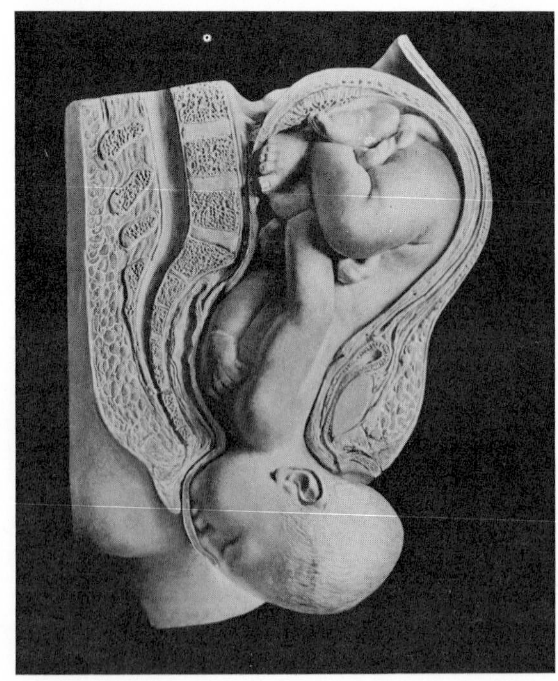

HORMONE CONTROL OF THE FEMALE REPRODUCTIVE CYCLE

The Role of the Ovary

One hint about how the female reproductive cycle is controlled is provided by closer observation of what happens in an ovary. We note two things. First, the cells of the follicle (Figure 26-8) in which the egg ripens secrete one or more female sex hormones called **estrogens** (ES·tro·jenz). The action of these hormones after they pass through the bloodstream to the uterus may have to do with starting the renewed development of the uterine wall. Second, we see that when the ripe follicle on the ovary bursts and releases the egg, the follicle "heals over" in a special way. The cavity of the follicle fills up with cells that have a good supply of blood capillaries. The structure formed by these cells is called the **corpus luteum** (KOR·pus LOO·te·um) because of its yellow color. There is ample evidence that this structure, too, is an endocrine gland, and that it secretes a hormone, **progesterone** (pro·JES·ter·ohn), into the blood. Can you conceive of just what kinds of experimental tests would prove these statements?

The hint that the ovary is somehow responsible for timing the cycle of development and deterioration of the inner wall of the uterus is made stronger by a simple experiment. Suppose we remove the ovaries from young female rats, so young that they have not yet begun to have a reproductive cycle. We find that the cycle does not start (Figure 26-11), nor does the uterus develop into its normal adult condition. Instead, it remains infantile.

What this experiment suggests is strengthened by further experiments. Let us now inject material from the follicles of mature rats into young rats from which the ovaries have been removed. Very soon after, we see the cells of the inner tissues of the uterus begin to divide and grow in each injected female.

Through further experiments of a similar nature we can now be reasonably sure that the

26-11 DETERMINATION OF THE CAUSE OF CYCLIC CHANGES IN THE UTERUS OF THE FEMALE RAT

Subjects: Young female rats of pre-reproductive age

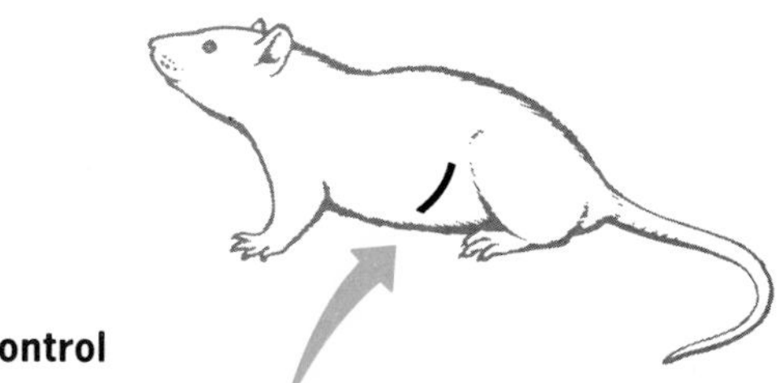

Control

Body wall opened and closed but ovaries not removed.

Reproductive cycle begins at age of expected maturation.

Experimental No. 1:

Body wall opened and ovaries removed.

Reproductive cycle fails to start.

Experimental No. 2:

Body wall opened and ovaries removed.

Reproductive cycle fails to start.

Injections of extract from follicles of mature rats result in changes in the uterus. Reproductive cycle begins.

two kinds of hormones produced by the ovary, estrogens and progesterone, are primarily responsible for the changes in the uterus. One of these changes is produced by one or more follicular hormones (estrogens) during the ripening of the egg. Estrogens are responsible for the commencement and continuation of the growth of the uterine wall. The other kind of hormone that effects a change comes from the corpus luteum. This hormone is progesterone, which serves to bring on further development of the uterine wall—additional thickening of the wall and added development of blood vessels and glands.

Reproductive Cycles

What do we mean by a cycle? The passing of day and night or the seasons of the year are common examples of cycles. We may define a cycle as a succession of events repeated regularly within a given period of time. The periodic repeating of structural and physiological changes in the female reproductive system is a complex reproductive cycle. The cycle has been studied extensively in laboratory animals.

The female laboratory rat goes through a short period of increased mating desire, which has been called **estrus,** or heat. The physiological changes occurring from one period of estrus to the next are called the **estrous cycle.** Ovulation, or the release of the eggs from the ovary, generally occurs during the period of estrus. Rats, mice, dogs, sheep, and many other mammals exhibit estrous cycles. The cycles of these animals vary in length and frequency. The laboratory rat has an average estrous cycle of five days. With the dog the cycles occur only twice a year: thus the female will mate and conceive only twice a year.

The reproductive cycle of the human female (and of some other primates) is quite different from the estrous cycle. It is called the **menstrual** (MEN·stroo·al) **cycle.** The outward indication of the human cycle is **menstruation** (men·stroo·AY·shun). Menstruation, which is a discharge of blood, mucus, and cellular debris, is brought about by the breakdown of the soft tissues lining the uterus, which pass to the outside by way of the vagina.

Changes in Ovary and Uterus During the Menstrual Cycle

The human menstrual cycle takes about twenty-eight days. There is, however, much individual variation in the length of cycle and time of ovulation. What events take place during this cycle? Let the first day of menstruation represent the first day of the cycle. Ovulation takes place sometime between two periods of menstruation, usually around the middle of the cycle.

To simplify the description, the human menstrual cycle will be divided into four stages. *Stage F* (for follicle stage) covers the period of time from the end of the menstrual flow to ovulation. *Stage O* is ovulation, the brief time in which the ovum is released from the follicle. *Stage L* (for corpus luteum stage) is from ovulation to the beginning of menstruation. *Stage M* (for menstrual flow stage) represents the period of menstruation.

During *stage F* only a single egg follicle enlarges, except in the rare cases that may lead to twin or other multiple births. An estrogen is released from the ovarian follicle and stimulates a considerable increase in the size of the uterus. The growth of the soft tissues of the uterus is due primarily to three effects of the estrogen: mitotic activity and cell division is stimulated; blood supply is increased; and tissue fluid accumulates.

After ovulation (*stage O*) and during *stage L,* progesterone secreted from the corpus luteum acts on the already estrogen-prepared uterus. Progesterone stimulates the thickening of the uterus, affecting gland and blood vessel development until the soft tissues form a rich spongy layer suitable for the attachment of a fertilized ovum. These changes in the uterus must take place before the fertilized ovum can become attached and develop normally.

If fertilization and the attachment of the embryo do not occur, menstruation will start. Normally the onset of menstruation, *stage M,* is closely associated with a decrease of progesterone. The cycle is now complete, returning once again to the beginning.

In the United States, human females usually start to menstruate at the age of thirteen or fourteen, but there is a great deal of variation. It is not uncommon for menstruation to start as early as nine or as late as twenty-one years of age. Generally some time during the forties, the menstrual cycle of the human female ceases—this is referred to as the **menopause** (MEN·o·pauz).

The Role of the Pituitary Hormones

Of course, this story of the hormonal control of the reproductive cycle raises certain further questions. First, granted that ovarian hormones regulate the uterus, what regulates the ovary? What controls the growth of an ovum and a follicle? What controls the formation of a corpus luteum from the follicle? Second, what is it that makes the difference between the corpus luteum stage (*stage L*) and pregnancy; that is, what maintains the high development of the uterus for the 280 days when an embryo is present? We cannot answer these questions completely as yet, but experiments have given some valuable clues.

Our first insight into these questions begins with the experimental evidence that removal of the pituitary gland, a small body near the base of the brain, interferes with reproduction. If the pituitary is removed from an immature male or female rat, there is no normal development of either testes or ovaries. If the pituitary is removed from a mature female rat, the ovaries as well as the uterus stop their cycles. With the adult male, the testes, which are not cyclic in activity, are not so strongly affected.

It is clear that the hormones released from the pituitary gland influence both the ovary and the uterus. Adding what we already know about the influence of the ovary on the uterus, we can tentatively summarize the relationships among pituitary, ovary, and uterus in this way:

$$\text{Pituitary} \xrightarrow{\text{influences}} \text{Ovarian activity} \xrightarrow{\text{influences}} \text{Uterine activity}$$

Many experiments indicate that there are three different hormones released from the pituitary that affect the reproductive system.

When one of the pituitary hormones is given to an experimental female animal whose pituitary has been removed, the ovaries increase in weight. This increase in weight is due to the development of many follicles. The pituitary hormone having this action is called the **follicle-stimulating hormone,** commonly abbreviated FSH. Even though this compound stimulates the follicles to grow, the uterus remains small. This fact shows that effective amounts of estrogen are not being secreted.

The second pituitary hormone is called the **luteinizing** (LOO·te·ny·zing) **hormone,** or LH. It brings about very little change in the ovary if the ovary has only small follicles. When LH is given to an animal that has well-developed follicles, ovulation occurs and the follicles change to corpora lutea (plural for corpus luteum).

Only when FSH is given at the same time as LH do the developing follicles secrete detectable amounts of estrogen. With certain combinations of FSH and LH there is maximum development of follicles, secretion of estrogen, and ovulation.

The third pituitary hormone is called LTH, or the **luteotropic** (LOO·te·o·TROP·ic) **hormone** (it is also called prolactin [pro·LAK·tin] because it stimulates the development of and secretion by the mammary glands). The corpora lutea secrete progesterone in response to LTH.

Especially noteworthy is the *feedback* control exerted by the ovary on the pituitary. The amounts of estrogen being secreted by the ovary, in the several phases of its cycle, inhibit the secretion of one hormone by the pituitary but trigger, or stimulate, the secretion of

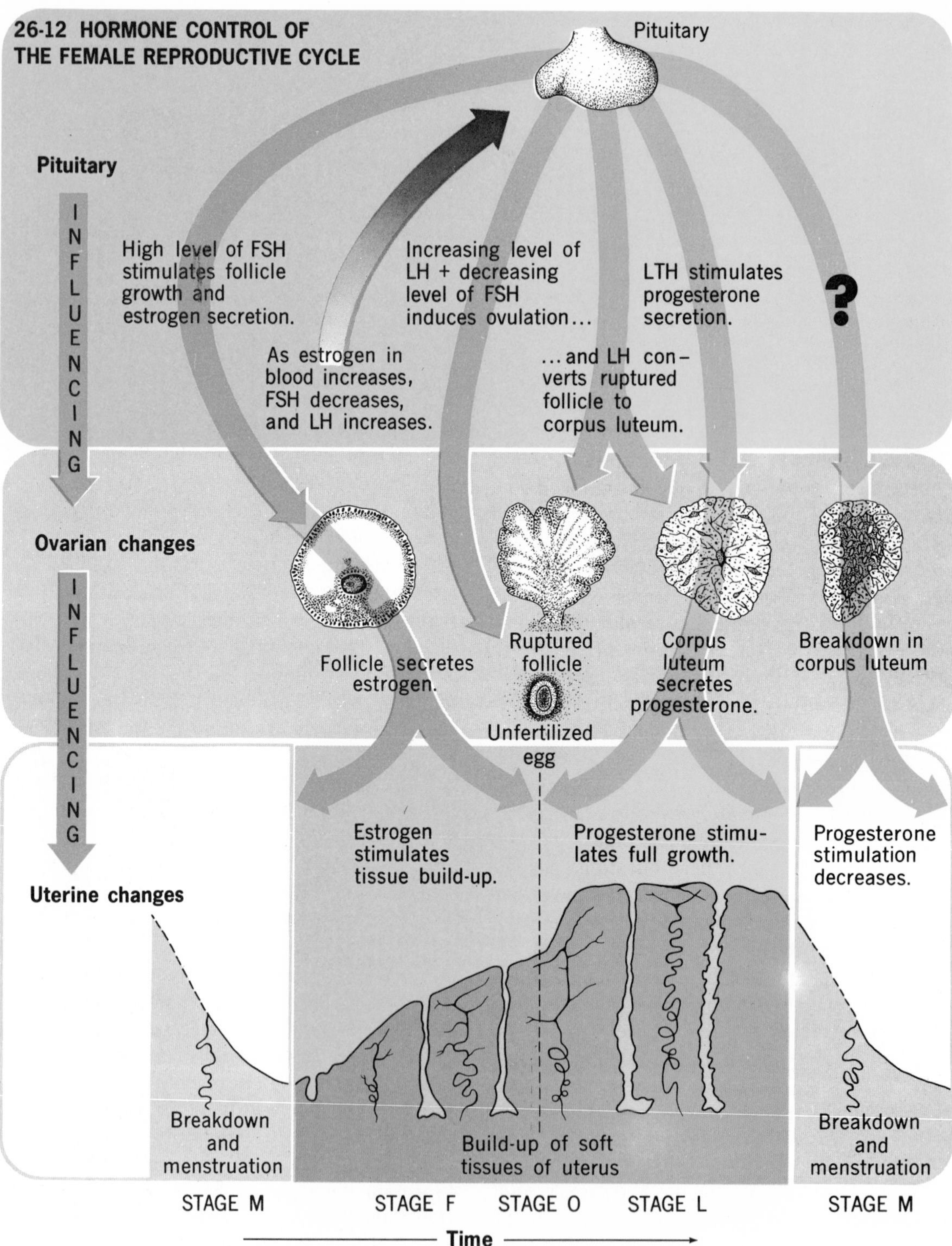
26-12 HORMONE CONTROL OF THE FEMALE REPRODUCTIVE CYCLE
Pituitary
Pituitary
INFLUENCING
High level of FSH stimulates follicle growth and estrogen secretion.
Increasing level of LH + decreasing level of FSH induces ovulation...
LTH stimulates progesterone secretion.
?
As estrogen in blood increases, FSH decreases, and LH increases.
...and LH converts ruptured follicle to corpus luteum.
Ovarian changes
INFLUENCING
Follicle secretes estrogen.
Ruptured follicle
Unfertilized egg
Corpus luteum secretes progesterone.
Breakdown in corpus luteum
Uterine changes
Estrogen stimulates tissue build-up.
Progesterone stimulates full growth.
Progesterone stimulation decreases.
Breakdown and menstruation
Build-up of soft tissues of uterus
Breakdown and menstruation
STAGE M
STAGE F
STAGE O
STAGE L
STAGE M
Time

another. Thus a rising concentration of estrogen inhibits pituitary release of FSH and stimulates the release of LH. There is another important point to add to this pattern of control of reproductive function by the pituitary. The pituitary itself is closely controlled by the part of the brain lying above and in close association with it.

Very much more could be said about the control of the reproductive cycle. But some of the evidence is still conflicting, and too many details may prevent one from seeing the main relations clearly. Figure 26-12 summarizes these relations.

Hormonal Control by the Placenta

How is the uterus maintained through the duration of pregnancy? There is good evidence that the placenta in some mammals (rats, mice, rabbits, man, monkeys, horses, and a few others) secretes hormones that function somewhat like those of the pituitary. These chemicals differ in structure and function from the pituitary hormones and are not the same from one mammal group to another. With the human embryo, the chorion has become specialized to produce a hormone that acts somewhat like LH but also has LTH activity. This placental hormone takes over the job of stimulating the corpus luteum to secrete progesterone until the placenta has developed to a stage where it is able to begin secreting progesterone and estrogen.

For some mammals, the ovaries are essential for the continuance of pregnancy. If the ovaries of female rats, mice, opossums, or rabbits, for example, are removed at any period during pregnancy (except, perhaps at the very end), pregnancy stops, and the young usually die. With other mammals, such as guinea pigs, the ovaries can be removed in the latter part of pregnancy without serious effect. Pregnancy usually continues, and birth of the young takes place at the same time as in the normal animals. In female mammals with the highest reproductive specializations (horses, monkeys, man), the ovaries can be removed even during the early stages of pregnancy without affecting the development of the young.

What is the explanation for these peculiar differences in the three groups? It seems that only in certain mammals has the placenta evolved the ability to secrete ovarian hormones as well as pituitarylike hormones. Thus with man, monkeys, and some other mammals, when the ovaries are removed the placenta takes over and carries the pregnancy to completion. Of course, the prolonged reproductive cycle comes to an end after the birth of the young and the ejection of the placenta.

CONCLUDING REMARKS

Methods of reproduction, and, more particularly, of sexual reproduction, vary widely among animals. In general we note that the number of eggs produced by the female bears an inverse relationship to the probability of fertilization of the eggs and survival of the individual offspring.

The main methods that animals have developed to insure the effectiveness of reproduction may be listed in a sequence leading up to placental mammals. Many of these methods are regulated by complicated hormonal interactions.

The sequence of reproductive specializations is as follows: (1) some means to insure internal fertilization; (2) a reduction in number of eggs produced; (3) storage (in the egg cell) of yolk, a reserve food supply for the nourishment of the developing embryo; (4) retention of the developing embryo in the reproductive tract of the female, affording the embryo greater protection during development; (5) development of a placenta (with the loss of yolk), which protects the embryo and brings to it a constant food supply; and finally (6) development of mammary glands, which supply the immature or newborn young with a source of continued nourishment (and along with the nourishment, a corresponding increase in maternal protection).

GUIDE QUESTIONS AND PROBLEMS

1. Evolution is thought to occur more rapidly in animals and plants that reproduce sexually than in those that reproduce only by asexual methods. What is the biological basis for this idea?
2. As a general rule, ova are considerably different in form and size from sperms. How are these differences related to the role each plays in the reproductive process?
3. How are the processes of internal and external fertilization related to the environment in which an animal lives?
4. Adult female mammals are capable of producing only a few offspring during their lifetime, while an oyster may give rise to millions of young oysters. To what can you relate this difference in reproductive capacity?
5. The structure of the reproductive system in the duckbill platypus, and the eggs that are laid, correspond to reproductive characteristics of reptiles. Other features of the platypus, such as its mammary glands, correspond to characteristics of the higher mammals. How can this kind of "in-between" reproductive pattern be accounted for?
6. Many myths surround human embryo development. One states: "If a mother during her pregnancy is frightened by a dog, the child will have a lifelong fear of dogs." How should such statements be evaluated?
7. In rabbits ovulation takes place only after mating. How does this pattern of ovulation compare with that in human females? Can you suggest what might control ovulation in the rabbit?
8. Suppose that a previously undetected gland is found in sheep, and that a biologist suspects the gland may be important in the control of part of the reproductive cycle in female sheep. What kind of experiments might he do to shed light on his idea?
9. The addition of certain reproductive hormones to cattle feed and chicken feed greatly increases meat production in these animals. Why would this use of hormones have to be carefully studied and regulated by law?
10. In your study of the endocrine glands in Chapter 24, you learned that the pituitary gland produces thyroid-stimulating hormone (TSH), which stimulates the production of thyroxin by the thyroid gland. You also learned that as the thyroxin accumulates in the blood it inhibits the further production of TSH by the pituitary gland; the inhibition lessens as the thyroxin is used up in the body. What similar situation exists in the human reproductive cycle, and what is such a mechanism termed?

RELATED READING

Books

For further accounts of animal reproduction and reproductive systems . . .

Davey, K. G., *Reproduction in the Insects,* Freeman, San Francisco, 1965 (paperback).

Corner, G. W., *The Hormones in Human Reproduction,* Revised Edition, Atheneum, New York, 1963.

Nalbandov, A. V., *Reproductive Physiology,* Second Edition, Freeman, San Francisco, 1964. Covers reproductive systems and reproduction in domestic and laboratory animals, and in man.

Magazines

Allen, Robert D., "The Moment of Fertilization," *Scientific American,* Volume 201 (July 1959), page 124.

Berelson, Bernard, and Ronald Freedman, "A Study in Fertility Control," *Scientific American,* Volume 210 (May 1964), page 29.

Levine, S., "Sex Differences in the Brain," *Scientific American,* Volume 214 (April 1966), page 84.

Rosenfeld, Albert, "Drama of Life Before Birth," *Life* magazine, Volume 58, No. 17 (April 30, 1965), page 54. Fascinating color photographs of developing babies before birth.

27

The Development of Animals

Animals and plants are exceedingly complex. An oak tree and a man are both composed of billions of cells, but they are not just masses of cells. Their cells are organized. In man, the cells are organized into a creature who lives, thinks, speaks, and in many ways controls his environment. How does this amazingly organized complexity develop from a single cell?

Development comprises the events that begin with fertilization and end with the formation of the adult body. The study of development is called **embryology** (em·bree·OL·o·gee). Many things occur during development. All are interrelated, but for convenience we can think of development as being composed of four main processes.

Four Processes of Development

First, there is an *increase in the number of cells*. The fertilized egg is a single cell. Its diploid nucleus contains the chromosomes of the sperm plus those originally in the ovum. The diploid nucleus divides into two nuclei by mitosis, and the cell divides into two cells (Chapter 7). Mitosis and cell division continue, and slowly the adult body forms. This may take a few days, weeks, months, or years—depending upon the species of animal or plant.

Cell division usually continues throughout life in some parts of the body. In our own bodies, the cells of the lower layers of the skin and of the lining of the intestine, and those giving rise to the blood cells, divide frequently. Cells in many other parts of our bodies (for example, the brain) divide rarely or not at all.

Second, development entails *growth*. Each of us began as a tiny cell, so small as to be just visible to the unaided eye. This first cell divided, and the daughter cells divided. Soon the young embryo began to take in raw materials from the outside and its mass increased. Now look at us!

A fertilized frog's egg is a sphere about 1.5 mm in diameter. From this minute beginning a large bullfrog may develop. A human fertilized egg is even smaller than a frog's egg, and the product of its growth is many times bigger than the bullfrog.

Third, many different kinds of cells are produced in the course of development. We call this process *cellular differentiation*. The many cells that have arisen from the fertilized egg are not mere fragments or duplicates of the egg. Instead, they have changed in many different directions. Some have become muscle cells and others have become skin cells; some have become gland cells, which produce hormones and other secretions; others have become ova or sperms.

Fourth, the many kinds of different cells undergo *organization into various structures*. That is, in the course of development, the cells become arranged and grouped in such a way that they can perform their specialized functions in an efficient manner. These arrangements of cells are the tissues and organs of the adult organism.

We have divided the large problem of development into four smaller problems to make our study simpler. The embryo makes no such division. Cells divide. As they divide, they begin to differentiate. Growth generally begins when the cells are just starting to differentiate. With differentiation comes organization into tissues and organs. If we remember, then, that development is the sum of all these processes, we may continue to study them as separate problems.

You already know something about the biology of cells. Cell multiplication, with nuclear mitosis, was discussed in Chapter 7. The physiology of cells was discussed in Chapter 6. There is nothing special about cell division or the general features of cell metabolism in embryonic cells. Hence, we need not reconsider cell division and cell physiology here. The *special* problems of embryology are those concerned with differentiation and organization. These are the problems we will talk about now, using the amphibian embryo as our example.

DEVELOPMENT OF THE AMPHIBIAN EMBRYO

Why do embryologists spend their time studying the development of frogs and salamanders? Would it not seem more appropriate to study the development of man? By now you should be able to give an answer. Biologists tend to investigate problems in those situations that are most likely to yield answers. A biologist would be more likely to study the problems of inheritance in some small, rapidly breeding animal or plant than in the much slower breeding elephant or oak tree! Embryologists have found the embryos of amphibians, chickens, sea stars, sea urchins, and some other animals far more useful than embryos of man.

Advantages of Studying Amphibian Embryos

What are the advantages of using amphibian embryos over those of man? Briefly, they are easier to get, easier to maintain, and easier to use in experiments. As you might imagine, very young human embryos are exceedingly difficult to obtain. Furthermore, they require special conditions for growth. The normal conditions, present in the uterus, have so far not been duplicated in the laboratory. The day of the "test-tube baby" is still a long way off.

If embryologists had been forced to restrict their studies to the embryos of man, our present knowledge of development would be scanty. But we have seen repeatedly that fundamental biological processes are very much alike in similar organisms. As a matter of fact, we do know a great deal about the development of the human embryo; but this knowledge is based on the far better data obtained from experimental studies of development of frogs, salamanders, chicks, and sea stars, and from some glances at the embryos of monkeys. Of all of these, it is probable that investigations of amphibian embryos have provided the best understanding of fundamental processes in development.

To begin with, amphibian embryos can easily be kept in the laboratory. A dish of pond water and a relatively cool room (15–20° C) suffice. No food is needed; the egg, when it leaves the body of the female, has a large supply of yolk granules.

The yolk of an amphibian egg is much like that of a hen's egg. It consists largely of protein. In the hen's egg there is enough stored food to supply the needs of the embryo during its entire development from zygote to hatched chick. A frog's egg, or a salamander's egg, has enough stored food material to supply the embryo's needs up to the time it becomes a swimming larva able to obtain its own food. The egg of the human being, and of all other placental mammals for that matter, contains only a small amount of stored food. The embryo of a placental mammal receives nearly all of the raw materials it needs for maintenance, growth, and development from the female, by way of the placenta (Chapter 26).

It is easy, therefore, to raise the embryos of frogs and salamanders in the laboratory. Another advantage is that in most parts of the world, amphibian embryos are easy to collect. Salamanders are common in many parts of North America, Europe, and Asia. Frogs are found on all the continents except Antarctica. The egg masses of amphibians are often familiar sights in ponds and streams. In many parts of the United States, the croaking and peeping of frogs and toads when they are at their breeding sites is one of the most prominent and familiar sounds of spring and summer nights.

The modern embryologist, however, does not have to wait for spring to carry out his experiments! Many species of frogs can be stimulated by hormones to ovulate. The technique is simple, as you will find in Laboratory Inquiry 27-1. A mature healthy female is injected with about four to six mashed pituitary glands from other frogs. After an interval of two or three days, the eggs are released from the ovary and collect in the uterus. If the female is squeezed gently, the eggs can be forced from her body into a dish containing a suspension of sperms. The sperm suspension is prepared by removing the testes from a mature male frog and cutting them into small pieces in about 10 ml of clean pond or aquarium water. This procedure liberates the sperms into the water. The embryologist can fertilize the eggs as needed for his experiments. Thus, amphibian embryos are readily available, in contrast to the embryos of man and many other mammals.

Amphibian embryos have another tremendous advantage – they are extremely hardy. In fact, they can be cut into pieces, and the pieces will survive. Possibly such an operation seems pointless to you. You will soon learn, however, that answers to some of the most basic problems in development have been obtained by cutting embryos into various pieces and observing what happens to the pieces. Chapter 29 considers these studies.

The Pattern of Development of a Salamander

The general pattern of development in the common species of salamanders and frogs that are found in the temperate regions of the northern hemisphere is much the same. We will use as an example the development of the marbled salamander, which has the scientific name *Ambystoma opacum* (am·BIS·toh·ma oh·PAY·cum – Figure 27-1). Fertilization is internal, and fertilized eggs are laid in the autumn. The females make little burrows near the edge of a pond, and in these the eggs are laid. The embryos shown in the photographs that follow were collected, brought into the laboratory, and kept at 20° C.

John A. Moore

27–1 A female marbled salamander, *Ambystoma opacum*. This particular female was the mother of the embryos photographed in Figures 27–2 through 27–17.

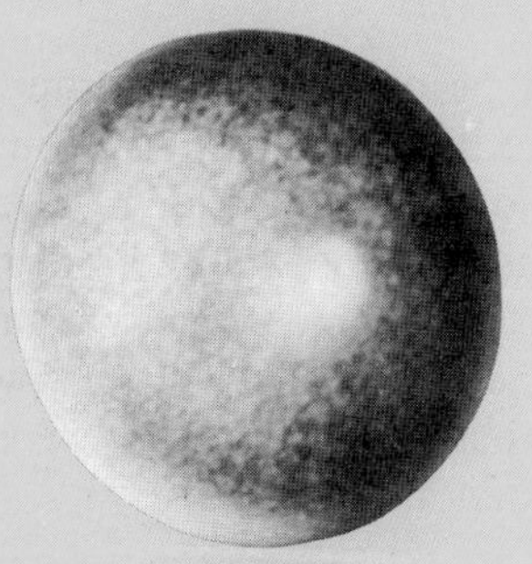

27-2

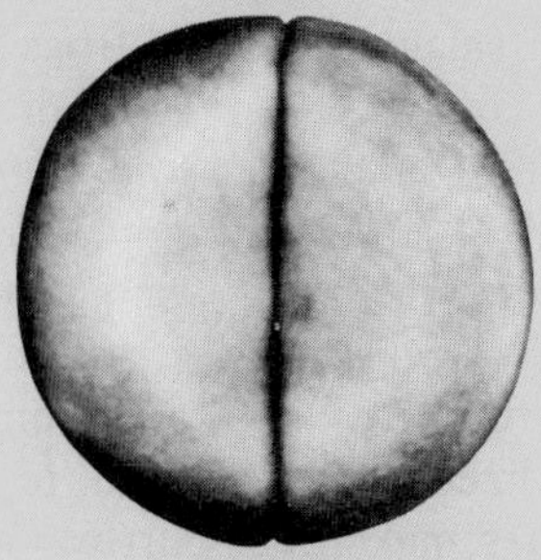

27-3

27-4

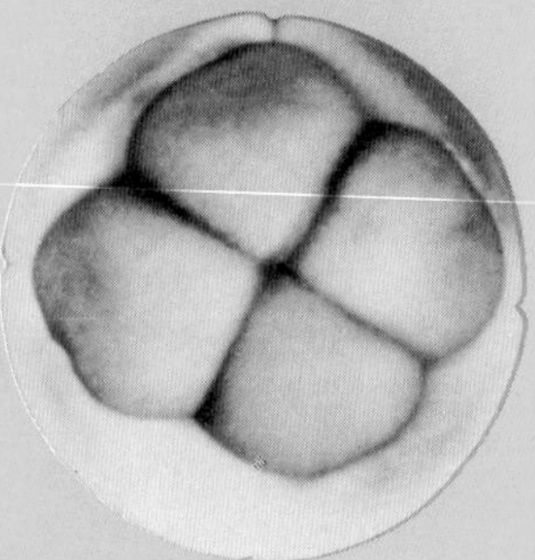

John A. Moore

27-5

Figure 27-2. The fertilized egg, when laid, is a sphere about 2.9 mm in diameter. The outer portion is pigmented, but not uniformly. Approximately one half is pale brown and the other half almost white. The darker half is called the **animal hemisphere,** and the paler half is the **vegetal hemisphere.** The vegetal hemisphere is heavier than the animal hemisphere. As a consequence, the embryo becomes oriented vegetal hemisphere down. In the photograph, we are looking down onto the animal hemisphere.

Figure 27-3. About 9 hours after the egg leaves the body of the female, a dramatic event occurs—the egg divides, or cleaves, into two cells. The first evidence that this is about to occur is the appearance of a thin pigmented line across the animal hemisphere. This line quickly becomes a deep groove, which cuts the single cell into two cells. The internal events are equally dramatic but are, of course, invisible. Each of the two cells formed has a diploid nucleus produced by mitosis.

Figure 27-4. About 2 hours and 20 minutes later, the embryo divides again. In each of the two cells the nucleus undergoes mitosis and the cell as a whole divides. Thus the two-celled embryo is converted into a four-celled embryo. Notice that the first two cleavages cut through the center of the animal hemisphere. The four cells are equal in size. Each contains a portion of the animal hemisphere and of the vegetal hemisphere. (In the photograph, we are still looking down on the animal hemisphere.)

Figure 27-5. After another interval of approximately 2 hours and 20 minutes, or about 13 hours and 40 minutes after the egg is laid, the third cleavage divides the embryo into four small and four large cells. The plane of this cleavage is at a right angle to the first two. The first two cleavages produced cells equal in all respects. The third cleavage is different. Not only are the two quartets of cells unequal in size, but they differ in the materials they contain from the animal and vegetal hemispheres.

Figure 27-6. The process of cell division continues, and the original material in the one-celled zygote becomes apportioned among many cells. More than thirty cells are visible in this photograph, which shows the animal hemisphere side of the embryo. Nineteen hours have passed since the egg left the body of the female. Cell division is slightly more rapid in the cells of the animal hemisphere than in those of the vegetal hemisphere. As a result, the cells of the animal hemisphere are smaller and more numerous. There is no overall growth of the embryo yet, but only cell division with some degree of cellular differentiation. Growth will occur in later stages.

Figure 27-7. Now the embryo is 29 hours old. The cells of the animal hemisphere are quite small, and there are many hundreds of them. If one were to cut this embryo in half, a large cavity would be revealed (Figure 27-18a, page 501). This cavity occupies much of the interior of the animal hemisphere. It is filled with a fluid, largely water but with some dissolved salts and proteins. An embryo consisting of many cells and with a cavity of this sort is called a **blastula** (BLAS·tyoo·la). The cells are nearly alike in their physical appearance, except in size and presence of pigment. Chemically, they may be considerably more different than they appear.

Figure 27-8. When the embryo is about 50 hours old, an event of profound importance begins—there is a rearrangement of cells. The embryo shown here has been rolled over so that we are looking at the vegetal hemisphere. A curved groove has formed, which is known as the **blastopore** (BLAS·toh·pohr). The cells on the outside of the embryo, both above and below the blastopore, move slowly toward the blastopore. Here, as shown by the small arrows added to the photograph, they disappear into the interior of the embryo. This process of rearrangement of the cells by the movement of some of them into the interior is known as **gastrulation** (gas·troo·LAY·shun).

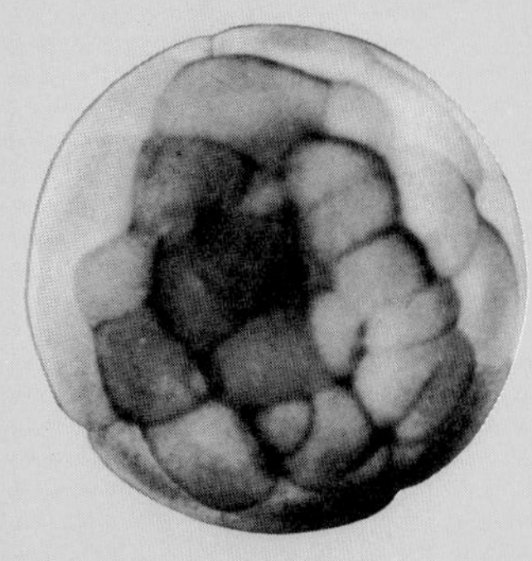

27-6

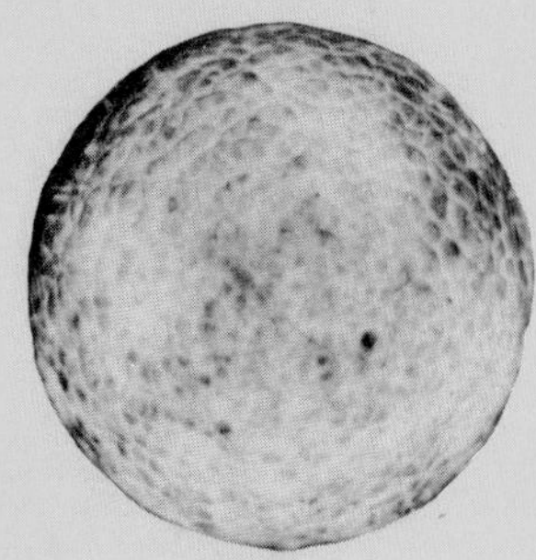

27-7

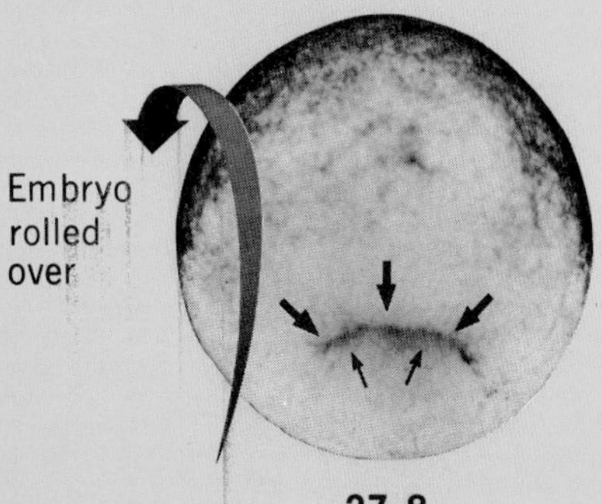

27-8

John A. Moore

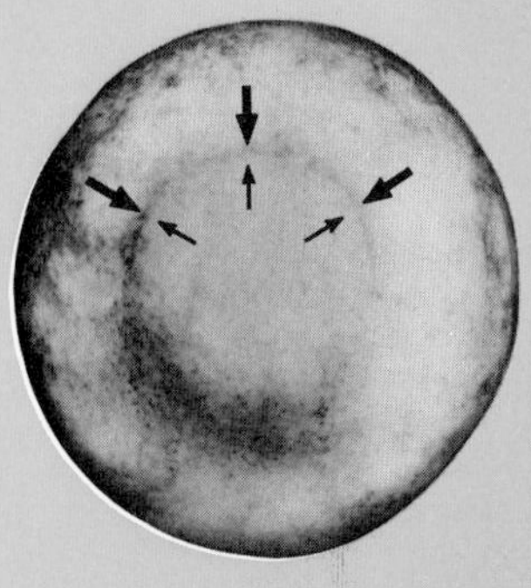

27-9

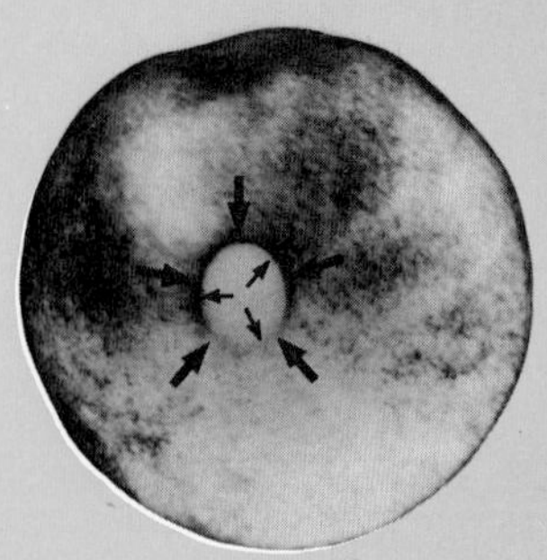

27-10

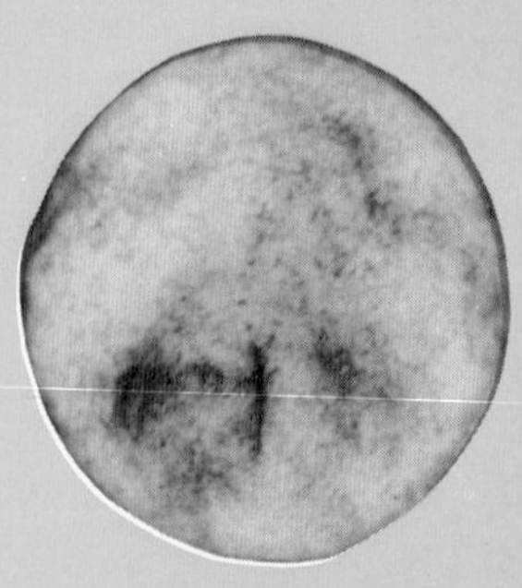

27-11

John A. Moore

Figure 27-9. Five hours later the blastopore increases in size; that is, the groove becomes deeper and extends farther around the sides. In fact, it now forms an arc of about 180°—halfway around the circle it will soon complete. The surface cells continue to move into the interior through the blastopore. [Before gastrulation began, the cells that are to form the **ectodermal** (EK·toh·der·mal), the **mesodermal** (MES·o·der·mal), and the **endodermal** (EN·doh-der·mal) structures (Figure 27–21, page 503) formed a continuous layer upon the outside of the embryo. During gastrulation the cells that will form the mesodermal and endodermal structures move to the interior.]

Figure 27-10. Eighty hours have passed since egg laying, and the blastoporal groove now forms a complete circle. The cells that will form the mesodermal and endodermal structures continue moving through the blastoporal groove to the interior of the embryo. The cells that remain on the outside are now largely those that will form ectodermal structures. Most of the cells that pass, or have already passed, to the interior of the embryo do so through the first part of the blastopore that took form, namely, the groove that was evident in the 50-hour-old embryo (Figure 27-8). This first part of the blastopore is known as the **dorsal lip.**

Figure 27-11. In this 90-hour-old embryo, the blastopore is reduced to a mere slit (seen vertically in the lower half of the photograph). Eventually it disappears entirely; but not too long after this happens the posterior end of the digestive tube breaks through in nearly the same place. In the 90-hour embryo the entire outer layer of cells is the **ectoderm.** This is the layer of cells that will form the nervous system and the outer part of the skin. The **mesoderm,** which is now inside, will form the muscles, skeleton, kidneys, circulatory system, and gonads. The **endoderm,** which is also inside now, contains the cells that will form the digestive tract, lungs, liver, and pancreas.

Figure 27-12. When the embryo is 95 hours old, it is no longer merely a spherical ball of cells. The nervous system begins to differentiate from the rest of the ectoderm. The beginnings of this are shown in the photograph. The closed blastopore is on the underside of the embryo, on the side toward the bottom of the photograph. Extending from the region of the blastopore up the side and over the top of the embryo are two lateral ridges. These are known as the **neural ridges.** The neural ridges are connected at their anterior ends, as can be seen in the photograph (where the neural ridges and the anterior connection have roughly the shape of an inverted "U").

Figure 27-13. This embryo is 10 hours older than the one in the preceding photograph. During this interval of time, the neural ridges become larger and also move together. Where the ridges meet, they fuse at their top edges. As a result, an internal tube is formed immediately beneath the fused edges. (This process can be more easily followed in the diagrams of Figure 27-19, page 502.) The neural ridges of the developing embryo are farthest apart near their anterior ends. It is this region that will form the brain. In the embryo pictured, the ridges have not closed in the anterior (brain) region. The part that has already closed will form the spinal cord.

Figure 27-14. By 110 hours the neural ridges have come together along their entire lengths. We are looking at the embryo from the side (slightly toward what is becoming its back) and from above. The enlarged portion of the neural ridges at the right will form the walls of the brain. One can still distinguish a line that runs along the back (in the upper portion of the photograph), marking the place where the neural ridges came together. This is the midline of the back in the developing embryo. Now the embryo begins to elongate slightly and acquire a new form. At this stage cilia begin to form in the cells of the outer ectoderm. Their beating slowly moves the embryo.

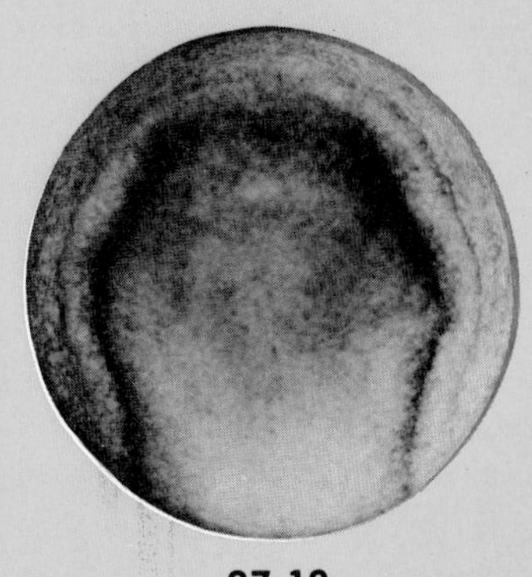

27-12

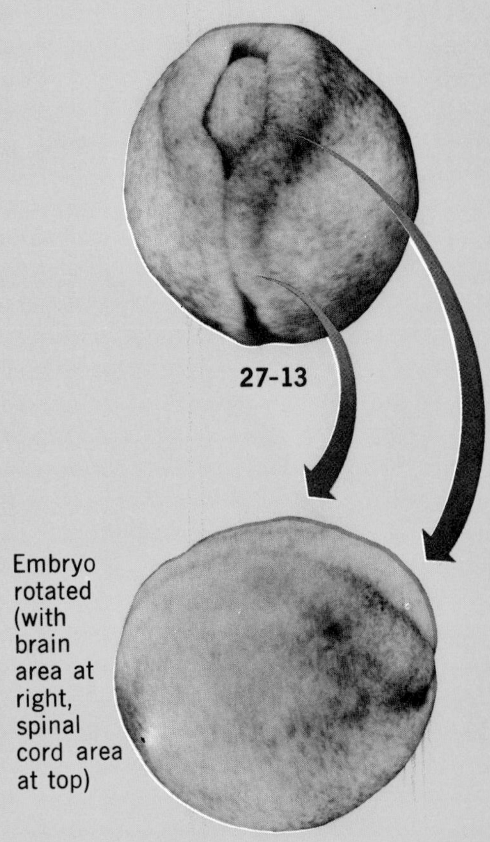

27-13

Embryo rotated (with brain area at right, spinal cord area at top)

27-14

John A. Moore

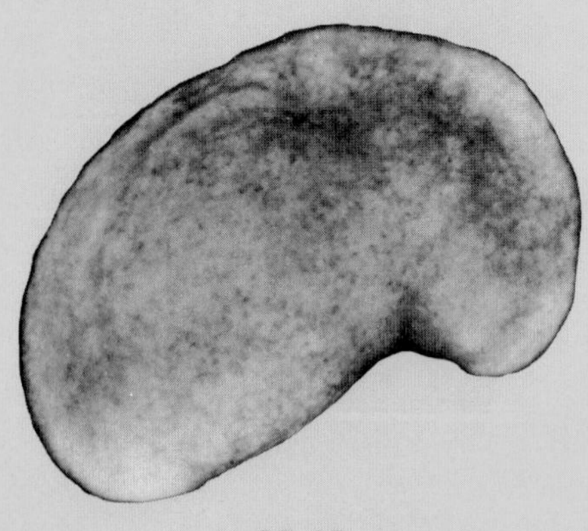

27-15

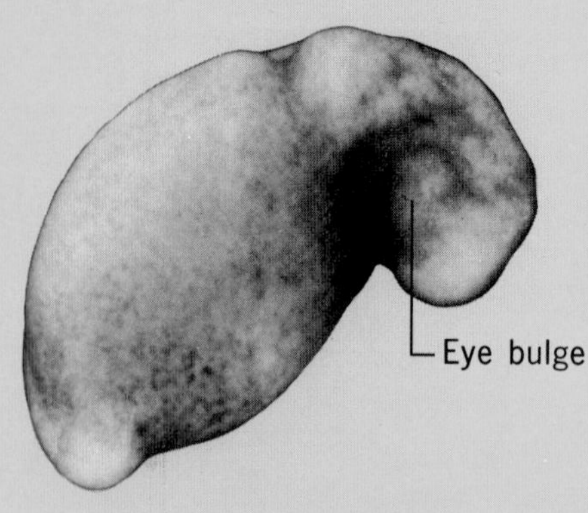

27-16

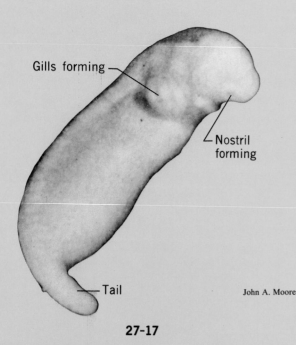

Gills forming
Nostril forming
Tail

John A. Moore

27-17

Figure 27-15. More than a day later, at 140 hours of age, the embryo is much elongated. We are looking at it from the right side, more or less the same perspective from which we viewed it in Figure 27-14. The bump at the right is the head, which bends downward. If you look closely about 3 mm below the top of the embryo and about halfway from front to rear, you can see a tiny ridge. This ridge marks the presence of an excretory organ, one of the embryo's kidneys, which form on either side from the mesoderm under the skin. Many other changes take place inside. For example, the digestive canal forms, though as yet it does not open at either end to the outside.

Figure 27-16. At 160 hours one can see a few more external developments of form. The head, which is still to the right in the photograph, has a bump on the near side of it (and also on the far side). This is caused by a bulging out of a part of the brain that forms the eye cup. Some cells of the ectoderm over the eye cup will differentiate as the lens. The eye, then, is formed in part as an outgrowth of the brain (which is derived from the ectoderm) and in part directly from the ectoderm that covers the embryo. The ears and nostrils also form as an ingrowth of the outer ectodermal layer, but they cannot be seen in the embryo at this time.

Figure 27-17. The embryo pictured here has been developing for nearly 9 days—for 209 hours to be exact. These times, you will recall, are for development at 20° C. (If we had kept the embryo at 10° C, it would have taken it about three times as long to reach this stage. If the embryo had been kept at 25° C it would have developed a little faster than at 20° C.) The dark spot near the front end is a nostril. The big bump, about one quarter of the distance from the front end, is where gills are forming. The tail is now fairly well developed. Internally, all of the organ systems are differentiating.

Now we have seen how the embryo changes as it develops from a spherical egg into a young *larva*. Let us go back and study some of the

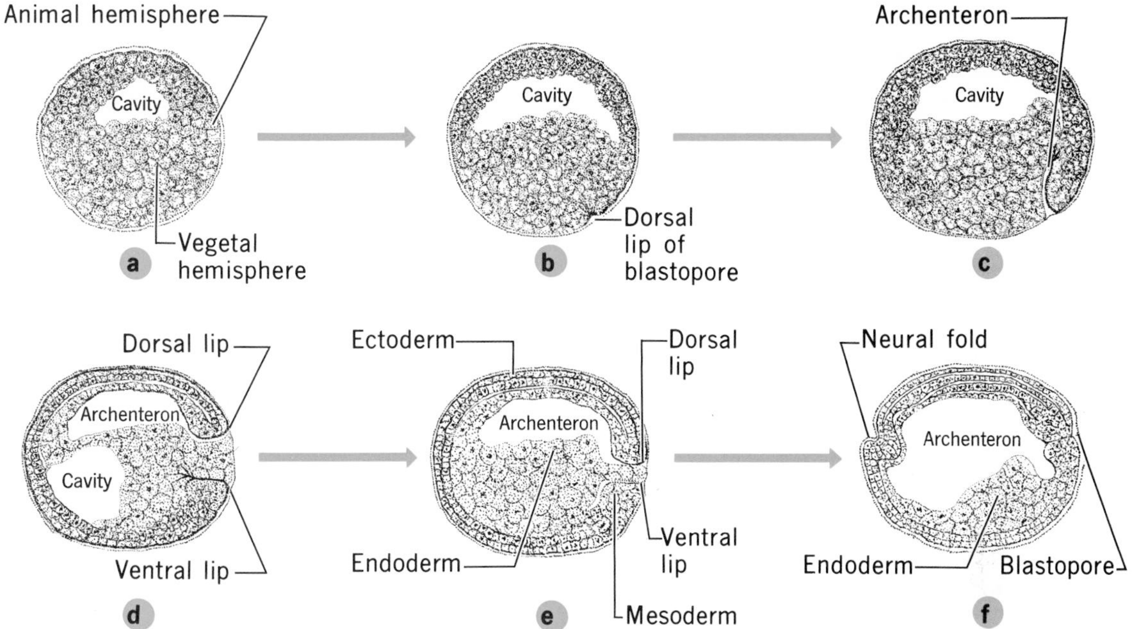

27–18 Early steps in the formation of a salamander embryo, as seen in sectioned embryos. A complex series of movements converts the blastula into a gastrula. Notice the gradual growth of the archenteron, which will form the alimentary canal. Can you relate these diagrams to the photographs of embryos in Figures 27–2 through 27–17? (Note especially the stages from Figures 27–7 through 27–11.)

events that take place *inside* the embryo. We have been aware of a few of these from the ridges and bumps that appear on the surface. Any detailed understanding of what goes on inside, however, can be gained only from making sections of the embryos and studying them under a microscope.

By a series of cell divisions, the fertilized egg becomes converted into a blastula (Figure 27-18), which is a hollow ball of cells. At gastrulation the cells become rearranged. Roughly speaking, those of the vegetal hemisphere and equatorial region move to the inside through the blastopore. The cells of these areas form the mesoderm and endoderm. These movements are shown diagrammatically in Figure 27-18. The small pocket that first forms at the dorsal lip of the blastopore gradually expands into a large cavity known as the **archenteron** (ar·KEN·ter·on). The archenteron in later development forms the digestive canal. The lungs, liver, and pancreas grow out from its walls. The cells lining the archenteron are endodermal, so all of the structures just mentioned have their origin in this layer.

The photographs of the developing embryo show that the nervous system begins as a pair of ridges forming on the dorsal side (Figure 27-12). The processes involved become clearer if we supplement our observations of external development with a study of sectioned embryos (Figure 27-19). Here we see how the neural ridges are elevated, and how they move together and then fuse to form the **neural tube.** The anterior part of this tube becomes the brain; the middle and posterior parts, the spinal cord. All of the nerves develop from the neural tube and the ectoderm adjacent to it.

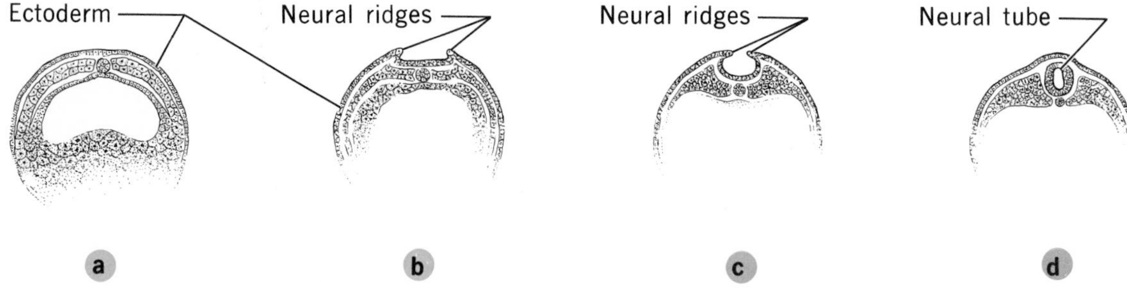

27–19 The formation of the neural tube in a salamander embryo. Dorsal parts of four developmental stages are shown in cross section. Compare these drawings with the photographs of neural tube development in Figures 27–12 through 27–14.

The eyes, which we noticed as mere bumps on the side of the head of the early embryo, develop from the brain region of the neural tube. The process is shown in Figure 27-20. The ears and nose are also formed from the ectoderm that covers the embryo.

Basic Features of Vertebrate Development

The basic features of development are much the same in all vertebrates. A three-layered embryo forms, the nerve tube rounds up from the ectoderm, and so on. Early embryos of fish, amphibians, reptiles, birds (Inquiry 27-2), and mammals resemble one another in many ways. As development continues, however, they resemble one another less and less.

This similarity of early developmental stages suggests that the "theme" of development is shared by most animals. The comparative study of early development of species that are really quite unlike as adults often provides strong evidence of descent from a common ancestor. From such studies we can even trace certain common features shared by the very primitive vertebrates with some of the invertebrates.

The Embryonic Layers

As we might expect, the formation of three layers of cells is a process shared by the embryos of all vertebrates. We call these three layers the **embryonic layers,** meaning that they are distinctive areas in the embryo that give

27–20 The formation of eyes in a salamander embryo. Cross sections of the anterior ends of embryos of four stages are shown. The youngest embryo is **a.** Optic cups can be seen growing out from the ventral part of the embryonic brain in **b, c,** and **d.** Simultaneously, the lenses of the eyes develop from the ectoderm that covers the embryo.

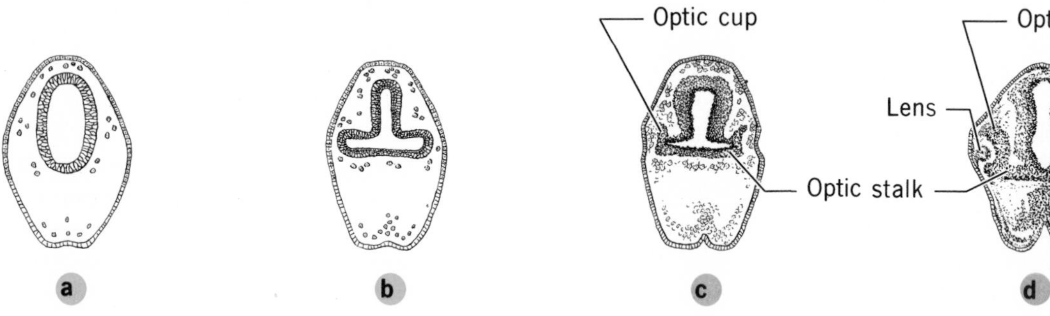

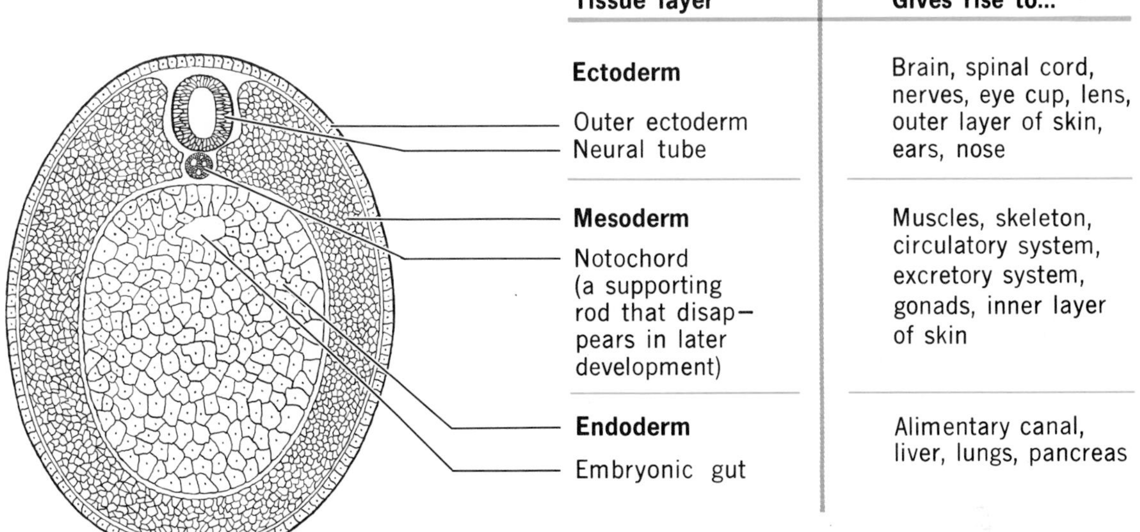

Tissue layer	Gives rise to...
Ectoderm Outer ectoderm Neural tube	Brain, spinal cord, nerves, eye cup, lens, outer layer of skin, ears, nose
Mesoderm Notochord (a supporting rod that disap- pears in later development)	Muscles, skeleton, circulatory system, excretory system, gonads, inner layer of skin
Endoderm Embryonic gut	Alimentary canal, liver, lungs, pancreas

27–21 A diagram of a salamander embryo in cross section, showing the three embryonic cell layers and the major body structures that originate from each. Can you see the relation between this diagram and one of the kind shown in Figure 19–10 (page 361)? Of what significance is such a comparison?

rise to all the organs and systems of the adult. Some organs are made up primarily of cells that come originally from two layers. The stomach, for instance, as well as the rest of the digestive system, is a kind of hollow tube. Its inner lining cells come from endoderm, but its muscular walls are made up of cells that come from mesoderm. The skin likewise has two components, the outer, tough epidermis (from ectoderm), and the inner layers (from mesoderm).

Figure 27-21 is a cross section of a salamander embryo. It shows the fundamental positions of the three embryonic layers and the main structures formed from each layer.

The corresponding embryonic layer in different vertebrates may produce different structures. In mammals, for instance, the ectoderm gives rise to the epidermis of the skin and to hair. In other vertebrates, however, the structures that emerge from and protect the surface of the body may be feathers (in birds) or scales (in birds, reptiles, and some mammals). Yet all of these surface structures arise from the same embryonic layer, the ectoderm.

CONCLUDING REMARKS

The problems of development, from fertilized egg to adult, are much the same in all organisms, and the solutions are also similar.

The fertilized egg is a single diploid cell. The adult may consist of many billions of cells, nearly all of which will be diploid. This increase in cell number is brought about by cell division.

Not only is there an increase in cell number, but ultimately there is also growth. Some fertilized eggs contain their own food supply—yolk—which makes growth possible. The hen's egg has a large amount of yolk—enough to carry the embryo to the chick stage. The amphibian egg generally has less—just enough to produce a swimming larva that can capture its own food. The egg of a placental mammal has little or none—it relies on its mother for food.

As the cells increase in number, they also differentiate; that is, they change in structure and function. The cells of the upper portion of the animal hemisphere of a blastula are much alike (Figure 27-7). They are all part of the embryonic layer known as the ectoderm. In the course of development, however, some differentiate into the cells of the neural tube or into the outer layer of the skin; others form the cell types found in the eyes; still others, the ears and nose. All neurons are differentiated from these cells.

The various cell types become organized into the specialized tissues and organs of the older embryo and the adult. They are organized to form stomach, kidneys, bones, muscles, testes, a pituitary gland, and so on.

What is responsible for the differentiation of cells and their organization into the parts of the adult? These are fascinating, though largely unanswered, questions. Nevertheless, in the next chapter we will review some of the observations and experiments that contribute to the answers that can be given today. Some day we will know more about these processes.

GUIDE QUESTIONS AND PROBLEMS

1. What four basic processes are involved in the embryonic development of complex animals?
2. How may the term "growth" be interpreted in the processes of embryonic development?
3. What evidence of evolution is suggested by comparison of the basic structural and functional features of all vertebrates?
4. Differentiation leads to organization into specialized cells, tissues, and organs. Initially in the embryo, it involves the formation of specific embryonic cell layers. What are these embryonic layers, and what structures in the mature animal are formed from each of them?
5. What are the practical advantages of studying embryonic development in animals other than man, rather than attempting to study human embryos directly?
6. What events occur in salamander embryo development between fertilization and the 29th hour after fertilization?
7. What major changes in development have occurred in a salamander embryo by the 50th hour? by the 80th hour? by the 110th hour?
8. What might account for the fact that the salamander embryo would take three times as long to develop at 10° C as at 20° C? What other physical environmental factors might influence the rate of salamander embryo development? Suggest designs for experiments that might determine the effects of these factors.

RELATED READING

Books

For more on the events involved in development . . .

De Beer, G., *Embryos and Ancestors,* Third Edition, Oxford University Press, New York, 1958.

Moore, John A., *Heredity and Development,* Oxford University Press, New York, 1963 (paperback).

Rugh, Roberts, *Vertebrate Embryology: The Dynamics of Development,* Harcourt, Brace & World, New York, 1965.

Waddington, C. H., *Principles of Development and Differentiation,* Macmillan, New York, 1966 (paperback).

Magazines

Edwards, R. G., "Mammalian Eggs in the Laboratory," *Scientific American,* Volume 215 (August 1966), page 72.

Etkin, William, "How a Tadpole Becomes a Frog," *Scientific American,* Volume 214 (May 1966), page 76.

Fischberg, Michail, and Antonie W. Blackler, "How Cells Specialize," *Scientific American,* Volume 205 (September 1961), page 124.

Konigsberg, Irwin R., "The Embryological Origin of Muscle," *Scientific American,* Volume 211 (August 1964), page 61.

28

The Analysis of Development

Look again at the series of photographs in Chapter 27 showing the gradual development of a salamander egg into a larva. Is this not an almost incredible series of events? A fertilized egg of a salamander seems to be a rather ordinary cell. In fact, it appears to be far less specialized than almost any cell in the adult. It is, seemingly, just a large spherical cell, with a lot of yolk granules in it. How does a larva that can swim, respond to stimuli, respire, excrete, and develop into an adult salamander arise from such a formless beginning? Variations of this question have been asked for at least 2,500 years. Today there is reason to hope for a solution to this fundamental biological problem within the next decade.

Now let us survey some of the questions man has asked about his own beginnings and those of other animals.

DEVELOPMENT – BY PREFORMATION OR EPIGENESIS?

Centuries ago, Aristotle proposed two different hypotheses to account for development. He pointed out that there are only two ways of explaining how an embryo arises from an egg. Either the embryo is already present in the egg, though not visible, or it is not in the egg but somehow appears during development.

Aristotle's first idea has been called **preformation.** Preformation implies that an egg or sperm is not as simple as it looks, but that it actually contains the new individual already formed (Figure 28-1).

Aristotle's other proposal is called **epigenesis** (ep·ih·JEN·e·sis). The idea is that the egg or sperm contains no preformed structures; rather, these structures somehow develop in their proper positions later, constructed from material in the egg.

For two thousand years after Aristotle's time, men argued whether preformation or epigenesis was the correct explanation for development. Scholars who believed in preformation thought that the animal was present in either the egg *or* the sperm (Figure 28-1). Of course, they did not think a preformed body could be in both (if it were, think of the confusion at fertilization!).

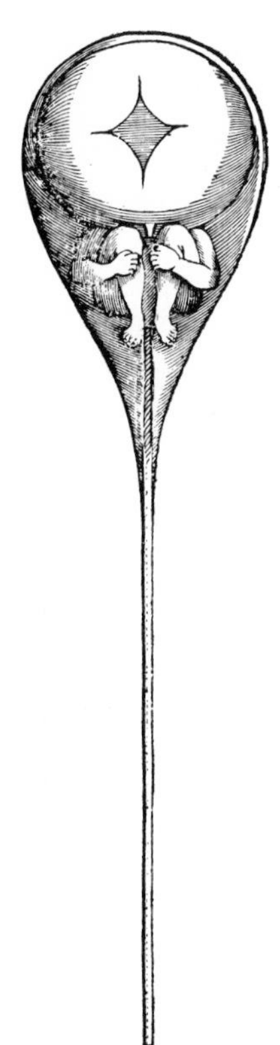

Nicolaas Hartsoeker, *Essai de Droptrique*, Paris, 1694

28–1 Some early embryologists imagined that a human sperm contained a tiny individual, shown here with a large head and folded arms and legs.

28-2 ROUX'S EXPERIMENT

a A fertilized frog egg is allowed to divide into two cells.

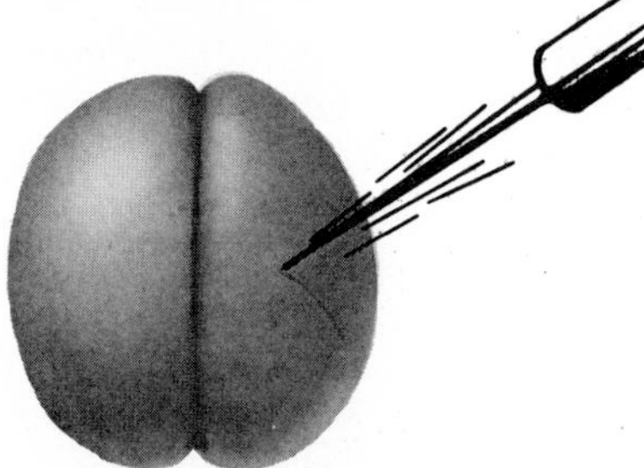

b One of the cells is killed with a needle.

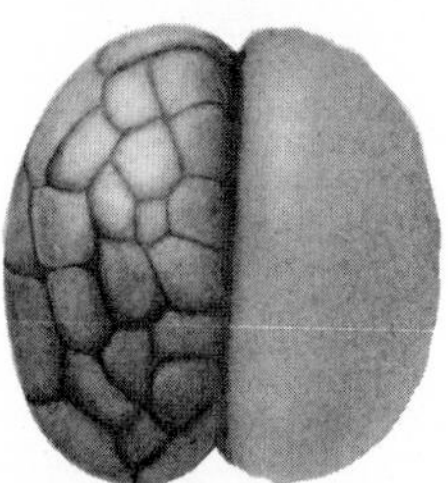

c The living cell divides to produce half a blastula.

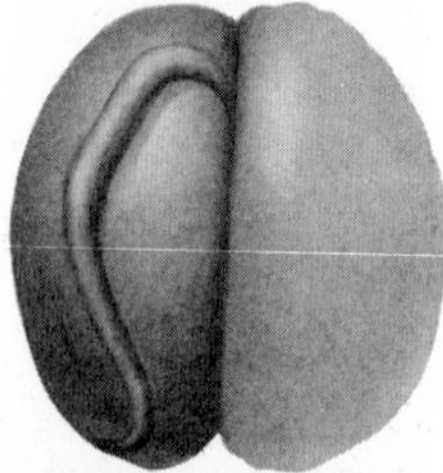

d The half-blastula may continue to develop and form half of the neural ridge.

Those who believed in epigenesis claimed that the idea of an animal in miniature inside an egg or sperm is false. They said that the egg *develops* into an animal—though they were at a loss to explain how.

During the past fifty to one hundred years, these arguments have been resolved, at least in part, by careful experimentation. One of the most important experiments was done in 1888 by the German scientist Wilhelm Roux (ROO).

Evidence for Preformation

Roux's experiment was so simple that we may do it in the school laboratory. He fertilized frog eggs and let them divide once. Then he poked a heated needle into one of the two cells, which killed that cell. The other cell was not injured by this procedure. Roux then found that the living cell developed into a *half* embryo—sometimes a head end, sometimes a tail end, sometimes a left half, and sometimes a right half, but always a half embryo, never whole (Figure 28-2).

Let us think about Roux's experiment. It *seems* to be evidence for some sort of preformation—not preformation of a body, but preformation of a pattern that controls development. If one of the first two cells develops into a left half of an embryo, that cell must have had only the pattern for this one side. The surviving cell is not able to change its organization and produce a whole embryo. Figure 28-2 summarizes this situation, from which Roux concluded that preformation is nearer the truth than epigenesis.

Evidence for Epigenesis

Roux's experiment was so interesting that many people began doing similar experiments. Some poked eggs with needles. Others worked instead to separate the first two cells in some way. One of these investigators was Hans Driesch (DREESH). He did an experiment similar to Roux's but with a different animal. He used sea urchin eggs that were at the two-cell stage, and completely removed one of the cells instead of killing it. The result was very different from that of Roux: the remaining cell produced an *entire* embryo. This result led Driesch to believe epigenesis is nearer the truth than preformation. If a half egg, which according to preformationist theory would normally contribute to only half an embryo, could actually produce a whole embryo, then the embryo is not preformed in the egg.

Roux and Driesch began a long argument. They wrote articles in scientific magazines, each saying the other was wrong. We now know they were both partly right. Modern biologists have repeated Roux's experiment and have discovered that half frog eggs do sometimes develop into whole embryos. Whether one gets a half embryo or a whole embryo depends on how the experiment is done. Thus if one actually removes one of the first two cells instead of killing it, the remaining cell usually gives rise to an entire embryo. In Roux's original experiment, apparently the mere presence of the dead cell prevented the formation of a whole embryo.

Driesch's experiments with the sea urchin have also been repeated and the same results obtained. However, sometimes a half sea urchin egg forms only a half embryo rather than a whole embryo. If the two cells formed *at the first division* are separated, either one can give rise to an entire embryo (Figure 28-3a). But, if the egg cell is cut through along the equator, *thus separating the animal hemisphere from the vegetal hemisphere,* neither half gives rise to a whole embryo (Figure 28-3b).

A whole series of experiments shows that most eggs behave this way. The results depend upon the way the experiments are done. The old debate of preformation versus epigenesis is essentially over. The basic answer is known —as a careful study of a developing embryo in the school laboratory will show (or a study of the series of photographs in Chapter 27).

Development is largely epigenetic. There is no preformed tadpole in a frog egg or sperm. There is no tiny human being, such as was described long ago (Figure 28-1), in a gamete of man. New structures do make their appearance in development. The ectoderm is originally a sheet of cells on the outside of the embryo. In the course of development some of these cells curl up to form a tube (Figure 27-19). Later the tube differentiates into a brain and a spinal cord. Still later the eye cup grows out from the brain (Figure 27-20). The brain and eye cups are not preformed as minute structures in the egg (or sperm). Their development is epigenetic.

But there is an element of truth in preformation—though not in the way it was first conceived. In a sense one can say that the embryo is preformed, because it receives genes from the parents. Its development will depend on the action of these genes. Thus, an embryo inherits a preformed genetic makeup. But this is very different from the theory of preformation that was believed for so long. The organization of the embryo arises by epigenesis, a process controlled by the genes.

THE PROBLEM OF DIFFERENTIATION

Roux and Driesch have left us a difficult problem. It would be easy to explain the "how" of development if preformation were correct: development would be just the enlargement of an organism already present in the egg. There would be only growth and cell multiplication, no differentiation or organization. Since preformation is not the explanation, we have a harder task. We must explain how a preformed genetic pattern, combined with epigenetic development, produces the adult organism.

Obviously, epigenesis is more difficult to explain than preformation. Many biologists thought it was so mysterious that it could not be explained strictly in mechanical, or physical and chemical, terms. (See Chapter 4, where the debates of the mechanists and vitalists were discussed.) Believers in epigenesis were often vitalists, while believers in preformation prided

28-3 WHOLE OR HALF? —AN EXPERIMENT WITH SEA URCHIN EGGS

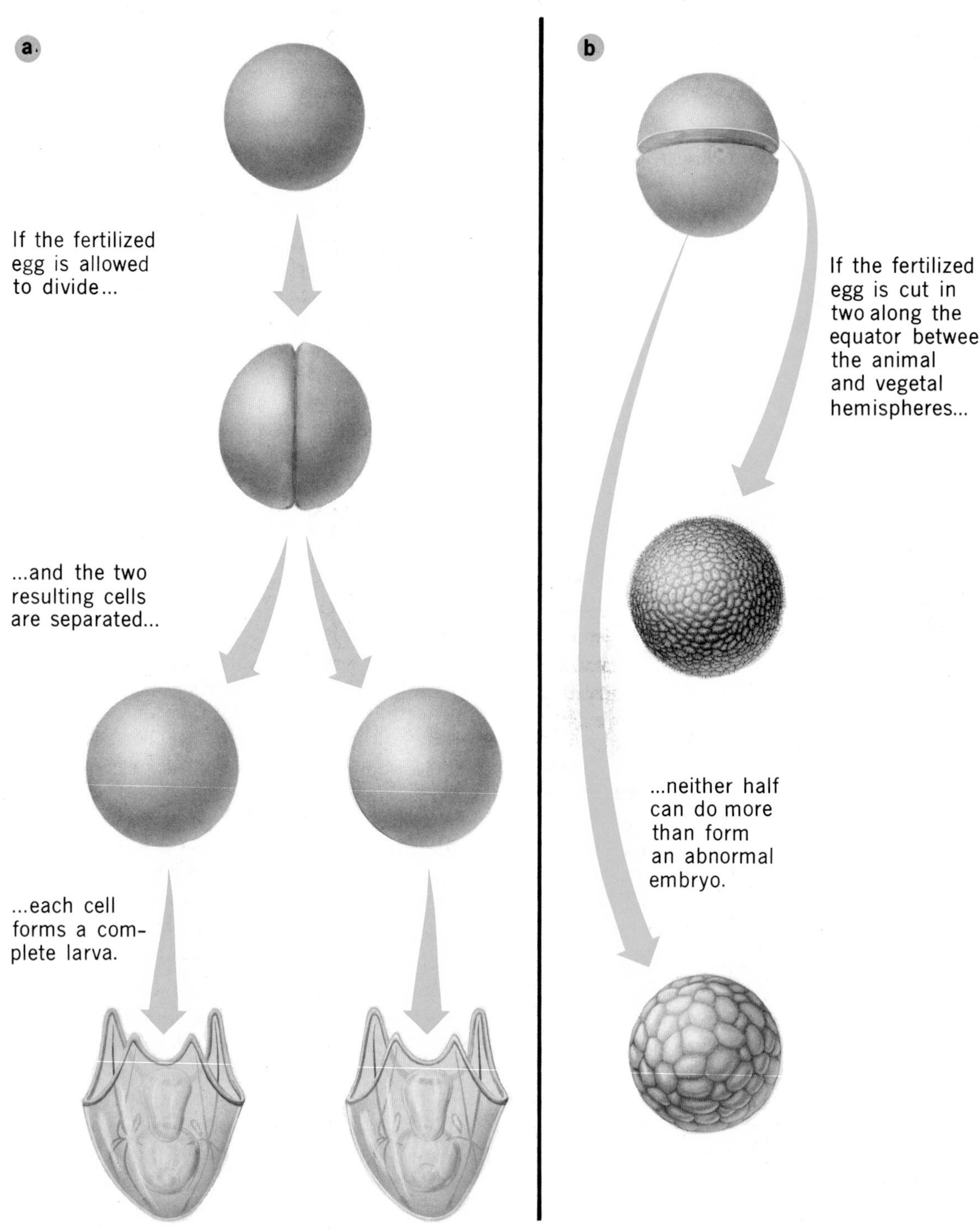
a
If the fertilized egg is allowed to divide...
...and the two resulting cells are separated...
...each cell forms a complete larva.
b
If the fertilized egg is cut in two along the equator between the animal and vegetal hemispheres...
...neither half can do more than form an abnormal embryo.

themselves on their rejection of mysterious vitalistic principles in interpreting life processes. This is worth remembering, because so many students (and biologists) think that mechanists are always right.

How does a simple egg develop into a complicated organism? How do the organs of the tadpole form from parts of the egg that are just like any other part? If all the parts of the egg cell are alike, it is hard to see how differences in the organism's cells can arise. Why isn't the tadpole made up of cells all of the same kind? From where do the differences come?

These are the questions of differentiation, one of the four aspects of development. It is quite easy to see how a cell can grow by taking up food; it is quite easy to see how a cell can divide by mitosis. It is more difficult to see how these cells differentiate into specific types.

One of the most revealing series of experiments on differentiation was carried out by Hans Spemann (SHPAY·monn) in 1924. Spemann was a student of a student of Roux's, and he continued the work of his "scientific grandfather" by inventing ways of doing more complicated surgery on amphibian embryos. Using very fine scalpels he was able to cut embryos into small pieces. He then made careful studies of how the pieces developed.

Spemann's Work on Development of the Neural Tube

Spemann's most famous experiments dealt with the differentiation of the embryonic nervous system. We have already described how the ectoderm folds up to form a tube and how the cells of the tube go on to form the nervous system. Spemann chose to investigate this act of differentiation and organization. From embryos he cut out the ectoderm that normally becomes the nerve tube and put the piece of ectoderm in a separate dish. An embryo from which the piece was taken healed and lived, but it had either a defective nervous system or none at all. Moreover, the isolated piece of ectoderm did not form a nervous system, though it remained alive and healthy. Why did the piece form a nervous system if left in the embryo, but not by itself?

Possibly something about the relation of the ectoderm to the rest of the embryo was necessary to start development of a nervous system. Spemann concluded that the piece of ectoderm needed to be attached to the embryo in order to develop properly. If you think back to the early structure of the embryo, you will remember that there is a layer of mesoderm underneath the ectoderm. Spemann thought that perhaps the mesoderm stimulates the ectoderm to develop into the nervous system. So he did a second experiment.

He cut a flap of ectoderm from the top of an embryo. He did not remove the piece of ectoderm but just folded it back. Then he cut out the mesoderm underneath and discarded it. Finally, he folded the flap of ectoderm back in place. The ectoderm healed and looked quite healthy, but it did not develop into a nervous system.

Spemann's hypothesis appeared to be proved. When the mesoderm is removed, the ectoderm does not differentiate into nerve tissue. The mesoderm must influence the ectoderm somehow to differentiate into nerve tissue.

Spemann did a third experiment that substantiated more conclusively the hypothesis that the mesoderm stimulates the ectoderm to form a neural tube. To understand this experiment, we must know that the mesoderm of an early gastrula forms a band extending around the equator of the embryo—in the zone connecting the animal and vegetal hemispheres (Figure 28-4). Spemann used two embryos, both in the early gastrula stage. From one he removed a piece of mesoderm from immediately in front of the dorsal lip of the blastopore. From the second embryo, he removed a similar-sized piece from the mesodermal area 180° from (or exactly opposite) the dorsal lip. In its place he put the piece of mesoderm from the first embryo. The transplanted mesoderm formed a blastopore and moved inside the embryo.

28-4 SPEMANN'S EMBRYO TRANSPLANT

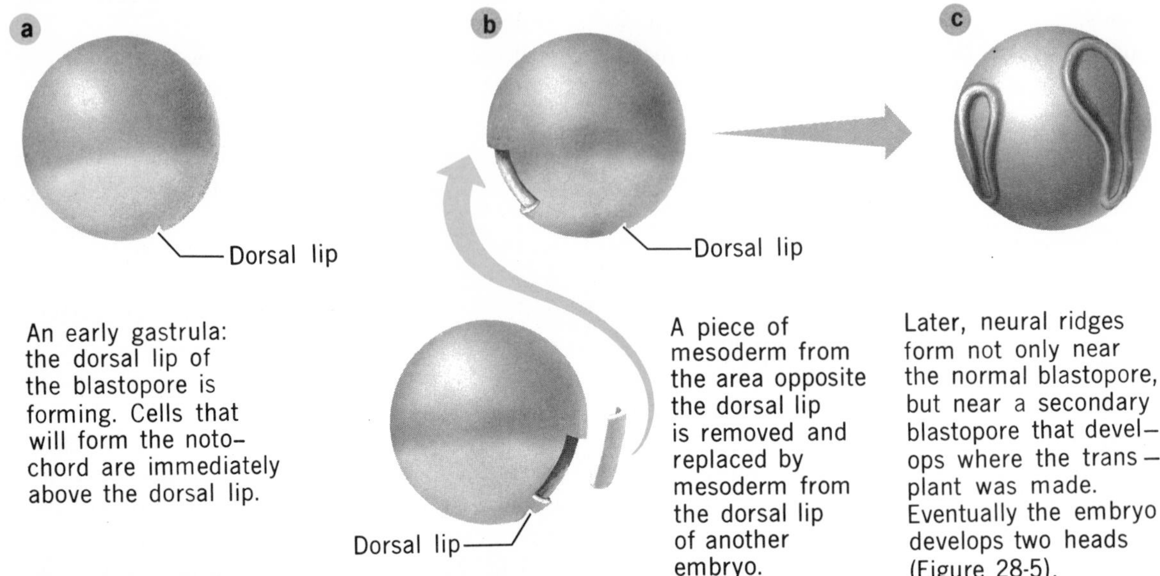

a
b
c
Dorsal lip
Dorsal lip
Dorsal lip
An early gastrula: the dorsal lip of the blastopore is forming. Cells that will form the noto-chord are immediately above the dorsal lip.
A piece of mesoderm from the area opposite the dorsal lip is removed and replaced by mesoderm from the dorsal lip of another embryo.
Later, neural ridges form not only near the normal blastopore, but near a secondary blastopore that devel-ops where the trans-plant was made. Eventually the embryo develops two heads (Figure 28-5).

John A. Moore

28-5 A salamander larva following an experiment similar to that in Figure 28-4. Notice the induced second head protruding from the belly of the larva.

Neural ridges, and later a brain and spinal cord, formed normally in front of the embryo's *original* dorsal lip. Of much greater interest was *the same occurrence in front of the blastopore that developed where the transplant was made* (Figure 28-4).

So a sort of Siamese-twin embryo was produced. From the belly of an otherwise normal larva protruded part of another with a brain and spinal cord (as in the larva of Figure 28-5).

Obviously there is something very interesting about the mesoderm of the dorsal lip region. If it is removed, the animal produces no nervous system in the normal place. If it is put in a strange place, the animal develops an extra nervous system. This area of mesoderm seems to control the differentiation of nerve tissue.

Spemann's work was considered so important that he was given a Nobel prize in 1935.

Embryonic Induction

The effect of mesoderm in stimulating ectoderm to become nerve tube was called **embryonic induction** by Spemann. Embryonic induction remains one of the very important mechanisms by which we explain differentiation. Basically it means that cells of one kind direct the development of other cells. In this case, mesodermal cells of the dorsal lip region *induce* the ectoderm to form a nerve tube.

Since the time of Spemann, induction has been discovered in other tissues of amphibian embryos and in many other kinds of animal embryos. Therefore, induction seems to be important for differentiation in all animals.

One of the most exciting recent experiments is that of another embryologist, J. Holtfreter (HOLT·fray·ter), who used the technique of tissue culture to study induction. He changed Spemann's experiment in the following way: He cut a piece of the ectoderm from an early frog embryo and put it in a small dish of special salt solution. Then he cut a piece of the mesoderm and put it in the same dish. He pressed the two pieces together so that the mesoderm healed in contact with the ectoderm.

You might expect from Spemann's experiment that this would cause the ectoderm to form a nervous system. So it did. It was not a very well shaped nervous system, because the pieces curled up in tissue culture, but it was obviously brain and spinal cord. This demonstration was the first example of induction of a tissue outside of the embryo. In control experiments, where the ectoderm alone was cut out and cultured, no brain or spinal cord formed.

Many other experiments on this same problem have shown that interaction between the parts of the embryo is common and highly important in bringing about differentiation.

For example, it is possible to mark out with stains certain areas on the blastula that are exactly the same in appearance but are destined to form ectoderm leading eventually to two different tissues—skin and nerve. If bits of tissue are exchanged between the two regions, their development is influenced by their new locations. Thus cells from the skin area develop into nerve tissue when placed in the area of nerve ectoderm. Similarly, cells from the nerve area develop into skin when placed in the area of skin ectoderm. The same seems to hold true for exchanges of tissue during the early gastrula stage.

But by about the end of gastrulation, these two areas are fixed so far as their future development is concerned. That is, cells from the skin area will develop into skin even when placed in the area of nerve ectoderm. And, cells from the nerve area will develop into nervous tissue when placed in the area of skin ectoderm. This is so because the underlying cells by the end of gastrulation have induced the ectoderm cells to differentiate in specific ways.

Still later in development, other changes occur that further restrict the sort of thing particular cells can do. It is as if each cell passes along a series of ever-branching pathways, and at each fork it must take one path or the other. Its possible goals are constantly more and more narrowly restricted. Thus a cell in the ectodermal area of an *early gastrula* is able to develop into skin, or any part of the brain or spinal cord, or part of the eye, nose, or ear. As time goes on, an ectodermal cell is no longer able to develop into *any one* of these parts; it can give rise to *only* skin cells, or *only* part of the nervous system, or *only* a part of the eye, and so on. These changes are apparently brought about by the interaction of one tissue layer with an adjacent one in which the process of induction is important. Such an interaction causes a tissue to develop in a particular way. The developed tissue then interacts with another one in turn. Thus, one tissue is a stimulus for the differentiation of another. This seems to account for the orderly, properly timed, and properly spaced differentiation of body parts.

You can see that embryonic tissues are influenced to differentiate in certain ways by other tissues. What kind of "message" is sent by the mesoderm to the ectoderm? How does the mesoderm "tell" the ectoderm to form nerve tissue? We suppose that the "messenger" the mesoderm sends to the ectoderm is a chemical substance. Recently a substance has been found that may be this "messenger."

The substance was found by an American embryologist, M. Niu (NEW), who took a piece of mesoderm from the dorsal lip area and let it stand in a salt solution for a few hours. Then he removed the piece of mesoderm and put in a piece of ectoderm. In the culture dish, the ectoderm formed nervous tissue. Niu did a control experiment in which he put a piece of ectoderm into plain salt solution that had not been exposed to mesoderm. The control piece of ectoderm did not form a nervous system.

Obviously the mesoderm leaves something behind in the salt solution, and this something stimulates the ectoderm to differentiate into nerve tissue. What is this something? Chemical analysis of the solution shows that it contains *nucleic acid.*

This exciting experiment tells us that perhaps induction occurs by the transfer of a nucleic acid from mesoderm to ectoderm. Perhaps substances other than nucleic acids are active as well. We cannot tell until more experiments have been done.

POST-EMBRYONIC DEVELOPMENT IN ANIMALS

Development does not stop when an adult animal has been formed from the egg. It continues, in a sense, from "cradle to grave." Once an animal has reached adulthood, changes in its body form and function occur much more slowly than in the case of the developing embryo. Yet such changes *do* occur.

Cell Replacement

In many tissues of the adult, cells continue to divide and differentiate, replacing older cells. Thus, the tissue remains apparently constant in form and function, yet is maintained by "turnover" of cells with all individual cells remaining fairly young. For instance, in adult amphibians like salamanders and frogs, as well as in all other vertebrates studied so far, individual red blood cells are destroyed and replaced at a steady rate, with a more or less constant number remaining always in circulation. The surface layers of skin are shed, and freshly matured cells lying underneath them take over the function of body protection.

Though such renewal of cells occurs in many tissues of adult animals, in other tissues the majority of cells are never replaced. Animals vary greatly in their patterns of cell replacement. In some, like *Hydra,* there seems to be a continuous turnover of all cells. In others, such as insects, the cells of the adult, once formed, are never replaced. Vertebrates seem to occupy an intermediate position on this scale—some cells are replaced (like blood and skin cells), but others are not (like nerve, muscle, and other highly differentiated cells). Cell replacement seems to be related to processes of regeneration, which you will read about on the next page.

Aging

Even in animals like salamanders and man, which can replace some of their cells, cell replacement does not go on forever. Gradually the adult animal changes. The changes represent a complex process which we term *aging.* Aging is most easily recognized, in all species where it occurs, by the increased probability of death. Frogs tend to live no longer than 12 to 20 years; and man's most probable life span is around 70 years (though the actual length of life varies greatly, depending on the individual's genetic background, history in terms of diet, disease, accidents, and so forth). There are other changes which have long been recognized as part of aging—both structural changes (like loss of weight, and altered skin form and hair color in man) and functional changes (loss of reproductive capacity; and slowing and decrease in accuracy of homeostatic adjustments). Many biologists are as much interested in the fundamental mechanisms of aging as in the processes at the other end of the individual's life—embryonic development. Aging is far harder to study, however, for in any given species it occurs far more slowly and is much less predictable and uniform than is embryonic development. Today, much research is being carried on in this field, both because of its scientific interest and its practical concern to members of our own species.

Why should aging—and the death which inevitably follows it—occur so predictably in some species, and not at all in others? In some tissues, cells can continue to divide, replacing worn cells up to a certain point. Why is this not true of all tissues, and indefinitely so, so that organisms need never die? Results of experimental analysis are not yet available to answer these questions. Some biologists suggest that aging and death are based on genetic mechanisms, especially mutations (Chapters 8, 30, 31, 32), which actually "program" the events leading to death—or at least do not protect the organism *against* aging and death. Others believe that the highly differentiated cells which do not divide—muscle and nerve cells in mammals, for instance—represent "points of weakness" where accidental effects of damage and disease accumulate gradually, destroying the cells and normal function of the animal as a whole. Viruses, radiation, and other factors have been suggested as possible agents causing such damage. Processes of growth and cell activity, too, may be closely related to aging. Recently it has been shown that aging can be greatly slowed and life lengthened in mammals (most of the experiments have been carried out with rats) in which growth is slowed by preventing the animals from feeding adequately when they are young. This effect is seen only when the diet is balanced in terms of its nutritional content (with plenty of minerals, vitamins, and so forth) but not given in the amounts which animals usually consume. Insects, too, can live far longer if their development is delayed.

Research in this field is progressing, although slowly. Biologists are looking for clues in changes in DNA and other cell compounds, in the structure of cells and extracellular substances of tissues, in enzyme patterns and homeostatic mechanisms. As in the case of the study of embryonic development, we must wait for more observations and experiments, to know more about the nature of aging.

D. P. Wilson

28–6 Regeneration in a sea star (viewed from the underside). Two of the animal's arms have been lost, and new ones are growing in their place.

Regeneration

If one (or more) of the arms of a sea star is removed, a new arm soon begins to regenerate (Figure 28-6). The regenerating arm continues to develop until it has the same size, form, and function as the arm it replaces. Similarly, after a lobster loses one of its larger pincer claws, it begins to grow a new one. In the lower animals we find even more dramatic instances of ability to form new structures. With planarians (flatworms) a variety of experiments can be done. If one splits the head end of a planarian between the eyespots, two new heads will develop. (Figure 28-7 shows the result of a similar experiment upon the tail end.) If one cuts a planarian

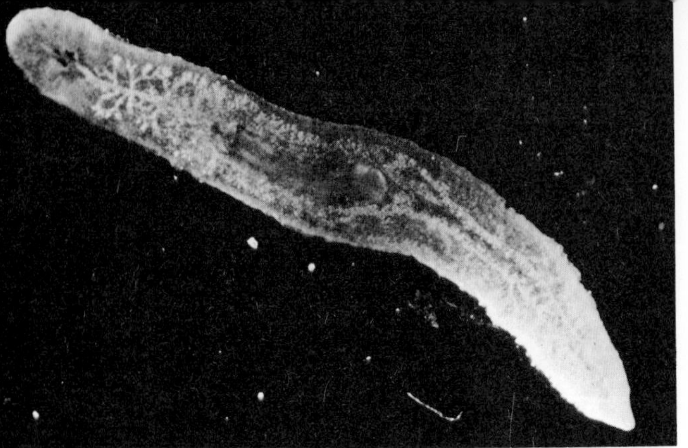

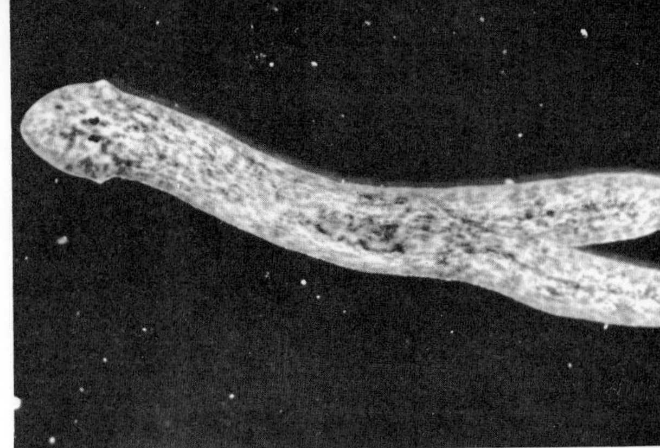

A. M. Winchester, from *Biology and Its Relation to Mankind*, D. Van Nostrand

28–7 Regeneration in a planarian. A normal individual is at the left. If its tail end is split, each half will regenerate the missing tissues, and an individual of the type at the right will be produced. What do you suppose will happen if the tail end is split into three parts, or if the head end is split into two or more parts?

in two halfway between the head and the tail, two new individuals will develop: the head end forms a new tail, and the tail end forms a new head.

In plants, regeneration is very common; the removal of large parts of a plant is followed by new development of the missing structures.

Among the animals, even some vertebrates display a remarkable capacity for regeneration. If one removes a leg from a salamander, for instance, a new leg will form. The leg is a duplicate of the one that was amputated. Every bone, every muscle, every nerve, every blood vessel is replaced accurately. The proper connections to the rest of the body are made in such a way that the leg functions perfectly. It is a fully normal replacement for the lost leg.

In such cases of regeneration we have all the biological problems of embryonic development: cell division, growth, differentiation, and organization. Since the development involved in regeneration occurs at a later stage in the life of the organism, and becomes correlated with the structures and functions that have already developed, the problems are even more complicated.

As you work with Laboratory Inquiry 28-1, you will appreciate that there is still a great deal to be learned about regeneration. The main conclusions are clear, however. The regeneration of lost parts involves the same kinds of processes that are characteristic of the initial development of an organism. It would seem that some cells of the adult retain their embryonic abilities to differentiate into a variety of cell types. These nonspecialized cells are more abundant in some species than in others—more abundant in salamanders than in frogs, for example, even though both are amphibians. If one amputates a frog's leg, the wound heals, but no new limb develops. Even man has some regenerative powers, although he cannot regenerate a limb, or even a finger. Skin wounds heal by a regeneration of the various cell types we find in the epidermis and dermis. In the case of severe loss of tissue, the wound heals somewhat imperfectly, leaving a scar. Some but not many of man's internal organs can also regenerate to some degree. The tongue, when injured, has good regenerative capacity. The liver will regenerate to its normal size when large portions have been removed surgically.

Abnormal Development

Although the processes of development are repeated with remarkable accuracy generation after generation, sometimes mistakes occur. These mistakes may have their origins in gene mutations or other changes in the hereditary material. If the genes that control developmental processes do not function properly, abnormal development may result. Outstanding examples are some kinds of dwarfism and giantism. Usually these patterns can be traced to a malfunctioning pituitary gland (Figure 24-9, page 453). Abnormal numbers of chromosomes also may result in defects (pages 559, 560, and 561).

Cancer is another kind of abnormal development. Ordinarily cells continue to divide by mitosis and to differentiate until the organism reaches its adult form. The rate of cell division then drops off gradually, and new cells are produced only as replacements for those that wear out in normal life activities. Red blood cells, for instance, are destroyed at a very fast rate, and the body must manufacture about 7 to 10 million new red blood cells every second, just to keep the number of these cells in the blood constant.

If the rate of cell division in an organ suddenly and abnormally increases, more cells are produced than are needed by the body. These rapidly developing cells get their raw materials for division and growth from the cells of organs that are already formed. Such cancerous growth may lead to the formation of tumors or to abnormal numbers of certain kinds of cells that upset the balance of function in the body. The disease "cancer" really refers to a large variety of different types of abnormal development. Leukemia, for example, is a condition in which large numbers of excess white blood cells are produced and released into the bloodstream. To complicate the example further, not even all cases of leukemia are identical. Apparently, there is not a single cause.

A great deal of progress has been made, but the problem of cancerous development is still a long way from solution. This is because the many kinds of cancer may each have a variety of causes. Although we are still uncertain about many of these causes, the techniques for detection of cancerous growth, and for its treatment, are being improved each year. We can be confident that our knowledge about cancer will continue to increase, and that eventually we shall be able to control such abnormal development effectively.

GENES IN DEVELOPMENT

As far as we know, every gene is present in every cell of a developing embryo. The orderly replication of DNA in mitosis guarantees that every daughter cell of the original zygote will have a full set of chromosomes with their accompanying genes. How, then, can we account for the fact that different cells become specialized in development to do different things?

This is a question to which we have no clear answer at the moment. The difficulty can be understood from an example. One enzyme, produced by the cells of the stomach lining, is very useful in digesting steak. Another enzyme, produced in the cells of the fingers and toes, helps form the protein **keratin** (KEHR·a·tin) of the fingernails and toenails. We are quite sure that the genes governing the production of both these enzymes are present in the cells of the stomach lining and in those of the fingers and toes. But we do not understand why it is that one kind of cell forms one sort of enzyme while the other kind of cell forms a different enzyme. If the nuclei are identical, as presumably they are, then perhaps we might look to the cytoplasm of the cells for clues. Perhaps their cytoplasms are *not* identical. Perhaps a gene can act in one sort of cytoplasm but be inactive in another.

The Nucleus-Cytoplasm Team

Possibly the study of simple forms of life, or early developmental stages of higher forms, might throw light on some of the relationships between nucleus and cytoplasm.

An organism that has been very useful in such studies is a large, one-celled alga, ***Acetabularia*** (as·e·tab·yoo·LAY·rih·a). This in-

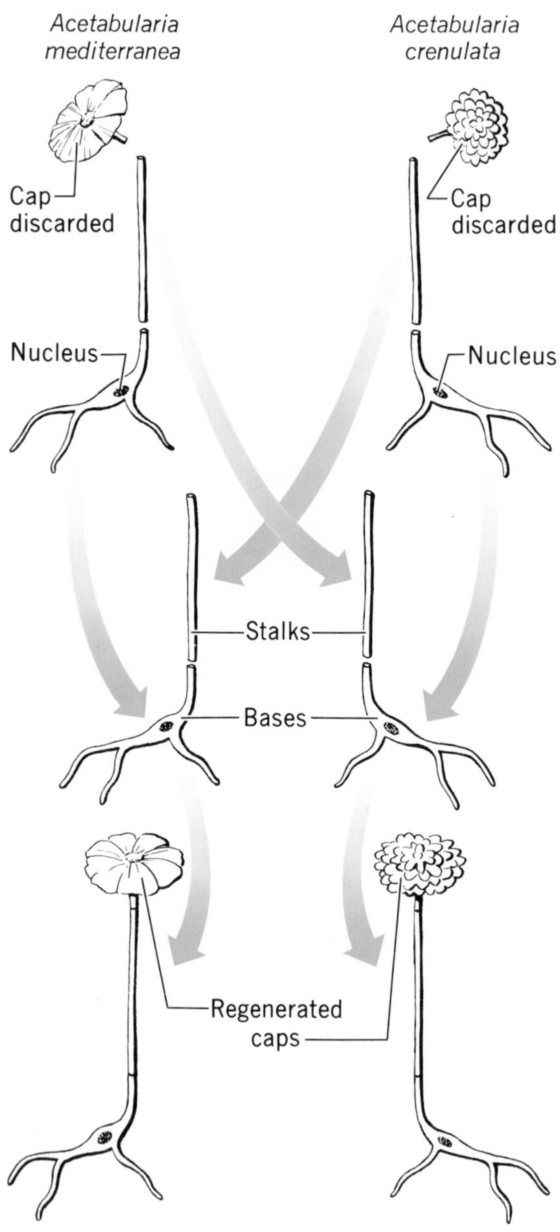

28-8 Evidence of nuclear control of cap structure in two species of *Acetabularia*. When parts of these algae are interchanged by grafting—leaving off the caps, which are discarded—the type of new cap ultimately grown is determined by the grafted part with the nucleus. Can you suggest other experiments with these species, to shed light on the relation between nucleus and cytoplasm?

teresting form (Figure 28-8) grows to a length of 6-9 cm (2-3 inches), a size easy to work with. Let us consider two distinctive species, *A. mediterranea* (med·ih·teh·RAY·ne·a) and *A. crenulata* (kren·yoo·LA·ta), that inhabit European marine waters. *A. mediterranea* has a cap shaped like an umbrella, atop a long stalk of cytoplasm. The nucleus of the alga is imbedded in the base of the cell. *A. crenulata* looks a good deal like *A. mediterranea,* except that its cap is very irregular in appearance.

Now we can carry out a very simple experiment. The cap is removed from one species and thrown away. Next, the cytoplasmic "stem" is cut off and grafted to the base of an alga of the *other* species (after the second alga has had its own "stem" and cap cut off, and the cap thrown away). In such an experiment a whole new alga forms from the joined pieces. The new organism becomes complete—with cap, "stem," and base. The crucial question is this: Will the newly developed cap resemble the species from which we took the "stem" (cytoplasm), or the one from which we took the base (nucleus)? As it turns out, the first cap regenerated may be intermediate in type, but if it, too, is removed, the next cap formed is always characteristic of the species supplying the nucleus. Therefore the nucleus of each grafted algal cell must exert its influence through "alien" cytoplasm in determining the form of the cap. We can conclude, then, that this is evidence for the *nuclear control* of the developmental processes forming a new cap. Here the effect of the nucleus must be transmitted to (and through) the cytoplasm. We have already considered how this might come about—the DNA of the nucleus transmits its instructions by way of messenger RNA molecules, which in turn direct the synthesis of the essential substances necessary for the development of a new cap.

In the *Acetabularia* experiment, which we diagrammed in Figure 28-8, the nucleus exerts a strong influence on the development of a cap characteristic of the species supplying the nucleus. Sometimes, however, the cytoplasm severely restricts what the nucleus can bring about. An example of this is seen in experiments on a certain species of sea urchin.

You will recall that Driesch was able to separate the two cells of a sea urchin embryo following the first division of the fertilized egg. He did this by vigorous shaking. More gentle methods were discovered later. If the early embryos are placed in sea water from which the calcium ions have been removed, the cells tend to separate. Thus it is possible to isolate the two cells formed by the first cleavage division, or the four cells formed by the second cleavage division. Each of the cells continues to develop and becomes, in time, a small but complete sea urchin larva. From this result we conclude that each half or each quarter of the original cytoplasm supplies all the substances and conditions necessary for the development of a complete embryo. Although the nucleus of the zygote undergoes two mitoses before the four cells are separated, each nucleus that results still controls the entire development of the embryo. In this case, the nucleus and cytoplasm of each cell function together as an effective team.

In the experiment just described, we let the embryos separate along the natural planes of cell division. These run from the top to the bottom of the egg, much like the planes between the sections of an orange. Let us now return to a second type of experiment; instead of dividing a sea urchin egg along the natural planes of cell division, we cut *across* the axis of an *unfertilized* egg (Figure 28-3b). This would resemble an orange cut in two before squeezing it for juice. Now we have two halves of an egg; sometimes the nucleus is located in the upper half and sometimes in the lower half.

Both halves heal, each forming an apparently normal cell. Then we add sea urchin sperms. A sperm will enter each half of the egg cell. If the half has a nucleus, the half will be diploid. If the half is without a nucleus, then it will have only the monoploid number of chromosomes contributed by the sperm. Both halves proceed to develop, but development does not continue normally (control experiments show that the abnormalities are not due to chromosome number). Typically, the *upper* half develops into a hollow ball of cells with many cilia, but it forms no internal tissues. It swims around for several days and then dies. The *lower* half, too, is very abnormal and incomplete, and dies before long. Neither of the "half-embryos," then, is able to develop into a normal embryo, or even to survive for long.

What conclusions can we draw by comparing the two experiments? Apparently the *cytoplasm* of the sea urchin egg, even before fertilization, is organized along an axis running from the top to the bottom of the egg. On the basis of this hypothesis, each of the first four cells of the embryo must receive similar cytoplasm; hence each cell must have the materials and organization necessary for normal development. In the second experiment, when an unfertilized egg is cut apart, the upper half of the egg must receive some of the materials needed, but not others. Similarly, the lower half of the egg must receive certain materials that are absent from the upper half, and must lack others that are present in the upper half. This means that different materials must be contributed to the two halves of the egg and thus to the cells of the developing "embryos" derived from these halves. Finally, we can conclude from many similar experiments that such materials of the cytoplasm indeed affect and limit what the genes in the nucleus are able to do in controlling the path of development.

CONCLUDING REMARKS

The study of development shows once again that observation, experimentation, and proper tools are necessary to answer biological questions. Observations with the unaided eye could not tell us whether the embryo was preformed in the fertilized egg or whether it developed epigenetically. One needed a microscope if critical observations were to be made. Observation alone would never have discovered the role of the dorsal lip. Experimentation was necessary to show how it influenced the formation of the nervous system.

By using a variety of methods, embryologists have discovered a great deal about some of the factors in development. They have, however, discovered only a little about the underlying control of differentiation. One of the most difficult problems today in all of biology is to explain how the cells of the body can have the same genes but become different from one another. Some possible hypotheses were suggested in this chapter. They might be correct or incorrect; only time will tell. But these hypotheses will suggest experiments to be done and, hence, the hypotheses will be made more probable or less probable. Embryology is a very active field today and there is a good chance that, in your lifetime, biologists will obtain much better explanations of the cause of differentiation.

GUIDE QUESTIONS AND PROBLEMS

1. Is an individual *preformed* in the fertilized egg? Comment upon the idea from the point of view of the original concept of it, and then from what we know today of DNA, RNA, and patterns of inheritance.
2. Originally, the idea of epigenesis must have been troublesome to defend (how could a "puddle" of unformed material in the egg yield an accurately reproduced offspring?). Suppose you were to coin a new term to help answer the old debate—say, *preformational epigenesis.* How would you describe what it means?
3. Roux and Driesch, by killing or removing one cell of a two-cell stage of the egg, both were investigating what half an egg could do—or were they incorrect in this assumption? Answer in terms of the amount of material involved (as compared to the original egg, undivided), and then answer in terms of your knowledge of mitosis and genetics.
4. How did the experiments of Holtfreter and Spemann support the hypothesis of a mechanism for embryonic induction?
5. What experimental evidence suggests chemical influences in cell differentiation?
6. Some regeneration is possible in most plants and animals. What can study of regeneration in an organism (a salamander, for example) add to our knowledge of development in the embryo?
7. Generally, the ability to regenerate missing tissues or organs *decreases* as complexity and specialization in body organization of animals *increases.* Can you suggest a reason why?
8. In what way is the medical problem of cancer related to an understanding of developmental processes?
9. How can biologists hope to learn more about aging and death by studying development earlier in life?

RELATED READING

Books

For the original accounts of embryological studies of Driesch, Spemann, and others . . .

Gabriel, M., and S. Fogel (editors), *Great Experiments in Biology,* Prentice-Hall, Englewood Cliffs, New Jersey, 1955.

For more on embryological principles . . .

Moore, John A., *Heredity and Development,* Oxford University Press, New York, 1963 (paperback).

Rugh, Roberts, *Vertebrate Embryology: The Dynamics of Development,* Harcourt, Brace & World, New York, 1965.

Waddington, C. H., *Principles of Development and Differentiation,* Macmillan, New York, 1966 (paperback).

For more information on processes of aging . . .

Strehler, B. L., *Time, Cells, and Aging,* Academic Press, New York, 1962.

Magazines

Comfort, Alex, "The Life Span of Animals," *Scientific American,* Volume 205 (August 1961), page 108.

Edwards, R. G., "Mammalian Eggs in the Laboratory," *Scientific American,* Volume 215 (August 1966), page 72.

Shock, Nathan, "The Physiology of Aging," *Scientific American,* Volume 206 (January 1962), page 100.

PART 3

CONTINUITY

Wallace Kirkland from Rapho Guillumette

29

Patterns of Heredity

In Chapters 7 and 8 you learned how biologists first suspected that the *nucleus* has a directing role in inheritance. This hypothesis was based on simple observation and experiment (refer to Figure 8-2, page 149, for one such experiment). Later the directing role in inheritance was narrowed to the *chromosomes* and finally to the *DNA* of the chromosomes (Figure 8-6, page 154). All of this seemed logical: the search was narrowed step by step. We began with hypotheses and ended with a well established theory: DNA has the instructions for making proteins, which in turn determine the structure and function of cells. These DNA instructions are transmitted from one generation to another via the egg cells and the sperm cells.

But the *full* story was not like that at all! The bulk of our information on inheritance was gained before anyone suspected that DNA was involved.

The History of Genetics

Early in our century the name *genes* was given to factors that control the way inheritance occurs in organisms. No one had ever seen the genes and no one knew what they were made of. Nevertheless, the manner in which they were passed from one generation to another, the relations of one gene to another, and even their precise locations on the chromosomes were worked out. This occurred almost 40 years before Watson and Crick proposed their model for DNA, even before Watson and Crick received their own hereditary instructions from their parents.

Thus in the first half of the twentieth century, geneticists were able to study the behavior of the units of inheritance without ever seeing them. In much the same way physicists and chemists built a whole science of matter that was based on atoms they never saw.

The history of genetics is a wonderful example of how man, by careful observation and experiment together with the controlled use of his mind, can explain the most difficult problems of nature. The modern part of the story begins with Gregor Mendel, who was trying to understand why some pea seeds were round and others were wrinkled. You might suppose this an unimportant problem – hardly worthy of attention. Yet this was the humble beginning of a science that is of great importance for the health and happiness of man. It has become of deep significance for agriculture, leading to improved crops and greater yields to feed millions more. It has helped us to understand some of the most profound events in life. . .and all because someone, who was not even a professional biologist, was careful in counting his peas! In Laboratory Inquiry 29-1 you can begin similar experiments with an animal widely used in genetics studies.

THE WORK OF MENDEL

Gregor Mendel (Figure 29-1) grew up in an agricultural district of what is today Czechoslovakia. Quite early he was attracted to the monastic life and was ordained an Augustinian priest at the age of twenty-five. Later he took additional training at the University of Vienna and taught in the high school in the town of Brünn for some years. It was during these years that he kept a small garden plot at the monastery and carried out his experiments with garden peas – experiments that threw the first clear light on the nature of heredity. His results were published in 1865.

Linda Hall Library

29–1 Gregor Mendel. The rules that he discovered for the inheritance of traits in peas have been found to apply to many other organisms.

The Study of Traits in Garden Peas

Mendel spent several years establishing known strains of pea plants. He did this by allowing plants with certain traits to produce seeds by self-pollination. If the offspring always had the same trait he knew that they were *true-breeding* or *pure* for this trait.

Mendel's experiments with these plants were novel in three important respects:

1. For each trait to be studied, Mendel bred many plants with the identical trait, enabling him to use many identical matings. Hence he was justified in pooling the offspring of these matings, just as if they were one very large family of a single mating. As a result, he had large numbers of offspring to study. You will appreciate the importance of this when you begin a similar study in Laboratory Inquiry 29-2.
2. Mendel used mathematics, especially the mathematics of probability. He used it in two ways: to analyze his data, then to arrive at a hypothesis explaining his results. Laboratory Inquiry 29-2 will also show you how important mathematics is to investigations in genetics.
3. Mendel made no attempt to study everything about the offspring at once. Instead, he limited his study of each cross (or mating) to a single difference at a time. In other words, each cross was between two types he was contrasting in just one respect, such as for round or wrinkled seeds, or for tall or dwarf plants.

One additional point we must keep in mind: when Mendel began his experiments, biologists knew nothing of chromosomes or the processes of cell division—nor even of the union of gametes. The principles Mendel established were based solely on the evidence from his breeding experiments. They did not depend in any way on knowledge of what changes were taking place in the cells. It was not until many years later that knowledge about the cell was successfully related to the hereditary principles established by Mendel (as you will see in Chapter 30).

Mendel selected garden peas for his experiments because he had found they possess many desirable features. The plants are easy to cultivate and cross, and the generation time is reasonably short. Numerous varieties were available to him, and the offspring of crosses between these different varieties are **fertile**—that is, able to reproduce successfully. Of great importance, the pea flower is usually self-pollinating, and not easily cross-pollinated by bees or other insects. Can you guess why this was important?

Let us look briefly at the structure of the flower of the pea and see how fertilization usually occurs (Figure 29-2). Refer also to the general description (Chapter 17) of fertilization in flowering plants.

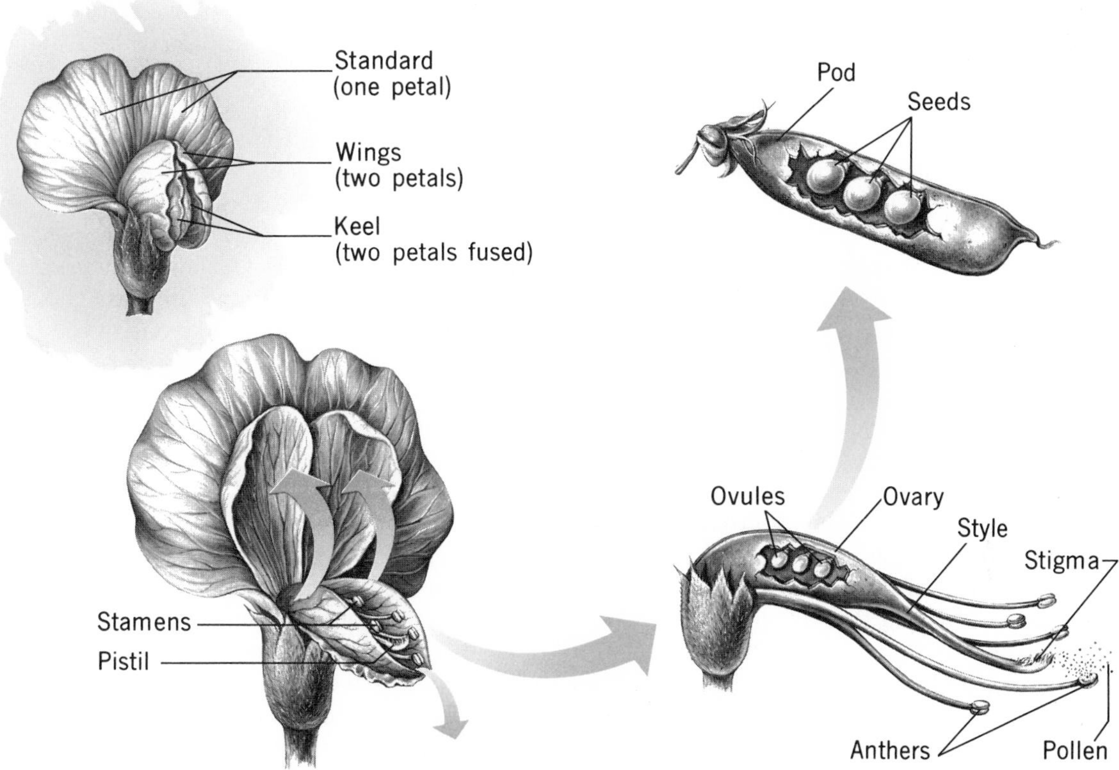

29–2 The flower and the fruit of the garden pea. The flower is normally self-pollinating because its stamens and pistils are enclosed by modified petals that usually prevent cross fertilization. Why was Mendel's choice of a self-pollinating flower an advantage in his experiments? At the lower left the petals are shown opened, and at the lower right is an enlarged view of the reproductive structures of the flower. At the upper right is a pea pod, partly cut away to show the seeds.

You will recall that the ovules are formed in the ovary. The pollen grains, which give rise to the male gametes, are formed in the anthers. Pollen from a pea flower's own anthers falls on the stigma above the ovary and develops pollen tubes that grow down through the style. One of the two male gametes in each pollen tube fertilizes an egg within an ovule. In the pea flower, the stigma and the anthers are completely enclosed by the petals. This means that egg cells within the ovules are normally fertilized by gametes from the anthers of the same flower. Thus the male and female gametes arise from parent cells of the same plant—cells that have *the same heredity.*

This would seem to mean that different varieties of peas could not be crossed. Not at all. One can cross peas experimentally. If a geneticist wants to pollinate one pea flower with the pollen from another plant, he removes the anthers from the first flower before the pollen is mature. Later, when the stigma of this same flower is ready to receive pollen, he can dust it with pollen taken from another plant. Thus, the geneticist can cross any varieties of peas that he wishes.

Mendel, having selected this favorable material and made his plans, was ready for his experimental work. First, as we have mentioned, he made sure that his plants were pure-bred for the single traits he wanted to study. He did this by letting plants of each type fertilize themselves (self-pollinate) for a number of generations, until he was sure that the offspring of each generation were all like one another and like the parent plant.

Then Mendel made hundreds of crosses by dusting the pollen of one kind of plant on stigmas of plants of another kind. He pollinated plants from the strain whose seeds were always *round,* with pollen from the strain whose seeds were always *wrinkled.* Laboratory Inquiry 29-3 involves a similar cross with fruit flies that have differences in their wings.

In every case of the round × wrinkled seed cross, Mendel found that all the offspring resembled *one* of the parents: the seeds were always *round.* This held true whether the pollen came from the plants with round seeds or the plants with wrinkled seeds. One trait seemed to dominate the alternative trait. Mendel, therefore, called a trait **dominant** if it alone appeared in the offspring of parents with contrasting traits. The trait that was masked was spoken of as **recessive.**

Let us now look at a summary of the results that Mendel found in this first series of experiments. He worked with seven different pairs of contrasting traits. What he discovered about their dominance is recorded in the table in Figure 29-3.

When a cross is made between two pure varieties, the parent generation is called the P_1 generation. The offspring of the P_1 cross are the **first filial** (FILL·ee·ul) **generation,** or F_1 generation. (The word *filial* means offspring.) These symbols, P_1 and F_1, will help us as we follow Mendel's work.

Mendel might have ceased his experiments at this point. After all, he had discovered some important rules for inheritance in peas. The offspring were always exactly like one of the parents. There were never intermediates, blending the hereditary characteristics. Many breeders had performed crosses much like Mendel's, and they usually stopped with the F_1 generation. Mendel did not, and went on to lay the foundation for the science of genetics.

Mendel next let the F_1 plants pollinate themselves. In the generation of plants that resulted (the F_2 generation), the dominant trait appeared in 75 percent of the offspring, while in 25 percent the recessive trait *reappeared*! Again he noted no intermediates. The new seeds were either round or wrinkled.

The table in Figure 29-4 gives some of the results when Mendel permitted members of the F_1 generation to produce an F_2 generation by self-fertilization. You can see that the ratios of plants with the dominant trait to those with the recessive trait are roughly the same, regardless of whether seed shape, length of stem, or any of the other traits is considered. One trait was always dominant, and it alone appeared in the F_1. In the F_2, there was always a ratio of 3 dominant to 1 recessive. *Such clear regularities*

29–3 Dominance in Seven Pairs of Traits in Garden Peas

1. Seed shape	**Round** seed dominant to wrinkled seed
2. Seed color	**Yellow** seed dominant to green seed
3. Seed-coat color	**Colored** seed coat dominant to white seed coat
4. Pod shape	**Inflated** pod dominant to wrinkled pod
5. Pod color	**Green** pod dominant to yellow pod
6. Flower position	**Axial** flowers dominant to terminal flowers
7. Stem length	**Long** stem dominant to short stem

29–4 Mendel's Results with Two Generations of Garden Peas

Traits Selected for P_1 Cross	*F_1 Plants*	*F_1 Self-pollination*	*F_2 Plants*	*Actual F_2 Ratio*
1. Round × wrinkled seeds	all round seeds	round × round	5,474 round seeds 1,850 wrinkled seeds 7,324 Total	2.96:1
2. Yellow × green seeds	all yellow seeds	yellow × yellow	6,022 yellow seeds 2,001 green seeds 8,023 Total	3.01:1
3. Colored × white seed coats	all colored seed coats	colored × colored	705 colored seed coats 224 white seed coats 929 Total	3.15:1
4. Inflated × wrinkled pods	all inflated pods	inflated × inflated	882 inflated pods 299 wrinkled pods 1,181 Total	2.95:1
5. Green × yellow pods	all green pods	green × green	428 green pods 152 yellow pods 580 Total	2.82:1
6. Axial × terminal flowers	all axial flowers	axial × axial	651 axial flowers 207 terminal flowers 858 Total	3.14:1
7. Long × short stems	all long stems	long × long	787 long stems 277 short stems 1,064 Total	2.84:1

could not be dismissed as accidental. Mendel made many crosses and *always* obtained the same ratios. What could all this mean?

Inheritance of a Single Trait

Mendel sought an explanatory hypothesis. He began by assigning symbols—letters of the alphabet—to represent each trait.

Mendel assumed that the *trait* of round seeds was caused by a *dominant element.* He used a capital *R* to symbolize this element. The *trait* of wrinkled seeds was caused by a *recessive element,* symbolized by a small *r.* Basically we use the same symbols today (along with the word *gene*, which we will use hereafter, although it came after Mendel's time).

An important distinction is being made here. We are differentiating between the *appearance* of an organism and what causes this appearance—the *hereditary basis* for it. Again after Mendel's time, two useful terms were introduced: **phenotype** (FEE·no·type) for the *appearance* of the trait being studied and **genotype** (JEE·no·type) for the *genetic basis* of the trait.

Thus the phenotype in the cross we have been discussing would be *round* or *wrinkled* seeds. The symbols we are using for the genotype or cause of these traits are R and r.

With the genotype thus assigned, Mendel was able to test his hypotheses about genes. If he knew the genotype of each parent, he could predict the kinds and proportions of *gametes* each parent could produce. Then he could, in turn, predict the kinds and proportions of offspring.

It seemed reasonable to assume that the gametes of a "*round* plant" would contain only the R gene. (For convenience a plant that produces round seeds will be called *round.* Similarly, "*wrinkled* plant" will indicate one producing wrinkled seeds.) Self-fertilization in such a *round* plant would unite an R sperm produced by a pollen grain with an R egg in an ovule. The result would be a *round* F_1 with only the R genes. Similarly, the gametes produced by a *wrinkled* plant would have only the r genes. Such a plant, when *selfed* (self-pollinated), would produce *wrinkled* F_1 plants with only the r genes.

What will happen if a *round* plant is crossed with a *wrinkled* plant? The hypothesis that we have already made is that the *round* plant will produce gametes with only the R gene and the *wrinkled* plant will produce gametes with only the r gene. The F_1 plants would then have both R and r. The phenotype of such a plant is *round.* We already know what will happen when such a plant is self-pollinated (refer again to the table in Figure 29-4). There will be a ratio of 3 *round* to 1 *wrinkled.* Mendel tried to make a mathematical model that would explain this constant result. On the basis of our scheme, we believe that the F_1 plant has both R and r genes. Such a plant could theoretically produce gametes that had only R, or r, or both R and r. One might expect, therefore, a wide variety of F_2 plants depending on which genes were in the gametes and the relative proportions of the different kinds of gametes. Thus, the ratios might be expected to vary widely from one experiment to another. But Mendel already knew this was not the case. Every time he did an experiment, and no matter which genes he used, the F_2 always gave almost precisely a 3:1 ratio (shown in the last column of Figure 29-4). Thus, the gametes must be produced in mathematically precise ways. Mendel made these assumptions:

1. A plant with both R and r genes will produce gametes that have either R or r but never both.
2. The R and r gametes will be produced in equal numbers. If we assume that our F_1 plant produces 100 pollen grains and 100 ovules, the sperms and eggs will be of these sorts:

   Sperms: 50 will be R; 50 will be r
   Eggs: 50 will be R; 50 will be r.
3. The sperms and eggs will combine at random. That is, a pollen grain that will produce an R sperm will have an equal chance of falling on any stigma. (If there are 100 ovules, with 50 R eggs and 50 r eggs, in half the cases an R sperm will combine with an R egg and in the other half with an r egg.)

From the information already given, could you work out the genotypes of the F_2 plants in this cross? It is worth a try. You may find it helpful to return to the discussion in Chapter 7, pages 142 and 144, and especially Figure 7-12, page 144, for hints.

We will now assume that you have made the attempt and are ready to check your results. If you used the checkerboard, you may have proceeded as follows:

		Eggs	
		50 R	50 r
Sperms	50 R	25 RR	25 Rr
	50 r	25 Rr	25 rr

Thus, there will be 25 offspring that are *RR*, 50 that are *Rr*, and 25 that are *rr*. We already know the phenotypes of these plants. The *RR* genotype is that of the pure-breeding *round*. The *Rr* genotype is that of the F_1 round plant we just crossed. The *rr* genotype is that of the pure-breeding *wrinkled*. Thus there would be 75 round to 25 wrinkled, or the 3:1 ratio that Mendel always obtained in the F_2 generation of a cross of this type.

There is a simpler way. In a cross of this sort, where the gametes are produced in equal proportions, you could have arrived at the answer from this simple diagram.

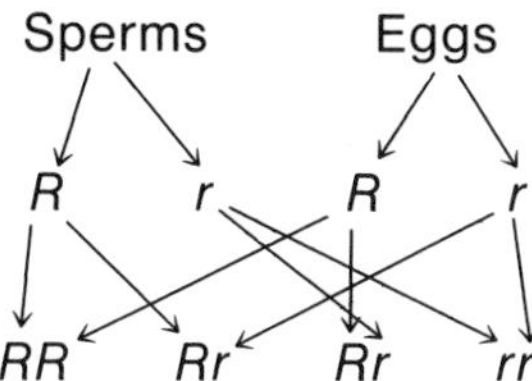

Here we have simply made all the possible combinations between pollen and ovules.

A third way you might have worked the problem is this. The frequencies of different genotypes in the F_2 is the *product* of the frequencies of the gametes. Thus:

R sperm × *R* egg: 50% × 50% = 25% *RR*
R sperm × *r* egg: 50% × 50% = 25% *Rr*
r sperm × *R* egg: 50% × 50% = 25% *Rr*
r sperm × *R* egg: 50% × 50% = 25% *rr*

The result again is 75 percent round to 25 percent wrinkled, or a 3:1 ratio. You may detect that this method is really the same as the checkerboard method. Laboratory Inquiries 29-2 and 29-3 are valuable in helping you understand these mathematical relations.

Mendel's three assumptions could, therefore, be used to construct a mathematical model that would account for the results of his breeding experiments. Figure 29-5 shows another of his crosses, using the same type of symbolism, which we will continue to use. Thus we will symbolize, as we already have done tentatively, the genotype of a pure-breeding *round* plant as *RR*, a pure-breeding *wrinkled* plant as *rr*, and the F_1 of a cross between them as *Rr*. You might ask why we are designating the pure-breeding plants as *RR* and *rr*. Why not call them *R* and *r*, or *RRRRR* and *rrrrr*? To a biologist working in Mendel's period any of these designations would be equally good. It was not until the early years of the twentieth century that biologists realized that it was not only convenient but also correct to refer to the genotype of the *round* plant as *RR* and not *R*. This is a bit ahead of the story, but you may be able to guess the reason.

As we work with designations for genotypes such as those for *round* and *wrinkled*—or any other pair of contrasting traits—we should become acquainted with three other useful terms in genetics. Two of these terms are **homozygous** (ho·mo·ZY·gus) and **heterozygous** (HET·er·o·ZY·gus). The prefix *homo* means "the same"; *hetero* means "different." *Zygo* means "a pair." So *homozygous* refers to a pair of the same units or elements, while *heterozygous* refers to a pair of different ones. In this case, we mean a pair of the same *genes* and a pair of contrasting *genes*. In short, an organism with the genotype *RR* is a **homozygote** (ho·mo·ZY·goht). So is one with the genotype *rr*. An organism with the genotype *Rr*, on the other hand, is a **heterozygote** (HET·er·o·ZY·goht).

The third new word is **allele** (a·LEEL). It is a Greek word meaning "belonging to one another." We use it to refer to the individual members of a gene pair. With the gene pair *Rr*, *R* is an allele of *r*, and vice versa. For the gene pair *AA*, *A* is an allele of *A*.

PROBABILITY IN GENETICS

The simpler problems in genetics are exactly like the problem of calculating the expected results of tossing two pennies, or rolling two dice and tallying odd and even. Nothing new is added except that we are using gametes instead of pennies or dice. And we get zygotes instead of combinations of pennies or dice.

29-5 INHERITANCE OF TERMINAL AND AXIAL FLOWERING IN PEA PLANTS

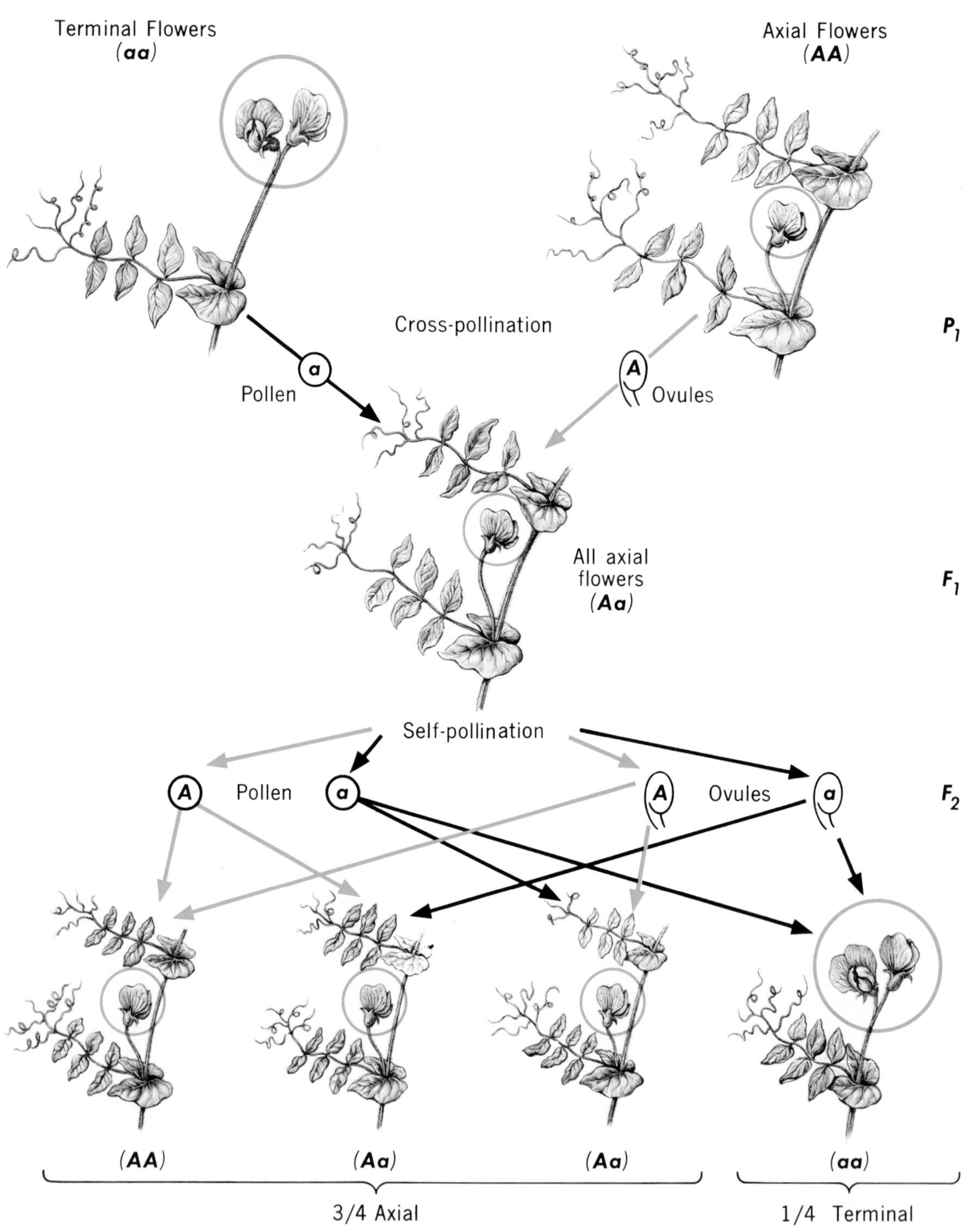

Let us take a problem in genetics in which one of the parents is the homozygote *AA*, while the other parent is the heterozygote *Aa*. What kind of offspring might we expect? Algebraic multiplication will really help us here.

Gametes of *Aa* parent: $\frac{1}{2} A + \frac{1}{2} a$
Gametes of *AA* parent: A

(Notice that we are shortening the statement of gametes for the homozygous parent. There is no need to say $\frac{1}{2} A + \frac{1}{2} A$ when it is equally accurate to say *A*.)

We multiply:

$$\begin{array}{r} \frac{1}{2} A + \frac{1}{2} a \\ \times \quad A \qquad \\ \hline \frac{1}{2} AA + \frac{1}{2} Aa \end{array}$$

Half the zygotes are expected to be homozygous *AA*, while the other half are expected to be heterozygous *Aa*.

Now let us take a problem in which both parents are heterozygous. Again, we begin by separating the alleles in the gametes:

$$\begin{array}{lr} \text{Gametes of} & \\ \text{one } Aa \text{ parent:} & \frac{1}{4}\!\!\!\!\quad \frac{1}{2} A + \frac{1}{2} a \\ \times \text{ gametes of other:} & \frac{1}{2} A + \frac{1}{2} a \\ \cline{2-2} & \frac{1}{4} AA + \frac{1}{4} Aa \qquad\qquad \\ & + \frac{1}{4} Aa + \frac{1}{4} aa \\ \cline{2-2} & \frac{1}{4} AA + \frac{1}{2} Aa + \frac{1}{4} aa \end{array}$$

Thus, we see again that with a cross between two heterozygotes, the *probabilities* are that 1/4 of the offspring will be *homozygous dominant* (both genes alike and dominant); 1/2 will be *heterozygous*; and 1/4 will be *homozygous recessive*.

Other Examples of Single Trait Inheritance

Mendel's principles were worked out in one kind of plant, the garden pea. Without doing the same kinds of experiments with other kinds of organisms, we cannot be sure whether the principles that Mendel established for his pea plants apply *in general*.

Let us take an example from animal heredity. If we cross a homozygous black male guinea pig with a homozygous white female guinea pig, all the F_1 offspring are black. If guinea pig inheritance is like inheritance in peas, we can conclude that the black trait is dominant to white in the guinea pig, and that the F_1 offspring are heterozygous. When the F_1 individuals form ova and sperms, 1/2 of the ova will carry the gene for black, and 1/2 will carry the gene for white. The same is true of the sperms. The expected ratios of the F_2 generation will be 1/4 homozygous black, 1/2 heterozygous black, and 1/4 homozygous white – the same ratios Mendel got in his peas. These are the actual results obtained in such an experiment. Mendel's principles are found to apply in guinea pigs just as they do in peas.

Let us turn the experiment around and see another way in which this sort of genetic analysis can be used. Suppose you had a black guinea pig whose parents were not known to you, and you wanted to know whether the guinea pig was homozygous or heterozygous for black. How would you go about finding out? One way is to make a *test cross*. We mate the organism we wish to test with one that has the *homozygous recessive* genotype for this trait. Each offspring from such a mating would receive a recessive gene from the homozygous recessive parent. The offspring's phenotype would depend on whatever it received from the parent being tested. In our example we mate the unknown black guinea pig with a white (homozygous recessive) guinea pig. If, among all the offspring, there is even a single white guinea pig (homozygous recessive), the tested black guinea pig must be a carrier of the recessive allele, and therefore heterozygous. If many offspring are obtained and all are black, we can assume that the black parent is homozygous black.

PROBLEM: Assign symbols for black and white, and diagram the guinea pig crosses just described.

PROBLEM: Show how the test cross works, using a round-seeded pea of unknown genotype.

PROBLEM: In sheep, white coat is dominant to black. Occasionally a black sheep appears in the flock. How can a farmer eliminate the genes for black coat from his flock? (He will wish to do so because the black wool is worth less.)

We have spoken of alleles as being dominant or recessive as if there were no other possibilities. But sometimes one allele of a pair is *not* completely dominant over the other. In shorthorn cattle, for instance, when a red bull (*RR*) is crossed with a white cow (*rr*), the heterozygous offspring (*Rr*) are neither red nor white, but *roan* (having intermingled red and white hairs). If a roan bull (*Rr*) is crossed with a roan cow (*Rr*), the calf has one chance in four of being white (*rr*), two chances in four of being roan (*Rr*), and one chance in four of being red (*RR*). (See Figure 29-6.)

PROBLEM: Using symbols, work out a cross of roan × red.

PROBLEM: A farmer wants to establish a pure strain of roan cattle that breeds true. Why is this impossible?

PROBLEM: If a four-o'clock plant having red flowers is crossed with a white-flowered four-o'clock, the F_1 plants are all *pink*-flowered. From this evidence alone, what ratios would you expect to find in these crosses: red crossed with red? red × pink? pink × white? white × white?

Multiple Alleles

We have learned how to deal with genetic problems in which there are two unlike alleles of a gene pair—*A* and *a*, for instance. For many traits there may exist more than two different alleles of the gene that affects the trait; in other words, there may be **multiple alleles.** These are all alleles of one another—any two may occur together in the same cell, and in any combination. The important thing to remember is that *only* two alleles of a given gene are normally present in the genotype at the same time. As always, one allele is contributed by the male parent, the other by the female parent.

A well-known example will illustrate what we mean. Whether a person has type A, type B, type AB, or type O blood depends on the presence or absence of specific substances on the red blood cells. There are two of these substances—**antigens** (AN·tih·jenz) **A** and **B.** Thus, a person with antigen A is considered to be type A, a person who is type O has neither of the antigens, and so on. It is interesting and important to know that a person's blood type is under genetic control.

In what way do the blood-type genes determine which blood type a person has? We now know that there are three alleles in this particular series: I^A, I^B, and *i*. (The *I* of each symbol indicates the allelic relation of one to another. *B* could not very well be used as a symbol for an allele of *A*, for you would be likely to forget that they form a pair and must separate as they go into the gametes.) The three alleles may be paired in any combination, but as we said earlier, only two of them can be present in a single individual. The dominance relationships of these three alleles are interesting, too. Both I^A and I^B are fully expressed in the presence of the other; that is, both *A* and *B* antigens are produced. On the other hand, both I^A and I^B are dominant to *i*, and it is only when both I^A and I^B are absent (when the genotype is *ii*) that a person is type O. Let us summarize these relationships in a chart:

Phenotype	Genotype	Antigen on Cells
Type A	I^AI^A or I^Ai	A
Type B	I^BI^B or I^Bi	B
Type AB	I^AI^B	A and B
Type O	*ii*	none

Because of the dominance relationships in this set of multiple alleles, it is possible to deduce immediately the genotype of persons who are type AB or type O. The table shows that type A and type B persons may have either of

29-6 INHERITANCE OF COAT COLOR IN SHORTHORN CATTLE

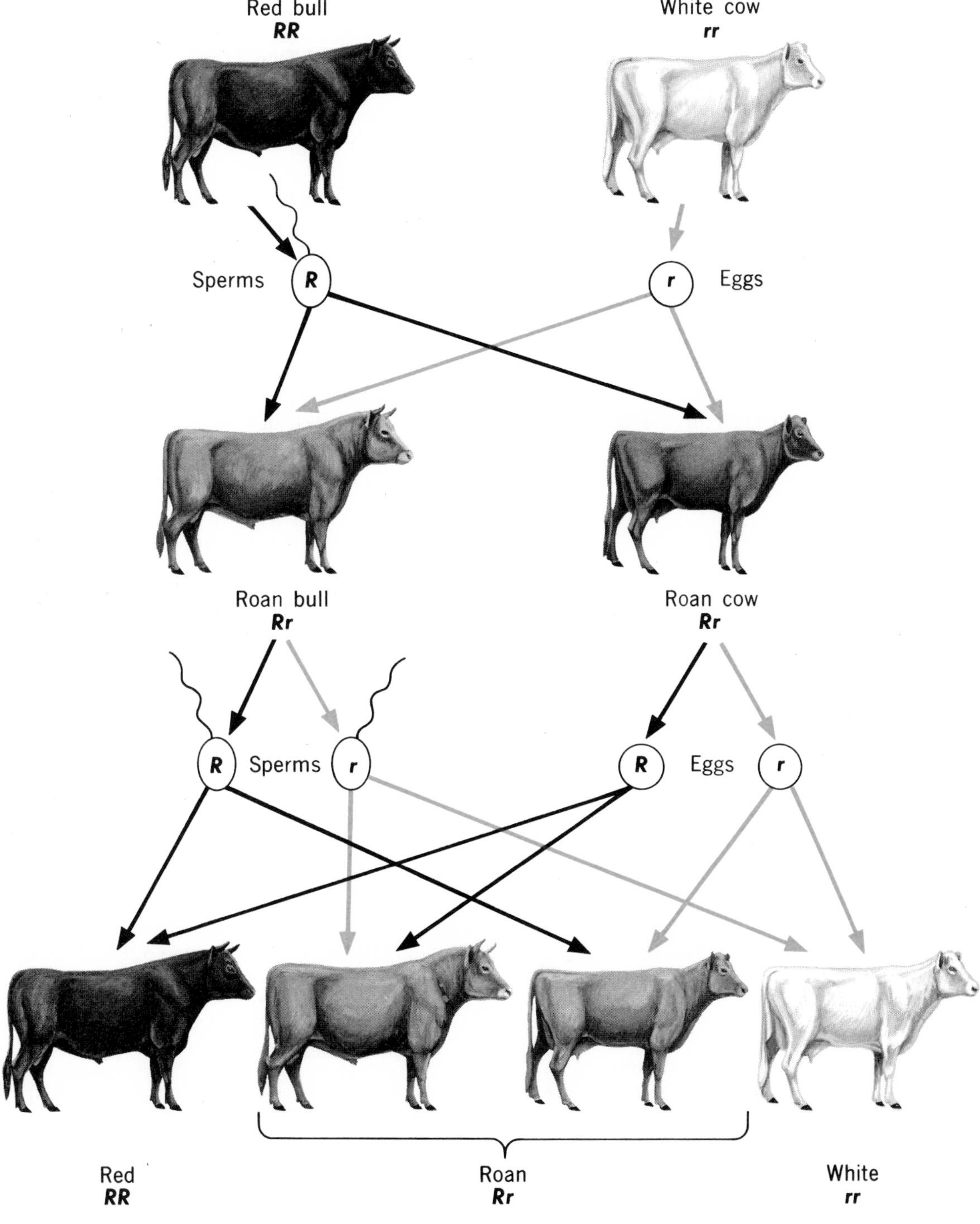

two genotypes, however. Which one they possess must be determined from the blood types of their offspring, or by sensitive laboratory tests.

We can become acquainted with the inheritance of blood types by working out the following examples:

PROBLEM: Suppose a man with type A blood marries a woman who has type AB blood. What blood types would you expect to find among their children? In this problem we have no way of knowing whether the man is homozygous or heterozygous for the I^A allele. What would tell you which of the genotypes he has?

PROBLEM: Suppose two newborn babies were accidentally mixed up in the hospital, and there was a question of which baby belonged to which parents. From the following blood types, determine which baby belongs to which parents:

Baby 1	Type O
Baby 2	Type A
Mrs. Brown	Type B
Mr. Brown	Type AB
Mrs. Smith	Type B
Mr. Smith	Type B

What is the genotype of each of the six persons?

In the years following Mendel, geneticists studied the inheritance of many genes in plants and animals. The results were often exactly the same as Mendel had discovered for peas. When the cross was between a homozygous dominant and a homozygous recessive, the F_1 heterozygote always showed the dominant phenotype. In the F_2 there was a ratio of 3 dominant to 1 recessive. There were other instances where dominance was not complete, as in the roan cattle illustrated in Figure 29-6. Here the F_1 would be intermediate and the F_2 show a 1:2:1 ratio. There were still other exceptions, some of which will be discussed later. But in all cases inheritance seemed to be following definite rules, rules that could be discovered if the experimenter used pure-breeding strains and obtained large numbers of offspring.

Inheritance of Two Traits

Were there also rules that could explain the inheritance of two different sorts of traits? For example, in pea plants, what would happen in a cross of a *round yellow* plant with a *wrinkled green* plant? Each pair of genes alone gives a 3:1 ratio (Figure 29-4). Will this also be the ratio for both traits together (Laboratory Inquiry 29-4)?

Mendel crossed a pure-breeding *round yellow* plant with a pure-breeding *wrinkled green* plant. All of the F_1 were *round* and *yellow*. These plants were allowed to self-pollinate. The F_2 consisted of

315 *round yellow*
108 *round green*
101 *wrinkled yellow*
32 *wrinkled green*

There does not seem to be any clear-cut ratio. Furthermore, there are four phenotypic classes instead of two. Two of the classes are the same as the original parents, but two are not: *round green* and *wrinkled yellow*. Thus, the two pairs of traits seemed to be combining in the four ways that were possible. This may have suggested to Mendel that each pair of alleles behaves independently. That is, the inheritance of *R* and *r* (for *round* and *wrinkled*) has no influence on the inheritance of *Y* and *y* (the symbols we will use for genes affecting *yellow* and *green*, respectively). So let us add as a fourth assumption to the list on page 526:

4. When two pairs of traits are followed in the same crosses, each pair is inherited independently.

Now if this assumption is correct, then from what we already know we can predict the ratios for the F_2 in the cross we are using as our example. Thus, considering *round* and *wrinkled* peas as at the top of the next page . . .

A. Of the $^3/_4$ of the F_2 that are *round*, $^3/_4$ should also be *yellow* and $^1/_4$ should also be *green*. Therefore,
   $^3/_4$ of $^3/_4$, or $^9/_{16}$, should be *round* and *yellow*
   $^1/_4$ of $^3/_4$, or $^3/_{16}$, should be *round* and *green*

B. Of the $^1/_4$ of the F_2 that are *wrinkled*, $^3/_4$ should also be *yellow* and $^1/_4$ should also be *green*. Therefore,
   $^1/_4$ of $^3/_4$, or $^3/_{16}$, should be *wrinkled* and *yellow*
   $^1/_4$ of $^1/_4$, or $^1/_{16}$, should be *wrinkled* and *green*

This is a ratio of $^9/_{16}$ to $^3/_{16}$ to $^3/_{16}$ to $^1/_{16}$, or 9:3:3:1. You should now check to see how closely the actual results that Mendel obtained correspond to the expected results. The cross is diagramed in Figure 29-7.

These 9:3:3:1 ratios for two pairs of traits in the F_2 generation demonstrate that the traits are independent of one another and that combinations turn up as expected according to chance. This is often called Mendel's **law of independent assortment.** It may be stated as follows: *When two pairs of traits are followed in the same crosses, they are found to be inherited independently.* Mendel found this true for all the combinations of the seven pairs of traits he used in his pea crosses. Yet, as we shall see, there are important exceptions.

Another Example of the Inheritance of Two Traits

In guinea pigs with colored hair, the hair color may be *black* (*B*) or *brown* (*b*). *Black* is dominant. Also the hair may be *short* (*S*) or *long* (*s*). *Short* hair is dominant.

In each cross described so far, we have begun with homozygous individuals. This time we will cross animals of heterozygous genotypes: BbSs × BbSs. What is their phenotype? What will be the genotypes and phenotypes of the F_1 individuals? Try this problem on your own. (Check your answer with Figure 29-8.)

Sperms \ Eggs	RY	Ry	rY	ry
RY	RRYY	RRYy	RrYY	RrYy
Ry	RRYy	RRyy	RrYy	Rryy
rY	RrYY	RrYy	rrYY	rrYy
ry	RrYy	Rryy	rrYy	rryy

29-7 A genetic checkerboard of Mendel's cross involving two traits. Genotypes of sperms and eggs of F_1 individuals appear at the left side and above the checkerboard. Genotypes of F_2 individuals appear in the squares of the checkerboard.

Continuously Varying Traits

In order to simplify his experiments, Mendel worked with traits that showed distinct alternatives: wrinkled as against round seeds, yellow as against green seeds, axial flowers as against terminal flowers, for example. But what about such traits as length of a giraffe's neck, or color of the human skin? In such cases as these, there may be dozens or even thousands of degrees of variation. These can hardly be accounted for by a single pair of Mendel's factors. Even with nondominance, one pair of alleles can yield only three genotypes. Some cases of varying traits are due to multiple alleles. But even this phenomenon does not account for many characteristics that seem to have a *quite continuous* variability—as height in man, for example.

To account for such continuously varying traits as human height, human skin color, and human intelligence, geneticists have developed the hypothesis that several different pairs of

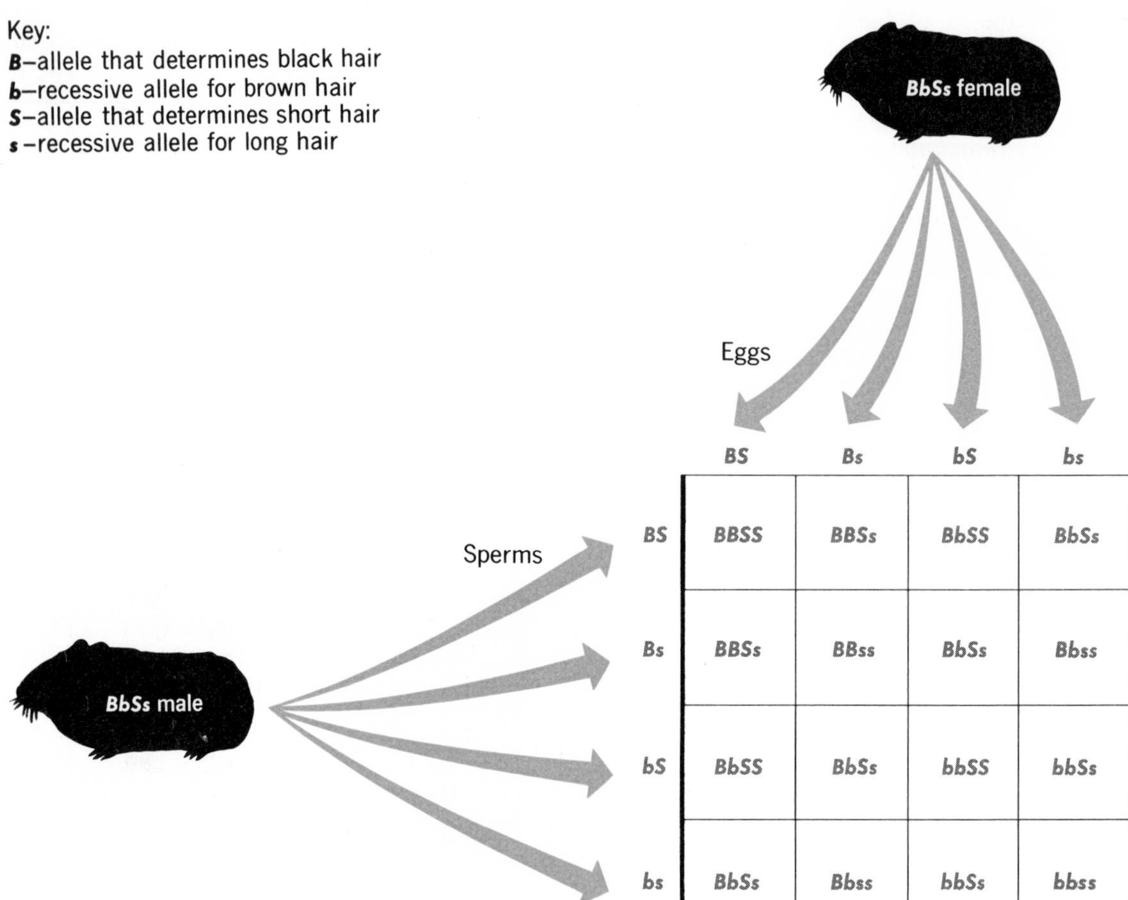

29–8 Checkerboard calculation of expected genotypes in offspring, when both parents are heterozygous for the same two traits. In this case, the parents are two guinea pigs, heterozygous for black hair and for short hair. Four kinds of gametes will be produced by each parent. Can you complete the calculations by adding together the identical genotypes wherever they occur in the checkerboard? How many different genotypes can be found in the offspring? how many different phenotypes?

genes may affect the same trait. An example for another organism will illustrate this idea.

Suppose that gene X produces a certain degree of red coloring, and that XX is redder than Xx. Suppose that gene Y also does the same thing, as does gene Z. In addition, suppose that x, y, and z, the recessive alleles of the three genes, produce no color. In such a case, an organism with the genotype $xxyyzz$ would be pure white. The genotype $XXYYZZ$ would have six doses of color-forming genes and would be very dark red indeed. $Xxyyzz$ with only one dose of red pigment would be a very light shade of pink. $XXyyzz$, $xxYYzz$, and $xxyyZZ$ would each have two doses and be a shade darker, and so on up through six possible shades. This is actually the way seed color has been found to be inherited in wheat.

Out of experiments and interpretations of this sort grew a great technological triumph—the first gift of the new science of genetics to the welfare of mankind. The American geneticists E. M. East, George H. Shull, and Donald F. Jones were responsible. The achievement was the development of hybrid corn, which has enormously increased the yield for the same input of acreage, fertilizer, and labor. The reasoning of these geneticists went as follows. Hybrids are often more vigorous than the parent types that produce them. This, according to the theory, might be because one pure parent strain is *WWXXyyzz* and the other is *wwxxYYZZ*. Cross them, and you should get *WwXxYyZz*. If any of these genes are dominant, the hybrid should then be better, in terms of the desired characteristic, than either parent type.

Pure strains of maize were selected and crossed. The hypothesis was indeed proved true. The F_1 hybrid plants were vastly better in yield than either of the pure parent strains. The F_2 generation, however, showed enormous diversity, ranging from the very best-yielding to quite worthless types.

Jones then worked out what he called a "double cross." He combined four pure lines to get his productive hybrid. Line A was crossed with line B, and line C was crossed with line D. Then, in the next generation, a cross was made between the hybrid A/B and the hybrid C/D. In this way recessive, poor-yielding genes become masked in effect. Only high-yielding, dominant genes remain effective (Figure 29-9).

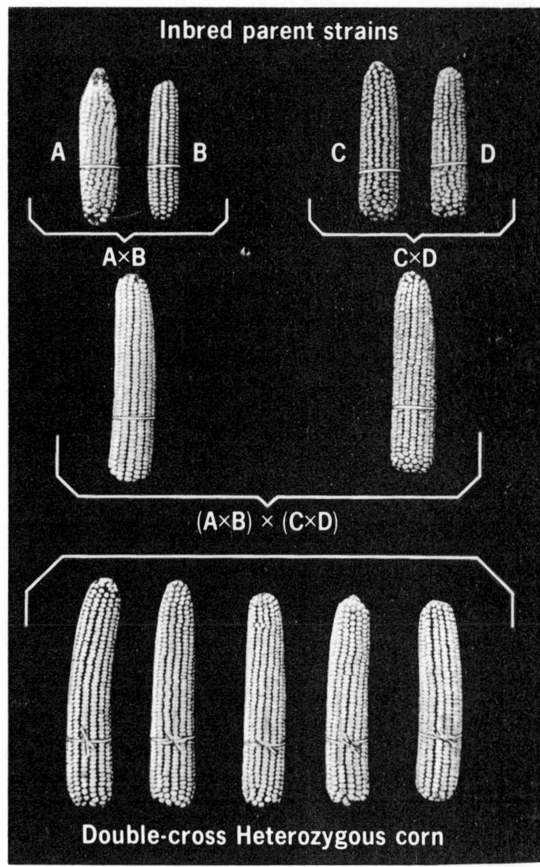

USDA Photos

29–9 How hybrid corn is produced. A, B, C, and D are four inbred lines. They are crossed as shown to produce F_1 hybrids. The two F_1 hybrids are then crossed to produce the F_2 double-cross hybrids, which are commercial hybrid corn.

Different sorts of hybrid corn have been developed for different areas. A type of hybrid corn good for Iowa will not do well in Mexico or the U.S.S.R. Local pure lines, with a genetic basis suitable for the climate, must be used. When hybrid corn is produced properly, the increase in yield is phenomenal. During the years 1942-1945 alone, the increased yield in the United States, from the *same* acreage and with *less* labor than had been expended before World War II began, amounted to nearly two billion bushels of corn. And, in the days of peace that followed, throughout the devastated and war-stricken countries of Europe, it was food supplied by the United States—made possible largely by increased production of corn—that prevented widespread famine.

Hybrid corn is one reason for the high average standard of living in the United States. We must remember that hybrid corn is not only a food for man but also for hogs and cattle. Hybrid corn, therefore, makes it possible for us to have more meat, milk, and butter than would otherwise be the case.

HUMAN HEREDITY

Biologists very quickly discovered that Mendel's rules applied to man. The table of Figure 29-10 shows a few of the human traits that have a simple Mendelian basis.

In spite of the very great interest in the subject, the study of heredity in man has been slow and difficult. The reasons can be brought out if we mention what the geneticist tries to do in the laboratory. The geneticist prefers to do his experiments with pure lines, which he obtains by generations of inbreeding. He repeats the crosses numerous times and tries to obtain as many offspring as possible. And, of course, he tries to keep his experimental organisms in a constant environment. You can imagine how difficult it would be to meet these conditions for man. Nevertheless, by carefully tracing the inheritance of traits in man, it has been possible to learn a great deal about his genetics.

Much of what we know about human heredity comes from the study of relatively rare traits. From a few of these studies we have learned how the traits are inherited and what the effect of environment is on their expression. For the more common traits possessed by all of us—such as blood type, intelligence, and so on—in some cases we know a great deal, in others our knowledge is scanty indeed.

We will list a few human traits and briefly indicate what we know of their heredity.

Blood types. Many different genes are now known to affect blood.

In one example, there is a dominant gene (*R*) that produces *Rh antigen* (Rh stands for *rhesus* [REE·SUS], the kind of monkey in which the antigen was first identified). If a person is *RR* or *Rr* we say he is Rh-positive. Such individuals comprise about 85 percent of the white population. The remaining 15 percent of the population is *rr*, known as Rh-negative. You can see that these are population data, not data of individual families. (Among Mongoloid populations the Rh-negative allele is almost wholly absent.)

29–10 Some Traits in Man That Are Inherited in a Simple Mendelian Fashion

Recessive	*Dominant*
red hair	not red hair
white forelock	normal
normal	premature grayness of hair
normal	no iris
normal	glaucoma
extreme myopia	normal
night blindness	normal
normal	congenital cataract
albinism	normal
polydactyl	normal
normal	split foot
normal	no incisor teeth
normal	rootless teeth
no A or B antigens	A and B antigens
normal	sickle cell
no Rh antigen	Rh antigen
attached ear lobe	free ear lobe
normal size	achondroplastic dwarf
St. Vitus' dance	normal
Friedreich's ataxia	normal
normal	Huntington's chorea
diabetes mellitus	normal

The Rh factor is sometimes very important to the health of newborn babies. If the mother is *rr* and the father is either *RR* or *Rr*, the offspring is, or may be, *Rr*. In some instances, the red blood cells (carrying Rh antigen) of the fetus pass through the placenta into the circulation of the mother and cause in her the production of antibodies against the Rh antigen. These antibodies may pass back into the circulation of the fetus and begin to destroy its red blood cells. If the damage is widespread, the fetus is killed, and a miscarriage results. If there is less damage, the baby may be born alive but suffering from severe anemia and jaundice (a greenish-yellow color due to pigments from the destroyed red blood cells). A complete substitution of the baby's blood by blood from a donor who does not possess anti-Rh antibodies may save the infant's life and allow it to begin making a fresh supply of red blood cells.

A transfusion of Rh-positive blood will also induce in an Rh-negative mother the production of anti-Rh antibodies; this greatly increases the chances of damage to any Rh-positive child she may bear. Clearly, it is of the greatest importance to know your Rh blood type. This is especially true if you are female, in order to assure blood transfusions of the correct type and thus prevent possible damage to unborn children. About 10 percent of all babies in the white population are Rh-positive babies born to Rh-negative mothers. Not all the mothers of these babies develop antibodies, at least in their earlier pregnancies; therefore, there are not as many damaged babies as the percentage just given would suggest. Still, about 1 in 150 of all babies in the white population is so affected. This is about 27,000 in the United States every year. The frequency of affected newborn is much less in the Negro portion of the population.

The ABO blood groups, already discussed, have been known since 1900. Yet a similar incompatibility of maternal and fetal blood in the case of these blood groups was discovered only after the Rh disorder had been explained in 1942. Why was this?

The ABO blood incompatibility is much more severe than the Rh type, and it kills the fetus during an early stage of its development, causing an abortion. It most often occurs when the mother is of blood type O and the fetus is of blood type A or type B. (Remember that persons of type O already carry anti-A and anti-B antibodies. Type-O persons do not have to be stimulated to make these antibodies as is the case with Rh-negative persons and Rh antigen.)

It is also possible for incompatibility to occur when the mother is of type B and the fetus of type A, or when the mother is of type A and the fetus is of type B. It is now thought that ABO incompatibility is responsible for a great number of the deaths among the unborn. Much of the apparent sterility in marriage is really due to ABO incompatibility, too.

Baldness. Hereditary baldness is dominant in males, recessive in females—that's just the way things are! The respective sex hormones promote or overcome its dominance.

Diabetes mellitus. In this hereditary disease, inadequate control by the hormone insulin causes inability of the body to utilize sugar properly. Many cases appear to be due to a single recessive gene (although you learned in Chapter 24 that not all forms of diabetes are identical). The disease may be mild or severe (are multiple alleles perhaps involved?), or it may not appear at all, depending on environmental factors.

Eye color. Eye color is a complex trait not at present completely understood. It seems that a true, pure blue eye is due to a single gene that is recessive to a gene for pigmented eye. We must lump together under "pigmented" any eye with even the least spot of brown pigment (including hazel eyes), and also green and gray eyes. There are probably other genes that affect eye color when the pigment gene is also present.

Skin color. The amount of dark pigment seems to be controlled by four to eight pairs of independently assorting genes with nondominance in each pair; many grades exist between white and black. (Exposure to sunlight also modifies the amount of color in the skin.)

The reddish and yellow pigments of certain races are different from the shading from white to black.

Height and weight. There is a definite genetic influence here, but environmental differences such as diet play an important role, too. Extreme variations in height, such as dwarfism and giantism, are usually due to activity of pituitary hormones, and these hormones, too, are under genetic control.

Resistance to tuberculosis. Probably many genes as well as environmental conditions play a part in resistance to this disease. The evidence from studies of identical twins shows that the amount of resistance to tuberculosis is strongly influenced by the individual's heredity.

Schizophrenia. The evidence from twins shows that this commonest type of mental disease is strongly influenced by heredity. One authority suggests that a single recessive gene is involved. Environmental factors are also highly important.

Mental retardation. There may be many causes for what is generally considered to be mental retardation. While normal intelligence depends on the proper functioning of many genes, a defect in the function of any one of these may result in an impairment of mental activity. Some conditions of mental retardation have a strong hereditary determinant; others may be due to injuries before or at birth. One special type of mental retardation, **Down's syndrome** (SIN·drome), is the product of a single extra chromosome (Chapter 30). Another well-known type, **phenylketonuria** (fen·'l·key·to-NYOO·rih·a), is a simple recessive trait caused by the failure to produce a certain enzyme that normally converts one of the twenty common amino acids in proteins into another—**phenylalanine** (fen·il·AL·uh·neen) into **tyrosine** (TY-roe·seen)—a process which takes place in the liver.

Intelligence. Intelligence is not easy to define and is even more difficult to measure. Individuals may appear to be highly intelligent in one field, yet be quite ordinary in others. The most common type of intelligence test is one that gives an intelligence quotient (IQ), measured by a particular level of response in visualizing objects in space, memorizing, and reasoning. Verbalization and vocabulary are important. Judging from IQ tests of identical twins, there is a very strong hereditary factor in intelligence. But environment also plays an important role, and it is the interaction of heredity and environment that finally determines the intelligence of an individual.

In all probability, many genes contribute to the determination of intelligence. If genes also are largely responsible for certain types of *motivation* toward learning, then the situation is still more complicated.

The information that has been reviewed here on human heredity is extremely limited, and there are good reasons why our knowledge of human heredity is not as far advanced as our knowledge of the heredity of some other organisms. The long span of years of a human generation, the difficulty of accurately measuring many human characteristics, the impossibility of using planned matings, and the relatively small number of offspring per family all represent handicaps to the geneticist. But in spite of these difficulties, the advances in our understanding of human heredity are taking place rapidly.

CONCLUDING REMARKS

The rules that Mendel discovered for peas were found to hold for the inheritance of many traits of plants and animals. The more important of these rules were

1. When two alleles affect the same trait, frequently one of them is dominant over the other. That is, when they occur together in a heterozygote, its phenotype is identical (or nearly so) to that of the pure-breeding dominant. This is not always the case. For example, in the four o'clock, a cross of a red and a white plant gives an F_1 that is pink. Similarly, when the blood group alleles I^A and I^B are together, both A and B antigens are produced.
2. If one pair of alleles shows a simple dominance-recessive relationship, the cross of a pure-breeding dominant and a pure-breeding recessive gives a 3:1 ratio in the F_2.
3. If two pairs of alleles are followed in such a cross, the ratio in the F_2 is 9:3:3:1. The inheritance of one pair of alleles is independent of inheritance of the other pair.
4. When a dominant and recessive allele are together in a heterozygote, neither affects the other in any permanent way. This is shown by the F_2: the recessive allele reappears in the homozygous condition and

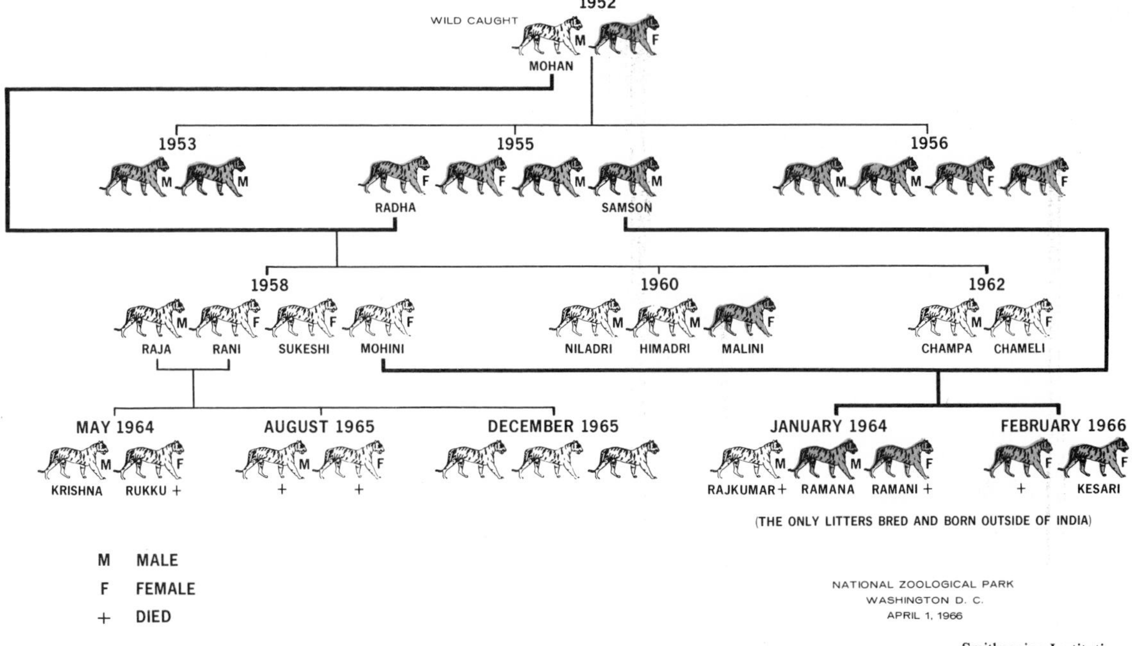

Smithsonian Institution

29–11 Can you work out the basis for the inheritance of white coat color in tigers from the data in this chart? See Problem 1 at the end of this chapter.

produces a phenotype exactly like that of a pure-breeding recessive (which, of course, it is).

5. A gamete can receive only one member of each pair of alleles.
6. At fertilization, gametes unite at random.

In case it has escaped your notice, this interesting point should be made: no mention has been made in this chapter of what the genes are and where they are situated. How different this is from our earlier study of inheritance (Chapter 8), which was concerned with DNA and how it acts. Mendelian genetics studied the appearance of traits in successive generations. Its main technique was the experimental breeding of the more complex animals and plants. Biochemical genetics is concerned with studying the substance of heredity. Its main techniques are biochemical and the organisms used are viruses and bacteria. Eventually the two lines of investigation merged to form the molecular biology of today.

We will learn in the next chapter that the simple Mendelian rules do not hold for the inheritance of all traits. Nevertheless, they do hold for the vast majority of cases. The exceptions, now to be discussed, will tell us much more about the nature of inheritance.

GUIDE QUESTIONS AND PROBLEMS

1. In 1952 a male white tiger was captured in India. A family tree of his descendants is shown in Figure 29-11. What is the evidence that white coat color is a recessive trait? In what ways do the relatively few offspring not reflect expected Mendelian ratios?
2. Suppose you were a cat fancier and were raising what you thought was a purebred line, but found that some of the cats had spots of white

hair at the tips of their tails, while others did not. How could you determine whether this trait is recessive or dominant? Assume that only one pair of genes is affecting this trait.

3. Corn is not self-pollinating as pea plants are, but rather may be self- or cross-pollinated by wind dispersal of pollen. What methods would have to be used to insure that corn kernels would be hybrids?
4. Why would offspring of families with a history of diabetes mellitus on both the mother's and father's side be more likely to develop the disease than offspring of families in which diabetes has occurred only on one parent's side of the family?
5. How can you account for the fact that in some cases organisms of the same genotype will not be of the same phenotype?
6. What kinds of gametes would be produced by organisms having the following genotypes?
   a. *AaBB*
   b. *aaBB*
   c. *AAbb*
   d. *AaBBCc*
7. Two white sheep produce a black offspring. What must the parents' genotype for color be? What is the probability that the next offspring will be black?
8. When crossing a red four o'clock plant with a pink one, what should you expect the offspring to be like?
9. Red fruit (*R*) is dominant to yellow fruit (*r*) in tomatoes. Tallness (*T*) is dominant to shortness (*t*) in these plants. What phenotype and genotype ratios would you predict for offspring of parent plants, one of which is red homozygous and tall homozygous, and the other of which is red heterozygous and tall heterozygous?
10. Among the following genotypes, which ones are heterozygous and which are homozygous? Which of the genotypes have the same phenotype? Pick out from the list one or more genes for which only two alleles are given. Also pick out a series of multiple alleles.

    AA, I^AI^B, ss, Bb, I^Bi, Aa, BB, rr, ii
11. What would be the results of a cross of *AaBbCc* × *AaBbCc* in which three inherited traits are observed? Let *A* represent the dominant gene for shortness, and *a* the recessive for tallness; *B*, the dominant gene for black, and *b*, the recessive gene for white; *C*, the dominant gene for curly, and *c*, the recessive gene for straight.
12. An extra finger in man is rare, but is due to a dominant gene. When one parent is normal and the other parent has an extra finger, but is heterozygous for the trait, what is the probability that their first child will be normal? their second child? their third?
13. Albinism (lack of pigment) in man is caused by a recessive gene. If normal parents have an albino child, what is the probability that their next child will be normal for color?

RELATED READING

Books

For Mendel's own account of his discoveries . . .

Mendel, Gregor, *Experiments in Plant Hybridisation,* Harvard University Press, 1963 (paperback).

For additional information on principles of genetics . . .

Brewbaker, J. L., *Agricultural Genetics,* Prentice-Hall, Englewood Cliffs, New Jersey, 1964 (paperback).

Moore, John A., *Heredity and Development,* Oxford University Press, New York, 1963 (paperback).

Sinnott, E. W., L. C. Dunn, and T. Dobzhansky, *Principles of Genetics,* Fifth Edition, McGraw-Hill, New York, 1958.

Stahl, F. W., *The Mechanics of Inheritance,* Prentice-Hall, Englewood Cliffs, New Jersey, 1964 (paperback).

Magazines

Bearn, A. G., and J. L. German, "Chromosomes and Disease," *Scientific American,* Volume 205 (November 1961), page 66.

30

The Chromosome Theory of Heredity

The paper in which Mendel reported his studies with the garden pea lay unnoticed for a long time. During the years following 1865, as before, many breeding experiments were performed with different plants and animals. Biologists attempted to make sense of the results they obtained, but these efforts were not successful. It was not until the year 1900, thirty-five years after Mendel presented his results, and some years after his death, that his paper was "discovered" by three biologists. All three were working independently on the same kind of problem that Mendel had investigated. The modern science of genetics was born with the recognition by each of these men that Mendel's work established the foundation upon which hereditary studies could build.

Where Is the Gene?

You will recall that the experiments with garden pea plants led Mendel to the view that heredity is controlled by a number of independent elements that we now call genes. Each inherited trait, such as seed shape, or flower position, or height of plants, is supposedly controlled, as we now express it, by a *pair* of alleles of a gene. One member of each pair—one allele—comes from the male parent (in the pea plant, from the male part of the flower, or anther). The other allele comes from the female parent (the ovule in the pea plant).

The new zygotes resulting from the parental or P_1 cross develop into seeds and then into mature plants. These in turn produce gametes. During the production of gametes, members of the gene pair again separate, and again only one of the two alleles enters any one sperm or egg cell. This segregation of the members of gene pairs to the gametes, and their pairing with new alleles in the zygote, we recognize as the rule in sexual reproduction.

Mendel assumed that the members of a gene pair are in no way modified by being associated with one another in the cells of a heterozygous organism. He believed this because the effects of the recessive genes can be observed again in homozygous offspring of heterozygous plants. The gene for white seed coat, for instance, remains the same "determiner" of whiteness, in spite of being associated with a gene for colored seed coat in a heterozygous plant.

This theory of Mendel's is all very well as far as it goes. It accounts beautifully for the experimental data obtained from breeding pea plants. Further investigation of the heredity of a variety of plants and animals shows that Mendel's principles can also account for the results in many different kinds of organisms. But an important question looms unanswered. If there are really such things as the genes, where are they? Shouldn't we see them behaving in the manner we have discussed—that is, pairing in each zygote, and separating before being assorted to the gametes?

CHROMOSOMES AND GENETIC CONTINUITY

At this time we must recall some of the things that we have learned about chromosomes and cell division.

First, we learned that all cells come from preexisting cells (Chapter 3). One cell divides into two, the two divide into four, and so on.

The events that occur during cell division are complex (consult Chapter 7). Some of the cell's contents seem to be passively divided when the one cell divides into two. The chromosomes, however, are always replicated and then

Victor A. McKusick

30–1 Walter S. Sutton (1870–1916). Sutton made his important contribution to genetics in 1902 and 1903. He subsequently practiced medicine.

divided exactly, by mitosis. The process actually begins some time before the cell is to divide. Each chromosome replicates, and thus, there come to be two of every original kind of chromosome in the cell. During cell division, one chromosome of each and every kind goes into each daughter cell. The two daughter cells, therefore, have identical chromosomes; and these chromosomes are identical to the chromosomes of the parent cell from which they were derived.

We have also learned that all individuals of the same species have the same number of chromosomes (later in this chapter we will consider a few exceptions to this generalization). The normal number for man is 46; for the potato, 48; for hydras and cherry trees, 32; for garden peas, 14; for the fruit fly, 8; and so on.

We have learned that most of the cells in an individual animal or plant have the same number of chromosomes. We call this the diploid number. But not all cells can have the diploid number. We saw in Chapter 7 that the process of meiosis reduces the chromosome number by half during the formation of eggs and sperms. (In plants, meiosis occurs during the formation of spores; but sooner or later the spores produce eggs and sperms, so these gametes have the reduced number of chromosomes.) Each gamete receives only one chromosome of each homologous pair.

You should review the details of meiosis from pages 138–44 of Chapter 7. We will use the information in the discussion that follows.

The Chromosome Theory of Heredity

Walter S. Sutton (Figure 30-1), a young graduate student working at Columbia University, provided one of the first leads to the solution of the problem, "Where are the genes?" Sutton recognized a parallel behavior between Mendel's genetic units and the chromosomes during meiosis. He argued that these parallels are too striking to be accidental. Let us follow some of the evidence and arguments, of Sutton and others, that convinced biologists that the genes are located at definite places on the chromosomes.

One step in the early argument ran as follows. The biological link between generations of multicellular organisms consists typically of two tiny cells—a sperm cell and an egg cell. Therefore, the genes that control heredity must be within these two gametes.

A second step in the argument is the fact that the egg cell and sperm cell appear to make precisely the same genetic contribution to the organism that develops from their union. Mendel himself supplied the evidence for this equal genetic contribution from the two gametes. He made *reciprocal* (re·SIP·ro·kul) crosses in which first the male and then the female plant carried the dominant trait he was studying. And yet, these crosses produced *exactly the same kind of offspring*. It made no difference which parent had the dominant trait.

Now, the argument ran, if the genetic contribution of the sperm and the egg are essentially the same, some structure, common to both gametes, must be responsible for inheritance. There is a single conspicuous candidate for this honor—the nucleus. Many sperm cells consist of a nucleus and little else. The nucleus of the egg is, in nearly all respects, a duplicate of the nucleus of the sperm. Only the cytoplasm of the egg differs vastly in both amount and nature from that in the sperm. On this basis we might conclude that the *nucleus* is the seat of heredity.

Within the nucleus lie the chromosomes. A careful study reveals that they seem to behave much as Mendel's hereditary factors are supposed to behave. An individual chromosome retains its structure throughout the cell divisions of meiosis, and indeed throughout numberless cell divisions that produce the cells of the body tissues of each generation. Clearly, this preservation of the individuality of each chromosome is required if the chromosomes are to serve as the carriers of heredity.

Sutton drew up a precise list of these parallel types of behavior:

1. At the conclusion of meiosis, a gamete has only one of each kind of chromosome, that is, one member of each homologous pair. This corresponds to Mendel's requirement that one and only one of each pair of genetic elements be present in each germ cell.
2. The union of sperm and egg, each with its single set of chromosomes, re-establishes the diploid number for the new organism. This corresponds to the requirement that the genes be contributed equally by each parent.
3. Each pair of homologous chromosomes segregates quite independently of every other pair during meiosis (page 143, Chapter 7). The four possible combinations of two pairs of chromosomes correspond exactly to what Mendel had found to hold true for different pairs of traits, such as *round* versus *wrinkled*, or *yellow* versus *green*, when they were followed together.

Sutton carefully calculated the *number* of combinations that would be possible in gametes and in zygotes with different numbers of pairs of chromosomes in the diploid cells. He found that the number of possible chromosome combinations is just the same as the number of combinations of genetic elements Mendel postulated in explaining the results of his crosses with pea plants.

After considering all these striking parallels, Sutton proposed this hypothesis:

> Let us assume that the genes are units located on the chromosomes, one member of each pair of alleles being located on each member of a chromosome pair. Then the behavior of the chromosomes in meiosis and fertilization will account for the results of the breeding experiments.

In Figure 30-2 two pairs of genes located on two pairs of chromosomes are indicated in a diagrammatic fashion. Follow the various genes through meiosis, and see how they provide a plausible explanation for the Mendelian ratios.

Sutton realized, of course, that there must be *more* than one gene pair to a pair of chromosomes. If this were not so, the number of traits under genetic control in an organism would be limited to the number of its pairs of chromosomes. Since some organisms have only one or two pairs of chromosomes and man has but 23 pairs, the number of hereditary traits would be very limited indeed. Sutton therefore assumed that many different genes are located on a single chromosome. This conclusion led him to a brilliant hypothesis. If several genes are linked together on a single chromosome, they can scarcely be transmitted independently of each other. One could then make the deduction that there should be groups of genes that do not assort independently. The number of these

30-2 SEGREGATION AND INDEPENDENT ASSORTMENT IN MEIOSIS

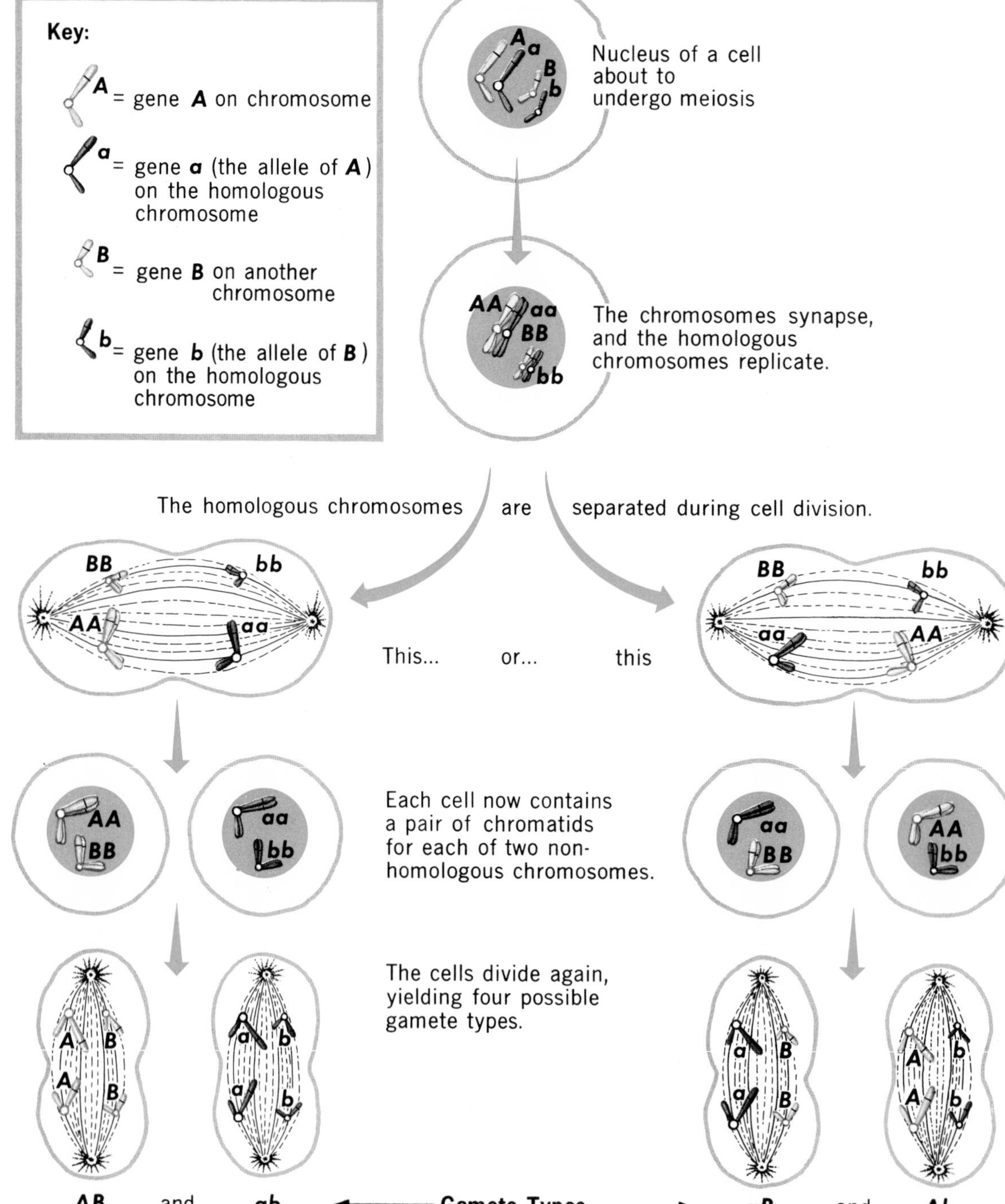

Key:
A = gene A on chromosome
a = gene a (the allele of A) on the homologous chromosome
B = gene B on another chromosome
b = gene b (the allele of B) on the homologous chromosome
Nucleus of a cell about to undergo meiosis
The chromosomes synapse, and the homologous chromosomes replicate.
The homologous chromosomes are separated during cell division.
This... or... this
Each cell now contains a pair of chromatids for each of two non-homologous chromosomes.
The cells divide again, yielding four possible gamete types.
AB and ab ← Gamete Types → aB and Ab

linkage groups of genes should correspond to the number of pairs of chromosomes.

Mendel did not find any linkage group in the pea, but in his experiments he tested only seven pairs of alternative traits. Mendel was fortunate in that each of his seven pairs of alleles was situated on a different pair of chromosomes. As a matter of fact, the pea has just seven pairs of chromosomes. If Mendel had studied an eighth pair of alleles, he would have found an exception to the independent assortment of different pairs of alleles. Sutton predicted that when the monoploid chromosome number of a species has been determined, it will correspond to the number of linkage groups in that same species. He was unable to confirm this idea himself. More than a decade was to pass before geneticists knew enough about the chromosome number and inheritance in any species to test the hypothesis. The fruit fly was the first species for which the data were available. Today we know much about the genetics of many species, and Sutton's hypothesis has been verified, with convincing evidence.

The Nature of Scientific Proof

What do we mean by "convincing evidence"? We have discussed frequently the accumulation of evidence for or against a hypothesis in biology. If the evidence favors the hypothesis, is the process something like proving a theorem in geometry?

Proof in geometry starts with axioms and postulates and moves by a series of logical steps to a conclusion. This conclusion is *unquestionable* if the assumptions (axioms and postulates) are granted, and if the steps of the proof are logical. "Proof" in science is quite different. The biologist gradually and haltingly accumulates data—by many steps and with many doubts. At intervals he tries to interpret his data. He seeks to find some pattern that will relate them to one another, and thus organize them into a reasonable whole, acceptable as *theory*.

A theory can do no more than take into account all the available data. If it does so, without any omissions or distortions, it is a very good theory indeed. One effect of a good theory is to spur scientists to search for new data, to advance new hypotheses, and to test these hypotheses. The very surest test is to make a hypothesis on the basis of the theory—just as Sutton did—and then make deductions from the hypothesis. The deductions can be tested with new data to see whether the hypothesis holds true or can be shown to be false. Whenever new data are found, the theory must be re-examined. If the new data do not support the theory, then the theory must be revised to take them into account, or abandoned if the new data contradict it entirely.

So in biology, as in all science, no theory is ever proved once and for all. However, if a theory continues to account for all new data as they appear over the years, then it is said to be established.

Discovery of the Sex Chromosomes

Let us return to the mounting evidence for the chromosome theory of heredity. Most of it came from the study of the small fruit fly, which you may have seen at times hovering around overripe fruit. Its scientific name is *Drosophila melanogaster* (dro·SOF·il·a mel·a-no·GAS·ter), meaning "black-bellied dew-lover."

Drosophila was first studied intensively in the laboratories of Columbia University in New York City, where Walter Sutton had earlier been a graduate student. Here T. H. Morgan (Figure 30-3), around 1910, raised thousands of the red-eyed flies in bottles, supplying mashed bananas as food. In the course of examining these flies, one fly was found that had *white* eyes instead of *red* eyes. What was the basis of this variation? Could it be due to genetic differences, such as Mendel had found in peas?

The white-eyed fly was a male. It was mated with a red-eyed female. The F_1 generation consisted entirely of red-eyed flies. This meant, if we follow Mendel's scheme, that the allele for white eyes is recessive; the allele for red eyes, dominant. The F_1 red-eyed flies were mated

California Institute of Technology

30–3 Thomas Hunt Morgan (1866–1945). His discovery of sex-linked traits in *Drosophila* indicated that genes are on chromosomes. He and his students worked out the details of inheritance in *Drosophila* to such an extent that this species is still a model for explaining genetic behavior.

to produce an F_2 generation. Among these offspring a ratio of $^3/_4$ red-eyed flies to $^1/_4$ white-eyed flies was obtained. This, too, agreed with Mendel's F_2 results for single trait inheritance—until Morgan noticed that *all the white-eyed flies were males.*

Not even one white-eyed fly was female. All of the F_2 females had red eyes, as did about half the males. Since the number of males and females in the F_2 generation was about equal, $^3/_4$ of the F_2 had red eyes and $^1/_4$ had white eyes. If this had been a true Mendelian ratio, as at first it seemed, the 3:1 ratio should have applied to the males and females separately, as well as together. In other words, both the males and the females would have been $^3/_4$ red-eyed and $^1/_4$ white-eyed. Work out this cross and convince yourself.

How could such a strange result be explained? One could have assumed that the rules for inheritance in peas are not the same as in *Drosophila.* After all, the two organisms are very different. Recall for yourself the great differences in structure and physiology between an angiosperm and an arthropod. But there were also reasons for assuming that the general rules for inheritance would be the same in all organisms. By the time that Morgan was doing his work, the genetics of many plants and animals had been investigated. For the most part their patterns of inheritance were the same as in Mendel's peas.

Remember that Morgan was working in the same laboratory where, a decade earlier, Sutton had suggested that the genes were on chromosomes. Morgan would have had this hypothesis in the back of his mind. Now if the allele for white eyes is on a chromosome, that chromosome must be behaving in a very strange fashion. Otherwise, the cross would give the expected Mendelian results.

Might we get a clue by looking at the chromosomes of *Drosophila*? Just before Morgan's discovery of the white-eyed male fly, some careful work on the cells of *Drosophila* had shown that there is a difference between the chromosomes of males and females. Of the four pairs of chromosomes in each cell, three pairs are identical in males and females. But one pair is not (Figure 30-4). The straight, rod-shaped

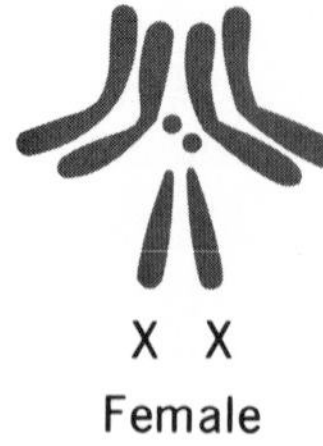

30–4 The four pairs of chromosomes of diploid cells in female and male *Drosophila*.

SEX DETERMINATION IN *DROSOPHILA*

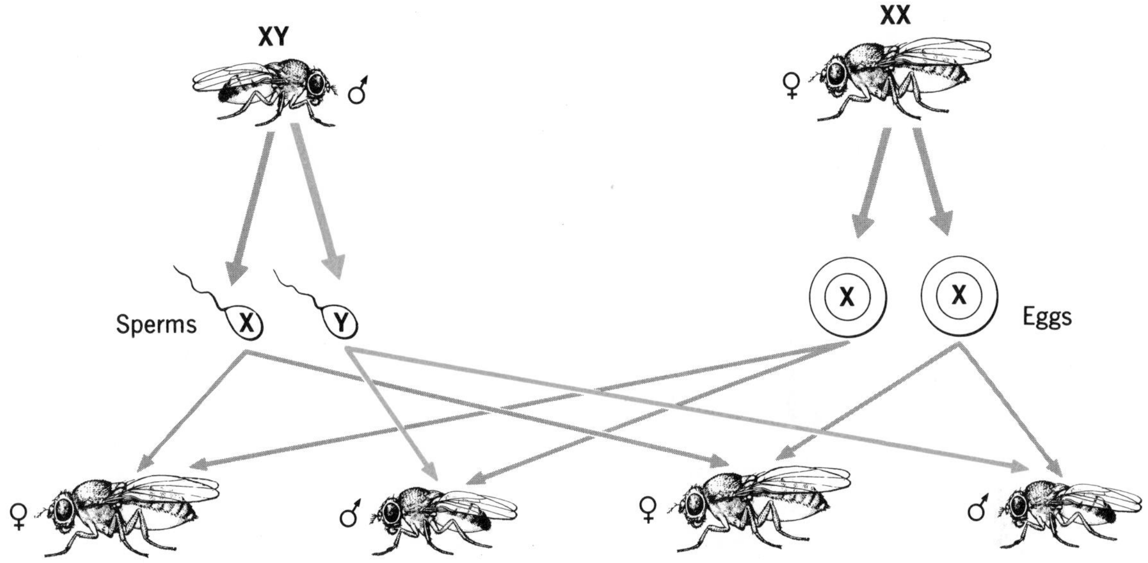

30–5 The relation of chromosomes to sex determination in fruit flies. ♂ is the symbol for male; ♀ for female. Which parent contributes the sex-determining chromosomes to the offspring? (Later you will qualify your answer, as you read page 555.)

chromosomes of this pair in the female are named X chromosomes. Only one of these occurs in the male, along with a hook-shaped chromosome (found in the male only), named the Y chromosome. Because of their connection with the sex of the flies, the X and Y chromosomes are called the **sex chromosomes**. All of the other chromosomes are called **autosomes** (AW·toh·sohms). Thus, the male of *Drosophila* has three pairs of autosomes, one X sex chromosome, and one Y sex chromosome. The female has three pairs of autosomes and two X sex chromosomes.

Recall that after meiosis, each gamete has one of each pair of homologous chromosomes. A female *Drosophila* would form egg cells with one of each pair of autosomes and one X chromosome. All of the egg cells would be alike. The sperm also would receive one member of each pair of chromosomes, but since there are two kinds of sex chromosomes in the male, half of the sperms would receive an X chromosome and the other half a Y chromosome.

Figure 30-5 shows how the sex chromosomes in *Drosophila* are inherited. Notice especially that the inheritance of the X and Y chromosomes determines the sex of the offspring. All egg cells contain one X. If a sperm with an X enters an egg, the result is XX, or a female. Similarly, if a sperm with a Y enters an egg, the result is XY, or a male.

This illustration shows something else about the inheritance of the sex chromosomes. The daughters receive one X from the father and one from the mother. Notice, however, that a son can inherit his X only from the mother (if he inherited an X from his father also, he would be a daughter!). This means that a son could inherit only from his mother the genes that are carried on the X chromosome.

Knowing these facts and the results of a cross between a white-eyed male × red-eyed female,

Morgan made this hypothesis:

1. The allele for white eyes and the allele for red eyes are located on X chromosomes.
2. The Y chromosome does not carry any allele of this eye-color gene.

If this hypothesis is correct, then a cross of a white-eyed male and a homozygous red-eyed female should turn out as shown in Figure 30-6. This, of course, was the original experiment that set Morgan on this line of research. The model and the experimental results were identical. This one test supports the hypothesis. This is not surprising, since the model was made after the results were obtained and for the purpose of explaining them!

Other tests would have to be made. If the hypothesis is true, then the following deduction could be made. In a cross between a red-eyed male and a white-eyed female, these results should be obtained:

F_1: all the males should have white eyes and all the females should have red eyes.
F_2: in both males and females, half should have red eyes and half should have white eyes.

You should compare these expectations with those of the opposite cross (Figure 30-6). You will observe that they are very different. When Morgan made this cross he obtained the expected results. You should work out the cross for yourself according to the plan shown in Figure 30-6.

Morgan was able to make other deductions, and all of them supported the original hypothesis. In every way he was able to test it, the hypothesis was found to be an adequate explanation of the experimental results. So far as he could determine, all the data could be explained by the hypothesis that the allele for white eyes and the corresponding allele for red eyes were situated on the X chromosomes. You can test this hypothesis yourself in Laboratory Inquiry 30-1. Also apply the hypothesis to the problems at the top of the next column of text.

PROBLEM: If you had a red-eyed female fly, but did not know whether it carried a gene for white-eye color, how would you plan a test cross to find out?

PROBLEM: What would be the result of the cross between a white-eyed male and a white-eyed female?

As the years went by, many genes other than those for white-eye and red-eye color were shown to behave in similar ways. Sutton's hypothesis, and its later extensions by Morgan, became well established. A large body of data based on observation and experiment was accumulated, explained, and interrelated. It became useful for making predictions. By 1915 one could even refer to the chromosome *theory* of heredity rather than to the *hypothesis* that genes are on chromosomes.

Morgan's work established that the sex chromosomes carry not only some of the genes that determine sex, but other genes, too—in the example you know, the alleles for white-eye color and red-eye color in *Drosophila.* The heredity of traits whose genes are located on the sex chromosomes is different from that of traits whose genes are on the autosomes. This combined pattern differs partly from that found by Mendel, for his results require us always to assume the presence of pairs of similar genes in *both* sexes. With this new chromosome picture in the male fruit fly, there came to be reason to doubt that all the X chromosome genes have corresponding partners (alleles) on the Y chromosome. In fact, Morgan's case of white-eye inheritance in *Drosophila* was explained by assuming that the alleles for white-eye and red-eye color are carried on an either/or basis by an X chromosome, and are absent from the Y chromosome. Since this also proves to be true of many other genes on the X chromosome, the Y chromosome in *Drosophila* may be said to be "inert" in inheritance. Consequently, even a recessive gene on the X chromosome always affects the phenotype and is recognizable in

SEX-LINKED INHERITANCE IN *DROSOPHILA*

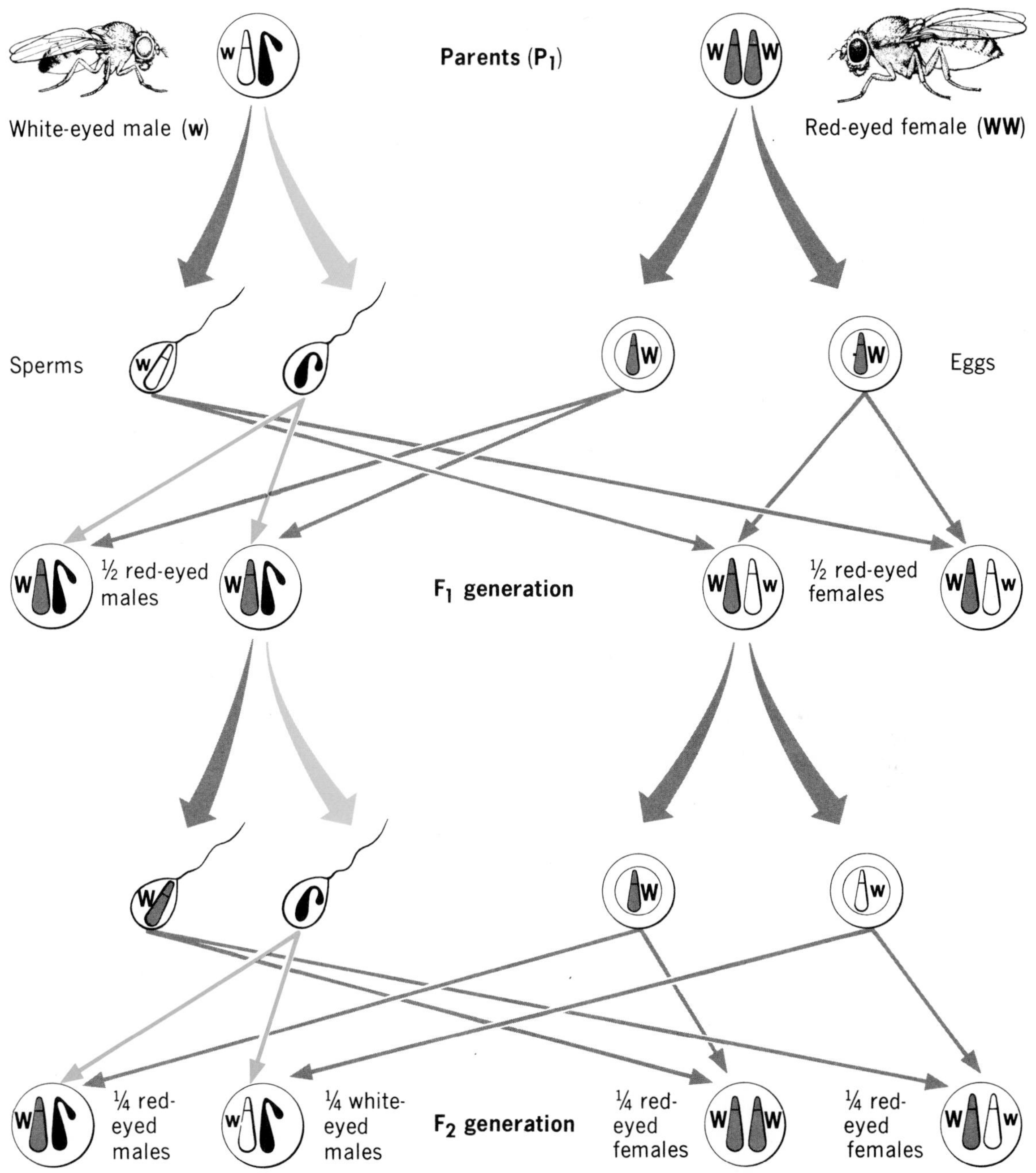

30–6 A diagram of two generations of *Drosophila*, showing the inheritance of a trait controlled by a gene located on the X chromosome. The gene in this case controls the production of white-eye color; its normal allele results in red-eye color.

the male fly, since there is no corresponding allele on the Y chromosome.

Whenever Y chromosomes have been studied in other organisms, they are found to have very few genes. They are not always without genes, however.

Sex-linked Inheritance in Man

In man the Y chromosome does have genetic effects, although for many genes carried by the X chromosome it is inert. Decide which of these possibilities is involved as we consider two sex-linked traits in man, color blindness and **hemophilia** (hee·mo·FIL·ih·a).

1. *Color blindness.* Sex-linked color blindness is a rather common trait. Persons afflicted have difficulty in distinguishing red from green. This type of color blindness can be detected by using special charts made up of a number of colored dots so arranged that colorblind persons see a different pattern (or word) than other persons do.

   PROBLEM: There are eight or ten times as many colorblind men as colorblind women. Use the model worked out for white-eye inheritance in *Drosophila* and show why you would expect more color blindness among men than among women.

2. *Hemophilia.* Genetic hemophilia is a much more serious human defect than color blindness, and fortunately a much rarer one. Hemophilia is a condition in which the blood fails to clot after a surface or internal injury, or clots very slowly. Persons with extreme cases can bleed to death from even a small cut.

   Hemophilia is a genetic defect with a royal history. The gene for the trait became so widely distributed in European royalty during the nineteenth and early twentieth centuries that the course of history was profoundly affected, especially in Spain and Russia. The gene probably appeared first as a mutation in one of the gametes that united to form Queen Victoria, since there is no record of hemophilia in her ancestry. Because of marriages among the royalty of Europe, the gene became distributed in other royal families. Figure 30-7 shows the pedigree for Queen Victoria's descendants. Note that the present royal family of Great Britain is free of the gene. How can one be positive about this?

   You will note in the pedigree that there are no female hemophiliacs. In order for a female to have hemophilia she would have to receive one X chromosome from her mother, the other from her father, both of the chromosomes carrying the hemophilia gene. This occurs very rarely, partly because few male hemophiliacs survive to marry and reproduce.

   PROBLEM: Determine what kind of inheritance is shown by each of the following human pedigrees:

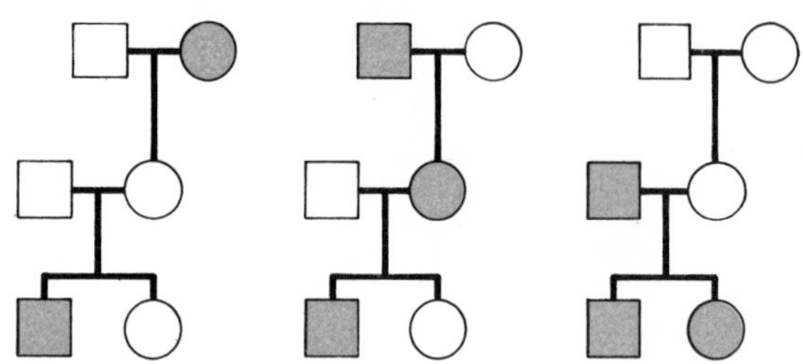

   Can two different hypotheses account for any of the preceding pedigrees? If so, what are they?

LINKAGE AND CROSSING-OVER

You will recall that Mendel found that each of the genetic differences he followed in his pea experiments is inherited independently. A heterozygous mating involving two different traits gave him a 9 : 3 : 3 : 1 ratio of the phenotypes in the F_2 generation. This ratio was a consequence of independent assortment of the two pairs of alleles. We can now express this more adequately by saying that the 9 : 3 : 3 : 1 ratio is obtained only if the two pairs of alleles are on different pairs of homologous autosomes. If genes are on the sex chromosomes or if two pairs of alleles are on the same chromosomes, Mendel's rules will not apply. For the inheritance of these linked traits, rules and ratios were emerging from the careful work of Morgan and his students. Yet Morgan's predictions, too, were to find exceptions.

Shortly after the white-eye gene was discovered in Morgan's laboratory, another unusual fly was found. It had a bright yellow body instead of the normal pale yellowish coloration. The yellow phenotype was found to be inherited in the same manner as white eyes, so it was assumed that the gene responsible for it, too, was located on the X chromosome. Now if this were true, what pattern of inheritance could one expect if a cross was made between a female that was white-eyed and bright-yellow-bodied and a male that was red-eyed with nor-

30–7 A pedigree of some of Queen Victoria's descendants, showing the hereditary distribution of hemophilia. The present British royal line descended through Edward VII. He did not have hemophilia and therefore did not inherit from his mother, Queen Victoria, the X chromosome carrying the recessive gene for hemophilia. Beginning with Queen Victoria, which women were clearly "carriers" of the gene?

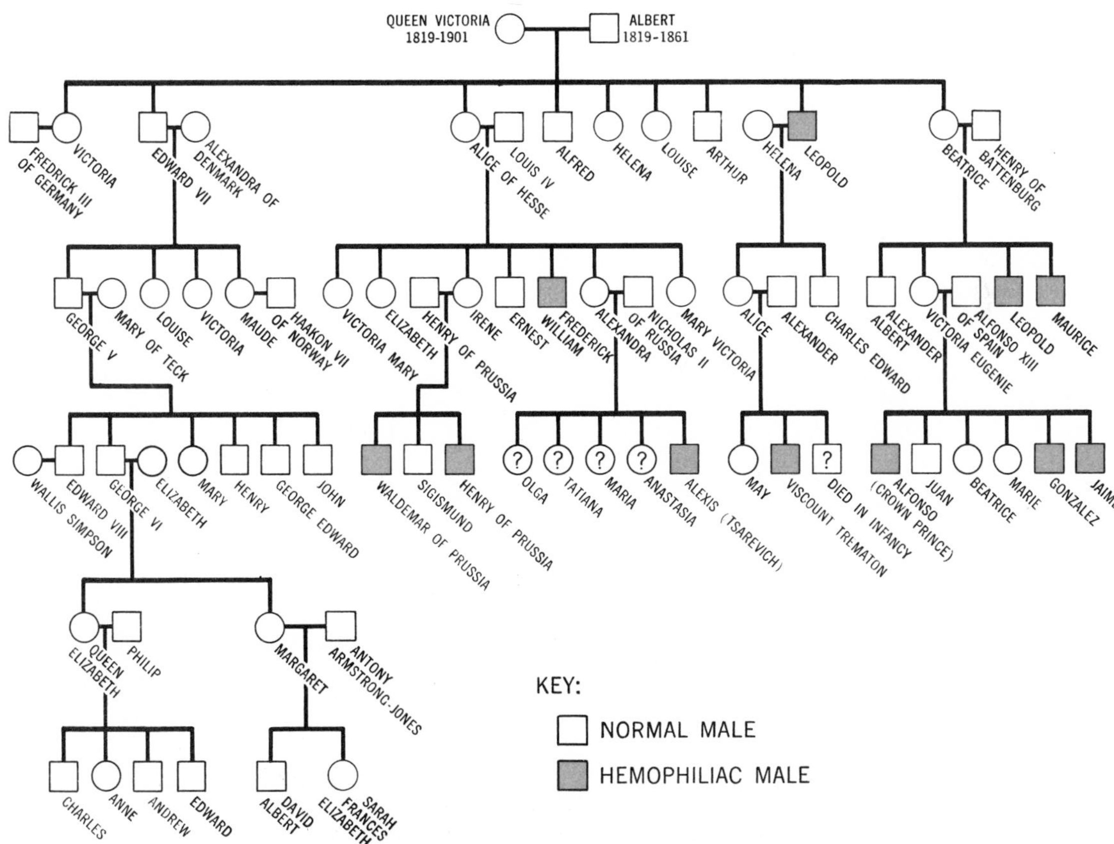

mal body color? We would assume that the white-eye and yellow-body alleles would be inherited as a unit since they are attached to the same chromosome. Where that chromosome went they, too, would go. The F_1 phenotypes should be

for all males—white eyes and bright yellow bodies
for all females—red eyes and normal body coloration

The predicted results appear in Figure 30-8.

When the cross actually was made the predicted results were obtained. This again was strong support for the hypothesis that genes are on chromosomes. Those genes that, when studied separately, behaved as though they were on the X chromosome were found, when studied together, to be linked in their inheritance.

Yet surprisingly, the linkage is not complete, as it should be if two genes are riding together on the same chromosome and cannot separate. Instead, Morgan and others noted that while

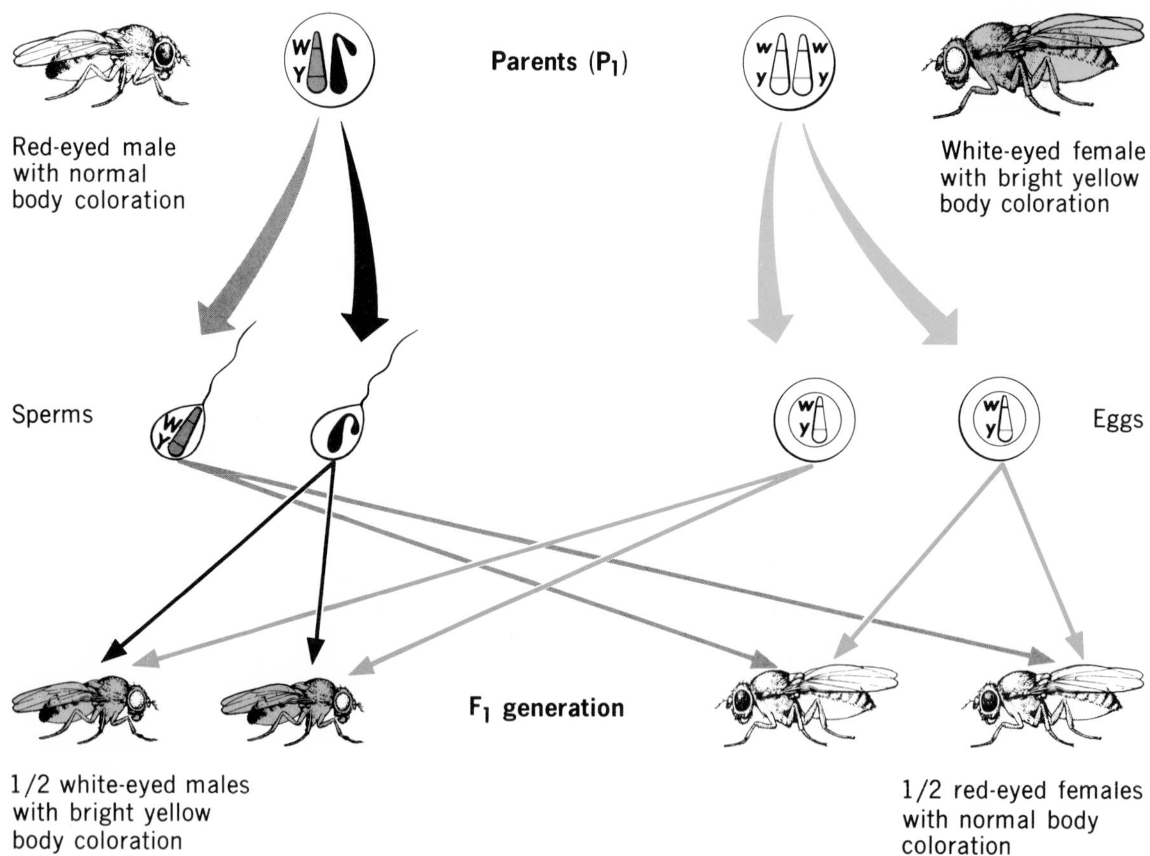

30–8 A diagram of the inheritance of two different traits determined by genes that are sex-linked. In *Drosophila*, the alleles of genes that determine white eyes and yellow bodies all occur on X chromosomes. Can you diagram the F_2 probabilities?

combinations of linked traits in the original parents tend to be preserved in most of the descendants, there are also *recombinations* in some of the descendants. And what is more, these recombinations always occur *with the same frequency* between particular linked traits. It does not matter at all whether an F_1 individual has received the alleles for both dominant traits together from a single parent, or has obtained one from one parent and the other from the other parent. The percentage of recombinations in the F_2 generation is the same. Thus, if the F_1 individual has inherited both *A* and *B* from one parent, and *a* and *b* from the other, the percentage of recombinations (*Ab* and *aB*) in the F_2 is, say, 10 percent. But if the F_1 individual has obtained *Ab* from one parent and *aB* from the other, the percentage of recombinations (*AB* and *ab* this time) in the F_2 is still 10 percent.

If two genes are located on the same chromosome, why do they not *always* stay together? The answer is related to an event that occurs in meiosis.

When chromosomes unite in synapsis, the chromatids of the homologous chromosomes may break and exchange parts in the process. New recombinations of linked genes result. What has happened is called **crossing-over.** Figure 30-9 shows how crossing-over in 20 percent of the meiotic divisions modifies the proportions of gametes (50 percent *AB*; 50 percent *ab*) that would be expected if genes *A* and *B* were always inseparable. In this case the break is close to the middle of the chromosome, and the two genes *A* and *B* (or the recessive alleles *a* and *b*) are at opposite ends. If *A* and *B* were closer together, we might suppose that a break between them would not occur as frequently. In fact, the farther apart two genes are on the same chromosome, the more likely they are to be separated by crossing-over. This assumes, of course, that the points at which crossing-over occur are distributed at random along the chromosome. This simple principle, pointed out by Morgan, has enabled geneticists to construct maps of chromosomes locating the genes in relation to one another. Of course, this can be done only for organisms that have been used in hundreds of genetic experiments involving many thousands of offspring. For the fruit fly, for corn (maize), and for a few other species, this has been done quite thoroughly. Mapping of the human chromosomes in this way is just beginning. Can you suggest why?

Sex Determination

The discovery of two kinds of sex chromosomes in *Drosophila* suggested that perhaps they would provide an explanation for the determination of sex. Flies with two X chromosomes are always females, and those with an X and a Y chromosome are always males. All egg cells are alike in containing a single X chromosome. The sex of a fly therefore depends on whether an egg is fertilized by a sperm with an X chromosome or one with a Y chromosome. Thus the male fly's gamete determines the sex of the offspring, since it carries either an X or Y chromosome. Figure 30-5 shows a diagram of this theory of sex determination.

In later years, when techniques were improved, it became possible to show that a similar difference in one pair of the chromosomes of males and females is a common pattern among animals. With most plants there are no individuals of separate sex—the same plant produces both male and female gametes. In plant species that do have separate male and female individuals, however, sex chromosomes can be distinguished—in mosses and liverworts, the ginkgo tree, and in some flowering plants, for example.

The study of human cells has revealed that man's pattern of sex chromosomes is similar to that of *Drosophila*. Man has 23 pairs of chromosomes in all. Twenty-two pairs of these are the autosomes, and one pair the sex chromosomes. In man, the Y chromosome is very small in size, compared to the X chromosome.

30-9 CROSSING-OVER DURING MEIOSIS

During meiosis crossing-over may occur between genes situated on the same chromosome. The amount of crossing-over depends on the distance between genes. In this example, crossing-over occurs between genes **A** and **B** or their alleles in 20 percent of the cells.

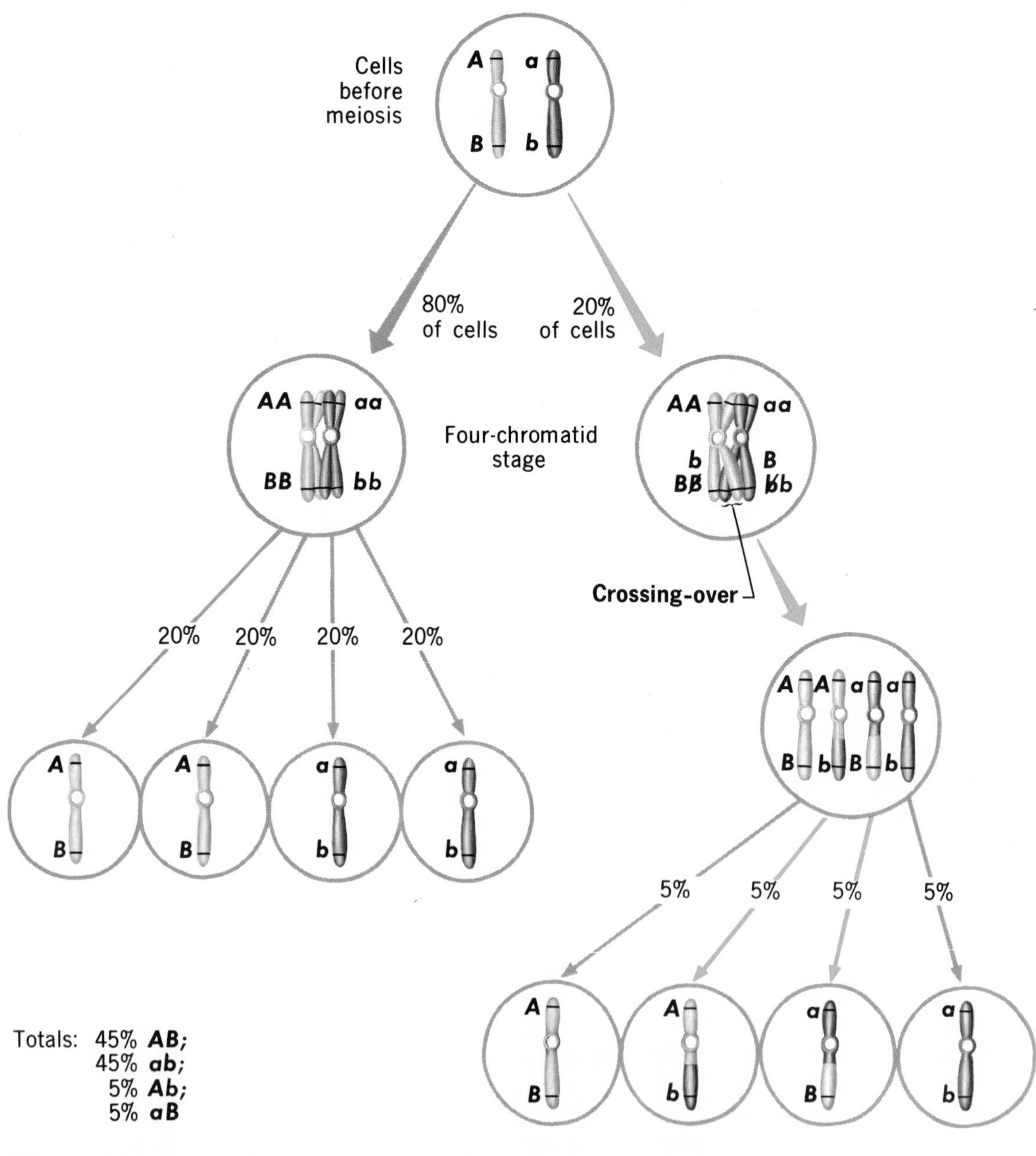

Totals: 45% **AB;**
45% **ab;**
5% **Ab;**
5% **aB**

Figure 30-10 on the following two pages shows the normal sets of chromosomes for a human male and a human female.

By applying our rule of keeping explanations as simple as possible, we can explain sex determination in humans the same way we do in fruit flies. The male produces two kinds of sperms. Half of them carry an X chromosome. The other half carry a Y chromosome. The female produces eggs all of which carry an X chromosome. If an egg is fertilized by a Y-bearing sperm, the offspring is a male. But if an egg is fertilized by an X-bearing sperm, the offspring is a female. Thus, as in *Drosophila*, the sex of a human offspring is determined by the male parent's gamete.

Not all kinds of animals have sex-determining sperms. In some, such as birds, butterflies, and moths, it is the *female* that has two kinds of sex chromosomes, and hence produces two kinds of egg cells. In these organisms all sperm cells are alike in respect to the kinds of sex chromosomes they possess. It is the kind of egg cell that is fertilized that determines the sex of the offspring.

In still other species one of the sex chromosomes may be missing entirely. In some grasshoppers, for instance, males have 23 chromosomes, but females have 24. In this case half the sperm cells have 11 chromosomes, and the other half have 12. The sex of the young grasshopper depends on the kind of sperm that fertilizes the egg.

Abnormal Chromosome Numbers

The effects of X and Y chromosomes are part of the normal pattern of inheritance for species that possess them. The other chromosomes—the autosomes—seem less dramatic in their effects only because *all* offspring normally are affected in the same or similar ways. What might one expect, however, if the chromosomes were juggled in abnormal ways? For example, what might be the result if there was one extra chromosome, a total of the normal diploid number *plus one*? Similarly, what might happen if one chromosome was missing? Many experiments have convinced geneticists that a normal set of chromosomes is required for normal development and life. When even small parts of a chromosome are missing, the individual usually dies early in life or is highly abnormal.

In recent years it has been possible to study human chromosomes. One of the basic methods is to remove a small amount of blood and culture the cells. Of course the red blood cells cannot divide, since they lose their nucleus early in their development. The white blood cells do divide, however, and it is possible to obtain many of them in mitosis. These can be stained and their chromosomes studied. When these methods were perfected, geneticists began to study the chromosomes of human beings. The chromosomes for the male and female in Figure 30-10 are shown twice—once as they were spread out for study under the microscope (at the top of each photograph), and again as arranged by pairs (at the bottom of each photograph). Each chromosome is made up of two chromatids characteristic of the stage in mitosis at which the cell was killed for study. No abnormalities are seen.

Of special interest are the chromosomes of human beings with abnormalities that seem to have a genetic basis, but for which there is no convincing evidence for Mendelian inheritance. The abnormalities described in the following paragraphs are examples. Each is named for the physician or biologist who first described the condition.

Down's Syndrome, formerly known as Mongolism, occurs about 16 times in every 10,000 births. The frequency seems to be related to the age of the mother. If the mother is 32 or younger it is very rare. The incidence increases after that age until it may reach a rate of 150 per 10,000 births in mothers over 40. The child is abnormal both physically and mentally, with a very low IQ. Most of these children die early in life. When the chromosomes of babies with Down's Syndrome are studied it

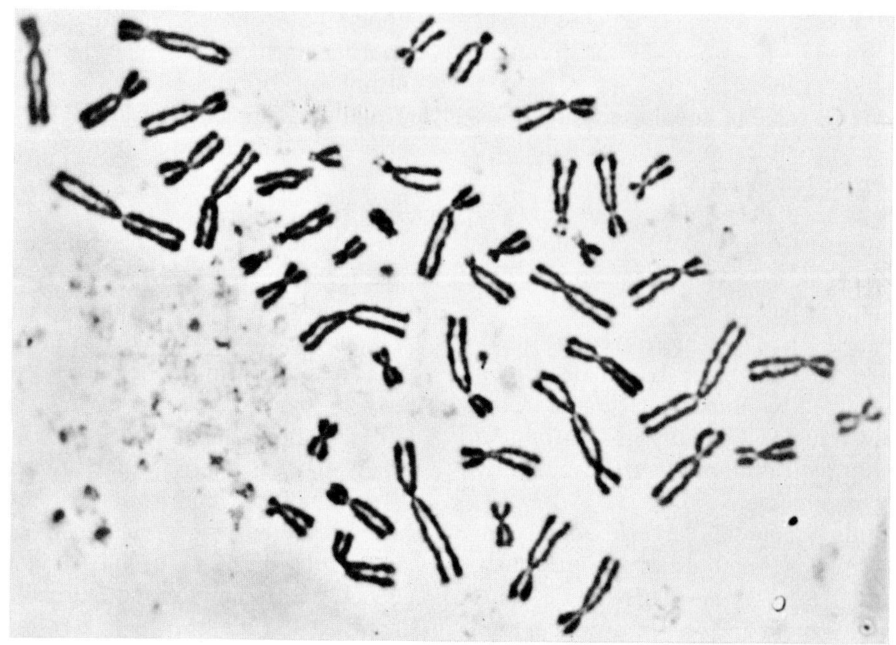

Margery Shaw, M.D.

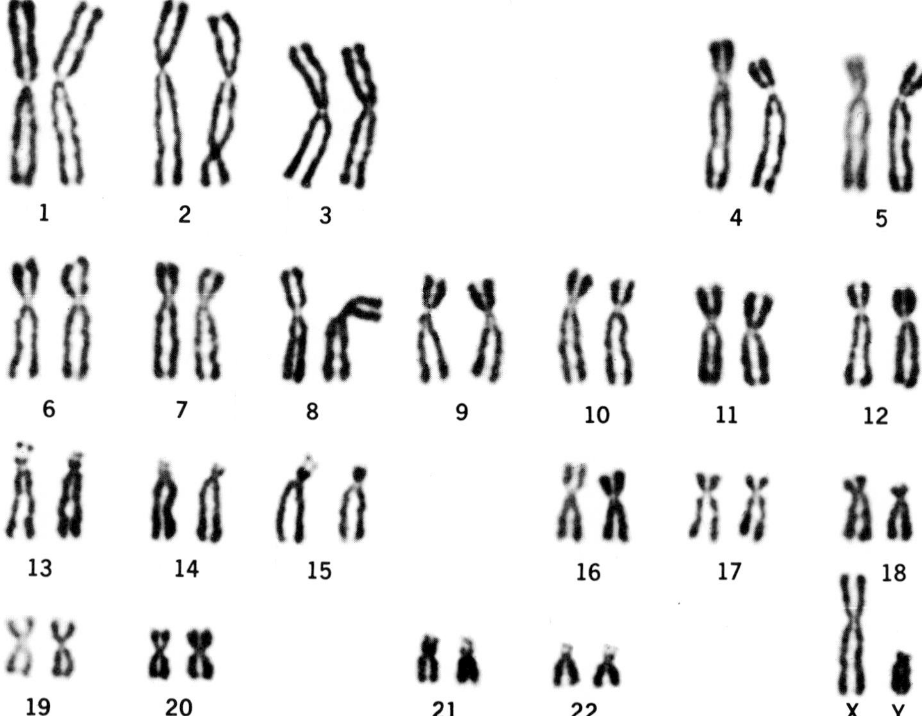

30–10 The chromosomes of a normal human male (this page) and of a normal human female (facing page). For each, a squashed cell is shown above, and the chromosomes

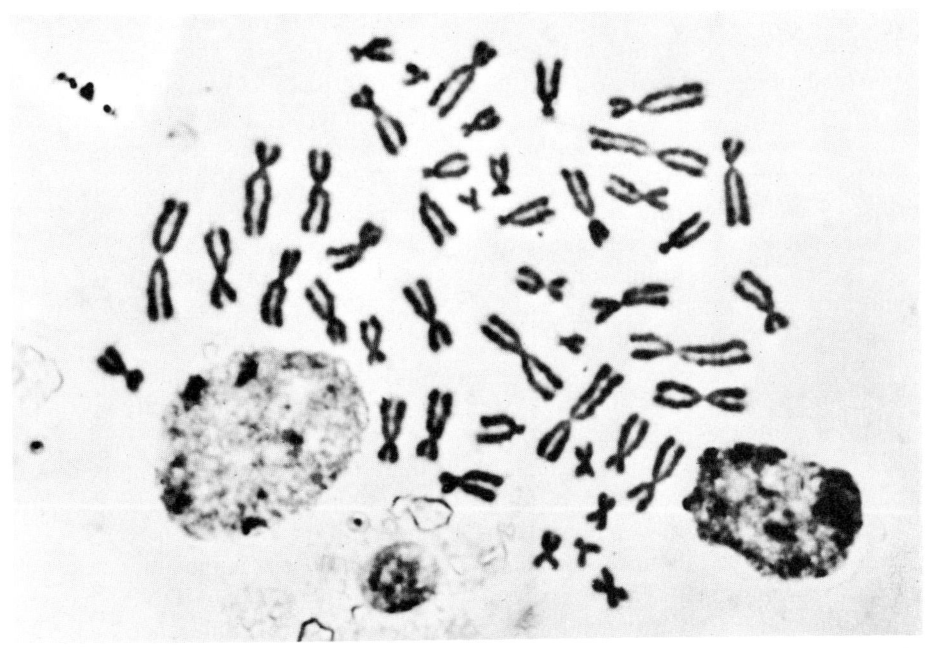

Margery Shaw, M.D.

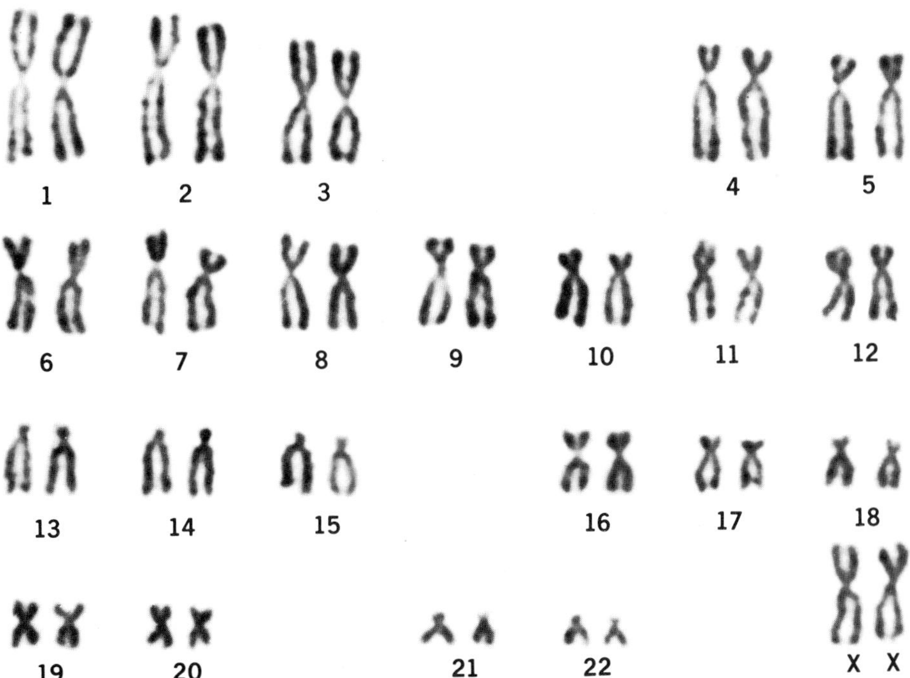

are cut out and arranged in homologous pairs below. How do the pairs of chromosomes of the male differ from those of the female? Which has the sex-determining chromosomes?

is found that there are 47 instead of the normal number of 46. This is the result of *three* autosomes instead of the normal two for the Number 21 autosomes (Figure 30-11).

Turner's Syndrome, a very rare disorder of human females, occurs in about 4 of every 10,000 births. The affected individuals may reach adult size, but they never become sexually mature. When their chromosomes are counted, only 45 are found. Careful study shows that one of the X chromosomes is missing (Figure 30-12).

Klinefelter's Syndrome occurs in about 10 of every 10,000 *male* babies. The babies grow to the adult size but fail to mature sexually. When chromosome counts are made, a total of 47 is found. This is the same number as in Down's Syndrome but, in this case, the male has an extra X chromosome. His sex chromosomes, therefore, are XXY (Figure 30-13).

The study of human chromosomes is a very active field of bio-medical research today. Many abnormal conditions, which were difficult to associate with any known cause, have been found to be associated with abnormal chromosomes. As you can readily understand, it is impossible to cure these patients. In some instances the condition can be helped with injections of hormones. Little is known of the causes of the chromosome abnormalities. It is assumed that they are due to defects in meiosis during the formation of the egg cell and the sperm cell that united to form the individual.

WHAT IS A GENE?

Two entirely different lines of research, each concerned with the nature of the gene, had merged by 1960. Geneticists who crossed *Drosophila,* corn, and many other organisms had demonstrated beyond a reasonable doubt that the genes were located on the chromosomes. They were able to trace the effects accurately through meiosis and fertilization and to account for the phenotypic ratios of successive generations. They had no good evidence for the chemical nature of the gene. It was another group of investigators who supplied this information. Working largely with viruses and bacteria, and using the techniques of biochemistry, these workers had not only localized the gene on chromosomes but had established, beyond a reasonable doubt, that genes were composed of DNA.

It was a major triumph to determine, as you read in Chapter 8, that DNA is the hereditary material. Once this was known, biologists wanted to know how one gene differs from another. It might be perfectly correct to say that the white-eye and the red-eye alleles of *Drosophila* were both composed of DNA. The next step would then be to find how the two alleles differ. In one case DNA is associated with white eyes; in the other case with red eyes. What is there about DNA that could be responsible for the difference?

Let us think about the problem, recalling what we have already learned. DNA controls the life of the cell through the instructions it sends out in messenger RNA. Messenger RNA, enzymes, transfer RNA, and ribosomes are responsible for uniting amino acids to form specific proteins. That is, the amino acids have to be lined up in an exact way. One error and the protein may be defective. Recall the case of hemoglobin in sickle-cell anemia (pages 168–69), an example of a single mistake that may mean the life of an individual.

The available data seem to indicate that amino acids are lined up on the messenger RNA in a specific order. They are then united to form a polypeptide chain for the protein (Figure 8-17, page 172). Thus there may be something about the structure of the messenger RNA that causes the amino acids to line up properly.

What *is* the structure of messenger RNA? We learned earlier that it is a long chain of the four RNA nucleotides of uracil, guanine, cytosine, and adenine (page 171). It is made by the DNA of the nucleus in a highly specific way (analogous to the way that one strand of

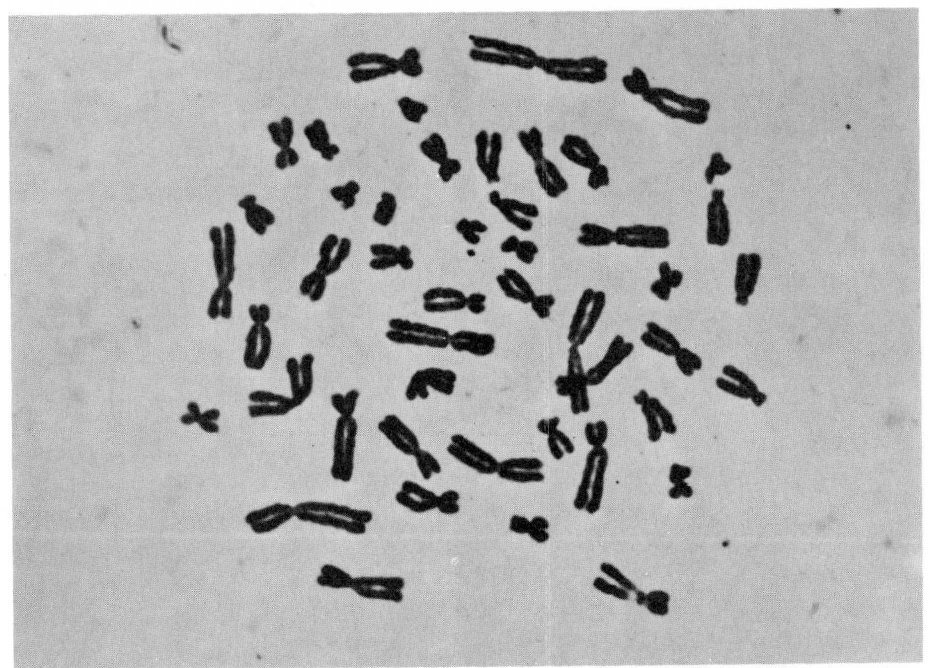

Margery Shaw, M.D.

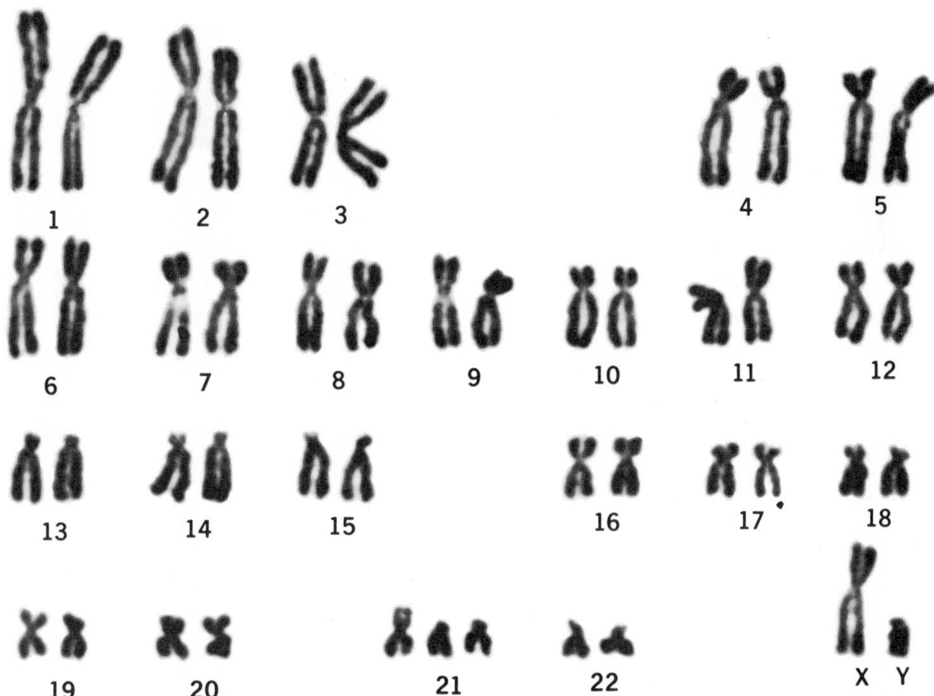

30–11 The chromosomes of a human male with Down's syndrome. Notice the extra Number 21 autosome. The abnormality occurs in females (XX) as well as in males (XY).

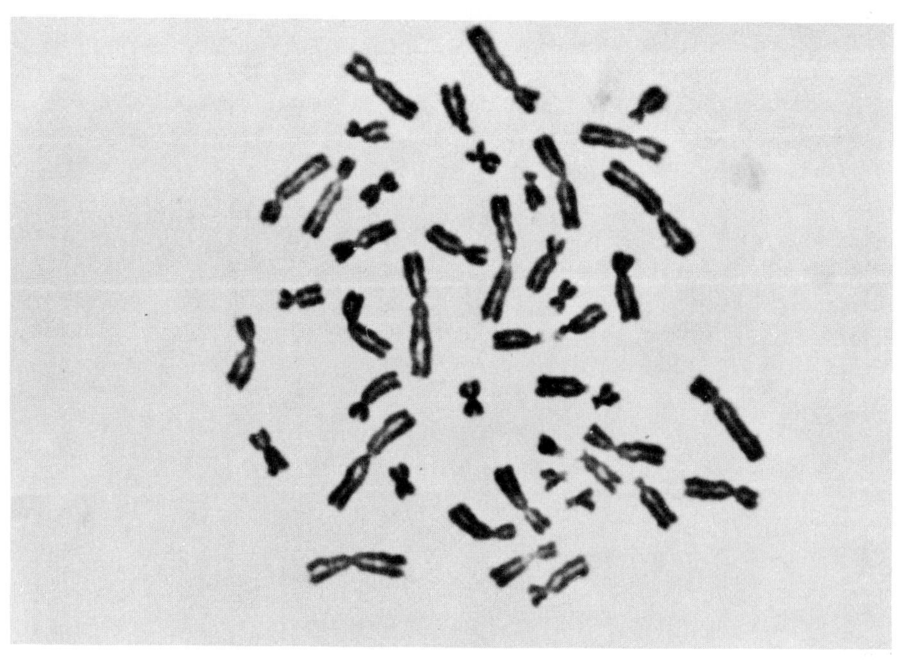

Margery Shaw, M.D.

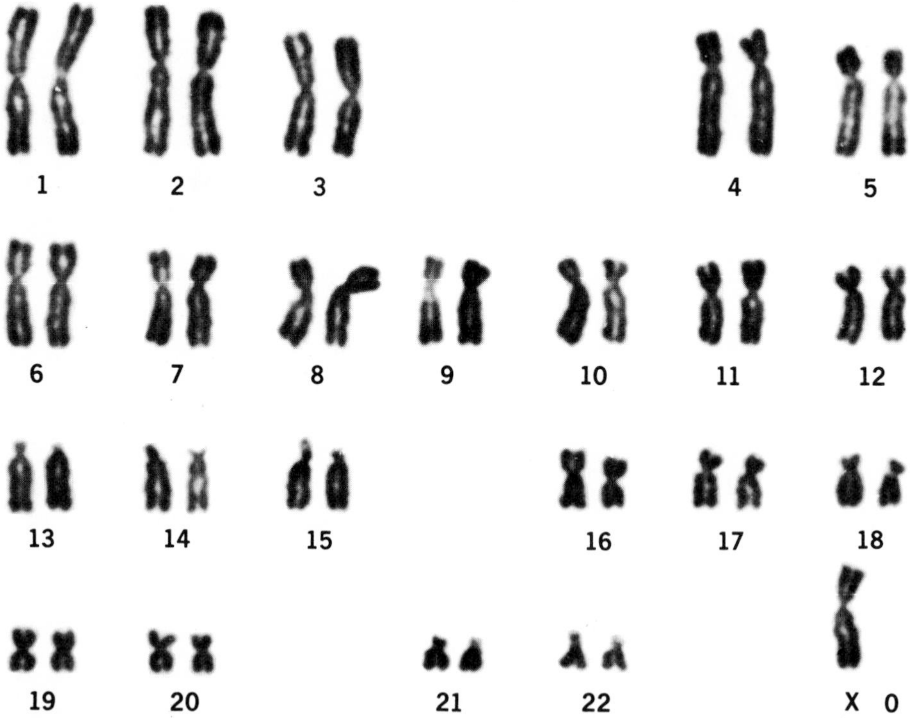

30–12 The chromosomes of a human female with Turner's syndrome, which prevents normal sexual development. Note that one of the two X chromosomes is missing.

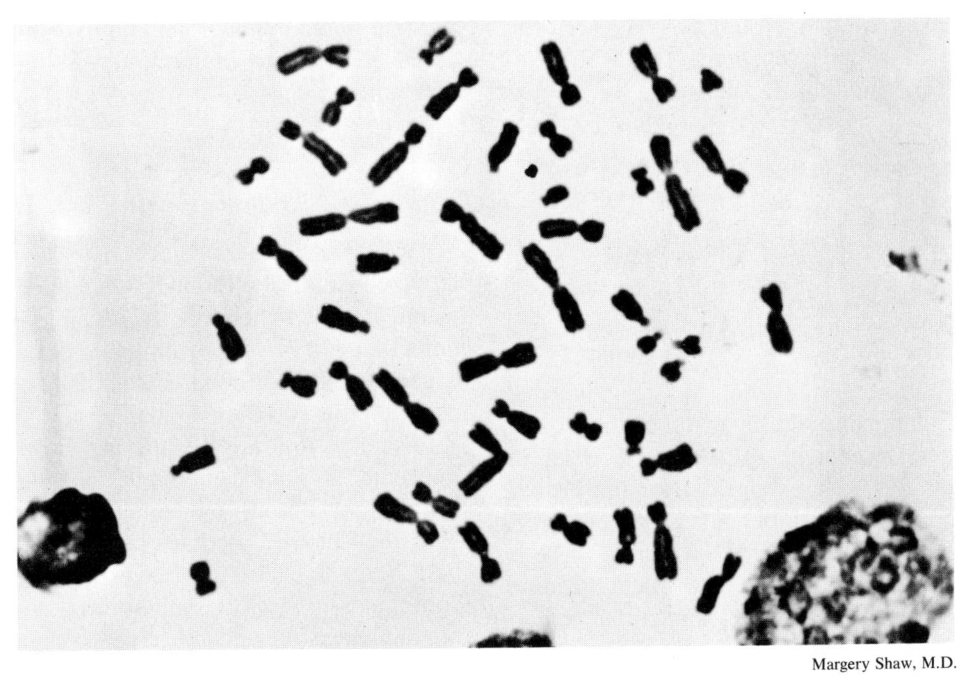

Margery Shaw, M.D.

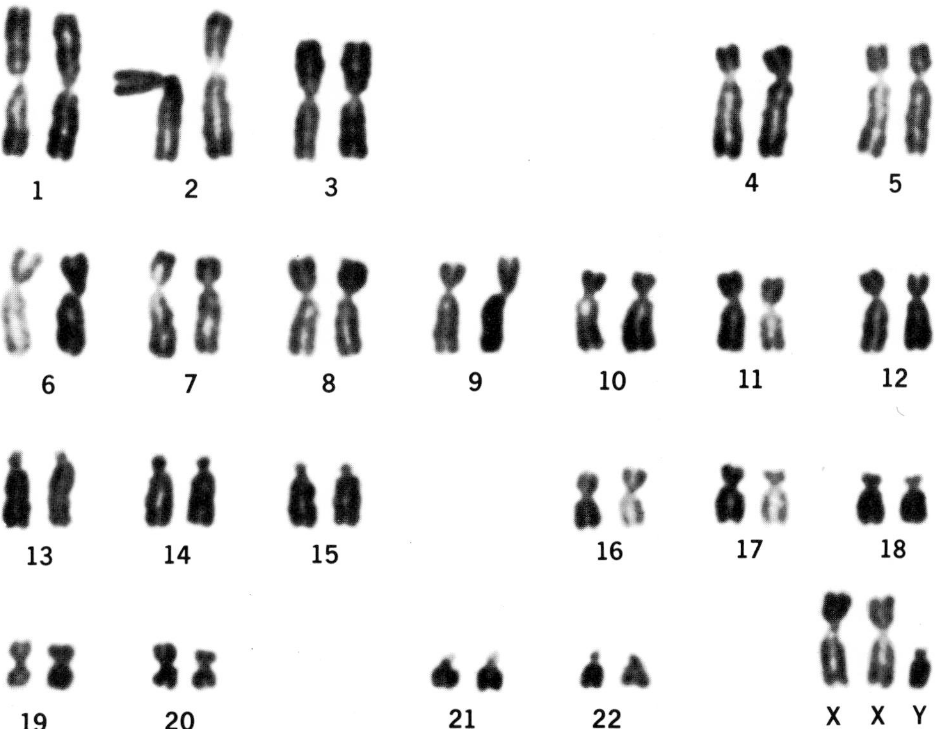

30–13 The chromosomes of a human male with Klinefelter's syndrome. Notice the extra X chromosome, which (with the Y and another X present) prevents normal development.

DNA makes another strand of DNA). In the presence of specific enzymes the RNA nucleotides are lined up as follows:

If the DNA nucleotide is. . .	*then the messenger RNA nucleotide opposite it will be. . .*
thymine	adenine
adenine	uracil
cytosine	guanine
guanine	cytosine

A reasonable hypothesis would be that somehow the *arrangement* of the nucleotides in messenger RNA is responsible for the proper lining up of the amino acids. For example, opposite every site of the RNA where there is uracil, the amino acid glycine might become attached; or opposite cytosine, the amino acid alanine might become attached, and so on, as follows:

If the order of nucleotides is. . .	*then the order of amino acids might be. . .*
uracil	glycine
cytosine	alanine
uracil	glycine
uracil	glycine
cytosine	alanine

Thus the arrangement of the nucleotides in messenger RNA would be a code for the arrangement of the amino acids of the protein. For every amino acid there would be a corresponding nucleotide in messenger RNA. It is possible to test this hypothesis without even doing an experiment. There are 20 amino acids and only 4 nucleotides. Thus the hypothesis cannot be true. Only if there had been 20 nucleotides could we have advanced the hypothesis that each is responsible for one amino acid.

If there are not enough nucleotides for each one to code for one amino acid, possibly pairs of nucleotides could do the job. Let us consider the two nucleotides uracil and cytosine. These could be arranged in combinations to code for four amino acids:

uracil – uracil
uracil – cytosine
cytosine – uracil
cytosine – cytosine

If we considered all four RNA nucleotides we would find that there are 16 possible combinations that can be made from pairs of them. This is almost, but not quite, the number needed to code for the 20 amino acids.

Possibly you are wondering how we get four combinations from the uracil and cytosine. Would not uracil – cytosine be the same as cytosine – uracil? Perhaps an analogy would help here. Pairs of the letters n and o can be combined in 4 ways: *nn, oo, no,* and *on.* In our language *nn* and *oo* have no meaning for us. They are nonsense words. You will be quick to realize, however, that it does make a difference whether we arrange *n* and *o* to be *on* or *no.*

If we go one step further and use groups of three nucleotides, then we will have enough possibilities. There are 64 combinations of the four nucleotides taken in groups of three. A triplet code, then, would be more than adequate to carry the instructions for the 20 amino acids. This is the hypothesis that biologists are using today: the instructions for inheritance are carried in a code that consists of triplets of DNA nucleotides. These triplets are copied in complementary triplets of messenger RNA nucleotides. Each triplet of the messenger RNA then serves as the site for the attachment of a specific kind of amino acid. Once these amino acids are lined up in a specific manner, they are united to form the specific proteins.

At the time this is being written the evidence is highly suggestive that this hypothesis is correct. At least it is a useful working hypothesis in a field that is rapidly advancing. From the laboratories of numerous scientists investigating the code there are now abundant data to suggest that the sequence of nucleotides determines the sequence of amino acids in a protein. The first conclusive data came from Marshall Nirenberg (NEAR·en·burg) and J. H. Matthaei (ma·THIGH) at the National Institutes of Health.

Nirenberg and Matthaei tried a method first developed by Severo Ochoa (o·CHO·a) of New York University. They made an artificial RNA consisting of nothing but endless repetitions of the *uracil* nucleotide. Then they put this artificial RNA into a preparation containing ribosomes (from bacteria) and all the usual amino acids found in cells. Surprisingly enough, a polypeptide chain is put together in a mixture of this sort, which is entirely without living cells. Nirenberg and Matthaei examined the polypeptide chain to see what amino acid or acids had been incorporated into it. Only phenylalanine (Chapter 29, page 538) had been used. So the code (assuming it to be a triplet) for phenylalanine must be U-U-U (meaning uracil–uracil–uracil) in the RNA. If the hypothesis is correct, the U-U-U sequence of RNA would be made by DNA with an adenine sequence of A-A-A. Thus the code word in DNA for phenylalanine is A-A-A.

We can summarize as follows:

If the DNA code is. . .	*then the message will be. . .*	*and the protein chain will be*
adenine	uracil	
adenine	uracil	phenylalanine
adenine	uracil	
adenine	uracil	
adenine	uracil	phenylalanine
adenine	uracil	
adenine	uracil	
adenine	uracil	phenylalanine
adenine	uracil	

Many others have studied this important problem of cracking the code. It seems more and more likely that the code is in fact triplets of nucleotides. At the present time, a tentative code triplet has been associated with each of the 20 amino acids. But already the experiments reveal that several different triplets of the DNA may be used to code the same amino acid. There are complications.

We might compare the code of the DNA molecule with the alphabet of a language. The English language is made up of thousands of words, and yet it has an alphabet of only 26 letters. Such an immense variety of words is possible because of the *number* of letters used in a word, and the *arrangement* of these letters within the word. With no more than the four letters N, O, E, and T—our analogy is to the *four* nucleotides in DNA that may be used in triplets—we can make such words as *net, one, ten, toe, too, ton,* and *not,* as well as many additional "words" that have no meaning in our own language.

It is possible to put such words together to form a meaningful message that is communicated from person to person. In an analogous way, it seems that the four nucleotides of chromosomal DNA and the complementary nucleotides of messenger RNA, in various triplets, "communicate" directions for the synthesis of proteins, especially enzymes. Such a control over protein synthesis thus becomes an indirect control over all the chemical reactions of the cell.

Modifying the Action of Genes

This discussion has emphasized the control of the cell's activities by the code of DNA. It may have left you with the impression that the effects of genes are constant and unchangeable. Such is not the case. There are many instances of the expression of the genes being modified by the environment. The environment might be within the cell or even outside of the organism. The genes determine what an organism *may* become, not what it *will* become. What an organism *will* become depends on both its heredity and its environment. It is these two causes working together that determine the final outcome. Let us look at a few examples of the relationship between genes and environment in different organisms.

1. In the fruit fly, *Drosophila,* there is a recessive gene that causes the wings to curl up sharply if flies are raised in a temperature of 25° C. On the other hand, if the flies are raised in a lower temperature, say 16° C, the trait appears but rarely; most of the wings appear straight, just like those of flies that do not have the curly-wings genes. The hereditary basis of the trait is still present in these apparently normal flies, however, and will be expressed in the next generation if the temperature is suitable (Figure 30-14).
2. Most plants inherit the ability to produce chlorophyll. But even in those plants that do so, can the chlorophyll be synthesized in the absence of light? If corn, or bean, or tobacco seeds are germinated and

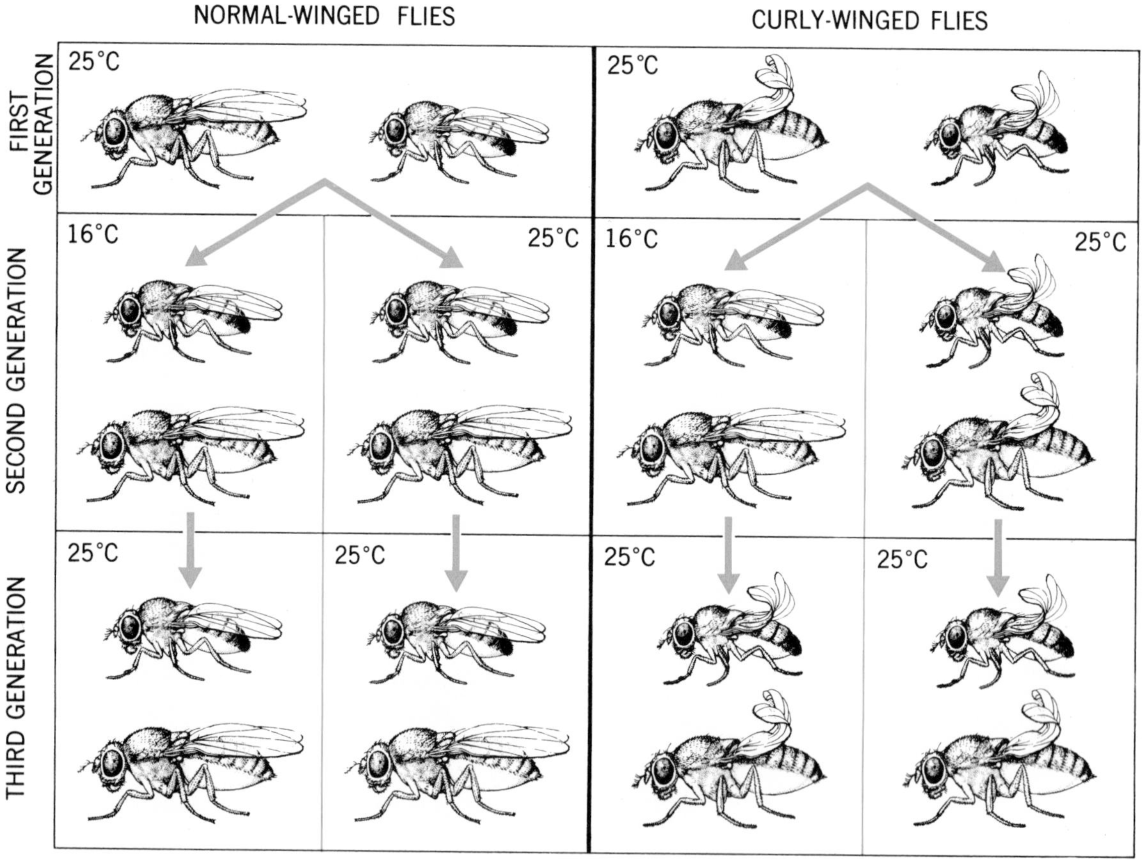

30–14 A chart of the effect of temperature, during development, on the expression of the curly-wings trait in *Drosophila*. Normal-winged flies have normal-winged offspring, no matter what the temperature. Curly-winged flies have offspring with normal-shaped wings if the offspring develop at 16° C. What happens when the offspring mature and the temperature is raised to 25° C? What kind of wings will the flies of the next generation have if they develop at the higher temperature?

allowed to grow in the dark, will the seedlings turn green and carry on photosynthesis? You can answer these questions in Laboratory Inquiry 30-2.

A few flowering plants, such as Indian pipe and dodder, are without chlorophyll. They are colorless or pale yellow. They live as parasites on other plants, or as saprophytes (Chapter 10, page 204). They do not have the proper hereditary makeup to produce chlorophyll, whether or not light is present.

3. There is a gene in man for *hereditary baldness*. The expression of the gene depends on the presence of male sex hormones. If the gene is present in women, or males that have been castrated, it is not expressed. In mature males, however, it is expressed.
4. In a similar way the genes for body form are influenced in their expression by the individual's diet. Tallness and fatness both have a hereditary basis. The action of these genes is much influenced by diet (Figure 30-15).

CONCLUDING REMARKS

In this chapter we have learned how two quite distinct lines of investigation have led to a general theory of heredity. It seems true beyond a reasonable doubt that genes are composed of DNA. One gene differs from another in the way its nucleotides are arranged, most probably in triplets. The specific arrangement of the nucleotides in DNA is the basis for the synthesis of specific kinds of messenger RNA. Again the specificity is thought to reside in the order of triplets of nucleotides. The specific messenger RNA's, in turn, are the basis for the formation of specific protein molecules. Each triplet in the messenger RNA is thought to direct the placement of one amino acid in the protein chain.

The role of DNA as *the* vehicle of inheritance has been emphasized because biologists believe that it is. We should recall, however, from long ago (Chapter 9) that some viruses have RNA, not DNA, as their hereditary material. There are also a very few instances of inheritance that does not depend on the nucleus. These cases are referred to as cytoplasmic inheritance.

Overall we have a coherent theory for the transmission of the hereditary instructions from one generation to another. This is short-term genetic continuity. Let us now turn to the long-term aspects of genetic continuity—evolution—and consider the factors that cause descendants to become different from their remote ancestors.

GUIDE QUESTIONS AND PROBLEMS

1. An investigator into the problem of heredity early in the present century might have ended his report of his work with the statement, "I therefore reach the conclusion that the nucleus is the seat of heredity." Write a definition for the word *conclusion* used in this sense, and then check with a dictionary. How does the dictionary definition compare with yours?
2. What would be the autosome number in an animal having 29 pairs of chromosomes?
3. If the percentage of recombinations of *Ab* and *aB* is 8 percent, of *Ac* and *aC* is 4 percent, and of *Bc* and *bC* is 12 percent, what can be said about the positions on the chromosome of these three gene pairs with respect to one another?
4. Suppose that in an individual heterozygous for *Aa, Bb*, and *Cc* crossing-over between genes *A* and *B* in a pair of homologous chromosomes occurs in 20 percent of the gametes, and between *A* and *C* in 8 percent of the gametes. How often would you expect crossing-over between *B* and *C*?
5. Suppose that a mutation occurs on an X chromosome in a human egg cell, and that the mutant gene is recessive to the normal gene. What kind of sperm must fertilize the egg if the mutation is to be expressed in the F_1 generation?
6. Why is it not possible for a male to be heterozygous for colorblindness?
7. What is the basis for saying that the sperm and the egg do not always contribute equally to the genetic make-up of the zygote?

8. If a woman who is not a carrier of genes for hemophilia is married to a man who is a hemophiliac, what percentage of their male offspring could be expected to be hemophiliacs?
9. If a colorblind man marries a woman whose father was colorblind, what is the probability of their first child being a colorblind boy?
10. What is the probable relationship between DNA, a gene, and protein synthesis?

RELATED READING

Books

For selections from the reports of Sutton, Morgan, and other famous geneticists writing of their own discoveries . . .

Peters, James A. (Editor), *Classic Papers in Genetics,* Prentice-Hall, Englewood Cliffs, New Jersey, 1959 (paperback).

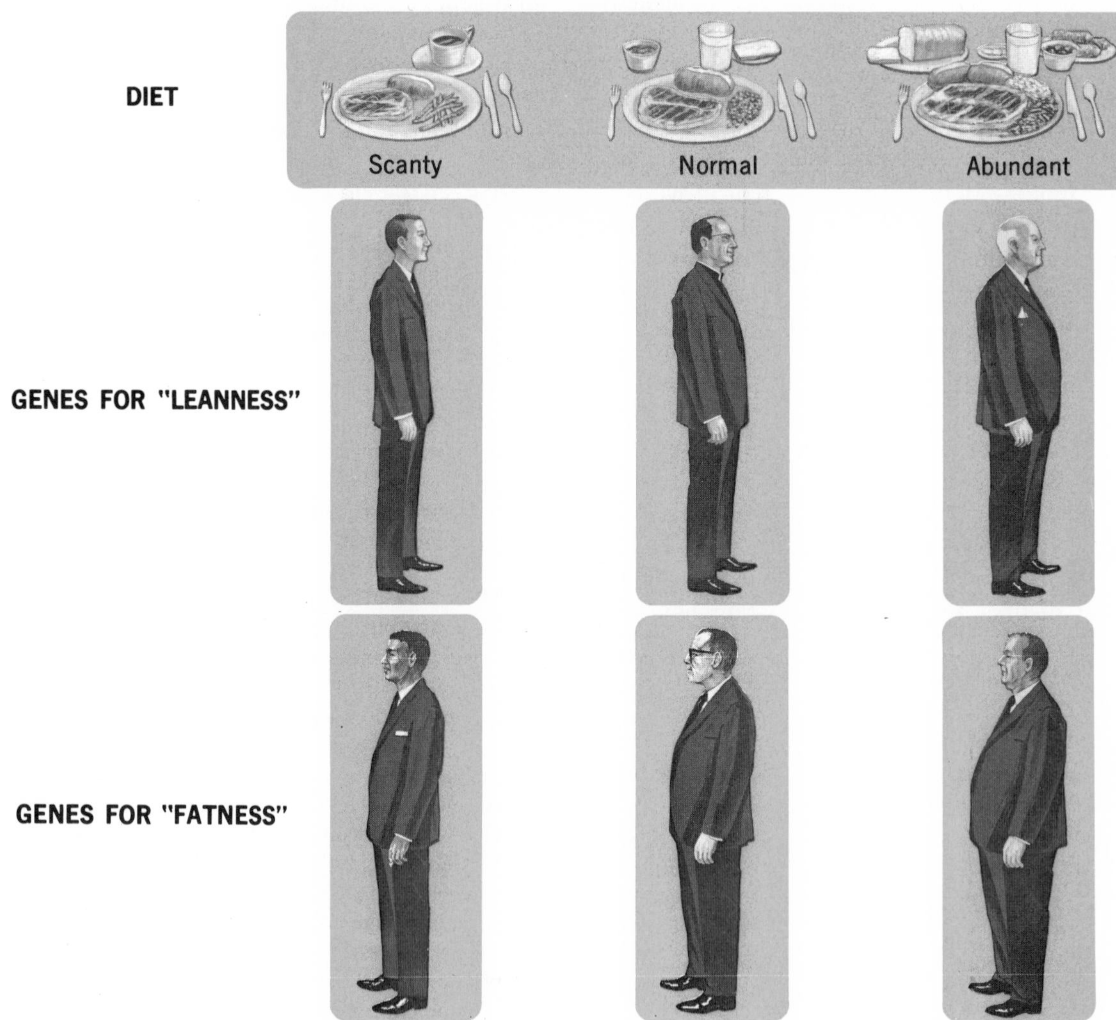

Adapted from *Mankind Evolving* by Theodosius Dobzhansky, Yale University Press

30–15 The interaction of genes and environment in the determination of one human characteristic, body weight—independent of height. As the chart suggests, the environment can mask different genotypes through dietary differences.

Watson, J. D., *The Double Helix*, Atheneum, New York, 1968.

For modern accounts of genetic principles, their applications, and the biochemistry of the gene . . .

Barry, J. M., *Molecular Biology: Genes and the Chemical Control of Living Cells,* Prentice-Hall, Englewood Cliffs, New Jersey, 1964 (paperback).

Moore, John A., *Heredity and Development,* Oxford University Press, New York, 1963 (paperback).

Watson, J. D., *Molecular Biology of the Gene*, W. A. Benjamin, Inc., New York, 1965.

For more information on human genetics . . .

Dobzhansky, Theodosius G., *Heredity and the Nature of Man*, Harcourt, Brace & World, Inc., New York, 1964.

McKusick, V. A., *Mendelian Inheritance in Man*, Johns Hopkins Press, Baltimore, 1966.

Stern, Curt, *Principles of Human Genetics*, Second Edition, Freeman, San Francisco, 1960.

Sutton, H. E., *An Introduction to Human Genetics*, Holt, Rinehart and Winston, New York, 1965.

Thompson, J. S., and M. W. Thompson, *Genetics in Medicine*, Saunders, Philadelphia, 1966.

Magazines

Crick, F. H. C., "The Genetic Code," *Scientific American,* Volume 207 (October 1962), page 66.

Nirenberg, Marshall W., "The Genetic Code – II," *Scientific American,* Volume 208 (March 1963), page 80.

Crick, F. H. C., "The Genetic Code – III," *Scientific American,* Volume 215 (October 1966), page 55.

Davidson, Eric H., "Hormones and Genes," *Scientific American,* Volume 212 (June 1965), page 36.

Fraenkel-Conrat, Heinz, "The Genetic Code of a Virus," *Scientific American,* Volume 211 (October 1964), page 46.

Sager, Ruth, "Genes Outside the Chromosomes," *Scientific American,* Volume 212 (January 1965), page 70.

31

Darwinian Evolution

Of all the theories you may study in biology, evolution is the most inclusive. It is so fundamental that biology can hardly be understood without it.

You have already learned how the theory of evolution can help us to understand the *unity* as well as the *diversity* of plants and animals. Once life appeared on earth (Chapter 9), it slowly evolved into many kinds of plants (Chapters 13 and 14) and animals (Chapter 19). But evolution has not made organisms *completely* different. Their common origin is responsible for their many biochemical similarities (Chapter 6), their frequently similar patterns of development (Chapter 27), and their nearly identical modes of inheritance (Chapters 8, 29, and 30). DNA nearly always carries the instructions for inheritance. ATP is associated with the energy reactions in all cells. All cellular events are controlled by enzymes. These are not accidental coincidences. Life has a common pattern because all life is interrelated through evolutionary descent. Much of biology would be a catalog of unrelated facts but for the unifying picture that evolution gives us. This would be especially true of classification (Chapters 14 and 19), which finds its scientific basis in evolutionary interrelationships.

What does evolution mean to the biologist? It means that living things change. A species may slowly change into a new species or even into two or more new species. It means, therefore, that the plants and animals that now inhabit the earth were not the first plants and animals. It also means that many plants and animals that once flourished are no longer alive, since if one species evolves into other species, the original species no longer exists. We know of the extinct species only by such fossil remains as we may be fortunate enough to discover.

Evolution also means the field of inquiry in which scientists try to discover how this process of change occurs. It is a field that is concerned with many questions. What is the origin of the individual changes that are the raw materials of evolution? What forces and factors control the direction in which a species may evolve? How rapidly does evolutionary change take place, and what factors control the rate? What is the past history of plants and animals living today? What plants and animals lived in the past but are no longer alive?

Evolution is now a scientific theory. In its present general form it began in 1859 as a hypothesis of Charles Darwin (1809-1882). It has grown and been revised as research reveals more and more facts about living things. A century of testing and accumulation of data has led to extension of the theory to explain more and more biological phenomena.

DARWIN'S HYPOTHESIS OF NATURAL SELECTION

Let us begin with an outline view of Charles Darwin's contribution to the theory of evolution. His views were published in detail in a book, *On the Origin of Species by Means of Natural Selection.* The first edition appeared on November 24, 1859, more than a century ago. Darwin was not the first to think about evolution. Many other ideas about it are older than his. Nevertheless, his first hypothesis is so close to the modern view that it serves as a convenient introduction to the subject. In very brief summary, here is Darwin's report.

First, there are many differences among the individuals of every species. Usually it is safe to say that no two individuals are precisely alike.

Darwin knew or suspected that many of the individual differences are inherited.

Second, the population size of all species tends to increase because of reproduction. One *Amoeba*, for example, divides to produce two. These two divide, and the next generation numbers four. Then there will be eight, sixteen, thirty-two, and so on in successive generations. Sexually-reproducing organisms can multiply even more rapidly, since two parent individuals can usually produce more than four offspring, and often very many more. A doubling (or any increase by a factor greater than one) per generation is known as a geometric rate of increase, or a **geometric progression** (Figure 31-1).

Third, it is clear that if this increase in the size of populations were to go unchecked, the number of individuals of any species would grow greater than the available food could support—or than space could accommodate.

Fourth, it is obvious that in nature this increase is checked. The number of organisms in a species does not continue to increase vastly over long periods of time. In fact, the sizes of most populations seem to remain nearly the same. How does this happen? Either reproduction must fail to approach a geometric rate of increase, or else many members of each generation must die before the age of reproduction. It is evident that many do die young. Why do some die but not others? Darwin thought there must be a **struggle for survival.** The individuals of a species must compete for food, light, water, places to live, and whatever else is important for survival.

In this competition, individuals with certain characteristics will more often survive to have offspring than the individuals that do not have these valuable characteristics. Hence, in each generation we should expect a slight increase in the number of individuals that do possess the valuable characteristics, and a decrease in the number of individuals that possess less valuable characteristics. Darwin called this differential survival **natural selection.** To Darwin, then, evolution involved several factors:

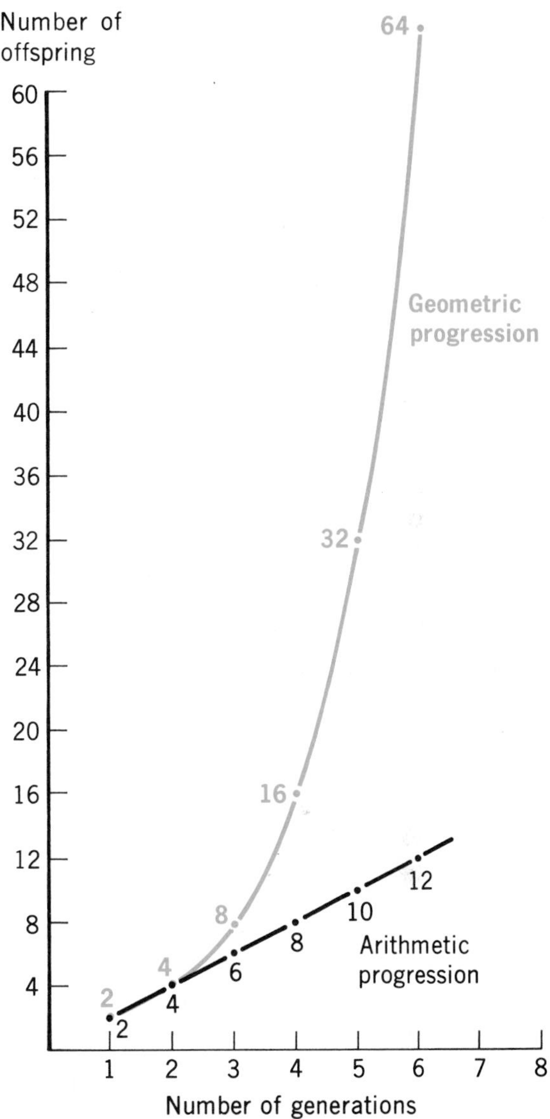

1. the presence of hereditary variation
2. the tendency of the size of populations to increase
3. the struggle for survival (or competition for the needs of life)
4. a difference in the contribution that different types of individuals make to succeeding generations—or *natural selection.*

American Museum of Natural History

31–2 Charles Lyell, the English geologist whose work on the history of the earth helped Darwin investigate and understand the history of life.

A species becomes *adapted* to its environment by natural selection. In the particular habitat in which it lives, it acquires, through the process of natural selection, characteristics that improve its chances of survival and reproduction.

Development of the Theory of Evolution

The clues that first led Darwin to the hypothesis of evolution emerged from his own studies and experiences as well as those of others.

Geology laid one foundation for Darwin's work. In the early 1830's, Charles Lyell, an English geologist (Figure 31-2), published a masterwork in geology. In it he pointed out that the earth's features need no longer be treated as an unsolvable mystery. The mountains, valleys, deserts, rivers, lakes, and coastlines could have come about through the action of existing forces and natural conditions. A river

31–3 Changes in the earth's surface. A glacial stream—a torrent in the early summer when the snows are melting—has eroded this deep valley. Lyell, and other geologists of the early nineteenth century, believed that such processes occurring now are of the same types that have altered the earth in the past.

John A. Moore

Both photos, American Museum of Natural History

31–4 Charles Darwin and H.M.S. *Beagle*, on which he sailed in 1831 as ship's naturalist. Observations that he made on this voyage suggested to him that a process of evolution occurs. The evidence that most impressed him was geographic variation of animal species, and the close resemblance of fossil and living species.

slowly carves a valley (Figure 31-3). Mountains are worn down to hills and finally plains.

Lyell described the evidence for believing that such changes had occurred throughout the ages, slowly changing the face of the earth. For this to occur at so slow a rate, the earth had to be much older than generally believed—a possibility that fired Darwin's imagination. If the earth of today is so old and so changed, what was it like thousands of years ago? Did it have the kinds of life we now have? What other life may have existed?

In 1831, when he was twenty-two years old, Darwin set out to study some of the earth's living things. He sailed as a ship's naturalist on H.M.S. *Beagle* (Figure 31-4) on a voyage to chart the coasts of South America and some of the islands of the Pacific.

In South America, Darwin spent long hours ashore collecting and observing. Strange animals greeted his eyes. He was impressed by the tremendous crowding of living things and the small chance for survival that any newly born individual would have. Later the *Beagle* sailed to the Galápagos (ga·LAH·pa·gus) Islands, some 600 miles off the west coast of South America. Here Darwin made observations that were most important in the development of his ideas about evolution. He carefully studied the organisms that lived upon these islands. There were huge tortoises, and much to his surprise, they were recognizably different on each island. The common birds were a group of finches. Closely related species had beaks of very different sizes and shapes (Figure 31-5), adapted to feeding on completely different kinds of food. How was one to explain all this diversity on a few small islands in the remote Pacific?

Darwin returned to England in 1836. Soon afterward, he read a work written by the English political economist Thomas R. Malthus (1766–1834), *An Essay on the Principle*

2
3
4
6
1
5
8
9
10
13
7
11
12

of Population. In it Darwin read that the rate of reproduction was such that the human population increases many times more rapidly than the available food supply. Malthus believed that the food supply increased arithmetically, but that the human population increased geometrically (Figure 31-1). Such a relation could result only in a struggle for food and, hence, for existence itself. Some men starved in Malthus' time, and some men starve today.

Darwin also studied variations in the breeds of domestic pigeons. By careful selection over some centuries, pigeon fanciers had developed numerous strange types. All of these originated from the common pigeon, like the kind now living in many cities. In a similar manner, plant breeders had developed many new varieties of plants by selecting those with desirable characteristics. These were clues, suggesting to Darwin that nature also selected.

With these observations, Darwin had the information needed to formulate a hypothesis of evolution. He worked slowly and carefully. In 1842 he wrote, for himself, a brief 35-page sketch of his theory. Two years later he enlarged this into an essay of 230 pages, which he showed his friends, but he did not publish it. For the next 15 years, Darwin continued to collect facts to support his ideas.

In 1858 Darwin received a letter from a fellow naturalist, Alfred R. Wallace (1823-1913), who was traveling at the time in Malaya. Wallace enclosed an essay that he had written, and he asked Darwin to read it and then forward it to Lyell. In the essay, Darwin found, almost in his own terms, the theory of *the origin of species by means of natural selection.* Darwin almost yielded to Wallace the honor of being the first man to announce the theory. However, his friends arranged to present the two papers under joint authorship using a single title, *On the Tendency of Species to Form Varieties; and on the Perpetuation of Varieties and Species by Natural Means of Selection.* The papers were presented to the Linnean Society in London on July 1, 1858.

Darwin then hastened to complete his book, *On the Origin of Species by Means of Natural Selection.* It appeared in November of 1859.

Darwin's ideas were well received by many scientists, and by a large segment of the public. There was much opposition, however. The defense and support of the theory was taken up by Joseph Hooker and Thomas Henry Huxley (1825-1895). Darwin himself scarcely entered the debate publicly.

Only a passing reference to man's place in evolution was mentioned in *The Origin of Species.* Twelve years later, Darwin's *Descent of Man* was published. This was the study of the evolution of man.

Darwinian Evolution and Its Relationship to Genetics

In the period immediately following Darwin's contributions, August Weismann (1834-1914) was able to focus the attention of biologists upon the reproductive cells of organisms as the basis of evolutionary changes. He pointed out that cells other than those involved in reproduction have no direct hereditary influence on the production of the next generation. Reproductive cells alone would be involved directly. And the reproductive cells, he thought, were isolated from changes brought about by the environment in the rest of the organism—changes resulting mainly from adaptation or accident.

In a test of whether environmental changes in parents influenced the nature of offspring, Weis-

31–5 The finches of the Galápagos Islands. These small islands, six hundred miles off the west coast of South America, are the home of numerous species of finches. There is much variation in the shape of the beaks and in the feeding habits among these different species. How could Darwin account for this diversity?

mann cut off the tails of *twenty* generations of mice, to find that the twenty-first generation still had tails just as long as those of the first generation. This made quite an impression on his fellow scientists, for it showed that cutting off body cells, or scars and mutilations, did not change the heredity of the organism.

From this time in the 1890's until today, the study of evolution has been closely intertwined with that of genetics. Genetics is concerned with characteristics that are inherited. It is these characteristics that are important in evolution, as Darwin recognized. We might say that evolution is chiefly the natural selection of genetic differences.

EVOLUTION, GENETICS, AND THE ENVIRONMENT

There have been other hypotheses to explain how evolution occurs, but none has been as useful as Darwin's. One of the most interesting and important was proposed by the French naturalist Jean B. Lamarck (1744–1829)., In an example often quoted, he tried to explain how the giraffe had come to possess such a long neck. Figure 31-6a is based upon Lamarck's thinking. For example, the need for food would create desires to satisfy the needs. If the giraffes lived in areas where other animals were eating the available grass, the giraffes might begin to eat leaves of the trees. Satisfying the desires would lead to the use or disuse of certain parts of the body. The neck and legs might become longer—a consequence of the constant stretching to reach the leaves. In time the changes would become inherited, or so Lamarck believed. Thus the environment would have directly changed the species.

This conception of evolution is different from Darwin's view. Darwin began by assuming that there are many hereditary differences among the individuals of a species (Figure 31-6b). He was not at all clear in respect to where these differences came from. We now know that they arise from mutations of the genes and from alterations of chromosomes (see Chapter 30).

There is an important difference between Lamarck's and Darwin's hypotheses. According to Darwin, hereditary differences (of *unknown origin*) that better adapt individuals will become established by natural selection. Lamarck supposed that adaptive differences *originate* in response to the environment, and that thereafter they are hereditary.

Lamarck's account of change is simple, clear, attractive—and wrong. Lamarck and many others have repeatedly sought confirmation of the hypothesis, but today no evidence exists to support it. Our knowledge of inheritance tells us that stretching the legs or neck does not affect the DNA of reproductive cells and cannot, therefore, change future generations.

The Expression of Genes in Different Environments

What is inherited by successive generations of plants or animals is the DNA that determines specific functions. Of course, environment may modify the way genes work to produce various traits (Chapter 30, pages 563–65), but there is no evidence that the environment causes *directed* mutations.

An example can be cited. Yellow fat and white fat are genetically determined characters in rabbits (Figure 31-7). Yellow fat can be formed only in rabbits whose diet includes carrots and leafy vegetables rich in yellow pigments. If we feed rabbits that are homozygous for yellow fat on a diet lacking carrots and leafy vegetables, they develop white fat. Other rabbits that have white fat alleles have an enzyme that breaks down the yellow pigment. Their fat is *always* white, on any diet.

The enzyme that breaks down yellow pigment is absent in the yellow-fatted rabbits, but a change in diet alters the appearance of the rabbits. Is there in consequence any change in their genetic constitution? Breeding tests show that the alleles are not changed. Further-

31-6 A COMPARISON OF LAMARCKIAN AND DARWINIAN THEORIES — THE EVOLUTION OF GIRAFFES

a Lamarck's theory

Ancestral giraffes probably had short necks that were subjected to frequent stretching to enable the giraffes to reach the foliage of trees.

The offspring had longer necks that also were stretched frequently in the quest for food.

Eventually the continued stretching of the neck gave rise to modern giraffes.

Existing data do not support this theory.

b Darwin's theory

Ancestral giraffes probably had necks that varied in length. The variations were hereditary.

Natural selection led to survival of longer-necked offspring at the expense of shorter-necked ones.

Eventually only long-necked giraffes survived.

Existing data support this theory.

31-7 FOOD AS AN ENVIRONMENTAL INFLUENCE UPON GENES IN RABBITS

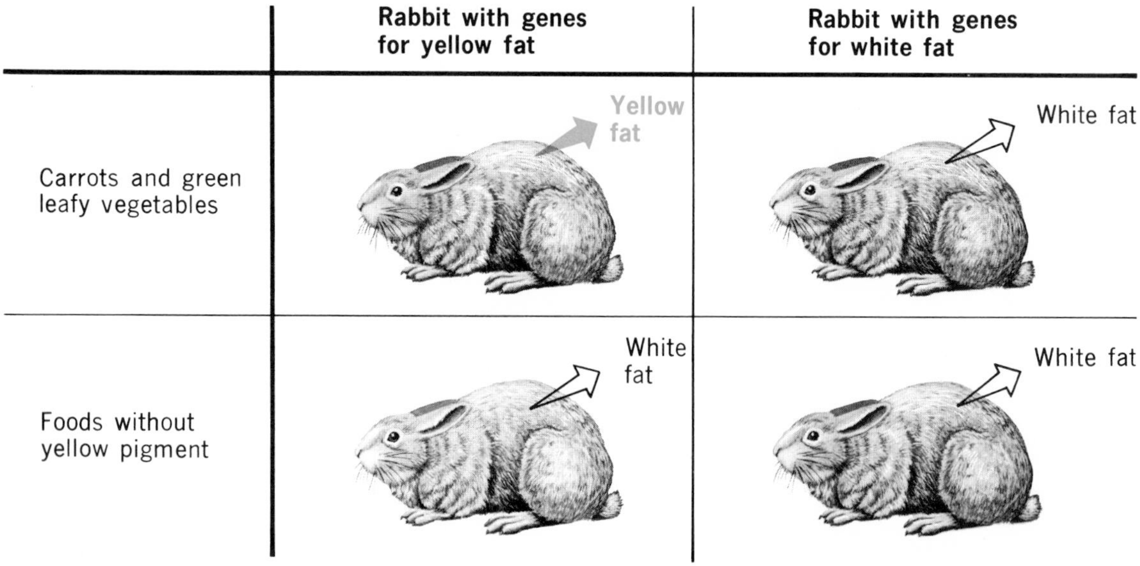

	Rabbit with genes for yellow fat	Rabbit with genes for white fat
Carrots and green leafy vegetables	Yellow fat	White fat
Foods without yellow pigment	White fat	White fat

more, when these rabbits are given a diet of carrots and leafy vegetables again, their fat turns yellow.

Another example of the effect of the environment upon the expression of genetic variability is the Himalayan rabbit, which normally has a black nose, black feet, and black tips of ears (Figure 31-8). By altering the environment we can change the appearance of the Himalayan rabbit to resemble that of a white rabbit, but the change is not hereditary.

You can see that the environment can alter the phenotypic expression of genes. However, the environment does not directly *cause* the appearance of a specific hereditary characteristic.

If a new hereditary characteristic arises by mutation and is beneficial, the individual possessing it has a better chance of surviving and leaving offspring. If the new hereditary characteristic is not beneficial, the individual's chances of survival and leaving offspring are reduced. The role of the environment is to select or eliminate modified hereditary materials that arise by mutation.

Adaptation and Selection

The modern evolutionist tries to duplicate in the laboratory some particular phases of nature in order to study natural selection. One example, with deer mice (*Peromyscus maniculatus* – pee·ro·MIS·kus ma·nik·yoo·LAH·tus), involves the two color varieties in this species, buff and gray. Under controlled conditions in a University of Michigan laboratory, these mice were exposed to the attacks of a barn owl. On alternate days the floor was covered first with pale-colored soil, which matched the buff-colored mice, and then with darker soil matching the gray mice. A "jungle" of interlacing sticks gave some cover to the mice. The room was kept almost dark, so that the owl could barely distinguish its prey. Each day, four buff-colored and four gray mice were exposed to the owl for 15 minutes. According to the kind of soil used on a particular morning, one set of mice was conspicuous, the other protectively colored. In 44 trials on each soil type, almost twice as many of the conspicuous mice were taken as of the better-concealed type (107 to 62).

Let us go to White Sands National Monument in New Mexico for an example from nature that is similar to the experiment we have described. Here we find dunes composed of white gypsum crystals. On these dunes there are white lizards, white grasshoppers, white beetles, and white mice. Outside the area, where the soil is reddish and darker, the animals of these same species are red-brown in color.

The light-colored animals that now live on the white sand dunes are the product of mutation and natural selection that have been going on for thousands of years. Any mutation that would give a paler coloration would be selected. Any mutation that would darken the animal would be eliminated. The white sand has no effect on the origin of the mutations. Mutations to dark or light occur by chance. But once they do occur, natural selection will determine what happens to them.

Most species of animals are relatively inconspicuous in their native environment. Throughout the ages the conspicuous individuals have been captured more frequently than the inconspicuous individuals. This often leads to remarkable resemblances between the animals and their surroundings. The ptarmigan on the left in Figure 31-9 is an example. The color and pattern of its plumage blend almost exactly with the plants, rocks, and soil of its habitat. The ptarmigan on the right is in winter plumage – white feathers against the white snow.

31-8 TEMPERATURE AS AN ENVIRONMENTAL INFLUENCE UPON GENES IN RABBITS

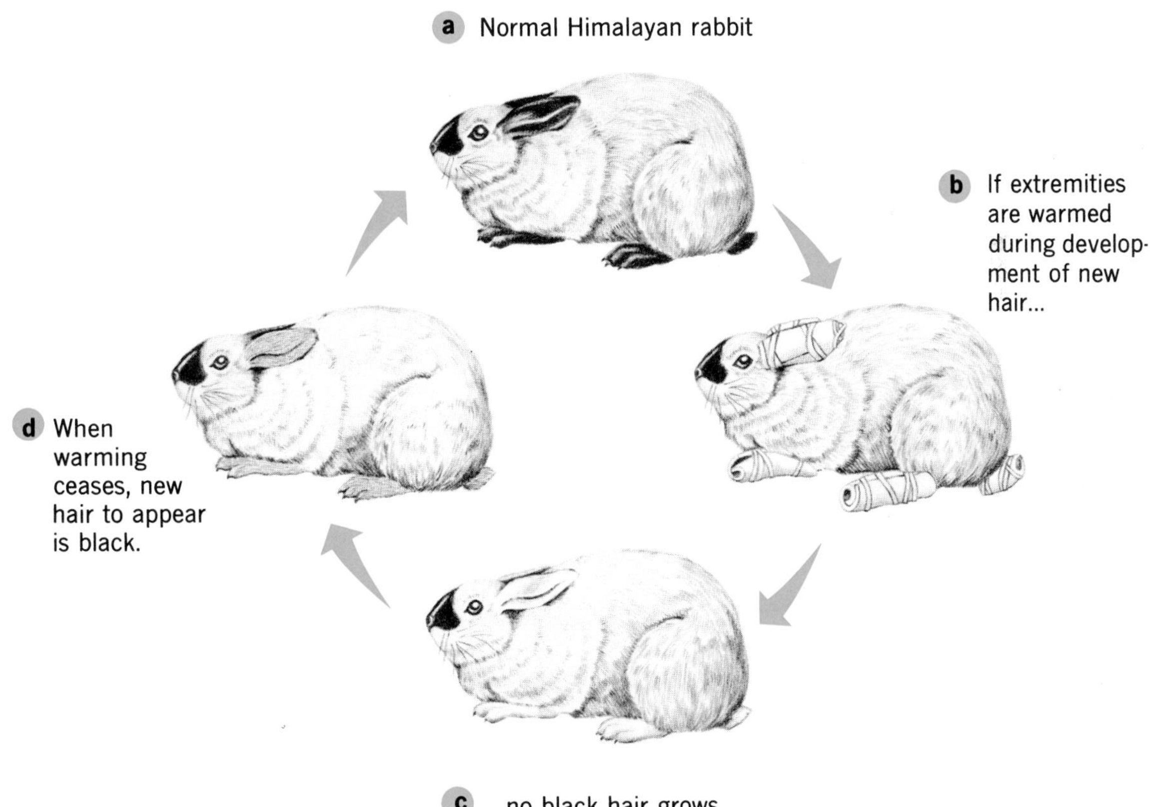
a Normal Himalayan rabbit
b If extremities are warmed during development of new hair...
c ...no black hair grows.
d When warming ceases, new hair to appear is black.

John A. Moore

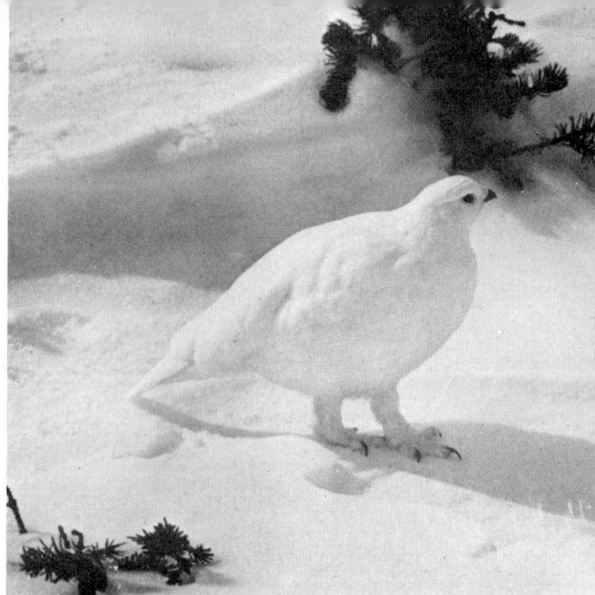

George Andrews from Colorado Game and Fish Department

31–9 Protective coloration in ptarmigans. Both birds are of the same species. The photograph at the left was made in summer, the one at the right in winter. Can you suggest hypotheses to account for the difference—that is, how the same individual changes with the season? What difference in environmental factors would you suspect?

In Laboratory Inquiry 32-3 you will work with another situation in which natural selection is effective because of the different degrees of protection afforded by hereditary differences of color—in this instance, in moths.

In recent years there have been many examples of selection in response to insecticides and drugs. You have probably heard that, when DDT was first used, it successfully killed houseflies. Now, a number of years later, we find that the houseflies have developed a resistance to DDT. How do we explain this resistance?

During the first year of DDT use, nearly all the flies were killed by the insecticide. However, there were a few flies that, because of their genetic makeup, were not killed by DDT. Since this type survived and reproduced, more of the resistant flies began to occur where DDT had been used. Hence, the insecticide became less effective. Eventually, wherever DDT was used for many years, only DDT-resistant flies were left. The DDT does the selecting. It does not cause the genes of the flies to mutate to alleles that give resistance.

When resistant flies are crossed with susceptible ones, the F_1 is found to have an intermediate degree of resistance. In the F_2 a complex segregation of resistant, susceptible, and intermediate types is found. That type of segregation indicates that the difference between full resistance and susceptibility is based upon many genes located at different points on the chromosomes.

Here a miniature of evolution unfolds before our eyes. The use of DDT was a selective factor that discriminated against the ordinary housefly and permitted the resistant variety to become the usual form.

Similar examples are known. You have read earlier that some bacteria can develop resistance to penicillin (Chapter 11). In one experiment a culture of about 100 million bacterial cells was exposed to a relatively weak dose of penicillin. Fewer than ten cells survived. These few cells became the parents of the succeeding generation. The progeny of these cells survived on the same weak dose. When the concentration of penicillin was doubled, nearly all were killed. A few survived. The survivors could then be isolated, cultured, and their succeeding generation exposed to an even stronger dose of penicillin. This process was repeated five times. Finally, a strain of bacteria was obtained that could withstand a dose 2,500 times as strong as the dose that killed most of the original culture of bacteria.

Many reports have been published of patients with bacterial infections that are resistant to antibiotics. These are recognized as resulting from the same kind of action as that just described. Again we see the work of natural selection. As the environment changes—that is, as more penicillin is added, the more resistant type of bacterium gains an advantage over the more susceptible.

The same process of natural selection by the environment applies to all other organisms as well as to flies and bacteria. After you have considered factors of populations in the next chapter and in Laboratory Inquiries 32-1 and 32-2, you will analyze a situation of special interest in human heredity and evolution in Inquiry 32-4.

A Summary of Natural Selection

Darwin proposed a mechanism for evolution: the selection by the environment of individuals with the best existing hereditary variations and whatever new variations arise.

Selection may be thought of as giving direction to evolution, since it results in better adaptation of organisms to their environment.

THE EVIDENCES OF EVOLUTION

In *The Origin of Species* Darwin did more than propose the theory of natural selection. He also summarized in a critical way the evidences for existence of evolution.

Now that we have examined the theory of natural selection and have seen on what a strong basis it rests today, let us see how Darwin recapitulated the evidences of evolution, and how they have grown since his time.

Darwin summarized his evidences of evolution under five principal categories:

1. Evidence from inheritance and breeding, especially evidence of variation under domestication
2. Evidence from geographical distribution
3. Evidence from fossils
4. Evidence from homologies
5. Evidence from embryology and rudimentary organs

We will begin our discussion with the evidence known to Darwin. Then we will draw on the vast fund of knowledge accumulated since his time.

The Evidences from Inheritance

Darwin had only a very crude idea of heredity. (Mendel's work was unknown to him.) Yet he emphasized that only hereditary variations would have any meaning for the evolutionary process.

Darwin was much impressed by man's successes in directing changes in plants and animals by selecting desirable hereditary traits. Although the plant and animal breeders could utilize **artificial selection** only on whatever variations they were able to notice, they had been phenomenally successful in breeding special types of domesticated animals and plants. Darwin noted the similarities of *artificial selection* (by man) and *natural selection* (by nature). An example with which Darwin was especially struck was the number of varieties of pigeons produced by artificial selection (page 573). The many domesticated varieties of plants and animals were a consequence of selection.

Evidence from Geographical Distribution

During his voyage on the *Beagle,* Darwin very early visited the Cape Verde (VURD) Islands, which lie near the equator off the coast of Africa. These islands are volcanic in origin. Their plants and insects, birds, and other animals resembled closely those on the nearby

John A. Moore

31–10 Formerly a forest, now a desert. Shown here are the fossilized trunks of trees in the Petrified National Forest. What was the region like millions of years ago?

shores of Africa. Several years later, when Darwin reached the Galápagos Islands, he was struck by the very great similarity of the climate and terrain to that of the Cape Verde Islands. But the plants and animals were totally different, this time more like the species on the west coast of South America, about 1,000 km (600 miles) to the east. The resemblance in each case to the flora and fauna of the nearby mainland made it reasonable to think that the organisms had come from there. Such an origin, followed by **isolation** and **adaptation** in their new homes, would best explain what had happened to these species.

The startling divergence of such groups as the finches of the Galápagos (Figure 31-5) reveals how wide a modification a few forms can assume in time, in a good habitat with no competitors.

Many other kinds of geographic evidence pointed to dispersal of species and colonization of new environments. Following isolation, evolution occurred in the new homes. Nothing was quite as dramatic as the evidence from the oceanic islands. Elsewhere, the barriers of the land—mountains, rivers, deserts—provided additional evidence. Similarly, the barriers to marine dwellers, such as the isthmus that formed between North and South America, long ago prevented fish only a few miles apart from mingling. With time this seemed responsible for great differences between those fish. The effects of isolation were again plain.

Fossil Evidences of Evolution

The most important evidence of evolution is given to us by the thousands of *fossil* animals and plants that scientists have dug from the rocks. These organisms lived thousands or millions of years ago, often under conditions very different from those now existing. For instance, one can go to the desert of southern Wyoming, more than a mile above sea level, and find hundreds of fossils of fish that once lived in the sea. Farther south, in the desert of Arizona, is the Petrified Forest (Figure 31-10). Trees of this forest, when they were alive many millions of years ago, must have lived in a mild, moist climate not even remotely similar to the desert where their remains are now.

Fossils have been found widely, over most parts of the earth. They are studied to discover trends in evolution, and to find out, if possible, which fossil animals were ancestors of what others. This kind of undertaking requires some method for dating fossils.

Relative age usually can be determined roughly by the position of the fossil in the sedimentary rock. Except where great upheavals have taken place in the past, the lower the layer, the older the rock (and the fossils it includes). Absolute age can be determined in some instances by measurements of radioactivity (Chapter 9).

With the use of such techniques, there have been many spectacular discoveries. For example, a small four-toed animal about the size of a large cat was found fossilized in strata

HISTORY OF THE DEVELOPMENT OF THE HORSE

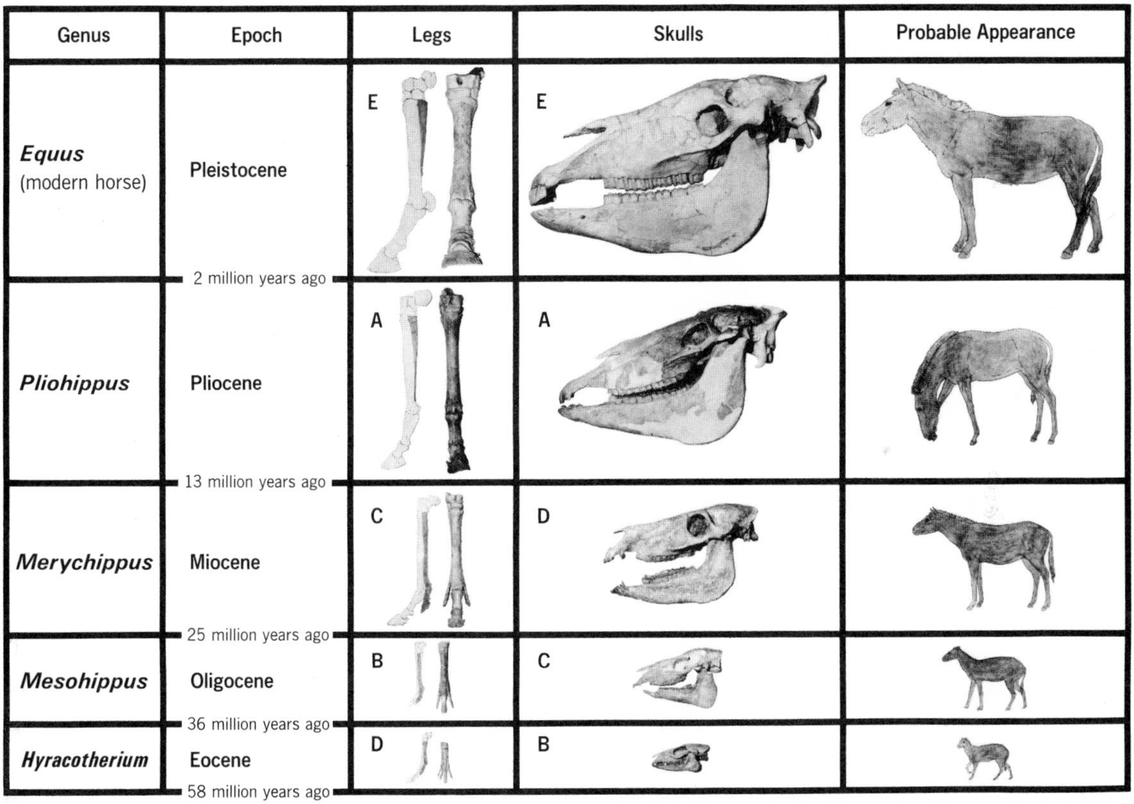

Genus	Epoch	Legs	Skulls	Probable Appearance
Equus (modern horse)	Pleistocene 2 million years ago	E	E	
Pliohippus	Pliocene 13 million years ago	A	A	
Merychippus	Miocene 25 million years ago	C	D	
Mesohippus	Oligocene 36 million years ago	B	C	
Hyracotherium	Eocene 58 million years ago	D	B	

Adapted with permission from The American Museum of Natural History

31–11 Five stages in the evolution of horses, as reconstructed from fossil evidence. The drawings at the right show comparative sizes, beginning at the bottom of the chart with *Hyracotherium* (hy·rak·o·THER·ih·um), the ancestor of 60 million years ago. At the top is an extinct member of the modern genus, *Equus* (EH·kwus). In the skulls at the left, note the relative sizes and the changing proportions. For example, follow the increasing size of the gap between the front teeth and the back teeth. The drawings of the front foot (front and side views) show the progressive loss of the side toes and the strengthening of the middle toe—the modern hoof.

some 60 million years old. From this animal can be traced a gradual line of descent, with continuing slight changes, to the modern horse (Figure 31-11). Similar evolutionary sequences have been established accurately for the elephant, the giraffe, and the camel.

This fossil evidence dramatically shows that life has been gradually changing over millions of years from one form to another. There is no longer any reasonable doubt that evolution occurs and that it has occurred all through the ages of the past.

Evidences of Evolution from Homology

Students of comparative anatomy have long known that the species of any larger group—such as phylum, class, or order—have numerous resemblances in structure (Chapter 19). For example, all the species of Phylum Chordata have at some time in their lives a notochord, gill pouches in the pharynx, and a dorsal nerve tube (page 370).

These resemblances are interpreted as a consequence of evolution from a common ancestor. The species of Phylum Chordata are alike because, at one time in the remote past, they had the same ancestor. The resemblances of the members of a class would be still closer, since they would have had their common ancestor more recently than the common ancestor of all the species of a phylum. The species of an order would resemble one another still more. The species of a genus might be so much alike that only a specialist could tell them apart.

During the course of evolution, the structures of the various descendants of the common ancestor became increasingly different. In many cases, however, some evidence of similarity still remains. Thus the wing of a bat, the arm of a man, and the flipper of a whale all have the same basis of structure in spite of their superficial dissimilarity (Figure 19-3, page 353). The explanation of their relationship is the origin of all three modifications of the limb from the same appendages of the primitive reptiles. This common pattern of structure is homology (Chapter 19), the principal basis for classifying plants and animals according to their relationships.

Evolution tends to be a conservative process. Rather than develop structures anew, it tends to remodel existing ones. For example, the fishes evolved gill arches that support the gills. In land vertebrates, these structures have become modified into other organs, such as the upper and lower jaws and the bones of the middle ear. The muscles of the human face are very largely derived from the muscles of the gill arches of ancient fish.

Sometimes an organ becomes reduced in evolution—and may even lose its function. Such organs are spoken of as **vestigial** (ves·TIJ·ih·al) **organs**. Good examples are the tailbone, ear muscles, and appendix of man.

The appendix (Figure 20-7) is a pouch that leads off from the large intestine. It has been removed from thousands of persons without ill effects. It has no known function. In other animals, such as the rabbit, the appendix is well developed and serves a useful function in digestion.

The muscles around the ear also are of little use to man, but in some animals (as dogs and horses) they move the ears, allowing them to be directed toward sounds (Figure 31-12a).

Vestigial organs are not confined to man. The whale has vestiges of hind limbs buried in the flesh where its tail begins. The python (a snake) has tiny bony structures beneath the skin which are all that remain of its ancestral hind legs. The vestigial wings of such flightless birds as the kiwi (Figure 31-12b) are also an example of organs that became useless but that were neither lost nor modified into different structures.

The unity of body plan that is so easily seen when comparative anatomy is studied is revealed in microscopic structures as well as gross anatomy. The fact that we can develop the concept of the "generalized cell" is one evidence of this. The remarkable uniformity of mitosis in all cellular organisms, and the essential likeness of meiosis and fertilization in all sexually reproducing organisms, are homolo-

Harbrace Photo

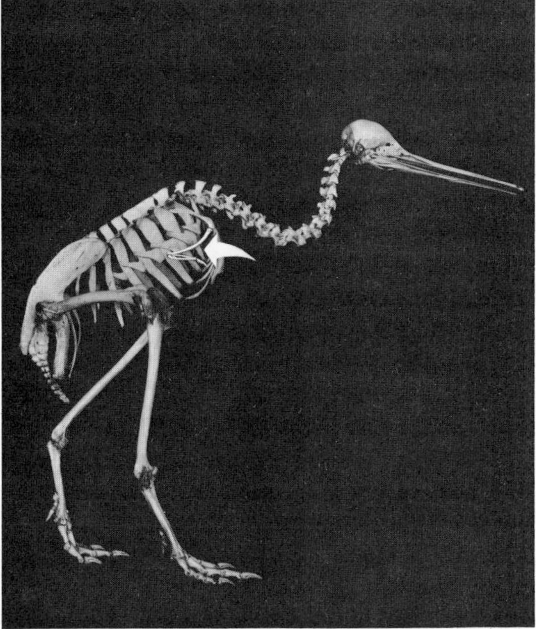

American Museum of Natural History

31–12 Vestigial organs. At the left are a man and his dog. In which of the two are the ear muscles vestigial? At the right is the skeleton of a kiwi. The arrow points to the small bones of a vestigial wing. (The wing bones appear somewhat like a "V" lying on its side; the small bones have been highlighted in white, so that they can be distinguished more easily.) Is the tail of the bird also vestigial?

gies. Then there are similarities of physiological mechanisms and of biochemical aspects that likewise reveal the unity of plan among living things. Is it not remarkable that all living things should use nucleic acids, and most of them a *particular* kind of nucleic acid, DNA, for the vehicle of heredity? Recall also that all organisms use ATP for energy transfers, and that almost all plants use chlorophyll for photosynthesis.

Whence comes this wonderful unity and similarity that is evident in the more than a million known *living* species of animals and nearly half a million species of plants? It need not, of course, come about because all of them have descended from a common ancestor. But since in our experience all organisms *do* inherit their characteristics from their ancestors, evolution is one way of explaining unity of basic plan combined with diversity in details.

Evidence of Evolution from Embryology

Embryology also gives us clues to paths of evolution. The similarities of embryological development among multicellular animals were intensively studied during the latter half of the nineteenth century. These studies led to the conclusion that the embryonic development of the individual repeated the evolutionary history of the race. Thus, it was thought to be possible to trace the evolutionary history of a species by a study of its embryonic development. This idea was so attractive as to gain the status of a biological principle.

Today the idea of embryonic resemblances is viewed with caution. We can see and demon-

31-13 COMPARISONS OF EMBRYOS IN FOUR ANIMALS

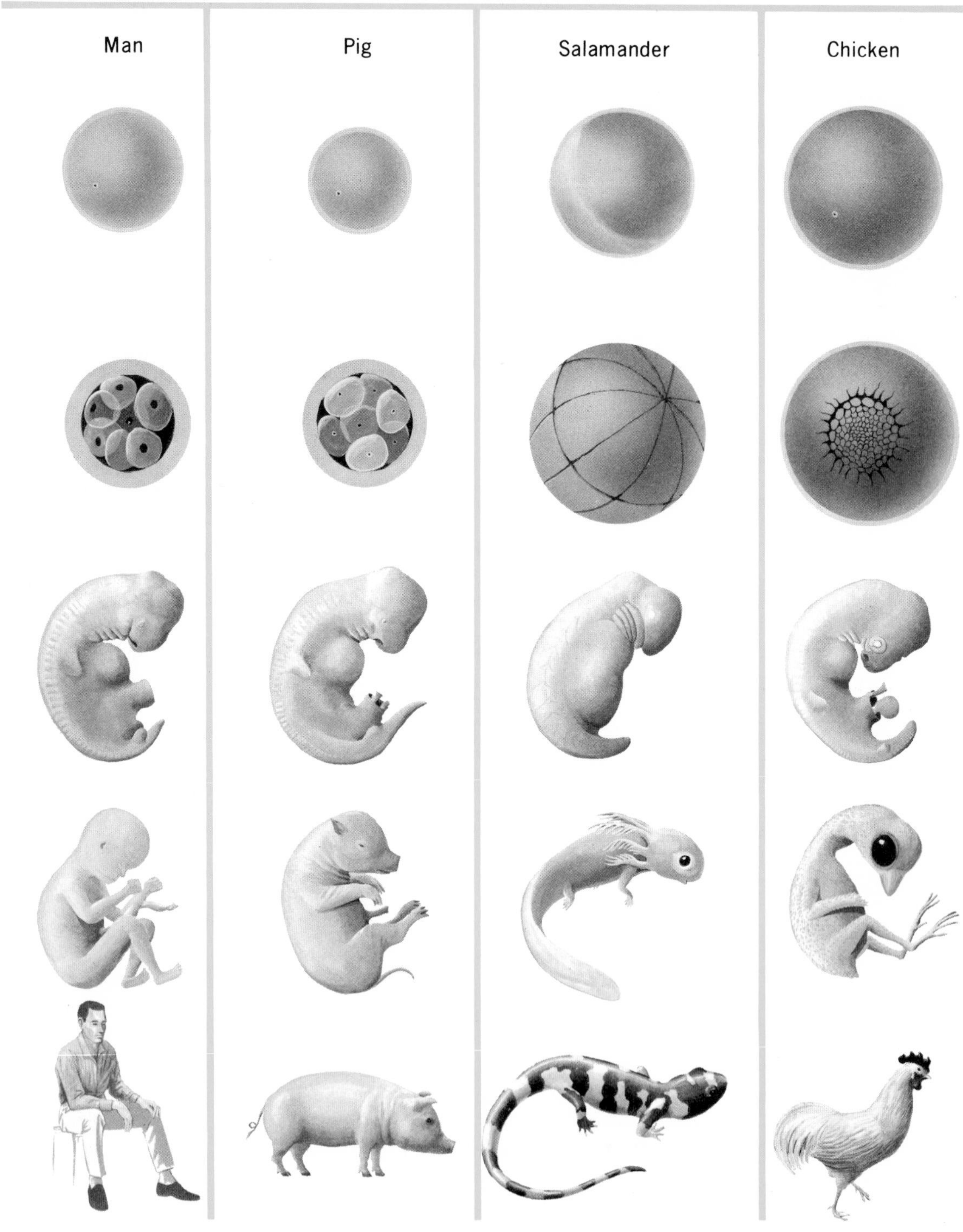

Man	Pig	Salamander	Chicken

strate similarities between embryos of related groups, as shown in Figure 31-13. However, while a certain amount of recapitulation is unquestioned, the old idea that a human passes through fish, amphibian, and reptile stages during embryonic development is not correct.

CONCLUDING REMARKS

We have now completed our discussion of some of the factors responsible for evolution. In the most general terms evolution results from the natural selection of inherited variations. Over the course of time one population may slowly change—becoming better adapted to its existing environment or to a changing environment. Or, if the area in which it lives is divided by barriers, the smaller populations of the isolated areas may evolve independently. In this case the single species may evolve into two or more different species.

Next, in Chapter 32, we shall make a closer study of the inherited variations and how they are acted upon in evolution. Much that follows is in the nature of reasonable hypothesis rather than fact. We can only assume that evolution as it takes place today is the same process that has been occurring on earth for hundreds of millions of years.

GUIDE QUESTIONS AND PROBLEMS

1. What evidence supports the idea that
   a. adaptations to the environment are not inherited?
   b. adaptations to the environment *affect* what is inherited?
2. What is your own impression of the kinds of influences that are at work upon different members of a species in the same natural environment? In what way are the offspring of surviving organisms a product of natural selection?
3. What kinds of influences are at work upon different members of a species of domestic animals or cultivated plants at a dairy farm, cattle ranch, or agricultural research station? How are artificial selection and natural selection alike? different?
4. Since Darwin had no idea why hereditary differences exist among members of a species, why do you suppose he declined an explanation similar to Lamarck's? (To answer this perplexing question to your satisfaction, you may wish to consult Darwin's book *On the Origin of Species by Means of Natural Selection.* A copy should be available in your school or public library.)
5. What role, if any, does natural selection play in the evolution of vestigial organs?
6. In Chapter 19 you read of the discovery of fossils of ancient reptiles, *flying* reptiles, and of *Archaeopteryx*, an early bird with reptilian features but with feathers such as modern birds have. How are these fossil discoveries—and others—of importance in evaluating Darwin's theory of evolution by natural selection? Why would the evolution of feathers have proved important in natural selection among flying organisms?
7. Anatomical and embryological similarities among animals today are striking. In what way are they evidence of evolutionary relationships? The discovery of what kind of evidence would be necessary to limit the usefulness of such comparisons?
8. In studies of evolution today, microorganisms are most frequently the subjects. What are the advantages of their use?
9. Man the hunter has eliminated numerous species of animals, such as dodo birds and passenger pigeons of historic times, and species of North American bison, mammoths, and camels of prehistoric times. Was this *natural* selection or *artificial* selection and why?
10. In what way does the theory of evolution explain the basis for another great theory in biology, the cell theory (Chapter 3)?
11. A basic principle of all the major sciences is the principle of **uniformitarianism,** pointing out that unless evidence can be discovered to the contrary, the basic laws of chemistry and physics known for natural events today must also have applied to natural events in the past—before there were any men to collect data and make scientific measurements and observations. Why is this principle important to the evaluation of evidence about the theory of evolution? Why is the principle a reasonable one?

RELATED READING

Books

For Darwin's own account of his travels, studies, and his theory of evolution . . .

Darwin, Charles, *On the Origin of Species by Means of Natural Selection,* Reprint of First Edition (1859), The New American Library, New York, 1958 (paperback).

Darwin, Charles, *The Voyage of the Beagle,* Reprint by Bantam Books, New York, 1960 (paperback).

For other accounts of the interrelation of life, genetics, and the theory of evolution . . .

Dobzhansky, Theodosius, *Evolution, Genetics, and Man,* John Wiley and Sons, New York, 1963 (paperback).

Dobzhansky, Theodosius, *Genetics and the Origin of Species,* Third Edition, Revised, Columbia University Press, New York, 1964.

Simpson, George Gaylord, *This View of Life,* Harcourt, Brace & World, New York, 1964 (and 1966, paperback).

Magazines

Bitterman, M. E., "The Evolution of Intelligence," *Scientific American,* Volume 212 (January 1965), page 92.

Eisley, Loren C., "Alfred Russel Wallace," *Scientific American,* Volume 200 (February 1959), page 70.

Napier, John, "The Evolution of the Hand," *Scientific American,* Volume 207 (December 1962), page 56.

32

The Mechanisms of Evolution

Darwin believed two conditions necessary for evolution to occur. First, genetic variability must exist among individuals of a species. Second, natural selection must operate. Over the course of time some of the genetic characteristics would be selected because they allowed the individuals possessing them a greater chance for survival and reproduction. Other individuals with less advantageous characteristics would tend to lose the competition for existence.

Darwin knew little about the cause or nature of genetic variation. Biologists had to wait until the beginning of the twentieth century, and the rise of modern genetics, before they were to understand the basis of variability. In Chapters 29-30 we learned that genetic variability originates in two main ways. First is the mutation of a gene, some alteration in its chemistry that changes the effect it has on the developing organism. Second is the recombining of existing alleles to produce *different combinations* of inherited characteristics. Now we shall learn how these processes contribute to evolution.

MUTATION

We begin with a consideration of mutation (see Chapter 7, pages 136–38), for without mutation there would be no different kinds of alleles that could be recombined. All individuals would be entirely homozygous.

One of the most curious aspects of mutation is that two characteristics of the process *seem* at first sight to make it improbable as a source of the heritable variety that we know exists in species. These two characteristics are (1) mutations are rare, and (2) most mutations are harmful. If they are rare, how can there be enough new variability for evolution to occur? If they are harmful, how can better adapted individuals evolve?

The Rates of Gene Mutation

There is no constant rate of mutation of genes. One of the genes needed to produce colored grains in an ear of corn, for example, may mutate as often as once in 2,000 gametes. Other genes are so stable that they fail to mutate during millions of cell divisions. The mutation rates of most genes fall between these two figures. A mutant form of any particular gene will be found about once in 100,000 gametes, as an average figure.

How, then, if mutation of a particular kind of gene happens so rarely, can mutation supply the raw material for evolution? The answer is that there are a great many opportunities for mutation, because

1. There are probably thousands of genes in each individual gamete.
2. For each species there may be thousands or millions of individuals producing gametes each generation.
3. There are many generations of individuals over the span of evolutionary time, and some opportunities for mutation occur at each generation.

Hence, though any particular kind of gene mutates rarely, the many genes, many individuals, and much time all add up to mean that mutation provides ample variability. In man there are probably more than 20,000 genes per gamete, and each person comes from a union of two gametes. Hence the probability that you have *some* freshly mutated gene among your 40,000 or more different genes or their alleles is roughly 40,000/100,000, or about 0.4, or two in five.

Life Photo, © Time, Inc.

32-1 Hermann J. Muller with an X-ray machine in his laboratory. Muller was awarded a Nobel prize in 1946 for his discovery and analysis of X-ray-induced mutations in *Drosophila*. Why was this discovery of such great importance?

The Effects of Gene Mutation

We can study the proportion of harmful to beneficial gene mutations by speeding up the mutation process. This can be done by means of X rays, as H. J. Muller discovered in 1927 (Figure 32-1). It can also be done by means of gamma radiation from radioactive isotopes (Figure 32-2).

When Muller used the X-ray method with *Drosophila*, he found by far the greater number of mutations to be harmful. They were so harmful, in fact, that often a fly made homozygous for the mutation died. Such mutations—and there are many—are called **lethals.** Apparently, most genes are so completely fitted into the chemical life of the cell that they are indispensable.

Other mutations, though not lethal, produce individuals that are less **viable** (VY·a·bul)—that is, they are less capable of living and developing normally or are less fertile in the normal environment. For example, we can put 20 normal *Drosophila* with 20 *Drosophila* that have the mutant gene for white eyes and let these flies interbreed. After a few generations we would observe that the entire population of flies will have red eyes. Natural selection will have eliminated the flies with white eyes. The white-eyed mutant flies cannot survive and develop to adulthood as well as flies that are wild-type. Most other mutant traits show a similarly reduced viability or fertility.

So, once again, we must ask how mutation can possibly produce individual variation that can serve as raw material for *adaptive* evolution. The answer seems to be that at least a few beneficial mutations do occur. Even if only one mutation in a thousand was beneficial, adaptive evolution could occur. Figure 32-3 is a set of calculations to show what is possible.

There is a second way in which the predominantly "harmful" nature of most mutations can contribute to adaptive evolution. This way is best seen in an illustration. Suppose that we are dealing with a species that lives in a climate with a temperature varying from 35° to 40° C. Suppose that the normal members of this species can survive in a temperature range from 32° to 42° C. Now suppose that in some members of the species a mutation occurs that shifts the range of tolerable temperature to 28° to 38° C. Clearly, the mutant organisms will not survive the hottest times of the year. But finally, let us now suppose that the climate changes so that the temperature ranges from 30° to 35° C. Which organism is best adapted to survive?

We can sum up by saying that the effect of any allele is neither wholly harmful nor wholly beneficial, but only relatively so. In our example of a changing climate, the mutant allele was harmful in the warm environment, but beneficial in the cooler environment.

Brookhaven National Laboratory

32–2 An aerial view of the "Gamma Garden" at Brookhaven National Laboratory, on Long Island near New York City. A radioactive cobalt source is in the center of the circular plot. Different kinds of plants are grown at varying distances from the center. Usually each kind of plant appears in several rows, for exposure at different distances from the radioactive source. In what respects is this plan more useful than one in which all the plants of a single kind would receive identical exposure?

32–3 Calculation of the Probable Number of Beneficial Mutations That Can Occur During the Evolutionary Lifetime of a Species

(Based upon conservative estimates of gene number, population size, and number of generations during which the species exists)

Estimates

1. Mutation rate per gene 1/100,000
2. Number of genes in the organism capable of mutating 1,000
3. Proportion of mutations that are beneficial 1/1,000
4. Population size of the species 100,000,000
5. Number of generations in the evolutionary life of the species 10,000

Calculations

6. Number of beneficial mutations per individual per generation equals No. 1 × No. 2 × No. 3, or 1/100,000 × 1,000 × 1/1,000 = 1/100,000.
7. Number of beneficial mutations in the species population per generation equals No. 6 × No. 4, or 1/100,000 × 100,000,000 = 1,000.
8. Number of beneficial mutations during the evolutionary life of the species equals No. 7 × No. 5, or 1,000 × 10,000 = 10,000,000.

This relativity of the "goodness" and "badness" of mutations would go a long way toward explaining how mutations can supply the raw material for adaptive evolution, except for one further matter – the simple fact that in the original environment in our first case, the allele was extremely harmful. How, then, could the mutation persist in the population until a climatic change occurred?

A solution to this problem is found in another characteristic of mutations. *Most mutations are recessive.* We can see immediately how this fact permits the gene to remain in the population for a long time. As long as it is present in an animal along with its normal allele (*Aa*), it will have little effect, either harmful or beneficial. Only when it is present in the homozygous condition (*aa*) will it produce effects that lead to its being selected against by the environment.

But you might guess that a recessive allele would be almost immediately swamped by its dominant allele. This leads us to a very important principle about the frequencies of alleles in populations.

THE FREQUENCIES OF ALLELES IN POPULATIONS

Suppose we begin with an experimental population in which the frequencies of a dominant allele *A* and its recessive *a* are both 50 percent. Let us also suppose that both alleles are equally adaptive. That is, the chance of survival and leaving offspring is the same for *AA*, *Aa*, and *aa* individuals. What would happen to our population in the succeeding generations? Would it not seem probable that the dominant alleles would increase and that the recessive alleles would be gradually weeded out? Let us see.

Calculating Allele Frequencies Resulting from Known Crosses

Turn back to Figure 29-5. Here is a cross of an *aa* × *AA* plant. There are equal numbers of *a* and *A* alleles in the P_1 generation, so the frequency of each will be 50 percent, just as in our experimental population. All of the F_1 plants will be *Aa*. What will be the frequency of each allele in the F_1?

Now on to the F_2. Here only four individuals are shown, but they have been selected to represent the mathematical proportions in which they would occur in a much larger sample. Once again we can determine the frequencies of the two alleles merely by counting all the *A*'s and *a*'s of these four individuals. How many are there of each?

What can you conclude about the changes in frequency of the dominant and recessive alleles in these three generations? Consider your answer a hypothesis and test it by determining the frequency of *R* and *r* in the three generations of cattle shown in Figure 29-6. A further test can be made by determining the frequencies of *R* and *r*, as well as of *Y* and *y*, in Figure 29-7.

You have discovered for yourself something very important about the frequency of alleles in successive generations of genetic crosses. This same principle applies to the frequencies of alleles in natural populations. There are special problems, however, when we go from the model crosses of the laboratory to genetics of large natural populations. In the laboratory the geneticist can control the cross; in the natural population he has to work his genetics problems backwards to determine from the existing population the frequencies of alleles affecting the crosses that have taken place, which he has not been able to observe. Let us see how this can be done.

Calculating Allele Frequencies from Unknown Crosses in Natural Populations

Our problem will be to determine the frequency of alleles in a population when all we know is the frequency of phenotypes. Let us return to Figure 29-5. We could have used a slightly different method of obtaining the F_2. Since the eggs in the ovules of the F_1 will be *A* and *a* in equal numbers, we could give each

Harbrace Photo

32–4 Sampling a population in a representative way poses many problems for the population geneticist. What would be wrong with sampling a city's population by selecting only people like these, who work downtown each weekday? What would be wrong with sampling only those who normally stay at home during the week?

a value of 0.5. The same would be true for the sperms produced by pollen. Therefore:

		Eggs	
		0.5 *A*	0.5 *a*
Sperms	0.5 *A*	0.25 *AA*	0.25 *Aa*
	0.5 *a*	0.25 *Aa*	0.25 *aa*

Thus the frequency of the genotypes in the F_2 is the *product* of the frequencies of the different kinds of sperms × the frequencies of the different kinds of eggs. In a field of pea plants, however, all we would see is whether the flowers were terminal or axial. We could not be sure whether the plants with axial flowers were *AA* or *Aa*. We would not have this difficulty with plants with terminal flowers. They would have to be *aa*. Thus, if we counted a large number of plants and found that 0.25 of them had terminal flowers, we would know that the frequency of the *aa* genotype is 0.25. Since the *aa* are in a frequency that is the product of *a* eggs × *a* sperms we can readily determine the frequency of *a*. Look at the example at the left and notice how the 0.25 *aa* value was obtained. We multiplied 0.5 × 0.5. If we want to obtain the frequency of the allele *a*, all we have to do is to take the square root of the frequency of *aa*. Thus $\sqrt{0.25} = 0.5$. If the frequency of *a* is 0.5, then the frequency of *A* is 1−0.5, or 0.5.

This has been an easy problem, since the values are the same as in the cross of Figure 29-5. Try another problem. We will overlook the difficulty of how to find out whether a sample population is representative of the entire population from which the sample is taken for study (Figure 32-4). Let us consider an arbitrary population of all the students in your school. Suppose that you had examined them all and found that 64 percent, or 0.64, had nonblue eyes and that 36 percent, or 0.36, had blue eyes. For the purposes of the problem we will ignore some of the genes that actually are involved in determination of eye color and assume that blue eyes are a simple homozygous recessive. Use the symbol b for blue eyes. We will use B for any nonblue eyes and thus not try to account for different colors of nonblue eyes. What are the frequencies of b and B in your sample population? Try working this out for yourself using the method described in the preceding paragraphs. If you have trouble, refer to a similar study in Figure 32-5. The answer and explanation of your own problem will be found at the end of the chapter. (In Laboratory Inquiry 32-1 you will analyze a similar situation for yourself, observing the frequency of a trait and setting up and working out the problem in population genetics.)

The frequencies of alleles in any generation, therefore, are the product of the frequencies of the alleles in the parents. Thus if we call one allele A and the other a, we could describe what happens in algebraic terms:

$$(A + a) \times (A + a) = A^2 + 2\,Aa + a^2.$$

The frequency of AA individuals will be A^2, of the heterozygous Aa individuals $2\,Aa$, and of the aa individuals a^2. All add up to 1 (or 100 percent).

The expression $A^2 + 2\,Aa + a^2 = 1$ describes the population at equilibrium. The values for the three genotypes will remain at the equilibrium values generation after generation, so long as these main conditions are met:

1. The AA, Aa, and aa individuals have equal chances of surviving and leaving offspring.
2. There is random mating. For example, the probability that an AA male will mate with an AA, Aa, or aa female depends only on the frequency of each type of female in the population.
3. The mutation rate of A to a is the same as a to A.

This mathematical relationship that we have derived was first recognized in 1908 by an English mathematician, G. H. Hardy, and a German physician, W. Weinberg. They realized that if random mating occurs, the frequencies of the different kinds of zygotes remain the same, generation after generation. Of course, this holds true only if there are no upsetting influences, such as mutation or selection.

Geneticists call this mathematical relationship the **Hardy-Weinberg Principle**. Usually they use the symbols p for the frequency of one allele and q for the other. Thus the Hardy-Weinberg Principle can be expressed: $(p + q) \times (p + q) = 1$; or, $p^2 + 2\,pq + q^2 = 1$.

In Laboratory Inquiry 32-2 you will consider whether the Hardy-Weinberg Principle applies to sex-linked genes.

HOW POPULATIONS CHANGE

We have concluded that the frequencies of various kinds of alleles in a population do not change *of themselves*; but over a long period of time changes usually do occur nonetheless. In fact, evolution can only occur if the equilibrium expressed by the Hardy-Weinberg Principle is no longer maintained.

Reasons for Change

Biologists who study the genetics of populations have found several important factors that cause gene frequencies to change:

1. *Mutation.* Mutations of the alleles of a particular gene occur very rarely under natural conditions. Little by little, the frequencies of the alleles change in favor of the one that is most stable, that is, has the lowest mutation rate. A more mutable allele tends to become relatively rarer.
2. *Natural selection.* Suppose that the allele A gives its possessors a slight advantage in viability (page 588) or fertility over indi-

32-5 A STUDY OF A POPULATION IN EQUILIBRIUM FOR A PAIR OF TRAITS

Traits: Ability / Inability } to taste PTC (phenylthiocarbamide)

64%

36%

Phenotype: PTC tasters
Genotypes: *TT* and *Tt* (but in unknown proportions)

Phenotype: PTC nontasters
Genotype: *tt* (known)

Working directly with *TT* and *Tt* is not possible, since their relative proportion in 64 percent of the population is not known. Begin with the proportion of *tt*, known to be 36 percent. The frequency of gene *t* in the population is $\sqrt{.36}$, or 0.6. Therefore, 60 percent of the total number of genes (*T* and *t*) in the population must be *t*, and the remaining 40 percent *T*.

Eggs

Sperms

	0.6 *t*	0.4 *T*
0.6 *t*	0.36 *tt*	0.24 *Tt*
0.4 *T*	0.24 *Tt*	0.16 *TT*

Genotype proportions:
0.16 *TT*
0.48 *Tt*
0.36 *tt*

viduals who have the allele *a*. Thus the frequency of *A* in the gene pool tends to increase and the frequency of *a* to decrease.

Natural selection is frequently made more apparent following *isolation.* It is possible for a large natural population to be broken up into smaller populations. Perhaps a mountain range or a canyon grows increasingly too wide or too rugged to be crossed by most of the individuals of a population, thus separating the population eventually into two parts. Each isolated population will be evolving almost by itself. If the environments are different in the isolated areas, natural selection will act differently, and the two populations will become increasingly divergent. Laboratory Inquiries 32-3 and 32-4 are studies of natural selection in moths and men. One of the traits to be studied appears at first unrelated to the health or life of the individual–it is color in moths. The other trait obviously affects natural selection in man.

3. *Emigration and immigration.* Very few populations are completely isolated. Terrestrial species that live on islands, far from the mainland, and that are not able to cross the open sea, are perhaps the most completely isolated. Even so, a few individuals of various species occasionally may be blown or rafted to or from such remote islands. In most populations, individuals leave or join the population more frequently. From an evolutionary standpoint, these emigrations (away from) or immigrations (to) may result in a change in the frequencies of some of the alleles in the population. In particular, individuals that come from another population with different frequencies of alleles change the frequencies in the population they join.

When the genetic difference of two populations becomes great enough, the populations may not be able to interbreed any longer. This final degree of genetic isolation usually takes a long time to come about. Many mechanisms are involved, but basically, mutation, recombination, and natural selection, together with geographic isolation over a long enough period of time, are sufficient. Eventually two new species arise, each in its isolated area.

Bees, Birds, and Columbines

An example will show some of the factors involved in the changes in the frequency of alleles in natural populations. A species of columbine with red flowers lives in the moist canyons of the Pacific Coast. The flowers are in a nodding position and have relatively long, straight spurs. Another species of columbine that lives in Europe has curved purple flowers and short spurs (Figure 32-6).

The differences between these two species represent adaptations to different animals that pollinate the flowers. The red columbine is pollinated by hummingbirds. Red is the brightest part of the spectrum to birds; hence the flowers of the columbine are bright and conspicuous to the hummingbird. The nodding position of the flowers is an adaptation to the way in which hummingbirds usually visit flowers, by hovering near them and putting their beaks in from below. Finally, the spur of the red columbine is the right length for the hummingbird's beak. When the bird is sucking up the nectar at the bottom of the spur with its beak, its head feathers deliver pollen to the stigmas and receive pollen from the anthers of the flower. Thus as the hummingbird goes from flower to flower seeking food, it also cross-pollinates the flowers.

The European purple columbine is pollinated by bumblebees, whose eyes are sensitive to violet and ultraviolet colors. The bees use their short, curved proboscis to suck nectar from the flowers. The curve of the short spurs of the European columbine just fits the proboscis of the bumblebee. As the bee gets nectar it pollinates the columbine.

32–6 It is no accident that **(a)** bumblebees pollinate European columbines, while **(b)** hummingbirds pollinate Western American columbines. The bumblebee is sensitive to violet and ultraviolet light; its proboscis is short and curved (folded away when the bee is in flight, as here). The hummingbird is sensitive to brighter colors; its bill is long and straight. Interdependence in evolution between flower and insect in **a,** and flower and bird in **b,** have led to differences in the length of the spurs and in the colors of the flowers. Which flower is red, and which purple?

These two flower species are easily crossed, and the hybrid is fertile. By artificial selection in the garden, we could easily get a flower with the red color and nodding position of the red columbine, but the curved spur of the purple columbine—or any other combination of characteristics that we might desire. But in nature we find *only the two combinations* of characteristics that have been described. This is because flowers with those particular combinations are most often pollinated and produce more seeds than do flowers with other combinations of characters. We can say, in fact, that mutations for long spurs in the columbine are beneficial in *combination* with genes for red flowers, but harmful in combination with genes for purple flowers.

Recombination and Selection

In higher animals and plants *genetic recombination* is as necessary as mutation, to provide the variability required for evolution. Since the only way in which genes can become recombined in higher organisms is by means of the sexual process, it is clear that sexuality is important in evolutionary change.

The great importance of genetic recombination in providing the immediate source of varia-

32-7 JOHANNSEN'S EXPERIMENT — SELECTION FOR SIZE IN BEANS

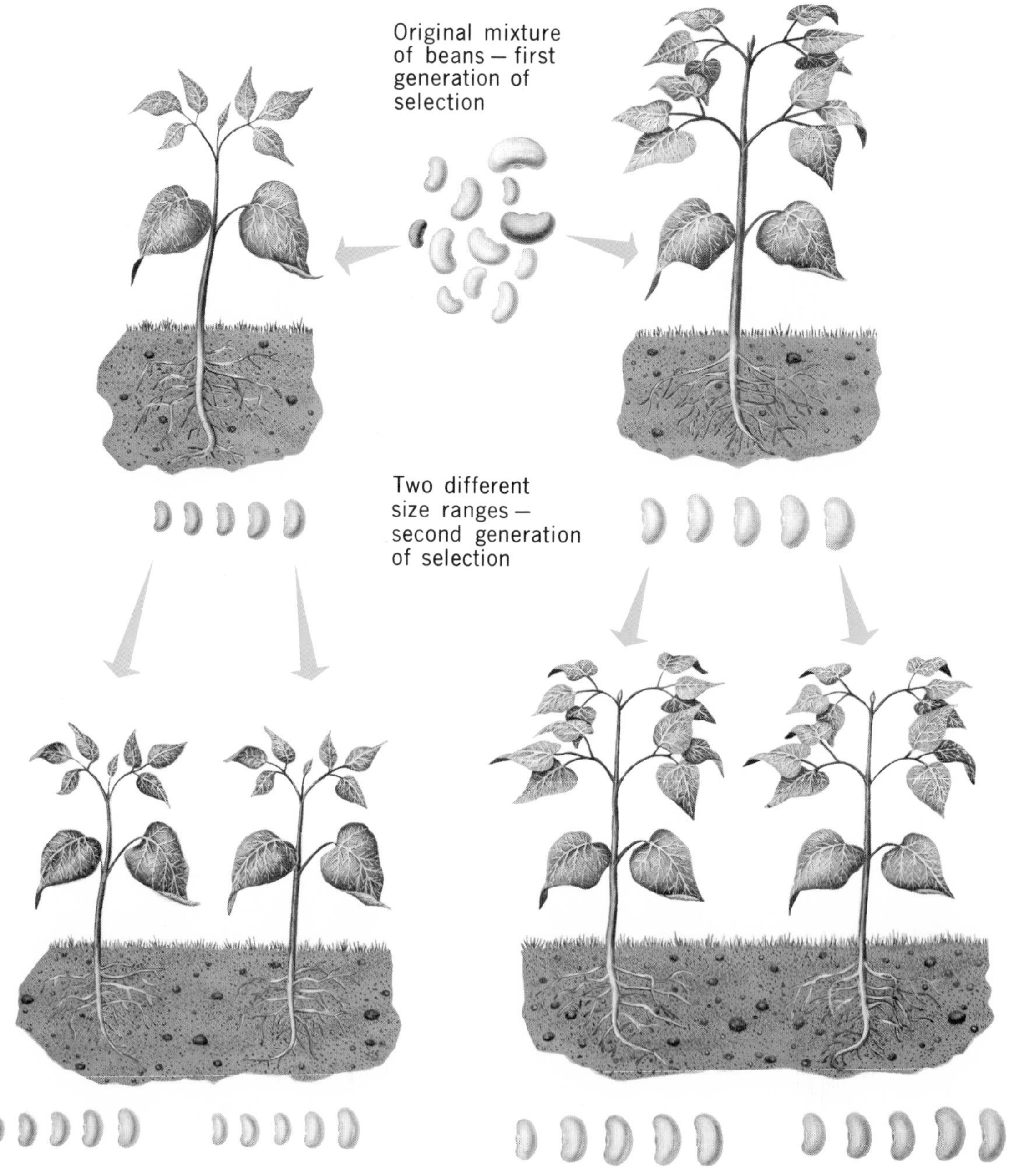

No further difference (only the first generation of selection produced measurable results).

bility upon which selection may act is shown by the contrast in the results of two experiments. The Danish geneticist W. L. Johannsen (yo-HON·sen) performed an important experiment with garden beans in about 1905. He selected the largest and the smallest beans from a bag of seeds of a well-known commercial variety. He then grew a crop from the largest beans and one from the smallest beans in separate plots of ground. The average size of the beans descended from the large seeds was larger (Figure 32-7) than that of the crop derived from the small seeds. In each of the two fields, he again selected the largest and the smallest beans, keeping them separated into four groups this time. The next year he found that this second generation of selection had produced no further effect. The smallest beans from each of the two fields of the second generation of selection gave rise to a third generation with beans just as large as those derived from the largest beans in the *same* field. Johannsen continued this selection for three more generations. He showed that after the first generation, selection had no effect in either increasing or decreasing bean size.

He explained this result by assuming that the original beans consisted of a mixture of two pure-breeding strains. One strain gave large beans and the other small beans. He also assumed that all of the size differences between the beans in the same field grown in the second and later generations were due to environmental modification. In the first generation of selection, he had managed to sort out the two pure lines. Each consisted of homozygous, true-breeding beans.

Johannsen thought that the homozygous pure line was the typical genetic constitution of organisms in nature. He therefore concluded that natural selection could not be important in evolution. Most geneticists of his day agreed with this conclusion. For this reason, Darwin's hypothesis of natural selection was regarded by many scientists during the period 1905–30 as either disproved or of little importance.

32-8 SELECTION FOR HIGH AND LOW OIL CONTENT IN KERNELS OF CORN

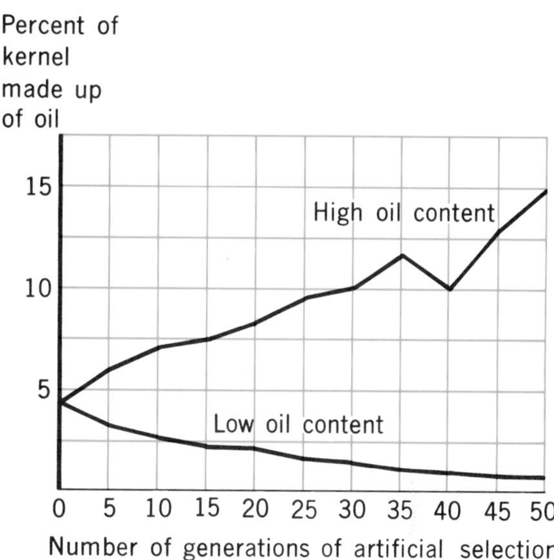

While Johannsen's experiments were being performed, another experiment on artificial selection had begun. In 1895 a group of **agronomists** (a·GRON·o·mists)—agricultural scientists—at the University of Illinois decided to find out for how many generations they could produce changes by continuous selection. They used field corn, which is normally cross-pollinated. They started with a hybrid produced by a cross between two of the varieties grown by farmers at that time. They selected for four different characteristics in the kernels: high protein content, low protein, high oil content, and low oil. This experiment was continued for fifty generations; the most recent published results were obtained in 1949 (the experiment was briefly interrupted during World War II).

In all four lines the population responded to selection for at least thirty-five generations. The results for oil content are shown in Figure 32-8. The kernels of the original population contained 4.7 percent oil. Fifty generations later, the average oil content in the high line was 15.4 percent; in the low line, 1.0 percent.

The results of this experiment with corn are completely different from those of Johannsen with beans. In corn, selection had a strong effect and was still producing some changes in the population even after 45 to 50 generations of continuous selection. How can we explain this difference?

For one hypothesis, suppose that the corn population responded to selection because mutations were constantly taking place in the desired direction, and that this was not happening in the bean population. But the facts that we know about mutation rates in plants, combined with the figures on the numbers of plants used by the Illinois agronomists in their experiment, both speak against this hypothesis. In each line of corn being selected, the number of plants raised per generation was between 200 and 300. If we multiply these figures by 50, the total number of generations raised in each line, then we calculate that the total number of plants raised in each of the four selected lines was between 10,000 and 15,000. We do not know the actual rate of mutation for changes in oil or protein content. But the rate of mutation for many other characteristics in corn has been measured, and for most characteristics it is as low as one mutation in 50,000 plants—or lower. Hence the occurrence of even one mutation in the desired direction during the fifty generations of the experiment is unlikely.

The slow, steady way in which the populations responded to selection suggests that many genetic differences were being sorted out. *The different genes for changed protein and oil content that were being selected must all or nearly all have existed in the population before selection began.*

Such different results for corn and bean selection can be explained by the difference in the way the two species breed. The bean is usually self-pollinated. Pollen from the anthers is deposited on the stigmas of the same flower. As a result of self-pollination, the beans have become much more homozygous for all or most of their hereditary characteristics.

Corn, on the other hand, is normally cross-pollinated. Pollen from the tassels of one plant is carried by the wind to the ears of another plant. Because of cross-pollination, corn plants are much more heterozygous than bean plants for many pairs of allelic genes. The different individuals of the same variety differ from each other in gene content much more than do beans of the same variety. (In this respect people are like corn, not like beans.)

In cross-fertilizing populations of plants and animals, there is a great store of genetic differences. Selection, whether artificial or natural, sorts out particular gene combinations, and so can bring about genetic differences between different lines derived from the same population. Each selected line has less variability than the unselected population from which it was derived. If selection does not occur too rapidly, mutations can gradually replenish the store of genetic variability and make still further selection possible.

It follows that in a cross-fertilizing population, the variability upon which natural selection acts has been acquired by mutations that have taken place in past generations and that have been passed on through successive generations. Since most populations of higher animals and plants are cross-fertilizing, this relationship between mutation and selection is the usual one. The results obtained by the Illinois agronomists are like those which we would expect if natural selection were acting on the usual type of population found in nature.

THE ORIGIN OF SPECIES

Thus far, the process we have been describing has produced no new species. Mutation, recombination, selection, and migration have merely brought about changes within species. To Darwin and other biologists of his day, however, the big question was, "Do new species evolve from previously existing species?" If so, how does this come about? This question loomed so large in Darwin's mind that he called

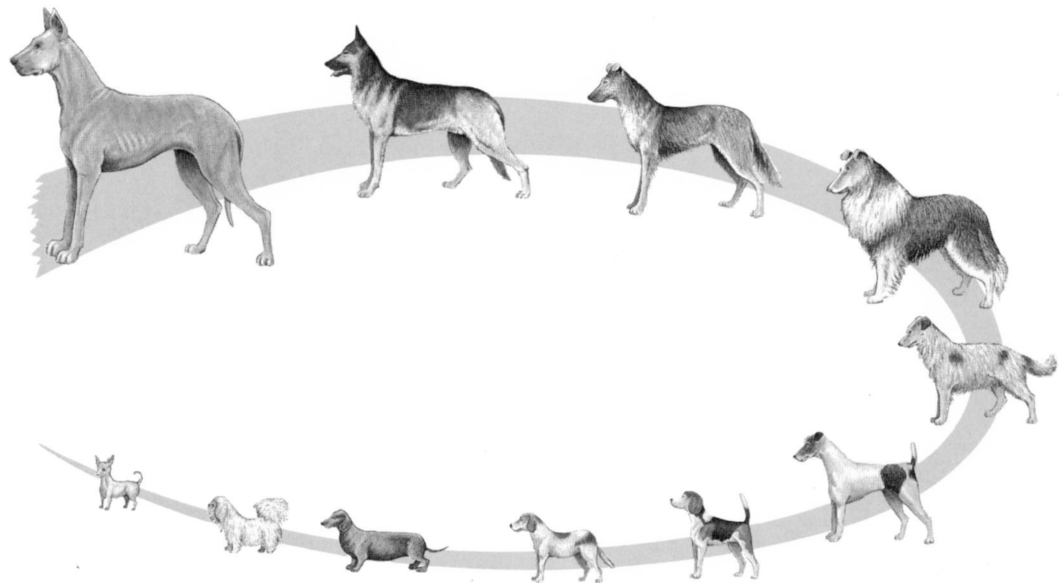

32–9 Variation in a domesticated species. The differences between some of these dogs are far greater than one observes between wild species of the same genus—or even between some related genera. Why are the dogs considered to be of one species?

his great book *On the Origin of Species*. In this section we shall study the way in which modern biologists are attacking this same question of the origin of species.

When we speak of the evolution of a new species we must keep clearly in mind what we are talking about. We are not referring solely to the evolution of differences. The domestic dog has evolved, largely through selection by man, into many different breeds (Figure 32-9). Why do we not consider these different breeds as separate species? The reason is that the different breeds can usually mate with each other to produce fertile offspring. A new species must be genetically *isolated*. That is, it must not interbreed with any other species to a significant extent, or its distinctness may disappear.

Selection in Populous, Widely Distributed Species

In a large continuous population of a species that spreads over a considerable geographic range, we often find regular increases or decreases in the frequency of an inherited characteristic as we pass from north to south or east to west. For example, in North America the red fox is subject to a mutation, incompletely dominant, that produces the beautiful silver fox when it is homozygous. Heterozygous individuals, with mingled red and silver hair, are known by fur trappers as the cross fox. The silver type is by far the commonest in the north, the red type in the more southern regions. The cross fox is found most abundantly in between. This geographic variation is most probably a consequence of natural selection. The silver fox is less conspicuous as it hunts its prey across the snow, and the red fox is less conspicuous hunting in woods and meadows where there is less snow.

A clearer picture of the relations of geographic isolation to the evolution of species is presented by what is called a **ring of races.** For example, in the coastal area of southern California there lives a salamander that is light and rather even in color. Farther north it gives

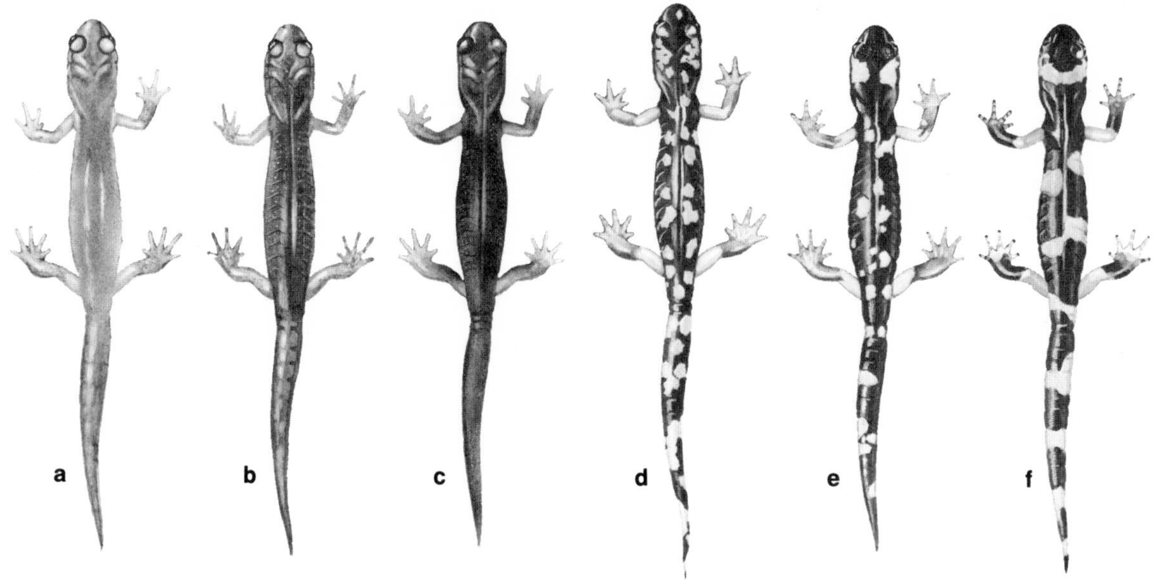

32–10 Geographic variation. The area of California where these animals live is roughly **O**-shaped—that is, the populations of these salamanders are distributed around the periphery of the state but not in the center. Salamanders **a** and **b** will interbreed, as will **b** and **c, c** and **d, d** and **e,** and **e** and **f.** But **a** and **f,** although they come in contact, rarely interbreed. How would you classify them—as subspecies or as different species?

place to a darker race (Figure 32-10), and this in turn is replaced in northern California by a still darker, uniformly colored type that ranges beyond the coastal regions into the interior. In the interior the dark type is replaced, toward the southeast, by a mottled form. Farther south, in the Sierra Nevada region across the hot, dry valley from the coastal habitat, this mottled form is replaced by a differently mottled form. Finally the ring is completed by another type of boldly mottled salamander, which overlaps the range of the even-colored form in Southern California.

Suppose we call these races or subspecies simply **a**, **b**, **c**, **d**, **e**, and **f**, in the order of the geographic ring described above; **a** and **b** interbreed where they meet. Similarly, **b** and **c** interbreed; and **c** interbreeds with **d**, **d** with **e**, and **e** with **f**. But to our astonishment we find that in evolution, things that are equal to the same thing are *not* equal to each other! *For* **a** *and* **f**, *where they overlap in territory, do not interbreed—or do so only rarely*. If some natural catastrophe would destroy the subspecies **b** through **e**, then **a** and **f** would be regarded as two species, instead of one.

A few rings of races of this kind are known in the world, especially among the birds of the Old World. Also known are rings of species in which each species is replaced in an adjacent area by a different but quite similar related species. We can easily imagine the rings of races becoming rings of species in the course of evolution.

On groups of neighboring islands, there are often similar but different species or subspecies of birds, or of other vertebrates. This, of course, was the situation Darwin found in the Galápagos Islands (Chapter 31). Originally the islands had no life, being of volcanic origin.

Very likely all the species of finches now found there are descended from one or a very few original males and females that reached the islands from the mainland at some time in the past. Since then, the geographic isolation from the mainland has permitted these island finches to evolve independently.

Genetic Isolation

Even if two populations look much alike, we assign them to different species if they do not cross successfully with each other and produce vigorous, fertile offspring in nature. For instance, the wild coyote looks much like a mongrel dog. Hybrids between coyotes and dogs are rare. Mating between the two species takes place less readily than between individuals of the same species. The male F_1 hybrids are sterile. Thus, dogs and coyotes can exist side by side and remain distinct from each other.

Reproductive separateness, or isolation, of species takes various forms:

1. Sometimes hybrids cannot be formed at all, or die when young. For example, the eggs of a bullfrog fertilized with sperms of the common leopard frog start to divide, but the embryos soon die.
2. The hybrid offspring may reach the adult size but be completely or partly sterile. A cross between a horse and a donkey gives us a mule. But a mule is sterile. The same is true of crosses between chickens and turkeys (or pheasants).
3. Individuals of two different species may not cross in nature, but they may form vigorous fertile hybrids if crossed artificially. The mallard and pintail ducks are an example. They are found in the same habitats throughout North America, and individuals intermediate between them are relatively rare. Yet when they are put together in the same pen, they will mate with each other, and the hybrids are fertile. The reason they do not cross in nature is that their mating instincts and nesting habits are very different.

Different courtship patterns may also isolate species. The male of the grouse or woodcock performs an elaborate dance in front of the female before mating takes place. This dance apparently stimulates the sex hormones in the female who watches it and causes her to release her egg cells. Since females are most strongly stimulated by the dance of males of their own species, there is little mating with males of other species.

Many flowers, such as orchids, milkweeds, and snapdragons, have evolved complex shapes and colors, which insure that flower-pollinating bees will visit only one kind of flower at a time. One experimenter planted alternate rows of a garden with two species of snapdragons having different flowers. When he watched the bees pollinating these flowers, he found that a bee would usually visit flowers of only one species during a particular flight. It would regularly bypass the row containing the second species. Other bees from the same hive would visit and pollinate the second species. Tests of the seeds from this field showed that only 2 to 3 percent of the seeds were hybrid. This showed how rarely the bees carried pollen from one species to another. Artificial cross-pollination, carried out as a control, yielded large numbers of vigorous hybrids.

Reproductive isolation is an important part of our definition of species. Therefore, the problem of the origin of species is basically one of discovering how reproductive isolation evolves.

We find that it almost always begins by physical or geographic separation of one part of a population from the remainder, as, for example, when a hurricane blows birds from the mainland to islands. Once separation occurs, natural selection may act differently on the two populations and lead to reproductive isolation.

Polyploid Species

In most groups of animals and in many plants, the origin of species is a process requiring hundreds of thousands of years. But there is one way in which species can originate almost

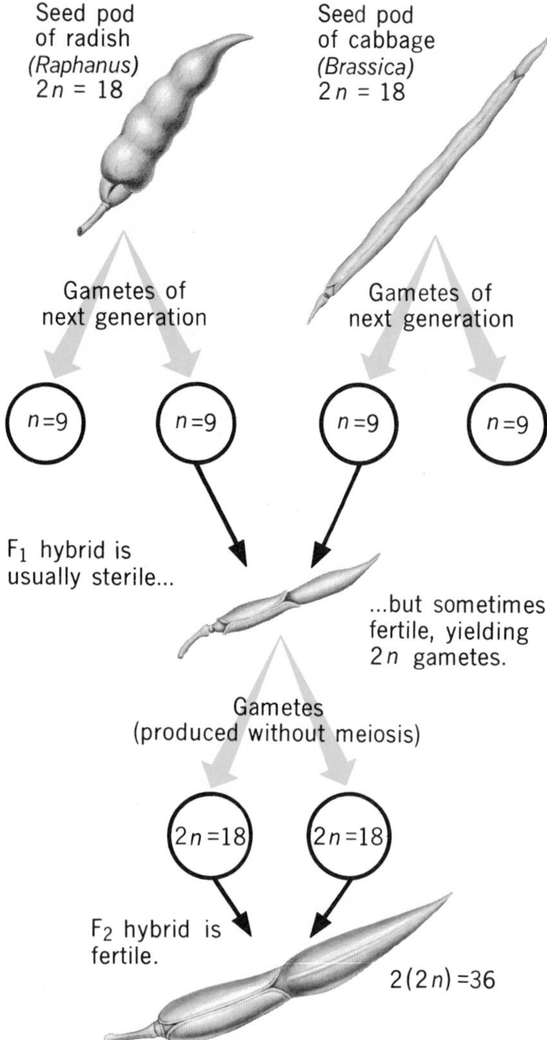

32–11 A diagram of Karpechenko's cross of a radish with a cabbage, showing the seed pods of the parent plants and of the hybrids. Meiosis in the F_1 hybrid was nearly always abnormal, producing defective gametes. Occasionally meiosis failed altogether and there was no reduction of chromosome number. In this case the gametes would have 9 radish chromosomes and 9 cabbage chromosomes. If two such gametes united, the F_2 would have 18 radish chromosomes and 18 cabbage chromosomes. In this plant, meiosis would be normal, and fertile gametes would result, with 9 chromosomes derived from each of the original parents.

instantaneously. This is through a cross between two existing species, *followed by doubling of the chromosome number of the hybrid.* For instance, in 1928 a Russian geneticist, Karpechenko (kar·PAYCH·en·ko), crossed a radish with a cabbage (Figure 32-11). The resulting plant was very large and vigorous, but when it blossomed it turned out to be completely sterile. Karpechenko studied this plant and found that the chromosomes did not pair in meiosis. The cause? The 9 chromosomes derived from a radish do not "match" the 9 derived from cabbage—i.e., they are not homologous. Because they are single, the chromosomes in the hybrid do not go to the equator of the spindle, and many of them are not included in the spores that result from meiosis. Hence the pollen grains formed by these spores are sterile and empty.

Occasionally meiosis fails altogether and there is no reduction in the number of chromosomes. Thus, quite rarely, pollen grains and egg cells are produced that have all of the 18 chromosomes (9 of the radish parent and 9 of the cabbage parent). Karpechenko learned that he could increase the frequency of these unusual gametes by subjecting the buds of the hybrid plant to various shocks and severe treatments. When gametes of this type unite, they produce a plant with twice the normal number of chromosomes—36 instead of 18. Since this plant has half its chromosomes derived from the radish and half from the cabbage, it is still intermediate, like the sterile hybrid. But when meiosis takes place in this 36-chromosome plant, the 18 chromosomes derived from the radish pair with each other, and those from the cabbage do the same. Consequently, meiosis is normal, and the gametes receive 18 chromosomes, 9 of the cabbage type and 9 of the radish type. Offspring from these gametes are fertile and breed true for an intermediate phenotype like that of the F_1 hybrid. Since the hybrid has more chromosomes than the plants that produced it, or actually two diploid sets, it is said to be **polyploid** (POL·ih·ploid).

When the polyploid hybrid is crossed with either of its original diploid parental species, the offspring are sterile. Consequently, a polyploid hybrid has all of the essential requirements of a distinct species. It looks different from any other species, including its original parents; it is fertile and breeds true; and it forms sterile hybrids when crossed with any other species, including its own original parents.

In recent years it has been discovered that many wild species of plants are polyploids. Polyploids in animals are rarer.

Karpechenko's polyploid species was the first species in all history to be made artificially by a man. Since his work, many doubled hybrids have been made in various groups of higher plants, and many well-known species have been shown to be doubled hybrids. Examples are cultivated wheat, cotton, and tobacco; garden flowers such as the cultivated marigold and larkspur; and wild species such as the blue flag iris and the Jerusalem artichoke.

Colchicine (KOL·chih·seen), a drug obtained from the crocus, has been found to be very effective in doubling the chromosome number of plant cells exposed to it. It does this by destroying the spindle on which separation of the chromosomes into two groups normally takes place. Through the use of colchicine, the artificial production of polyploid species has become a major achievement in man's control of the evolutionary process in plants.

The Origin of Genera and Larger Groups

The final question which we must ask about the forces of evolution is this: can mutation, recombination, selection, and barriers to crossbreeding explain the major trends of evolution, such as the divergence of catlike from doglike animals and the evolution of the horse from its small primitive ancestors?

The mechanisms that govern these major trends of evolution cannot be studied directly: they took place many thousands or millions of years ago. Nevertheless, a study of populations today, and of fossils, provides strong evidence that the same evolutionary forces in operation today have guided evolution in the past. One species evolves into two (or more). All the new species continue to evolve, becoming more different from one another until eventually we would classify them as different genera.

IMPROVING GENETIC LINES

We generally think of evolution as occurring only in nature and generally over millions of years. But man himself has been a force in the evolution of some species. He has, in these instances, replaced natural selection with artificial selection. The result is not a population better adapted to its environment but a population better adapted to the needs of man.

Long before he had an insight into the principles of evolution and genetics, man sought to improve the quality of his domesticated plants and animals. These are the organisms that provide him with food, clothing, transportation, and protection. He wanted fruit and vegetable plants that would produce more food on less land and with less of his labor. He wanted cows that produce more milk, chickens that lay more eggs, cattle and hogs that have more flesh usable for meat, and grain plants that give large crops and are resistant to disease.

The processes man used to bring about these desirable ends are essentially the same as the natural processes that change populations. Man did not know how to introduce more mutations into his stocks, and hence more variation. He certainly took notice of the variation already there and selected as parents of the next generation those organisms with the traits he desired. This was artificial selection, as distinguished from natural selection. Natural selection promotes the increase of certain genotypes adapted to a particular set of environmental conditions. Artificial selection promotes the increase of genotypes that man wants for his own purposes (Figure 32-12).

32-12 VARIETY THROUGH ARTIFICIAL SELECTION

All photos by Grant Heilman

Man also recognized the importance of reproductive isolation, for he kept separate the lines of domestic plants and animals he desired—by preventing their breeding with types he considered less desirable. Even today the owners of pedigreed stock take special care that their animals are mated only with other animals that have similar pedigrees.

In recent years, armed with genetic knowledge and techniques, man has applied new tools to old problems. The effectiveness of these techniques in increasing the quality and quantity of his farm animals, his food plants, and even his ornamental plants has been truly phenomenal. One of the most dramatic examples of the application of known genetic principles is the development of hybrid corn, which was discussed in Chapter 29.

One example of how special traits are developed in domestic animals is provided by American cattle breeders. Some diseases of Shorthorn cattle are transmitted by insects that pierce the thin skin of the animals. Shorthorn cattle are good meat-producers. Brahman cattle have thick, almost insect-proof skins. However, they are not such good meat-producers. The raw material available to the cattle breeder, therefore, was an insect-susceptible, good meat-producing strain and an insect-resistant, poor meat-producing strain. Clearly a little genetic recombination was desirable!

Breeders crossed American Shorthorn cattle with Brahman cattle. From among the offspring, animals with the desired characteristics – good meat-production and thick skin – were selected for future crosses. After repeated selection, a true-breeding strain was developed. The result was a beautiful breed of cattle known as the **Santa Gertrudis** (ger·TRUE·dis). These animals have a thick, almost insect-proof skin stretched over the fine beef of American Shorthorn cattle. These cattle can graze unharmed in areas that would be deadly to thin-skinned cattle.

A few other examples of the application of genetic and evolutionary principles to improvement of plants can be given. One of the worst problems with cultivated tomato plants is wilting caused by a fungus known as *Fusarium* (few·SAY·rih·um). It was discovered that a wild tomato species from Peru possesses a gene for resistance to *Fusarium* wilt. This wild species, however, produces poor fruit. By crossing the cultivated tomato and the wild one, a hybrid with resistance was obtained. This did not solve the problem, however, because most of the desirable qualities of cultivated tomatoes were diminished in the hybrid. A tasty and resistant tomato was obtained by repeatedly crossing the hybrid plants back to the cultivated tomato, and by selecting in subsequent generations. This amounted to introducing the gene for resistance to wilt into the best cultivated varieties.

In wheat, the stem rust fungus causes enormous losses. A cross between the high-yielding Marquis (MAR·kwis) wheat developed in America and a Russian variety gave a variety resistant to the stem rust. This new variety was named Ceres (SIR·eez). Released in 1926, it had become by 1934 almost the exclusive variety grown in the Dakotas and neighboring regions. Unfortunately, mutations and hybridizations occur not only in wheat and other crop plants, but in wheat stem rust and other disease organisms. In 1935 a disaster of enormous proportions occurred. Either a mutation in the stem rust enabled it to overcome the resistance of the Ceres wheat, or a natural hybrid of different strains of stem rust arose and produced the same effect. The wheat crop was almost wiped out wherever Ceres had been planted!

The wheat breeders had to begin again, trying to produce by hybridization and selection a new variety that would be resistant to the new strain of stem rust. In time they were successful; but this process is often slow and difficult. The same process may be required again in the future, for we must watch for further evolutionary change in the stem rust fungus.

In the growing of cotton and tobacco, fruits and vegetables, flowers, and even trees for timber, the work of the plant breeder has utilized the growing knowledge of genetics and evolution. By producing hybrids, by inducing mutations, by doubling chromosome number to make vigorous plants, the plant breeder has the basis for developing desirable strains. These first steps are followed by selection and the breeding of pure lines. By these biological techniques, the supply of useful plant products, and the food of the world, have been multiplied many times.

CONCLUDING REMARKS

We have learned that mutation, recombination, and selection, combined with geographic isolation – or the effects of emigration and immigration – are the principal mechanisms of evolution in animals and plants. Doubling the chromosome number in a sterile hybrid may create new species abruptly, especially among plants.

Far from being of theoretical value only, a knowledge of the principles of evolution is helping man to develop better domestic animals and plants. With even more knowledge, it may enable him to direct his own evolutionary changes. That degree of knowledge will have awesome possibilities and awesome dangers.

Answer to the Problem on Page 592

We cannot tell whether an individual with nonblue eyes is *BB* or *Bb*. Therefore, we cannot take the square root of the frequency of nonblue eyes to determine the frequency of any *B* alleles. But we know the frequency of blue-eyed individuals, which is 0.36, and hence the frequency of *bb*. The frequency of *b* will be $\sqrt{0.36} = 0.6$. Since the frequency of *b* is 0.6, the frequencies of *B* will total $1.0 - 0.6$, or 0.4. Knowing these frequencies, check the problem by finding what would be the phenotypes and genotypes of offspring if you crossed males and females for which the average frequency of *B* gametes is 0.4 (or 40 percent) and the frequency of *b* is 0.6 (or 60 percent).

GUIDE QUESTIONS AND PROBLEMS

1. Genes vary in mutation rates. What might be the result if a species of organisms had a very high percentage of genes that mutated frequently? If a high percentage of genes mutated at an abnormally low rate or never?
2. By natural selection a species becomes adapted to its environment. How might the *individual* abilities of members of the species to adapt to seasonal or fluctuating changes in the environment be considered one of the species' adaptations through natural selection?
3. Phenylthiocarbamide (PTC) is a substance that is bitter in taste to some people, while to others it is tasteless. The ability to taste PTC, as in the problem illustrated in Figure 32-5, seems to be due to a dominant gene (*T*). Nontasters are homozygous recessives (*tt*). Suppose that a group of students and their families are tested and found to be 70 percent tasters and 30 percent nontasters of PTC. Use this information to calculate the probable frequencies of the genes and the genotypes in the sample.
4. Why is it significant to know the distribution of alleles in human populations?
5. What factors can cause gene frequencies in a population to change?
6. How can enough beneficial gene mutations occur among species to provide raw materials for adaptive evolution, if only rare mutations have beneficial effects?
7. How may some gene mutations be either harmful or beneficial, depending upon special circumstances? Explain how the European and American columbines are one illustration of your answer.
8. How did Johannsen's choice of an experimental plant affect his conclusion that natural selection was not a significant factor in evolution? Account for the difference between Johannsen's results and the experiments in Illinois with corn.
9. Under what conditions can polyploidy be considered "instant species"?
10. List some ways in which a population may become divided into two or more geographically isolated populations. What are some of the factors determining whether such isolation eventually will lead to the establishment of separate species?

RELATED READING

Books

For more information on how evolution occurs . . .

Dobzhansky, Theodosius, *Genetics and the Origin of Species*, Third Edition, Revised, Columbia University Press, 1964 (paperback).

Dowdeswell, W. H., *The Mechanism of Evolution,* Harper and Row, New York, 1960.

Srb, A. M., and B. Wallace, *Adaptation,* Second Edition, Prentice-Hall, Englewood Cliffs, New Jersey, 1964 (paperback).

Magazines

Crow, James F., "Ionizing Radiation and Evolution," *Scientific American,* Volume 201 (September 1959), page 138.

33

The Evolution of Man

Charles Darwin's general hypothesis was that species of today have evolved from other species that lived in the past. Although he did not discuss the evolution of man in *On the Origin of Species,* his belief was clear: since man is a species of animal, he also must have evolved. In 1859 Darwin went no further, saying only that because of his hypothesis of evolution "light would be thrown on the origin of man and his history."

If modern man evolved from other species, what were the other species? When did man evolve from them? Darwin knew that if man had a past history, the best evidence would be provided by the fossil record. He did not know of the existence of any fossil men.

In one of the strange accidents of history, a fossil man had been discovered just a few years before Darwin published *On the Origin of Species.* In 1856, an unusual skull was discovered in the valley of the Neander River in Germany. It has come to be known as the **Neanderthal** (nee·AN·der·thahl) skull ("–tal" means valley in German). The skull was much like that of modern man; however, the bones of the top of the skull were very thick, the teeth were large, and there were heavy ridges over the eyes. There were many suggestions for the origin of this somewhat brutish looking skull. Virchow ("*omnis cellula e cellula,*" page 48) and some other anatomists pronounced it to be nothing but an abnormal skull. Others suggested it was the skull of a Russian soldier or an ancient Celt. Biologists had not begun to think of an evolutionary past for man.

It was not until many years had passed that the true significance of the Neanderthal skull came to be understood. Far from being a freak, the skull belonged to a race of man that had lived in Europe during the Pleistocene epoch, or Ice Ages.

Attempts were made to see what Neanderthal man really looked like. His bust was sculptured by using a cast of the skull as the base and then adding clay to represent the muscles and skin. You may believe this to be an impossible task, but it is not. The muscles of the human head are thoroughly known. A skillful anatomist can tell from the ridges on the bones not only the points of attachment but also the sizes of the muscles. You can feel your own skull and note how thin are the layers of muscles and skin. The cast of the Neanderthal skull was given a layer of clay muscles, skin, and hair, as in Figure 33-1.

But Darwin, and others of his time, did not understand the significance of that strange skull from the Neander Valley. Thus there were no fossils for him to use in trying to understand man's past. There were other methods that he could use, and with these he set about to inquire into man's past. In 1871 his findings appeared in *The Descent of Man.*

A basic deduction that Darwin could make from his hypothesis of evolution is that all the organisms of a related group in biologists' classifications must have a common ancestor. Man is placed in the genus *Homo,* of the family **Hominidae,** of the order **Primates,** of the class **Mammalia,** of the phylum **Chordata,** of the kingdom **Animalia.** Thus man's place in nature was given by his position in the scheme of classification. But was this scheme of classification correct? Man had been classified long before biologists thought in terms of the hypothesis of evolution.

Was man a chordate? Biologists had already discovered that in his embryonic stage he possesses a notochord and strange gill pouches in

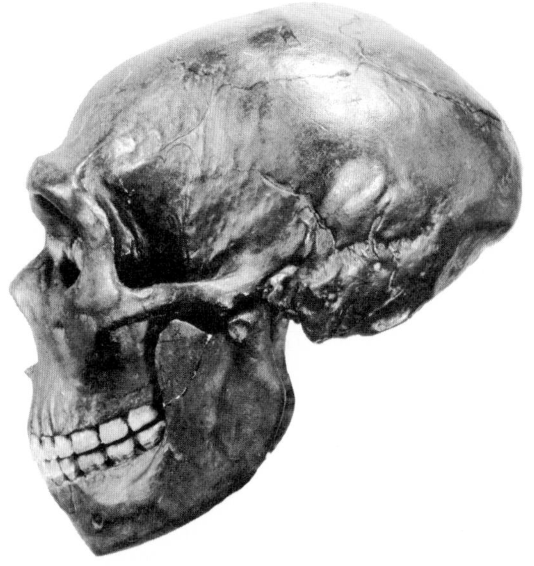

Both photos from American Museum of Natural History

33–1 A fossil skull (**left**) and a reconstruction of the probable appearance of a Neanderthal man. Neanderthal remains and tools have been found in Europe, North Africa, Gibraltar, and in the Near East. Enough specimens have been discovered to establish that there was considerable diversity within Neanderthal man, just as there is in modern man. The skull shown here is an unusually large one (1600 cc cranial capacity).

his pharynx, and that throughout life he has a dorsal nerve tube (Chapter 19, page 370). These are the three diagnostic characteristics of the chordates. Any animal that has them is, by definition, a chordate. So the inference was that man was related to all other chordates. The first chordates would have been not only his ancestors but also the ancestors of all other chordates. We know now a good deal about the evolution of the early chordates. The known ancestral chordates go back to the ostracoderms (page 376) of 450 million years ago. Then slowly the line evolved through stages of more advanced fishes, the primitive amphibians, the primitive reptiles, which gradually lost their reptilian characteristics and evolved those of the mammals.

Was man a mammal? Man is covered with hair, his young are nourished by the mother's mammary glands, his red blood cells are without a nucleus, a diaphragm extends across the cavity of his body. In these and many other ways he meets the criteria for being a mammal.

Linnaeus (pages 348-49) did not hesitate to place man in the order Primates. He did so a full century before Darwin's *On the Origin of Species*, so he was unaware of Darwin's hypothesis of evolution. Linnaeus classified organisms by their structural resemblances. It was his opinion that man bore more resemblances to the monkeys, apes, and other primates than to any other mammals. If these resemblances could be shown to be due to homologies (pages 352-53), then Darwin could speculate that modern man shared a common ancestor with the other primates at some remote time in the past. The only way to prove this would be to discover fossils that showed this evolution.

Recall that biologists in Darwin's time who were interested in the past history of man had no fossil record to study. The best they could do was to study the living primates, in the hope that these could throw light on what was surely one of the most interesting of all biological problems. This was a very indirect method but it had to suffice if there were no fossils to study.

The order Primates is large and includes many different species. Most of the characteristics used to define the order are details of bone and tooth structure, but some characteristics are more general and should be mentioned. Both the hands and the feet are rather primitive. This may come as a surprise to you, but stop for a moment and look at your hand—five fingers attached to a broad palm. This same basic structure was present in the first amphibians that invaded dry land. Think how unspecialized your hand is compared to the hand (wing) of a bird, the hand (wing) of a bat, the hand (flipper) of a whale, or the hand (hoof) of a horse—the last so modified in the course of evolution that it now has but a single finger.

This primitive hand of man has been one of the main reasons for his accomplishments. Later we will learn that one of the key events in man's evolution occurred when he began to make and use tools. How many of the animals with which you are familiar have hands that could make and use tools?

Other characteristics of the primates are possession of a clavicle (collarbone) and primitive molars (grinding teeth). In the living primates, the toes and fingers usually end in nails (rather than claws or hoofs). So far as the sense organs are concerned, the eyes become increasingly important in the more advanced primates. Correlated with this, the organs of smell and the associated areas in the brain become less important. This, in turn, results in a change in the shape of the skull. The area devoted to the nose becomes shortened, giving the primates, especially the advanced ones, a flat and almost human type of face. Last, but certainly not least, the primates are characterized by very large brains in proportion to their body size. The brain of a whale is only about 0.01 percent of its body weight. For man the value is 2 percent. Possibly this happy comparison should not be ruined—but the value for the capuchin (CAP·you·chin) monkey is 5 percent!

The more biologists continued to study the primates—including man—the more these were found to resemble one another. The resemblances often were slight between the lower primates and man. But in the case of the gorilla and chimpanzee, the resemblances often were striking. For example, it has recently been found that the hemoglobin of man and the hemoglobin of the gorilla differ in a single amino acid out of several hundred.

What biological conclusion could be drawn from this tremendous wealth of data? Such data could suggest the hypothesis that man must have shared a common ancestor with all of the primates a very long time ago, and that later he shared a common ancestor with the more advanced species.

Special attention was paid to these advanced primates. The gorilla and the chimpanzee were so much like man in general structure that the differences seemed trivial. The two other great apes, the orangutan and the gibbon, seemed less close in their resemblances to man. These observations suggested the hypothesis that man's closest relatives in the living world were the gorilla and the chimpanzee. If so, the three species must have had a common ancestor, and fossils, if found, would reveal some of the evolutionary interrelationships.

Thus began the quest for fossils that would tell man about his past. These fossils alone could indicate what *did* happen. Studies of living species of primates could only suggest what *might* have happened. Where and how should one look for his remote ancestors?

FOSSIL FINDS AND EMERGING MAN

A Dutch anatomist, Eugene Dubois (doo-BWAH), knew of fossil-rich strata in Java (an island of Indonesia). He became convinced that this would be a likely place to look for evidences of prehistoric man. In 1889, he resigned his position and took a government job in Java to be near the fossil site.

The Species *Homo erectus:* Java Man and Peking Man

The strata Dubois wanted to examine are thought to have been laid down by volcanoes about 700,000 years ago. In two seasons of searching along the banks of the Solo River, he unearthed a small piece of human jawbone, several teeth similar to those of apes, and a partial skull. A study of the fragment of the skull suggested that the original owner would have possessed a brain too big for an ape and too small for any known man (Figure 33-2). The next year Dubois located a fossil thighbone which was very straight. This was interesting because the great apes all have curved femurs, and do not walk fully erect. Man is the only truly erect primate, and his femur is nearly straight. These fossils from Java, therefore, seemed to be from a primate that lived long ago, walked like man, and had a brain smaller than modern man's but larger than the brain of an ape.

Dubois named the fossils *Pithecanthropus erectus* (pith·e·KAN·thro·pus e·REK·tus), commonly known today as the Java man. Thus Dubois thought that the fossils were different enough from the bones of modern man that they should be put in a different genus. In recent years biologists have thought it more accurate to put the Java fossils in the genus *Homo* and call them *Homo erectus.* These remains of Java Man were the first examples of *Homo erectus,* an extinct species of man that has since been found to have lived in other parts of Asia and in Africa and Europe.

In Dubois' time the arguments about his fossil discovery were bitter and far too often more emotional than scientific. Under tremendous pressure from arguments on both sides, Dubois finally disclaimed his interpretations of the fossils as human, locked up the specimens, and refused to let anyone study them. They remained unavailable until the 1920's when he was finally persuaded to exhibit them publicly. In recent years other specimens have been found in Java.

In 1924, a skull referred to as Peking man but also classified today as *Homo erectus* (Figure 33-2) was discovered in China. During the next twelve years parts of more than 40 other individuals similar to this one were dug up from a cave floor at Choukoutien (JO·ko-TYEN), near Peking, China. Earlier, in Java, a few crude flint tools had been found near the fossils of Java man. In China a whole array of chopping tools (rough stones chipped to an edge on one end, somewhat like a modern chisel) were found among the split bones and punctured skulls of Peking man and the animals he ate. Charcoal was found nearby, indicating that Peking man used fire.

Recently, a skull and three jaws closely resembling those of Java man were uncovered in Algeria and were given the distinctive title of Atlantic man. Supplementing the fossils of Java man and similar finds are widespread deposits of chipped pebbles and a few hand axes from the same period, indicating that tool-using men similar to Java man lived over many areas in Asia, Africa, and Europe. The fossils and other remains of *Homo erectus* place man on earth more than 500,000 years ago. Were these early men the oldest manlike primates?

The Southern Apes

On a June day in 1938, Gert Terblanche played on his school desk with "four of the most beautiful fossil teeth ever found" while waiting for the teacher to call a recess of his one-room school near Kromdraai (KROM·dry),

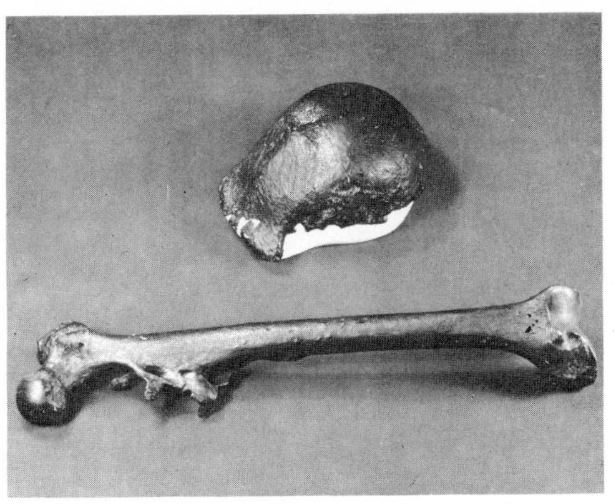

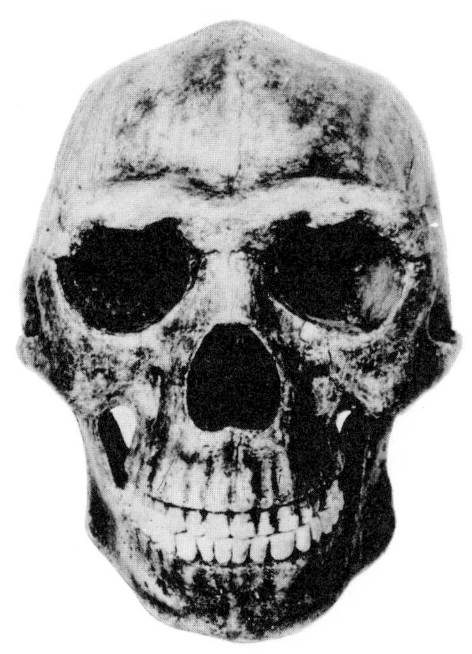
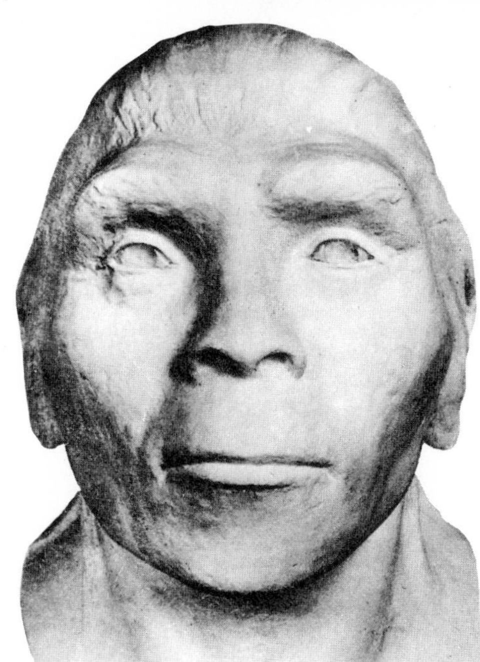

All photos from American Museum of Natural History

33–2 *Homo erectus*. The upper part of a skull and a thigh bone **(top left)** are two of the specimens originally found in Java. The bust **(top right)** suggests the probable appearance. **(Below)** A skull and a reconstruction of *Homo erectus* from China.

South Africa. He had knocked five teeth out of a rock on his father's farm with a hammer. One had been given to a Mr. Barlow, the foreman at a local quarry. It was not until his teacher interrupted the recess ball game, and introduced him to the great paleontologist Robert Broom, that Gert realized the teeth had any scientific importance.

Dr. Broom had been alerted by Mr. Barlow. He spent the afternoon telling Gert and his

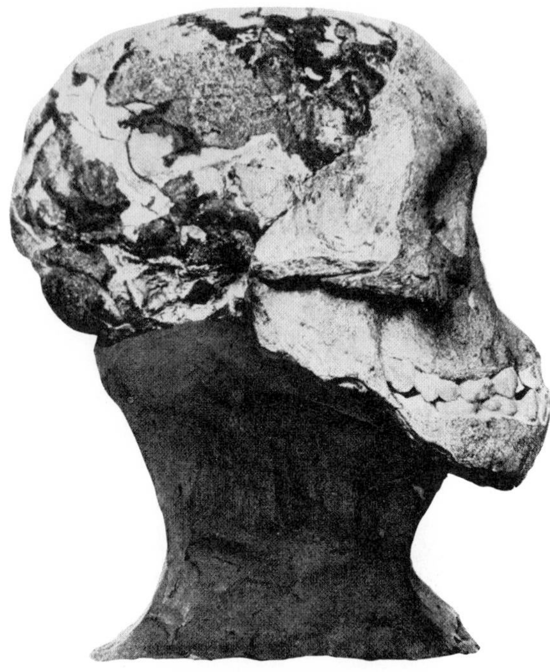

American Museum of Natural History

33–3 The fossil skull of an australopithecine child. Many fragments are missing, but the basic characteristics of the skull are clear. What is not too clear is how this "southern ape-man" is related to other types of early man or of pre-man.

classmates many fascinating tales about fossil men. When school was finally over, Gert somewhat reluctantly led the paleontologist up the hill to look for more fossils. Together they exhumed many teeth, a right lower jaw, and most of the left side of a fossil skull. These well-preserved fossils added greatly to the incomplete knowledge of the "southern apes," as newspapers had been calling the fossils previously collected in South Africa. This common name is no more than a translation of the scientific name first used for them—*Australopithecus* (aus·tray-loh·PITH·e·cuss).

Additional specimens, belonging to something like 100 individuals, have been collected since then by Robert Broom and Raymond Dart. Interestingly, some of the specimens of the southern apes were older than Java man, while others survived to be his contemporaries.

Except for features of the lower jaw and teeth, the skulls (Figure 33-3) of the australopithecines (aus·tray·loh·PITH·e·seenz) resemble those of modern apes. Their jaws, however, do not protrude as much, and the back of the skull does not have as large ridges for the attachment of muscles. The opening in the australopithecine skull, through which the brain and spinal cord connect, is farther forward than it is in apes. Also, the teeth and jaws resemble those of man more than those of apes. Moreover, the pelvic girdle is more broadly bucketshaped than those of apes. This evidence is interpreted to mean that the australopithecines walked erect.

The australopithecines are now placed with man in the family Hominidae. They stand at an *earlier* place than *Homo erectus* and modern man in time, although some of their fossils and those of the earliest known members of *Homo erectus* appear to overlap in time. In structure and features of appearance the australopithecines are *intermediate* between the great apes and *Homo*.

Since 1959 numerous fossils have been discovered by Dr. and Mrs. L. S. B. Leakey in Olduvai (OLE·duh·vye) Gorge in Tanganyika (tan·gan·YEE·ka). These include both australopithecines and some of the oldest known examples of fossils somewhat like Java man. The Leakeys have also discovered some of the most primitive tools of man. The fossils and the tools range in age as far back as almost 2,000,000 years. Some of the tools apparently were made by australopithecines, others later by men of the genus *Homo*. The remains are now being studied intensively to see what light they can shed on man's past. The presence of tools makes us suspect that their makers had some simple method of communication. This may have been by simple speech or even by hand signs. We cannot imagine how the young could learn from their elders to make even a simple tool, unless the parents could somehow find a way to instruct them.

In 1967 Professor Bryan Patterson of Harvard University discovered a still older fossil bone fragment from a member of the human family—a piece of the **humerus** (HEW·mer·us) bone of the upper arm (Figure 33-4). Careful dating of the ancient lava deposit in which the bone fragment was found places its age at 2,500,000 years ago, with a probable range of error of about 200,000 years or less. To date, this is the most ancient evidence of a member of the family Hominidae.

Tertiary Ancestors

The Cenozoic era, with two periods and a number of epochs, began some 63,000,000 years ago and includes the earliest fossil evidences of man's evolution from ancestral primates. We can represent this span of time as in the table at the upper right.

ERA	PERIOD AND EPOCH with approximate time since beginning	
CENOZOIC	**Quaternary Period**	**Recent** **Pleistocene** –2,500,000 years ago
	Tertiary Period	**Pliocene** –13,000,000 years ago
		Miocene –25,000,000 years ago
		Oligocene –36,000,000 years ago
		Eocene –58,000,000 years ago
		Paleocene –63,000,000 years ago

Many fossil remains of man are known from the various parts of the **Pleistocene** (PLYS·toe-seen) epoch. All the evidence, taken together, suggests that our toolmaking ancestors were

33–4 New evidence of early man. At the left, almost natural size, is a fragment of humerus believed to be the oldest fossil from the human family—2,500,000 years old. At the right, Professor Bryan Patterson, who discovered the fossil in Africa, compares it to a modern arm bone.

Harvard University News Office

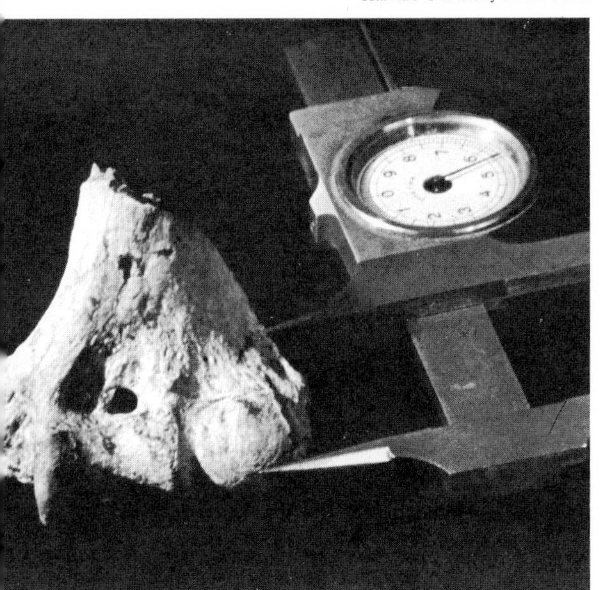

Harvard University News Office

already well along the evolutionary path to modern man by 2,000,000 or more years ago. The hypothetical common ancestor of man and the great apes would be still older, and therefore would have to be sought in older deposits. The Pliocene epoch, which immediately preceded the Pleistocene, covered a long period of about 12,000,000 years. During this time great evolutionary changes must have been occurring in pre-man. Fossils of *Ramapithecus* (ram·a·PITH·e·cuss) belong here. Although little has been found of them, they clearly were even more primitive than the australopithecines. From the partial evidence, they seem to be on the evolutionary line leading to man. Unfortunately there are so few fossils from the rocks of this epoch that the evolution of pre-man cannot be traced accurately.

The **Miocene** (MY·o·seen) epoch preceded the Pliocene. There are no remains from the rocks of this epoch that are even close to modern man. There are, however, fossils of *Dryopithecus* (dry·o·PITH·e·cuss) that some biologists regard as ancestral to the apes (Figure 33-5). Others insist that *Dryopithecus* is primitive enough to have come before the division between the hominid (man) and ape lines of descent. The exact position of *Dryopithecus* in the family tree is thus in question. Until we have more fossils of this and other Miocene **anthropoids** (AN·throw·poyds—manlike primates) the point of divergence of the hominid and ape lines will remain uncertain.

In our search for the history of our past among the deposits of the Pleistocene epoch and the earlier epochs of the Tertiary, we have found what Darwin predicted. There have been men more primitive than those living today. Still earlier fossils seem to represent a pre-*Homo* stage of evolution, and before these, fossils are being found that might represent a common ancestor of the evolutionary line leading to man and the line leading to the great apes. There is not yet enough material for biologists to do more than outline the evolution of man and the other primates. Many more fossils will have to be discovered before we have even a reasonably satisfactory account of the details of the evolution of the primates.

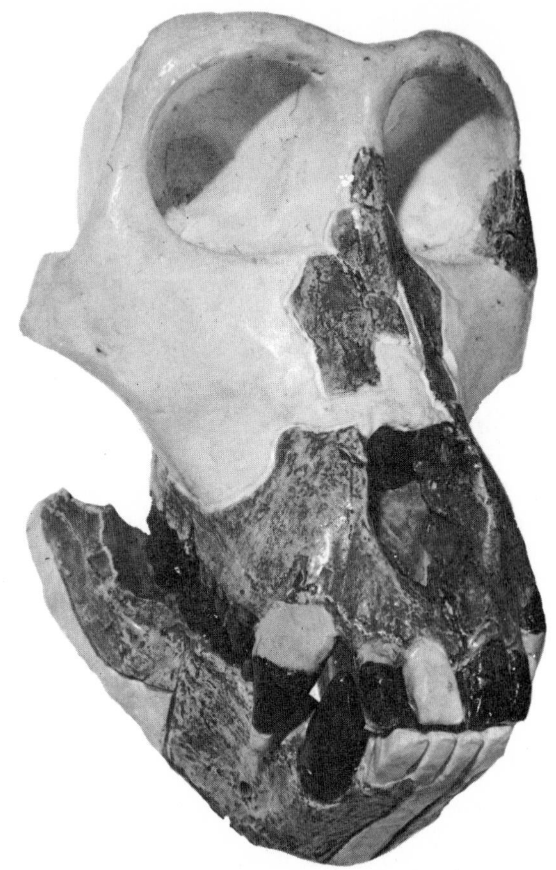

P. R. Pilbeam

33–5 A reconstruction of a skull of *Dryopithecus*. The gray and black portions are fossil bones and teeth; you can see that they represent only a small part of the skull. The white areas are reconstructions—a hypothesis for what the rest of the skull must have been like. How can so many missing parts be reconstructed in this way? How reliable are the results of these efforts?

Dating Man's Evolution

Fossils older than 30 million years can be dated fairly accurately by the uranium-lead method (Chapter 9, pages 192-93). Organic material as recent as a few thousand to not quite 40,000 years ago can be dated by the carbon-14 method. But dating fossils from the period in between has until recently been a problem. Man emerged more recently than 30 million years ago but earlier than 40,000 years ago. Neither uranium-lead nor carbon-14 dating methods will serve to cover this interesting time in his evolution. Fortunately, new methods that fill in the gap have been developed, including potassium-argon dating. This method is similar to the others but measures the decay of a radioactive isotope of potassium to argon and other products.

An additional guide to dates is available for the last 600,000 years. At least four times during this period, great glaciers have extended southward into the mid-latitudes of the Northern Hemisphere. Each time the glaciers retreated as the earth warmed up.

We know about these glacial changes through a careful study of the fossils (and rock itself) in the strata deposited during each glacial and interglacial period. Deposits from the glacial periods in southern Europe contain fossils of plants and animals that are characteristic of cold environments. The fossils of the interglacial periods are of plants and animals characteristic of warm environments.

MAN'S PAST RECONSTRUCTED

Man appeared only after hundreds of millions of years during which the other vertebrate and invertebrate animals evolved (see Chapter 19). You have considered the forces shaping the course of plant and animal evolution. There is every reason to believe that the evolution of man is a result of the continuing action of these same forces, principally mutation, recombination, natural selection, and isolation.

Early Mammals and the First Primates

Long before the dinosaurs disappeared from the surface of the earth, ancestors of mammals were evolving from the other reptiles. Very early, a line of small **insectivorous** (in·sec·TIV·o·rus) mammals, which we know today only from fossils, took to the trees. From them evolved the first primates. These creatures were enough like the hedgehogs and shrews of the present that we can assume that they had sensitive noses, ears that distinguished clearly between sounds of different pitch, and a rather fine sense of balance. Life in the trees must have encouraged them to rely upon the senses of sight and hearing rather than upon the sense of smell. Ground-living animals, by contrast, seem to profit more from their sense of smell than from good vision—especially if they live in the thickets or woods.

These ancient insectivores gave rise to one group of descendants, the **lemuroids** (LEM·yoo-roids), most of which retained less specialized grasping feet and hands. We suspect that they had bushy tails useful for balancing when leaping from branch to branch, much as a squirrel's tail helps him. We know these facts from the close correspondence between skeletons of fossil lemurs and those of lemurs living today (Figure 33-6) in the Malagasy (mal·a·GAS·ee) Republic (formerly Madagascar).

Fossils of different descendants of the ancient insectivores have flatter snouts and enlarged eyes. They demonstrate progress toward greater emphasis on vision and less on smell. This line of descent led to the **tarsiers** (TAR·see-ers). The shift in eye position from the sides of the head to the front (Figure 33-7) was of very great importance. It meant that objects could be seen by both eyes at once. This in turn made **stereoscopic** (stehr·ee·o·SKOP·ik) vision possible. In stereoscopic vision, the images from each of the two eyes are so blended that the brain is able to make accurate judgments of the relative distance of objects. Evolution toward stereoscopic vision gave the tarsiers a considerable advantage by helping them in judging distances as they leaped from tree to tree. Despite these gains, most of the tarsiers died out, leaving a single modern species in the East Indies (Figure 33-7) in comparison with numerous **Eocene** (EE·o·seen) species.

New York Zoological Society

33–6 A ring-tailed lemur. For its evolutionary relationship to other groups of living primates, see page 620 (Figure 33–10).

Further descendants of the primitive insectivore stock became specialized in other directions about 36 million years ago as the **Oligocene** (OL·ih·go·seen) epoch began. Fossils of these animals indicate the same reduced snout and increased reliance upon stereoscopic vision. The fingers and toes had nails. Some of this group became ancestral to today's **marmosets** (MAR·mo·zets) and to New World monkeys with **prehensile** (pre·HEN·sil) tails—that is, tails that grasp (Figure 33-8, left). Others evolved toward mankind and toward Old World monkeys with slender or stubby nonprehensile tails (Figure 33-8, right).

The Parting of the Way for Man and the Apes

Possibly as early as the Miocene, more than 15 million years ago, the ancestors of the apes and of man began evolving along separate lines. Both apparently evolved from upright terrestrial primates, probably from relatives of *Dryopithecus* (Figure 33-5). The ancestors of today's great apes apparently returned to the trees—if they had ever really left. Swinging through the trees on arms that grasped the branches became a selective factor of increasing importance. Apes' arms became even stronger, well muscled, and longer—eventually becoming longer than their legs (Figure 33-9).

33–7 A tarsier. Only one species survives today, despite the possession of characteristics that have helped make other primates successful.

New York Zoological Society

New York Zoological Society

Carl Frank from Photo Researchers

33–8 New and Old World monkeys. **(Left)** A long, grasping tail, covered with hair to the tip, characterizes most New World monkeys. They are native to South America. **(Right)** Slender or shorter tails characterize Old World monkeys. The baboon you see is promoting, if unintentionally, an interest in the capital of Kenya in East Africa.

While the apes ranged among the trees and developed sharply crested teeth and long arms, the human family evolved as upright ground animals. Human types progressively developed longer and straighter legs, with feet for striding instead of shuffling. Prehensile use of the big toe tended to disappear. The early pre-men retained, however, their relatively acute mammalian hearing and excellent three-dimensional vision. Their grasping hands, freed for new uses, were served by an enlarging cerebrum. Presumably their upright position was served by the evolution of a double-curved backbone and a broad, basin-shaped pelvic girdle, upon which the trunk of the body balanced easily.

An additional evolutionary change that occurred in pre-man's skull allowed him to assume a truly erect posture. The hole through which the brain connects with the spinal cord gradually shifted underneath the cranial cavity, toward the jaw. This allowed him to look forward while his back was vertical. Great apes look forward too, but only by leaning forward and slightly hunching the back.

These changes, completed within 15 million years of the present time, produced an upright primate able to move quickly along the ground. He could undoubtedly focus his eyes on objects he held and manipulated in his pliant hands. Pre-man, if not man the thinker, had arrived.

Claude Schoepf

Russ Kinne from Photo Researchers

Ylla from Rapho-Guillumette

Ylla from Rapho-Guillumette

A synopsis of our discussion of primate evolution is shown in Figure 33-10.

Homo erectus

The first animals to which the name *man* is now definitely assigned were those now known as *Homo erectus,* first discovered in Java. Some scientists would also classify the tool-using australopithecines as men. Early men are now known to have been widely distributed in Asia, Europe, and Africa during Pleistocene time. *Homo erectus* stood upright, to a height of five feet or more. The brain was about midway in size between the brain of the australopithecines and the brain of modern man (see the table at the right). The forehead was low, usually with pronounced brow ridges above the eyes. The jaws protruded (forward), but below the lower jaw was little or no bony chin. *Homo erectus* used fire, made crude stone tools, and had a crude culture.

Average Cranial Capacities of Apes and Men

Name of Living or Fossil Primate	*Cranial Capacity*[1] (in cubic centimeters)
Modern apes	
Gibbon	100 cc
Orangutan	395 cc
Chimpanzee	400 cc
Gorilla	510 cc
Australopithecines	600 cc
Early men	
Java man	870 cc
Peking man	1050 cc
Neanderthal man	1450 cc
Modern men	
Cro-Magnon man	1660 cc
Living man	1450 cc

[1] Average for males. The average for females is somewhat less.

Neanderthal Man

In late Pleistocene time, just before the beginning of the last glacial advance, Neanderthal man (Figure 33-1) appeared in Eurasia and northern Africa. He was rather short, heavily built, and exceedingly strong. Like most specimens we know of *Homo erectus*, he had heavy brow ridges above the eyes, with protruding jaws, little chin, and a sloping forehead. He gives the impression of having been rather brutish. Yet Neanderthal man had a large brain, made excellent flint tools, and buried his dead with considerable ceremony. Biologists now believe that Neanderthal man should be included with all modern men in the same species, *Homo sapiens*. Neanderthal man may not have been the first *Homo sapiens*. There is increasing evidence that *Homo sapiens* may have evolved much earlier, even when *Homo erectus* was still alive.

During the last glaciation, perhaps 50,000 years ago, Neanderthal man disappeared. Various theories have been advanced to account for his extinction. It seems likely that he was overwhelmed and replaced by other races of *Homo sapiens* that were very similar to ourselves—men who came out of the east. Perhaps the Neanderthals may have intermated with the newcomers; or perhaps they perished or were exterminated because of their inability to compete with a culturally more advanced type of man, with better tools and weapons.

33–9 (Facing page) The four living types of great apes. The gorilla **(upper left)** and the chimpanzee **(upper right)** both are native to Africa. The orangutan **(lower left)** is native to the East Indies, and the gibbon **(lower right)** is native to southeast Asia and the East Indies. All are found in the Old World. Do the observations that all the great apes live in the tropics, and that none lives in the New World, suggest to you a hypothesis for where early man may have evolved and lived?

33-10 A SUMMARY OF THE EVOLUTION OF PRIMATES

Epoch	Prosimians	Monkeys	Apes and hominids
Recent	Tree shrew, Lemur, Tarsier	New world monkeys, Old world monkeys	Apes, Man
11 thousand years ago			
Pleistocene			
2.5 million years ago			
Pliocene			
13 million years ago			
Miocene			
25 million years ago			
Oligocene			
36 million years ago			
Eocene			
58 million years ago			
Paleocene	Ancestral tree-dwelling insectivores		
63 million years ago			

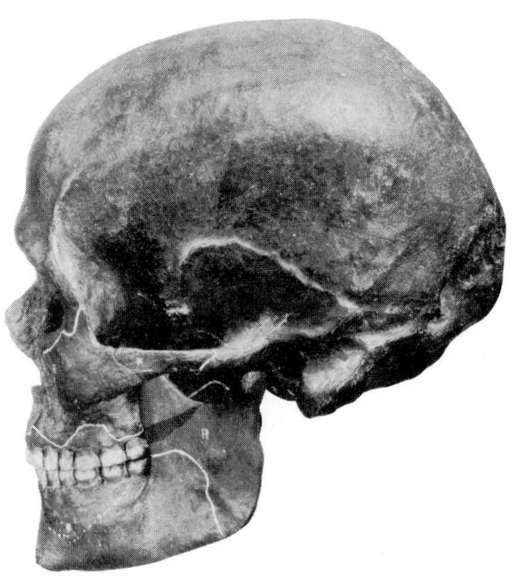

Both photos from American Museum of Natural History

33–11 A skull of Cro-Magnon man **(left)** and an attempt to portray his appearance. Cro-Magnon man was of our species, *Homo sapiens*. He differed from living man in being larger in average size. He made beautiful tools, was a skillful hunter, and left us some remarkable paintings (Figure 33–12).

Cro-Magnon Man

The successors to Neanderthal man were another variety of *Homo sapiens*, known as **Cro-Magnon** (kroh·MAN·yon – Figure 33-11). Theirs was the peak of Stone Age Culture. They lived in a world inhabited by woolly mammoths, woolly rhinoceroses, cave bears, wolves, bison, reindeer, wild horses, and other large mammals. They drew superb pictures of these animals deep within the caves of southern France and northern Spain (Figure 33-12). They carved tools and ornaments from ivory, and manufactured finely chipped stone arrow and spear points. They were vigorous, intelligent people of large stature.

During most of Pleistocene time, man shared the earth with many large mammals. To a Stone Age hunter, life was indeed uncertain, for he had to struggle with these large animals for his place on the earth. About 8,000 or 10,000 years ago there was a worldwide extinction of many of the large mammals that so characterized the Pleistocene epoch. The reasons for this extinction are obscure, but whatever may have been the causes of the late Pleistocene disappearance of large mammals, the event must have had considerable effect upon the cultural evolution of man.

TOOLS AND CULTURE

We know that the attainment of an upright position predated the use of tools. We also have some evidence that the use of tools began in men with rather small brains. Probably the development of tools and culture, and further development of the brain, proceeded simultaneously. Perhaps each reinforced the other.

When tools were first developed, those men with the more efficient brains were able to use their tools more effectively than others, in hunting and in protecting themselves. They prevailed over men of lesser capabilities—and developed still better tools. This, too, is natural selection. Man's way of life improved, and his level of culture gradually rose. As the process repeated itself, the progressive increase in human brain size came as a product of evolution through natural selection. It contributed toward greater mental efficiency, invention of superior tools, a higher level of culture, and selection of people with still more advanced brains.

For evidence of the earliest cultural developments of mankind, we must rely upon fossil remains of his food and his discarded tools. It seems clear that early man was a hunter and a meat eater. In the cave near Peking where remains of *Homo erectus* occur, there are split bones and skulls of many wild animals and of man as well. They are associated with the remains of fire pits. Charred bones suggest that man had already learned to cook meat, perhaps to make it easier to chew.

The early tools were relatively simple. Gradually man, in his evolution, improved on the crudely flaked pebbles of the australopithecines and the chipped flints and stone tools of early men in Africa and Europe (and later, in America). As man's tools improved, he no doubt hunted more efficiently (Figure 33-13).

Rapid improvement in tools during the last advance of the continental glaciers shows that

33–12 The dawn of painting. Caves in France and Spain contain examples of the oldest known paintings, done by Cro-Magnon man as early as 20,000 years or more ago. Many of the animals portrayed no longer are found in Europe. Can you suggest why?

The Louvre

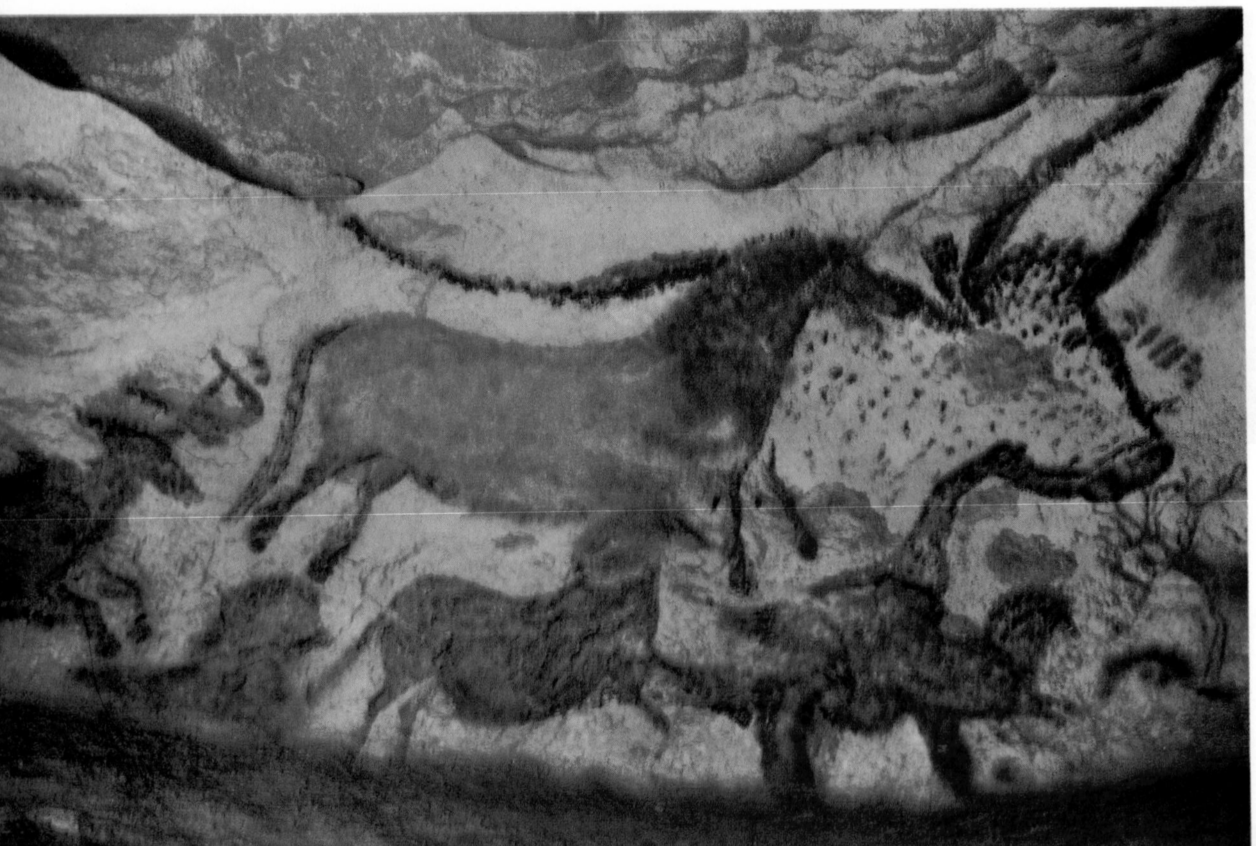

J. T. Robinson, upper right; all others, British Museum

33–13 The dawn of toolmaking. **(Upper left)** These chopping tools are crudely chipped pebbles. Dr. and Mrs. L. S. B. Leakey excavated them from Bed I (lower, older deposits) of Olduvai Gorge in East Africa. They may be more than 1,500,000 years old. **(Upper right)** This rare handaxe and a chopper also are among the oldest known tools. They were excavated from Sterkfontein in South Africa by Dr. J. T. Robinson of the University of Wisconsin. **(Middle left)** Three later handaxes from Bed II of Olduvai Gorge are compared with the more advanced tools of Neanderthal man—handaxes, hide scrapers, and pointed hunting tools **(middle right** and **lower views).**

modern men were highly inventive. Among these tools is a large variety of long flint blades of triangular cross section. They were made by splitting off one edge from a squared block of flint, then chipping and pressure-flaking to shape a useful and often beautiful tool. Blades of other shapes presumably served as knives, scrapers, borers, and spear points. Since huge piles of bones from mammoths, bison, and horses of this time have been found, men are assumed to have hunted these animals, perhaps making seasonal drives for meat. As men gained some control over nature, human social organization became both more complex and more efficient. Presumably language grew more useful, too.

Bone tools dating to between 10,000 and 6,000 years ago indicate that *Homo sapiens* had devised clothes and learned new skills in food gathering. We do not know exactly when this occurred, but it began much earlier than the known bone tools themselves indicate, for a frozen hunter of more than 30,000 years ago in Northern Siberia was found ceremonially buried in a well-stitched suit of animal hides. From a later time, we have found such bone tools as pins, needles with eyes, spool-shaped buttons, spear throwers, fishhooks, and arrow-straighteners somewhat similar to those used by Eskimos today.

Primitive man may have begun to support specialists in tool-making and cave-painting (Figure 33-12). Engravings and paintings from this period cover the walls of more than 60 caves in Spain alone. Tools and sacred objects placed in graves, both in the Old and New Worlds, suggest that man believed in a life after death.

CONCLUDING REMARKS—THE NATURE OF MAN TODAY

Scientists who specialize in studying man of recent times are known as **anthropologists** (an·thro·POL·o·jists). They believe that a long history of comparative isolation, extending back perhaps 25,000 years, is responsible for the measurable differences between native peoples today in different geographic localities. All men can be classified, in a rough way, into such groups as the Negroid, Mongoloid, and Caucasoid races. But anthropologists recognize that each of the features by which people might be so classified show tremendous variation within any given population.

In Africa, the East Indies, and Australia, the native population today has a high proportion of dark-skinned people. In Europe, the majority have light skin color. In eastern Asia, the greatest numbers have a skin shade between fair and dark. But many south European "whites" have darker skins than some of the lighter complexioned African "blacks." Often there is considerable diversity of skin color among the children even of one pair of parents.

Similarly, many Oriental people have "slanted" eyes because of a slight difference in the distribution of fat above the lids. When the eyes are open, the upper lids disappear under overhanging folds (Figure 33-14). Some Western people have similar folds, and some Orientals do not.

The effects of prolonged geographical isolation and inbreeding can still be seen in some parts of the world. All South American Indians, for example, have blood type O; Australian aborigines have about 49 percent O, 48 percent B, 2 percent A, and 1 percent AB. Similar differences are evident in the incidence of the sickle-cell trait (Chapter 8, pages 168-69) or the relative numbers of people in isolated groups afflicted with buck teeth.

Despite the fact that we can divide *Homo sapiens* into races on the basis of percentage differences of many inheritable traits, the different members of the human species are still much more alike than they are different. All possess strictly comparable organs and physical characteristics, and remarkable uniformity in most chemical characteristics. All racial types are known to be completely interfertile, and persons of mixed racial ancestry are in their turn fully fertile. They reveal no evidence of any

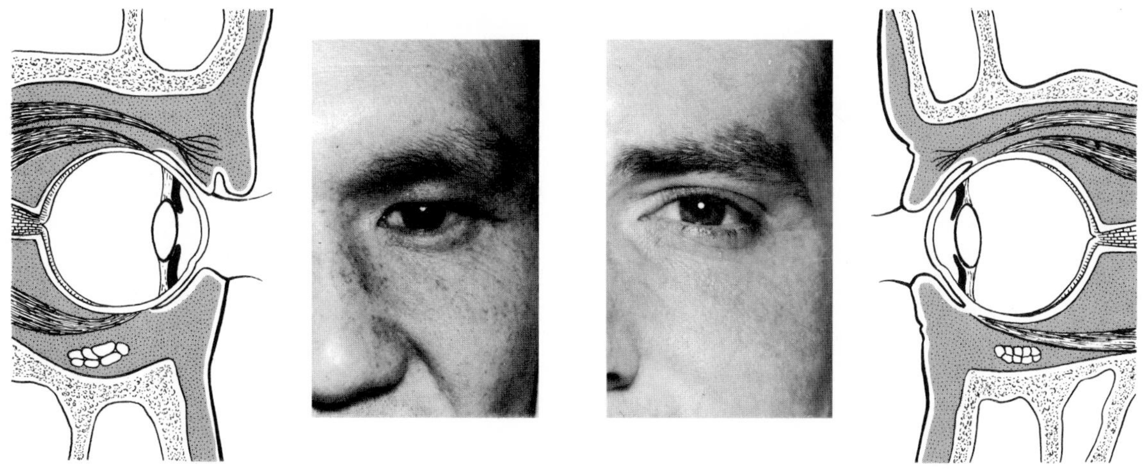

33–14 A comparison of the appearance of Mongoloid **(left)** and Caucasoid **(right)** eyes. The superficial difference is due to distribution of fat above the eyes. The skin hangs down over the upper eyelid at the left, but not at the right.

biological lack of harmony among their traits. By biological criteria, all men living today are of one species.

Anthropologists who study cultures of men of different backgrounds from ourselves—Indian tribes, native tribes of Australia, New Guinea, and other remote regions—agree that people who have been brought up in completely different surroundings, with cultural traditions very different from ours, can think and behave so differently from ourselves that many of us would consider them to have basically different human natures. Nevertheless, if a small baby is moved from his place of birth to a very different environment, he develops ways of thought and an outlook on the world that comes from the society in which he is brought up, rather than the culture of his parents. These facts have led many scientists to believe that differences in human nature, while affected by both physical environment and heredity, are nevertheless most strongly influenced by the physical environment—culture and tradition. In short, we are all modern men, as our ancestors apparently have been for hundreds of thousands of years.

GUIDE QUESTIONS AND PROBLEMS

1. What evidence and data support a history of evolution for man, as for other organisms?
2. Of what possible significance is the fact that hemoglobin in the blood of man and in the blood of gorillas differs in only a single amino acid out of several hundred? Try to estimate the biochemical probability that the two molecules could have originated independently of one another in separate lines of ancestry.
3. With a few exceptions, the older the hominid fossil, the smaller the brain size as indicated by fossil bones of the skull. Yet brain size, even today, does not correlate closely with intelligence. With these facts in mind, why would you consider the discovery of tools and their relationship to fossils of primitive hominids as especially important in interpreting whether the fossil hominids were men?
4. The age of the earliest known men is variously estimated from as little as 750,000 years ago to as much as 2,500,000 years ago. All of the biologists who make these estimates have access to the same fossil discoveries dating back as far as 2,500,000 years. Why does the difference of opinion occur, and what eventually may resolve it?

5. Why is there uncertainty about the time when the "manlike" and the "apelike" types of primates diverged in their evolution?
6. What reasons would you offer to criticize or support the decision of scientists to concentrate the search for man's ancestors in Africa and other parts of the Old World, rather than, say, in North America?
7. What is the justification for reconstructing a whole animal from the fossil bones of only parts of the skeleton?
8. Some who are unfamiliar with the theory or the evidence of evolution keep alive a misconception that scientists believe "man has descended from monkeys or apes." All three groups of primates alluded to by the statement are living primates rather than ancestral ones. How would you clarify the evidence and correct the statement?
9. What seems to be the biological basis for what are known as "racial differences" among men today? What seems to be the cultural basis for some of these differences? Which is the greater influence?
10. What observations suggest to you that men today are all of one species?

RELATED READING

Books

For more information about the evolution of man . . .

Coon, C. S., *The Story of Man,* Second Edition Revised, Knopf, New York, 1962.

Dart, Raymond, and D. Craig, *Adventures with the Missing Link,* Harper and Row, New York, 1959.

Dobzhansky, Theodosius, *Heredity and Evolution in Human Populations*, Revised Edition, Atheneum, 1965 (paperback).

Magazines

Howells, William W., "The Distribution of Man," *Scientific American,* Volume 203 (September 1960), page 112.

Napier, John, "The Evolution of the Hand," *Scientific American,* Volume 207 (December 1962), page 56.

Napier, John, "The Antiquity of Human Walking," *Scientific American,* Volume 216 (April 1967), page 56.

Simons, Elwyn L., "The Early Relatives of Man," *Scientific American,* Volume 211 (July 1964), page 50.

34

The Cultural Evolution of Man

Sometime between 50,000 and 75,000 years ago, the gradually evolving populations of mankind reached the stage at which they were biologically like ourselves. If we could dress some of our ancestors of that time in modern clothes and parade them down the streets of our cities, people would probably not recognize them as different.

By 25,000 years ago, all men on the earth resembled one or another of the modern races of man. The thin, delicate, beautifully sculptured arrow and spear points that these men made out of hard flint required the greatest of skill and craftsmanship (Figure 34-1). Some of these early men entered the caves of southern Europe, and by the light of smoky torches, painted pictures of horses, mammoths, and oxen that show a high degree of artistry (Figure 33-12). Engravings and paintings from this period cover the walls of more than 60 caves in Spain alone, as you read in Chapter 33. Furthermore, these men buried their dead in carefully constructed graves, and surrounded the corpses with spears, bows and arrows, ornaments, and other implements that they presumably thought would be useful to the dead in an afterlife.

We can be sure, therefore, that by at least 25,000 years ago, men had acquired some of the abilities that make modern life possible. These are the abilities to use tools; to talk and teach so that the young generation can profit from the experiences of the elders; to work together and respect wise, intelligent leadership; and to

34–1 The Hindsgavl dagger. Anthropologists know how it was made and have practiced the technique, but no one has matched the beauty of this example. It began as a piece of freshly quarried flint from which channel flakes were struck lengthwise to produce a long, narrow form. A prominent ridge extending down the middle of each face from top to bottom was left between the broad, long flakes that were removed. This appearance changed, however, because the final flaking was done *across* the face of the point, taking away the long, central ridge and leaving many smaller ridges running the opposite direction, back and forth across the blade. One portion of the original long ridge was preserved, in the thicker stem near the bottom of the photograph. You can spot it from its decoration with tiny, leaflike pressure-flaking. Delicate flaking and grinding around the edges completed a beautiful work of art from the late Stone Age.

Australian News and Information Bureau

34–2 The aborigines of Australia live in a harsh environment where food and water are often scarce and the climate severe. The boomerang and the spear are their principal weapons for hunting.

look into the future toward a better life. The fruits of these abilities have become the story of mankind.

THE GREAT TRANSITION

In a great many ways, the men of 25,000 years ago were still at the mercy of their environment. They got their food by hunting game and gathering wild fruits, seeds, nuts, and roots. If game was scarce, or if a drought cut down the supply of wild food plants, men starved. They had to protect themselves from lions, tigers, and other carnivores, and from the large herbivorous mammals such as mastodons and mammoths.

Since these primitive people could talk to each other, they may have had elaborate religious ceremonies. Even today the Australian **aborigines** (ab·o·RIJ·ih·neez) and the African Bushmen, who live as food gatherers, practice complex rituals. The culture of each group includes music, a rich vocabulary of spoken literature, and belief in a supernatural power.

Remnants of the Past: Hunting and Food-gathering Peoples

Anthropologists have studied men who live today in primitive social and economic states in the hope of learning about the life of prehistoric man. The Australian aborigines and the African Bushmen have been studied extensively. It comes as no surprise that their knowledge of nature is very extensive. Both these groups of people have detailed knowledge of the plants and animals they eat. They know about seasonal fluctuations in winds, in temperature, and in humidity; about tidal changes when they live by the sea; and about the movement of planets in the sky, as well as the phases of the

34–3 The art of the Australian aborigines is highly stylized and often abstract, resembling the work of many modern European and American artists. These paintings of fish and turtles are on bark.

Australian News and Information Bureau

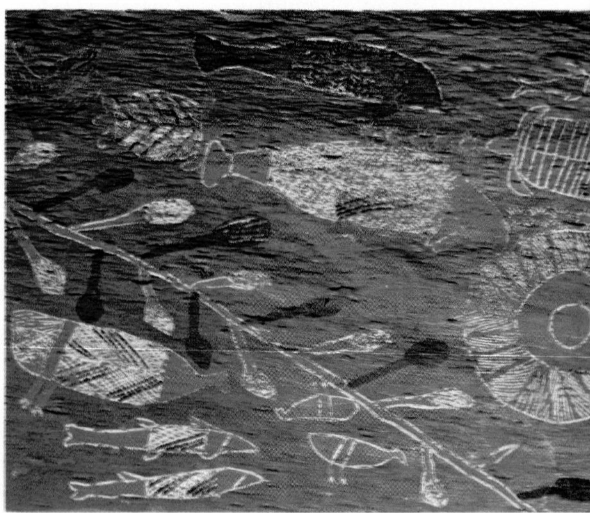

Laurence K. Marshall

34–4 A family group of African Bushmen of the Kalahari Desert. Like the hunting and foodgathering peoples of 10,000 to 25,000 years ago, they are nomadic. They live in small bands, gathering roots and tsama melons and hunting animals for food.

moon. This knowledge is intricately woven into living habits and is needed for survival.

In their use of the parts of kangaroos, the Australian aborigines (Figure 34-2) demonstrate how fully they exploit their environment. They bind their spears with its sinews, eat its flesh, and make tools and pins from its bones. Its fat is mixed with red ochre to make cosmetics. Paint is made by blending the kangaroo's blood with charcoal. (A bark painting appears in Figure 34-3.) The kangaroo's teeth and claws are strung as beads.

The Bushmen of the great Kalahari Desert (Figure 34-4) have devised a comparable number of uses for the tsama (SAH·muh) melon. The pulp of the melon is used for food. It yields water for quenching thirst and for boiling meat. Splinters from shoulder blades of the gemsbok (GEMZ·bok) antelope are thrust into the green tsama melons. This softens the bone splinters so that they can be carved into arrow points. The melon seeds are roasted and eaten, or ground into flour for cakes. Children bait mousetraps with the seeds. The dried rinds are used as mixing bowls, cooking pots, and dishes from which to eat. The rinds are filled with urine into which hides are put to be cured. Children use the dried rinds as toys, drums, and targets. Adults use them as resonators by holding them against musical instruments.

Undoubtedly the earlier hunters and food gatherers of 10,000 to 25,000 years ago had a similar knowledge of their environment and made a comparable use of materials in it. They probably cooked their food in open fires or in huge pits, as do many tribes of modern times. And they may have used forest or grass fires to drive game animals into places where they could be captured. Because game and edible plants became scarce from time to time, these ancient men could not always live a settled life in villages, but often had to be moving in search of food.

The Dawn of Agriculture

The conditions that made a settled life possible, and laid the groundwork for the rise of civilization, were the cultivation of plants and the domestication of animals. We believe that this happened some time between 10,000 and 7,000 years ago. The remains of men who, according to the radiocarbon method of dating, are more than 10,000 years old are associated only with hunting tools, remains of wild plants, and implements for preparing such plants for food. More recent remains begin to include hulls of grains related to modern wheat and barley, as well as such tools as sickles, which would be useful in harvesting grains. The dates given for the beginning of agriculture should be regarded as estimates only. Many of the plants and other items that could tell us about early culture are fragile and only rarely leave traces. You can guess, for example, how difficult it would be to study the history of clothing; only the fortunate discovery of a Siberian hunter frozen in his grave over 30,000 years ago has confirmed that neatly sewn and tailored garments are that old. Changes in our estimated dates for agriculture and for domestication of animals may also occur, with new evidence.

We who take agriculture for granted can hardly imagine how many skills had to be learned before men could raise sufficient crops to support themselves. To work with seed crops, men had first to learn which seeds could be saved and which would grow quickly into mature plants. Then they had to learn how to clear the ground, and how to dig it up or plow it to gain a loose, well-aerated soil. Next they had to learn *when* to plant to avoid freezes and drought, which would kill the young seedlings. But they could not plant too late if they hoped to get a ripened crop before the killing droughts or the frost of a later season.

During the long months when the crop was growing and ripening, these early men had to learn how to keep out destructive animals such as wild cattle, birds, and insect pests. They also had to defend their crops at all times from tribes who had not yet started to learn about agriculture, but were willing and ready to raid the fields of those who had. Finally, they had to learn how to harvest the crop quickly and store it in an edible condition for the winter months.

The Origins of Cultivated Plants

These early men learned not only how to cultivate wild plants but also to improve them. This involved conscious, artificial selection for characteristics that are very different from the traits that fit plants to survive in the wild. If the seeds were to be eaten, plants were selected with as large and as many seeds as could be found. Such seeds contain more stored food than the seedlings actually need, and are so heavy that they cannot easily be dispersed by natural means. *Natural selection* does not favor them, but *artificial selection* by man does.

The early cultivators had to rid their plants of a characteristic that is found in all wild, seed-bearing annual plants. This is the tendency for the seeds to break away from the plant as soon as they are ripe. In all of the wild grasses related to wheat, barley, rice, and other grains, the seed head shatters or breaks up into pieces containing one or two seeds when the seeds have become ripe. This trait is of great advantage to the plant in seed dispersal. It would be disadvantageous to man, since the seeds might fall off and be lost before they could be collected. Early man was able to select strains of cultivated grains with stiff seed heads that hold their seeds until they can be harvested.

Studies in genetics have shown that the differences between shattering and nonshattering seed heads are usually determined by one or two pairs of alleles. Hence the most important step in the evolution of cultivated cereals from the wild ancestral grasses was taken when the early cultivators found and selected plants having alleles for stiff seed heads.

Another difference of selection is that in the wild plants the hulls stick more closely to the grains than in cultivated varieties. The seeds of the wild plants are closely protected until they are ready to germinate. Man, on the other hand, wants his grain free of hulls. Hence mutations that cause the grains to fall out of the hulls easily during the threshing process are desirable. Plants carrying these mutations were long ago selected by man from among the many cereal species.

As a result of many generations of artificial selection for the kinds of characteristics mentioned above, our cultivated food plants have come to differ from their wild relatives in a large number of alleles. They are beautifully adapted to serve our needs, but they cannot grow without man's help.

The Domestication of Animals

The domestication of wild animals also required time and patience. The wild relatives of many domestic animals, which in some instances belong to the same species, are noted for their intractability, savageness, and ferocity. This is particularly true of the Eurasian wildcat, wild cattle (now extinct), and wild boars, which are the ancestors of our domestic cats, cattle, and pigs. Genetic studies of wild and tame rats have shown that tameness is largely under the control of genes. All domestic animals differ genetically from their wild relatives.

The domestication of animals, therefore, must have involved much more than simply capturing animals and keeping them penned up. It is very unlikely that early men could have caught and handled the adults of these wild beasts. They probably began by raising the young animals. As they grew up, these wildlings often became too unruly to handle, but some of them undoubtedly were tame enough to keep and even breed in captivity. The first domestication of animals must have been brought about in some such fashion.

Beginnings of Village Life

At first glance, we seem to have introduced a dilemma—a question of how tribes of nomadic hunters could have spent enough time in one place to learn about agriculture and the domestication of a wide number of different animals. The hunters had to move from place to place in order to find enough game to keep themselves alive. But they could not find the time to learn cultivation of plants and domestication of animals until they were able to stay in one place. How, then, could they have learned these arts?

Recent observations of modern tribes, and of the remains of ancient settlements, have suggested one possible solution. Many of the Indians of California and elsewhere were very poor hunters and did not cultivate plants. They lived on the seashore or along lakes and rivers, and got most of their food by fishing or gathering shellfish. Fishhooks are among the tools found in the remains of some of the settlements that existed before the dawn of agriculture.

This suggests that some of the first people who settled down and lived in villages were fishermen. Those living on lakes had to stay on the same lake most of the time, because boats were difficult to build and could not easily be carried overland. Also, the supply of fish in those days was probably almost inexhaustible. Once a tribe had discovered a good place for fishing they could stay there indefinitely. This was particularly true in the tropics, where the supply of both seafood and edible plants was unusually large.

While the men were fishing, the women were probably hunting for edible seeds and roots. They brought the best kinds in large baskets and roasted the biggest roots with the fish, as do many of the South Sea Islanders today. After the meals, the fish bones and other refuse were discarded near the settlement, eventually forming large mounds. As the rains mixed these mounds of refuse with dirt, the growing mounds became loose, well-fertilized soil. The women probably threw some of the smaller, tougher roots onto these dumps, where they must have grown very well since they found an ideal soil texture, good fertilization, and little competition from other plants. From such accidents, people probably got the idea of purposely bringing in extra roots and planting them around the refuse heaps. The roots that grew to the largest size and had the best flavor could then have been broken into pieces, some for eating and some for planting. Agriculture may have begun in this way in some of the early settlements – possibly with the cultivation of tropical roots such as yams, taro, and sweet potatoes.

You will be sure to recognize this as a hypothesis, not fact. The change from hunting and food gathering to food production took place not once but probably many times – for the earliest villages both of the New and Old Worlds were isolated settlements. Furthermore, some were in areas where fishing could not be an important source of food. Different plants and animals were domesticated at widely different locations. Some of the domestications apparently took place almost simultaneously, before the news could have gotten around (even if there had been a means of communication). Migrating early peoples then influenced domestication as they moved to new locations.

In regions like the Middle East, parts of Africa, and the highlands of Mexico, the climate was more suited to grains than to tropical roots. The seedlings of wild grasses related to wheat and barley – or in the New World, corn – must have grown very well on refuse heaps in these dryer, cooler areas. We can imagine, then, that the cultivation of these grains, which is much more difficult than raising root crops in a tropical climate, may first have been tried by people who migrated out of the tropics. Perhaps they settled in such areas as western India, the Middle East, parts of China, and the highlands of Mexico, Central America, and the Andes. They may or may not already have been in the habit of cultivating root crops. If so, they turned to seed crops because the tropical root crops would not grow well in the new environment.

Or perhaps certain tribes discovered agriculture independently of the early tropical peoples, by learning how to domesticate wild grasses. For example, the American Indians who domesticated maize (corn) and the potato are not likely to have learned about agriculture from the Old World. They were descended from primitive hunters who made their way into North America long before the dawn of agriculture. At least some of them, in the highlands of south central Mexico, first were hunters, then plant gatherers (as game became scarcer?), then breeders of corn from its wild parental type. There is no evidence in this instance that they first settled in villages as fisherfolk, but rather that they settled down in one place because *that place was a very good one indeed* – a series of protecting natural caves, with edible wild plants and at least *some* game nearby.

Some of the oldest known villagelike settlements, which include evidence that plants were cultivated and animals were domesticated, have been found in Israel, northern Iraq, and other sites in the Middle East. They occur in the hills surrounding the great fertile valley of the Tigris (TY·gris) and Euphrates (yoo·FRAY·teez), which considerably later was the scene of the oldest known civilizations, We cannot be sure, however, that these were actually the oldest communities that practiced agriculture. They are the oldest discovered so far.

We are unlikely to find any remains of primitive communities that may have existed in such regions as eastern India, Burma, and Malaya. All organic material would long ago have decayed; the great rivers and torrential rains would have covered the stone tools with many feet of dirt and silt. Later people cultivating

34-5 THE GEOGRAPHIC ORIGINS OF SOME IMPORTANT DOMESTICATED PLANTS

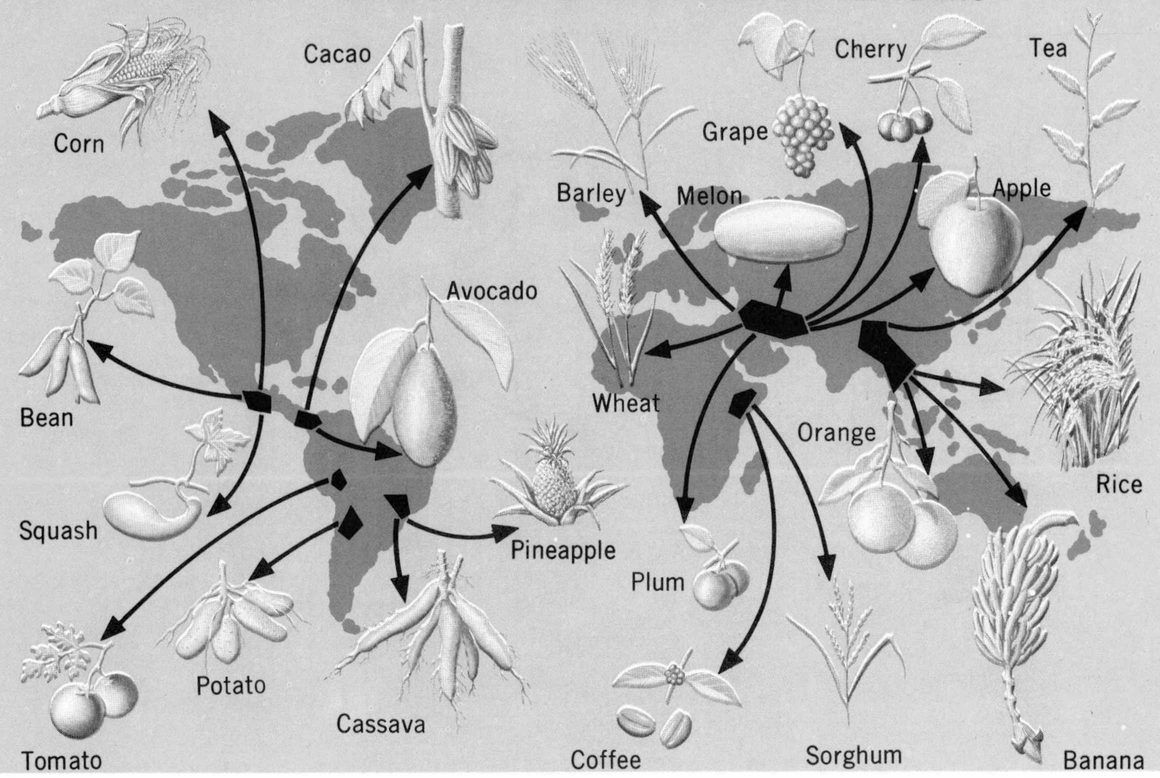

the same areas would long ago have destroyed any chance remnants, which might otherwise have survived.

Centers of Origin of Important Crops and Domestic Animals

Indirect evidence that agriculture appeared in other regions before it appeared in the Middle East is suggested by the probable origins of some of our cultivated plants and domestic animals. Evidence, chiefly from the distribution of wild relatives of these plants and animals, suggests that they arose in restricted parts of the earth and spread from these centers, either through being carried by migrating people or by trade between tribes.

Although many of these centers have been recognized, as few as four of them have probably contributed the great majority of man's most useful plants and animals. These are (1) tropical southeastern Asia; (2) temperate southwestern Asia; (3) subtropical or temperate Mexico and Central America; and (4) the central Andes of South America (Figures 34-5 and 34-6).

We do not know whether agriculture originated independently in each of these four centers, or whether the ideas of cultivating plants and of domesticating animals arose in one or two of them and were carried to the others. A final answer to this particular question will probably never be given.

Southeastern tropical Asia extends from eastern India to Burma. The cultivated plants that probably arose in this center of agriculture are rice, bananas, sugar cane, bamboo, and tropical root crops, particularly yams and taro. Here the first animals may have been domesticated.

34-6 THE GEOGRAPHIC ORIGINS OF SOME IMPORTANT DOMESTICATED ANIMALS

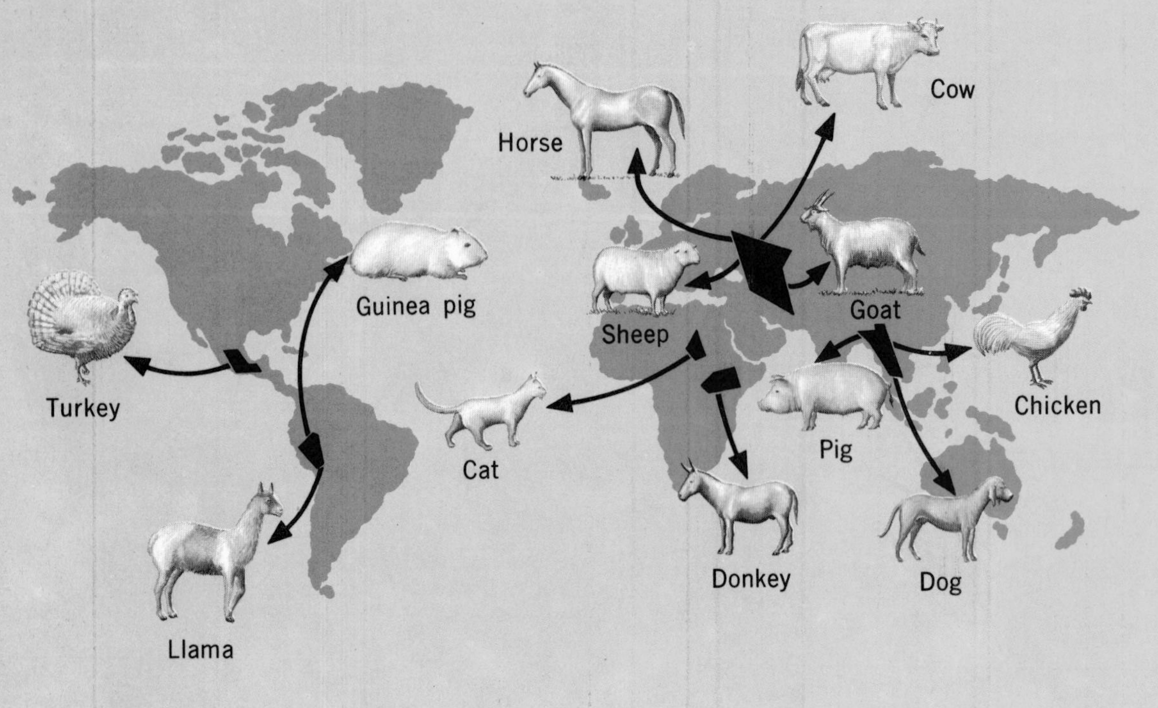

These were household animals: the dog, pig, and chicken. The pariah (puh·RY·uh) dogs of India and the wild dingo of Australia are more like mongrel domestic dogs than are any other doglike animals. They are probably descended from a jackal-like animal, which at some very early time learned that the refuse heaps of early village folk were filled with food. After they had come to be familiar sights about encampments, they were domesticated—perhaps because the puppies were taken for pets.

Wild pigs related to domestic ones are still to be found, from Europe through Asia to the islands of the Pacific. Both the living breeds of pigs and fossil bones of pigs found in association with early cultivators are more like the wild pigs of southeastern Asia than like other wild types. The modern wild pigs of that region still visit farms and villages and root in the plantings and the exposed refuse.

Chickens are clearly descended from jungle fowl of southeastern Asia.

The south*western* Asiatic center of cultivation extends from the hills of Israel northward to the mountains of eastern Turkey, Armenia, northern Iraq and northwestern Iran, and eastward to Afghanistan and Soviet Central Asia. This is the ancestral home of most of our familiar crops and farm animals. The wild ancestors of wheat, barley, rye, and oats are found here, as well as those of the forage plant alfalfa. Peas and flax also originated here, and probably muskmelons, cantaloupes, and their relatives. Apples, peaches, apricots, plums, grapes, almonds, and walnuts apparently were cultivated first either here or somewhere in the mountains of Asia farther to the east.

This center is also the place where our larger meat, milk, and draft animals were probably domesticated. Most likely the first of these were sheep and goats, since they could be more easily captured and tamed than could cattle and horses. At a time when game was abundant, the few animals that could have been raised probably contributed little to the people's supply of meat. Perhaps these animals were originally used for milk and wool, rather than meat.

Wild cattle, which were much larger and fiercer animals, were probably domesticated later, although their remains are found in the ruins of the earliest agricultural villages of the Middle East. Oxen, which are bulls castrated to render them docile, were the first draft animals. Some of the earliest records that we have show them pulling ceremonial carts. In this region the moon goddess was regularly worshiped. The resemblance of the cow's horns to the "horns" of a crescent moon is believed to have been one reason why cattle were regarded as sacred animals by many primitive peoples. It is entirely possible that at first the domestic cow was a "holy cow."

Another animal domesticated for doing work, the donkey, originated in northeastern Africa. Its popularity as a draft animal helped it spread quickly to the Middle East. Camels probably were domesticated in Arabia. This is uncertain, however, since the camel is the only domestic animal that at present has no living wild relatives. Horses were first domesticated in the Middle East or central Asia. They were the latest of all farm animals to be domesticated. The first tame horses known to us pulled war chariots in the early days of civilization. There is no evidence that horses were used for peaceful purposes as draft animals until later.

The only centers of cultivation in North America that have contributed many of our crop plants are highland Mexico and Central America. They appear to be the original home of maize (corn), beans, pumpkins, squashes, tobacco, and probably upland cotton. These crops were cultivated in the southwestern United States, in Central America, and in many parts of South America for thousands of years before Columbus. The only domestic animal of the New World that is of any general importance, the turkey, was probably first domesticated in Mexico.

Two other American centers may be as old as, or older than, the Mexican one. One is the northwest coast of South America, which contributed the sweet potato, the cocoa tree, and perhaps the pineapple. The other is the central Andes, from which came the potato and tomato.

Clothing

Next to food, probably nothing was more important to primitive man than clothing—except in the tropics. The early men of Europe undoubtedly made their clothing from skins of animals they killed. One may guess that early men were quite hairy, for until man learned to make clothes for himself hairiness would have had great importance in natural selection. By the time of Cro-Magnon man, within the past 35,000 or more years, the hides of animals were cut and neatly sewn together with thongs of rawhide, just as the Eskimos make their clothes today.

Clothing took an entirely new turn with the invention of weaving. The weaving of cloth is almost as old as agriculture, having started in Egypt and Mesopotamia (mess·up·a·TAY-mee·uh) with linen woven from the stiff, strong fibers of the stalks of flax plants. Wool and cotton fabrics were later inventions, since they both involved the more difficult problem of spinning short fibers into longer threads. The cotton that was first utilized was Old World cotton. It was derived from the hairy seeds of diploid species of cottons found in India and Africa. There are wild diploid cottons in North and South America, too. The cotton used for cotton fabrics woven by the Indians of Mexico, as well as for our modern cotton culture, is a polyploid. No one knows its origin. The data suggest that it began as a hybrid between an Old World and a New World species that doubled its chromosome number. If so, its origin is similar to that of the radish-and-cabbage fertile hybrid (Figure 32-11, page 602).

Was weaving invented quite independently in the Old and New Worlds? How did cotton come to be recognized on both continents as an ideal natural fiber? Wool, woven from the hair of domesticated llamas (LAH·muz) and alpacas (al-PAH·kuz), was made into cloth by the Indians of Peru. How and when did they learn to do this? No one knows, but one thing is sure: the inventiveness and ingenuity of the human species are not recent developments.

The Rise of Civilization

Civilized communities, with houses, public buildings, governments, laws, and written records, could not arise until people had solved the problem of staying in one place. This, in turn, meant having an assured supply of food. Thus is agriculture necessary for civilization. A second requirement for civilization is organization and division of labor. According to all of our records, the first organizations of this type began under the direction of a powerful leader. One way of gaining power over other men was by owning land. Hence, when land became the source of food through agriculture, the head of a landowning family could marry his sons and daughters into other landowning families, so that his eldest or most aggressive son could control more property, and so on. Fathers or leaders of large families thus became local "kings." About these rulers were grouped soldiers, priests, tradesmen, artisans, and others. By conquering neighboring people, they acquired large numbers of slaves who built cities, palaces, temples, and pyramids. Possibly in this way the first great civilizations were born in Egypt, Mesopotamia, and the Indus valley of western India.

CULTURAL EVOLUTION AND ITS FUTURE

You can see from this brief account that the change from a Stone Age existence to modern civilization took only a tiny fraction of the time needed for man to evolve from his apelike ancestors. Furthermore, if we list in order the various discoveries that gave man his increasing control over nature, we see that they have been made at a pace that has been increasing with terrifying rapidity.

If we bring the succession of changes down to a scale that we can more easily understand than the thousands of years actually involved, we can get a hint of the speed with which man's evolutionary line is racing toward unknown accomplishments. Suppose that we reduce to one "year" the last 730,000 years of time on the earth (Figure 34-7). In this case, each hypothetical "day" represents 2,000 actual years.

January 1 would find man's ancestors able to walk erect and use primitive tools, to hunt in bands and call to each other, but probably unable to talk in recognizable words. Speech evolved slowly, during January and February. Fire probably began to be used during March or April—for protection, for driving game to places where it could be killed, and finally for cooking. During the whole summer, man's ability to talk, make tools, and use fire was gradually improving. The size of his brain was increasing. The first men with a brain size comparable to ours, the Neanderthals, appeared about September 1. Burial in graves, indicating belief in an afterlife, appeared among the Neanderthals about December 6 of this hypothetical year.

By December 18, all people on earth, the Cro-Magnons and their contemporaries, resembled modern men in appearance. The beginnings of agriculture (Figure 34-8) came about December 26, while the entire span of known civilization occupies only the last three days, December 29 through 31. The birth of Christ would have been at about 12:30 A.M. on the morning of December 31. American Independence would date from 9:59 P.M. of the same day. The invention of the steam engine and the discovery of electricity would be noted at about the same time. Railroads, steamships, factories, and the telegraph would appear between 10:00 and 11:30; and the last half hour would see man con-

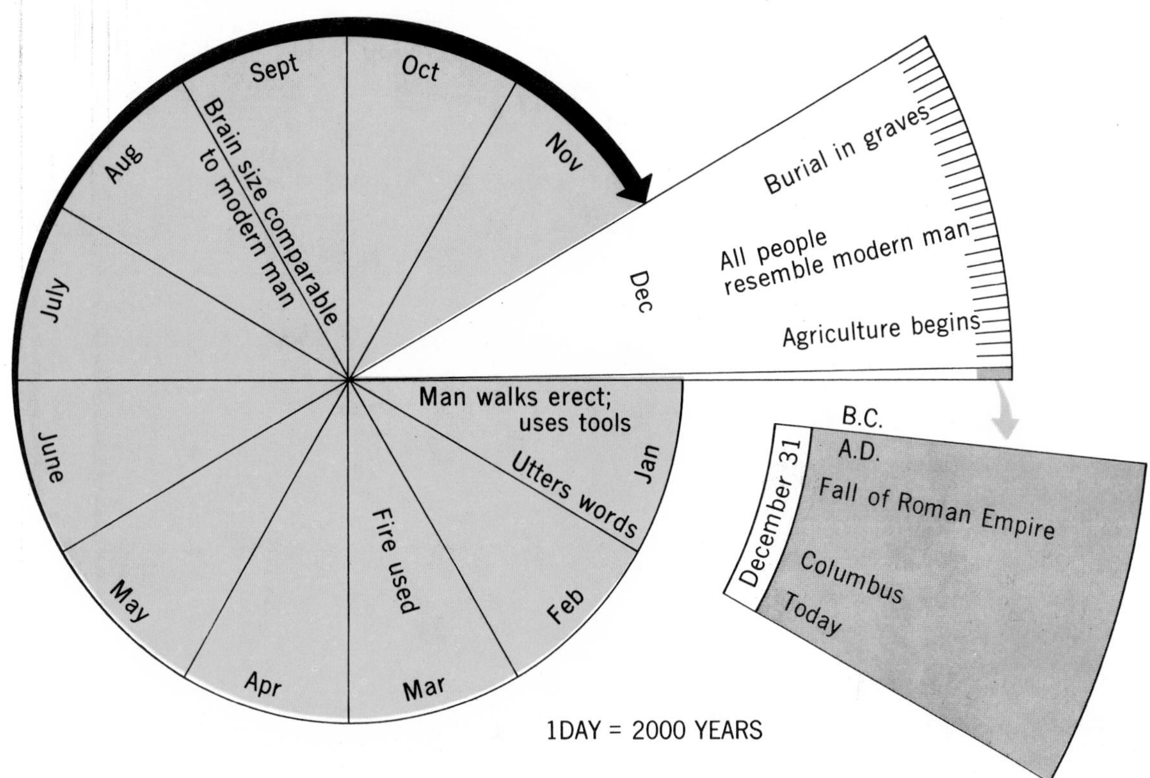

34–7 Roughly three quarters of a million years of human evolution on a one-year time scale. January 1 corresponds to 730,000 years ago, when man walked erect and used tools. On the time scale he is thought to have begun to speak late in January. He was still very primitive in early December and began agriculture late in the month. Civilization has been a very short period in human history.

quering the air, talking to anyone anywhere by radio, and learning how to destroy every living thing, including himself, if he wills.

We can measure evolution in terms of a change in the relationship of a species to its surroundings, as well as in terms of changes in the bodies of organisms. If we do, we find that human evolution, which went on for several hundreds of thousands of years at a fairly rapid pace compared to the evolution of other organisms, has in the last 25,000 years speeded up tremendously. No slackening of the pace is in sight for the future. The remarkable fact is that man has carried out this phenomenal transformation of his way of life without changing noticeably his physical makeup or his outward appearance. Man has discovered a new kind of evolution, *cultural evolution*, which has been independent of physical changes in his body. In order to have any idea of what the future has in store for mankind, we must understand fully the differences between cultural evolution and organic evolution.

The first new feature of cultural evolution is that it involves *cultural inheritance* in a manner analogous to physical heredity via the genes. We can think of heredity in the broadest sense as the transmission of traits from one generation to the next. In animals that cannot learn, this has to be done only by genes. The genes

Duncan Edwards from F.P.G.

34–8 Agriculture in ancient Egypt, as portrayed in a tomb painting. A crude plow is being drawn by two animals. Plows similar to this one are still used in some parts of the world. Can you identify any of the plants? What was the artist attempting to represent by the areas marked by zigzag lines? Thousands of years separate this scene from us, and also separated these Egyptians from the dawn of agriculture.

make an animal like its parents, quite independently of anything the parents may do. Once animals are able to learn, however, certain traits of behavior can be handed down from parents to offspring by the learning process itself.

We see the beginnings of this new kind of "heredity" in such animals as birds. The young of some birds learn how to fly by imitating their mothers. Careful studies of bird songs have shown that the birds of a species in one particular region have songs slightly different from the same species in a different region. This is because the young birds imitate the songs of their parents. But in birds and other animals, heredity by learning is much less important than heredity via the genes. Man is the only organism whose every act, from eating and sleeping to traveling over the earth and reproducing his kind, is greatly influenced by what he has learned. But we must not forget that his ability to learn is also a product of his genetic inheritance and his evolution.

A second feature of cultural evolution becomes clear when we think of man's relationship to his environment. About a century ago, Alfred Russel Wallace, the evolutionist who with Darwin proposed the Theory of Natural Selection (Chapter 31), remarked that while animals become adapted by changing themselves to fit the environment, man alters the environment to fit his needs. Animals become adapted to cold weather through natural selection of alleles that cause their bodies to become encased in fat or fur, or through selection of alleles that cause them to go to sleep in a warm shelter during the winter months. Man has become adapted to cold by learning how to make and wear warm clothes, and to build and heat houses. He provides a new environment for himself, like that of the tropics, in which he can function normally throughout the winter.

Birds and bats are able to fly because they have evolved great changes in their front limbs, backbones, and other structures. Man has succeeded in flying by building machines that carry him through the air much faster and farther than any bird.

A third feature of cultural evolution is that it has enabled man to modify his environment by learning to cooperate with his fellow man. Cooperation is highly developed in many societies of animals. The life in anthills and beehives provides familiar examples. But the individuals of these societies have instincts for cooperation given them by the action of their genes. They do not have to learn how to work together. Man must be *taught* to cooperate with his fellow men, for he has many remnants of antisocial behavior. All of our laws, morals, and codes of ethics are based upon this inescapable duality of man's nature: the inner warfare between his social yearnings and his selfish egoism. The manufacture and operation of complex machines, such as airplanes, radios, and electronic computers, require cooperation between more people of different abilities and skills than existed in a whole tribe of primitive men. As society and its material goods become more complex, the emphasis on cooperation will have to become greater.

Fourth and finally, man's cultural evolution has been determined in large part by the ability of some men and women to look ahead and foresee a better world than the one in which they have lived. This quality of foresight is uniquely human; no other animal has it. We must admit, sadly, that far too few men possess this quality. Furthermore, many of the ways that have been used to develop cooperation, particularly slavery and the rigid decrees of dictators, tend to stifle the capacity for foresight that many people might otherwise have. Here we are faced with the great dilemma of modern times. How can we maintain the cooperation among men of all sorts, which is needed to keep our complex society running, without stifling the individuality and initiative that we need for further progress? We in the United States believe that we have found the answer to this problem in democracy. Our own progress over the last two centuries supports this belief better than words could do. But we must remember that democracy is one of the cultural traits that, more than any other, must be passed down from one generation to another by teaching, learning, and setting examples. If we should ever take for granted this democratic heritage, we shall surely begin to lose it.

In the last four centuries man's cultural evolution has entered a culminating phase. This is the period of the Scientific-Industrial Revolution, which began modestly and inconspicuously with the introduction by Galileo (page 41) and Redi (pages 23-26) of critical observations and experiments in physics and biology. Who would have foreseen the tremendous technological developments that would so swiftly follow the discoveries in pure science? The circumstances of human life have changed faster and faster (Figure 34-9). The pace can best be assessed only in terms of a logarithmic increase. Three times in human history the sizes of human populations have increased at a logarithmic rate: once when toolmaking began; a second time when agriculture was introduced; and now a third time, when science has been broadly applied to the problems of human existence. In the first two cases, the progress in technology later diminished and came to a relative standstill; and the population likewise

NASA

34–9 Man in space. What will the circumstances of life be in the future? While no one can say, you may be sure that the circumstances of today will undergo change.

leveled off at a plateau where the means of subsistence for the population was in balance with its numbers. Will this happen again? The outcome would seem to depend on whether or not the scientific advance, upon which our present technological civilization is based, will continue indefinitely, or will come to a halt. What do you think? Will we soon know everything about nature? Will the era of exploration and discovery in science come to an end, like the era of geographical exploration and discovery that waned when all the world had been penetrated and mapped? At least we can say that at this moment no one can see any end to the scientific enterprise, no day when history will come to an end because everything is known and everything is managed for the best possible welfare of humanity.

Cultural evolution depends upon the transmission from each generation to its successors of all that has been learned, invented, and created. As modern industrial society comes to depend more and more upon technological advances that grow from scientific discoveries, what should be emphasized? Education in science would appear to be more essential than ever before, but not to the exclusion of other equally valid subjects. Science is advancing so rapidly and is so essential in our civilization that it cannot be ignored.

What is it about science that is of paramount importance in our cultural evolution? In the course of studying this book and doing the laboratory work that forms an integral part of your study of biology, has it become clear to you that a knowledge of facts is not enough? Neither, by itself, is a broad understanding of biological concepts and principles, although that is far better and indeed quite essential. You must also see the science of biology as a part of man's cultural evolution, the sweep of which is daily changing our ways of life. You must appreciate the nature of this human conquest which, more than toolmaking and more than agriculture, makes man like the ancient gods in his power to control nature and to work "miracles." What is it, behind this conquest, but the methods you have so often tried and found fruitful—the methods of science that involve careful, often quantitative observations, accurate reports, experiments with controls, hypotheses that you can test, and sound logic?

GUIDE QUESTIONS AND PROBLEMS

1. The abilities to use tools, to talk, and to teach and learn from one's experience and the experience of others are the basis for man's cultural evolution. What special characteristics of human evolution have led to these abilities?
2. During the time prehistoric men were developing domesticated varieties of plants and animals, they were in a sense putting into practice certain fundamentals of genetics. Which of their activities would support this view?
3. What were some of the major problems that had to be solved before nomadic ways of life could be replaced by settled community life?
4. How was the development of settled communities related to the rise of civilization? What immediate changes in human relations probably took place in the first durable settlements of prehistoric times?
5. What justification exists for the statement that most of the major discoveries responsible for modern civilization were made in prehistoric times?
6. Why is the study of cultural evolution important to the future of civilization? Consider the political, social, and technological problems facing man as you search for your answer.

RELATED READING

Books

For more information on our cultural evolution . . .

Bates, Marston, *Man in Nature,* Prentice-Hall, Englewood Cliffs, New Jersey, 1961.

Clark, John G. D., *World Pre-history—An Outline,* Cambridge University Press, New York, 1961.

Coon, C. S., *The Story of Man,* Second Edition, Revised, Knopf, New York, 1962.

Hall, H. R. H., *The Ancient History of the Near East,* Barnes and Noble, New York, 1962.

Roslansky, John D., *Genetics and the Future of*

Man, Appleton-Century-Crofts, New York, 1966.

Tylor, E. B., *Researches into the Early History of Mankind and the Development of Civilization,* University of Chicago Press, 1964 (paperback).

Magazines

Braidwood, R. J., "The Agricultural Revolution," *Scientific American,* Volume 203 (September 1960), page 130.

Butterfield, H., "The Scientific Revolution," *Scientific American,* Volume 203 (September 1960), page 173.

Dobzhansky, Theodosius, "The Present Evolution of Man," *Scientific American,* Volume 203 (September 1960), page 206.

MacNeish, Richard S., "The Origins of New World Civilization," *Scientific American,* Volume 211 (November 1964), page 29.

Rodden, Robert J., "An Early Neolithic Village in Greece," *Scientific American,* Volume 212 (April 1965), page 82.

Wheat, Joe Ben, "A Paleo-Indian Bison Kill," *Scientific American,* Volume 216 (January 1967), page 44.

PART 4

INTERACTION

Cesar from Annan Photo Features

35

Animal Behavior

On the sunny summer morning when this chapter was being written, one of the authors was sitting in a garden in Seattle, Washington. Bees were buzzing around the flowers in the garden, and a pair of white butterflies came fluttering over the fence. The butterflies darted about, flying closely together up and down, back and forth, in an intricate pattern above the flowers. A caterpillar was crawling up the stem of one of the garden plants. On the lawn nearby, a bird hopped about, occasionally pecking at the ground. Once, as it did so, it jerked up its head and the author saw an earthworm hanging from its beak. Then the bird flew up to a tree branch, and this called the author's attention to a half-grown bird perched on the branch. This young bird chirped loudly, opening and closing its beak. At one instant when the beak was open, the grown bird dropped the worm into the young bird's mouth. Then the grown bird flew back to the lawn and started hopping about again.

The author was about to get back to the job of writing when something happened in the garden. The bird flew up to the tree and began to make loud chirping sounds. At the same time, a dog that had been sleeping near the writer's chair woke suddenly, pricked up his ears, and gave a low growl. The half-grown bird on the branch became completely quiet and motionless. The author sat up (much more slowly than the dog) and looked around the garden. Only the caterpillar, the bees, and the butterflies seemed undisturbed as they continued their crawling or flight around and above the flowers.

What was it that had changed so suddenly the activity of the birds and the dog, when the insects seemed undisturbed?

Soon it became clear. A large gray cat had crept along a fence and into the garden. The cat's eyes were fixed on the half-grown bird, and the dog's eyes were fixed on the cat.

The Study of Animal Behavior

We will not continue the account, though what happened next was quite exciting (on a small scale). This much information is enough to introduce a chapter on animal behavior. Animal behavior is the sum of everything animals do—flying, walking, sitting, sleeping, eating, mating, rearing young, and so forth. It is a difficult field to study because, as you know from your own experience, there is an enormous range of *kinds* of behavior. This is true whether you think of a single animal, or of all the individual animals of one species, or—most complex of all—all of the individuals of every animal species. Yet this is one of the most fascinating of the areas of biological science—for the activities, the capacities to adjust to the environment, and the very survival of animals are fundamental aspects of behavior.

It is impossible to imagine a time, no matter how far back, when people did not make observations of animal behavior—their own and the activities of animals they hunted. Yet we are still at an early stage of organizing the observations, designing hypotheses and experiments to test them, asking further questions, and carrying out all the other processes needed in full development of a scientific field. Today, methods for studying behavior include direct observation of animals; recording activities with a great variety of sensitive measuring devices; and changing an animal's living conditions by specially designed cages, or by use of surgical operations, drugs, and other techniques. Some generalizations about animal behavior are beginning to be clear. Behavior ranges from the simple to the very complex.

Certain behavior is very consistent, occurring under similar conditions in almost all members of a given animal species. Thus, it appears to depend chiefly on the animal's hereditary makeup, and we often term it **innate** or **instinctive behavior.** Other behavior is much less predictable, for it differs from individual to individual, and changes from time to time with the individual's experiences. Such behavior can be *conditioned* or *learned*, resulting in changing patterns of nerve and endocrine activity. We often term it **conditioned** or **learned behavior.** It may also be based on even more complex and less understood brain processes, like human reasoning.

There are certain *patterns* of behavior which we can recognize over and over again, although they differ greatly in detail from species to species. Some of these patterns, which we will discuss at greater length later in this chapter, are food-seeking behavior; defense and escape behavior; patterns of behavior related to place; exploratory behavior; social behavior; and reproductive behavior—mating and care of the young. Can you recognize in the introductory account whether some or all of the animals were showing any of these general patterns of behavior? (After you have answered this question, you can check your guesses against ours, which are given in Figure 35-1.)

Other important ideas of behavior concern the types of information animals obtain from their environment; the nervous and endocrine mechanisms involved in coordination; and the ways in which patterns of behavior have become established through evolutionary processes.

PROBLEMS IN STUDYING ANIMAL BEHAVIOR

The account given in the introduction can be used to illustrate some major problems that arise in studying animal behavior. We can consider these under two headings—problems of observation and problems of interpretation.

Observations

Among the problems of observation, we can name the difficulty of making *enough* observations so that we are sure that we have representative data about the behavior of any given organism. What can we conclude, for instance, from our observations of the bees in the Seattle garden? Very little except that bees can buzz around flowers. It would take far more study before we could say anything significant about bee behavior. Often biologists are forced to place animals in controlled conditions (for instance, in a laboratory, or in a restricted environment in the field) in order to observe their behavior. But having done this, they must make a real effort to find out whether the behavior they have observed is "normal," or is a pattern which exists only under abnormally controlled conditions.

Another problem of observation arises from the fact that we usually see and measure only a small fraction of the total behavior of an animal. We can watch the bird fly, but we have no outside evidence about the adjustments in its nerves, endocrine glands, respiration, circulation, and so forth, that take place before and during the bird's flight. Yet these are all a part of the bird's pattern of behavior in responding to the cat's entrance into the garden.

Finally, we have a great problem in observing behavior because we do not know exactly what information any other organism obtains from a given environment. (Although you and the authors of this book all belong to the same species, we are not sure whether you see the setting and the forms in Figure 35-1 in the same way that we do. Is there any way that you can tell whether you and your best friend see or hear *exactly* the same things, even when you are talking and looking at the same book, or watching the same movie?) In the illustration from the Seattle garden, you may remember that the bird and the dog discovered the cat before the author did. In general, it has been found that birds have much sharper vision than people, and that dogs react to smells and sounds of

35–1 A scene in a Seattle, Washington, garden. Behavior can be simple, ②, or very complex, ①. Types of behavior easily recognized in this illustration include food-seeking, ③, ④, ⑦; behavior related to reproduction, ⑤, and ③'s relation to ⑥; and social behavior, ④. The events described on page 645, which took place just after the moment illustrated here, involved other behavior: defense and escape, ⑥ (assisted by ③); behavior related to place, ⑧; and curiosity and exploration, ①; plus other types of behavior. Patterns of behavior vary depending upon many factors, including the animal's state of alertness (compare ⑦ with ⑧); its stage of development (compare ③ with ⑥); and its relation to other organisms (⑥ and ⑦, as opposed to ⑦ and ⑧, in which ⑦'s behavior is quite different in the two associations).

which people are entirely unaware. No doubt the garden looked very different to the bird from the way it looked to the author—and also looked, smelled, and sounded very different to the dog. As for the bees, the caterpillar, and the butterflies, you may recall that their behavior did not change in particular when the cat came into the garden. From the data given, could you conclude that these insects did not have the sensory equipment to enable them to sense the presence of the cat?

Interpretations

Perhaps you may have felt like answering the question in the last sentence by suggesting that the insects might have seen the cat, but did not change their behavior because they did not feel concerned. After all, cats normally do not eat bees, caterpillars, or butterflies. This answer implies a human type of approach to the problem of the cat coming into the garden. We almost hope that you did think this, because it would be a good illustration of one of the big problems in the scientific study of behavior—the tendency to interpret animal behavior in human terms. The danger of this approach is that it seems to give a quick, easy answer to questions about how animals behave. In this way, it can block further scientific inquiry. Almost as strong, and equally false, is the tendency to interpret human behavior in terms of the patterns of activity of other animals. (In common, everyday usage, we sometimes compare clever people with foxes; lazy people with slugs; a strong man with an ox; a hard-working man with a beaver; and so forth.) But science must be built with careful observations, analysis of data, and interpretations of the data in their own terms. Valid comparisons between behavior patterns in different animals can be made only after we are quite sure that we know all the most important factors involved. This is not yet true of most cases of animal behavior we are studying today.

Biologists must be constantly on guard against oversimplifying, or drawing conclusions from too narrow a range of data. As people, we tend to be particularly interested in the behavior of people and the mammals which resemble them most closely. Thus, there is a great deal of research carried out using man, apes, and a few other mammals, including the convenient and widely studied rat. Knowledge of behavior in other forms is being gathered more slowly. Yet we need to know about a wide range of animals in order to build a complete understanding of animal behavior. This branch of biological science is termed **ethology** (eh·THOL·o·gee). **Psychology** is also a term for the study of behavior and other complex activities dependent on nerves and other coordinating systems. Often, though not always, psychological studies are concerned with man. Although it is useful for you to know the terms ethology and psychology, since they will help you if you want to learn more about this subject, there is little point in trying to distinquish sharply between the meanings of the two. Only some ethologists and psychologists know for sure which is which.

STABLE PATTERNS OF BEHAVIOR

A highly predictable sort of behavior is the movement of an animal or positioning of its body in relation to an aspect of the environment like light, temperature, humidity, or gravity. For instance, many animals have a definite tendency to move toward or away from a source of light. You will have an opportunity to study such behavior in Laboratory Inquiry 35-1. Similarly, many animals orient themselves in space so that they have a definite up-down position with respect to gravity. Often it is easy to show that these relatively simple behavior patterns, termed **taxes** (TACK·seez—the singular is **taxis**—TACK·sis) are of adaptive value to the organism. Thus, a positive taxis toward light may make it easier for an animal to find food, while a negative light taxis (the animal moves away from the light) may protect an organism from being used for food. A taxis related to gravity may literally assist an animal like an insect or crab in "keeping its feet on the ground." Taxes have been discovered as basic behavioral patterns in a wide range of animals, although they are difficult to detect in man. This may not mean necessarily that man does not have such behavior, but rather that the total picture of human behavior is so complicated that the separation of its individual parts is often difficult.

Another type of behavior pattern recognized by biologists as occurring in many animals may be termed a **reflex.** Like taxes, reflexes are quite simple and predictable. They are responses to specific stimulation, often involving only a few sensory neurons. The form of a reflex response is limited, too. We have mentioned a variety of reflexes in connection with our discussion of animal physiology. The change in breathing pattern in mammals, correlated with oxygen level in the blood, is one such reflex. A second well-known reflex is the blinking of the eye (closing of the eyelids) when the surface of the eyeball is touched. Like taxes, reflexes operate to adjust the organism to its environment. Although we usually describe them in terms of the obvious external effects only, taxes and reflexes almost always involve internal physiological adjustments as well.

More complex patterns of behavior can easily be recognized in most animals, and are very conspicuous in highly evolved forms like insects and many vertebrates. These complicated behavior patterns occur very predictably under certain sets of circumstances, and seem largely independent of an animal's past experience. They are the patterns we have referred to as innate or instinctive.

One such case of complex behavior is the series of activities in preparation for mating, in courtship behavior, and in care of the eggs in the small freshwater fish, the three-spined stickleback. We can describe this most easily in illustrations, as in Figure 35-2, which represents observations made by the biologist Nikolaas Tinbergen. Behavior patterns somewhat similar to these responses in the stickleback occur in many animals in connection with defense and food-seeking, reproduction, and other activities. One of the characteristics of this sort of behavior is that quite complex patterns of activity are built up by relationships among varied specific reactions to environmental stimuli. For instance, the behavior of the female stickleback in following the male is dependent on visual stimulation. The female will follow almost any red-colored object shaped somewhat like the male fish's red-colored belly, if it is moved through the water. Thus her mating behavior is not really triggered by the presence of the male, but rather by the presence of a suitable *red* and *moving* object. If the male fish sees a similar red, moving object, his response is to show attacking behavior (much as he attacks an invading male). Other features of the behavior of sticklebacks depend on other specific stimuli, or **releasers,** as we have suggested in Figure 35-2. Putting together *the normal series of responses to the normal series of releasers* results in the complex, predictable series of activities of this reproductive behavior.

An Approach to Understanding Behavioral Patterns

How can we account for the occurrence of such predictable patterns of response? This question can be answered in part in terms of our growing knowledge of three major areas on which behavior depends—(1) the kind of information an animal *can* and *does* receive; (2) coordinating mechanisms for behavior—neurons and endocrine glands; and (3) the kinds of responses an animal can make with its effectors.

To illustrate this approach to understanding behavior, we might consider two examples—a simple reflex, and the complex innate pattern of courting behavior in the stickleback.

Recall the illustration we gave in Chapter 24 (page 443) of the reflex response to painful stimulation of the human foot. Sensory receptors in the skin are excited. Nerve impulses travel to the spinal cord. There they excite particular associative neurons connected through synapses with the sensory neurons. These associative neurons are also connected through synapses in the spinal cord with motor neurons having processes which go out to the muscle cells of the leg. When the motor neurons are excited by the associative neurons, they in turn excite the muscle cells to contract, moving the leg—and thus the foot—away from the site of (painful) stimulation. Thus, the entire response can be described in terms of the chain: sensory stimulation—central association—effector response. Slight differences in the information received or in the central mechanisms involved can result in great differences in the response of

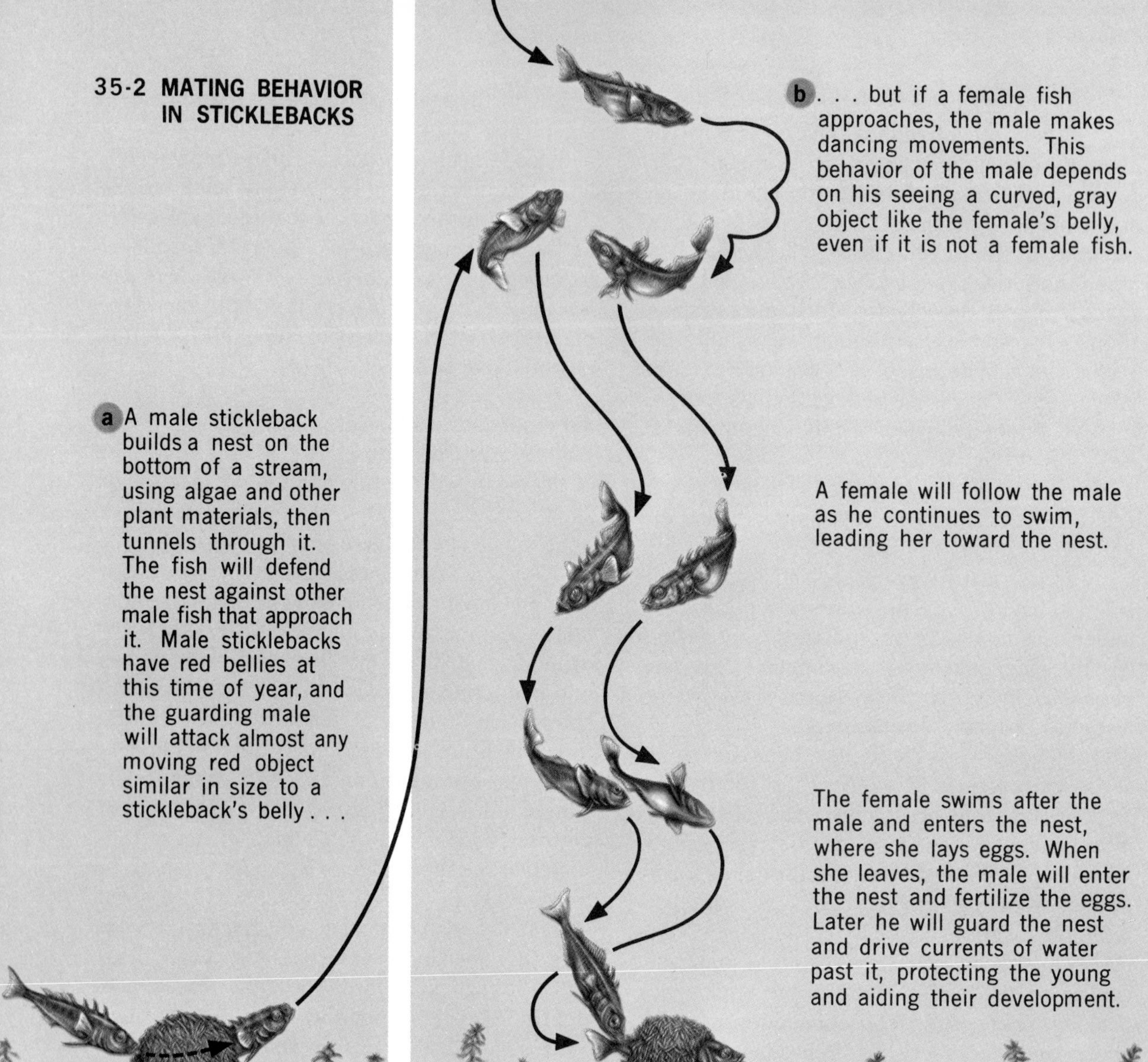

35-2 MATING BEHAVIOR IN STICKLEBACKS
a A male stickleback builds a nest on the bottom of a stream, using algae and other plant materials, then tunnels through it. The fish will defend the nest against other male fish that approach it. Male sticklebacks have red bellies at this time of year, and the guarding male will attack almost any moving red object similar in size to a stickleback's belly . . .
b . . . but if a female fish approaches, the male makes dancing movements. This behavior of the male depends on his seeing a curved, gray object like the female's belly, even if it is not a female fish.
A female will follow the male as he continues to swim, leading her toward the nest.
The female swims after the male and enters the nest, where she lays eggs. When she leaves, the male will enter the nest and fertilize the eggs. Later he will guard the nest and drive currents of water past it, protecting the young and aiding their development.

Adapted from *Social Behavior in Animals*, Second Edition, by N. Tinbergen, Methuen and Co. Ltd. Publishers, London

effectors. For instance, muscles in the leg, in the example we have just given, can be affected in quite a different way by stimulation arising in a different place. If sensory receptors in the muscles of the feet and legs are activated by stretching the muscles, stimulation through another associative path *but the same motor neurons* results in a different response—stronger contraction of the muscles so that the legs are held straight, rather than bending or moving. The difference in the reflex responses can be explained in terms of the difference in sensory stimulation and coordinating pathways in the spinal cord. By knowing many reflex pathways, we can often predict very accurately what will happen to a particular structure of an animal when a particular stimulus is given.

Now let us review the behavior pattern of courting in the stickleback. Here, many more stimuli (releasers) are involved than in the simple reflex response, and many more effectors are activated. You might guess from this alone that much more complicated central coordination is involved than in the reflex patterns we have just described. This is undoubtedly true. Visual stimuli (releasers) representing color (of the male) or form (of the female) must excite particular muscle activity ("dancing" in the male; and swimming movements following the male, in the female). These chains of events involve specific pathways in each fish's spinal cord and brain, but also depend in part on endocrine regulation. For these behavior patterns do not occur in the absence of the sex hormones present in characteristic levels during times when reproduction takes place. Observations on rats and other mammals have shown that here, too, reproductive behavior is dependent on endocrine control as well as on nerve stimulation. Thus, recent experiments have shown that an infant female rat, if injected with even a single dose of male sex hormone, matures into an adult that never shows normal patterns of female reproductive behavior. Similarly, injections with female sex hormones can disturb the reproductive behavior of males. More and more evidence is accumulating that many patterns of activities, even such complex ones as we have described here, can be accounted for in terms of such stable coordinative pathways of neurons and endocrine glands.

Associative Mechanisms Involved in Stable Patterns of Behavior

Quite recently it has become possible to discover something about organization of neurons, within the central nervous system, basic to such behavior. Do you remember in Chapter 24, page 450, the experiments in which stimulating electrodes were placed in particular parts of the brain of experimental animals like rats? It is possible to place such electrodes in surgical operations, then allow the animal to recover completely. Tiny electrical connections on the head can be used to attach the electrodes to devices which deliver specified electrical stimulation to the brain. When the electrodes have been placed in a certain part of the brain—in this case, in a region called the **hypothalamus** (hy·po·THAL·a·mus), closely related in position to the pituitary gland—and electrical stimuli are delivered, the rat will start to seek food and eat. It will continue to eat food as long as the stimulation is continued—long past the point where even the hungriest of rats would have stopped eating under normal conditions.

Destruction of the "feeding region" of the brain results in a remarkable disturbance—now the rat does not eat even though it may be losing weight for lack of food, and plenty of food is always available in its cage. The rat can still be fed—it is able to swallow, digest, and absorb food. The problem seems to be that it has lost the central nervous function involved in motivation for eating, or the tendency to carry out behavior involved in feeding.

In somewhat the same way, in a variety of animals specific regions of the central nervous system have been discovered which are involved in other major patterns of integrated behavior—drinking, reproductive behavior, fighting, escape reactions, and so forth. Although the details are far from clear, it appears that there are many such organizations of neurons within the central nervous system which represent a basis for much of the complex behavior of animals. But there are still many unanswered questions about such behavior. Why sometimes does one pattern of behavior dominate the animal's activities as a whole—or, to put this question in another way, why does an animal sometimes seem fully motivated by feeding behavior, at other times by mating behavior, and so forth? Endocrine control may play a part in such adjustments, as we have suggested already. Past experience, the play of stimulation from the environment, and other factors which we cannot as yet define may allow for the adjustments by which behavior changes from moment to moment, yet shows consistent patterns in the long-range adaptation of the animal to its environment.

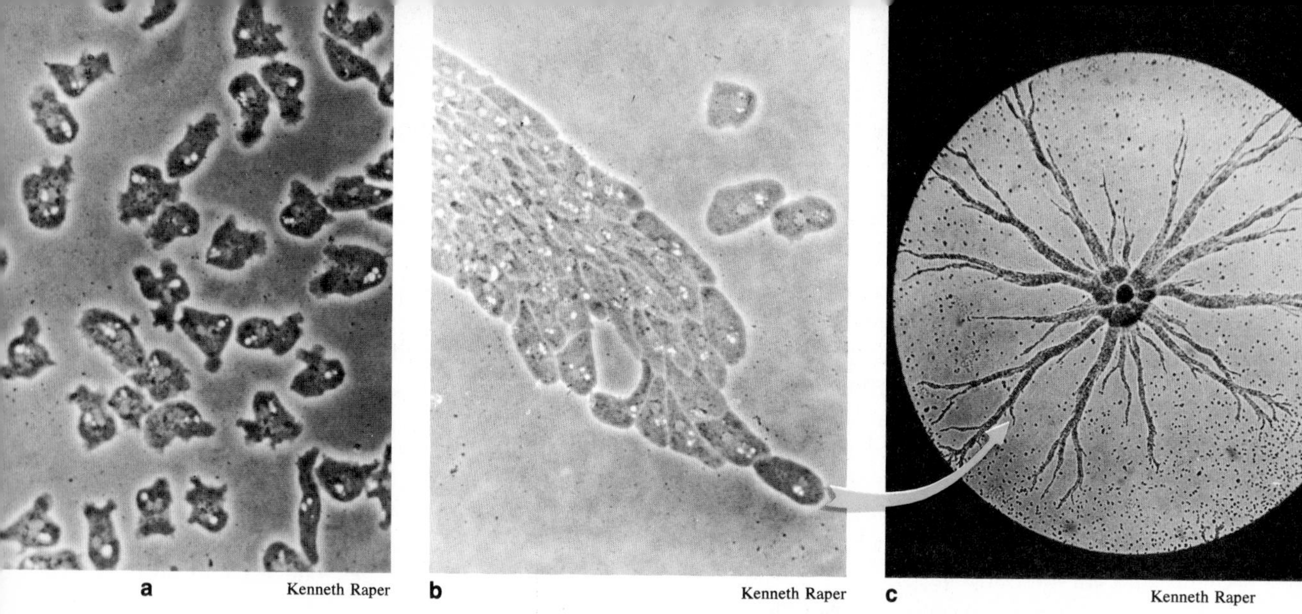

35–3 Communication in slime mold cells. Individual slime mold organisms, **a,** each like a small *Amoeba*, crawl over the surface of their surroundings feeding on bacteria. When all the bacteria have been consumed, the individuals begin to come together as in **b,** which shows only a small part of the mass streaming together in **c.** Half a million individuals ultimately may come together and begin to move about as in **d,** like a single organism—a "slug." After a while the slug settles down, and the individual organisms crawl over one

Receptors and Effectors

In the last two paragraphs, we have considered some general ideas about the associative mechanisms for behavior dependent on the coordinating systems (nervous and endocrine). You will see some other interesting problems if we touch on a few additional points related to effectors and to the sensory processes for receiving information. In the case of effectors, we may remind you of much of what you have learned in Chapters 18 to 26 about animal function. The stickleback fish shown in Figure 35-2 can and do respond to appropriate stimulation by *swimming* since they have the effectors and coordinative equipment with which to swim. Obviously, an animal's pattern of behavior can be expressed only in terms of its effectors—cilia, pseudopods, flagella, muscles and glands (and in some invertebrates and fish, cells which produce light, or even bursts of electric current).

Single-celled organisms like *Amoeba* (Chapter 18) and *Paramecium* (Laboratory Inquiry 35-2) react to many stimuli, including mechanical, chemical, and heat changes in the environment. More complex animals, from *Hydra* to mammals (Chapter 24), have special nerve cells or nerve endings and associated structures that detect a wide variety of environmental changes. You have studied some of the properties of these sensory structures in man (Laboratory Inquiry 24-1), and you are aware of the fact that sense organs can often detect extremely slight changes in the environment. These may be mechanical (touch; pressure; sound waves in air, liquids, or solids), or chemical (smell; taste; sensitivity to carbon dioxide, oxygen, and so forth), or light (vision), or heat or electrical changes. These sensory structures give an animal information about events within itself, about its nonliving environment, and about the presence and activities of other living things. Communication between organisms is of the greatest biological importance. Information passed from one individual to another of the same species may signal presence of

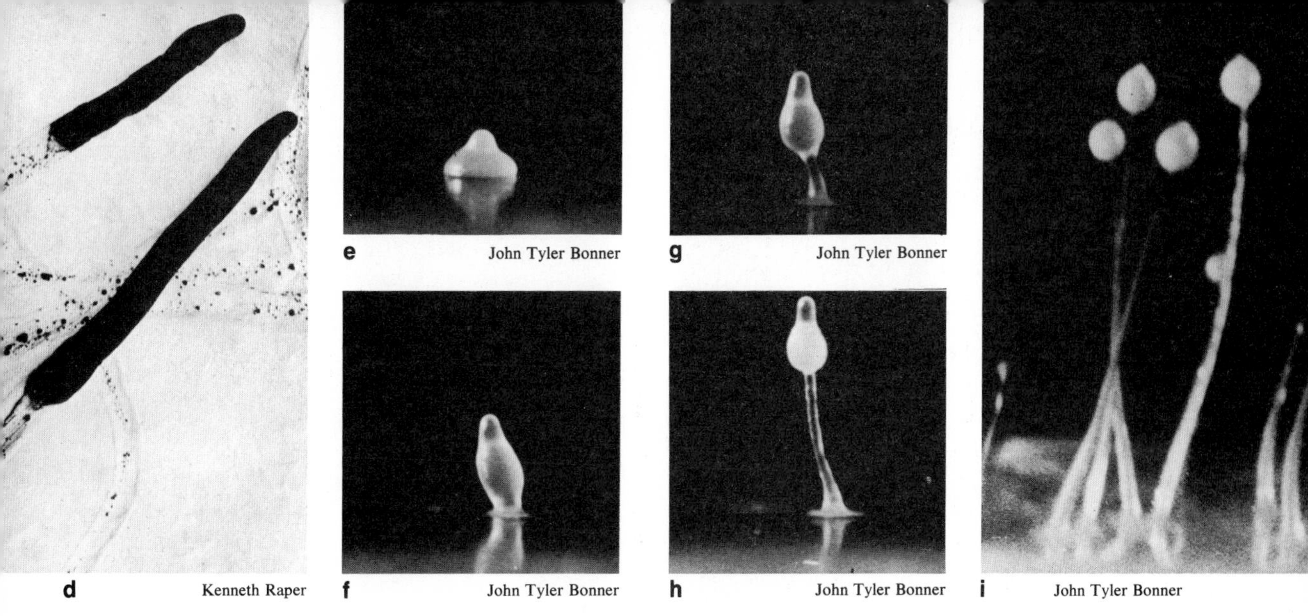

d Kenneth Raper e John Tyler Bonner f John Tyler Bonner g John Tyler Bonner h John Tyler Bonner i John Tyler Bonner

another upward (**e** and **f**), forming a structure with a stalk and head (**g** and **h**). The stalk differentiates further, as in **i**, and the head produces spores. Experiments have shown that water in which aggregating individuals, as in **b** and **c**, have been growing can cause non-aggregating individuals to move together. The water used in these experiments has been found to contain an unstable substance that serves as a *chemical signal* for aggregation—an example of communication by chemical means.

food, danger from enemies, or readiness for mating. Even single-celled organisms sometimes exchange information in this way. Figure 35-3 shows some evidence that slime mold organisms (Chapter 12) can communicate by the use of specific chemical substances. Two other interesting investigations, among many reported, of communication between animals of the same species, are illustrated in Figures 35-4 and 35-5, involving behavior related to food-seeking in fire ants and honeybees.

Animals also use sensory information in their behavior in relation to organisms of different species. This may involve search for food, and you can study such a case in Laboratory Inquiry 35-1. A dramatic illustration is the behavior of bats (small, winged mammals) in their night-hunting for flying insects, especially moths. Donald Griffin, of Harvard University, and his associates discovered by sensitive recording methods that bats utter a stream of high-pitched sounds as they fly about. Though these are far beyond the range of sensitivity of human ears, the bat's ears can easily hear the sounds reflected from objects even as small as the moths which the bat hunts. This natural sonar (echo location) system allows the bat to detect moths in the dark. Next it was discovered by Kenneth Roeder and Asher Treat that the moths have sensory receptors ("ears") which can detect the sound waves emitted by the bats. When the moth "ears" pick up bat sounds, the moth shows a variety of change in flight path—responses which must often help the moth in escaping from the bat as it zooms in on the moth, guided by sonar. Another note to be added to this story is that it has been discovered recently that some moths can emit sounds, too. The sounds are of nearly the same high pitch as bat sounds. There is some evidence that the moth sounds may confuse the bat so that it changes its interpretation of its own sonar. We have described this case in some detail, for it illustrates clearly the importance of communication in animal behavior—in this case involving both food-seeking and defense-escape.

35-4 COMMUNICATION AMONG FIRE ANTS

a Control

Fire ants communicate with one another about the position of food or danger. Here a foraging ant has found food . . .

. . . and returns to the colony, periodically touching the ground with its sting, which extends rearward from its abdomen.

Other ants quickly travel out to the food, taking the path of the foraging ant's return. Has the foraging ant left a "trail message"?

CHANGING PATTERNS OF BEHAVIOR

Up to this point in our discussion of behavior, you may have formed an impression that patterns of activity are quite fixed, at least in the sense that a given animal under given conditions (including its endocrine state, the presence of environmental releasers, and so forth) will show a predictable response. This certainly is true in the case of many behavioral patterns. It is equally true, however, that many behavioral patterns in animals undergo change in the course of time. They can, for instance, be *modified by experience.*

Habituation

One of the simplest cases of modification of behavior is **habituation** (huh·BICH·oo·ay·shun) —a change in response pattern which we can observe even in single-celled organisms. An animal may respond to a particular stimulus in a particular way, but often if the stimulus is repeated over and over at frequent intervals, the animal's behavior changes. It is as if it were "growing used to" the stimulus and beginning to disregard it. Thus, a spider will crawl quickly to the place in its web which moves, as a fly becomes entangled in the web. If a biologist moves the web with a glass rod, the spider also rushes over to the moving area.

b **Experimental**

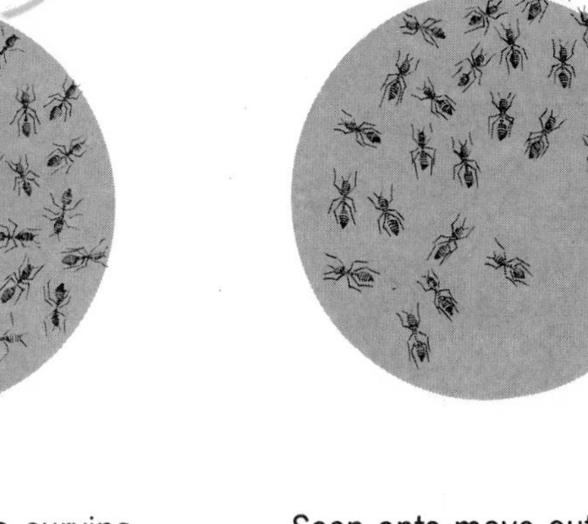

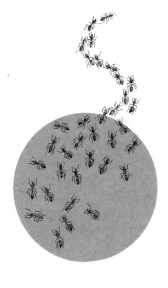

A biologist draws a curving line from the colony to a distant spot, using a stick dipped in an extract of one of the glands of the ants.

Soon ants move out of the colony, following the path traced by the stick – a demonstration that ants can use chemical information.

An hour later, the trail of ants is gone. No chemical information is left. Of what value to the ants is the instability of this substance?

Adapted from E. O. Wilson, "Pheromones," *Scientific American*, May 1963

But as the biologist does this a second time, a third, fourth, fifth time—and so forth—the spider becomes less and less responsive. Finally it does not respond at all until it is left undisturbed for some time.

Conditioned Responses

Another case of change in behavior with experience is the *conditioning* of simple responses. The great Russian biologist, Ivan Pavlov (PAV·lof), carried out in the nineteenth century many clever and carefully controlled experiments which convinced the scientific world of the occurrence of conditioning of reflexes. When a stimulus which normally results in a reflex action is given over and over again at the same time, or just after an *unrelated* stimulus, the reflex response can become associated with the unrelated stimulus. Perhaps you know something already about Pavlov's famous work with dogs. Dogs normally secrete saliva when they see or smell food (just as people do, as you may remember from Chapter 20). Pavlov found that he could *condition* a dog to secrete saliva when a bell was rung just at the same time, or just before, food was given to the dog. After this combination of stimuli (bell ringing and presentation of meat) had been repeated often enough, the dog secreted saliva whenever the bell was rung—even if meat was not given.

35-5 HOW HONEYBEES COMMUNICATE — A PROBLEM IN RESEARCH

a Observers first noted that when a foraging honeybee returns to the hive after discovering a nectar source . . .

b In one famous investigation, Karl von Frisch found that the returning bee gives nectar to other bees, then begins a dance on the vertical face of the hive.

If the dance is a *round dance* other bees follow it with their antennae against the dancer's abdomen, then leave the hive and search for plants nearby. Does *round dance* mean that *the nectar is near the hive?*

If the dance is a *figure 8 with wagging* of the abdomen, bees that follow the dance leave the hive and search at a distance. But *how far?* The dancer's rate seems involved. And *in what direction?* The middle line of the figure 8, if danced directly upward, indicates the direction of the sun. Other angles indicate other directions.

Part b only: Adapted from *The Dancing Bees* by Karl von Frisch. Reproduced by permission of Harcourt, Brace & World, Inc., New York, and Methuen & Co. Ltd. Publishers, London

d The problem grows more complex. In still further investigations, Johnson and Wenner found that when more than one scented feeding bowl is placed in the same line of direction from the hive, bees that follow the dance of a forager tend to fly to the correct distance (the bowl the forager visited) only if bees from another hive are not influencing them toward other feeding bowls . . .

. . . other bees soon leave the hive and fly to *the same source*, ignoring other flowers. The bee that already has fed is not along as a guide. How does it inform the other bees where it obtained the nectar?

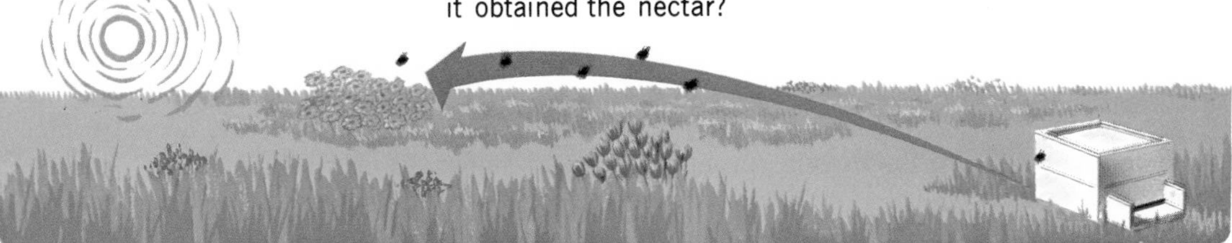

(c) Do bees actually use the information of the dance? In another investigation, Dennis Johnson and Adrian Wenner found that experienced bees locate an experimental nectar source without following the dance of the forager bee . . .

. . . while other bees seemed to follow the dancer *with their antennae to his thorax.* Sounds issuing from the dancing bee's thorax have a pattern correlated with distance to the nectar source. Does this information supplement the dance—or offset the dance's importance?

. . . and in the reverse situation, when more than one feeding bowl lies at the correct distance, but in somewhat different directions, bees that follow the dance are influenced by several factors—in part by the central feeding sites in the arrangement, still more by the correct feeding site, but most of all by bees from another hive visiting all the dishes.

Other unrelated stimuli—a flash of light, for instance—worked just as well as the ringing of the bell. Though this classic experiment is well known, many people do not realize how widespread is the occurrence of such conditioning. Similar patterns are seen in animals ranging from simple forms like planarians to complex animals like the octopus (a mollusk), and birds and mammals. You almost certainly have many conditioned responses yourself. One that is common in man, and particularly easy to demonstrate, is the increased rate of flow of saliva in response to the sound (or even the thought!) of words like *lemon, vinegar,* and *dentist's drill.*

Behavioral Changes Classed as "Learning"

Perhaps related to conditioning of responses, but far more complex, are the ways in which experience changes behavior by processes of learning. Learning may result in a combination of activities in ways which would not occur without experience. Also, activities not seen in inexperienced individuals may appear as a result of learning. Learning is seen in all animals with organized nervous systems, though it varies greatly in complexity, and may even depend on several basic mechanisms.

Experiments designed to test how learning takes place have uncovered several aspects of the process. In the first place, learning takes place best—and perhaps only—in connection with some *motivation.* A hungry rat can learn to follow a complicated path if it finds food at the end of the path. But the same rat, kept constantly fed, is not likely to show evidence of learning such a path. Hunger, thirst, sex drive, the drive in females to care for their young, and the tendency to avoid pain may serve to motivate learning throughout the great range of multicellular animals so far tested.

A second major characteristic of learning is that it often depends on *repetition of a given experience.* Sometimes the hungry animal finds food in a particular situation, let us say, and sometimes it does not. If tests (or trials) are repeated over and over (in which the animal is placed in the situation and succeeds in finding food), the chance that the animal will make an error (not get the food) gets less and less. As an illustration of this kind of trial-and-error learning, we can describe an experiment with a hungry land snail placed in a special container shaped like a **T** (**T**-maze). If food is placed at the end of the **T**'s right arm, an inexperienced snail starting from the base of the **T** will have a 50-50 chance of finding the food when it crawls down one or the other of the arms of the **T**. Once having found the food, this same snail (again allowed to become hungry) may still have only a 50-50 chance of turning towards the food on the next trial. But if the test is repeated again and again, the snail gradually learns by trial-and-error; after as many as 60 tries, it has nearly a 100 percent chance of taking the right turn and receiving food at the end of the test.

Animals with more complex nervous systems can learn much faster and learn far more complicated paths than a land snail can. Rats can master complex paths, or mazes, like the one shown in Figure 35-6 in a relatively small number of trials. Primates, porpoises and whales, and other higher mammals show still faster learning, and the situations which they learn can be extremely complex. Unfortunately we have too little data as yet to have more than the beginnings of an understanding of comparative animal learning. Learning is an area in which man excels, for his capacity to learn is very great indeed. He is aided by other types of capacities which are present in some animals but developed in man to a unique degree—insight (or reasoning) and symbolization. We will come back to these abilities later (page 662).

Quite different in its characteristics from conditioning, or from trial-and-error learning, is a type of behavioral change resulting from **imprinting.** This has been observed in young animals, and studied especially in young birds. It is a type of learning in which just a single

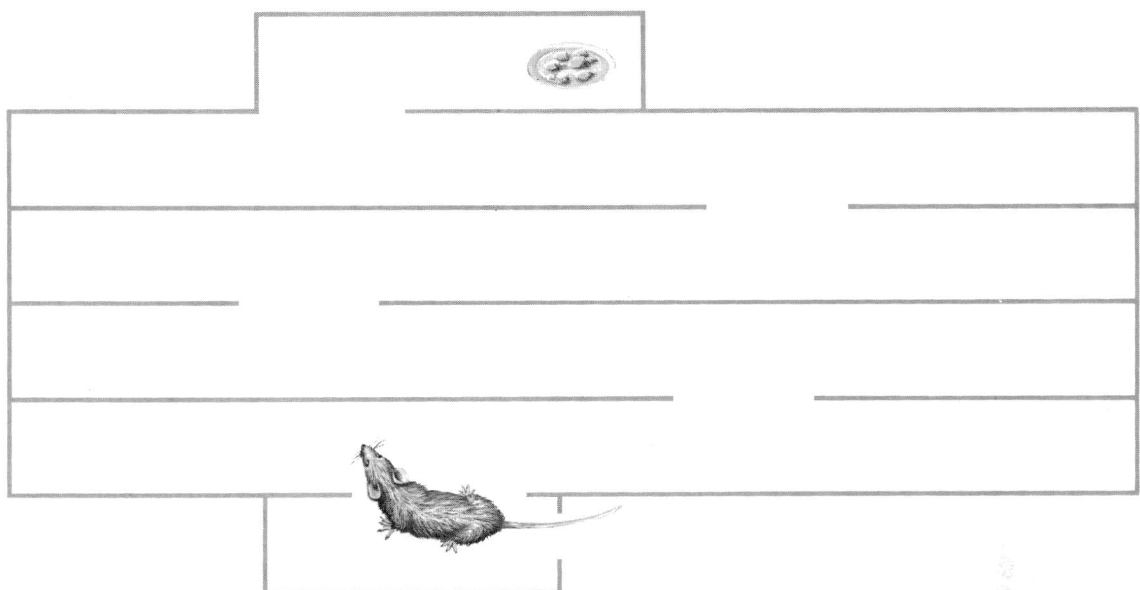

From *Brain Mechanisms and Intelligence* by K. S. Lashley, Dover Publications, Inc., New York, 1963. Redrawn with permission of the publisher

35–6 In his classical studies, the American psychologist K. S. Lashley used a maze with a structure suggested by this diagram. How many ways are there to make an error on the route to the food? A normal rat can learn to go directly from the starting point to the food, without making any errors, after 20 or fewer trials.

experience (or at most a very few experiences) has a long-lasting effect in changing the animal's behavior. We can describe this curious process best by giving an example. In normal life, geese hatch from eggs in the presence of the mother goose. Soon after hatching, the baby geese (goslings) begin to follow their mother about, as she leads them to suitable areas to feed, or protects them from predators and other dangers. The Austrian biologist, Konrad Lorenz, made a remarkable discovery—if he hatched goslings from their eggs in the laboratory, and immediately began to walk along slowly making gooselike sounds, the newly hatched goslings would follow him around all through their period of immaturity, just as if he were a mother goose! Even when they saw their real mother, the goslings paid no attention to her, but continued to follow the biologist (Figure 35-7). In fact, all through their lives the behavior of these geese towards Lorenz was like the behavior of normal geese towards other geese. Later experiments carried out by Lorenz and other biologists showed that geese, ducks, and other birds will respond in a similar manner in the first few hours of life to many objects which move slowly and give off sounds—somewhat as a mother bird does. Even a moving and ticking alarm clock will do! Such an object becomes fixed in the memory and behavior patterns of the young birds. The brief exposure time needed, and the long-lasting effects of the experience, have led biologists to call this sort of process **imprinting.** It has been observed in a variety of animals, characteristically occurring only in the earliest hours of independent life. In the ducklings, for instance, the capacity for imprinting lasts for only about 30 hours after the birds hatch.

What is the explanation for change in behavior with experience? On one level, we can answer this question by saying that such change,

Tom MacAvoy, *Life* Magazine © Time, Inc.

35–7 A demonstration of imprinting by its discoverer – Konrad Lorenz. Goose eggs were kept in an incubator until they hatched. The young goslings, in the hours immediately after hatching, were not permitted to see their mother or another adult goose. Instead they saw Konrad Lorenz. He substituted for "mother," and this photograph shows how well he was accepted.

whether it is reflex-conditioning or more complex learning, can be of great advantage to the animal. Consider the case of a hungry land snail which follows a **T**-maze and learns after many trials always to turn to the right, thus always finding the food which the experimenter places in the right arm of the **T**. By learning to locate the food in the **T**-maze, the snail actually gets more food. Thus, it benefits from its learned behavior. Of course in this case the learning is experimental, and the experimenter would feed the snail even if it did not find the food. In nature, however, an animal that learns certain ways of finding food consistently has a better chance of surviving than an animal without such learned responses. Baby geese or ducks with imprinted memories of their mother benefit from the mother's care and protection as they follow her about. Similarly, learning in other situations is likely to increase the organism's chances of surviving and reproducing successfully.

This sort of answer to the questions about how conditioning and learning occur may help explain their biological significance, but it does not tell anything about the actual mechanism in terms of nerves and endocrine glands. How can sensory stimulation affecting the ears or eyes (ringing bell, flashing light) become linked with the normal reflex path to the salivary glands in conditioning of salivary secretion? As you may remember from Chapter 24, the brain contains an enormous number of associative neurons. These have so many interconnections through synapses that any neuron in the central nervous system could be affected indirectly by any other one through paths of associative neurons. We suppose that reflex paths can become linked with unrelated sensory paths in some manner through associative neurons. Repeated stimulation (*at the same time*) of such different neuron paths allows them, in some unknown way, to become related so that activity in one regularly comes to be associated with activity in the other. Thus, when nerve impulses are moving along two neuron pathways, the paths may be linked together by chemical changes or response patterns in associative neurons lying between the pathways. The exact manner in which this could happen remains unknown — but an active area of biological research.

Even less well understood are more complex processes of learning and memory. What change in the chemistry of nerve cells, or in the patterns of nerve connections, allows certain types of information to become associated so that, for instance, a snail motivated by hunger and crawling along a **T**-maze learns to turn always to the right? Modern engineering research, in devising computers which have "memories," has stimulated many ideas about possible mechanisms of memory. A computer's "memory" may involve magnetic tape which records patterns of electrical change corresponding to particular bits of information fed into the computer. This may have no direct bearing on animal memory, but it does, perhaps, suggest how change in pattern of some function of nerve cells could result in storage of past experience.

Several hypotheses have been proposed to explain learning and memory. For instance, in the case of the snail learning the **T**-maze, it is possible that new nerve cell connections are formed in the central nervous system, linking the neurons concerned with movement and those concerned with feeding. This is a difficult hypothesis to test, since the numbers of nerve cell connections even in a simple nervous system like the snail's are so enormous. It would be far harder yet to test in the case of a more complicated animal like a fish or a person. A second hypothesis would explain learning and memory by continuous nerve activity, started by a particular stimulation, and maintained indefinitely in the extremely complicated neuron circuits of the brain. A third popular hypothesis is that memory may be based on chemical changes in the brain cells — for instance, in the types of proteins or RNA molecules within them. A given experience, for instance, might result in stimulation of nerve cells, and this would change their pattern of RNA formation. As a result of formation of new types of RNA, the activity of the neurons would change, and we might recognize the nerve's changed activity in terms of memory. Chemical data seem to support this hypothesis, for RNA metabolism does change in certain parts of rat brains when the animals are being trained experimentally. There is other evidence in support of this interesting hypothesis. At the time this book is being written, however, the authors do not feel able to suggest definite conclusions. Rather, we would advise you to watch for new developments in this field, which is almost certain to make fast and important advances during your lifetime.

Are the changes which we have described in behavioral patterns — conditioning and learning — permanent? Apparently not. If a conditioned reflex is well established, but then not tested again for a long time, it often grows harder and harder to demonstrate, and may disappear altogether. Learning, too, is often temporary. But we do not understand what happens to remove the effects of conditioning or learning. We are not even sure whether only one major type of process, or many, is involved. Clearly some behavioral changes are made more easily, and some have much longer-lasting effects, than others. They differ in other ways, too. As you may recall, for instance, imprinting and related processes can occur only very early in an individual's life. Memories may be easily established by a few repetitions of a stimulus pattern, or may require a long series of training experiences. Experiments involving damage or removal of different parts of the brain suggest that different kinds of memory may be associated with activities of different neurons or neuron interconnections. Thus, an octopus can easily be trained to avoid reaching for a crab — tasty food it normally attacks eagerly — when it is offered a crab at the same time that it is shown a plastic square and given an electric shock. After some trials, the octopus develops a stable change in behavior — it will reach for a crab alone, but will not reach if it sees the plastic square at the same time that it sees the crab. Even if the test is not repeated for one or two weeks, the octopus can avoid the shock by avoiding the crab *plus* plastic square. Removal of part of the octopus brain leaves the animal still able to learn to react differently to *crab* and *crab plus plastic square*—but this learning lasts for only about two hours. The results of such experiments suggest that different parts of the octopus brain are associated with short-term memory and the long-term memory of the normal animal. It is interesting, too, that certain diseases, drugs, and other unfavorable conditions disturb memory in man; these are being studied as clues which may help answer some important and puzzling questions about memory.

Conditioning, trial-and-error learning, and imprinting all play parts in modifying behavior of many animals on the basis of experience. In higher mammals, and in man in particular, there are other special processes which, though poorly understood, are easily recognized as of major importance in adjusting behavior. These include reasoning and symbolization. We can give in the short space of this chapter only a few illustrations to suggest such processes. Consider the case of a hungry bird or mammal which is placed in a cage with one square cup and two round cups. Under the square cup is food. The animal will find the food, sooner or later, and almost certainly could be trained—with more or less difficulty—to associate *square cup* with the reward of food. It could also be trained always to look for food in the cup on the right (or on the left—or in the center). But instead of being placed in that sort of situation, the animal is placed in a series of situations of this form:

Test one:	round cup (FOOD)	square cup	square cup
Test two:	square cup	square cup	round cup (FOOD)
Test three:	round cup	square cup (FOOD)	round cup
Test four:	square cup	round cup (FOOD)	square cup

. . . and so forth—

As a human being, you have no doubt seen what the animal must do in order to find the food in every test—it must always go to the kind of cup of which there is only *one*, and not to either of the other cups. It may surprise you to realize that even a mammal as capable of learning as a rat cannot learn to find the food on every test in this situation! A rhesus monkey may need 400 to 1500 trials before it has a 90 percent chance of finding the food at once in any test. You can judge for yourself whether this would be a difficult task for man. It requires a certain capacity to recognize an odd (different) member of a group and to reason at least this far—that food will be associated with whatever there is *one* of, not with what there is more than one of. We could give many other illustrations, but these probably are not needed, for you are well aware of the processes of reasoning. You also know how reasoning plays a part in modifying human behavior. Think of a simple case in your own day, for instance. You feel hungry, and want to go to the school cafeteria. You look at the clock and see numbers (symbols representing the position of the sun with respect to the earth) and decide not to go yet. Your capacity to reason and your knowledge of symbols make you aware of the fact (probability) that the cafeteria will not be open for half an hour. If you were a rat, apparently similar behavior (postponement of feeding for half an hour) would probably be based on quite a different process that modified behavior—repeated trials that were not rewarded by food because a door was locked at the time the rat attempted to enter.

In man, the capacities to learn quickly and to modify his behavior by such complex processes as reasoning and symbolization are vastly greater than those of other mammals—or, for that matter, of any other animals. Man himself attributes his special abilities to his large and highly complex brain. (The porpoise and related sea mammals are among man's nearest competitors in complexity of behavior and brain structure.) Brain injury or lack of oxygen almost always disturb memory, reasoning, and other higher processes to a greater or lesser extent. So do many drugs and chemicals, like alcohol, LSD, and narcotics. In some cases of such change and injury, the effects on these specially developed capacities of man may be permanent. We cannot say for sure, however, whether some parts of the brain are related to particular brain processes. Sometimes damage to a small part of the brain may have very disastrous effects. On the other hand, occasionally in disease or accidents, people have lost large parts of the brain, yet seemed to retain quite normal higher processes.

At an early stage in his history, man added to his other abilities two immensely powerful tools: (1) language—a common scheme of sounds for communicating with other men; and (2) writing—a technique for storing information in symbols so that it can be transmitted effectively from generation to generation. Thus, partly because of his basic behavioral patterns, and partly because of the social and cultural evolution these have made possible (Chapter 34), man today shows behavioral complexity unique in the Animal Kingdom.

CHANGE IN BEHAVIOR IN THE COURSE OF LIFE—DEVELOPMENT, SLEEP, AND WAKING

Even during the course of the life of a single animal, patterns of behavior may change greatly. As you know, some of this change may result from the individual's particular experiences, through processes like conditioning, imprinting, and trial-and-error learning. But we also recognize trends in behavior changes which are found in all or most of the members of a given species.

Development

Certain animals—for example, frogs—have lives divided sharply into different developmental periods. The life history of the frog is much like that of the salamander, which you studied in Chapters 27 and 28. The frog egg is laid in water. Here, much of the early development of the animal takes place. Then, quite abruptly in the course of one to two weeks (Figure 35-8), the frog turns into a land-living organism. Before this occurs, the behavioral patterns of the young frog as a tadpole include movement by swimming in water; breathing patterns using gills; feeding patterns with plant material as the main food; and complete absence of reproductive behavior. With the change into an adult frog, the same individual shows a remarkable change in behavior. Now it moves by using its four legs for hopping on land or swimming in water (but it swims in a manner quite different from its earlier swimming ways as a tadpole). As an adult it feeds on other animals, which it catches by its own particular and highly adaptive behavior. It breathes by swallowing air, using its lungs. It also shows very special reproductive behavior. What is it that happens to the frog tadpole so that its behavior changes sharply to the behavior of an adult frog? Cellular changes and structural changes in the animal's body are associated with the behavioral changes. We could answer in general terms the question we have asked about the cause of the behavioral changes by saying that the tadpole's nervous and endocrine systems are the basis for its tadpole behavior, while the adult frog's nervous and endocrine systems are the basis for its adult frog behavior. Unfortunately, this unsatisfactory answer is almost the only one we can yet give to this puzzling and fascinating question.

We do not know much more about the biological bases for changing behavior, with development, in other animals. The striking processes of imprinting occur, as you will recall, only during a brief early phase in a bird's life. What are the conditions in the central nervous system that allow imprinting to take place? What are the later changes that account for its disappearance? Even in higher mammals and man, the very first part of life after birth appears

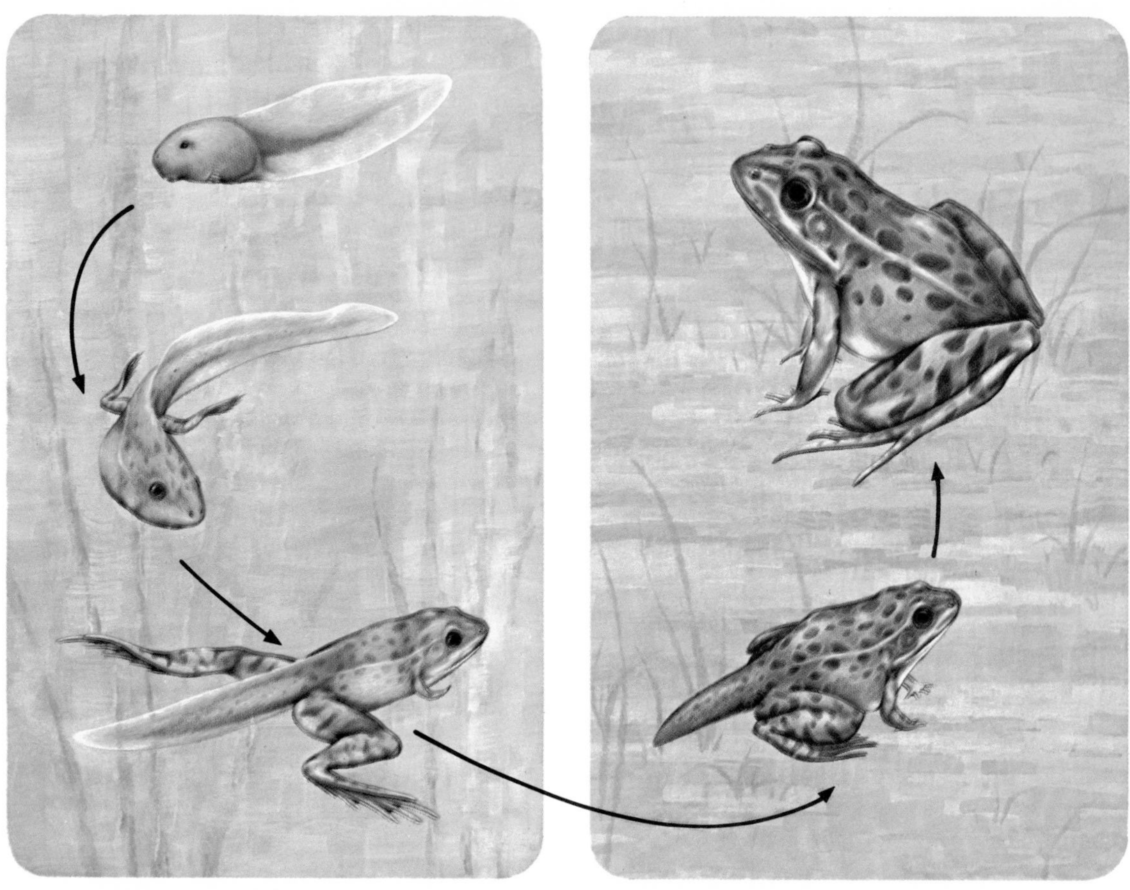

35–8 In the life history of a leopard frog (*Rana pipiens*), the animal changes rapidly from a tailed tadpole, with structure and behavior adapted for life in water, to a tail-less adult frog, with structure and behavior adapted for life on land.

to be a critical period when many behavioral patterns are established. If these patterns are not built up adequately in this early period, they may never be established at all in the animal's life. In this connection, it is interesting that much evidence suggests that the playing of young animals is not just a way of spending time – rather, many of the behavioral patterns of play seem to lay out important foundations for adult behavior. Young mammals – including people – which are prevented from playing, as normal little mammals do, may grow up and show poorly developed or unfavorable patterns of adult behavior.

Since behavior is closely regulated by endocrine glands, as well as by the nervous system, it is not surprising that changing levels of endocrine secretion in an individual's lifetime may be related to changing patterns of behavior. Young mammals – again including people – show particularly abrupt changes in behavior at the time of maturation of reproductive functions. General activity, quite apart from specific reproductive behavior, shows marked change. For centuries, farmers have recognized that infant cattle and horses (calves and colts) are quite gentle, with only slight differences in behavior patterns in males as compared with females. When they mature, male horses and cattle (stallions and bulls) become far more active and aggressive—even dangerous—while females (mares and cows) remain gentler and easier to handle. Again, we have taken this as one of many examples we could have given. As in so many other aspects of behavior, the problems of change in behavior during the course of an individual's life have direct bearing on human life in particular. You may find it interesting to think back over your own life, and the lives of relatives and friends with whom you have associated through several years, and see whether there are trends of changing behavior that you can recognize in human beings. As you do this, you will immediately face one of the problems that faces all students of human behavior: to what extent are any consistent changes which you may note the result of "growing up" (individual maturation, as in the tadpole turning into a frog), and to what extent are they based on experience, education, and pressure from society? These are the types of questions that complicate the efforts of scientists who study human behavior. For many reasons they cannot subject people to arbitrary, long-term laboratory conditions (even if we knew what conditions to control) in order to study the effects upon behavior.

Sleep and Waking

Besides all the long-range changes in behavioral patterns during an individual's life, can we detect other kinds of consistent change? You can answer that question easily if you think about it for a moment. In vertebrates and other animal groups, there are periods in an organism's life when it is active, and others when it is inactive. Many animals are inactive for months in a cold (or hot-dry) season, or throughout the night (or throughout the day). In most vertebrates, cycles of activity and inactivity are correlated with day and night (we will return to timing of behavior later in this chapter). Inactivity is often recognized as *sleep*, and activity as *waking*.

During sleep, behavior is completely different from waking activity—we will leave to you the task of filling in the details of how these behavior patterns differ in man. Why should sleep occupy so much of the time of an active vertebrate like a mammal? In your own case, why have you spent the equivalent of as much as five to seven years of your life asleep? We cannot answer that question, though much research is being carried out to do so. We *are* beginning to understand something about how sleep occurs, however. There are special regions of the brain—grouped together under the term **reticular** (reh·TIC·yoo·lar) **formation**—which receive sensory stimulation from all over the body. No special reflexes or sensations are dependent on these regions, as far as we know. Rather, impulses go out from them to other parts of the brain and act to increase or decrease their general level of activity. When this general level is high, reasoning and memory processes are brisk, reflexes all over the body are easily excited, and muscle activity is likely to be vigorous. Such a state is termed arousal, or waking. Under controlled stimulation from the reticular formation, nervous function in general can also become depressed. In a person, we would say that drowsiness sets in, and later, perhaps, sleep. Our growing knowledge of the reticular formation can explain such observations as these: general sensory stimulation often makes you (or another vertebrate) more alert; if you wish to sleep, you are likely to seek conditions where sensory stimulation is as slight as possible (a comfortable bed in a quiet, dark room with a temperature neither too hot nor too cold). We also begin to understand the effects of drugs like caffeine (in coffee and cola drinks) or medicines like sleeping pills and tranquilizers that may act in relation to the reticular formation, making a person more alert or more sleepy. But we do not yet understand why sleep comes in its typical cyclic fashion, or—most puzzling of all—why sleep is so necessary for health and normal mental and behavioral processes.

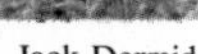

Jack Dermid

Richard Dranitzke from Photo Researchers, Inc.

35–9 Life for the deer and for the lion involve quite different types of behavioral and structural adaptation. The deer has keen senses of sight, hearing, and smell, and is easily aroused by sensory stimulation. Using its long slim legs, light body, and powerful muscles, it takes refuge in flight. The lion's sensory apparatus, body structure, and behavior are adaptations of a different sort. Behavioral patterns in general have evolved in close association with each animal's special body structures.

SOME GENERALIZATIONS ABOUT ANIMAL BEHAVIOR

One of the most obvious aspects of behavior is that it is adaptive. This is another way of saying that the sum of an animal's activities tends to increase its chances for survival and successful reproduction. Why should this be so?

When we discuss behavior, there is a certain temptation to interpret an organism's actions in terms of plan or purpose. We might say about a worm that it burrows into an apple "to find food and shelter." A bird digs its beak into the same apple "to find the worm." This sort of explanation is undesirable in biology, for the same reason that interpreting animal behavior in human terms is not helpful. The kinds of answers we get using these approaches do not lead us anywhere. We can say that a certain action has a purpose, and that ends the matter. Far more useful in terms of suggesting hypotheses and ways of testing them is to look at behavior in the same way that we look at structures and processes within living cells. We can explain the origin of structures and cell processes in terms of evolution. Like these, behavior has *evolved.* After all, behavior represents the sum of activities of the organism's structures—activities based on its cell processes. An animal living today is the product of animals of the past which succeeded in reproducing. From these, it inherited structures, cell processes, and behavior patterns which it may pass on to its offspring. Its chance of doing so is much greater if its behavior is such that it is well adapted to its environment (Figure 35-9). If you think back to the relationship described in Chapter 32 between Pacific coast columbine flowers and hummingbirds, you will recall that we pointed out that the *structure* of the flowers is related to the *behavior* of the birds. It would be just as fair to say that the *behavior* of the birds is related to the *structure* of the flowers. Hummingbirds that suck honey from the flowers feed better and are more likely to survive than individuals with behavior patterns unfavorable for feeding (for instance, not skillful enough or not "patient" enough to suck out the flowers' nectar).

Although animal behavior is, then, clearly adaptive, this does not mean that a given pattern of activity will always help the individual which shows it to survive. We can illustrate this by describing a particular example. Aphids are small insects that suck juices from plant leaves and stems. In some species of aphids, it has been observed that the adults emerging from larval form either may have wings or may not. The wingless forms cannot travel, and they immediately begin to feed on whatever plants they happen to be on when they emerge. The winged forms show quite a different pattern of behavior. As soon as they have completed the change from larval to adult form, they fly directly upwards into the air. This is believed to be because of a positive taxis toward the light in the sky. As they move upwards, they are likely to be caught by the wind and carried some distance before the wind dies down, dropping them wherever they happen to fall. From the point of view of the whole aphid population, this appears to be a highly adaptive mechanism, for it insures the distribution of the newly emerged insects over a relatively wide area. Thus, the wingless and winged individuals do not compete with one another for a limited local food supply. From the point of view of a given winged individual, however, the pattern may or may not be advantageous. This particular individual may be dropped by the wind on a juicy leaf where it can feed, or it may be dropped into a lake where it will drown. As you continue your study of behavior—in this chapter and later (for you cannot help making observations of animal behavior throughout your life)—you will find it helpful to analyze each pattern of activity in terms of its adaptive value for the species, as well as its possible direct effects on the life of the individual organism.

It is interesting, too, to speculate about how behavioral patterns have evolved. So far, we have much less convincing evidence about details of behavioral evolution than about the evolution of structure. For one thing, the fossil record is not of much help here (could you recognize fossil behavior?). We do have some clues from the comparison of behavior patterns in related animals. This is one reason why comparative studies in a wide range of animals is rewarding. In spite of the lack of much detailed information, it is clear that many behavioral patterns have been established through well-known evolutionary processes—interactions of genetically based variation and natural selection. Basic to this conclusion are observations showing that aspects of behavior can vary markedly, depending on the individual's genetic background. As one of many illustrations, the data in Figure 35-10 show how biologists have been able to use standard methods of selective breeding (Chapter 30) in rats, and thus develop from a single stock divergent strains which learn by trial-and-error either especially quickly or especially slowly.

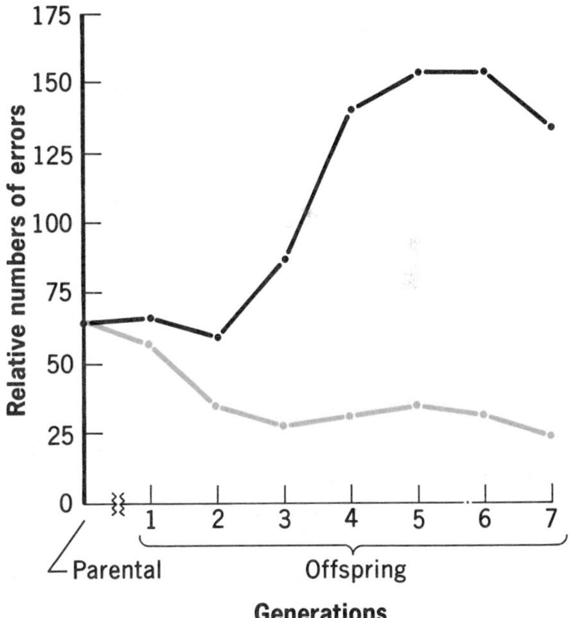

National Society for the Study of Education

35–10 Selective breeding of rats for relatively few generations can produce strains that show marked differences in the average number of errors made by individuals in trial-and-error learning under a given set of conditions.

As we look over the entire range of activity patterns in animals, some general ideas emerge. In comparing more complex with less complex animals, we find that more highly evolved forms tend to show more complex behavior patterns. Simple taxes and reflex activity tend to be less conspicuous in the range of activities of higher as compared with simpler animals. Among the arthropods and some of the mollusks and vertebrates, elaborate innate patterns of behavior are often found. In some higher mollusks and vertebrates in particular, there is remarkable capacity for modifying behavior in relation to experience, through learning and in other ways. In mammals and especially man, the remarkable brain processes like insight and reasoning occur. Finally, we can note as a generalization that animals show many patterns of behavior closely related to *space, time,* and *interactions with other organisms.*

Behavior Related to Space

Most animals show behavior specifically related to space or place. Many seek food in a relatively wide area, yet tend always to return to a particular home base. Insects like bees and ants have established nests or hives where the reproductive members of the community, the young, and the food stores are kept and protected. Other members of the community range widely, collecting food and bringing it back to the nest or hive. Sometimes these animals find their way back to home base by following chemical trails laid out as they travel. In other cases, they follow clues given by light from the sky and the sun as they navigate long distances. A fascinating study of how bees use special properties of light to guide themselves has been carried out by Karl von Frisch (fone FRISH) and other scientists. Birds and mammals show somewhat similar behavior, especially when they are caring for young.

Animals often recognize places not only as evidenced by the fact that they return again and again to the same nest or special spot, as we have mentioned in the foregoing paragraph, but also as evidenced by the behavior of some animals as if a particular area was under their special rule or care. This latter kind of behavior is called *territorial.* The animals guard their territory, driving away other members of their own species (usually *not* members of other species) which come into the particular territory. This type of behavior has been carefully studied in many species of birds. Typically, birds of a given species build nests at fairly wide intervals. A male and a female bird can forage all around their nest without interference from other birds of the same species, for these do not enter the couple's territory. The borders of the territory are defended by the male bird. He will attack intruders, although usually this is not necessary since members of the species tend to stay out of the territory. Apparently this interesting behavior is dependent on the characteristic song of the male bird, which serves as a warning or "advertisement" of the boundaries of his territory. Somewhat similar patterns of territoriality are seen in some mammals.

A third important case of behavior in relation to place is *migration.* Many species of insects and vertebrates travel long distances during the course of their lives. Birds often nest and rear their young during warm seasons at latitudes far from the equator (in North America and Europe, or South America and Africa, for instance). Then, as winter approaches, they move toward the equator, spending a few months there, then travel north or south again as spring comes to the regions more distant from the equator. The distances traveled in migration may be thousands of miles. Even though much of the route lies over oceans, some birds are nearly unbelievably accurate in their ability to return year after year to the same place. Often the young migrate before the adults. How do they find the way? Some mammals and insects show somewhat similar migration patterns. Certain fish species have still another interesting type of migratory behavior. They may hatch from eggs in freshwater lakes or streams, then move downstream and out to sea to spend most of their adult lives. When they are ready to reproduce, they migrate back to the shore, then upstream to the freshwater streams or lakes where they deposit eggs and sperms. Here the next generation of young fish hatch out. In some cases it has been proved that a fish of a given species (for instance, salmon) will return to the *very same stream* where it was hatched—not merely to a *similar* stream or lake (Figure 35-11). Other species of fish (eels, for instance) may live as adults in fresh water, yet migrate to sea to carry out reproduction.

Though much research has been carried out, little is yet known for sure as to how animals orient themselves in long migration. Apparently they sometimes use cues like the position of the sun or stars, and the character of light from the sky. Recognition of a landmark—a mountain, or lake, or patch of forest—may help some animals traveling over land. But this certainly would not help a small bird in its flight overseas from Hawaii to Alaska. Recognition of place by chemical senses may play some part, at least in fish migration. But on the whole, we find it easier today to ask questions than to answer them as we study patterns of animal migration.

Behavior Related to Time

A major problem for any animal that orients itself in relation to the position of the sun in the sky, or light from the sky, is that these clues are not constant. The position of the earth with respect to the sun, and the light from the sky, vary during the course of each day and night. A person can decide direction by looking at the sun. In the morning he looks toward the sun and says that he is looking in the eastward direction. If he did not know it was morning (that is, if he had no sense of time) he would not be able to tell whether the direction of the sun was eastward or westward. But how about bees and other animals that guide themselves by sky light or by the position of the sun—are they able to correct the information they receive according to the time of day? Biologists were surprised to find that the answer to this question must be yes. These animals, like man, must be able to "tell time."

Although we do not know exactly what we mean when we say that animals can "tell time," timed activities are easily observed in all multicellular animals—as indeed they also are in plants and single-celled organisms. Often the changing activity is closely correlated with the great cyclic events of the environment—the movements of the earth and moon with respect to the sun, and correlated events like the patterns of day and night, seasons, weather, and tides. Almost without exception, the timing of activities of organisms is clearly adaptive. Thus, reproductive activities of plants and animals occur at favorable times of year. Organisms grow when there is a rich food supply, and migrate (in the case of animals) or enter into a protected and metabolically inactive state (microorganisms, plants, and animals) at unfavorably hot, cold, or dry seasons of the year. Many animals are inactive during the daytime, when light is abundant and they would be easily detected by organisms hunting them. Rhythmic behavior patterns allow them to be active at night, seeking food themselves and carrying on their various other activities. Often we can recognize that the activities of animals are closely timed in relation to the activities of other organisms. When certain plants bloom, behavioral patterns of particular species of insects allow the young insects to mature to the point that they can not only use the flowers' nectar as food, but also pollinate the flowers (Chapter 32). Oysters and many other sea-dwelling invertebrates which shed their reproductive cells into the water do so in close coordination with other members of their species, not at random. Even when such reproductive behavior occurs in only a very short time (for instance, in one 24-hour period out of a year), all the organisms of a given species carry out their reproductive activities at once.

At present, we do not understand the mechanisms involved in timing the activities of ani-

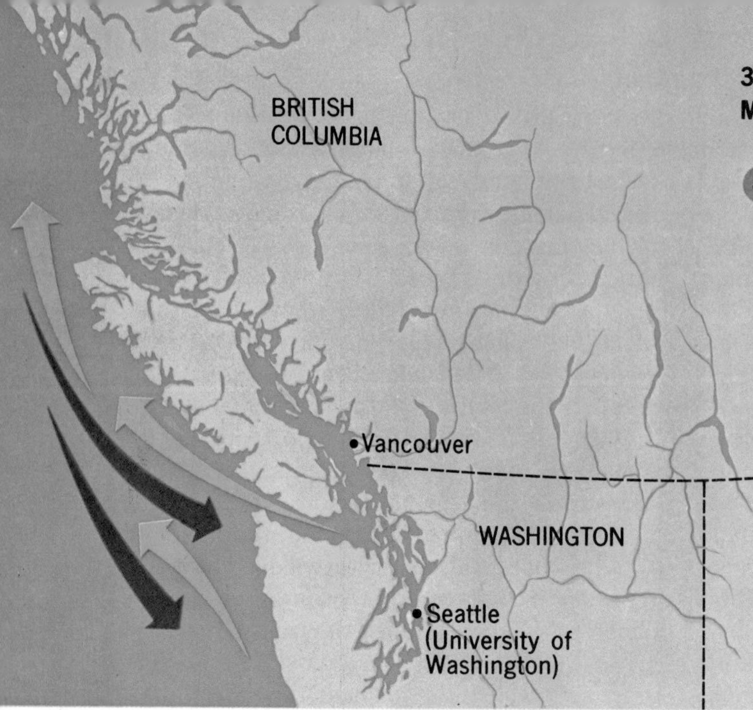

35-11
MIGRATORY BEHAVIOR IN SALMON

a Salmon breed in fresh water lakes and streams along the northwest coast of the United States and Canada. After the eggs hatch, the young salmon grow for a period of time in fresh water, then migrate to sea (orange arrows). They spend two to five years growing to adults, then return to breed in the lakes and streams where they hatched. They may travel for more than a thousand miles on their way to their breeding waters (gray arrows.) At the University of Washington, L.R. Donaldson has developed a strain of extra-large salmon by selective breeding. The fish are marked before they migrate to sea.

b After three years at sea, an adult male Chinook salmon swims upstream to his home breeding pond at the University of Washington.

James O. Sneddon, University of Washington

c L.R. Donaldson identifies the mark on an adult salmon. How can such an animal find its way back from the open ocean to *this particular pond* where its life began?

James O. Sneddon, University of Washington

mals. It seems probable that there must exist basically rhythmic patterns within the organism itself, but we have very little evidence about what these may involve in terms of cell structures and processes. Even though the cycle of timing originates in processes within the animal itself, it apparently can be started up or checked by major characteristics of the environment that also show timing (like average length of day, or maximum height of tide at one coastal region). Thus, many biologists believe that timing of behavior results from a combination of effects of rhythmic internal processes and timed events of the environment. There are some puzzling cases which do not fit in with this explanation, however, in which an animal's activities do not seem to be directly controlled by any known environmental events. Whatever the future may promise for explaining rhythmic activities, capacity for timing (or for maintaining rhythmic processes related to time) apparently is basic to all living things.

It is no doubt obvious to you that time is a major factor in regulating behavior in all people, including yourself. Such timing is often based on cycles that are roughly 24 hours in length, as you know from your own cycles of activity and sleeping. Though human-timed cycles are partly dependent on social conditioning (at least in the setting of the actual hours of work, recreation, and rest), they are clearly shown by individual cell function as well as by more obvious bodily activity. General cell metabolism, mitosis of the cells of the skin, hair, and fingernails, nerve sensitivity, body temperature, excretion of water and salts, and many other aspects of human physiology vary more or less consistently during daily cycles. (These are often referred to as **circadian** [ser·KAYD-i·an] – a term which means "*about* one day," admitting a good deal of individual variation in the actual number of hours in many animal rhythms of approximately day-length.) You may not feel your best when the school day begins, but some time during the hours between morning and sunset you have a peak of alertness, muscular activity, nerve sensitivity, body temperature, and so forth. Similarly, you doubtless show a *minimum* in many of these variables around 12 hours later. If you flew by jet to another country where 8 A.M. today at home corresponds to 2 A.M. there, you might easily feel lively late at night (your body's morning) and very sleepy and tired at 6 P.M. (your body's midnight). Although you might adjust to the new timing cycle rather quickly, the experience would convince you that your body processes run by "clocks" which are not reset as easily when you travel as is your watch or alarm clock. Bodily timing cycles and abrupt changes in local time are probably important features in much of today's popular "jet fatigue."

Other cyclically timed events which you know about in man are the rapid rhythms of heart contractions and breathing movements, and the approximately monthly rhythm of changes in the female reproductive system. Some of these rhythms are clearly reflected in human behavior, while others are never noticed because they recur so often and rapidly, or because they are masked by environmental factors or social adjustments. It would be profitable for you to think of and list as many human activities as possible which you can recognize as timed. Would it be possible to determine in each case which processes show timing because of social control, and which represent actual body-timed cycles? Human behavior and its variation in relation to time is an interesting study – but only one of thousands which we could have chosen – illustrating the importance of timing in behavioral regulation in animals.

Behavior in Interactions with Other Animals

Perhaps the examples of behavior you know already, and some we have described in this chapter, will give you a basis for drawing some conclusions about interactions among animals. They vary enormously in complexity. Thus, there are single animal-single animal encounters: examples are competition for a given food

R. D. Estes

35–12 Dividing the spoils. When different species use the same resource, their relationships may range all the way from competitive behavior to behavior that regulates or even prevents competition. This kill was made by a lion, who was the first to feed on the carcass. With the lion now gone, a hyena **(left)** and two jackals **(right)** compete for their portions, with the jackals periodically withdrawing under threat from the hyena. Two vultures **(background)** wait their turn; they are last in this hierarchy.

source (Figure 35-12), predator-prey relationships (Figure 35-13), and mating activities. At the other end of the scale are highly elaborate patterns of social behavior in insects and primates. Many animals show interactions with others which are fairly long-lasting, or even lifelong. Good examples of these are formation of stable pairs of animals which mate and care for young throughout their lives. Often many individuals of a given species associate in a relatively small space, and some sort of social interaction may then occur. Sometimes this is no more than the chance encounter of many individuals at feeding places or in regions offering protection. Among insects, fish, and birds, behavior patterns in which great numbers of individuals travel together in great numbers are seen quite frequently. It is not yet clear whether there is any stable organization within such groups (for instance, swarms of locusts, flocks of birds, schools of fish).

Social organization at a rather simple level is often seen in groups of birds and mammals living together in restricted space. This may take the form of establishment of a sort of order among the individuals so that some (often stronger members of the group) have first chance at food supplies. A stronger or dominant individual in the group may attack another without itself being attacked in return. In flocks of chickens and other birds, a definite pattern of dominance and submissiveness (the pecking order) is established between individuals. In every flock of chickens, there is usually one chicken at the top of the pecking order. At the opposite end of the scale is a bird which does not resist if pecked by any other member of the group. Intermediate individuals show tendencies to peck or allow themselves to be pecked in rather consistent order. This can be interpreted as the beginning of social organization. It indicates clear recognition on the part of each bird of the other members of the flock, and of the position of each in the established order. Mammals living in herds and other groups show rather similar organization based on dominance and submission of the individuals within the group. In some cases, the activities of a leader—often an old and experienced male—dominate and guide the behavior of the group as a whole.

Far more elaborate is the social organization which is seen in some groups of insects (for instance, some bees and ants). Thus, in a given species of ant, great numbers of individuals may live together in a single community (Figure 35-14). Each individual is closely specialized in body structure and behavior so that it fulfills special functions that benefit the community as a whole. Generally there is a single mature female (queen) which founds the community and lays eggs that hatch into separate classes, or castes, of ants. These include workers, which seek for food, bring it back to the nest, and feed and care for the queen and the young. Sometimes there is a special caste of fighters, with powerful jaws and poison glands. A few males are hatched and may be retained in the community to fertilize the queen. Certain individuals of a special caste may serve merely to store reserves of food in their bodies. Moreover, in some ant communities, entirely unrelated organisms such as fungi or aphids, which can provide food, are maintained with great care by the workers. Such an elaborate social organization requires an immense number of adaptations, ranging from adjustment of body size and function to behavior of individuals and their interaction and communication with one another (Figure 35-4). Touch and chemical stimulation and hormonal control play major parts in establishing and maintaining these interrelationships. The problems of evolution of social organization in insects are among the most fascinating in the field of animal behavior. This is not to underrate, however, the puzzling and remarkable problems of social organization in higher mammals and man. Primate and human societies depend on quite different techniques of social organization from insect communities. You will find it interesting to think over human society as you know it and consider to what extent it is based on cultural, rather than biological, evolutionary processes.

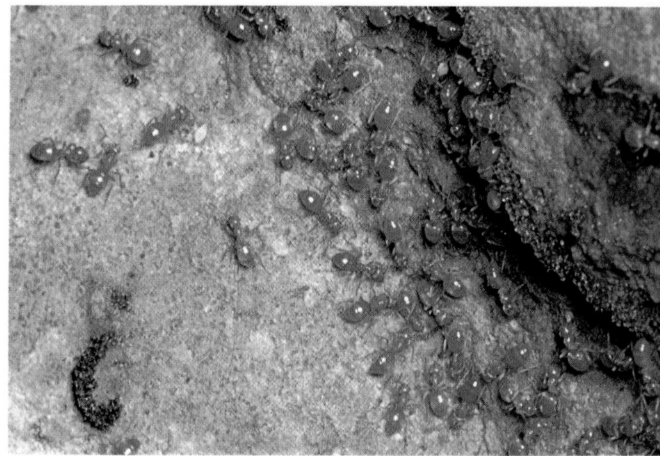

H. Green from Annan Photo Features

35–14 An ant community consists of hundreds or thousands of individuals. In this photograph only a small number can be seen. There are usually several types of individuals that differ in structure and behavioral pattern. Each has its specialized function in the colony. Organized behavior of many individuals requires rapid and efficient communication (see Figure 35–4).

35–13 Learning to be successful as predators is part of the education of lion cubs. By the time they are a year old, they are given lessons in stalking by their parents. The behavioral changes help set them apart clearly from animals that are learning a different lesson—how to hide or flee.

Norman Myers from Black Star

CONCLUDING REMARKS

If you look back over this chapter, you will see that we have mentioned behavior ranging from simple to complex. Some is very stable and predictable, other behavior can be readily modified by conditioning and learning, and by the special "higher" brain processes so characteristic of man. The whole field of behavior is so vast, and interpretation of any particular case so difficult, that we are still not able to describe or account for the entire range of behavior in any species—or even in a single animal! But it is interesting to see how far one can get in such an attempt, and we invite you to try this in Laboratory Inquiry 35-2. Perhaps this exercise will give you some direct understanding of the present state of the study of behavior—a field in which scientists are working with excitement, much argument, and a keen sense for the importance of the work they are doing.

Although the study of animal behavior is a relatively new field in biological science, a vast amount of information has been collected already. We have selected a few topics to discuss in this chapter, but there is far more that we could tell and that you would find interesting. The short space left in this book forces us to stop our account here. But now that you have a start on understanding animal behavior, you can continue this study by yourself by observing animals (a caterpillar on a lettuce leaf; a bird flying past the window; your pet dog or cat; even your friends and yourself). This observation, supplemented by further reading and study, will prove to be very rewarding. The world of animals about you becomes far more interesting as you begin to understand more about patterns of behavior.

Perhaps you will even find more direct rewards in this study, for it may assist you in making your own activities more effective. If you are willing to admit that you can be motivated by specific rewards, and strongly affected by external and internal conditions, you will be able to control your activities more closely according to your wishes. For instance, consider your present activities as a high school student. Experiments have shown that mammals, including man, are more alert and can learn more quickly when they are in surroundings which offer a moderate amount of stimulation to the various senses. Likewise, great monotony in the surroundings slows the learning process and may result in drowsiness. On the other hand, too much stimulation is correlated with slower learning, and animals make many errors and become restless and irritable when there is so much stimulation that the environment becomes distracting. Perhaps you can apply these findings in your own case, as you consider whether you can best study for an examination by yourself in a quiet room, with or without a radio, or in a roomful of people with the television turned on full blast. Another interesting case in which behavioral research might be applied to your own case is the observation on both people and other mammals that curiosity is a strong source of motivation. Perhaps you realize already from your own experience that it is easier to learn well and quickly if you are interested in what you are studying. This means, too, that if you feel that it is important to learn something, you might begin by finding what is really interesting to you about the subject, and concentrating on that as you study. A third application of behavioral experiments to your life as a student can be made in connection with knowledge of timed (circadian, for instance) patterns of activity. You can easily discover by experiment what times of day are best used for study, and when you can most efficiently spend time relaxing or sleeping. Although you may decide to study throughout a 24 hour period, you will do so at the cost of lowered efficiency—you cannot escape from the limitations imposed on your behavior by your "internal clocks."

Nowadays there are many scientists actively engaged in applied research in behavior. They study both man and other animals. Such study can be applied to an enormous range of problems—from law, education (we have just sketched an example), and advertising, to milk production by cattle and the training of animals for TV shows and circuses. The information obtained can be of great value to man. Unfortunately, it could also be misused. One of the basic principles of a free society is that people should be able to decide for themselves what they want to do, and make and enforce laws so that the majority of people can do these things. But if a particular group of people could discover how to influence other people's behavior, guiding them to do things they really do not wish or intend to do, freedom of society could be endangered. Right now, this is not a particularly great threat, because so little is known about the basis of human behavior that it is still difficult to influence people very predictably. But the situation may change as more and more is learned about behavior, and it will be important for you to keep up with what is going on in this field.

GUIDE QUESTIONS AND PROBLEMS

1. Criticize the statement, "Squirrels bury acorns for the winter." What other common expressions about animal behavior are subject to misinterpretation?
2. Check the meaning and pronunciation of the word *anthropomorphism* in a dictionary. What is the basis for saying that students of animal behavior must avoid anthropomorphic phrases when making interpretations from their studies?
3. Many insects seem attracted to lights on summer evenings. How would you investigate whether this is a positive taxis toward light?
4. How could you find out if bees are more often attracted to yellow flowers than to red flowers? Suggest an experimental plan.
5. What adaptive significance might be attached to *imprinting*?
6. Suppose you were a fish and game biologist on the West Coast of the United States and were assigned the problem of stocking salmon in a freshwater stream that runs into the Pacific Ocean. The salmon should use the stream as a breeding ground from year to year, if your work is to be effective. How would you go about making your plans and carrying them out? What factors in the behavior of salmon would you have to take into account?
7. What might be some problems you would encounter if you set out to make observations about dog behavior using your pet dog as the experimental animal?
8. Considering what you have learned in this chapter, would it be correct to say that a theory has been established which explains the physical basis of memory and learning? Support your answer by reviewing your understanding of the term *theory* in relation to the evidence that has been presented about memory and learning in this chapter.
9. What evidence suggests that specific areas of the brain, such as the hypothalamus, affect behavior?
10. Suppose you feel drowsy in biology class. Suggest some factors that might change your behavior from drowsy to alert.
11. How do innate behavior patterns differ from learned behavior patterns? What would be some of the difficulties involved in distinguishing clearly between these types of behavior in a human being?
12. Certain cyclic behavior patterns are correlated with the lunar month, which is slightly shorter than a calendar month. What might be the adaptive value of the timed behavior patterns? How can their existence be accounted for?
13. Social hierarchy exists in many animal groups where one animal, usually a mature male, becomes the recognized group leader. What significance might this have for the survival of the group? What might be some detrimental effects of this type of leader-follower organization?
14. Peck order in chickens may be changed by giving testosterone injections to submissive chickens, which then become more aggressive and move up in the peck order. What other things might affect an established peck order? What experiments might be designed to test your ideas?
15. Male and female mockingbirds seem to be identical in appearance. How might sex difference be communicated in a pattern of reproductive behavior?

RELATED READING

Books

For accounts of behavior illustrated by examples from a variety of animals . . .

Dethier, V. G., and E. Steller, *Animal Behavior,* Second Edition, Prentice-Hall, Englewood Cliffs, New Jersey, 1964. An introductory account.

McGill, T. E., *Readings in Animal Behavior,* Holt, Rinehart and Winston, New York, 1965. An advanced account.

Portman, A., *Animals as Social Beings,* Harper and Row, New York, 1961 (paperback).

Scott, John P., *Animal Behavior,* The Natural History Library, Anchor Books (Doubleday and Company), Garden City, New York, 1963 (paperback).

For behavioral studies of animals of a single species . . .

Adamson, Joy, *Born Free: A Lioness of Two Worlds,* Pantheon Books, New York, 1960 (and Macfadden-Bartell Corp., 1962 – paperback); and Adamson, Joy, *Living Free,* Harcourt, Brace & World, New York, 1961. The story of Elsa the lion, raised as a pet and later taught by the author to live as a lioness in the wild. Later accounts cover the early life and training of Elsa's cubs, including observations of their behavioral development.

Darling, F. F., *A Herd of Red Deer,* The Natural History Library, Anchor Books (Doubleday and Company), Garden City, New York, 1964 (paperback).

Schaller, G. B., *The Year of the Gorilla,* University of Chicago Press, 1964 (and Ballentine Books, New York, 1964 – paperback).

For studies of animal communication . . .

Frings, Hubert, and Mabel Frings, *Animal Communication,* Blaisdell Publishing Company, Boston, 1964.

Gilbert, Bill, *How Animals Communicate,* Pantheon Books, New York, 1966.

von Frisch, Karl, *Bees: Their Vision, Chemical Senses, and Language,* Cornell University Press, Ithaca, New York, 1956.

Magazines

Berlyne, D. C., "Conflict and Arousal," *Scientific American,* Volume 215 (August 1966), page 82.

Bonner, J. T., "How Slime Molds Communicate," *Scientific American,* Volume 209 (August 1963), page 84.

Boycott, Brian B., "Learning in the Octopus," *Scientific American,* Volume 212 (March 1965), page 42.

Esch, Harald, "The Evolution of Bee Language," *Scientific American,* Volume 216 (April 1967), page 96.

Frings, Hubert, and Mable Frings, "The Language of Crows," *Scientific American,* Volume 201 (November 1959), page 119.

Harlow, Harry F., and Margaret K. Harlow, "Social Deprivation in Monkeys," *Scientific American,* Volume 207 (November 1962), page 136.

Kortlandt, Adriaan, "Chimpanzees in the Wild," *Scientific American,* Volume 206 (May 1962), page 128.

Lorenz, Konrad Z., "The Evolution of Behavior," *Scientific American,* Volume 199 (December 1958), page 67.

Roeder, Kenneth D., "Moths and Ultrasound," *Scientific American,* Volume 212 (April 1965), page 94.

Seilacher, A., "Fossil Behavior," *Scientific American,* Volume 217 (August 1967), page 72.

Tinbergen, N., "The Evolution of Behavior in Gulls," *Scientific American,* Volume 203 (December 1960), page 118.

Wenner, Adrian M., "Sound Communication in Honeybees," *Scientific American,* Volume 210 (April 1964), page 116.

BSCS Pamphlets

Brown, F. A., *Biological Clocks,* D. C. Heath and Company, Boston, 1962 (Pamphlet No. 2).

Carr, Archie, *Guideposts of Animal Navigation,* D. C. Heath and Company, Boston, 1962 (Pamphlet No. 1).

Collias, N. E., *Animal Language,* D. C. Heath and Company, Boston, 1964 (Pamphlet No. 20).

Farner, D. C., *Photoperiodism in Animals,* D. C. Heath and Company, Boston, 1964 (Pamphlet No. 15).

Mayer, William V., *Hibernation,* D. C. Heath and Company, Boston, 1964 (Pamphlet No. 19).

Meyerriecks, A. J., *Courtship in Animals,* D. C. Heath and Company, Boston, 1962 (Pamphlet No. 3).

36

Checks and Balances in Nature

In the preceding chapter you learned of some of the ways organisms behave, including how they interact with one another. Biologists learned long ago that organisms also interact with their physical environments. In fact, the interaction between evolving organisms and the environment is so intimate that all organisms are, in part, the product of their environments. The study of the interactions between the changing physical environment and evolving organisms will help us to understand why and how plants and animals live where they do. This, essentially, is what **ecology** (ee·KOL·o-jee) is about.

The study of interactions of plants and animals with one another and with the physical environment is a complex subject. The scene pictured in Figure 36-1 suggests the environmental components that may determine how and where an organism will live. Let us list these environmental components and separate them—as Figure 36-1 has done—into physical factors and biological factors.

Physical Factors	*Biological Factors*
1. Energy	1. Green plants
2. Temperature	2. Animals
3. Water	3. Nongreen plants
4. Atmosphere	
5. Fire	
6. Gravity	
7. Topography	
8. Geological substrate	
9. Soil	

Keeping this list of environmental components in mind, look at the two photographs in Figure 36-2. Which of the components in the list are shown in the left-hand photograph? Which components are not shown by the photograph but are ones that would affect giraffes in their natural environment? In what ways do giraffes have an effect on the physical and biological components of their environment? Clearly we could ask the same questions about any kind of organism from the smallest bacterium to the largest redwood tree or whale, for no individual organism or population of organisms is complete in itself. Each has numerous and complex interactions with other individuals of the same and other species as well as with the physical environment. The interacting plants and animals, as they exist in nature, are part of an ecological system or **ecosystem** (EEK·o·sis·tem or EK·o·sis·tem).

An ecosystem may be in a square meter of prairie, the edge of a pond, a tide pool, an alpine meadow, a few cubic meters of surface water of the ocean, or a closed bottle containing some algae and protozoans. In Inquiry 36-1 you will prepare just such a closed ecosystem. All it needs is light and a proper temperature. A tide pool (Figure 36-3), on the other hand, is influenced by what occurs in the nearby ocean and on the shore. It has no sharp boundaries—nor do most other ecosystems.

PHYSICAL FACTORS OF THE ECOSYSTEM

Energy

We might guess that practically all of the energy in an ecosystem originates as radiation from the sun. Light energy (visible light) from the sun is captured by green plants in the process of photosynthesis and converted into chemical energy, a process we have discussed in some detail (Chapter 15). Light energy, with wavelengths between 400-760 mμ, is also important in heating the environment. Solar radiation with wavelengths over 760 mμ is in-

36-1 INTERACTION OF PLANTS AND ANIMALS WITH THE ENVIRONMENT

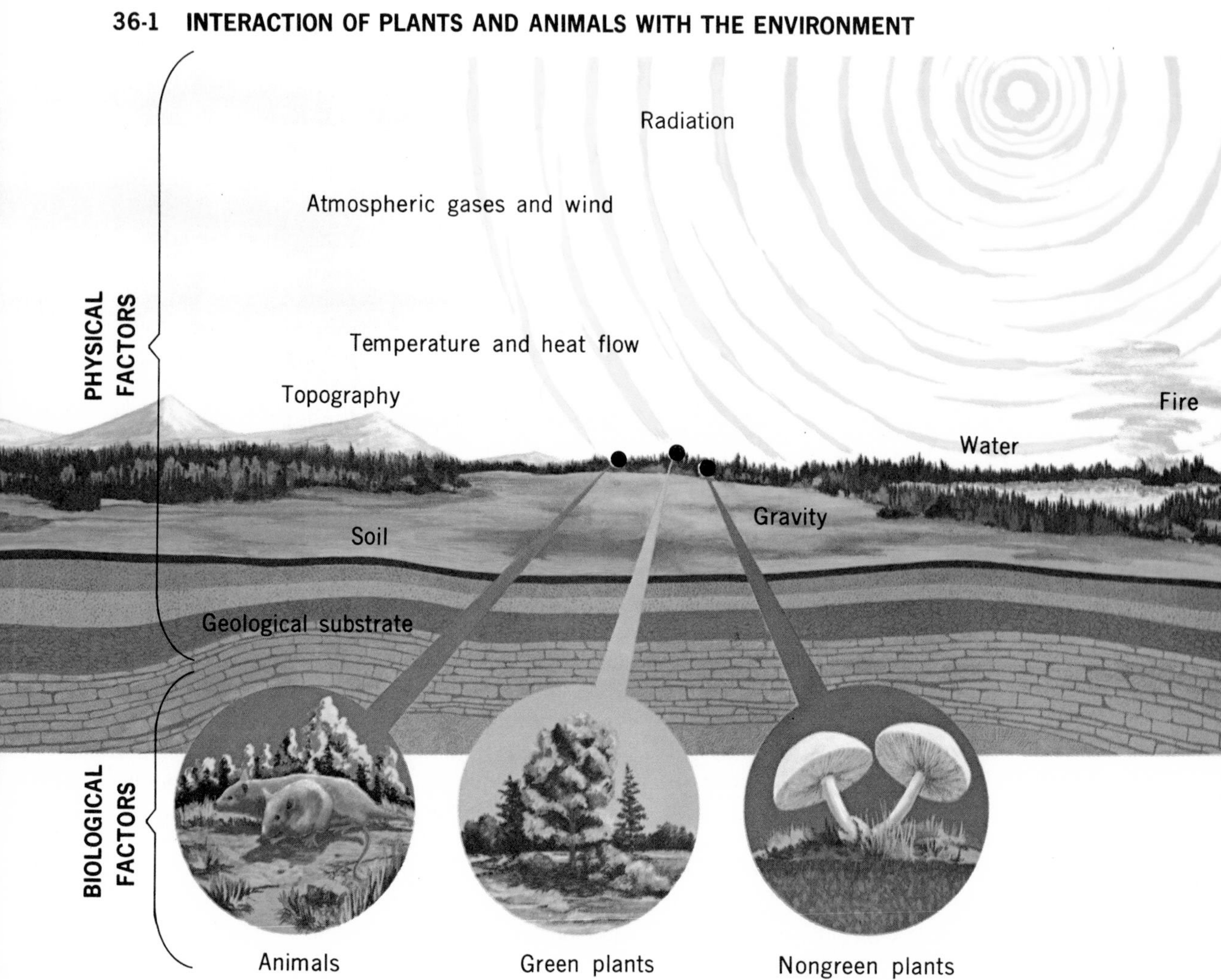

visible to the eye but can be felt as radiant heat. An even smaller part of the radiant energy that influences an ecosystem is ultraviolet radiation with wavelengths shorter than those of visible light. Ultraviolet light in large doses may be harmful to the cells of living organisms. Fortunately, most of the ultraviolet light is absorbed by a part of the atmosphere called the ozone layer. This layer is approximately 16 miles above the earth's surface. Other parts of solar radiation also decrease as they pass through the atmosphere. Thus ecosystems in the seas or at sea level receive less radiant energy than ecosystems of mountains.

Temperature

Gases, liquids, or solids that occur in the ecosystems may also absorb radiant energy. The result will be an increase in the temperature of the absorbing substances. If, for example, the temperature of the soil or ocean is higher than the temperature of the surrounding atmosphere, heat energy will flow from the warmer to the cooler part of the environment. Such a flow of heat energy is spectacularly displayed by the warm winds that blow on to the coast of Oregon and Washington from the Pacific Ocean. These warm winds modify the environment by providing the area with mild temperatures and abundant rainfall. One of the results is a luxuriant growth of plants some of which would not normally be found growing at such northerly latitudes (Figure 36-4).

Heat flow, the movement of heat in the ecosystems from high to low temperatures, can occur by molecular conduction, movement of air or water currents, or by reradiation. Much of the radiant energy received by the ecosystem is, however, lost as heat energy.

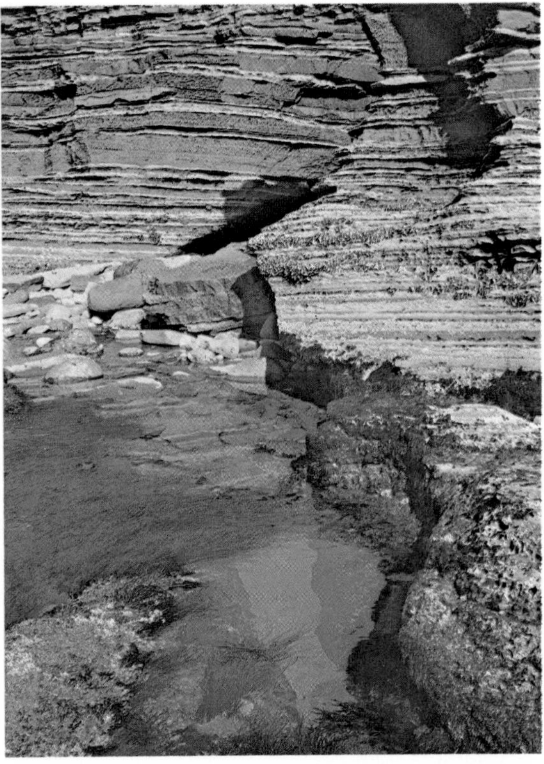

Dennis Brokaw

36–3 (Above) A tidal pool. The environment of the tidal pool may change radically several times a day, as the tide moves in and out. The organisms inhabiting the pool must be able to endure these changes. Look ahead to Figure 37–5 and compare it to this photograph; then try to identify the clusters of organisms on the rocks at the upper right.

36–2 (Below) An animal in and out of its environment. The importance of the environment to our understanding of the organisms that inhabit it is suggested by the obvious differences between the two photographs. Both show the same giraffe. But the photograph at the right conveys nothing of this particular animal's way of life—where it lives, what it feeds upon, whether its habitat is warm or cold, or densely overgrown by plants, or partly open and sunny—or even, as indicated in the photograph on the left, a suggestion of how cumbersome it is for the animal to eat or drink. How does the spotty pattern of coloration on the giraffe suggest the nature of its appearance when it is hidden in a thicket of trees?

H. W. Kitchen from Photo Researchers

G. R. Roberts

36–4 A monkey puzzle tree. This tree may be found growing in a tropical rain forest or in a garden in Seattle, Washington. Would you expect to find it growing in Maine?

Water

Water is one of the most important factors of the ecosystem. It is not evenly distributed over the earth. It is most abundant in aquatic ecosystems and least abundant in deserts.

The supply of water in the earth's atmosphere has been estimated to be only enough to provide a one-inch rainfall for the entire world, or about a 10-day supply. This limited supply means that cycling of water (Figure 36-5) by precipitation, transpiration from plants, and evaporation must be rapid and continuous.

The abundance of water, or the lack of it, has a striking effect on the ecosystems of a given region. This is well illustrated in the state of Washington. The primary source of water for this region is the Pacific Ocean. Water vapor from the ocean is carried in from the northwest by storm systems that originate in the Aleutians and the Gulf of Alaska. As the moisture-laden Pacific air moves inland (Figure 36-6) over the coastal ranges of the state (the Olympic Mountains), the air rises, expands, and cools. The

36-5 THE WATER CYCLE

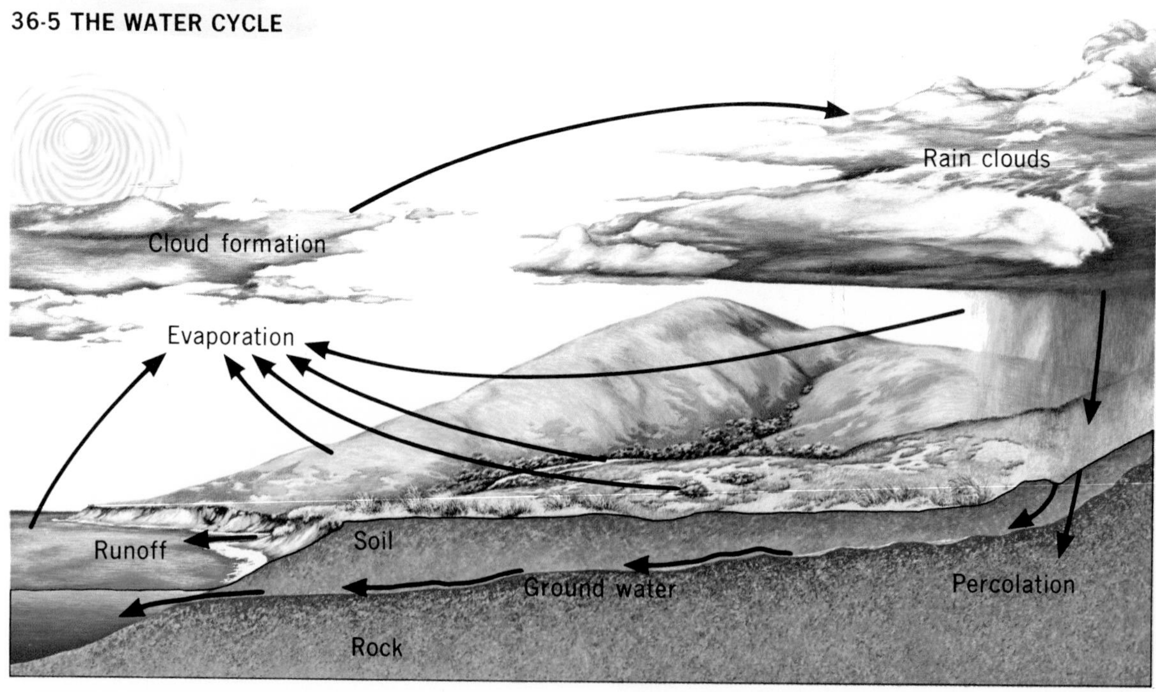

All photos by John A. Moore

36–6 Climatic conditions in western Washington. The coast **(a)**, with its Olympic rain forest **(b** and **c)**, receives more than 350 cm (140 inches) of rainfall each year. Just east of the Olympic Mountains, where the Cascades begin to rise **(d** and **e)**, are forests of Douglas fir, with some western hemlock and Sitka spruce. Little moisture gets past the Cascades; near-desert conditions prevail beyond **(f)**, where crops must be irrigated.

result is a very heavy rainfall on the seaward side of the mountains. The average annual precipitation in certain places on the west side of the Olympic Mountains is 355 centimeters (142 inches).

The ecosystem produced by this abundant rain and moderate temperatures is, in many ways, similar to a tropical rain forest except that in place of the exotic trees of the tropics we find magnificent specimens of Douglas fir, Sitka spruce, and hemlock (Figure 36-7). Like the tropical rain forest, the trees of the coniferous rain forest have an abundance of **epiphytes** (EP·uh·fites), plants that grow on the surface of other plants. In the coniferous rain forest many kinds of mosses and liverworts hang from the branches (Figure 36-8). One of the more unusual epiphytes is *Selaginella* (sel·AG·in·ella), a species of vascular plant. This plant gets water for its growth from the moisture-laden atmosphere and from the mosses that act like a sponge holding rain water on the branches high above the ground. Because of the intense shade provided by the trees, only shade-tolerant plants such as certain ferns and mosses survive on the forest floor. These are some of the characteristics that identify this ecosystem as a coniferous rain forest.

After moving inland over the mountains, the air, which has lost some of its moisture, descends into the trough formed by Puget Sound. As it descends, the air is warmed and tends to hold more of its remaining moisture. This reduces the precipitation so that Seattle receives only 87.5 centimeters (35 inches) of rainfall a year. As it continues eastward from the Sound, the air encounters yet another range of mountains, the Cascades. Once again the air cools

John A. Moore

36–8 Epiphytes growing in the temperate rain forest of the state of Washington. The epiphytes consist chiefly of species of mosses and liverworts. What principal characteristics of the climate of the rain forest support such a luxuriant growth of plants, so far north of the tropics?

36–7 Sitka spruce and western hemlock growing in the temperate rain forest of Washington. Magnificent trees such as these and Douglas firs make the temperate rain forest the greatest timber-producing ecosystem on the earth.

Ruth Kirk

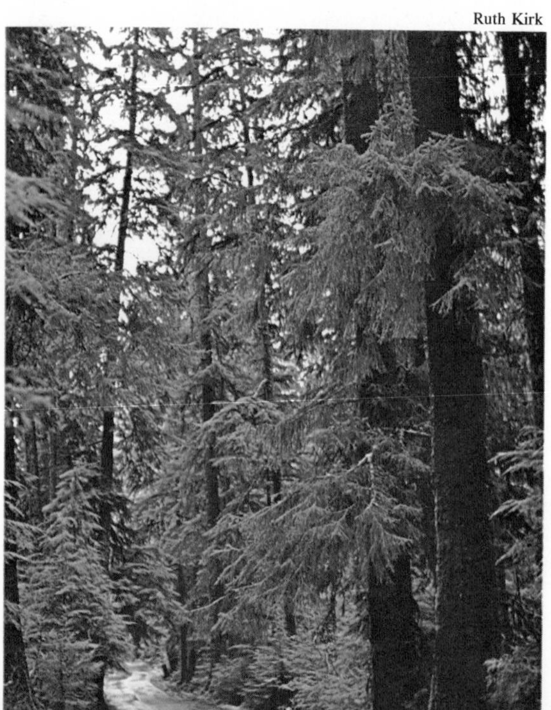

rapidly and the moisture it contains condenses into rainfall. But remember that the air is drier than when it passed over the Olympics. The amount of precipitation on the west slopes of the Cascades therefore will be less than in the Olympics. At about 600 meters (2,000 feet), the annual rainfall in the Cascades is 200 to 250 centimeters (80 to 100 inches), noticeably less than in the Olympics.

By the time the air mass crosses the Cascades, it has lost most of its water vapor. When the air descends the east side of the Cascades into the Columbia River Valley, little or no moisture remains to be precipitated. Even though you may never have been in the Columbia River Valley, where there may be less than 18 centimeters (7 inches) of rainfall a year, you can guess that it has the characteristics of a desert ecosystem (Figure 36-9). Here we see outcrops of columnar volcanic rocks, scattered sagebrush, and a few tufts of drought-resistant bunch grasses. Nowhere can we see any resemblance to the luxuriant coniferous rain forests of the Olympic Peninsula.

The availability of water to organisms in an ecosystem is related to many factors, such as the rapidity of **runoff** (water not absorbed by the soil), which in turn may be determined by the slope of a hill, the nature of the soil, or the kind of vegetation that is present in the ecosystem. If the soil has much sand and is composed of large rocky particles, most water drains rapidly into gullies and normally dry stream beds. Little of it is held by the soil where it can be utilized for plant growth. If the soil is fine grained and contains much decaying vegetable material, the water will soak in and be held as in a sponge. Clearly the water in the latter type of soil will be held better against the force of gravity than in a loose, sandy or rocky soil without decaying material. Sandy, rocky soils are often characteristic of desert ecosystems, while soils rich in organic material are often found in grasslands and in forests. The interaction of soil,

36–9 A portion of the Columbia River Basin, which lies east of the Cascades in the state of Washington. The sparse annual rainfall is probably the limiting factor in this ecosystem. What special characteristics would you expect to find in the plants and animals living here, which would enable them to adapt to their environment?

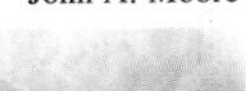

John A. Moore

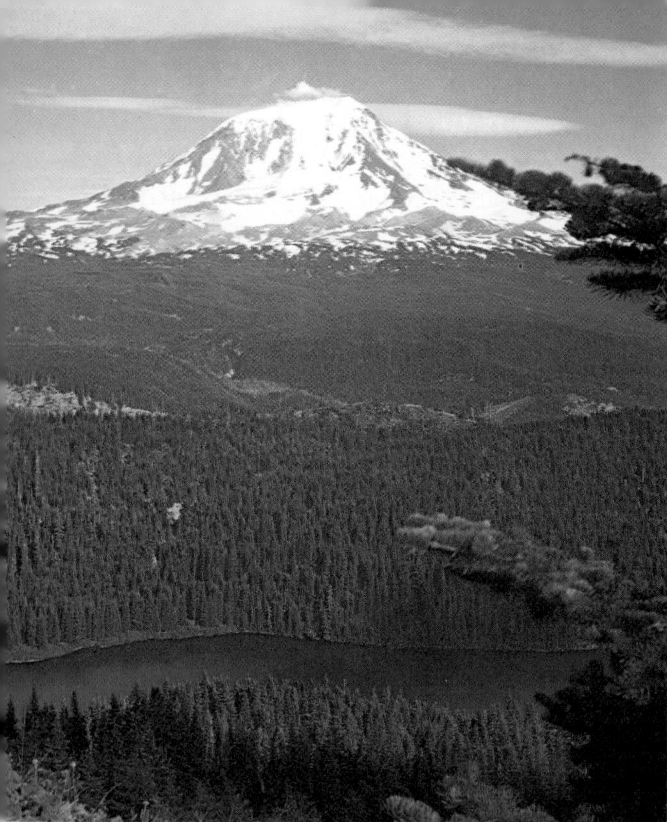

Annan Photo Features

36–10 Timberline on Mount Adams in Washington. Above a certain elevation on high mountains, trees will not grow except as stunted, shrublike plants. What are some of the environmental factors characteristic of high elevations that limit tree growth and determine a timberline?

topography (the configuration of the earth's surface), and water is as important an interaction as any in a terrestrial ecosystem.

Atmosphere and Wind

Because we usually cannot see the atmosphere, we may overlook it as an important part of an ecosystem. The atmosphere *is*, however, a storehouse of some very important substances needed by living things. The CO_2 required for photosynthesis and the O_2 so vital in respiration are both found here. Some nitrogen of the atmosphere is used in building the proteins of living things in the ecosystem.

Atmosphere in motion is wind. These air currents created by heat flow redistribute the components of the atmosphere. By increasing the rate of evaporation and transpiration, the air currents increase the accumulation of water vapor in the atmosphere, which is then precipitated on the earth as we have described.

Wind is the chief factor responsible for timberline on mountains (Figure 36-10). Large plants cannot withstand the blasting of their stems and leaves by ice and snow in the terrific winds. Trees near timberline (Figure 36-11) are characteristically "flag-form," or one-sided trees which are the result of the influence of strong winds. Hurricanes and tornadoes also have drastic effects on ecosystems.

Fire

Of all of the physical factors that may bring about sudden changes in an ecosystem, fire is the most common. A fire of a few minute's duration can drastically change an ecosystem that has been centuries in the making. Man and lightning are the most frequent causes of fires. Where fires are frequent, there is a tendency for a change to occur in the ecosystem that will favor fire-resistant organisms.

Gravity

Of all the physical components of ecosystems, gravity is one of the most constant. We expect the roots of plants to grow down and stems to grow up. We have learned that this is a response to the stimulus of gravity. Much energy is needed to move anything against the pull of gravity. However, many of the structural adaptations of plants and animals are related to the environment. Some of these adaptations enable organisms to overcome the pull of gravity. Striking examples are birds flying and tall trees lifting a water column more than 115 meters (380 feet) into the air against the force of gravity.

The moon with its gravitational pull has an indirect effect on ecosystems, especially those in the tidal regions along the shores of oceans, for as the tide ebbs, organisms that were submerged in the tide pools are often exposed to the harsh environment of the atmosphere.

Topography

We have already seen how the topography may have an effect on the ecosystem. The slope of a mountain may determine the rate of water runoff. The height of a mountain will determine the amount of precipitation, solar radiation, wind, and shade that organisms of the ecosystem receive. The furrows in an Illinois cornfield provide a microtopography where there may be more moisture, thus more weeds. Topography provides the setting for ecosystems.

Geological Substrate and Soil

The soil and the underlying rocks from which it comes—the geological substrate—are closely related. Both provide the all-important reservoir of water and minerals required by organisms inhabiting the ecosystem. It is here that available compounds of iron, calcium, magnesium, and other elements so necessary to the growth of organisms are found. The absence or excess of any one of these or many other elements may have a drastic effect on the organisms that are found in the ecosystem.

Soil is derived from the geological substrate by erosion, which breaks the rocks into particles of silt, sand, or clay. Water and air occupy the spaces between the particles. Countless microorganisms, mainly bacteria and fungi, cause the decay of dead organic material that mixes with the particles of silt, sand, or clay to form part of the soil.

BIOLOGICAL FACTORS OF THE ECOSYSTEM

Green Plants

Green plants and a few other organisms are unique in the living world because they take energy from the nonliving environment and incorporate it in compounds that can be used by all living things. They are the **producers**. By photosynthesis, the green plants bind energy from sunlight into organic compounds needed for their own growth and reproduction. So plentifully do they store these compounds that they supply nearly all the nourishment for all nongreen plants and all animals. Energy from the sun, trapped by photosynthesis, is the power for living things. And oxygen, one by-product of photosynthesis, is required by almost all organisms in order to release this power.

36–11 "Flag-form" trees growing near timberline. The strong prevailing winds in this high-altitude ecosystem cause these trees to look like weathervanes.

Rexford Daubenmeier

Animals

We prefer to describe animals, including ourselves, as the **consumers.** Directly or indirectly all animals live at the expense of green plants. They could be regarded almost as parasites of plants. A community without green plants could not exist; a community without animals could—and probably has!

The beetle grub eating a root, the grasshopper chewing up stems and leaves, and the mouse eating seeds and fruits all live directly upon green plants. These animals are **primary consumers**. The mole eating a beetle grub, the coyote pouncing upon a grasshopper, and the hawk catching a mouse are all **secondary consumers**, because their food consists of the primary consumers. The cat that eats the mole, like the bat that catches a mosquito full of coyote blood, is a consumer, too—of a still higher order, since the energy of the sun has been handed on by further chemical steps of digestion and synthesis into still different compounds.

Nongreen Plants

When the cat, bat, hawk, and coyote die, they become food for bacteria and molds, which are the **decomposers** in nature. Decomposers work also on fallen leaves, dead trees, and other plant remains. They operate in relay teams, simplifying, step by step, the organic constituents of each dead body. In this way they obtain energy and chemical substances for their own growth and reproduction. Their activities make chemical substances available for other living things. Thus chemical substances pass constantly from organism to organism and between organism and the nonliving environment. We call these repeating patterns in the movement of materials in the ecosystems, **cycles**.

As we review the first part of this chapter we should have a fairly clear picture of the requirements of an ecosystem. Important among the physical factors is a source of energy that organisms can use directly or indirectly. There also must be available a supply of all the elements required by the organisms in the ecosystem. There must be organisms or processes that cycle the elements between organism and nonliving environment. Finally there must be suitable temperatures, humidities, and so on. An ecosystem, then, involves organisms, energy, matter, cycles, and climates—all interacting to constitute living nature.

CYCLES IN THE ECOSYSTEMS

If the decomposing body of a plant or animal is in a pond, the decay bacteria that attack it can become food for mosquito wrigglers, which belong to a new generation of consumers. If the decomposing body is in a forest or a field, some of the products of decay are almost sure to go into the soil and become raw materials for green plants. The same atoms are used over and over in cycles. Some of the atoms present in the earliest living things were re-used in the giant dinosaurs and are still being used in plants and animals today.

We have learned that even water is constantly on the move into the roots of plants and out again by transpiration, and into and out of animals. Over the surface and through the earth it flows to the oceans. In the form of rain and snow it returns to the land (Figure 36-5).

We know that the living substance of all organisms is composed chiefly of carbon, hydrogen, oxygen, and nitrogen. In the balance of nature, the inflow and outgo of these four elements, as they cycle through living organisms, are especially important. Because the cycles of carbon, hydrogen, and oxygen are so intimately related, it is best to consider these three elements as if they formed one great cycle, the **carbon-hydrogen-oxygen cycle.** It is sometimes called just the **carbon cycle** for short. The **nitrogen cycle** has special features that deserve separate attention.

The Carbon-Hydrogen-Oxygen Cycle

All organic compounds—the building materials of which all living things are constructed—contain carbon. We have already seen this in the variety of carbohydrates, fats, proteins, and nucleic acids to which we have been introduced (Chapter 5). But where does all the carbon come from? In the nonliving world there are only two conceivable sources of abundance:

1. The carbon dioxide of the air (0.03 to 0.04 percent), and that which is dissolved in water.
2. The rocks (such as limestone) containing carbonate in the earth's crust.

There are large amounts of carbon in coal and petroleum, but this does not become available to organisms unless it is burned to produce carbon dioxide. And coal and petroleum have their origin in trees and other vegetation that grew on the earth millions of years ago.

Our attention has already been directed to one carbon-trapping process, photosynthesis. In photosynthesis, carbon dioxide is absorbed from air (or from the water in which it has dissolved) and is then united with hydrogen (from water) and converted into molecules of carbohydrate. No source of carbon other than CO_2 used in photosynthesis is really important for living things.

The pure carbon of coal or graphite, the solid carbonates of limestone, and the like, must be burned or changed chemically before they become available to living organisms. When CO_2 dissolves in water, some of it reacts to form carbonic acid (H_2CO_3), which immediately yields carbonate (CO_3^{-2}) and bicarbonate (HCO_3^-) ions. Today the richest store of carbon in the waters of the earth is in the form of these ions. To an extent, they, as well as dissolved CO_2, are used by marine organisms.

A mollusk, which deposits carbonate in its shell, cannot use the insoluble carbon so accumulated as a part of its fuel supply, or for its protein or nucleic acid, unless the carbonate is converted into carbon dioxide or soluble ions. Neither the mollusk nor any other animal is able to use large amounts of CO_2 directly. For most of its supply of carbon and oxygen, each animal depends upon carbohydrates, fats, amino acids, and other carbon compounds that are in its food. So we come back to the green plants—the primary producers. The green plants, and they alone, take the carbon dioxide of the environment and make it into food. This is the meaning of our general equation for photosynthesis:

$$6\ CO_2 + 6\ H_2O + \text{light energy} \rightarrow C_6H_{12}O_6 + 6\ O_2$$

When sugar or fat or any other fuel molecule is broken down in a living cell, and its energy is transferred to molecules of ATP, what happens to the carbon, oxygen, and hydrogen atoms? The general equation for respiration in plants and animals is simply the reverse of the photosynthesis equation:

$$C_6H_{12}O_6 + 6\ O_2 \rightarrow 6\ CO_2 + 6\ H_2O + \text{chemical energy}$$

In Chapter 6 you saw that not all respiration is so complete. Many microorganisms, known as fermenters and decomposers, respire in the absence of free oxygen. However, insofar as the carbon-hydrogen-oxygen cycle is concerned, they too produce CO_2 when they utilize glucose. Their other final products of respiration, such as ethyl alcohol, acetic acid, or lactic acid, are released and are utilized by organisms that are able to use free oxygen as a final hydrogen acceptor. The end of the matter is therefore that these microorganisms also help to carry out the chemical transformations of the cycle. The carbon dioxide and water formed during respiration go back into the air and the waters of the earth. Here, then, we see a tremendous cycle that involves carbon, hydrogen, and oxygen—all three at once. The cycle as it occurs for land organisms is shown in Figure 36-12. The same cycle, with a few changes and additions, occurs in the oceans. The bodies of living organisms contain a tremendous quantity of chemical substances. Generally these are not available to other living creatures while the organism is alive. Suppose there were no bacteria, molds,

36-12 THE CARBON-HYDROGEN-OXYGEN CYCLE ON LAND

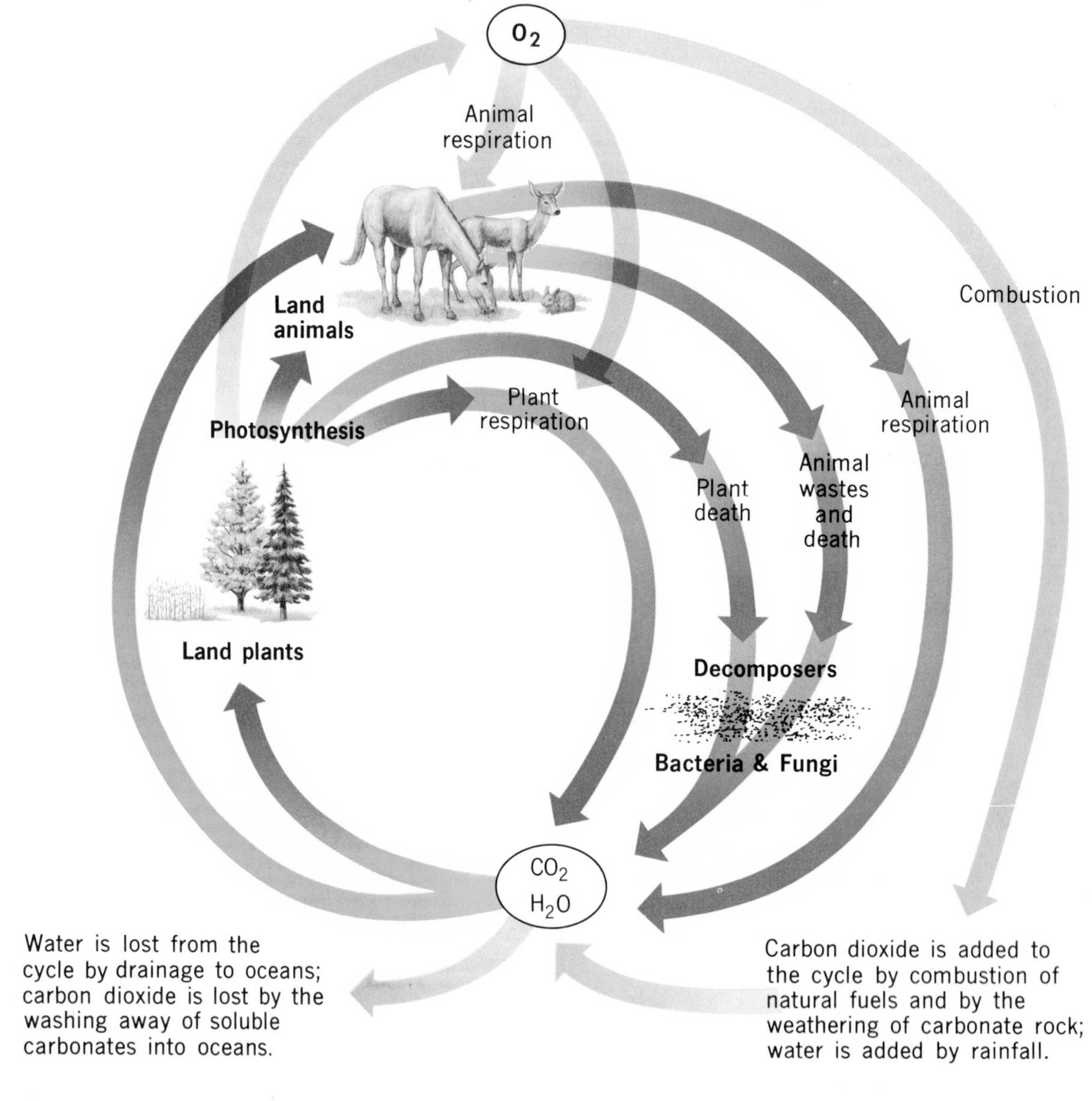

O_2
Animal respiration
Land animals
Combustion
Photosynthesis
Plant respiration
Animal respiration
Plant death
Animal wastes and death
Land plants
Decomposers
Bacteria & Fungi
CO_2
H_2O
Water is lost from the cycle by drainage to oceans; carbon dioxide is lost by the washing away of soluble carbonates into oceans.
Carbon dioxide is added to the cycle by combustion of natural fuels and by the weathering of carbonate rock; water is added by rainfall.

fungi, or other organisms to *decompose* dead plants and animals, or break down their wastes. We can imagine that dead organisms and the wastes of living organisms would then accumulate everywhere. We might try to burn them to get carbon dioxide back into the atmosphere, but this would dispose of only a small fraction of all things dying on the land, to say nothing of those in the oceans, where perhaps 85 percent of all living things occur. Clearly, burning dead organisms is not a realistic possibility. What could we do even to dispose of human sewage without bacterial decomposers to assist? The problem would be great indeed!

Without the decomposers the carbon in wastes and dead organisms would quickly become "fixed." It would no longer be returned to the carbon-hydrogen-oxygen cycle in the form of CO_2 resulting from "biological combustion." If we stop and think about this for a moment, it becomes appallingly clear that the small amount of *available carbon* (CO_2 or CO_3^{-2} or HCO_3^-) in our world would soon be used up by green plants in their photosynthesis. The carbon-hydrogen-oxygen cycle would slow down and come to a halt, blocked by failure of carbon dioxide to return to the atmosphere. If that were really to happen, why would nearly all life on earth halt abruptly?

We have called this the carbon-hydrogen-oxygen cycle. Let us now see what happens to the hydrogen and the oxygen in the cycle. First consider the hydrogen. It is abundantly present in the environment in water molecules (H_2O). In photosynthesis the water molecules are split into hydrogen and oxygen. The hydrogen becomes part of the sugar molecule, and then goes into the various organic compounds that are made from glucose, directly or indirectly. When glucose is broken down in respiration, or when the decomposers get to work on organic compounds of wastes and dead organisms, hydrogen atoms are oxidized to form water again. This seems quite straightforward.

Now think about the oxygen in the cycle. This part of the cycle may be easier to understand if we treat oxygen as though it were a separate part of the cycle (see Figure 36-12). Oxygen (O_2) is necessary for all combustion, and it is the ultimate receiver of hydrogen atoms in respiration (Chapter 6). Combustion and respiration are the important sources of carbon dioxide in the atmosphere; thus, without O_2 there would be no combustion or respiration, no CO_2 production, and no carbon cycle.

Is the converse true? Could there be an oxygen cycle without a carbon cycle in nature? Green plants, during photosynthesis, release molecular oxygen to the atmosphere and to the earth's waters but—and this is crucial—these same plants require CO_2 from the atmosphere or water to carry on their photosynthesis. There is good reason to believe that the amount of CO_2 actually limits the process. If photosynthesis were to stop, it would not take many thousand years for the combined respiration and combustion going on in the world to use up all the available oxygen—a point realized by Priestley long ago (page 64). The oxygen would become combined in the form of organic and inorganic compounds such as water, and therefore would not be available for respiration.

Clearly, we human beings and all other animals require the presence of the green plants and their photosynthesis, not only to supply us with food substances, but also to keep replenishing the atmosphere with the oxygen we require for respiration. On their side, the green plants must have the bacteria and other decomposers to replenish the supply of usable carbon (mainly CO_2) in the atmosphere and in water. The carbon, hydrogen, and oxygen cycles are really inseparable and combine to form one cycle. The producers, consumers, and decomposers all play essential roles in keeping the combined cycle going.

The Nitrogen Cycle

Nitrogen is found in all proteins and nucleic acids. For this reason it is, consequently, an essential element in living substance. One might suppose that plants and animals could capture the nitrogen they need directly from the air, since four fifths of our atmosphere is pure nitrogen. But no! Animals must have their nitrogen in the form of amino acids. Plants must have soluble nitrogen salts, from which, together with carbohydrates, they can make their proteins and nucleic acids. When amino acids are broken down in the bodies of animals, or when the animals die, the products are generally useless for green plants. It is the decomposers, especially some species of bacteria, that convert these useless compounds into compounds that the green plants can use for synthesizing their proteins. The decom-

36-13 THE NITROGEN CYCLE ON LAND

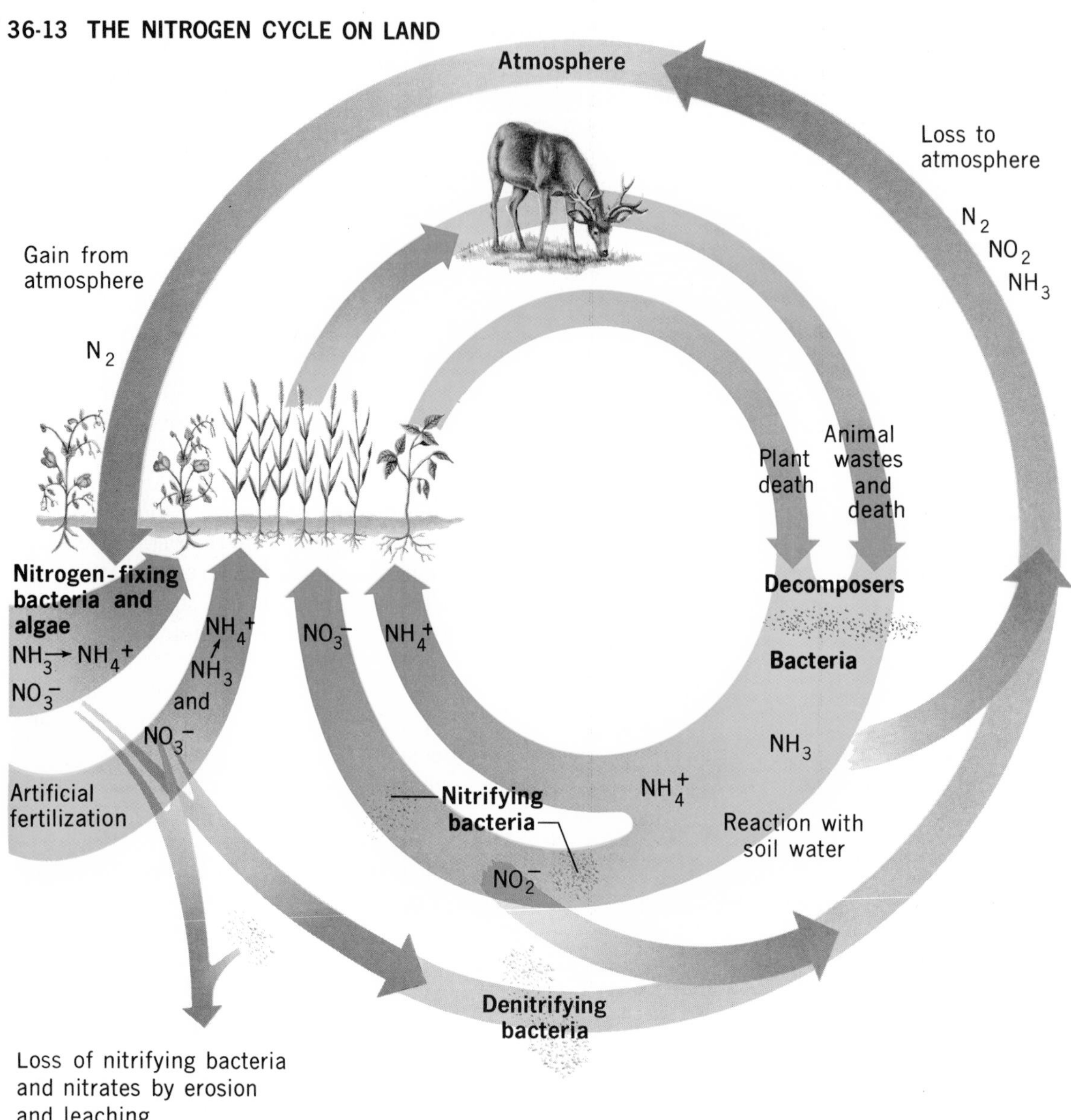

posers are consequently of prime importance in the nitrogen cycle (Figure 36-13).

Essentially, the nitrogen cycle involves about five main steps. First, when a plant or an animal dies, when leaves fall from a tree, or when an animal excretes its waste products, the nitrogen compounds pass into the soil or water. Next, certain bacteria in the soil, or in water, begin to break down these organic nitrogen compounds. This process converts much of the organic nitrogen to ammonia. (In freshwater communities and in the oceans, many forms of life other than bacteria also produce ammonia as a metabolic end-product.) Yet even when combined in this relatively simple form, the nitrogen is of little use to green plants.

In the third step, chemical reactions occur in which ammonia gas is changed to an ammonium compound, a soluble salt. The salt ionizes to produce ammonium ions (NH_4^+) as well as some ions with a negative charge. Some green plants can take ammonium ions directly into their roots.

The fourth step is carried out in the soil by bacteria called **nitrifying** (NY·truh·fy·ing) **bacteria.** Some of these oxidize ammonium ions to water and **nitrites** (NY·tryts—salts containing the nitrite ions NO_2^-). Others oxidize nitrites into **nitrates** (NY·trates—salts containing the nitrate ion, NO_3^-). In the fifth step, the highly soluble nitrates, dissolved in the soil water, are taken up by the roots of plants.

When ammonia is oxidized by bacteria to nitrites, and the nitrites are then oxidized by other bacteria to nitrates, energy is transferred and made available to the bacteria. The bacteria use this energy for their own vital activities. The nitrates produced are waste products as far as the bacteria are concerned. The nitrates are of vital importance to green plants, however.

Another way in which nitrogen is made available for protein synthesis is by **nitrogen fixation**. Some nitrogen-fixing algae and bacteria are free-living microorganisms in the soil. Other nitrogen-fixing bacteria grow in the roots of plants called **legumes** (LEG·yoomz). Examples of legumes with which you may be familiar are garden beans, soy beans, peas, vetches, alfalfa, and clover. After these bacteria invade the roots of the host they form **nodules**—little warty growths on the roots (Figure 36-14). It might seem that these bacteria would be harmful for the legumes. Actually, they improve the growth of these green plants. The bacteria utilize atmospheric nitrogen in their own metabolism and convert it into nitrogen-containing substances. These substances are used by the legumes in making the proteins and nucleic acids which they need for growth.

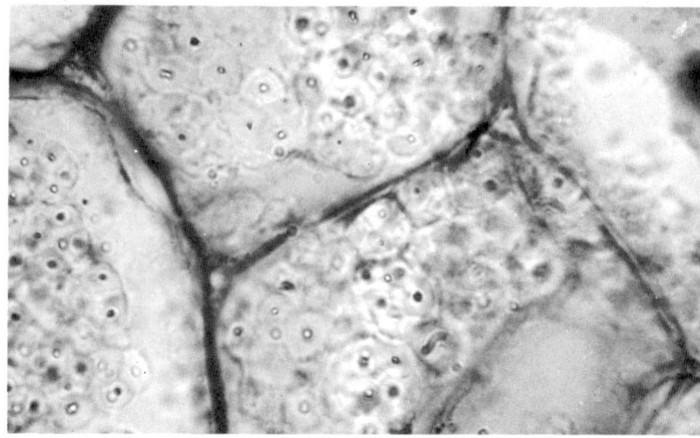

Both photos by Hugh Spencer

36–14 The nodules on the clover roots in photograph **a** are the homes of nitrogen-fixing bacteria, which can use atmospheric nitrogen in the synthesis of nitrogen-containing compounds. These nitrogen compounds offset the "leaks" that occur in the nitrogen cycle (Figure 36–13). In photograph **b,** a cross section of part of a single nodule is shown enlarged. The nodule is a structure of many partitions and cells; the inner cells are the ones that contain the nitrogen-fixing bacteria.

Nitrogen-fixing bacteria need energy to fix nitrogen. To meet this requirement, carbohydrates and oxygen are needed by the nitrogen-fixing bacteria. The leguminous plant provides these. Thus, both the green plant and the bacteria benefit from their close association.

To a limited extent man supplies green plants with nitrogen from commercial fertilizers. In the great agricultural section of North America it is common to see farmers applying ammonia or nitrates to their fields to increase the yield and protein content of the crops. Green plants thus have at least three possible sources of nitrogen, but where do you and I and all of the other animals get nitrogen for proteins? We get it either directly from plants (when we eat a salad or some green vegetable, peanuts, beans, etc.), or indirectly when we eat meat or cheese, or when we drink milk; for remember, the steer that provided our meat had to eat alfalfa and corn to get nitrogen in the form of amino acids to synthesize its own proteins.

For their part in the nitrogen and carbon-hydrogen-oxygen cycles, and in many other ways, bacteria are indirectly beneficial. Without them, plants could not get nitrogen to make proteins, and without the plants none of us could exist. In a way, nitrogen-fixing and nitrifying bacteria are, like the bacteria of disease, of life-and-death importance—but the nitrogen-fixing and nitrifying bacteria aid life instead of making it more difficult.

The nitrogen cycle as we have just described it is simplified. It is actually more complicated. Some of the additional details are shown in Figure 36-13 where you can see that there are some "leaks" in this cycle. One such leak occurs when certain bacteria of the soil convert some of the all-important nitrates into nitrous oxide (NO_2), a gas that is lost to the atmosphere. Another leak involves loss of nitrifying bacteria. They are most abundant in the top six inches of soil and they will be lost if soil erosion occurs. Still another leak occurs when nitrogen-containing compounds are washed away from the places where they could be absorbed by plant roots. In spite of these and other losses the cycle remains in balance. Can you say why?

INTERACTION BETWEEN ORGANISMS AND THEIR ENVIRONMENT

Usually we think of the environment as something that acts on living things, and we tend to think of the living things as merely being acted upon. Our discussion of the carbon-hydrogen-oxygen cycle and of the nitrogen cycle has shown that this is not so. The action goes in both directions. Our surroundings—atmosphere, soil, oceans, fresh waters—possess many of their present characteristics because of the presence of earlier plants and animals. Life is certainly affected by its environment, but it also modifies that environment and thus indirectly affects future generations of living things. This is another example of interaction in an ecosystem.

The cycles we have already discussed provide striking examples of interaction between living organisms of an ecosystem. Animals as we know them could not exist without oxygen. Yet until green plants began carrying on photosynthesis millions of years ago, the atmosphere did not contain enough oxygen to support animal life. Someone has calculated that if photosynthesis were to cease, future populations of animals, no more numerous than those today, would use up all the oxygen in the atmosphere within about 20 centuries.

THE CLOSED ECOSYSTEM AND SPACE TRAVEL

Algae and Space Travel

"Thirty days out—everything A-OK." This might well be the message from space in the not-too-distant future as man attempts his first trip to Venus or some other planet. Not long ago such a trip seemed impossible, yet at the time of this writing many of the technological devices—the rockets, the space vehicles, the propellants—are available. It has been determined that such a trip, lasting over thirty days, would require "nonexpendable or regenerative life-supporting systems." What this means is that man will have to construct and maintain closed ecosystems within space vehicles, space platforms, or other structures used for extended habitation away from the earth.

What are some of the problems that must be considered in building such a closed system? Spacemen will need sources of oxygen and food. At the same time, some means of getting rid of CO_2 and other body wastes must be devised. How can this be done? Does the way in which the carbon-oxygen-hydrogen cycle or the nitrogen cycle work on land suggest any ideas to you?

In addition to the spacemen and their equipment, the spaceship could be supplied with some photosynthetic organism—one which can grow rapidly and supply food and sufficient oxygen. Certain microscopic, unicellular algae have been tested for possible use. Among these is the green alga *Chlorella pyrenoidosa* (klo·REL·a py·re·noy·DOE·sa). To simulate conditions that might be encountered in a space vehicle, investigators devised a closed system (Figure 36-15) using the alga and a *Cebus* (SEE·bus) monkey. The closed ecosystem consisted of 55 liters of alga suspension connected to a 230-liter closed gas system containing the monkey. The alga delivered O_2 into the system at rates from 1.3 to 2.6 liters per hour, while the monkey consumed O_2 at rates between 1.0 and 2.1 liters per hour. The monkey produced CO_2 at rates from 1.4 to 2.6 liters per hour, and the alga absorbed it in photosynthesis at rates from 0.9 to 1.9 liters per hour.

At the end of 50 hours—the end of the experiment—the oxygen level had increased from 21 percent to 25 percent. At no time did the carbon dioxide content of the atmosphere exceed 1 percent. From the standpoint of gaseous exchange, the experiment could have run longer. However, the problem of providing food during such an experiment must be considered.

During the experiment the alga produced from 1.0 to 1.8 grams (dry weight) of energy-containing cells per hour. This represents a possible source of food in the closed system for a human being. (*Chlorella* is one of several unicellular algae that can be made palatable for human consumption.) To be an effective food producer in the closed ecosystem, the alga must have a source of nitrogen for the synthesis of protein. One obvious nitrogen source, as indicated in Figure 36-15, is human wastes—urine and feces. Methods for utilization of both materials have been tested. One of the most promising methods resulted from the discovery that some species of algae can grow in diluted human urea. Hence this substance can be used as a nitrogen source for protein synthesis.

The algae have been harvested and fed to mice. They appear to have nutritive value for these animals, and there is reason to believe that these algae could be food for man.

The algae in these experiments are of particular interest in the investigation of space travel because they participate not only in the carbon-oxygen-hydrogen cycle but also in the nitrogen cycle. Bacteria are not required to recycle the nitrogen; everything necessary is accomplished by the one organism—the alga. Once again, we see how an understanding of certain basic principles of nature may help to solve technological problems—this time in the realm of space travel.

In considering the cycles of an ecosystem we have emphasized organisms and their environment, mostly at the molecular level. You have learned that carbon, hydrogen, oxygen, nitrogen, and many other elements that have not been discussed, move from organism to organism and to and from living and physical parts of the ecosystem. All of these changes require a great deal of energy. What is the source of the energy? What form or forms does it have? Is it cycled in nature as are the elements we have talked about? These are a few of the questions we hope to answer in the discussion of the ecosystem in the next section.

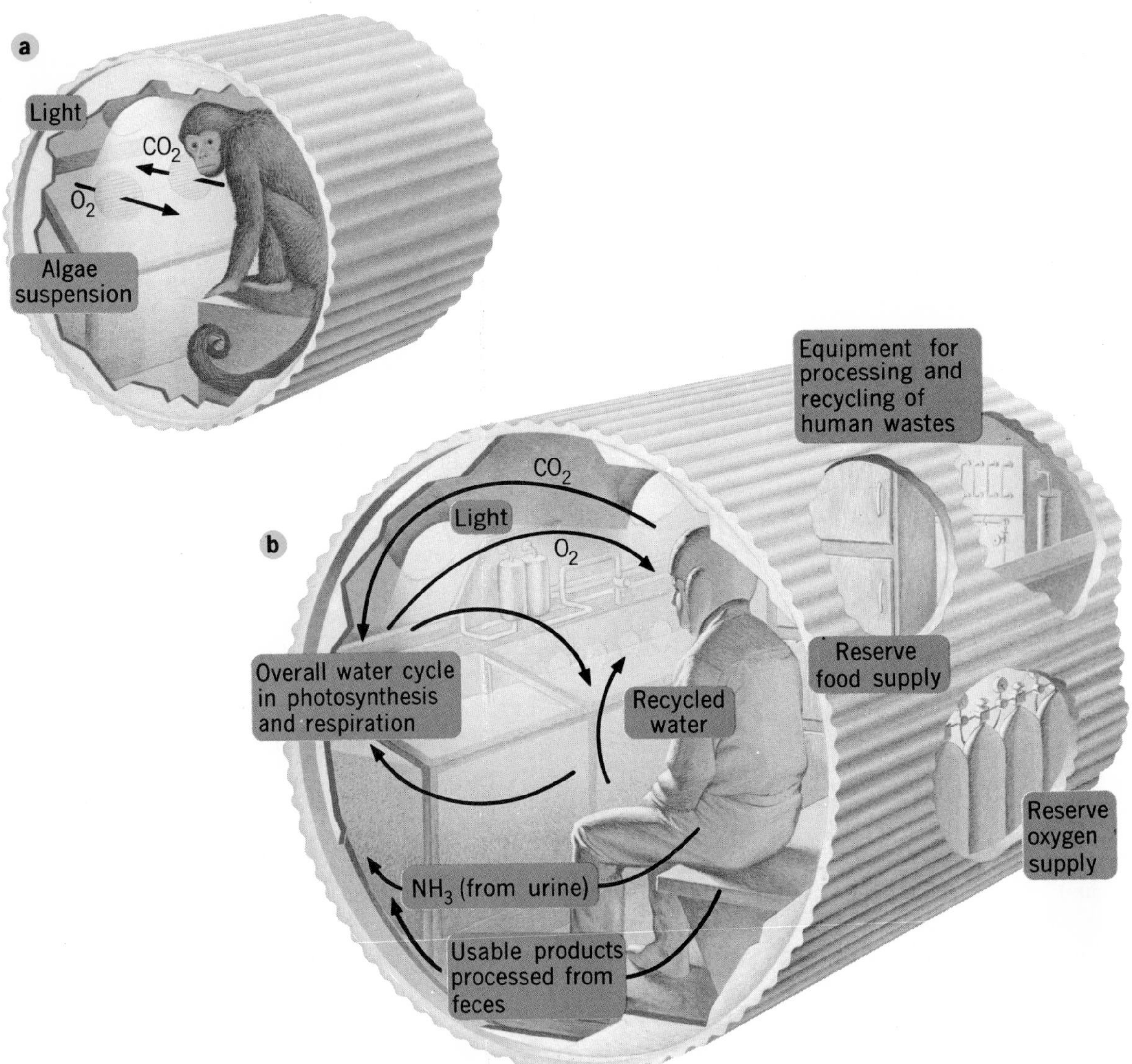

36–15 **a** A Cebus monkey in a temporarily closed environment. The monkey and the algae could survive for days—the algae longer—but not indefinitely. Can you guess why this experiment, unlike the one in **b,** would have to be terminated soon? (Would the monkey be able to feed himself and supply the algae with nutrients?) **b** Compare this hypothetical closed environment (for space travel exceeding thirty days) with the experiment in **a.** What justifies the more complex environment for man?

Energy Flow in the Ecosystem

Perhaps the best way to understand the energy relationships in the ecosystem is to review briefly and in a general way some of the basic principles of energy relationships in nature. You can get some help in doing this by looking at Figure 36-16. The illustration reminds us that the ultimate source of nearly all energy in nature is the sun. By photosynthesis, light energy from the sun is fixed in the form of chemical energy holding together the carbon, hydrogen, and oxygen of the glucose molecule. Only green plants containing chlorophyll and a few pigmented bacteria are able to fix light energy in this way. This is the reason these organisms are called producers. As you follow the arrows in the diagram you will see that an animal consumes some of the energy-rich compounds stored by the plant, releasing the energy for its own metabolism. Since animals, fungi, and most bacteria are not able to fix light energy, they rely on the energy stored by green plants

36-16 A SUMMARY OF ENERGY RELATIONSHIPS IN LIFE

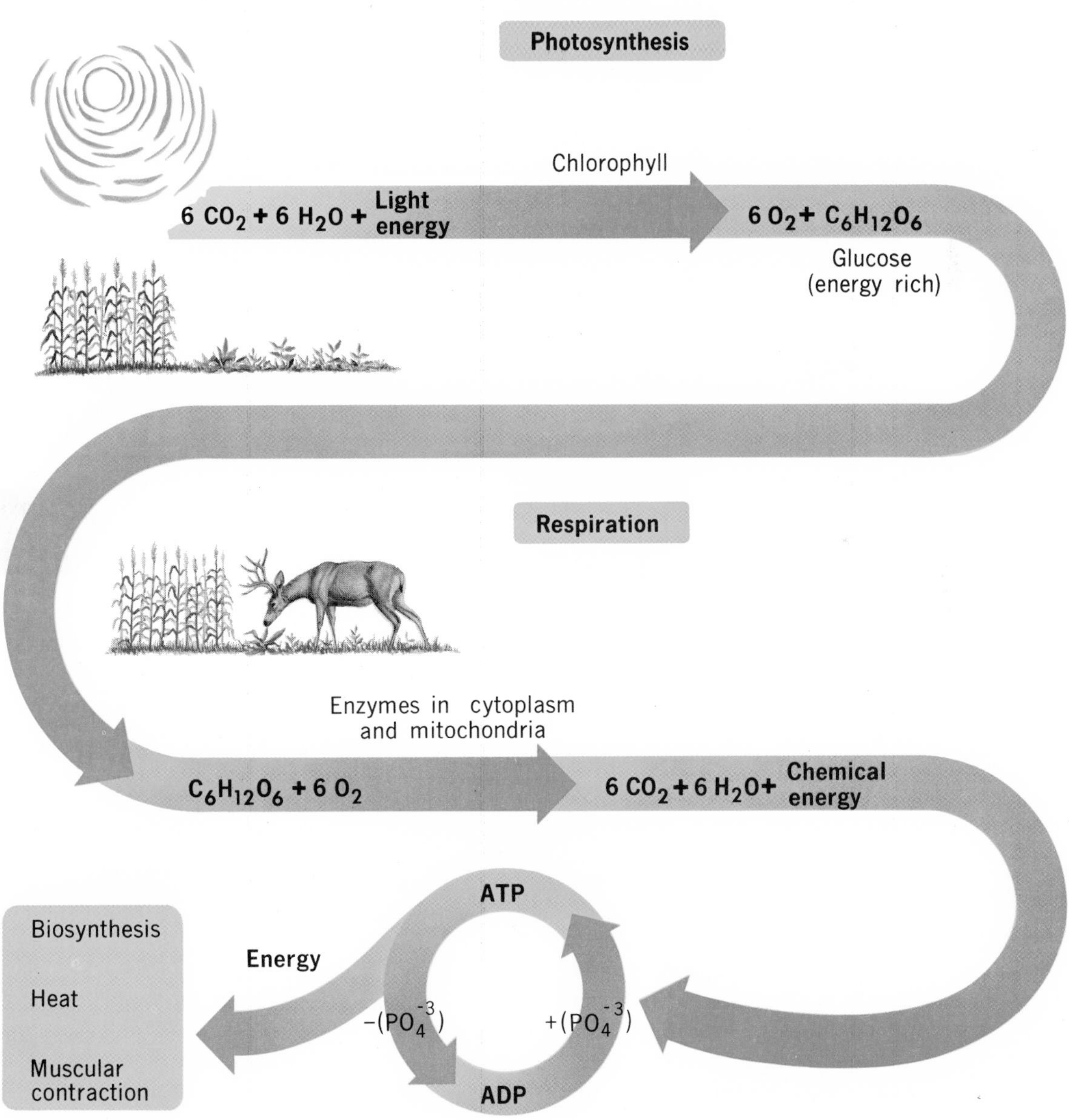

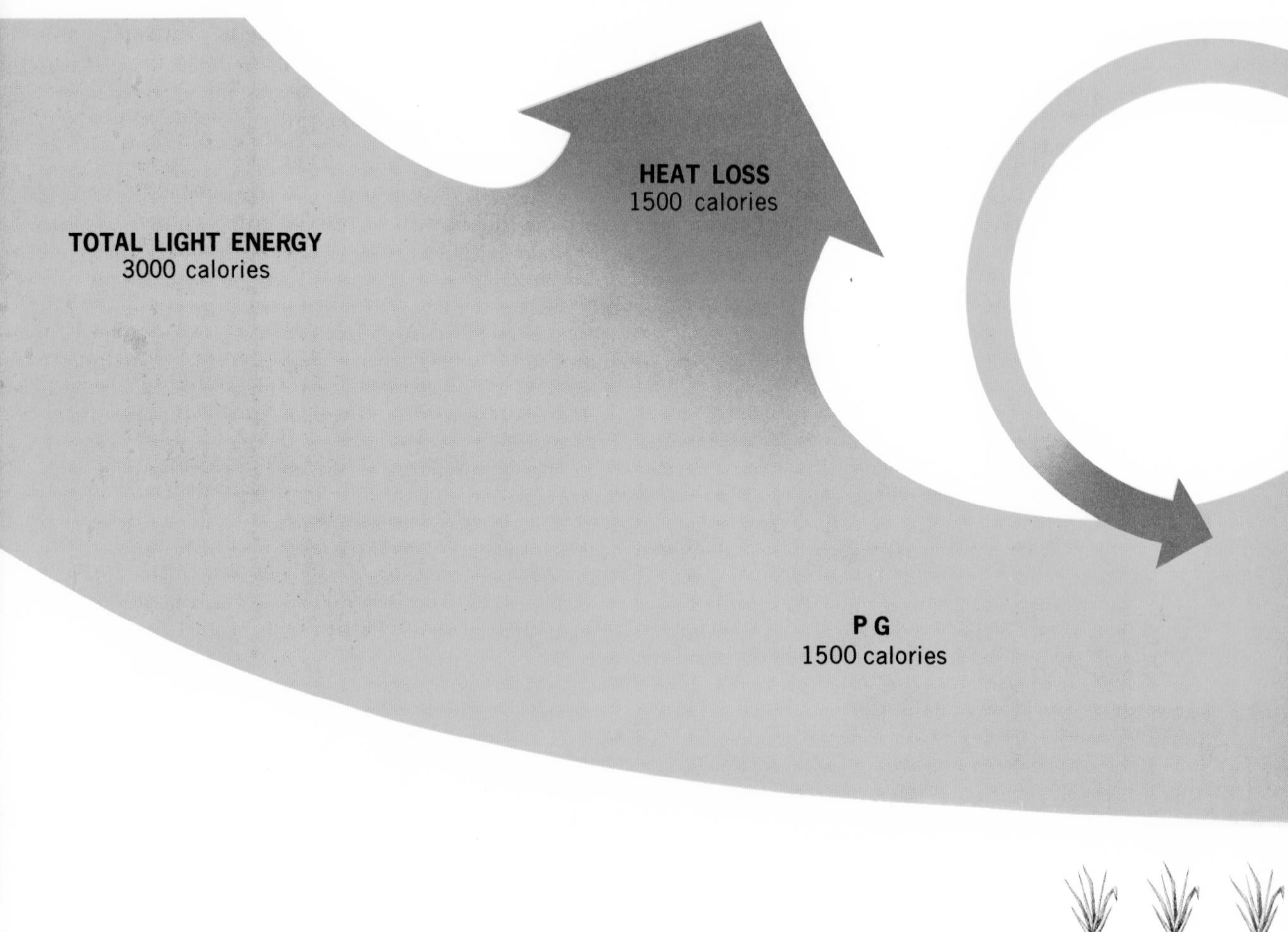

36–17 Energy flow in an ecosystem. In the diagram, PG stands for the gross productivity of the ecosystem. This includes all of the energy fixed by the green plants plus energy that is lost as heat and energy that is converted to the plants' use by respiration. PN stands for net production of the ecosystem, or the amount of energy that is available after heat loss and constructive respiration have been subtracted. It is the energy available in a head of

for their growth and reproduction. Much of the energy transferred by respiration is chemical energy, some of which is trapped in ATP molecules. This energy in ATP is used in a thousand ways – some in biosynthesis, some in muscular contraction, and some is dissipated to the surroundings as heat. Most important of all, the diagram shows that much of the energy is not cycled in the ecosystem as are the carbon, hydrogen, and oxygen. A large part of the energy flow is in one direction only. The rate at which the energy flows through the ecosystem will determine the number and kinds of organisms found in the ecosystem.

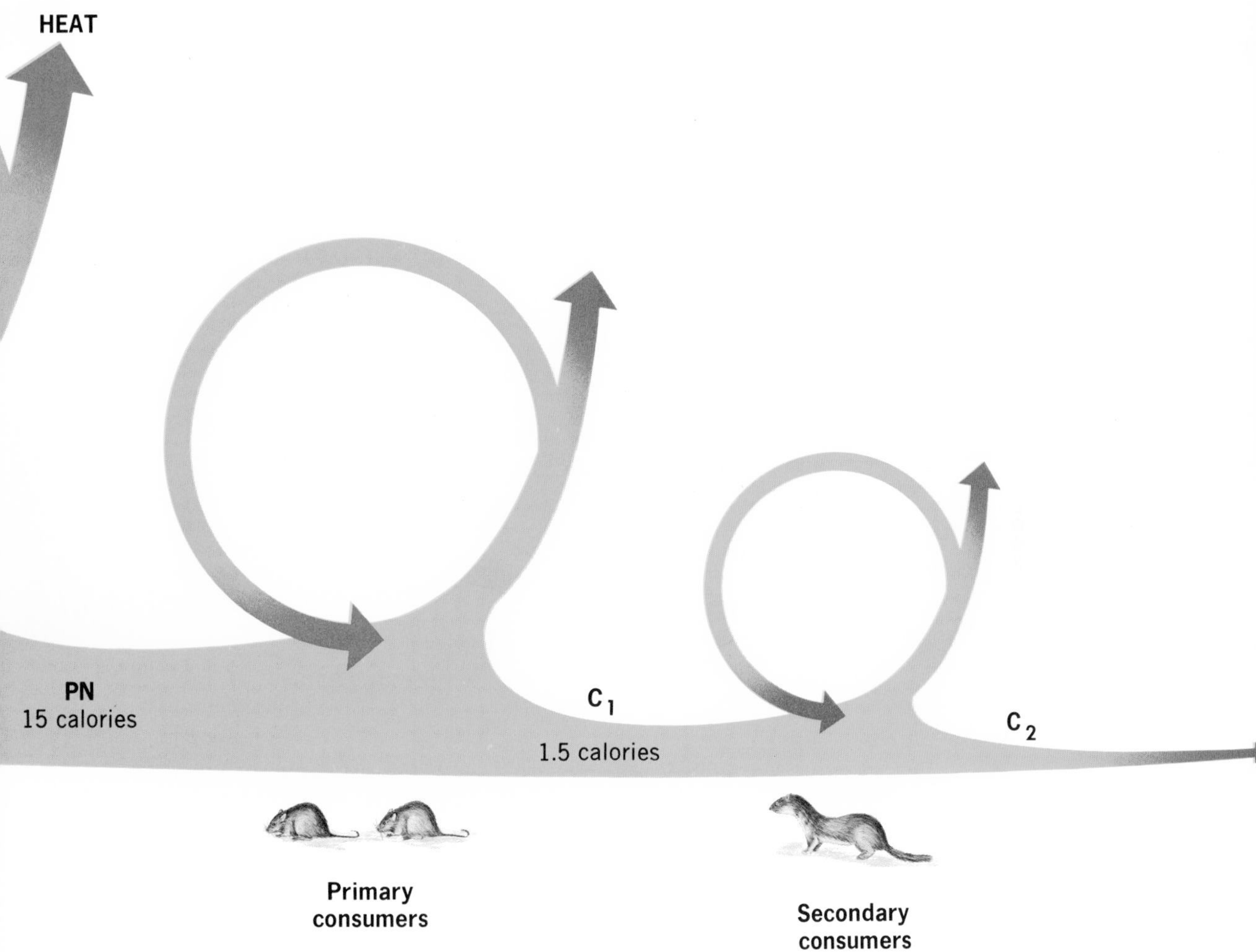

cabbage when we eat it in a salad, or the amount of energy in a tuft of grass eaten by a grazing deer. This amount of energy is a very small fraction of the total amount of light energy that hits a square meter of the ecosystem in one day. The primary consumers in the diagram are mice, which are captured and eaten by a weasel. How many of the original 3,000 calories are available to the weasel?

The fact that energy has, in the long run, a one-way flow in nature is explained by basic concepts of physics. You have already learned that energy may be transformed from one type into another, but it is never created or destroyed. Another physical principle states that transformation of energy always involves an overall energy change from concentrated to dispersed form. Thus, in photosynthesis—the conversion of light energy into chemical energy—much energy is always dispersed unavoidably as heat energy (Figure 36-17). The *useful* conversion of one kind of energy into another is never 100 percent efficient.

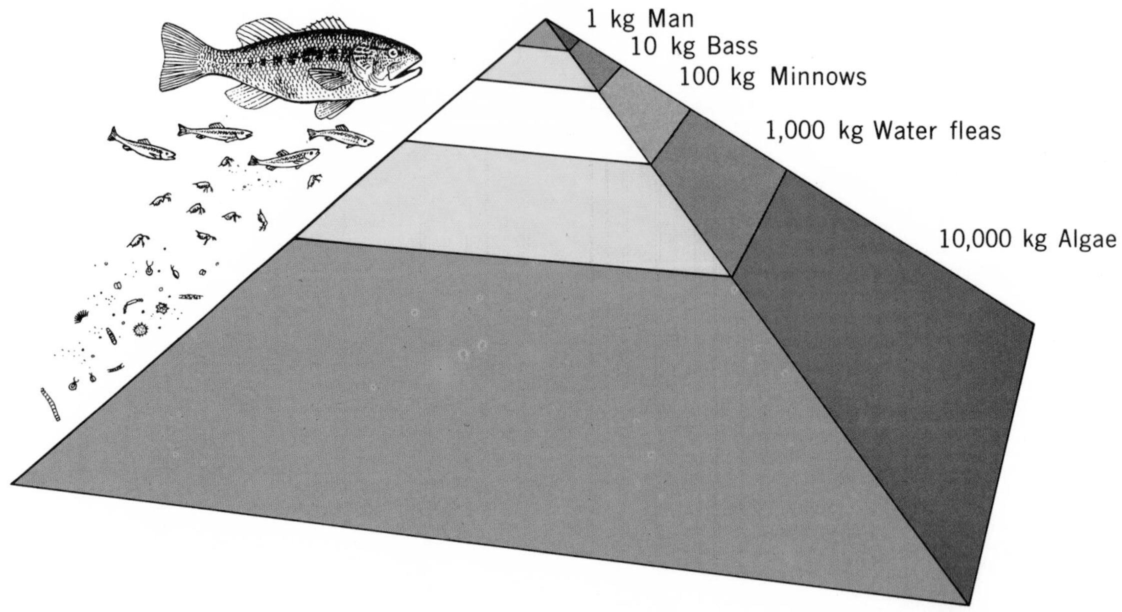

36–18 Comparative masses of predator and prey. It takes about 10 units of prey to support 1 unit of predator. If man could fill all his nutritional requirements by eating algae, how many men of average weight (80 kg) would 10,000 kg of algae support?

As energy flows through the ecosystem and is converted into other forms, there are many points where energy is lost or dispersed. We might say there are many leaks in the system and new energy must be added continually. The source of the new energy is, of course, solar radiation.

Let us examine a simplified energy-flow as it might apply to an ecosystem (Figure 36-17).

Let us take the example of one square meter of an ecosystem. Suppose it receives 3,000 calories of indirect light energy in a day. In a 100-percent efficient system all of this energy would be absorbed and converted into chemical energy. Part of the total amount of light, however, never enters into the light reactions of photosynthesis. Much of it is never absorbed by the chlorophyll of the producer. Some light energy is reflected from the surface of the photosynthetic organ, some is transmitted through the leaf, and some is dispersed in the form of heat energy.

Of the 3,000 calories of total light energy, perhaps only half of it is absorbed by the producers. Of the 1,500 calories, only 15 to 75 are converted into chemical (food) energy. Much of this energy is used by the plants in their metabolism. But green plants absorb and store more chemical energy than they can use. It is this energy that is available to animals and other heterotrophs such as bacteria and fungi.

Plant-eating heterotrophs, such as deer, cattle, antelopes, and certain insects and other invertebrates, are the primary consumers. Of the energy potentially available to them in the ecosystem, much again is dispersed. Some is lost as heat; some is converted into other forms of energy during respiration.

As the energy flow passes through the secondary-consumer level of the ecosystem, it is once more depleted by loss of heat energy and the energy of respiration. We might ask what part of the energy flowing through the ecosystem is left for the owl (third-level consumer) that eats the weasel (secondary consumer)? Look at Figure 36-17 and determine the percent of energy available to an owl in an ecosystem that receives 3,000 calories of total light. Remember that Figure 36-17 is a model and is used to help you understand what happens in a hypothetical ecosystem.

Food Chains

The sequence of events and changes in energy levels illustrated by Figure 36-17 are the events and changes that occur in a **food chain.** Another way of showing these events is illustrated by Figure 36-18. Here we see a food chain of an open fresh-water ecosystem. In this case the producers are the algae growing in the water. The primary consumers that eat the algae are rotifers, paramecia, water fleas, and other small invertebrates. Second-level consumers are the small fish that eat the smaller invertebrates. A third consumer level is represented by a large fish that eats smaller fish. At the top and at the fourth consumer level is the fisherman who caught the large fish and ate it. Note how many kilograms of producer at one end of the chain are required to make one kilogram of a human at the other end.

As far as available energy is concerned, the fewer steps in the food chain, the greater the availability of energy. The longer the food chain, the more energy is dispersed as heat or utilized in the respiration of the consumers.

Productivity of the Ecosystem

The productivity of an ecosystem is determined by measuring the rate at which radiant energy is fixed by photosynthesis and how much of this fixed energy is available to heterotrophs. By making careful measurements, ecologists have discovered that ecosystems vary considerably in productivity. On an annual basis the productivity of an alpine environment is much lower than that of a tropical rain forest. What determines the difference in productivity between the two ecosystems? The alpine ecosystem is photosynthetically active for only about two months a year. The tropical rain forest is photosynthetically active the entire year. The greater the productivity of an ecosystem is, the greater the amount of living material that can be supported or maintained in the ecosystem. In short, the amount of living material, the **biomass**, is directly related to the amount of energy fixed by the producers of the ecosystem.

Food Webs

In our discussion of energy relationships within an ecosystem, we have portrayed the movement of energy as a linear relationship. The producers were eaten by the mouse, the mouse by the weasel, and the weasel was eaten by the owl. We called this sequence a food chain. But are the relationships between organisms in the ecosystem always this simple, or are the interactions often more complex? Let us consider another food chain.

A bat ate a mosquito that had bitten a coyote that had eaten a grasshopper that had chewed a leaf. All these living things together comprise a food chain. This sequence is incomplete, however, for it does not show that many animals other than those mentioned eat grasshoppers and mosquitoes, or that coyotes and bats eat and are eaten by a great many other organisms. Grasshoppers and mosquitoes are related in similar ways to many other species. When we consider also that the kind of plant a grasshopper might eat may also be eaten by various other primary consumers, and these by several different secondary consumers, we start to build a picture of the food web that links together a whole community of living things (Figure 36-19).

The alternative pathways in a food web help maintain the stability of the ecosystem. If the rabbits in an area decrease in number, perhaps because of some disease, the owls might be expected to go hungry. However, this is not the case. Because there are fewer rabbits, less vegetation is consumed. The greater number of plants therefore produce more fruits and seeds and furnish better hiding places for mice. Soon

36-19 A FOOD WEB

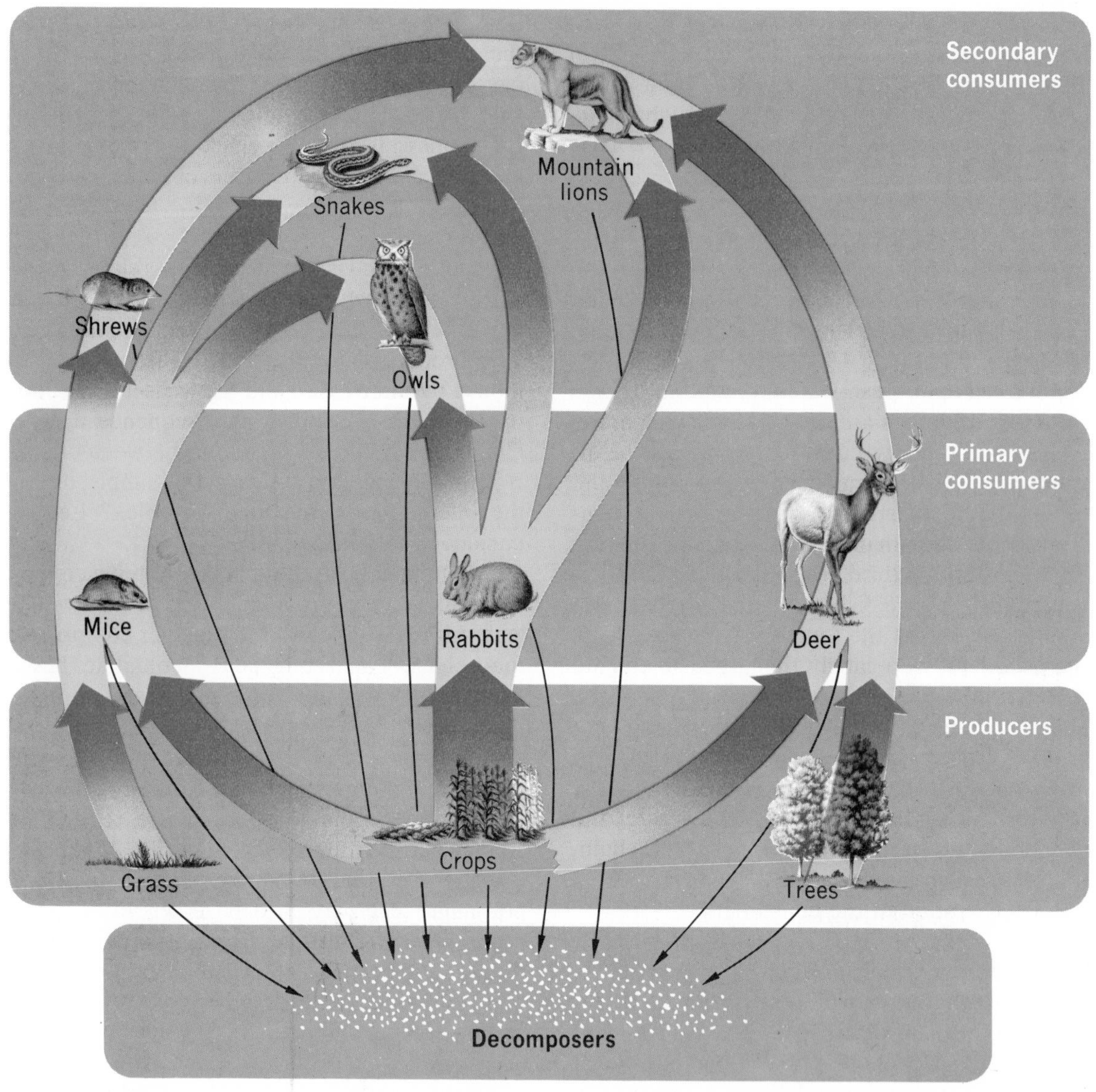

a larger population of mice is present. The owls transfer their attention from rabbits to mice. This reduces the danger for surviving rabbits, and these primary consumers have a better chance to rebuild their numbers. The greater the number of alternative pathways a food web has, the more stable is the community of living things which make up the web.

Stability in an ecosystem results because, on the average, only a few of the possible offspring of a plant or an animal survive to reproduce. Of all the seeds a plant forms, all but a few are eaten by animals or succumb to diseases or are killed by adverse weather conditions, either as seeds or somewhat later in life, as young plants that have not yet formed seeds of their own.

The world could not otherwise accommodate all the offspring that might be produced. Under normal circumstances a pair of meadow mice, for example, born early in the year, can produce 13 litters totaling about 78 young before the winter reduces their food supply. If each of these young were to survive and reproduce at the same rate, and all further generations likewise, the original pair would be ancestors to about 50,000 descendants and be great-great-great-great-great-grandparents before the year was out. If we consider that just one meadow mouse requires about 10 kilograms of plant food per year and ruins far more than this, we can begin to see why the world could not accommodate all the offspring. The 50,000 mice would eat or destroy more than 1,500 metric tons of vegetation in a year's time. (One metric ton equals 1,000 kilograms.)

Actually, the meadow mouse population is fairly stable. About two offspring actually survive from each pair of parents. The others die of diseases or are caught by hawks, owls, foxes, martens, and other secondary consumers.

We are so used to thinking of the welfare of our own species that we tend to regard as "wasted" all the offspring of any organisms that do not survive to reproductive maturity. But there is another side to the picture. Not only does the world lack space for so many individuals of any one kind, but also these individuals are needed as food by a great variety of consumers. Without the fruits, seeds, young plants, and foliage that are produced and "wasted," the primary consumers could not exist. Without the primary consumers, the plants would die of overcrowding, or weaken from excessive competition for nutrients and light. Without the primary consumers produced and wasted, the secondary consumers would be reduced in numbers because of competition, or would become extinct. Through the presence of all these components in the food web, each species is held in check, and the ecosystem maintains its stability.

Colonization and Succession

Occasionally living things have a chance to spread into an uninhabited region. It may be a mountain slope exposed after a landslide, new beach filling in at a pond or lake (Figure 36-20), or the land devastated by a forest fire, a flood,

36–20 Sand dunes along the shore of Lake Michigan. Although the dune environment is very hostile to living organisms, over a long period of time biological succession can change it into a much more productive ecosystem.

Wilson N. Stewart

or a glacier. Some kinds of life prove more efficient than others as colonists, and quickly occupy the area. Others begin to follow the pioneers, and eventually crowd them out. These changes in the kinds of species are known as **succession**.

Let us visit some such beaches and the wooded areas that border them. Here we may see some wonderful examples of succession—a succession that may take hundreds of years to accomplish.

The average tourist and beachcomber spend most of their time walking along the edge of the beach, where the breakers wash the sand and deposit the multiformed driftwood, water-logged butterflies, ladybird beetles, dead fish, and sea gulls.

Rather than walking *along* the beach, let us walk *across* the beach toward the small dunes. The clean white sand unmarked by any vegetation is called the middle beach (Figure 36-20). In the summer the sand of the middle beach is hot and dry. It is constantly shifting in the wind, making life difficult for any organisms except a few burrowing insects and spiders.

Beyond the middle beach we may find the first evidence of producers. These are perennial grasses—hardy plants indeed! They resist drying and require a minimum of mineral elements. They have a remarkable ability to bind the sand that blows over them from the middle beach. These pioneer plants form the windbreak against and around which the first small dunes are formed. As the plant roots and leaves die, organic material is added to the sand. At this stage the small dunes gradually shift or move higher and higher on the beach under the influence of the wind. As the sand grasses increase in abundance, their roots bind the sand more and more so that the movement of the dune slows and finally stops. After a dune stops, we can see the next step in succession. Birds bring in seeds of sand cherry, cottonwood, and willow that grow in the moister spots of the dunes. With the additions of these plants, the productivity of the changing ecosystem increases. A reflection of this is the increase in numbers of species of insects, rodents, birds, and predators that are found here. The plants and animals of the *cottonwood* stage add to the organic material that accumulates in the sand. This paves the way for the introduction of the next change in the ecosystem, which is the *pine forest*. Before we reach the dense pine forest we go through a transitional zone of old cottonwoods and pine seedlings.

The accumulation of leaves from broad-leaf plants and needles from the pines increases the amount of organic material in the soil and this sets the stage for the development of the *oak forest*. Again there is a change in the kinds of

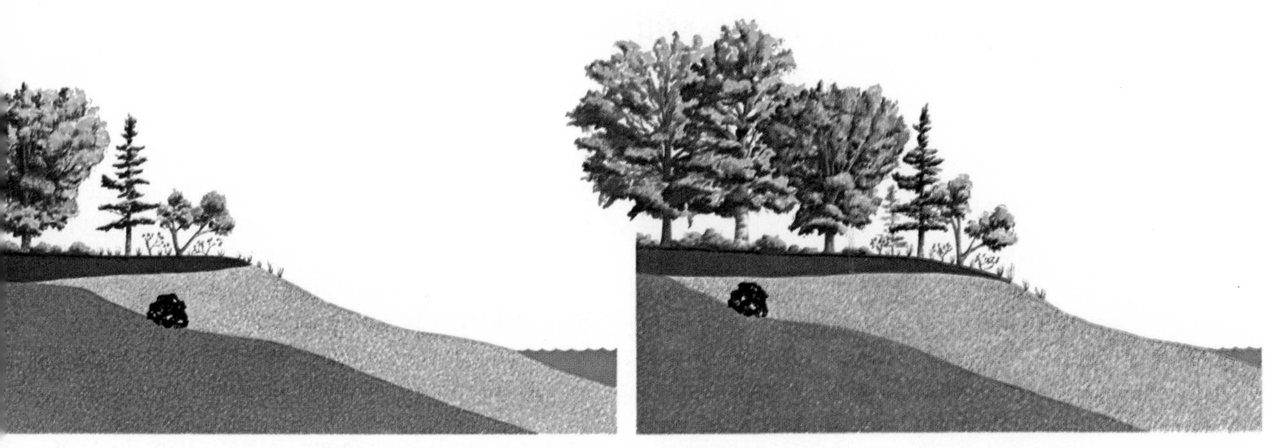

animals and a great increase in their numbers. Hoards of insects and tree-living animals inhabit this productive ecosystem. Groundhogs, foxes, wood mice, and squirrels are abundant. On the forest floor, under rotting logs and dead leaves, we find earthworms, crickets, slugs, snails, and millipedes.

Continuing our walk through the woods away from the beach we will notice another change. The forest seems to be more shaded and parklike. The dense shade is provided by the luxuriant foliage of beech and maple trees that form a dark canopy. The shade prevents the rapid evaporation of water from the forest floor. So as we walk over the dead logs and fallen leaves, we have the impression of walking on a spongy surface. The shade has another effect. It prevents the growth of most other kinds of plants except mosses, lichens, a few ferns, and the seedlings of beech and maple. Since few new plants can grow in the dense shade except the maple and beech seedlings, this stage in succession remains essentially the same provided nothing changes in the environment to upset the balance that has been achieved. Because it is a stable stage in succession, the *beech-maple forest* is considered to be the **climax** stage for this region.

From what we know of productivity (energy use) in an ecosystem, it must be apparent that there is an increasingly efficient use of energy with each stage of succession starting with the sand beach. Most of the radiant energy is lost as heat energy on the barren, bright beach. The beech-maple forest is probably the most efficient ecosystem, not only in utilization of energy, but also in making maximum use of water and increasing the soil fertility.

In our walk from the shore into the forest that borders the sand beach, we have seen a succession of changes in the ecosystem with the youngest at the edge of the lake and the oldest farthest from it. During a walk that may have taken a few minutes we have seen a succession of changes that has taken hundreds of years. Figure 36-21 shows the main stages in succession occurring through time at a given place along the shores of Lake Michigan.

Succession is going on in ecosystems of all kinds everywhere in the world. If you live in a forested area you may have seen the succession that often occurs after a forest fire. It is a more rapid succession than the succession on the beach. Only one season may be needed before the burned area is again green with blackberry bushes, fireweed, and other plants whose seeds are dropped by birds. Winds and birds bring the seeds of pioneer trees: poplar, birch, and sumac, all of which are quick growing and able to dominate the lower vegetation. Gradually oak and beech or evergreens rise above the pioneer trees and provide so dense a shade that

Betty Moore

36–22 A thermal spring in Yellowstone National Park, so hot that steam is rising from the surface. The white areas are deposits of salts. The colors are those of algae and bacteria that are adapted to the extreme environment of the pool.

the quick-growing pioneer kinds can no longer survive. The interaction between forest and environment is fairly stable and a climax is reached. An equilibrium has been established between the physical and biological components of the ecosystem, and the succession of plants and accompanying animals has essentially ended. The wound in nature has been healed by the process of succession.

Tolerance in Food Webs

Wherever some one feature of the environment limits the number of species that can live in an area, the food web is simpler. A tundra on a mountaintop or in the Arctic, for example, shows evidence of stress from winter cold. Comparatively few species inhabit it throughout the year; many migrate in during summer and away again in autumn. When the weather is warm on the tundra, insects and small plants reproduce to astonishing numbers, only to vanish as cold weather kills them, or as they become dormant in response to the cold. Nowhere on earth do mosquitoes, blackflies, and flower-visiting bees reach greater abundance. Nowhere more than in the Arctic do animals show such cyclic variations in abundance.

On a much smaller scale, the water of a thermal spring is a living space for plants and animals that can tolerate stress caused by high temperatures. Bacteria and blue-green algae (Figure 36-22) form crusts, often with bright pastel colors, in hot springs with water temperature as high as 85° C. At an elevation of 6,000 or 7,000 feet, as in Yellowstone National Park, this is not much below the boiling temperature of water. Few animals or plants, except the bacteria and blue-green algae, can live at temperatures above 50° C. Fish, for example, occur in thermal springs, but seldom tolerate temperatures above 40° C.

From these examples we see that the ecosystem is not static, nor is it fixed. It is a flexible system and varies from place to place and time to time. It is a system of checks and balances, like a good system of human government. But the checks and balances are not conscious choices made by the organisms; they are automatic responses to the changes produced in nature by natural forces and by living things.

The Biosphere

Spread out over the earth's surface, between the solid rocky crust of the earth and the upper reaches of the atmosphere, extends the world of life, like a film of living matter. It is made up of grass, shrubs, and trees, of worms, fish, rabbits, and wolves, of microorganisms and all other sorts of living things. This world of life is called the **biosphere** (BY·o·sfeer).

Every organism within the biosphere affects the life of every other, directly or remotely. Man, for example, cannot continue to live without the bacteria in the soil, the green plants on land and in the sea, and even the scavengers of the dead. And what man does to the environment matters immensely to all other living creatures. The biosphere is a concept that embodies the balance of nature, but it is even broader than that idea. It includes every relationship—

insignificant as well as significant—that binds all living beings into one inseparable world. It is the highest level of organization involving living organisms.

CONCLUDING REMARKS

We have observed that harmony and coordination exist at all levels of organization. The living system is always in balance with what is outside it and around it—its environment. Individuals of the same species form populations with relationships between young and old, parents and offspring, males and females. Populations exist in ecosystems made up of many interdependent kinds of organisms—plants, animals, and microorganisms interacting with one another and the physical environment. Consumers live at the expense of producers, and decomposers return the materials of the dead to the reservoirs of the atmosphere, fresh waters, seas, and soil.

The cycles of nature are illustrated by the movements of carbon, hydrogen, oxygen, and nitrogen, and those of other elements such as phosphorus and calcium. These elements pass through the bodies of living organisms and reenter the soil, water, and atmosphere. Some of these cycles are quite complex. They reveal to us the interdependence of living things.

Energy flow in the ecosystem is a one-way flow, with a dispersion of energy in the form of heat energy starting with the producers and ending with the highest order of consumer.

Food webs constitute another way of looking at the interdependence of living organisms. Food webs must have existed in the remotest past, ever since the time when life first arose on the earth and different species assumed the roles of producers, consumers, and decomposers. We can see a dramatic bit of the adjustment that takes place when life is wiped out or grossly disturbed somewhere and then gradually returns to normal through a succession of relationships, leading up to a climax when the fullest possible balance of nature is restored. The invasion of a new volcanic island by living things, or the renewal of life in an area devastated by fire, offers a picture of this kind.

The biosphere includes all living things on the earth. Each of them affects all the others, directly or indirectly, for all of them are a part of the balance of nature; all take part in the cycles of nature and form the food webs.

In this chapter we have explained how an ecosystem works. We should be able to see how similar it is in operation to systems at the other end of the scale of organization—at the molecular and cellular levels. In the ecosystem we have stressed the interaction of organisms with other organisms and the physical environment. To bring about these interactions, energy must move into and through the system. Basically this is little different from the interaction of a DNA molecule with the environment in a cell. To bring about the replication (reproduction) of the DNA strand, certain substances must be present in the cell. Nitrogen is one of the more important of these substances. If nitrogen is removed from the environment of the cell, no proteins, thus no enzymes that interact with the cell environment, will be formed. Since enzymes are required in the replication of DNA, the reproduction of the vital substance cannot occur. In short, the interactions among the environmental factors of the cell will not occur, and life at this level of organization will cease to exist. We might say that the "ecosystem" of the cell has been put out of balance.

At the level of the ecosystem we could remove the source of nitrogen from the environment by eliminating the microorganisms that are responsible for making nitrogen available. Indeed, there are many places in the biosphere where there is very little available nitrogen, and organisms will not—cannot—grow here. We know that the reason for this effect on the whole organism is related to what happens in the environment of the cell, where the nitrogen from the external environment is required in making enzymes vital to the cell's activities.

The point is, that to really understand interactions of organisms with their external environment, we must also understand the interactions of molecular systems with the internal environment of the organism. No matter where the interactions occur, whether in the ecosystem or at the molecular level of the cell, it takes energy to bring the interactions about. How much clearer the whole picture of biology becomes when we understand the origin of this energy and how it flows through the ecosystem. We must learn to study biology with a broad perspective relating all levels of organization with one another. These relationships form the real unity of biology.

GUIDE QUESTIONS AND PROBLEMS

1. In what characteristics do producers differ from consumers?
2. Light is the fundamental energy source for all ecosystems. What communities exist in perpetual darkness? How is energy fed into such communities? In what way is a city similar to an ecosystem in perpetual darkness?
3. What might happen in a pond community if the population of green algae increased greatly? Would any of the changes that occur be permanent? Would it make a difference if the expanding population was of fishes?
4. Suppose we were to remove all the microorganisms from a closed ecosystem that contained many leguminous plants. What changes might we expect to occur in the atmosphere of the closed system? How would these changes affect the consumers? What effect, if any, would the lack of microorganisms have on protein synthesis?
5. In comparing two ecosystems, an investigator found that one ecosystem had only first and second order consumers, but the other had these two as well as third, fourth, and fifth order consumers. Which of the two ecosystems would be more stable? Why?
6. An ecosystem in a valley on the leeward side of a mountain range in the western United States is apt to consist of sagebrush and cactus plants. Why do we not find a rich growth of conifers or hardwoods in this particular place? Why are the latter plants more apt to be on the windward side of the mountain range?
7. An island devastated of all living things by the eruption of a volcano will eventually become repopulated.
   a. How are organisms able to repopulate this island?
   b. What types of organisms would be most likely to appear first on the island?
   c. What characteristics would you expect to find in the climax ecosystem?
8. Refer to the graph below, and answer the questions that follow it.

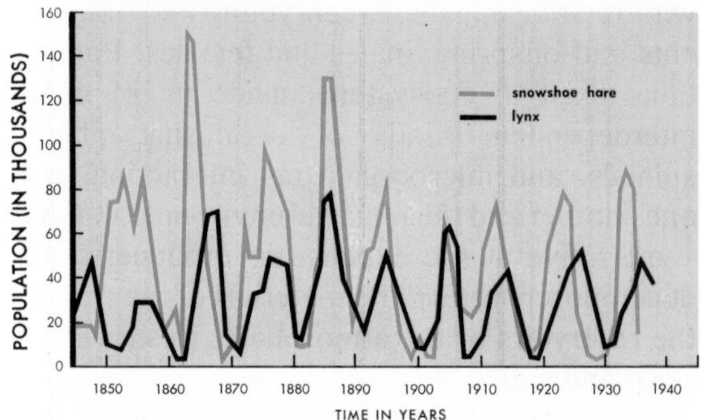

   a. What would happen to the lynx population in some subsequent year if a severe drought affected the grasses in their hunting range?
   b. During every ten-year interval shown by the graph above, the lynx population was always less than the hare population. What factors might account for this?
   c. Suppose the hare population was eliminated by hunters. What would happen to the lynx population?
   d. During the winter months the producers in the hare-lynx ecosystem are unable to function. What is the source of nutrient energy for the hare? the lynx?

RELATED READING

Books

For stimulating general accounts of the interrelations of organisms . . .

Bates, Marston, *The Forest and the Sea,* New American Library, New York, 1959.

Buchsbaum, Ralph, and Mildred Buchsbaum, *Basic Ecology,* Boxwood Press, Pittsburgh, 1957.

Storer, J. H., *The Web of Life,* New American Library, New York, 1956.

For more detailed accounts of ecological principles . . .

Billings, D. W., *Plants and the Ecosystem,* Wadsworth Publishing, California, 1964.

Dowdeswell, W. H., *Animal Ecology,* Harper and Row, New York, 1961.

Odum, E. P., *Ecology,* Holt, Rinehart and Winston, New York, 1966 (paperback).

Wallace, B., and A. Srb, *Adaptation,* Second Edition, Prentice-Hall, Englewood Cliffs, New Jersey, 1964 (paperback).

For a description of ecological techniques . . .

Phillips, Edwin A., *Field Ecology,* D. C. Heath and Company, Boston, 1964.

Magazines

Anderson, A. J., and E. J. Underwood, "Trace-element Deserts," *Scientific American,* Volume 200 (January 1959), page 97.

Inexler, P. C., "Germ-free Isolators," *Scientific American,* Volume 211 (July 1964), page 78.

McNeil, Mary, "Lateritic Soils," *Scientific American,* Volume 211 (November 1964), page 96.

Plass, Gilbert N., "Carbon Dioxide and Climate," *Scientific American,* Volume 201 (July 1959), page 41.

Wald, George, "Life and Light," *Scientific American,* Volume 201 (October 1959), page 92.

Woodwell, George M., "The Ecological Effects of Radiation," *Scientific American,* Volume 208 (June 1963), page 40.

Woodwell, George M., "Toxic Substances and Ecological Cycles," *Scientific American,* Volume 216 (March 1967), page 24.

The entire September 1965 issue [Volume 213] of *Scientific American* is devoted to the physical, biological, and sociological problems that face cities as populations and technology grow.

37

A World of Ecosystems

When we think of the tremendous complexity of the activities in a single cell, with all of the synthesis, breakdown, energy storage, and energy transformation, all interacting with one another at the right time and right place, we wonder how there can be any life at all! Yet there is—and organisms are so successful that they are present in nearly every nook and cranny of the earth. We will now survey some of the major world habitats and explore the problems of living in these places.

LIFE IN THE OCEANS

As land animals, we tend to forget that the most extensive habitat for life is the world's oceans (Figure 37-1). The oceans occupy about 70 percent of the earth's surface. Even this figure does not give a true estimate of the space available for marine life. On land, organisms occupy a flat and narrow zone from several meters below the surface to rarely more than 30 meters above it. Nearly all terrestrial life is restricted to this zone about 40 meters thick. The average depth of the oceans, on the other hand, is roughly 4,000 meters. Since organisms are found throughout the depths of the oceans, the actual space available for marine life is about 300 times as great as the space available for terrestrial life.

Life in the earth's oceans—or in the sea, as we usually refer to ocean waters—depends, as life does elsewhere, on the presence of light. Where there is light in the sea, plants carry on photosynthesis, develop, and reproduce. These plants, the primary producers, are eaten by

37-1 THE WORLD'S OCEANS

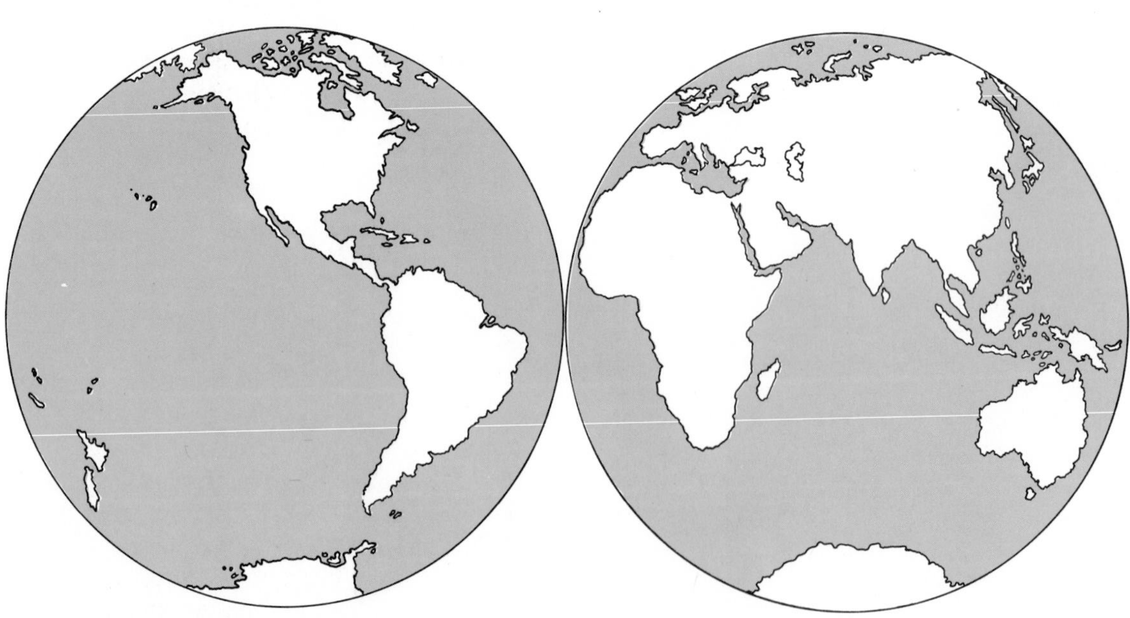

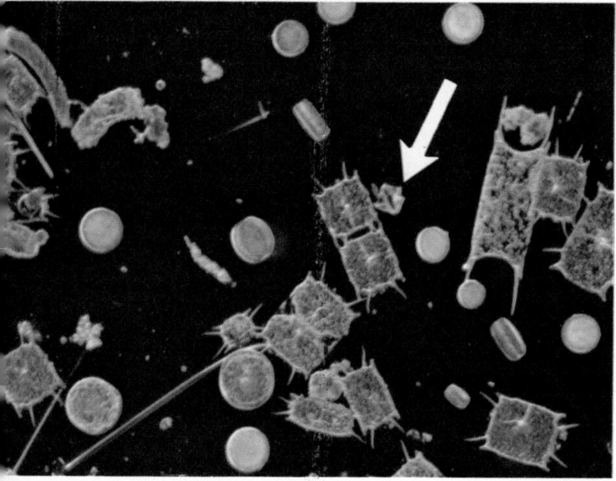

D. P. Wilson

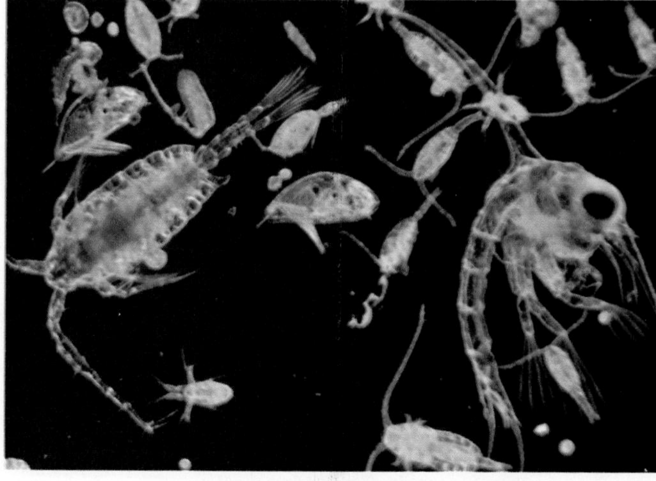

D. P. Wilson

37–2 Microscopic life in surface waters of the open sea. **(Left)** Diatoms (many are shown) and dinoflagellates (see arrow) are the world's leaders in food production. They account for perhaps 85 percent of the world's photosynthesis. **(Right)** The primary consumers of the sea include these minute crustaceans—copepods and a crab larva.

animals. These animals are the primary consumers. They, in turn, are prey for the secondary consumers, and so on.

With light, the sea becomes a factory for life. The energy of light is stored in carbon compounds, which are used for the substance and energy of all organisms. The mass of living matter present in the sea is far greater than that on land. This life is not at all obvious. If you were to examine the surface waters of the North Atlantic, the chances are that you would see only water. Yet a liter of this water might contain 500,000 bacteria, 1,000,000 microscopic plants, and 150 microscopic animals.

Many of the animals move by means of cilia, flagella, or legs of some sort. A few of the plants move by means of flagella. For the most part, however, all of these organisms of the surface waters of the open sea are at the mercy of wind and waves. These more or less helpless drifters are known as **plankton.** They are insignificant to the unaided eye, but they play a vital role in the life of the sea. Under the microscope they take on a truly wondrous variety of forms and colors.

The primary producers of the open-sea plankton are single-celled plants. The most abundant are diatoms (Figure 37-2, left). These are algae having an outer skeleton composed largely of silica, which is almost identical to glass. Diatoms contain a chlorophyll similar to that of green plants. It enables them to transform the light energy into the chemical energy of carbon compounds that are characteristic of the green plant's way of life.

The primary producers next in order of abundance are the dinoflagellates (dy·no·FLAJ-e·lates). Each dinoflagellate has two flagella—a structural characteristic that we usually consider animal-like. Some dinoflagellates possess chlorophyll and are photosynthetic. Others lack chlorophyll and are heterotrophic. Obviously the usual distinction between green plants and animals breaks down in the dinoflagellate group.

Diatoms and dinoflagellates, plus a few other microscopic algae and some of the larger floating seaweeds, green, brown, and red, are the basis for all other life in the open sea. Being photosynthetic, the marine algae can live

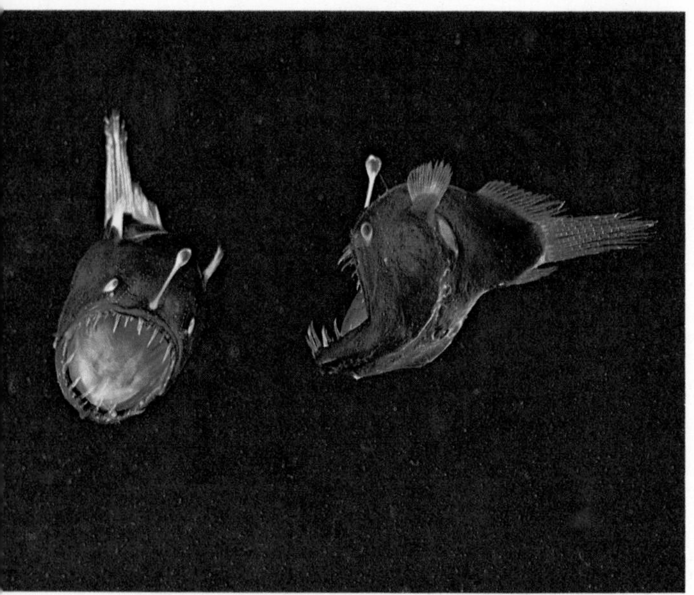

Peter David

37–3 Ocean depths have no producers—only consumers, as vividly portrayed by these angler fish.

only where there is light. It is not surprising, therefore, to find them restricted to the surface layers of the water—nearly always to the top 100 meters. Here they serve as food for a variety of small animals, which are the primary consumers. Among these are protozoans, various crustaceans, larval fishes, and representatives of nearly every other group of animals (Figure 37-2, right). The primary consumers serve as food for secondary consumers, which range in size up to the giant whales, whale sharks, and giant squids (Figure 37-4). And, of course, there are numerous decomposers, primarily bacteria, that change the bodies of dead organisms into inorganic and simple organic compounds. The food web near the surface of the open sea is not unlike that on land as we studied it in Chapter 36.

In other parts of the sea, conditions of life may be quite different from those just described. In deep waters, the absence of light means that there can be no photosynthesis, no local producers (Figure 37-3). All life in the lightless depths is ultimately dependent upon food materials that drift down from above.

Life near the shore is greatly affected by the land. Rivers bring not only fresh water but also organic and inorganic materials from the land masses. Organisms living at the edge of the sea are subjected to greater environmental extremes than those living in the open sea. The rise and fall of the tides may cover and uncover shore organisms, and water temperatures vary more than in the open sea. The **salinity** (salt content of the water) is also variable, being decreased by river water and runoff of rain water.

Many organisms along the shore, attached to rocks or pilings, show a remarkable vertical zonation. Even more remarkable is that the order in which the organisms occur in this ecosystem is similar whether we are looking at it on the coast of South Africa, the Atlantic coast of Maine, or the Pacific coast of California.

A tidal area can be divided into three distinct zones (Figure 37-5): an *above tidal zone*, which receives spray from the water at highest tide; the *tidal zone*, which is successively covered and uncovered by most of the tide; and the *subtidal zone*, where there are permanent tide pools. When we look at the diagram representing this zonation, even without knowing what the organisms are, we can see that certain kinds of organisms are restricted to a very specific part of this ecosystem. The zone in which an organism lives is determined to a large extent by the degree of drying the organism can withstand.

Note that algae do not cover the whole surface of the rocks bordering the tide pool. The exposed edges are constantly acted on by surf, which makes it impossible for algae to grow here. Algae do grow on the more protected faces of the rock. The kind of algae that occurs in a particular zone is again determined by its tolerance to drying. Some algae at the base of the lower zone cannot withstand drying and have most of their bodies continually covered by water of the tide pool.

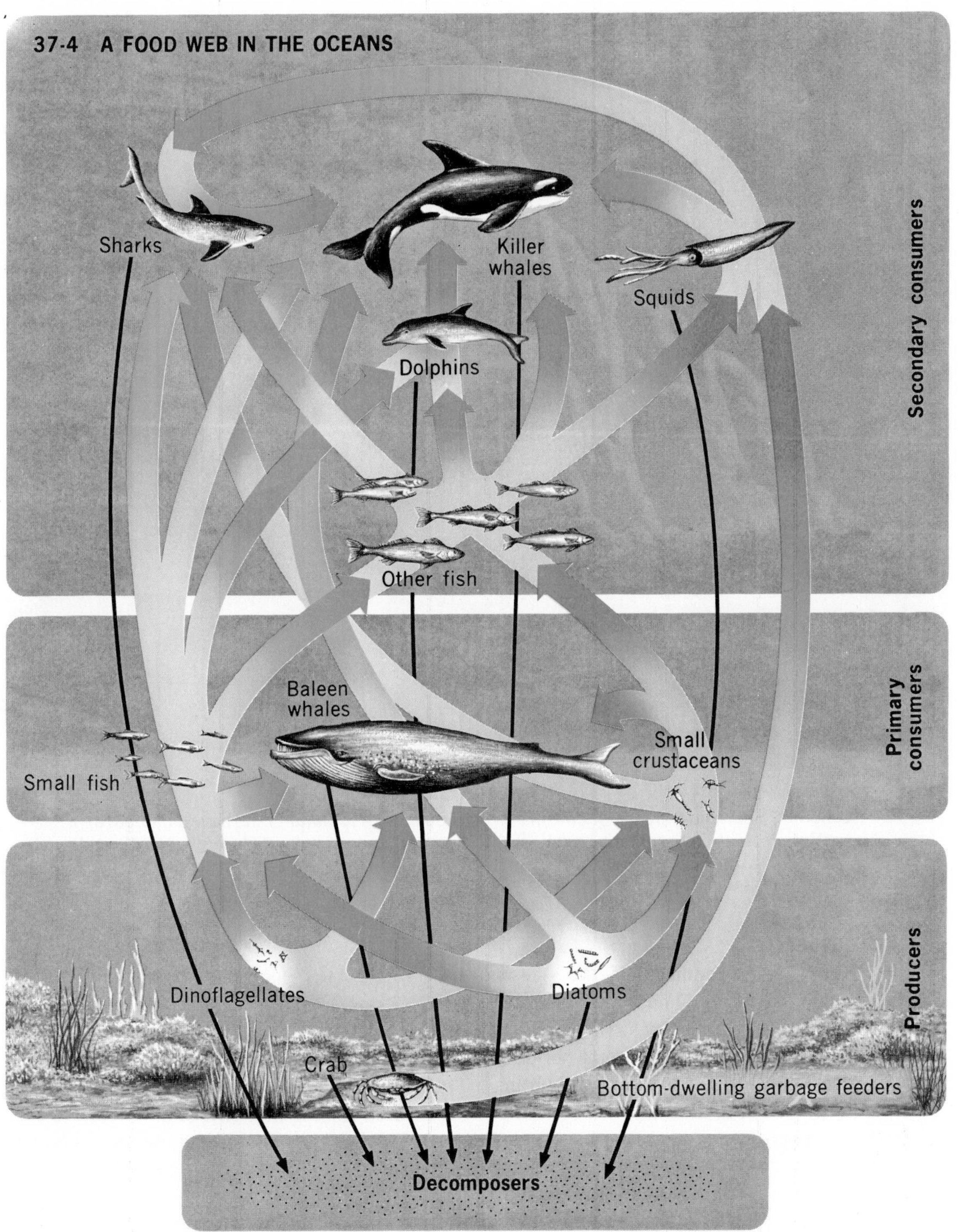
37-4 A FOOD WEB IN THE OCEANS
Sharks
Killer whales
Squids
Dolphins
Other fish
Secondary consumers
Baleen whales
Small fish
Small crustaceans
Primary consumers
Dinoflagellates
Diatoms
Producers
Crab
Bottom-dwelling garbage feeders
Decomposers

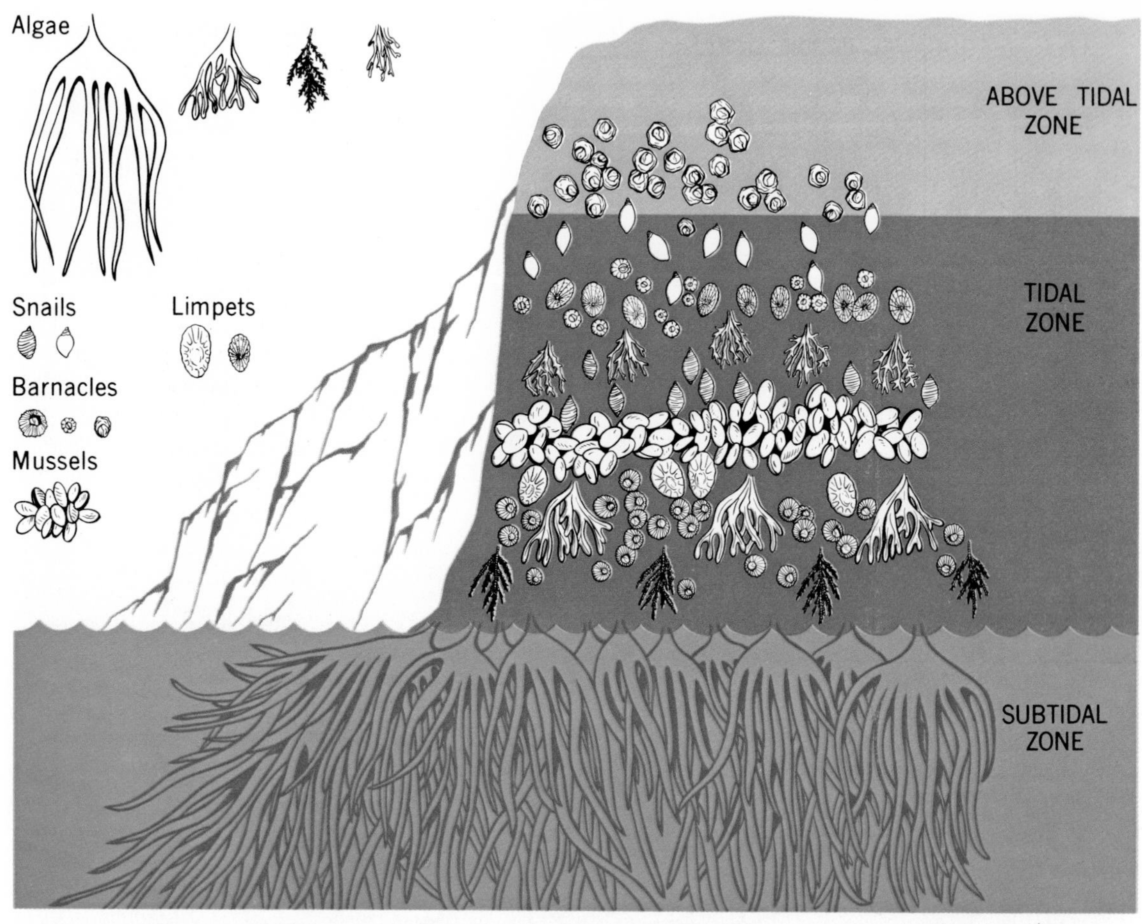

37–5 A tidal ecosystem. Organisms living above the *subtidal zone* have adapted to a semi-terrestrial environment by being able to withstand periods of drying when the tide is out. How do you account for the difference in abundance and types of organisms in the upper and lower portions of the *tidal zone*?

Generally, the environment of the ocean is the most stable of any. The oceans existed before life on earth began. They have expanded and contracted in different geological periods, but, by and large, they have provided a continuous medium—in space and time—for the life of organisms. Their temperatures are more uniform than those of the land masses at the same latitude. There is plenty of oxygen, except in deep waters of some seas cut off from the main masses of water. The Mediterranean is a sea of this type. Also there is plenty of water—not always the case on land.

The seas then provide one of the most reliable environments. It is here that life originated. It is also to this habitat that organisms were restricted for the first two billion years of their existence. Enormous evolutionary changes took place before organisms could live on land. Only the most advanced animals and plants—seed plants, higher vertebrates, and arthropods—developed into their present forms on land.

LIFE ON LAND

The seas are characterized by constancy; the lands by variability. The seas have always existed and been connected. Land masses, by contrast, have had their ups and downs. At one time or another nearly every bit of land has been covered by sea. Even areas where we now find great mountain ranges were once under water. Probably no more than 10 percent of the land today has been above water continuously since the Cambrian period began.

General Problems of Life on Land

A jellyfish in the ocean maintains its body form; on the shore it collapses into a shapeless mass. All marine organisms are supported by water. Land plants and land animals lack such support. They have, however, other means for supporting their living substance, which is so largely water. Plants have evolved rigid cell walls; animals have evolved skeletons and other supporting devices (see Chapter 25).

Most aquatic organisms except those in a tidal zone die rapidly when exposed to air. The water evaporates so quickly from their bodies that cellular metabolism is disrupted and then destroyed. The conservation of water is therefore a major problem for organisms that live on land. Terrestrial plants and animals have special devices that conserve water. As a rule, the body has a waterproof covering to keep water *in*. Respiratory surfaces, which are always areas where water would be lost by evaporation, are internal. Recall the example of lungs in terrestrial chordates, tracheal tubes of insects, and air spaces behind the stomata in plants.

While the chemical composition of sea water remains quite constant, the composition of land masses varies greatly. On land we encounter great variations in the amount of water —ranging from marshes at one extreme to waterless deserts at the other. Soils vary tremendously in their relative amounts of particular mineral substances and of dead organic material. Oxygen and carbon dioxide are the only required substances that are nearly constant in amount. They are constant for the same reason that the sea is constant—they are part of a continuous and ever-moving mass. The sea of water and the sea of air are fairly uniform chemically. Land is not.

The temperatures of the sea are nearly always between 0° and 30° C. Temperatures vary greatly on land, not only from place to place but also with the season. The surface temperatures in some deserts may fall below 0° C in the winter and rise above 50° C in the summer. No organism, in its active state, can withstand all of the tremendous environmental differences encountered on land. (Man is the most widely distributed species, but solely because he is able to provide a tolerable environment for himself wherever he goes.) Each species has evolved adaptations for life in a specific ecosystem. Part of this great variety is shown in Chapter 39 of your book. Look at the different organisms, decide what kind of ecosystem each inhabits, and how it is adapted to its particular environment.

What gives a particular ecosystem its distinctive features? The soil and climate of a locality are two of the most important factors. They determine what green plants will grow there, and the plants often determine what consumers can exist there (Inquiries 37-1 and 37-2). If the climate and soil will support a forest, one type of ecosystem exists; if they can support only a desert, another type of ecosystem prevails. For the most part, the animals that can live in a forest are quite different from those of a desert or other ecosystem.

On the land masses of the earth, there are four major types of ecosystems: forest, grassland, desert, and savanna ecosystems.

The Forest Ecosystem

Wherever sufficient moisture is available and the temperatures are not too low, the land supports forests. Man has destroyed many of the forests that once blanketed broad areas of the earth (Figure 37-6), but some remain. Forest trees belong to many different species. Some are gymnosperms, others are angiosperms.

A mature tree is generally much taller than plants that are not so woody. Its height is an adaptation enabling it to obtain light. In an old, well-established forest, the large trees support the photosynthetic tissue far above the ground. The smaller plants that grow in the shade on the forest floor are of two kinds. Some are shade-tolerant species, plants which can grow in dim light. The second group consists of the young trees of the species that make up the forest. The young trees begin their growth, but most of them soon die. There is not enough light for them. In a mature forest, the young trees are generally doomed unless one of the larger trees is blown down. If this happens, the small trees nearby begin to grow rapidly in the newly available space. Usually many more compete for the place to live than can be supported by it. The smaller or weaker individuals become excessively shaded and perish. After years have passed, probably only a single tree will stand in the place of the one blown down long before.

The numbers of such doomed individuals is staggering. How many thousands of acorns will an oak tree produce during its life? Yet on the average, only a single one will ever become a full-grown tree. The acorn that does survive is not only the fittest in the evolutionary sense, but also the luckiest! This is frequently the way in evolution. Many of the young oak trees that perish in the shade of some larger individual may possess superior genes—yet, unless some "lucky" accident occurs, they never have a chance to mature and reproduce.

Temperate Deciduous Forest

The white settlers who first came to North America had a profound effect on the magnificent deciduous forests of the region (Figure 37-7). For centuries prior to the coming of white settlers, American Indians had depended on this forest ecosystem for their food and

37-6 THE WORLD'S FORESTS

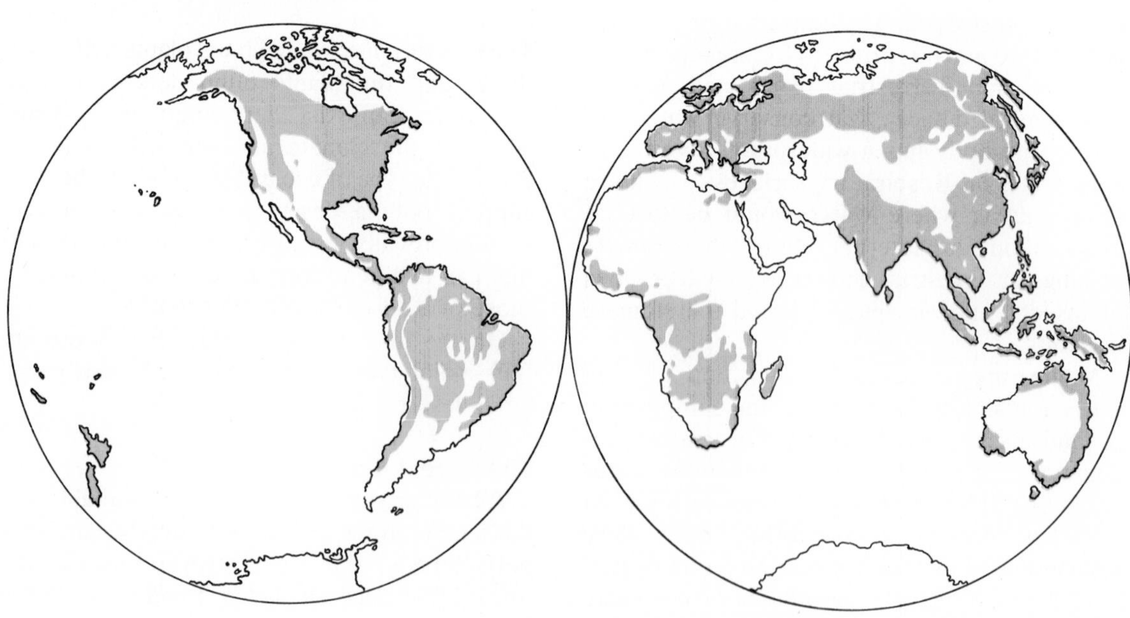

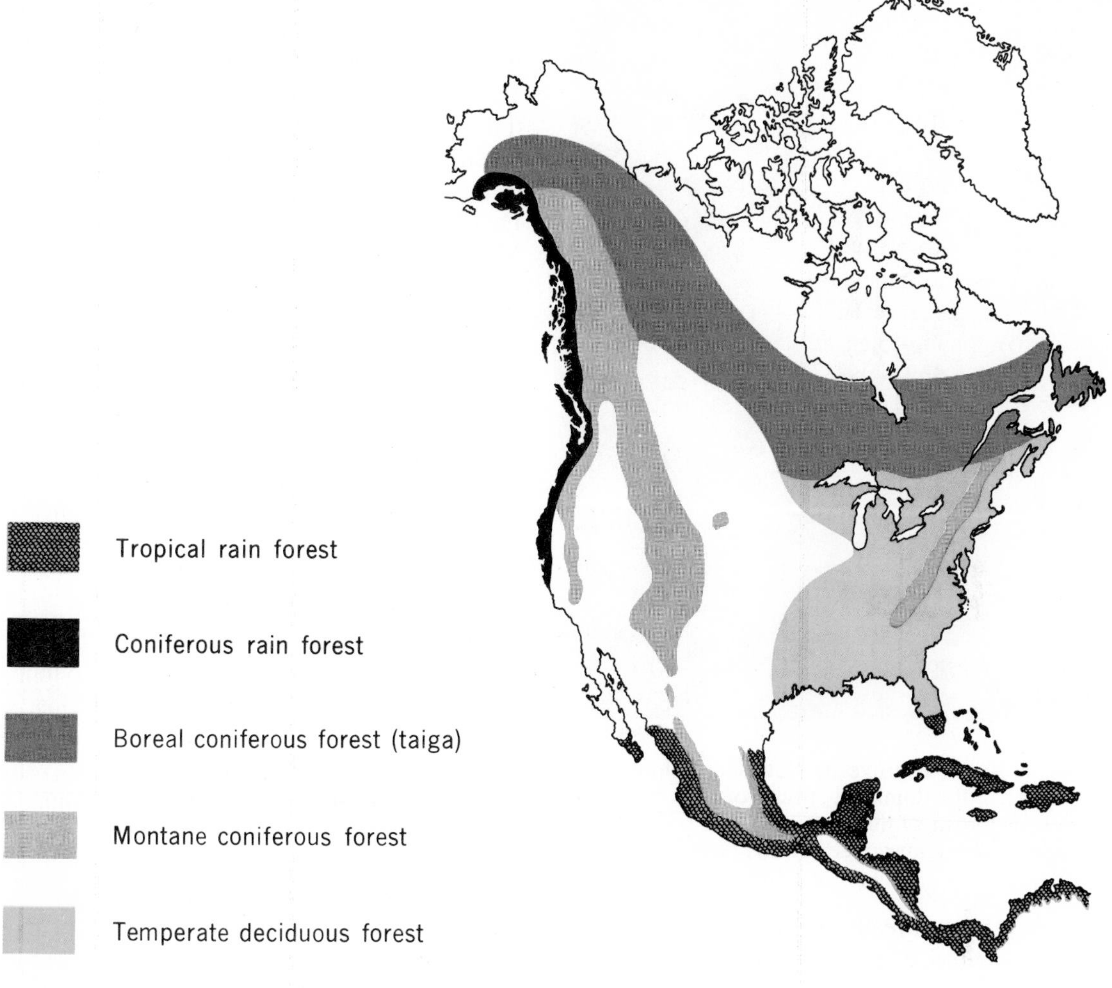

37–7 The distribution of forests in North and Central America before land was cleared for cultivation. The white areas are grasslands, deserts, tundra, and glaciers.

shelter. They hunted the plentiful deer, bear, panther, squirrel, and wild turkey. They harvested wild fruits, seeds, and roots. Their agriculture was restricted to a few small garden plots associated with their villages. The Indian was a part of the deciduous forest ecosystem and did little to alter it. All this changed with the appearance in North America of European colonists with axes and plows. One by one the forest trees began to fall.

Today only small isolated and protected segments of this ecosystem remain in the eastern United States. The white settlers cleared the land for cultivation, and the once extensive forests gradually decreased until few are left. Some deciduous forest ecosystems are still preserved. The most extensive examples are in the Great Smoky Mountains National Park of North Carolina and Tennessee. Here we can get some idea of what the original forest was

Dick Smith

37–8 This maple grove in New Hampshire illustrates one of the dominant species of trees in climax deciduous forests of the eastern United States. What are some other climax trees of this region?

like. We have already mentioned the animals that characterize the original forest in this region. The trees may be well known to some of you. The buckeye, basswood, beech, tulip trees, and many others are in the forests of the Smoky Mountains. In the more northerly states of New England we are more apt to see beech and maple (Figure 37-8), while at the southern end of the Appalachians oaks and hickories are common. All of these deciduous trees are hardwoods. In some regions, however, conifers, especially hemlocks, may be present.

Biologists have noticed that the vegetation of the forest tends to be in layers, not unlike the zones of a tide pool. In a deciduous forest (Figure 37-9) the upper level is composed of deciduous trees forming a crown or canopy 25 to 60 meters (75 to 175 feet) above the ground. The second layer is also deciduous trees, but their tops are rarely more than 6 to 16 meters (18 to 48 feet) above the ground. A third layer is composed of deciduous and evergreen shrubs 0.30 to 2.5 meters (1 to 8 feet) tall. Familiar spring flowers, such as hepaticas, Dutchman's breeches, wild ginger, bloodroot, May apple, and many others compose the fourth layer, the cover of herbaceous plants on the forest floor (Figure 37-10). Intermixed with these and on the fallen logs and rocks is a fifth layer, of mosses and lichens. The layering effect is primarily the result of an interaction between organisms and available light energy and humidity. As we go downward through the layers, light intensity decreases, while humidity increases.

Coniferous Forest Ecosystems

Anyone who has traveled through the Sierra Nevadas of California or the Rocky Mountains is aware that in ascending the mountains, we go through several rather specific climatic zones in a short time. For example, when traveling westward toward the Rocky Mountains of Arizona we come up out of the Painted Desert into a semi-barren foothill country dotted with rather scrubby looking piñon pines and junipers. This open coniferous forest extends from about 1,600 meters (5,000 feet) through a rather dry zone to about 1,900 or 2,200 meters (6,000 to 7,000 feet). Continuing upward to the 2,500 meter (8,000 feet) level, we see a change in the conifers, reflecting an increase in moisture. Here are the ponderosa pines, especially on the north-facing slopes where less drying takes place. A little higher, around 2,800 meters (9,000 feet), and again more prominently on the north-facing slopes, Douglas fir and the limber pine are abundant. Douglas fir, you will recall, is an important element of the coniferous rain forest (Chapter 36) of the state of Washington. It is a good indicator of greater amounts of moisture. Above 2,800 meters, the Douglas fir merges with spire-like Engelmann spruce. In this zone in early June, melting snow covers parts of the forest floor. The temperatures remain fairly cool as the flowering plants appear (Figure 37-11). The spruce forest extends to timberline zone (Figures 36-10 and 36-11) at about 3,800 meters (11,500 feet), where wind and low temperatures are the limiting factors. Above timberline and over the pass to the other side of the mountains we travel through the treeless alpine tundra, which we will describe in another section.

Some animals, especially birds such as the ptarmigans (Figure 31-9) and piñon jays, are restricted to certain zones—ptarmigans to the upper zones, piñon jays to the lower zones. Pikas and certain marmots are in harmony with the rugged environment above timberline, while larger mammals such as deer and elk move up or down from zone to zone with seasonal changes that regulate the availability of food.

The coniferous forest of the mountains is a variable one and changes in character from one altitudinal zone to the next. However, not all coniferous forests are this diverse. In the north woods, or boreal forest (Figure 37-7), the coniferous forest is much more uniform, being composed of spruce, pines, and firs. In parts of Canada and Russia, the trackless northern spruce forests are known as the **taiga** (TY·guh). The climate in these forests is severe and similar to the climate of the spruce zone of a mountain. In the more northerly latitudes, however, the summers are shorter, the rainfall less, and the winters more severe. Very few trees other than spruce have become adapted to the physical environment of this kind of ecosystem. One of the larger mammals that is

37–9 The layering effect in a deciduous forest. The upper two levels are composed of deciduous trees. The third level is composed mainly of shrubs, and the fourth layer is occupied by herbaceous plants that produce spring flowers (see Figure 37–10).

J. Cikel from National Audubon Society

Arthur W. Ambler from National Audubon Society

John H. Gerard from National Audubon Society

John H. Gerard from National Audubon Society

37–10 Some of the flowering plants commonly found in deciduous forests include: **(left, top to bottom)** May apple, hepatica, bloodroot; **(right, top and bottom)** Dutchman's breeches and wild ginger.

George Regensburg from National Audubon Society

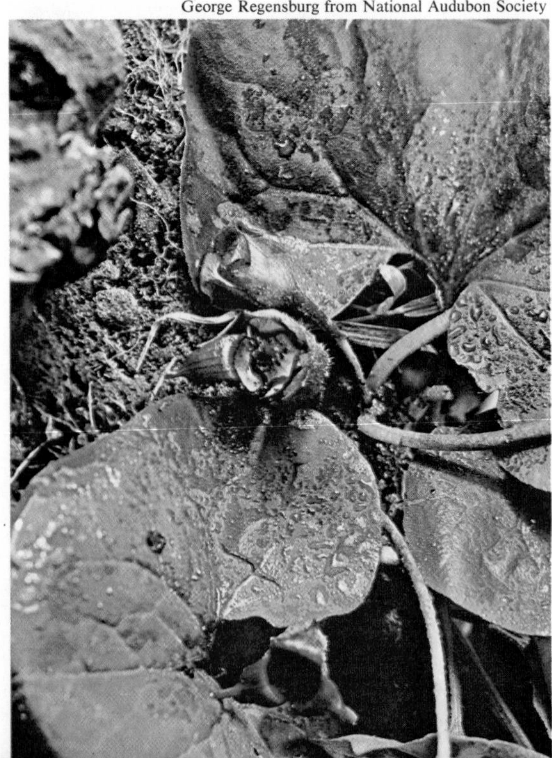

H. R. Booth from National Audubon Society

John A. Moore

37-11 Flowering plants of higher altitudes endure low temperatures. **(Above)** Columbine; **(above right)** mountain marsh marigolds; **(below)** Indian paint brush; **(below right)** bluebells.

John A. Moore

John H. Gerard from National Audubon Society

John A. Moore

John A. Moore

John A. Moore

John A. Moore

John A. Moore

John A. Moore

John W. Marr

37–12 A variety of plant life occurs on alpine rocks and slopes. Most of these plants were photographed on Mt. Rainier. **(Left, top to bottom)** Lupine, red mountain heath, saxifrage; **(right, top to bottom)** sedge, phlox, lichen, and grasses.

very much a part of the boreal forest is the moose. The association is so close that the ecosystem is sometimes referred to as the spruce-moose ecosystem.

Tundra

The rugged tundra ecosystem is intimately associated with the climatic conditions of the coniferous forest.

In our trips across the mountains, above timberline (Figure 36-10) we encountered the alpine zone where no tree forms can grow. The alpine zone with its lichens, mosses, and diminutive flowering plants (Figure 37-12) crowding the protected faces of slopes and rock depressions is sometimes called the **alpine tundra** ecosystem. On certain mountains the alpine zone is subjected to winds in excess of 160 kilometers per hour (100 mph) and temperatures down to −57° C (−70° F) or lower. Light energy and ultraviolet radiation are intense at this high altitude. Water is also in abundance and, when thawing occurs, the soil is usually boggy at the surface.

With this rugged environment in mind, we can better understand why no large plants grow in the alpine zone. Most of them are small perennials that reproduce in a very short time. They only have a month or two of favorable weather for growth and reproduction.

Although there are no big trees, there are miniature willows and birches that never exceed two to four inches in height. Clearly these plants have evolved from ancestral tree forms and have become adapted to the special environment of the alpine tundra, with its lower temperatures but bright sunlight. The predominant plants of this ecosystem are grasses, sedges, and lichens. The latter seem to be everywhere, especially on barren rock faces and well-drained slopes.

You may be surprised to know that similar specialized organisms grow far away in the vast tundras (Figure 37-13) of North America north of the Arctic Circle. However, if we stop and think for a moment, the physical factors of the two widely separated ecosystems have much in common. The temperatures are low, winds are strong, and water is available only during a relatively short growing season.

Among the producers in the ecosystem are lichens and mosses, the miniature birches and willows, and other diminutive flowering plants. Trees are mostly lacking, making the Arctic tundra one of the most desolate of all places. The gray-green, matlike blanket of lichens and mosses covers the thin layer of soil of the tundra. In the one or two summer months, the poorly drained ponds of the marshes and lakes make an ideal breeding ground for ducks, geese, and countless other waterfowl.

As we might expect, the productivity of the ecosystem is low. Very little energy is left for consumers after the plants have met their own energy requirements. Very little of the energy that *does* flow through food chains and food webs is wasted by the consumer at the end of the chain. Consumers such as hares, lemmings, caribou, reindeer, and musk-ox move from place to place through the rather uniform ecosystem, obtaining the limited amount of

37–13 Arctic tundra. Beyond the northernmost reaches of tree growth, tundra begins. In the summer it resembles grasslands or alpine tundra with diminutive flowering plants, but the chief plant cover is lichens and mosses.

Charles J. Ott from National Audubon Society

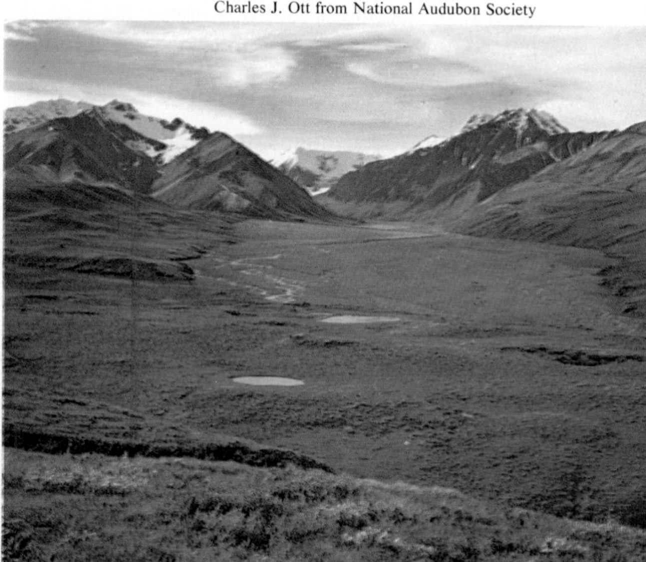

37-14 AVERAGE MONTHLY VARIATION IN TEMPERATURE AT THREE SELECTED LOCATIONS (TUNDRA, TEMPERATE FOREST, AND TROPICAL RAIN FOREST)

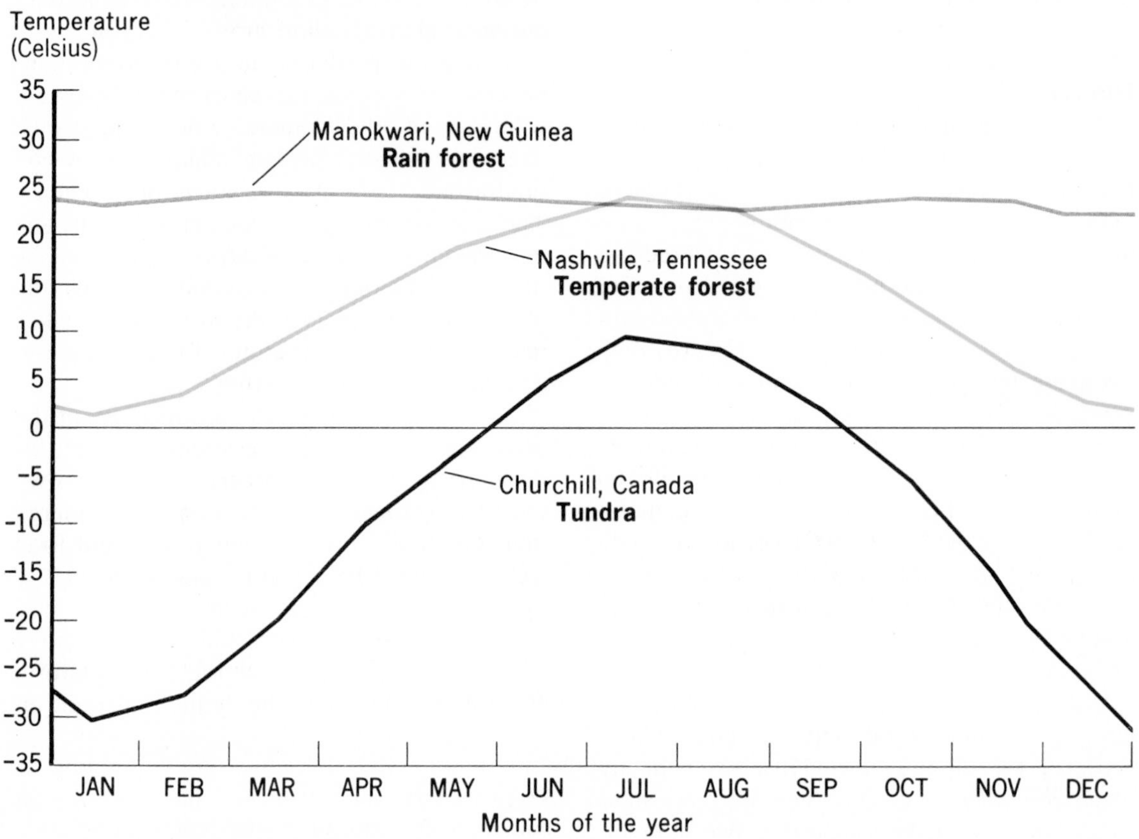

energy from vast expanses of vegetation. Populations of second-level consumers, such as the great snowy owl, foxes, and weasels, fluctuate greatly with the changes in populations of hares and lemmings.

Of all the ecosystems, the tundra is probably the most inhospitable, least productive, and least utilized by man. Only the Eskimos of North America and the Lapps of northern Europe have managed to survive in the tundra.

The Rain Forest Ecosystem

Great forests also occur in many parts of central Africa, southern Asia, and the tropical parts of the New World. The trees are usually broadleafed; the leaves, however, are shed irregularly, not seasonally as in a temperate-zone deciduous forest. The tropical forest is always green, never presenting the barren, winter appearance of a deciduous forest in the temperate zone. Many tropical forests are **rain forests,** referring to the copious rainfall that occurs. Here the temperature and humidity are always high. Frequently the trees have such a dense mass of leaves that little light reaches the forest floor. Once again, only the most shade-tolerant of species can survive at the lower levels of the forest.

The richness of life in a tropical rain forest staggers the imagination. In a tropical rain forest, you might have to search a long time for two individual trees of the same species. Where there are a few dozen species of insects in an eastern deciduous forest, there are hundreds or thousands in the Amazonian rain forest.

The richness and diversity of life in the tropics is due to many factors. First of all, the environment has been stable for a very long time (reminding us of the stability of the marine environment mentioned earlier). In contrast, the great Pleistocene glaciers covered much of Canada, the northeastern United States, and Europe as recently as 10,000 years ago. The tropics were almost unaffected by these recurring periods of stress.

As examples of the uniformity of conditions over long periods of time, tropical forests are uniform in two important ways—water and temperature. Two chief problems for terrestrial organisms are those of securing water and finding tolerable temperatures. Generally, plenty of water is available in rain forests, and temperatures are high and nearly constant throughout the year (Figures 37-14 and 37-15).

In the warm, moist rain forest, plants grow in situations that would be impossible for them in the temperate zone. If dehydration is not a danger, many plants can cling to the trunks and branches of trees. Thus we find that many trees in the rain forest are covered with epiphytes (Figure 36-8, page 682) which obtain their moisture chiefly from the air. There are many species of epiphytes in the tropics. The pineapple, orchid (Figure 37-16), and fern families contribute a large number. All are reaching for the sun, so to speak, for in the lower levels of the forest there is too little light for most of them to grow.

In such a highly productive ecosystem we might anticipate a great variety of animal life in the different layers of the ecosystem. In the

37-15 AVERAGE MONTHLY VARIATION IN RAINFALL AT THREE SELECTED LOCATIONS (TUNDRA, TEMPERATE FOREST, AND TROPICAL RAIN FOREST)

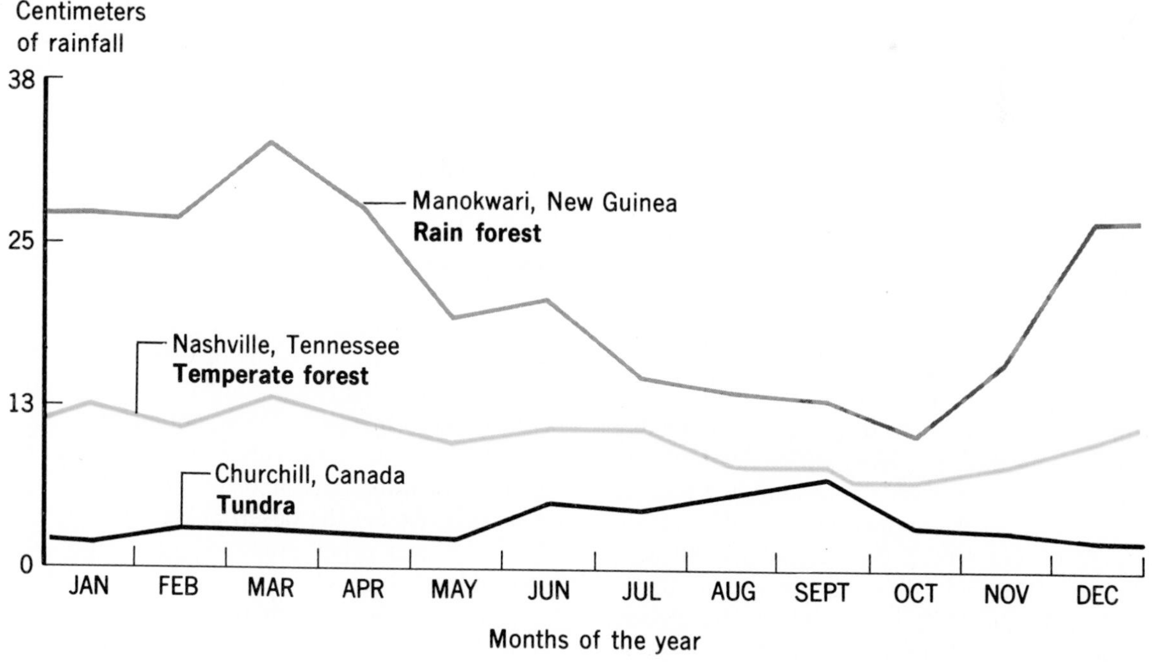

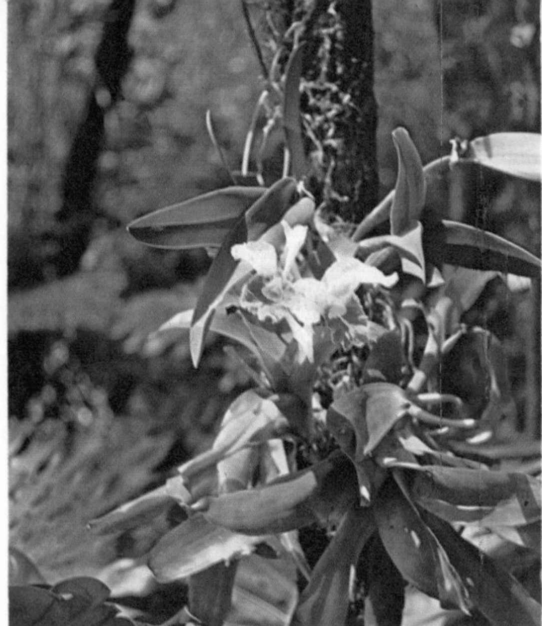

Annan Photo Features

37–16 An orchid plant—a winner in the competition for sunlight. A perch on a tree, or among its branches, characterizes the tropical epiphytes.

canopy of the rain forest, which may be more than 30 meters (100 feet) above the ground, we find monkeys, lemurs, snakes, birds, and insects. All show remarkable adaptations to this tree-top environment. This variety of consumer life decreases as we go downward to the forest floor, where productivity decreases because of increased shading.

A brief review of Chapter 36 (pages 680-82), which describes the coniferous rain forest of the Olympic Peninsula, will show you that the coniferous rain forest is similar in many ways to the tropical rain forest ecosystem, even though the two ecosystems are found in different parts of the world. By now you may have realized that when a certain set of conditions is found in the physical environment, we can predict, to a degree, the kinds of organisms that will live within the limits imposed by the environment. Thus we find rain forests where the temperature is mild and fairly uniform and where the rainfall is 330 centimeters (130 inches) or more per year. It does not make any difference whether these conditions exist in the state of Washington or the Island of Ceylon. Likewise, tundra can be found near the top of a mountain 3,600 meters high (12,000 feet) or above the Arctic Circle. The same can be said for deserts, grasslands, and other ecosystems of the world.

The Grassland Ecosystem

Water is always a necessity for plants, but the requirements vary from species to species. More water is required to support a forest than is available in large areas of the temperate zone and the tropics. Where there is less than enough water to support a forest, a grassland ecosystem develops. With still less water, the result is a desert. As a rough rule, grasslands occur where yearly rainfall averages 25 to 75 cm (10-30 inches). But more than the amount of rain is involved. For the growth of a forest, rains must be reliable—they must come every year. Characteristically, grasslands are regions of frequent, and often severe, drought. These lands might receive enough water for tree growth during many years; but then a dry period will come during which the trees are killed. Thus, there can be no forests. The type of ecosystem that develops in a region depends not on the years with the most favorable conditions but on the years with the least favorable conditions.

The relation of water to the type of plants supported is often vividly illustrated in a grassland (Figure 37-17). Most of the area supports grass, but along stream beds a narrow ribbon of trees clearly indicates that, given a little more water, trees could grow here.

The principal grassland ecosystems of the world are the Great Plains of Canada and the United States, the pampas and other grasslands extending from southern Argentina to Brazil, the steppes extending from southern Russia to central Asia, the grasslands of much of central Australia (except the desert at the center), and the veldt and other grasslands of south and central Africa (Figure 37-18).

Grasslands have been the home of grazing animals for millions of years. The Great Plains of North America were the home, until comparatively recently, of the bison (or American buffalo). The grasslands of Africa are the home of many species of antelopes. Kangaroos are common grazing animals of Australian grassland. Man now uses many of these grasslands to pasture the cattle and sheep that provide his meat, hides, and wool.

Compared to forest ecosystems, the grasslands are ecosystems of stress. Forests provide shade and protection from the winds. They release tremendous amounts of water into the atmosphere by way of transpiration. In this way, humidity, always important for terrestrial animals and plants, is kept higher than it would be without the trees. The evaporation of water by forest transpiration also moderates the temperature. Grasses and other relatively short plants of the grasslands, on the other hand, are not able to provide so effective an umbrella. Winds sweep across a grassland and the organisms living there are exposed to the sun, and to greater variations of temperature than organisms in the more protected forest.

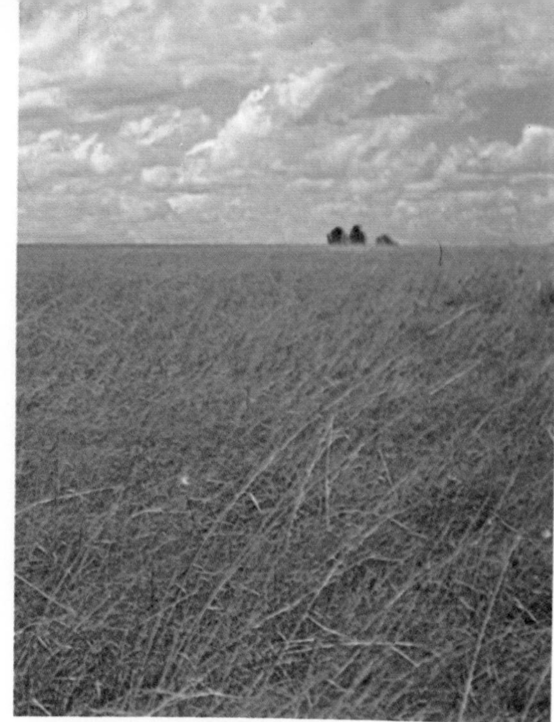

Clair Kucera

37–17 Virgin grassland in Missouri. In the central and southwestern United States, vast regions that now are under cultivation were native grasslands in the time of the Plains Indians.

37-18 THE WORLD'S GRASSLANDS

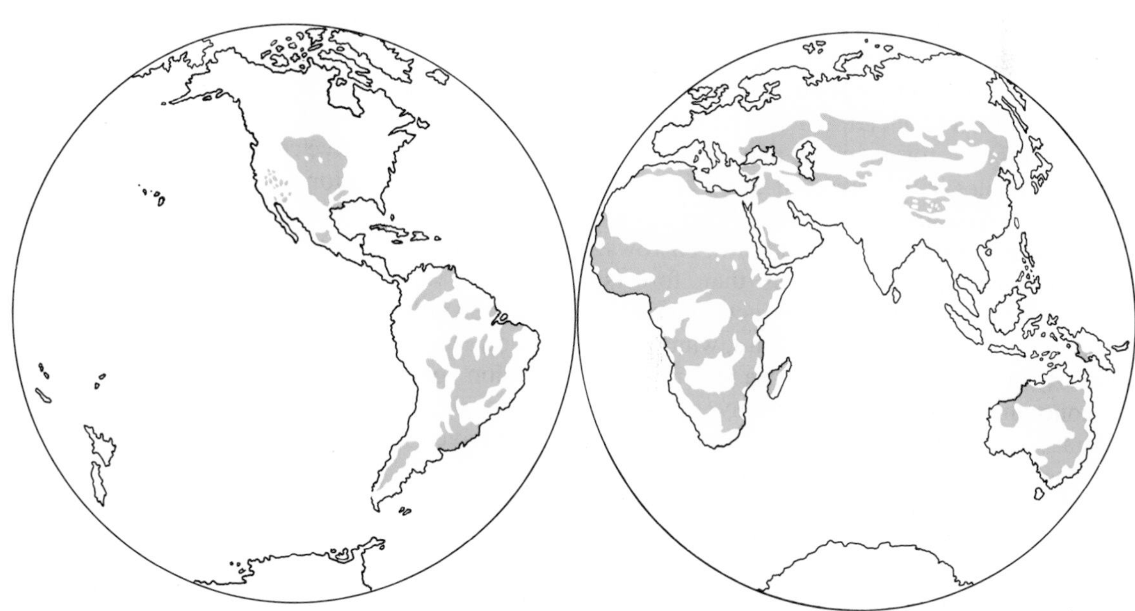

Roger T. Peterson from Photo Researchers

37–19 A waterhole in a tropical savanna of Africa. Grasses are the dominant form of vegetation, but widely spaced trees are also found. Water may be scarce, so that where it occurs, the animals congregate to drink.

A forest ecosystem provides a greater variety of habitats than does a grassland. Animal life on land generally is restricted to the zone between the tops of the tallest plants and a few centimeters below the surface of the soil. In a forest the thickness of this zone may be as much as 30 to 45 meters (100 to 150 feet). In a grassland community, on the other hand, this zone is generally less than 2 meters (6 feet) thick. The birds of a forest, for example, may nest on the ground, in holes in the trunks of trees, or at any level of the branches. In a grassland community birds usually nest on the ground or in burrows.

As regions of greater stress than forests, grasslands continually are subject to greater variations of temperature, moisture, winds, and intensity of sunlight; and there are fewer places of concealment for animals. Many grassland animals have evolved the burrowing habit. In burrows they withdraw from unfavorable conditions, particularly heat or cold. Grasslands are the homes of a variety of animals that are swift of foot—wild horse, antelope, gazelle, ostrich, and many others.

Since the grasslands are regions of stress, they are subject to easy destruction by man. We see this in the United States, where large areas of grassland have been converted to crop land. Sometimes these areas have enough rain in the "good years" for abundant crops, principally wheat—which, of course, is a grass. But grasslands are regions of frequent drought, and when the "bad years" come, crops fail. Since the land has lost its protective cover of permanent grass, it is subject to erosion. Large areas of the United States became a "dust bowl" during the 1930's, when land that should have remained covered in grass was plowed. Even where grasslands are used only for grazing animals, they are often overgrazed. The grass mat is destroyed, and erosion begins. Thus, areas throughout the world that were grasslands in their natural state have been converted to near desert by improper use.

The Tropical Savanna Ecosystem

Those of us living in North America are not familiar with this kind of ecosystem. Yet it is a very important one in large parts of South America, Africa, Australia, and parts of Asia, especially India.

The savanna might be described as a semiforested grassland (Figures 36-2 and 37-19). Often it is a very arid place with a few scattered waterholes in a setting of tall grasses and flat-topped, thorny trees. In parts of Africa the savanna is populated with large numbers of first-order consumers, such as zebras, giraffes, antelope, and rhinoceroses. Second-order consumers, including lions, jackals, hyenas, and vultures abound. The productivity of this ecosystem is highest during the rainy season, decreasing when the dry, hot weather arrives.

The Desert Ecosystem

Forest, grassland, desert: this is a sequence of increasingly rigorous environment. Grasslands cannot support trees in any great number, but conditions are favorable enough for a continuous mat of vegetation. Deserts are the next step. Here, lack of water permits only isolated plants with much bare ground between them.

In a true desert, perennially insufficient rainfall prevents the existence of permanently flowing streams. Some deserts have rivers flowing through them. The Nile, for example, flows *through* the desert of Egypt, but its headwaters are in the well-watered areas of the interior. There may be rivers in the desert—torrents after heavy rains, but otherwise dry gullies. Deserts generally have less than 25 cm (10 inches) of rain during the year. Even this modest amount of rain may be most unreliable. Rain may be relatively frequent in one year, but then there may be almost none for the next several years. This unreliability of water is a condition to which many desert plants and animals are adapted (Figure 37-20).

Without a protective blanket of vegetation, the desert environment is highly variable. In nondesert regions plant growth retards runoff of rainwater. In a desert, with its widely spaced plants, runoff is rapid. Thus, what little rain does fall is not as available for plants as it would be in a grassland or forest. The few desert plants lose little water into the atmosphere, so the humidity is always low. Winds sweep unhindered across the land. Data on average tem-

37–20 The Mohave Desert of California. Most of the plants you see are growing in the lowland area between the foreground and the hills in the distance. Can you suggest why?

John A. Moore

peratures do not reflect the fluctuations, which are generally extreme. Frequently, deserts are hot by day and cold at night. It is not unusual for the fluctuation to be as great as 30° C in 24 hours.

The great deserts of the world (Figure 37-21) occur on all the continents except Europe and Antarctica. The Sonoran Desert is in the American southwest and north central Mexico. Near-desert conditions exist as far north in the United States as the central part of the state of Washington. Deserts stretch across north Africa (the Sahara), through the Arabian Peninsula, and, with interruptions, across central Asia and Mongolia almost to the Pacific coast. The central portion of Australia is also a desert. In South America much of the west coast, from central Chile to Ecuador, is desert or near desert.

A permanent abundance of organisms in a desert is impossible. There is far less food than in the other major terrestrial habitats, since the primary producers are less numerous. Water is a chief limiting factor for plants as well as for animals. Both groups show numerous interesting ways for obtaining and conserving water.

Some desert plants have very shallow roots that may extend over a wide area. When rains come, the plants rapidly take up water and store it in specialized tissues. Cacti and euphorbias store large amounts of water in their fleshy stems—water that tides the plants over long periods of drought. Other desert plants have deep root systems that take up water far below the surface.

Plants lose water through their leaves (Chapter 15). When you remember this fact, you will not be surprised to learn that in deserts natural selection has promoted the development of plants with fewer and smaller leaves. There is nothing on a cactus plant that you will immediately recognize as a leaf (Figure 37-22 and righthand photographs of Figure 37-23). Actually the spines are modified leaves; you can see that their exposed surface is very small. Most of the photosynthetic tissue of the cacti

37-21 THE WORLD'S DESERTS

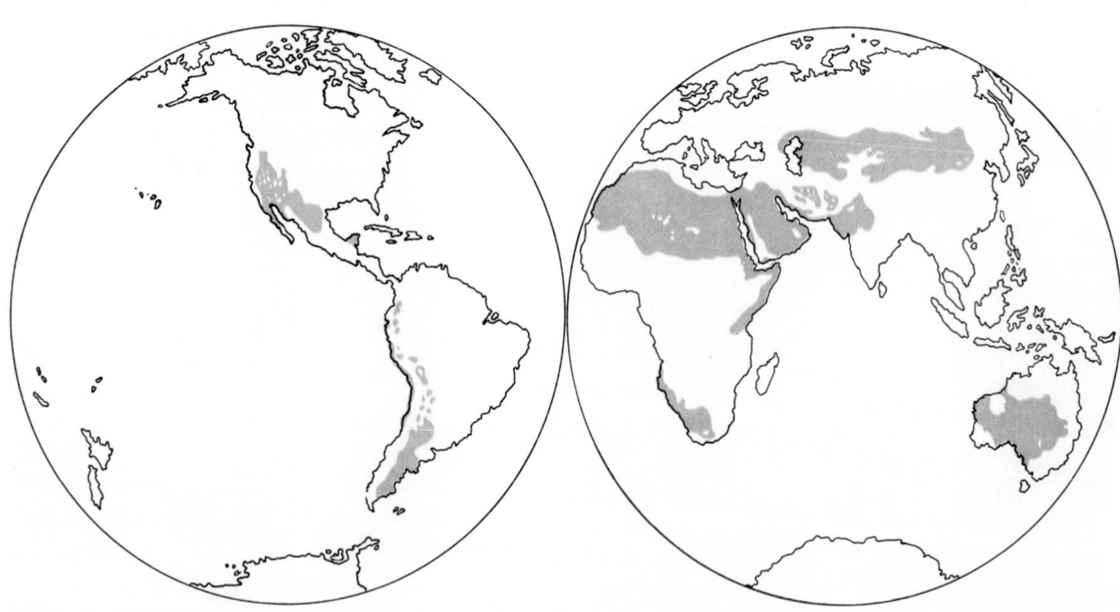

is in their enlarged stems. When more typical leaves are present on desert plants, they are usually small, thick, and either leathery or easily shed (Figure 37-23, upper left). Not infrequently the stomata are sunk in little pits. All of these adaptations reduce water loss.

The structure, physiology, and behavior of desert animals are evolved adjustments to the desert ecosystem. Many species live in burrows, where the humidity is greater and the temperature fluctuations are less extreme than on the surface. Many desert animals are nocturnal—they are active only at night when the temperature is lower and the humidity is greater. The water requirements of desert animals are often far less than those of their relatives living in the grasslands and forests. Many never drink at all. They rely solely on the water from their food and on what is produced during respiration. One of the main requirements for water in terrestrial vertebrates is for the removal of nitrogen wastes. Some desert animals excrete uric acid—the advantage to them being that uric acid, unlike urea, requires very little water for its removal (Chapter 23, page 432). Others excrete a very concentrated urine that contains urea.

An inhospitable-appearing desert may become a luxuriant garden after heavy rains. Flowers grow rapidly from seeds that may have lain dormant for a decade. Animals, which were biding their time in an inactive state, begin to stir. The desert becomes a colorful living world (Figure 37-24)—only to relapse into its usual condition when the rains pass and the water evaporates. We find that in a desert both animals and plants may grow with startling rapidity. Plants must grow, flower, and produce seeds while enough moisture remains for them to be active.

How Ecosystems Are Established

In describing the various ecosystems, we have used such words as "adapted," "survival," and "selected" to indicate the kinds of organisms that may be found in a particular ecosystem. These words we associate with the concept of evolution. Without relating the ideas of evolution to our study of ecology, we have little real understanding of why certain kinds of organisms are found in a certain kind of environment.

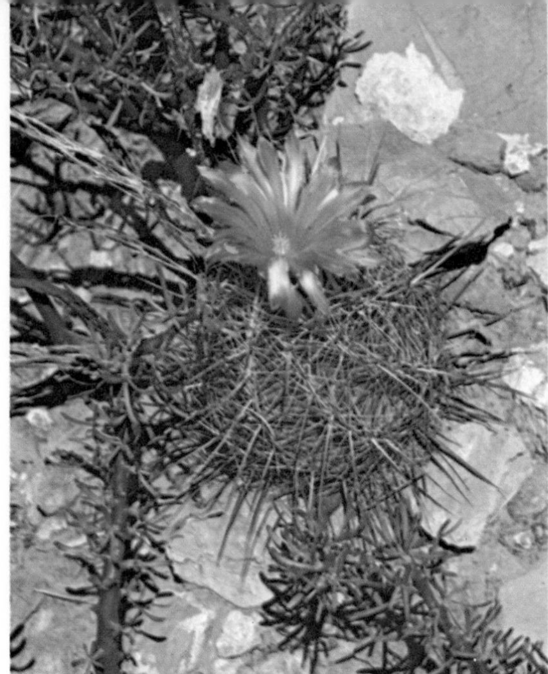

John A. Moore

37–22 A cactus plant in bloom. The leaves are reduced to spines. What adaptation to desert life does a minimum of leaf surface suggest?

The idea of the physical environment and the interaction of its parts on the organisms of the world has been noted in Chapter 36. Historically, we must remember that physical aspects of the world environments existed long before there were living things. With this in mind we can make the generalization that through time living things have come to occupy various areas or habitats of the physical environment which the organisms themselves modify. But what determines the first kinds of organisms that will occupy a specific habitat? We may be able to answer that question if we review the basic principles of organic evolution.

First, there must be a source of variability in a population of organisms. As Darwin noted,

John A. Moore

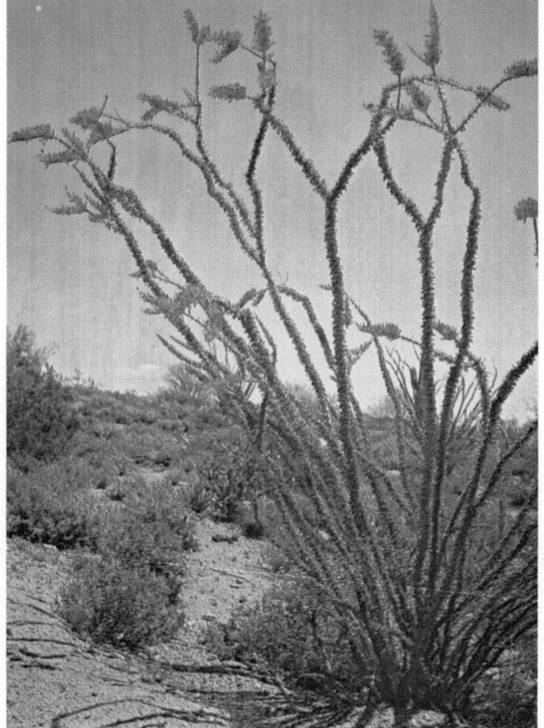

Willis Peterson

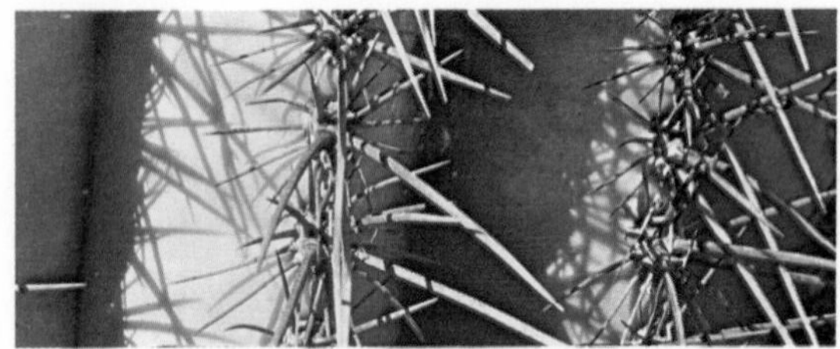

Ruth Kirk

Saguaro National Monument

37–23 (Lower left) The ocotillo, or cat's claw, of the Sonoran Desert has very small leaves **(enlarged at upper left).** During periods of drought, the leaves are shed. When rains come, new leaves are grown. Compare this adaptation with that of the saguaro cactus **(lower right),** which has spines **(enlarged at upper right).** The fluted stem of the saguaro expands with absorbed water during rains. During periods of drought, the water stored in the stem is used for the plant's needs. The thick covering of the stem, and the modification of leaves into spines, are protections against water loss.

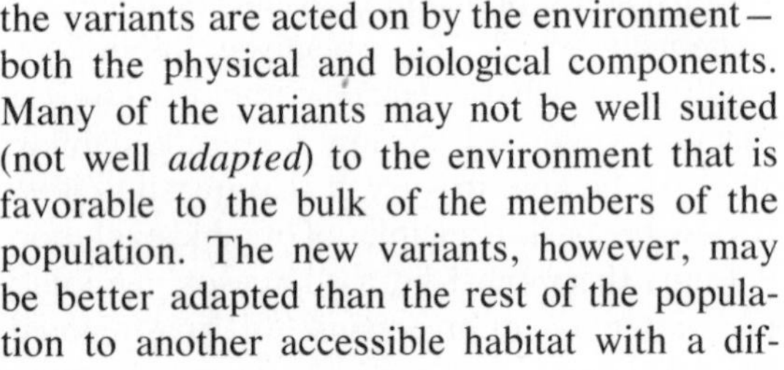

the variants are acted on by the environment—both the physical and biological components. Many of the variants may not be well suited (not well *adapted*) to the environment that is favorable to the bulk of the members of the population. The new variants, however, may be better adapted than the rest of the population to another accessible habitat with a different physical environment than the one in which the bulk of the population exists. Thus, in the environment of the population the new variant may be *selected against.* In the new habitat, however, the variant may be *selected for.* Here is a simple example to illustrate the point. A rather common mutation in fruit flies is vestigial wings. In the usual environments of fruit flies, around sheltered garbage cans and areas of little or no wind, vestigial wings would be detrimental to the population. Clearly the insects could not get from one place to another as freely. They would be less able to reproduce and to get to a source of food. But let us suppose the mutation occurred in a population on an island where there are strong prevailing winds. Which would be better adapted—flies with normal wings or with vestigial wings? It seems that flies with vestigial wings might be selected for simply because they cannot fly and be blown away from the garbage cans where the food is and where they can reproduce.

Not all variations in a population are of adaptive significance. Most mutations, for example, are harmful, and even some that are not harmful have no known adaptive significance. Adaptive importance requires a favorable interaction between the new variant and the environment. Thus, the usual environment of fruit flies around a garbage can would be decidedly unfavorable to vestigial-winged flies. If, however, the garbage can is placed where there is a strong and constant wind, vestigial-winged flies will be in a much better competitive position and are more likely to propagate.

Similar reasoning would apply to trees of related species that are quite different in height. Consider the miniature willows and birches of the alpine tundra (page 721) and their relatives that by comparison are "giants" in the lowlands—the willows and birches you know. How did a situation of such contrast come to exist?

37–24 Compare this view of the Sonoran Desert with the view of the Mohave Desert in Figure 37–20. How do you account for the striking differences? Seeds of many species of flowering plants lie dormant on the desert floor until sufficient rainfall occurs.

Orlo Manwarren

At the beginning of Chapter 36 we emphasized that the study of ecology was a study of interactions between organisms and the physical and biological components of their environment. But what interacts with what? In light of the evolution concept, it is clear that the interaction is really one between the environment and the genetic makeup of the individuals of the population. To really understand the complex interactions of the organisms of an ecosystem, biologists must understand evolutionary biology. They must be able to identify organisms and their characteristics; they must understand the physiology of the organisms; they most know how the organisms operate at the molecular level; they must understand physics and chemistry to understand the environment interacting with organisms; they have to know about soils and the geological history of the ecosystem. In short, ecology is an area that brings together nearly all aspects of biology that we have studied in *An Inquiry into Life*.

CONCLUDING REMARKS

Nearly every nook and corner of the earth's crust contains a host of organisms. Life is rich and varied wherever conditions are very favorable – in the surface waters of parts of the sea and in the tropical rain forest. Here the combination of light, warm temperatures, and plenty of water permits a luxuriant growth of the primary producers – green plants. With this bountiful base, there are numerous individuals at all levels of the food chain. As one moves from favorable areas to areas of extreme stress – the deserts and the lightless depths of the oceans – the primary producers decrease, and so do all the animals and plants that depend on them. Yet no matter how severe the conditions, there is usually some life. There are algae that grow only in melting snow. Many animals and plants spend their entire lives in lightless caves. Some algae and bacteria live in hot springs where temperatures are always near the boiling point of water. That all these habitats are populated by organisms is evidence of the effectiveness of genetic variability and natural selection. The processes of evolution have perfected organisms for almost every conceivable way of life.

GUIDE QUESTIONS AND PROBLEMS

1. In what ways does the food web in the surface waters of the open sea resemble the food web on land?
2. In what ways are environmental conditions in the oceans more stable than those on land? What problems faced by terrestrial plants and animals are not problems at all for most aquatic plants and animals?
3. What are some of the ways in which terrestrial plants and animals conserve water?
4. Describe the ecosystems that occur in your community. You may have difficulty in finding one in your book that corresponds with one in your community. What are some of the reasons for this?
5. Rearrange the following ecosystems in order of their productivity, starting with the most productive and ending with the least productive: savanna, tropical rain forest, desert, tundra, grassland, and sea 75 meters deep. Explain in terms of productivity why each ecosystem is put in the position in the list that you have given it.
6. Darwin's *On the Origin of Species by Means of Natural Selection* was published in 1859. What effect might this have had on the development of ecology?
7. Suppose that you are a farmer in central Iowa and your chief cash crop is corn. You grow corn every year and do not rotate crops – a practice called intensive agriculture. High school students from a large city school have been visiting your farm in order to gain insights into practical ecology. One of the students observed that your farm was not operating as a normal ecosystem would. How would you comment on this observation if you were the farmer?
8. One characteristic of desert plants is that they seldom grow close together. The spacing between them may vary but is rarely close. How can you account for this growth pattern? What adaptations might be involved?

RELATED READING

Books

For an excellent and beautifully illustrated description of the world's biomes . . .

Barnett, Lincoln, and Editors of *Life* Magazine, *The World We Live In,* Time, Inc., New York, 1955.

For general accounts of ocean ecosystems . . .

Bates. Marston, *The Forest and the Sea,* New American Library, New York, 1960.

Carson, Rachel, *The Sea Around Us,* New American Library, New York, 1954.

Carson, Rachel, *The Edge of the Sea,* New American Library, New York, 1959.

For a guide to the life of freshwater habitats . . .

Morgan, Ann H., *Field Book of Ponds and Streams,* Putnam, New York, 1930.

For a description of patterns of life in the deserts of the southwestern United States . . .

Krutch, Joseph W., *The Desert Year,* Viking Press, New York, 1960.

See also references for Chapter 36.

Magazines

Hutner, S. H., and J. J. A. McLaughlin, "Poisonous Tides," *Scientific American,* Volume 199 (August 1958), page 92.

Irving, Lawrence, "Adaptations to Cold," *Scientific American,* Volume 214 (January 1966), page 94.

Wecker, Stanley C., "Habitat Selection," *Scientific American,* Volume 211 (October 1964), page 109.

Wynne-Edwards, V. C., "Population Control in Animals," *Scientific American,* Volume 211 (August 1964), page 68.

38

Mankind: a Population out of Balance

Much of what has been written in the two previous chapters has been about plants and animals in their ecosystems. By now it should be easy to see the place of producers in an ecosystem, or the part played in a food web by the many consumers. It is a little more difficult to think of yourself as an organism that is part of an ecosystem. But if you stop and think about it, even for a moment, you will realize that you are affected by the same biological and physical factors (Chapter 36, page 678) that affect all organisms. This chapter is about you and your interaction with these factors. The emphasis is on the source of energy (energy in food) and on your relationship to other organisms. It is about the effect you and others like you have had and will have on your ecosystem. Thus, what you read in the rest of this chapter is about you and what the future has in store for you.

Each one of us lives in an ecosystem that is a little different from any other. If we live in London, New Delhi, Tokyo, or New York we are part of a highly urban ecosystem where many people live close together. Or we might live on a cattle or sheep ranch in the down-under country of Australia or a dairy farm of Wisconsin, where there is plenty of room. In each of these places there are those who are fortunate to have the proper food, clothing, housing, and schooling. Others are less fortunate and have barely enough food to keep from starving and little or no shelter. A school to go to might be unheard of.

You might argue that you and your neighbor go to the same school, the same church, walk the same streets, and have the same friends. It might seem that you are part of the same ecosystem. But remember you are a product of the *interaction* with the environment. Do you have the same effect on the people around you? Do they affect you the same way as your neighbor? Probably not. We are *individuals*, each reacting in different ways to the physical and biological factors that make up our environments. If we do not like our environment, we try to change it to meet our needs and desires. We build great dams to provide power so that where there was no manufacturing, an industrial center rises. The water from dammed rivers is directed into the desert so that where there were only cactus plants and sagebrush before, citrus fruits, cotton, and other crops are grown. *In this ability to intentionally adjust or change our ecosystem to suit ourselves, the human species is different from all other living things.*

It is true that many plants and animals affect their ecosystems, but in all cases this is unintentional—unreasoned.

What should our intentionally designed ecosystem be like? We suppose that one of the things that comes to the minds of young people who might be reading this book is having "a good place to live." After all, this means that our ecosystem should have in it plenty of food; it should have a supply of clothing and a house that allows us to adjust to the physical parts of our environment; a room that one would like to call his own; and friends to work and play with. In short, there should be a place where one can live in dignity as an individual as well as a place where one can make a contribution to the welfare of other members of his society. Each person, in his own way, can make such a contribution that will bring about the gradual change of the ecosystem—to make it what we might wish it to be. However, many of the things we do to our ecosystem, even though done with the best intentions, have turned out to be harmful.

Let us consider a few ways that we as individuals and populations of humans have altered our ecosystem (Figure 38-1). Anyone who lives

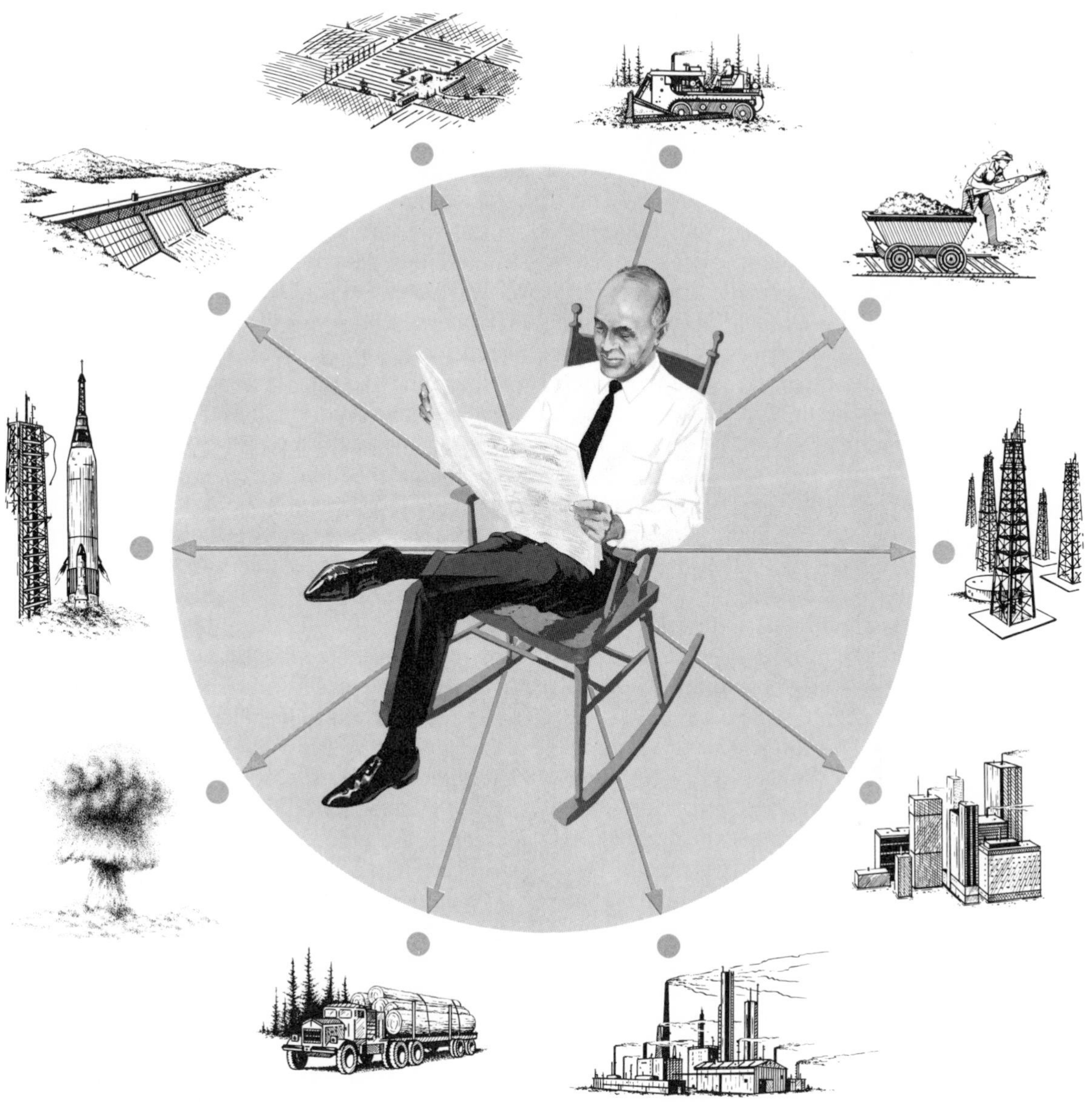

38–1 Leisure time today is one result of the many ways we have changed the environment to suit our needs. The clothes this man wears may be traced to three or more of the environmental modifications pictured around him. The rocking chair with its paint or varnish, and the newspaper with its ink, also can be traced to several environmental modifications. Try to find a way in which your life has *not* been affected by such changes.

on a farm realizes that every time a new field is prepared for cultivation, there is a drastic change in the ecosystem. Where there were many native species of plants before, there will be only a single cultivated species. This might be a crop of potatoes, rice, wheat, corn, or soybeans, which can provide us with food energy. Much that is grown can be eaten by humans directly. This is true of potatoes, rice, wheat, and soybean products. Corn is usually fed to livestock, which use the food to make their own proteins. We in turn consume the livestock, using their proteins to make our own.

What we have just described, you will recognize as a food chain. The crop plants are the producers, livestock such as cattle and pigs are the primary consumers. Human beings are, in this case, secondary consumers. You will recall that as the light energy captured by the producers is pushed on through the food chain, there is a tremendous loss of energy in the form of heat from producers and consumers alike, so that only a little energy is left to be utilized by humans. Which, then, is more economical as far as energy utilization by humans is concerned, the direct consumption of the producer or consumption of a primary consumer? The answer to this question is of major importance in solving the problem of feeding people everywhere, as we will soon see.

To make sure that we do not have to share what little energy comes to us through the food chain, we have altered the pattern of the food web by eliminating all those organisms that in some way would subtract from the energy supply. Weeds growing in a corn field take water away from the corn plants or shade the young seedlings, impairing their growth and productivity. Insects of all kinds visit the crop plants to consume their share of our producers. Birds and other first order consumers add to the problem of energy diversion from man by getting into the act. What do we do to prevent the normal interaction of organisms in the food web? We get rid of the unwanted ones—the pests and weeds—by spraying with insecticides and herbicides and by eliminating other predators (Figure 38-2). In altering our ecosystem in these ways we have eliminated the food web and established a fairly efficient food chain in which little energy is diverted into unwanted parts of the web.

In making alterations in our food webs, what do we do to the balance of nature? There are many things that happen. Cultivation changes the physical properties of the soil and unless carefully controlled, starts erosion and other undesirable changes.

By using insecticides we may eliminate one part of the insect population only to discover that another part is resistant to the chemical sprays. These resistant bugs soon take over in place of those we have eradicated. Thus, where we have gotten rid of one pest, we find another ready to take its place, one which may be more difficult to eliminate.

We get rid of the predators of our livestock by trapping or killing foxes, wolves, and birds of prey. The result may be a great increase of undesirable first-order consumers such as rabbits, rats, and mice that are normally controlled by the second level consumers. Another obvious effect is the elimination—the extinction—of many species. In these and many other ways we have placed much stress on our ecosystem by attempting to increase the amount of energy that will be available to us.

We have other ways of increasing food production besides modifying food webs. We have increased the amount of energy obtained from producers by crop improvements.

We cannot stress too much the great contributions made by plant and animal geneticists who are responsible for tremendous improvements in the productivity of crops and the livestock that use the crops for food. Among these improvements are hybrid corn, disease-resistant strains of wheat, rice, and other cereal crops. We have improved productivity of these crop plants by using fertilizers that add more nitrogen, thus more proteins, to our plants. We improve the primary consumers—the pigs and cows—so that they make better use of the producers. All of this is done with one purpose in mind: to channel the maximum amount of energy into our foods.

Nowhere in the world has the science of agriculture reached such a peak as in North

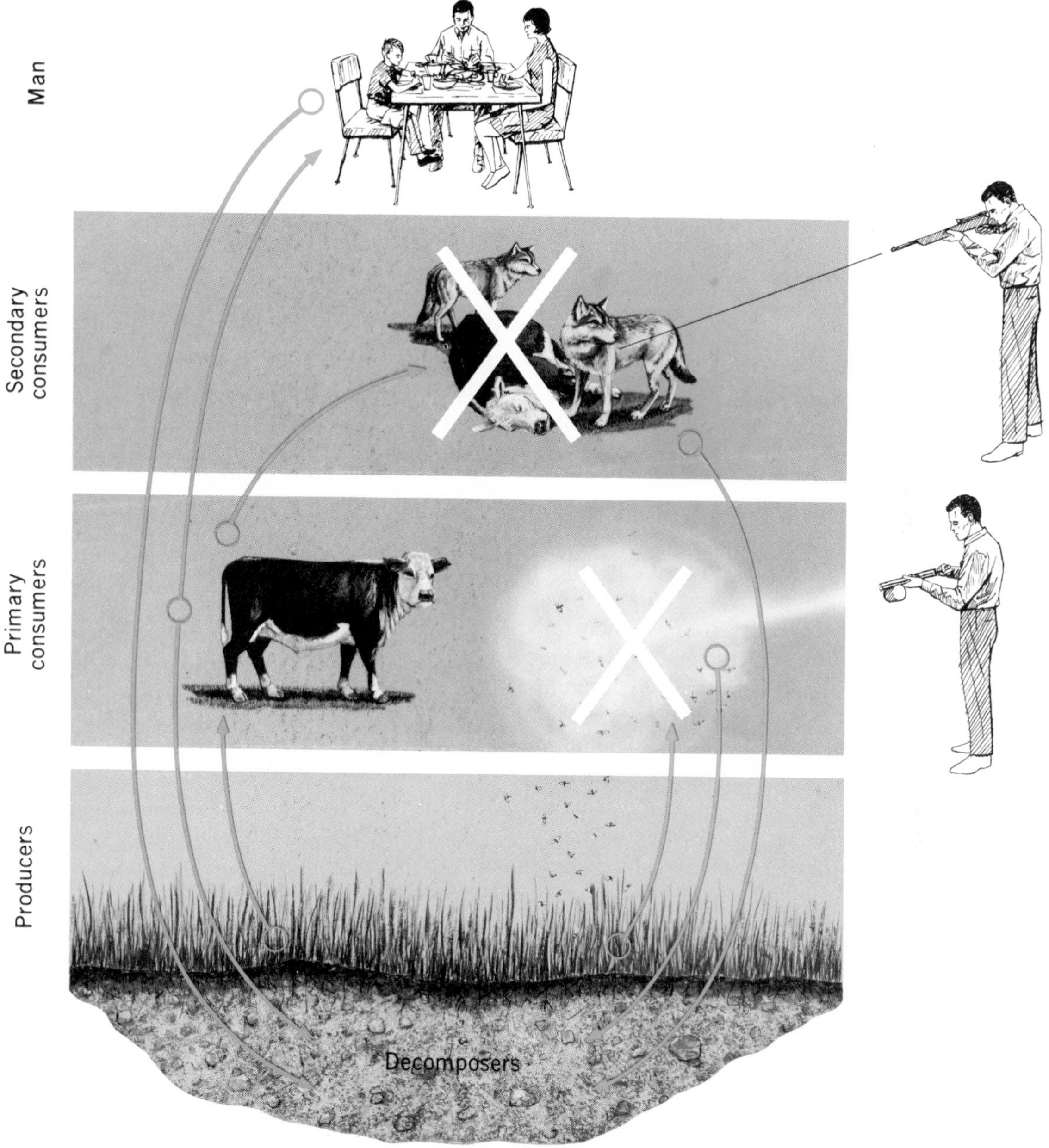

38–2 Competition and the food chain of man. Each step in the elimination of competitors involves problems that must be weighed from many points of view. A man kills a wolf because it killed his cow. But did the wolf also help to control populations of other animals that were troublesome to man? Or, consider the consequences of insect sprays. Will the sprays leave harmful residues on edible crops? Will they destroy helpful as well as harmful insects, and perhaps kill other small animals as well?

America. Here every farmer feeds himself and 36 other people. This is nearly twice as many as he fed ten years ago. Where are all of the other people? Who are they? They include those who live in the cities and must go to the market to buy meat and vegetables. They also include the one out of 20 people of Asia, South America, and Africa who for many reasons are less fortunate than we. The latter are the people who live in an ecosystem where only a minimal amount of energy is available to them. To survive, their energy supply must be supplemented by importing large quantities of grain and other foods.

What are the minimal energy requirements that half of the world's population exists on? A survey conducted by the United Nations showed that much of the population of Asia, Egypt, Central America, parts of South America and Africa exist on something less than 2,250 calories a day. The recommended amount for the average adult is 2,800 calories. In most of North America, much of Europe, Australia, New Zealand, Argentina, and parts of the Soviet Union — about 30 percent of the world's population — the average intake was 2,750 calories. About 50 percent of the world's population was on a caloric allowance that is described by the United Nations as "low." The remaining people were on a medium diet of 2,250 to 2,750 calories per day.

The Statistical Office and the Population Division of the United Nations collected information and estimates for the year 1950 to get figures on food production and on world population. From their records, the combined food production of all land and water areas added up to some 5,760 billion calories a day. The total world population was about 2,400 million. If the food produced had been divided equally among the 2,400 million people, each of them would have had 2,400 calories daily — the recommended minimum. The world had enough calories of food for everyone in 1950. But having enough calories is no solution to the problems of malnutrition and famine that have occurred in less technically developed countries since 1950. Even in the face of starvation, in certain parts of the world there are those with plenty of food who are not willing to share it with those who have little or none. Transportation from places of abundance to places of short supply also presents a problem in a world of bumper-to-bumper traffic. Or there may be difficulties in the fair distribution among the people who need the food and the energy it contains.

The calories of food energy are not the only things that are important in the daily diet. Human beings must have a reasonable balance of different kinds of foods such as carbohydrates, fats, and proteins. Calcium that can be absorbed must be present. Vitamins A, B_1, B_2, B_{12}, and C are all required. But of greatest importance are the proteins. Without them there would be no life. Proteins in human beings, like those of other organisms, are made from about twenty different amino acids — all available in suitable foods. Actually we can synthesize ten of the 20 we need. The remaining ten must be present in protein foods.

Some of the fatty acids, available through the digestion of fats, may also be essential in our diets. Carbohydrates, the prime source of energy, are less critical. For health, a person must have an adequate food supply, and in the ratio of approximately four pounds of carbohydrate for each pound of protein and each pound of fat.

Animal proteins are the most efficient sources of the amino acids we cannot synthesize. Plant proteins contain them, too, but in proportions different from those we need. Hence, to get all we need of the ten critical amino acids from plant foods, we must eat much larger quantities of proteins. People whose diets are primarily of vegetable food often get far too little protein. Their diets fall much below the recommended ratio of 1 protein : 4 carbohydrate : 1 fat.

In Java, where the total daily intake averaged only about 2,000 calories, the proteins eaten included only 4 grams of animal origin as compared to 39 grams of plant origin. In the United States, by contrast, the average daily intake stood above 3,000 calories, with most of the 88 grams of proteins coming from animal sources.

About 50 percent of the world's population cannot afford the recommended animal proteins for the simple reason that an acre of land will yield 15 to 24 times as many dietary calories when planted with crops for human consumption as it will when used for crops to feed meat animals (which will later be food for man). Fifty pounds of beef per acre per year, with 1,765 calories per pound, is regarded as efficient production on a ranch. An acre of average farmland will give 3,715 pounds of wheat per year, or 4,158 pounds of potatoes, or 4,450 pounds of shelled corn, or 5,368 pounds of rice. As dairyland, the same acre will yield 6,000 pounds of milk.

From information on the food values per pound (Figure 38-3), these figures on productivity of land can be converted to more meaningful numbers. An acre can furnish 2,400 calories per day per year for 3.54 people if planted in rice, 2.09 people if in corn, 1.91 people if in potatoes, 1.48 people if in wheat, 1.13 people if used for milk production, and only 0.83 people if used for raising beef.

From the dietary analysis we see that there is more to feeding people than just providing a sufficient number of calories. What they are fed is of equal importance if they are to be healthy, productive members of our ecosystem.

At the time this chapter is being written, most of the populations of the world had once more been fed without a major famine. Not all —just most. Even this imperfect record was possible only because of redistribution of available supplies of food to India, China, Africa, and parts of Latin America. In 1965–66 some 50 nations (with the United States the largest contributor) poured 1,000,000 tons of grain into India each month. One of the reasons for this great need is shown in Figure 38-4 better than all of the words that this author could possibly use.

Can this redistribution of food to help prevent extensive starvation go on and on? This is a question that each one of you who reads this should consider most seriously. When we read newspaper and magazine articles about famine in other parts of the world, the problems seem remote and not of any great importance to us as individuals. We have our 2,750+ calories a day. We are one of the best-fed nations.

The seriousness of the problem of feeding members of our species in the future is emphasized by a brief study of world populations —past, present, and future.

The total human population about the year 12,000 B.C. has been estimated at 10 million. By 1650 A.D. the population had grown to 545 million. This became 728 million in 1750 and 1,171 million in 1850. In 1950 the total was 2,400 million.

Now, if we take the figure of 10 million people in 12,000 B.C. and the figure 545 million in 1650 A.D., we can calculate the rate at which

38–3 Food Values per Pound for Various Foods, After Cooking by Recommended Methods

	Calories	*Proteins* (grams)	*Fats* (grams)	*Carbohydrates* (grams)	*Calcium* (grams)	*Phosphorus* (grams)
Beef (hamburger)	1765	107	146.0	0	.044	.766
Milk (whole)	330	17	19.0	24	.057	.451
Corn (sweet)	412	13	3.0	98	.024	.252
Rice (white)	577	12	.5	127	.039	.218
Potatoes (boiled, peeled)	403	10	.5	93	.053	.272
Wheat (whole meal)	349	13	1.5	77	.044	.403

(Data from U. S. Dept. Agric., Agriculture Handbook No. 8, June 1950.)

Peter Keen, Reproduced from *UNESCO Courier*

38–4 Drought, vivid in its presence and in its implications. What are your solutions for the problems shown here?

the population grew in those early years of human history. These calculations show that the population doubled less than six times in that 13,650 years. The average time required for each doubling was about 2,000 years.

After the mechanization of farming, which came with the Industrial Revolution between 1650 and 1850, we find a different story. The 545 million people in 1650 grew to 1,171 million by 1850. This doubling required only 200 years. By 1950, the 1,171 million became 2,400 million. The greater availability of food and better sanitation and medical care had allowed another doubling in less than 100 years.

Modern public health measures have been extraordinarily successful in the more advanced nations of the world in preventing the spread of contagious infections (Figure 38-5). Since the

38–5 Death Rate and Cause, per Hundred Thousand of the Population, in the United States, 1900–1965

Cause	*1900*	*1910*	*1920*	*1930*	*1940*	*1950*	*1960*	*1965*
Infectious diseases								
Influenza and pneumonias	202	156	207	103	70	31	37	32
Tuberculosis, all forms	194	154	113	71	46	23	6	4
Bronchitis	46	23	13	4	3	2	3	3
Diarrhea and intestinal diseases	133	117	54	26	10	5	4	4
Diphtheria	40	21	15	5	1	0.3	—[1]	—
Typhoid and paratyphoid fevers	36	26	8	5	1	—	—	—
Syphilis and sequels	12	14	17	16	14	5	2	1
Measles	13	12	9	3	0.5	0.3	0.3	0.1
Whooping cough	12	12	13	5	2	0.7	0.1	—
Scarlet fever	10	12	5	2	0.5	—	—	—
Malaria	8	2	4	3	1	—	—	—
Smallpox	2	0.4	0.6	0.1	—	—	—	—
Degenerative diseases								
Heart diseases	137	159	160	214	293	357	366	367
Cerebral hemorrhage and thrombosis	72	76	82	81	91	100	110	110
Cancer, all forms	64	76	83	97	120	140	147	153
Cirrhosis of liver	13	13	7	7	9	9	11	13
Appendicitis	10	11	13	15	10	2	1	1
Diabetes mellitus	11	15	16	19	27	16	17	17
Kidney diseases	89	99	89	91	82	21	15	11
Senility	—	26	14	10	8	13	11	12
Congenital malformations	12	15	15	11	10	12	12	10
Other causes								
Suicide and homicide	11	20	17	25	21	17	15	17
Accidents	72	84	70	80	73	61	52	56
All other causes	520	325	271	239	183	149	137	132
ALL CAUSES	1719	1468	1299	1132	1076	964	946	943

[1]Dash lines indicate death rates that are significantly less than 0.1 per 100,000.

beginning of the century, because of these advances more than 22 years have been added to the average life span (Figure 38-6); this is due largely to a reduced infant mortality. Little change is seen in the number of people reaching 90 or 100 years of age, for in our country, people saved from death by improved controls over infectious diseases usually die of degenerative changes before reaching the age of ninety. In some less technically developed countries, the use of DDT to reduce malaria and antibiotics to curb infectious diseases has cut the death rate by as much as one-third since 1940. Because of this, the population growth that was progressing at a slow rate prior to 1940 has now skyrocketed.

In the United States and other countries where medical care is most highly developed, a good many people with inherited disorders are now saved. They survive, reproduce, and pass along their genetic handicap. Natural selection no longer eliminates them as rapidly as in earlier times. In this and other ways, we have changed the genetic balance in our own species. We have become a force affecting our own evolution as well as our own ecosystem.

In 1963, a committee of the National Academy of Sciences reported

> "The present world population is likely to double in the next 35 years, producing a population of six billion by the year 2000." And further: "To appreciate the pace of population growth we should recall that world population doubled in about 1,700 years from the time of Christ until the middle of the 17th century; it doubled again in about 200 years, doubled again in less than 100, and if the current *rate* of population increase were to remain constant, would double every 35 years. Moreover, this rate is still increasing . . . Had this rate existed from the time of Christ to now, the world population would have increased in this period to 70,000,000-000,000,000; in other words, there would be about 20 million individuals in place of each person now alive, or 100 people to each square foot."

Look at the graph shown in Figure 38-7 and keep in mind that your chances are good of living well beyond the year 2000. You will see that you are already a part of a fantastic population growth.

Our population growth is affected by the same laws that maintain checks and balances in population growth of other organisms in nature (Chapters 36 and 37). You know that they are laws of supply and demand for energy in the ecosystem. They are the laws of survival. These are the laws that apply to all of us and that will, sooner or later, bring about the stabilization of mankind in his ecosystem. In nature we see how these laws work. A tree shades a smaller plant from its energy source—the sun. The smaller plant dies. It starves because of the lack of energy. The oyster produces 20 million eggs, but only a few grow into mature oysters. The rest provide an energy source for the consumers in the ecosystem.

38–6 The Changing Pattern of Births, Deaths, and Expectations of Life in the United States, 1900–1965

	1900	*1910*	*1920*	*1930*	*1940*	*1950*	*1960*	*1965*
Live births per thousand of population	32.3	30.1	27.7	21.3	19.4	24.1	23.7	19.4
Deaths per thousand of population	17.1	14.7	13	11.3	10.8	9.6	9.5	9.4
Excess of births over deaths	15.2	15.4	14.7	10	8.6	14.5	14.2	10.0
Expectation of life at birth	47.3	50	54.1	59.7	62.9	68.2	69.7	70.2
Average increase in longevity since 1900	—	2.7	6.8	12.4	15.6	20.9	22.4	22.9

Knowing what goes on in nature, can you suggest what could happen to mankind in the next four or five decades if his population growth continues at the rate shown in Figure 38-7 and the amount of food production does not increase proportionately? The answer could be an unpleasant one. It could involve more of what we read about in the paper every day: more famine, malnutrition, with the threat of famine; spread of disease; conflict of nation with nation, and people with people – until our population growth is once more stabilized or until the energy available in the ecosystem, and the rate of its use, are approximately equal.

How can we go about getting our ecosystem back into equilibrium once again and dispose of the hypothesis that the human race is doomed to starve because the population will outstrip the food supply? The first thing that must be done is to make sure that everyone understands what the problems are and that it will take the effort of every individual to resolve them. It is equally important that young people today recognize the urgency with which solutions to the problems must be sought, for you are members of the generation that is likely to be most concerned with a solution.

The first solution that may come to mind is to grow more food and in this way put more energy into the ecosystem so that the increasing population can be supported. When suggesting this we must keep in mind the size of the increase. It has been predicted that the population will more than double in the next 30 years. Can we double the food supply in the same period of time? If so, how can it be done?

One obvious answer is bring about greater gains in food production by exporting our agricultural technology to less fortunate parts of the world, and seeing to it that the technology is applied wisely. We must work with the awareness that machinery, fertilizers, and genetically improved crop plants that produce large crops in one part of the world do not necessarily work as well in another part. For example, when commercial fertilizers were applied to the native

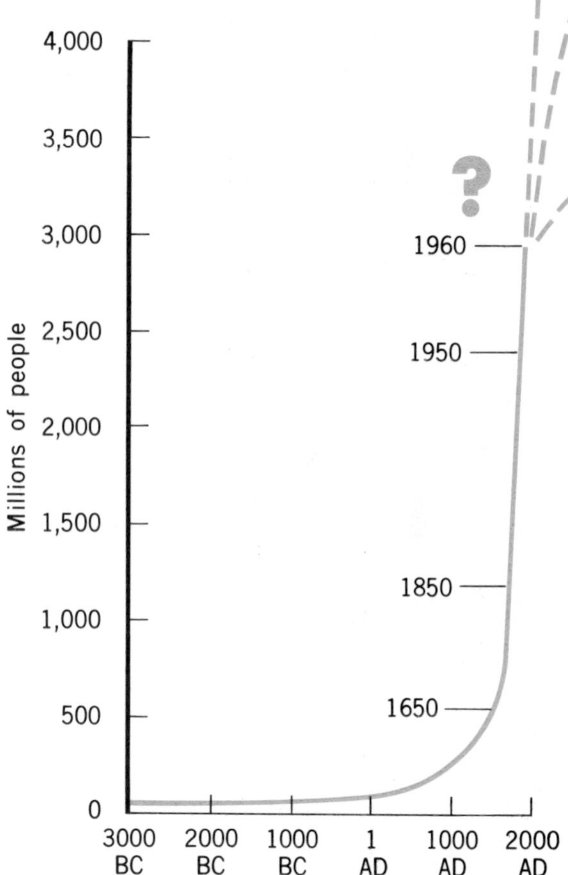

38–7 World population growth, from 3,000 B.C. until the present. Only one of the three possible courses shown for the future is known to be safe. This means that every individual has a responsibility for his or her share of reducing the rate of human population growth.

Jack Ling – UNICEF, Reproduced from *UNESCO Courier*

38–8 Food production on this farm in southeastern Asia could be improved by better farming practices. But this is not always easy. What should the first step be – the substitution of a tractor and a modern plow? Unfortunately, this man could not afford to purchase a tractor – or to maintain one if given to him. His farm may even be too small to warrant efficient modernization according to his scale of living.

Mexican wheat, the plants grew tall, then toppled under their own weight. To overcome this difficulty, new high-yielding wheat varieties had to be developed that were stubby and strong even under maximum fertilization. The result of these improvements has been a spectacular increase in Mexican wheat production.

In his travels to some less technically developed countries, one of your authors has had an opportunity of seeing places of unbelievable contrast in technology. In one place there is a large modern locomotive factory. Surrounding the factory are small farms of one to two acres that are farmed in much the same way as they were 2,000 years ago. In many countries it is possible to take a journey of a few steps and go from a modern technology to one that is 20 centuries old.

Let us imagine that we visit one of the farms where the land is being tilled for the planting of corn or rice. A wooden plow with a metal tip (Figure 38-8) is used to scratch a furrow an inch or two deep. This plow is usually pulled by a pair of oxen that respond to the touch of a pole the driver carries in one hand. The other hand is used to guide the plow. This method of plowing has been handed down from father to son for hundreds of generations.

Can more advanced technology be used to improve this ancient method of farming and increase the farmer's returns from his labors? For example, we might suggest using an American single-furrow, metal plow. You might think it would be desirable, because this type of plow has worked so successfully for American farmers. The American plow is constructed to cut a deep furrow, thereby turning under organic matter to improve the fertility of the soil and improving the physical characteristics of the soil by breaking up hard, compacted soil particles. The American plow, however, is designed to be operated with *both* hands. The animals that pull the American plow are guided by reins rather than a pole. Although this method of plowing may seem to you only slightly different from the first type described, remember that it means changing a centuries-old tradition, re-educating millions of farmers (and re-training their animals) – and may be no better than the traditional type of plowing. Even in North America, farmers recognize that different methods of plowing and farming must be used for different local climates, soil types, crops, and other factors. This knowledge has accumulated from many years of testing, mainly by trial and error.

Another possible improvement might be to use a tractor for plowing. A tractor for each small farm would be inefficient. Yet one tractor might be used to plow many farms. Unfortunately, the pooling of agricultural machines and tools has often not worked out for the simple reason that the tradition of independence and self-sufficiency among farmers – coupled with a limited trust of each other – has prevented meaningful cooperation.

In visiting southeast Asia, everyone who travels to a small village is impressed with the amount of unused protein available to a people having a minimum of this needed substance in their diet. The countryside abounds in water buffalo, oxen and cattle of every description. Many wander the countryside unattended, consuming crops and other forage plants to build their own proteins. The seas bordering the countries abound in fish, another important source of proteins, yet there is a steadfast refusal by a large segment of the population, even in the face of starvation, to use these important sources of food energy. The reason for this is that Hindus, because of religious custom, are typically vegetarians.

These examples of the effect of traditions, mistrust, and religious custom are given to impress you with the problems that face you and your classmates in bringing balance back into the world ecosystem. There is no simple solution to these complex problems, and it makes little difference in what part of the world we are confronted by the problem. Workable solutions will be provided only by the well-informed. This is one reason why you are studying biology.

Another approach to increasing productivity that will support our population explosion is to exploit farming in the tropics. At the moment only 10 percent of the earth's land surface is cultivated. Of this land 60 percent of the energy in foods comes from grains and soybeans grown in the cool temperate climates. Although many improvements in agricultural methods have been made in parts of Central and South America, there are places in the tropics where crops are grown in the same ways that the South American Indians did it 2,000 years ago. The technique is to burn the vegetation on a tract of land, farm it for three years or until all of the mineral nutrients and nitrogen are exhausted, then abandon the land. Vast tracts of land in our own country have been abandoned because of the effects of overgrazing. As the plants disappear, erosion sets in and the valuable topsoil is lost forever. With the problems of feeding twice as many humans in the next three decades, we are in no position to have the productivity of the land destroyed.

Another problem related to the use of land is the expansion of cities, parks, roads, and dams as the population increases. Every year new dams whose backwaters cover thousands of acres of land are constructed. We cannot complain, however, because the dams supply energy not only for the refrigerators, radios, and the many other electrical items we consider essential to modern life, but they also provide energy for industrial use and water for irrigating farmland.

Laid across rich agricultural states such as Iowa, Kansas, and Illinois are some of the most magnificent freeways ever constructed. These are needed to speed transportation across a nation whose highways are already overcrowded. Yet under every mile of the billion-dollar roads are hundreds of acres of some of the most fertile land in the world. As our population continues to expand, the primary problem is not finding new land to cultivate (except in the tropics there is very little of that) but to preserve the land we have. We are running out of space not only for crop production but for a place to live.

Waste of food is yet another problem that must be faced by every individual, everywhere. How many times have you refused to eat a salad or some other vegetable simply because it did not taste good? Yet this same food that is disposed of provides some needed vitamins and carbohydrates in your diet. Every bite that you waste removes energy that should be available to another human somewhere.

Waste extends to the harvesting and storage of food. In some underdeveloped parts of the world it is estimated that as much as 30 percent of the harvest is wasted by spoilage due to inadequate storage, rodents, insects, and poor harvesting techniques.

Earlier in the book we suggested that there were other kinds of food waste caused by the diseases of crop plants and spoilage in the market place. Although we take refrigeration of meats, milk, and other food supplies for granted, there are many countries in the world where there is little or no refrigeration. Without refrigeration the supply of foods containing the necessary animal proteins is all but eliminated. People who lack these proteins and exist instead on a diet of carbohydrate are victims of such dwarfing diseases as **kwashiorkor** (KWASH-e·or·core). If prolonged, this disease produces skin sores, bloated bellies, swollen limbs, and feeble minds that cannot be trained by any educational system. It is estimated that of the some 3.23 billion people on earth, one seventh of them suffer from some kind of malnutrition. Such people have little chance of contributing to the improvement and welfare of their nation or of their ecosystem.

Although much improvement has been made in combating plant diseases – by breeding disease-resistant varieties of crop plants, by sanitation, and other methods of control – disease still wastes millions of bushels of corn, wheat, rice, and other grains each year. One of the most destructive diseases of cereal crops is called wheat rust. The organism causing the disease is a fungus with a very complex life cycle that involves an alternate host, the common barberry plant. By eliminating the barberry plant, it has been possible to bring about partial control of wheat rust, but complete control has never been possible. Another approach has been the breeding of rust-resistant varieties of wheat. Often, however, as soon as the resistant variety of wheat has been produced by plant breeders, mutant forms of the rust fungus appear to which the new variety of wheat is susceptible. Thus far plant breeders have managed to stay a jump ahead of the fungus. In the area of disease control alone a large number of different kinds of biologists are needed. To control plant disease requires the knowledge of the life cycle of the organism and a knowledge of the kinds of plants that harbor the disease. The services of a geneticist are needed to develop the resistant varieties of grain. Inspectors are required who can recognize disease and stop it before it spreads. But where do we find the multitude of people who will have the training in biology required to do these important, life-saving jobs? We hope that some of you will have found an interest in biology and will continue to do your part in helping to solve the problems of food production faced by people everywhere. You will be needed.

Untapped sources of food energy may make it possible for us to support a population double its present size. One exciting possibility has been developed by the petroleum industry. A process has been invented whereby it is possible to produce an edible, protein-rich substance from petroleum. Also, experiments on an industrial scale have been performed by Japanese scientists that demonstrate the possibility of producing protein-rich algae on a commercial scale.

The Japanese and other people living in coastal regions utilize the food energy stored in the great beds of kelp that lie off the ocean shores. Cultivation of the beds has been practiced for many, many years. Thus far, however, the food energy in the sea has been little used. Some biologists see the day when there will be great kelp farms and fish will be raised and tended in herds like cattle.

The open oceans make up 70 percent of the earth's surface. We might expect the open oceans to be highly productive of food. This is not the case, however, for in the deep oceans, nutrients tend to accumulate near the bottom where they are lost as far as growth of photosynthetic organisms is concerned. Because of this, the open ocean has been described as a "nutritional desert." Only in certain places, along the coast of Peru, for example, is there an upwelling in the ocean that brings the nutrients to the surface. In this region the productivity is greatly increased, as evidenced by the increased amount of plankton and large fish and bird populations.

Only recently there have been advances in making the energy stored in unpalatable plants and animals available to us in an edible form. One of these foods is an inexpensive, tasteless, high protein flour made from fish.

A few years ago biologists were hopeful that they would unlock all of the secrets of photosynthesis and be able to perpetuate the process outside of the living green cell. If such an accomplishment were possible one might look forward to the day when unlimited amounts of energy would be available to our ecosystem. However, as the years have passed and more has been learned about photosynthesis, the hope that an efficient synthetic process of reasonable expense would be discovered seems to fade. The process is exceedingly complex, and many biologists in many parts of the world are still trying to fathom it. Whatever its difficulties, this kind of basic research has provided many of the solutions to human problems in the past. We can expect more solutions in the future.

Although there is no general agreement, many biologists believe that it is possible to increase the energy input of our ecosystem sufficiently so that our "shrinking" world can support a population of 6 to 7 billion people, which is about double what it is today. This, they say, can be done by maximum utilization of what is available to us.

What actually will happen in the next 30 years to the balance between the size of our population and the energy required to support it is just a guess. The most optimistic, or the indifferent, think that somehow all of our problems will be solved. Whether optimistic or pessimistic, one point on which everyone agrees is that people everywhere must understand the problems and do what they can to help put our ecosystem back into balance.

Harbrace photo

38–9 Orchard Street, New York City. What will you plan to do to help keep cities and towns today from choking with people in future years?

Thus far we have suggested that some ways to maintain the balance are to cultivate more land to grow more crops, grow better and bigger crops, harvest the food from the sea, reduce waste due to spoilage, disease, insects and other pests, and utilize other sources such as petroleum to increase the amount of food energy. Let us suppose that this works indefinitely and the rate of population growth continues at its present speed. It must be clear to the most optimistic that within a short time after the year 2000 you and I, and especially those belonging to the younger generation, will run out of space in which to live. Those of you who live in large urban communities such as New York City, Chicago, Los Angeles and other large cities know what it is to run out of space. You know of the rush-hour traffic with automobiles bumper to bumper, the crowded schools, and the crush of the subway. You know of the smog that comes in areas of high population concentration. You may know what it is like to have a family of a dozen crammed into two or three rooms. You have watched the people move from these centers of high population concentration to areas around the fringes, trying to escape the pressures of high population density. Some, because of the influences within our society, have been prevented from making these moves and they are the ones who really understand what it is to live in overpopulated areas (Figure 38-9). It is in just such areas that we find the greatest deteriorations of human dignity. These are the slums and ghettos.

To emphasize the seriousness of our present rate of population growth, mathematicians, using certain assumptions about the rate of population increase for the last 2,000 years as a basis (Figure 38-7), have calculated that by Friday, November 13, 2026 A.D., the human population will reach infinity. As one mathematician put it, "... our great, great grandchildren [your great grandchildren] will not starve to death. They will be squeezed to death." Biologists and mathematicians know that this could never come to pass. We know that the laws of nature cannot be stretched that far—that some kind of catastrophe such as famine will precede the squeezing stage. Nonetheless, a prediction of this kind should concern us all about the future of our species.

Compared with many other organisms, humans have a rather low reproductive potential.

Without the restrictions imposed by society a human female is capable of producing about 30 offspring in her lifetime. This figure hardly compares with the oyster which can lay 20,000,000 eggs in its lifetime. With these figures in mind, we might well ask why the seas are not crowded to overflowing with oysters and why we must be concerned about the numbers of humans with such a low reproductive potential. By now you know the answers. Unlike the oysters, we humans have intentionally adjusted our environment to favor our low reproductive potential. This we have done by curbing the spread of disease, reducing infant mortality, and improving agriculture. These things are impossible for the oyster whose offspring become food for all sorts of predators, or are killed by disease and eliminated in the competition for food and space. When we think about it, it is fortunate that there are any oysters at all. The fact that we not only survive but increase in numbers in spite of our low reproductive potential is related to our ability to reason and adapt our ecosystem to our own use. In spite of our ability to reason, we are on the verge of letting our population growth exceed the rate at which we can increase food production. Several ways have been suggested for increasing food production, thus increasing the amount of energy we can supply to support the population. At best, however, this can be only a temporary solution. Sooner or later we will run out of space in which to live with any degree of privacy and dignity. So we must look for a more permanent solution to our complex problem if we are to live as human beings.

The surest solution to the problem is by checking population growth, to regulate the rate of births so that there will be one instead of two babies born every second. This idea is not new and in many countries, especially Japan, positive results have been obtained from a nationwide program of fertility regulation and family planning. In Japan where there are, on the average, 259 persons crowded into each square kilometer (about 650 people per square mile), the birth rate has been cut by one half during the last 15 years. The Japanese are making every effort to stabilize their population at about 100 million. In India, where there is one of the greatest growths in world population, family planning centers have been established in cities and villages throughout the country. Every major country has committees and delegations examining the problem of population growth. The degree of success in affecting control of the size of the world population is going to be decided, in part, by the rapidity with which all people everywhere become aware of the problem and what they decide to do about it.

AN ADEQUATE SUPPLY OF FRESH WATER

With the increase and spread of humans, we have had other effects on the balance in our ecosystem. Equally important to satisfying our energy requirements by food production is our requirement for water.

Although each human being continues to need approximately half a gallon of drinking water daily, our other uses for fresh water have changed markedly in the last century. Only 100 years ago, nearly everyone in America depended upon water from wells or springs. Water was carried by hand into the house. Gutters collected rainwater from the roof to be stored in cisterns for use in washing clothes and people. A few gallons of water sufficed for each person daily.

Today a half gallon of pure drinking water is needed by more than twice as many people as a century ago. Moreover, we have come to regard an abundance of fresh water as part of our high standard of living. We expect it to run freely from a faucet for washing dishes, clothes, the dusty car, or to carry away heat from air-conditioning equipment. Large reserves must be on hand for use in fire fighting.

The second greatest use of water today is for transportation of wastes, particularly sewage and the discharge of industrial plants. Three gallons are required to flush a toilet and 30 gallons to take a shower. The number of gallons required per person for domestic use per day in the United States varies from 20 to 80 gallons. Every year the demand rises. Moreover, domestic use accounts for less than ten percent of the water used. The remainder is about equally divided between irrigation and industrial use.

The United States and inhabited parts of Canada are fortunate in having an average annual rainfall of about 30 inches. Half of this fresh water evaporates unused. One sixth sinks into the ground and flows to the sea by way of subterranean streams. One sixth flows over the surface in the form of rivers. The remaining sixth is absorbed by vegetation; most of this is lost to the air.

Methods and Difficulties in Providing More Fresh Water

If we are to maintain our food supply, we cannot divert water from the plants. To grow more food on arid lands, we need extra water for irrigation. However, the amount available from rivers and artesian wells is already too small to provide enough water for everyone to have the standard of living he would like. In many countries the water situation is far worse than it is in the United States and Canada.

Every move to conserve fresh water is important. Yet only in remote mountain streams can unpolluted water be found today. Elsewhere, communities dump sewage and industrial wastes into streams and lakes from which other communities obtain their water supply. The money saved in dumping the raw sewage instead of rendering it harmless or disposing of it otherwise is largely lost in purifying this same water for later use.

Different schemes have been proposed or put into operation to increase the amount of fresh water available in specific areas. The most basic scheme is to trap more rain, to reduce evaporative losses and pollution from eroding soil, and to channel the moisture into springs, into rivers on the surface, and also into underground rivers where artesian wells can penetrate. Forests provide the most efficient trap for rain. They are valuable also in supplying wood, in sheltering wildlife, and in affording areas for recreation. Interwoven tree roots protect the soil from erosion; they help keep streams flowing with clear, unpolluted water.

The person who owns a forest often sees no personal gain in the river that flows away, or the wildlife, or the soil protection, or the recreational values. He sees only timber he could use for fuel, for paper making, for lumber, or for some other technological use. If he is a farmer or rancher, he is likely to regard a forest as occupying land on which cultivated crops or domesticated animals could be raised. Why not fell the forest?

Forests the world over are still being cut and burned almost as fast as they are being replaced. On the exposed forest soil, in many places, erosion is rapid. Spring rains produce disastrous floods with mud-laden water carrying the topsoil to the sea. Summer drought is common. The subterranean water supply sinks below the roots of crop plants. Rivers shrink, often to a series of stagnant pools. Yet, with more people needing more food it is hard to be foresighted and turn cropland back into forest. Over most of the world few men work in this direction.

Another possible source of water for industry and agriculture is water from the sea. Devices for extracting fresh water from the sea are already in operation on a limited scale. That scale must be increased many times over if the supply of fresh water is to keep pace with demands.

OUR LIVING RESOURCES

Our high standard of living in North America depends partly upon the fact that our population is still small enough that food, water, and space have only begun to limit us. It depends also upon a combination of accessible raw materials, industrial power, and skill. These advantages are not always to be found in many other parts of the world.

Uses and Abuses of Our Living Resources

Part of our technology is concerned with preparing chemical compounds such as solvents, detergents, fibers, drugs, fungicides, and insecticides. For many of these, man makes use of living organisms that carry on syntheses he cannot duplicate efficiently. Examples are endless: alcohols from bacterial fermentations; silk from silkworms fed on mulberry leaves; special fibers from cotton and flax; paper from a variety of different wood pulps; antibiotic drugs from soil fungi; the insecticide rotenone, from a South American plant; rubber from the protective juices of many kinds of plants; pyrethrum, another insecticide, from a daisy of the Middle East.

No list that includes only the presently known uses of other living things is complete. At irregular intervals (often by accident), new and important uses are found for organisms that previously meant nothing to man. The whole concept of the use in medicine of antibiotic substances from molds and other organisms arose from Sir Alexander Fleming's discovery of bacterial inhibition by *Penicillium* in 1928.

Unfortunately, as he increases his need for food, water, and nonliving raw materials for technology, man for the most part overlooks the wealth of living things with which he still shares the earth. To overlook them is to press them progressively toward extinction (Figures 38-10, 38-11, 38-12, and 38-13).

Animals, particularly large ones, seem in greater danger of extermination than do plants. Island animals, such as the flightless dodo of Mauritius (exterminated in 1692), are especially vulnerable. Mainland animals are imperiled, too. Europe's bison (the wisent) and Africa's white-tailed gnu exist today only in zoos and sanctuaries provided for them (Figure 38-10). Our own American bison (Figure 38-10) almost disappeared before it was saved through special Congressional action. In the last century and a half, America has lost the great auk (1844), the Labrador duck (1878), the Carolina parakeet (1920), the Eskimo curlew (1932), the passenger pigeon (1914), and the heath hen (1933). (See Figure 38-11.) Some others among almost 600 different kinds of warm-blooded animals, or birds and mammals, most in danger of extinction are shown in Figure 38-12.

38–10 Three animals saved from near extinction. **(Top)** A white-tailed gnu; **(center)** the European bison; and **(bottom)** the American bison.

38–11 Endangered and extinct birds. **(Left)** The ivory-billed woodpecker, now very rare; **(center top)** the passenger pigeon; **(top right)** the Carolina parakeet; and **(below)** the heath hen. The last three now are extinct.

Some of the more unusual and conspicuous plants have been saved from extermination. Lamas in Tibetan lamaseries are credited with rescuing the last wild ginkgo trees and propagating them. Eventually the world elsewhere became hospitable to having these trees introduced for shade. Today no wild ginkgo trees are known; they are entirely domesticated. The Save-the-Redwoods League in California was principally responsible for the setting aside of a few groves of these tallest trees at a time when timber companies were ready to fell the last of them (Figure 38-13). The cypresses of California's Monterey Peninsula represent another

38–12 Four animals threatened with extinction. **(Upper left)** The whooping crane; **(upper right)** the trumpeter swan; **(lower left)** the key deer; and **(lower right)** the musk ox. All are North American species (the musk ox, from the Far North).

kind of plant protected for the future after all others of their species had been destroyed.

Similar efforts on a smaller scale, to protect such plants as wood orchids, trailing arbutus, and other wild flowers, have been needed in many parts of the country to insure continuation of the native flora. The establishment of national parks and of wilderness areas, where the ecological balance is left as free of human influences as possible, are larger endeavors. They are aimed at preventing the extinction of living things that are interesting now and may be highly useful in years to come.

We have reached a stage where enormous numbers of species are dwindling toward disappearance because their habitats are being destroyed. We simply leave them too little room. In some instances this is deliberate, aimed at greater efficiency in food production. By spraying a thousand-acre rice field with one chemical compound from a low-flying airplane, all plants other than monocotyledons can be killed—thus eliminating almost all "weeds" among the rice. By similar methods, using a variety of poisons, every animal—mollusk, crustacean, fish, amphibian, reptile, bird, and mammal—can be exterminated, but not always without the possibility of contamination of the food product.

Few people would criticize man, or any other animal, for defending his food supply. Defense, however, implies invading competitors. We have only a few real competitors. Most other species are either helpful to us or essentially neutral to our interests. In the process of eliminating a few species thought to be harmful, it is probable that many useful species also will be exterminated. In some areas, attempts are being made today to restore a balance and let man benefit from cross-connections in food webs.

38–13 A grove of redwoods in northern California. Redwoods are the tallest organisms on earth. For scale, notice the automobile (almost white) at the base of the trees on the left. The tallest grove of redwoods belongs to a private lumber company, but may one day be included in a national park.

John A. Moore

G. Ronald Austing from National Audubon Society

38–14 Friend of man, or foe? You see both, but the foe is dead. The hazards of chemical pest control make our natural allies all the more valuable. This owl has captured a rodent of a species that causes extensive crop damage both in the fields and in grain elevators.

Biological control of pests that affect us has become more highly regarded in the last decades. It consists in encouraging birds (Figure 38-14) and mammals that hunt crop-destroying pests, in aiding those insects that parasitize crop-destroying insects, in spreading disease-producing organisms that affect only destructive animals and plants. These procedures emphasize old and new relationships within the living communities. As pest numbers increase, so do the populations of predators, parasites, and disease organisms. When pest numbers shrink, so do these dependent populations. Living control agents evolve as their victims do.

By contrast, chemical control has not proved as satisfactory. Since the 1940's when DDT and other synthetic insecticides came into wide use, many kinds of insects have evolved into insecticide-resistant strains. Houseflies, body lice, mosquitoes, and various insect pests of crops are not always destroyed by chemical agents that once seemed 100 percent effective. The few immune survivors gave rise to the physiologically different insects we meet today. In the field of medicine, a comparable change is seen in antibiotic-immune bacteria.

Where they are not destroyed by mass applications of insecticides, honeybees still pollinate flowers, dragonflies continue to destroy mosquitoes, and ladybird beetles devour sapsucking aphids (plant lice). Chickadees hunt for aphid eggs on tree bark during winter. Continuation of these links in familiar food webs depends on us. Through poisoning campaigns we may gain higher yields from croplands for a few years—until the insects grow immune to the chemical agents. But do we gain enough to pay for ignoring and eliminating the agents of biological control, which work without charge at slightly less efficiency?

CONCLUDING REMARKS

The human species, as the sole survivor in the hominid line of the anthropoid primates, has developed and come to dominate the living world in less than one million years. Dinosaurs held a somewhat comparable position for 100 million years—then they became extinct. We would like to believe that man is here to stay. Yet permanence, even when measured in thousands rather than millions of years, depends upon an ecological balance that can provide over-all stability for microorganisms, plants, and animals.

The present explosive increase in human population, worldwide, represents a completely unstable situation, one with a highly questionable future. The presence of so many human beings has brought stress to the lives of most kinds of plants and animals from the arctic tundras to the equator and as far south as inhabitable land extends. Everywhere the number of species is shrinking, the food webs are tearing and permitting wide fluctuations in populations of organisms, including man himself.

From our present vantage point we can look back into time and reconstruct the long, impressive pattern of evolving nature. Can we claim a respectable place in it? As in the past and at present, and for as long into the future as man permits, plants and animals will interact with each other and with us. They serve us, far more completely than we know today, in maintaining a dynamic balance throughout the natural world. This balance is the sole stabilizing feature of the ecosystem in which mankind continues to evolve—and to make his own changes, some of them dangerously abrupt and with little foresight. Are we about to lose the stability of our ecosystem? Time will tell. And time is running out!

GUIDE QUESTIONS AND PROBLEMS

1. List ways in which your own ecosystem could be made better. How can you personally help to bring about these improvements?
2. Devise a daily diet that you think would be adequate. Determine the relative amounts of plant and animal protein in the diet; the amount of fat and carbohydrate. How does this compare with the minimum requirements? Compare the number of calories consumed daily in your diet to that consumed by an average Asian Indian.
3. What are the limiting factors that prevent the world from supporting a human population of indefinite size? Why is increasing food production only a temporary solution to the problem of overpopulation?
4. If you were the president of a country where the population growth clearly exceeded the productive capacity of your country, what programs would you attempt in order to solve the problems? What difficulties might you encounter in accomplishing your programs?
5. Describe the growth curves of bacteria, oysters, and human beings. Account for their similarities and differences.

6. In one day, what are all the ways you can think of in which you affect your ecosystem? What effects does your ecosystem have on you during the same period?
7. What are the consequences to an ecosystem of establishing national parks and wildlife areas? of building new roads? a new dam? an atomic energy plant? of otherwise providing services for a human population several times as large as the population now?

RELATED READING

Books

For a controversial account of the effects on ecosystems of chemical warfare against other species . . .

Carson, Rachel, *Silent Spring,* Houghton Mifflin, Boston, 1962.

For a factual report of the human birth rate and overpopulation . . .

The Growth of World Population, National Academy of Sciences (National Research Council Publication 1091), Washington, D.C., 1963.

See also references at the end of Chapters 36 and 37.

Magazines

Myrdal, G., "The World Is Heading for a Collision." UNESCO *Courier,* (February 1966), page 21.

Sen, B. R., "To Be or Not to Be," UNESCO *Courier* (February 1966), page 10.

Valters, Eric N., "Our Shrinking Planet," UNESCO *Courier* (February 1966), page 4.

Wynne-Edwards, V. C., "Population Control in Animals," *Scientific American,* Volume 211 (August 1964), page 68.

39

A Perspective of Time and Life–Molecules to Man

Now for a last look at life and its nonliving surroundings. Much of the biology we have discussed is centered about biological problems—how cells divide, the exchange of energy in living cells, patterns of inheritance, the interrelation of the organisms in a community. The specific nature of organisms was submerged in a quest for general principles that pertain to all life. But one does not encounter principles directly—they are what the mind of man abstracts from nature. So, in closing this book, let us look at matter as it exists. We will begin with nonliving matter and show examples of its occurrence in the complexity of the cosmos and in the complexity of atoms and molecules. The existence of matter as life will then be illustrated with many examples of life's variety. Hopefully this chapter will give you a table of reference and, to the extent that you become familiar with it, you will see the objects of nature in their proper positions in the general scheme of things.

The stage for the drama of life is below—in a photograph taken from a satellite. The gentle curve of the earth is seen against the blackness of outer space. The view is northeast to the Strait of Gibraltar, separating Europe and Africa (Spain center, Africa right). Beyond Gibraltar lies the Mediterranean. Its shores saw the birth of Western civilization and of science. Greece—over the horizon at the eastern end of the Mediterranean—was the home of Aristotle and others who, seeking a rational explanation for the phenomena of nature, became the first men of science. The explanations we seek today are in some ways not so different. We are still concerned with the nature and origin of life, and of the earth.

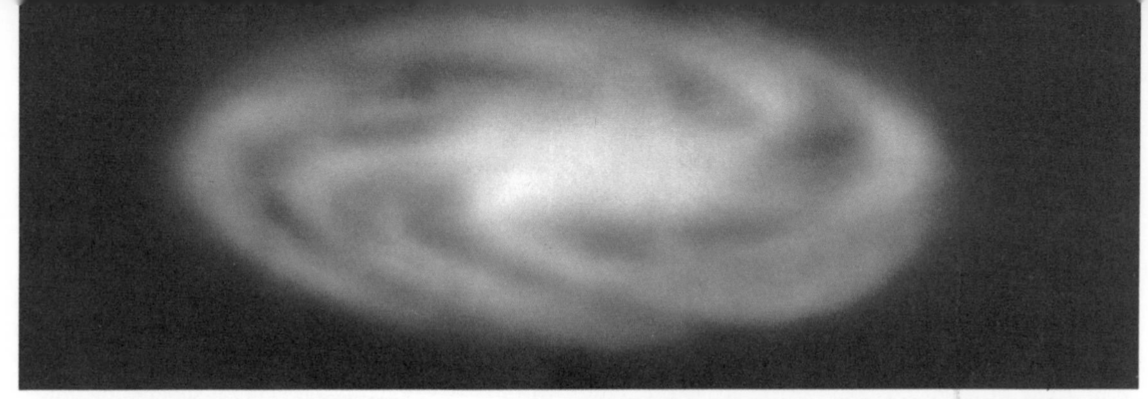

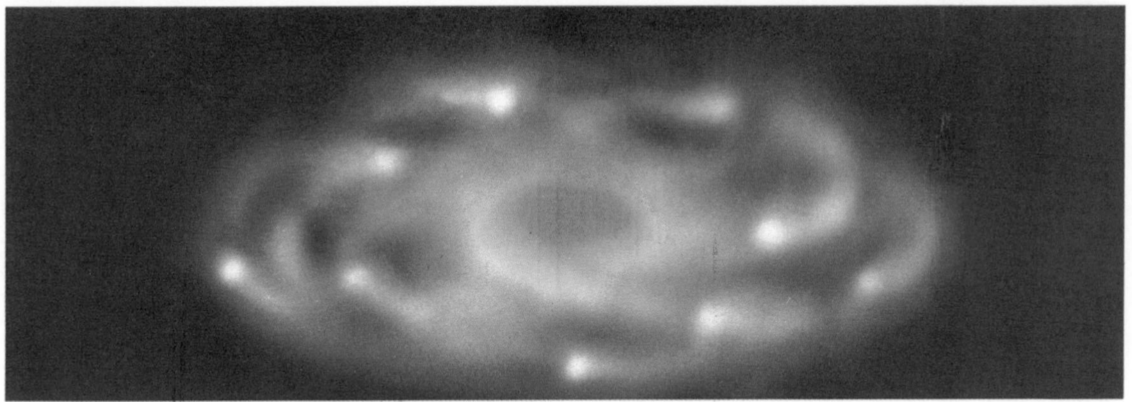

One hypothesis of the earth's origin is that the sun and planets gradually condensed from a vast cloud of hydrogen and other elements (top two views). Hydrogen may have been the ancestral element, from which others in the universe evolved in thermonuclear reactions. (Helium is formed from hydrogen, and carbon from helium, in such reactions in our sun today.) Gradually many elements were formed in the first stars. As these stars grew old, some exploded, and their debris was added to the gaseous clouds from which other stars, including our sun, have evolved. If the hypothesis is correct, then our sun and its larger planets condensed directly from their seminal cloud about five billion years ago. Smaller, inner planets (Mercury, Venus, Earth, Mars) are believed to have formed somewhat less directly, by accumulation of lesser condensations.

The primitive earth in its gaseous form may have had an atmosphere largely of hydrogen, which was later lost to space. A secondary atmosphere of heavier gases, forced from the interior of the planet as it solidified, may have included ammonia, methane, water, and hydrogen sulfide. Energy sources were abundant, in ultraviolet light from the sun, in electrical storms, and in decay of radioactive elements. In such circumstances sugars and amino acids probably formed, as can be demonstrated in the laboratory today.

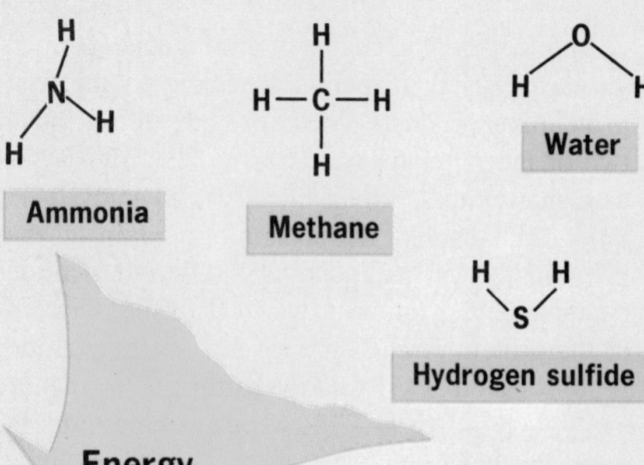

Energy

Some typical amino acids

Glycine

Alanine

Cysteine

Tyrosine

A continued supply of energy would have led to peptide linkages. Even today, heating a mixture of amino acids produces proteinlike products. (Try to identify the order in which the illustrated kinds of amino acids are linked.)

Energy

The lengthening chains of amino acids formed an early variety of peptides leading to the first proteinlike products. Most proteins today have two or more long chains of some 20 amino acids used many times. Atoms of sulfur (S) in cysteine units of chains like the portion of a chain on the preceding page can bond two different peptide chains together into a protein (as in the diagram of the protein *insulin* on page 92, where cysteine is abbreviated "Cys" and the sulfur bonds appear as "——S——S——" between cysteine units in opposite chains).

Early proteins or "proteinoids" in the primitive seas could have taken the shape of blobs with membranelike coverings; even in the laboratory today, these blobs appear to take material from their surroundings and "grow."

Amino acids and proteinoids were not the only products of early syntheses from an atmosphere of ammonia, methane, water, and other reduced compounds. Sugars (diagrams, above right) could have been produced under the same circumstances that produced the amino acids; and amino acids themselves, upon heating, have been shown to yield not only proteinoids but purines and pyrimidines (page 158). The purines and pyrimidines in the diagrams at the right are the five that, with sugars (above right) and phosphoric acid, form ATP (below, and pages 117-18) and the nucleotides of DNA and RNA (below right).

SUGARS

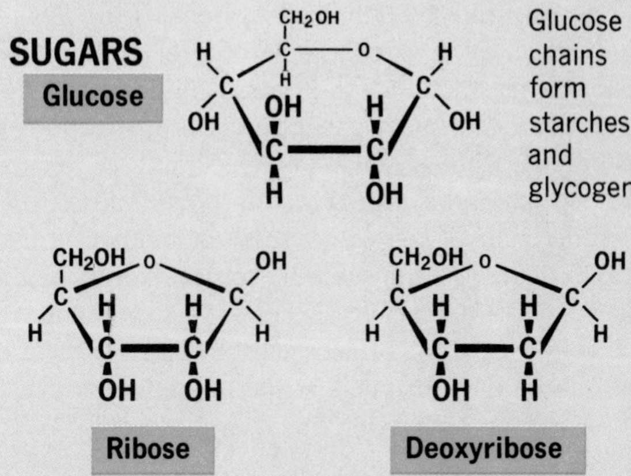

PURINES AND PYRIMIDINES

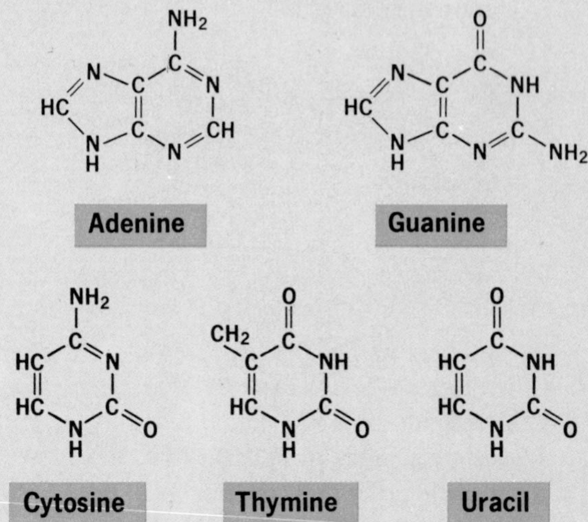

ATP-THE NUCLEOTIDE USED IN ENERGY TRANSFER

Triphosphate (phosphoric acids)

Ribose

Adenine

NUCLEOTIDE STRUCTURE IN DNA AND RNA

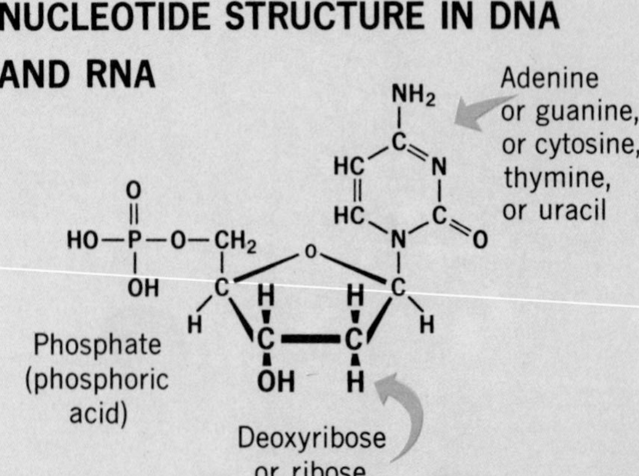

The first self-organizing, self-reproducing blobs appeared in an environment of amino acids and proteinoids, sugars, possibly ATP as well as nucleotides of DNA and RNA, and many other molecules including long chains of carbon and hydrogen in fatlike molecules. We can imagine the early living blobs feeding upon other organic molecules in the seas, until such "food" became scarce. Mutations that produced new proteins—enzymes capable of synthesizing needed molecules from simpler available materials—eventually must have occurred, until, as today, some cells could take energy from the sun and combine carbon dioxide and water into sugars and amino acids.

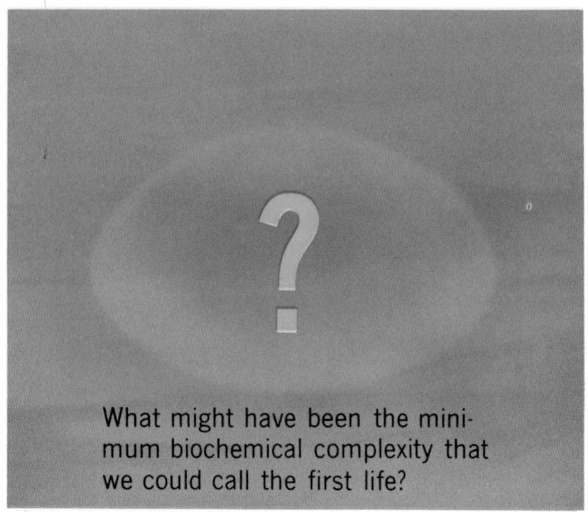

What might have been the minimum biochemical complexity that we could call the first life?

FOSSILS AND THE PAST

The mutant cells that first took energy from the sun and successfully combined carbon dioxide and water into sugars and amino acids must be considered the first plants. Presumably they were algae, or much like algae. When we find plant fossils today, we usually find only fossils of land plants, which came much later (photos at right and below).

A very few fossil traces of algae survive, and many living species of algae still thrive today. You will see them as we examine the Plant Kingdom on the following pages.

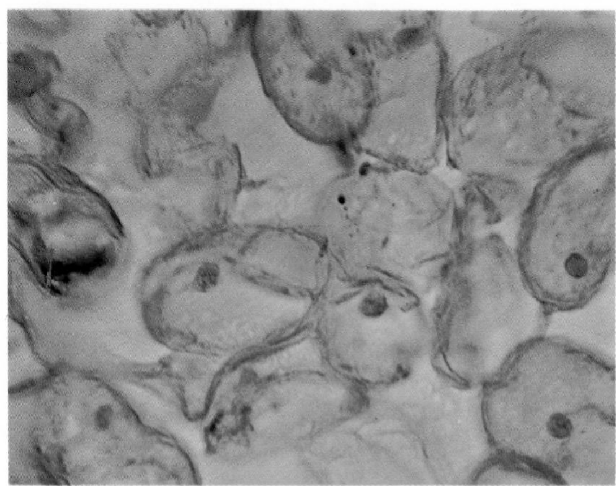

Spores with nuclei (Carboniferous period)

Cells in a fossil seed (Carboniferous period)

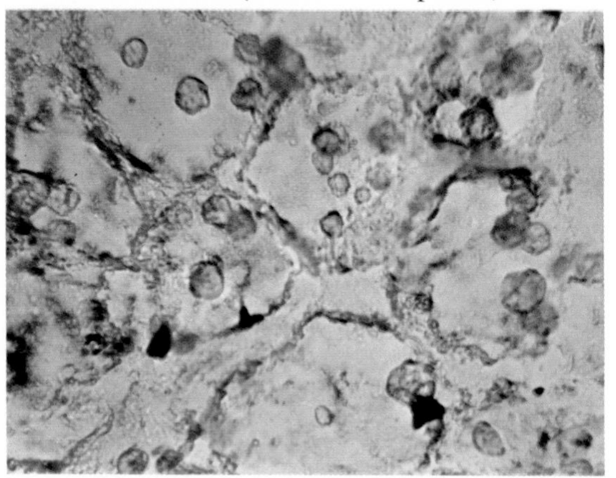

Fern tissue (Devonian period)

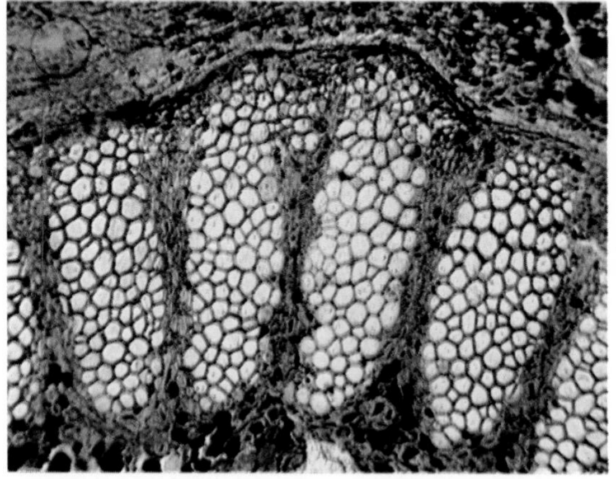

THE PLANT KINGDOM

PHYLUM SCHIZOMYCOPHYTA—Bacteria

Bacteria are one-celled organisms with cell walls but no highly organized nuclei. Almost all of them are heterotrophs (Chapters 10, 11). Fossils date to several billion years ago.

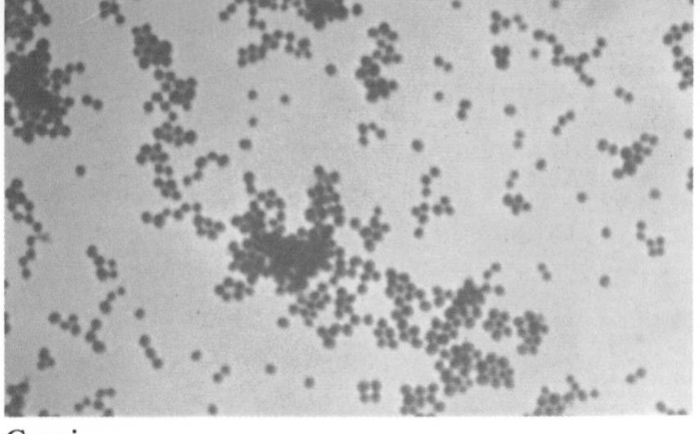

Cocci

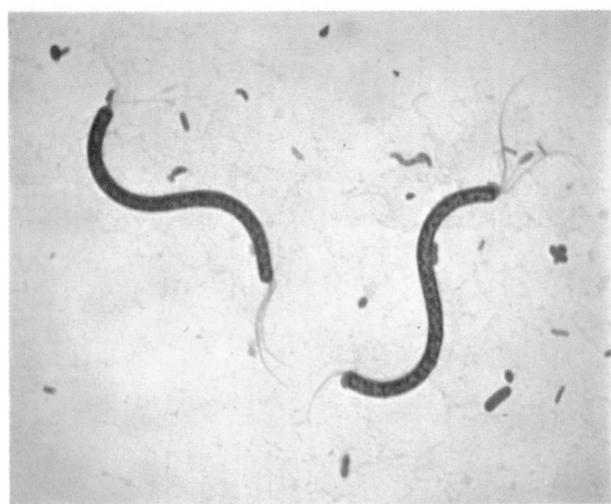

Spirilla

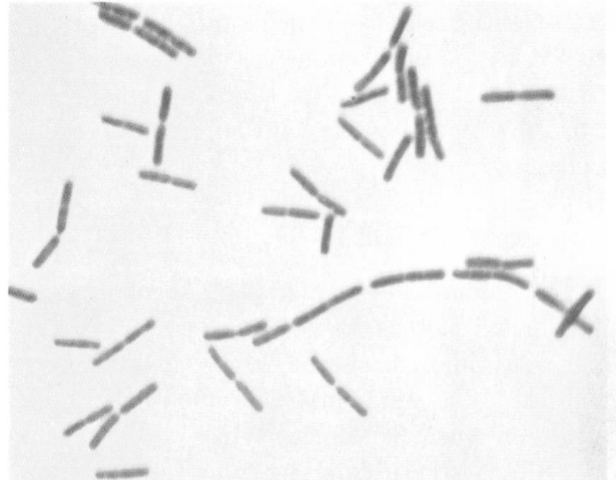

Bacilli

PHYLUM CYANOPHYTA—Blue-green Algae

The blue-green algae have a fossil record more than three billion years old. They are primitive autotrophs (Chapter 13) with chlorophyll that is not organized in chloroplasts. Like the bacteria, blue-green algae have cell walls but no highly organized nuclei in their cells. Fossil examples from the Gunflint Chert formation in Ontario, Canada, are shown at the right.

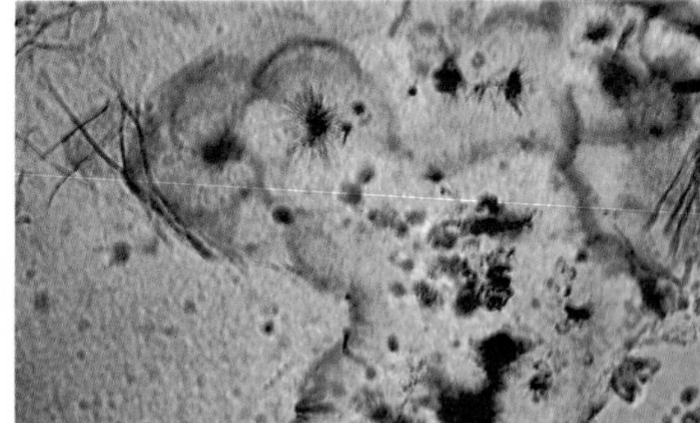

Fossil blue-green algae (Pre-Cambrian)

Oscillatoria, a freshwater blue-green alga

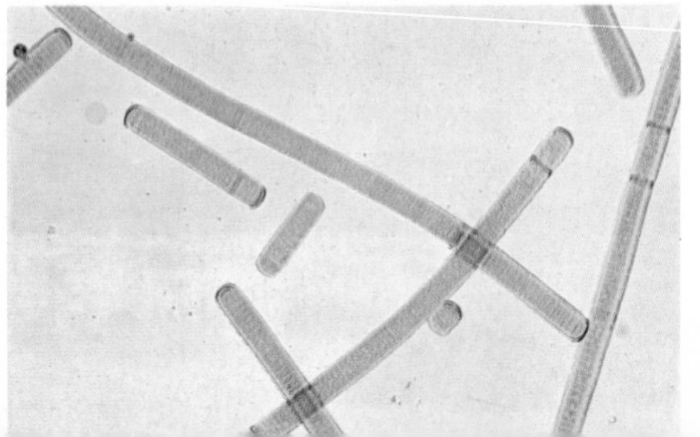

Nostoc, a freshwater blue-green alga

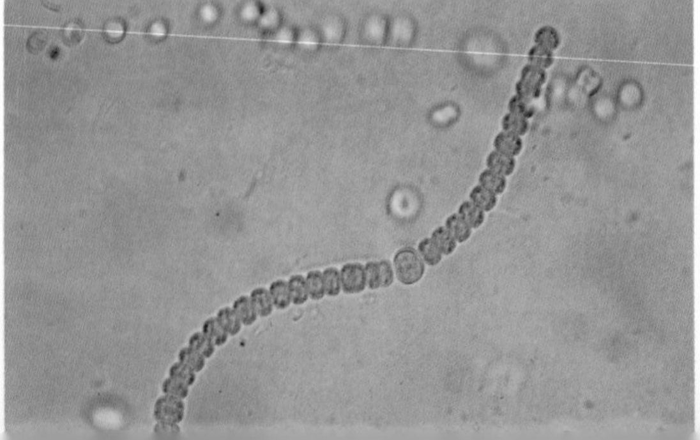

Stemonitis, a slime mold

Graterium, a slime mold

Another species of *Stemonitis*

PHYLUM MYXOMYCOPHYTA—Slime Molds

The slime molds lack chlorophyll and feed chiefly on bacteria. Their life cycles have two distinct phases—an amoeboid plasmodium with no cell walls (see pages 230, 652) and a fruiting stage (above) that produces thick-walled spores. Little is known of their fossil history.

PHYLUM CHLOROPHYTA—Green Algae

Chlorophyll in chloroplasts, cell walls, and starch, a stored food, link green algae to today's green land plants (Chapters 13, 14).

Ischadites, a fossil green alga (Ordovician)

Spirogyra, a freshwater green alga

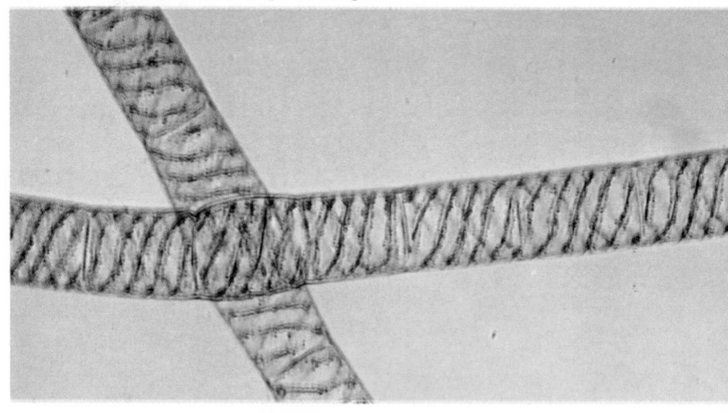

PHYLUM CHRYSOPHYTA—Golden-brown Algae

Golden-brown algae (page 277) contain a yellow pigment in addition to chlorophyll. One group of them, the diatoms (right), have a glass-like substance in their cell walls.

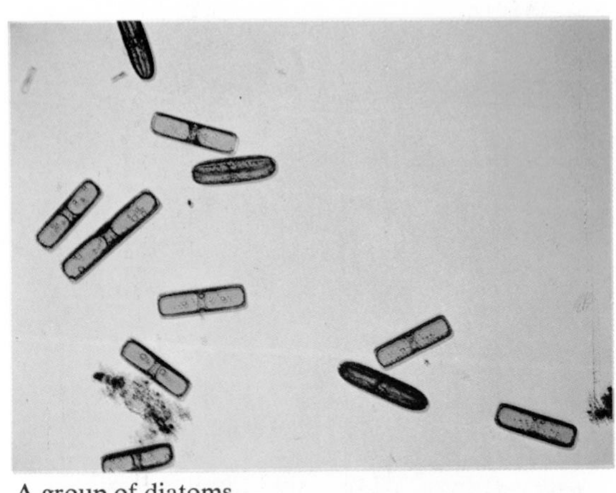

A group of diatoms

PHYLUM PHAEOPHYTA—Brown Algae

Brown algae (page 277) contain brown and yellow pigments in addition to chlorophyll. They are multicellular, with tissues that often form stemlike, rootlike, and leaflike parts.

The brown algae *Fucus* (above) and kelp (below). Like all brown algae, they are marine organisms.

The brown algae *Sargassum* (above) and *Ascophyllum* (below). Brown algae inhabit cooler seas.

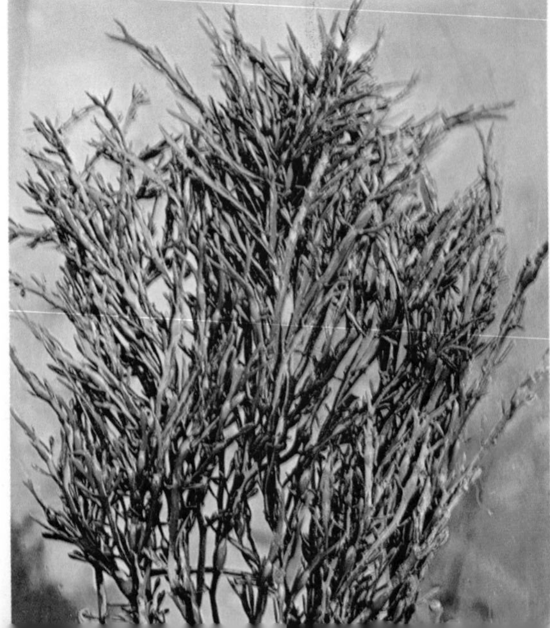

Agardhiella, a red alga

Stenophycus, fossil red algae (Devonian)

Rhodymenia, another red alga

PHYLUM RHODOPHYTA—Red Algae

Red algae (page 277) contain a red pigment in addition to chlorophyll. They are marine organisms, generally inhabiting tide pools in warmer seas. Most are multicellular.

Boletus, a mushroom

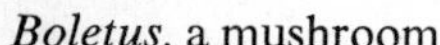

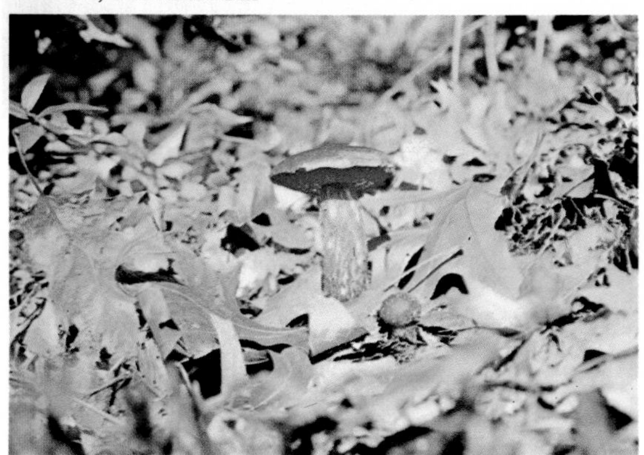

PHYLUM EUMYCOPHYTA—True Fungi

Fungi are heterotrophs (Chapter 12). They and the slime molds (page 763) probably evolved from early protozoans and never had chlorophyll. The fruiting stage produces thick-walled spores.

Another mushroom

Polyporus, a bracket fungus

Marchantia, a liverwort (female gametophyte)

Moss gametophytes with sporophytes

PHYLUM BRYOPHYTA—Liverworts and Mosses

The bryophytes are green land plants that have no true vascular tissue and no true leaves, stems, or roots. They have remained small and primitive, inhabiting moist environments.

PHYLUM TRACHEOPHYTA—Vascular Plants

(this page and the next nine pages)

SUBPHYLUM PSILOPSIDA

Psilopsids are the most primitive known vascular plants (see *Rhynia,* Chapter 14). The plant body is a system of forked branches in which xylem forms a solid core.

A living (left) and a fossil psilopsid (below)

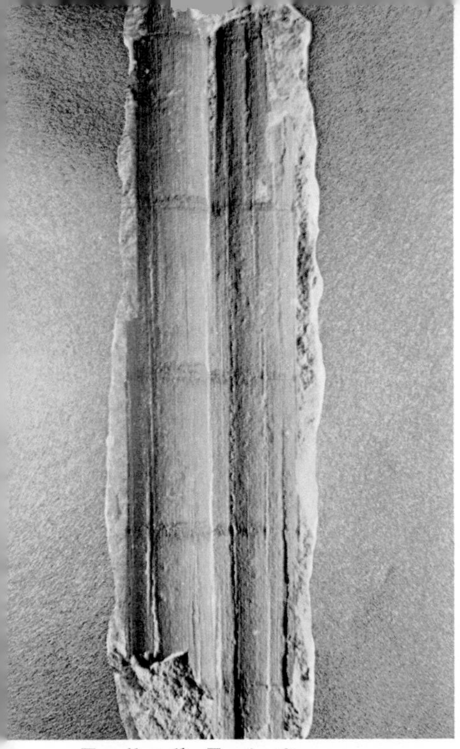

Fossil stalk, *Equisetites*

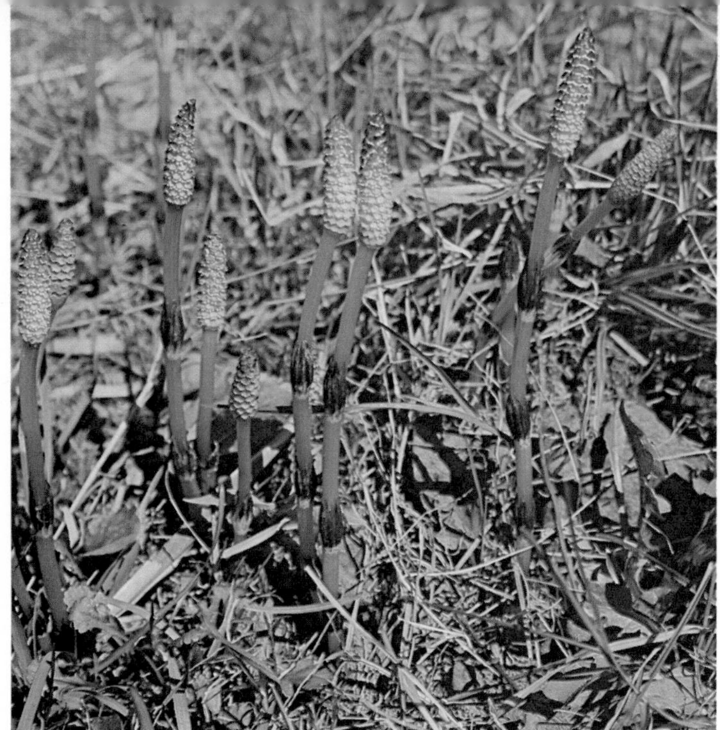

Living horsetails, *Equisetum*

SUBPHYLUM SPHENOPSIDA

Horsetails and their relatives date from Devonian times. Their vascular stems bear whorls of small leaves at regular intervals (photograph, lower left). The stems have terminal cones.

SUBPHYLUM LYCOPSIDA

Plants of this group date from the Silurian period. At their major stage in Carboniferous forests, some were treelike (see fossil trunk pattern, below). Small club mosses survive today.

Fossil *Sphenophyllum* branch

Trunk cast, *Lepidodendron*

Lycopodium, a club moss

SUBPHYLUM PTEROPSIDA—
From Ferns to Flowers

CLASS FILICINEAE (Ferns)

Fronds of subdivided leaves typify most ferns. The Carboniferous period was their peak.

Living tree ferns, New Zealand

Living fern, showing rhizomes in soil

Living sword ferns, *Nephrolepis*

Fossil *Pecopteris* fronds (Carboniferous)

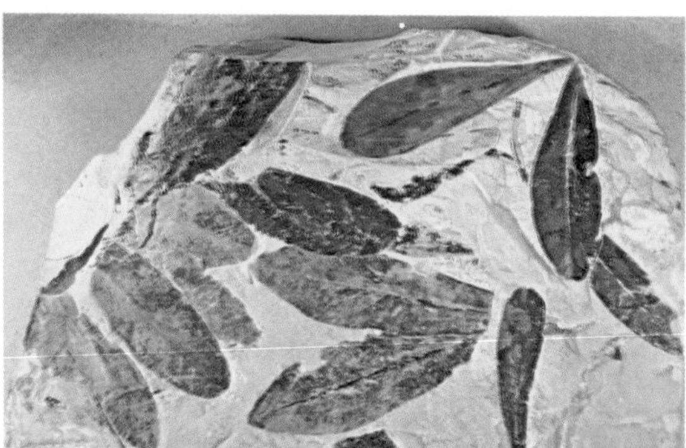

Two fossils that are not true ferns. Above, *Glossopteris,* probably a seed fern (Permian), and below, *Archaeopteris,* a pro-gymnosperm (Devonian).

CLASS GYMNOSPERMAE

Conifers, *Ginkgo*, and cycads typify this class of plants. Most produce seeds in cones. Their seeds are not contained in an ovary. Fossil and living gymnosperms are shown on this page and the following two pages.

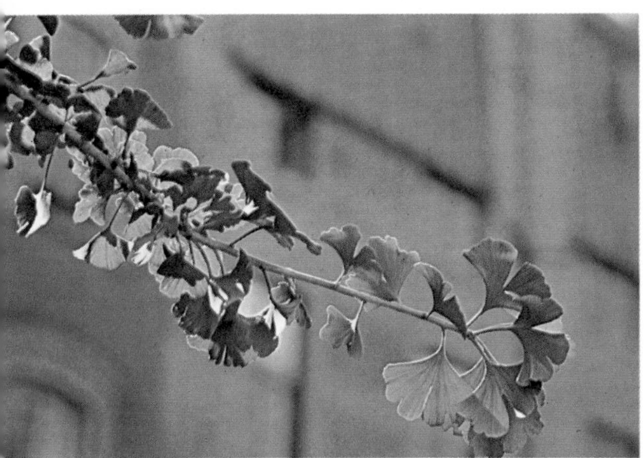

Living *Ginkgo* branch

Living monkey puzzle tree, *Araucaria*

Fossil *Ginkgo* leaf (Paleocene)

Living *Ginkgo* trees

Douglas fir (*Pseudotsuga*) and Western cedar

Fossil sprig and cone of an extinct species of *Sequoia* (Oligocene)

Fossil trunk of *Sequoia* (Eocene)

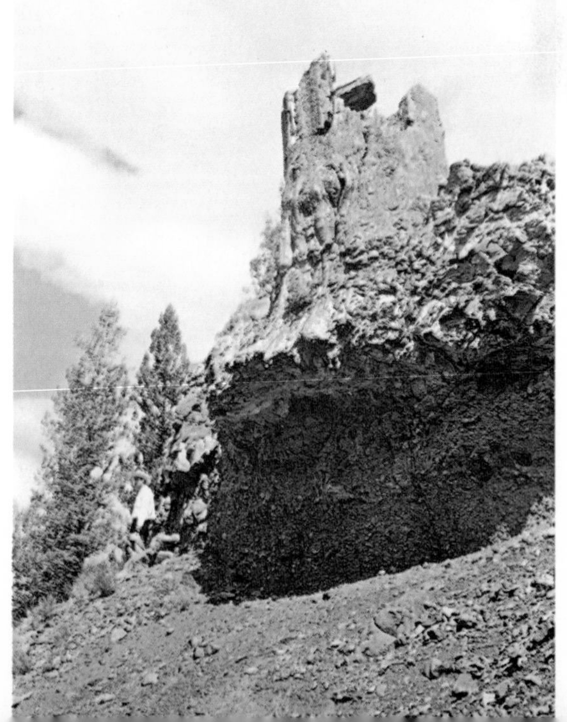

Like the ferns, gymnosperms once were much more abundant than they are today. About 600 species survive. Some, like *Ginkgo* (previous page), survived in a single area and have been reintroduced to others.

The tallest and the largest organisms in the world are two species of *Sequoia* trees; these are the only species of *Sequoia* that survive (see fossils, this page, and photograph, page 754). The cycads (facing page) also are rare.

Living white pine branch, *Pinus*

Living white pine tree, *Pinus*

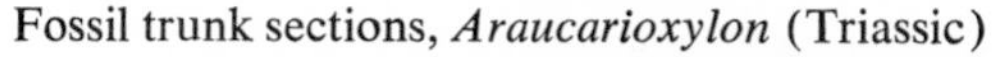

Fossil trunk sections, *Araucarioxylon* (Triassic)

Fossil cones, *Proaraucaria* (Eocene)

Close-up of cycad cones, *Microzamia*

Living cycad, *Microzamia*

CLASS ANGIOSPERMAE—Flowering Plants

The dominant land plants of our time are the flowering plants—vascular plants that flower and form fruits with seeds (Chapters 14, 15, 16, 17). The origin of the angiosperms and how their reproductive patterns evolved remains a mystery. Fossils first occur in the Triassic period, making angiosperms the relative newcomers among vascular land plants.

Angiosperms are of two subclasses, monocots and dicots. The plants on these two pages are monocots. Some dicots are illustrated on the succeeding two pages.

The angiosperms evolved as the great reptiles were disappearing from the animal scene and mammals were replacing them. These were the last great transitions in the dominant plant and animal types on land.

Bamboo, *Phyllostachys*

SUBCLASS MONOCOTYLEDONEAE

The monocots usually have parallel-veined leaves, often have floral parts in threes or multiples of threes, and usually have only one seed leaf (cotyledon) in the embryo within the seed. Grasses and grain crops are monocots, as are some trees and decorative flowering plants.

Banana tree, *Musa*

Winter wheat, *Triticum*

Skunk cabbage, *Lysichiton*

Fan palm, *Thrinax*

Narcissus

Fossil leaf of fan palm (Eocene)

Wild grass

Young corn plant, *Zea*

Lily, *Lilium*

SUBCLASS DICOTYLEDONEAE

The dicots usually have netted-veined leaves, often have floral parts in fours or fives, and have two seed leaves (cotyledons) in the embryo within the seed.

There are more than 200,000 species of dicots, compared to about 50,000 of monocots. All of the common deciduous trees and most decorative flowering plants are dicots.

Waratah, *Telopea* (Australia)

Bunchberry, *Cornus*

Fossil sycamore leaf, *Platanus* (Cretaceous)

Trollius, a primitive flowering plant

Living sycamore tree, *Platanus*

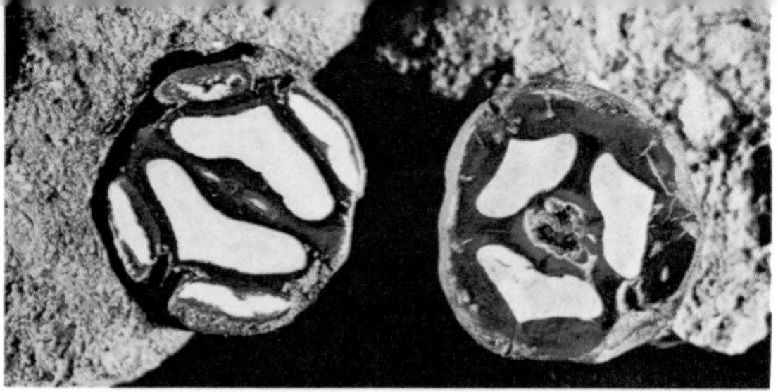

Fossil walnut, *Juglans* (Eocene)

Living white oak tree, *Quercus*

Fossil oak leaf, *Quercus* (Miocene)

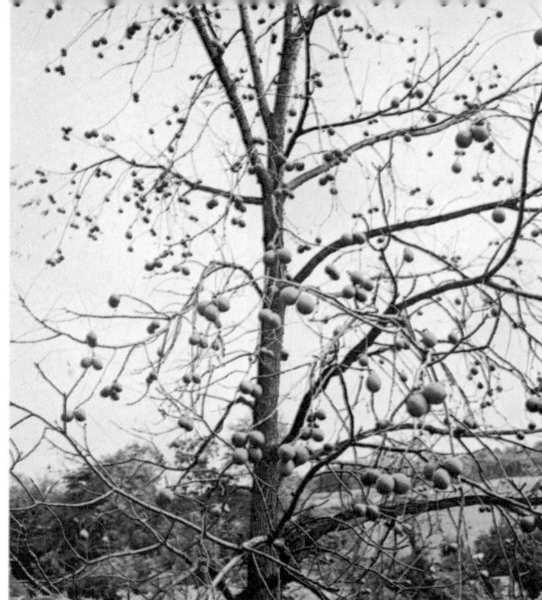

Living black walnut tree, *Juglans*

Fossil acorn, *Quercus* (Eocene)

Living white oak branch, *Quercus*

THE ANIMAL KINGDOM

PHYLUM PROTOZOA—Variations on the Cellular Theme

The primitive living blob illustrated on page 761 was a heterotroph. From it both plants and animals are believed to have evolved. Even today, certain algae can live as heterotrophs if their chloroplasts are removed.

Most protozoans carry on their life processes with a body that resembles somewhat an individual cell of a more complex form. About 16,000 living species are known (see also page 355).

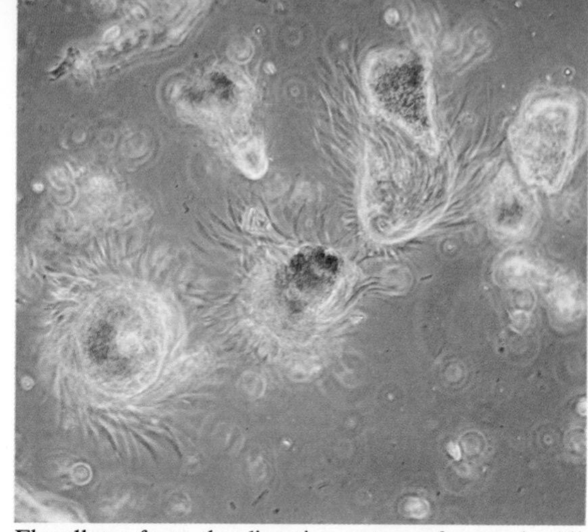

Flagellates from the digestive system of a roach. All the species on this page are microscopic.

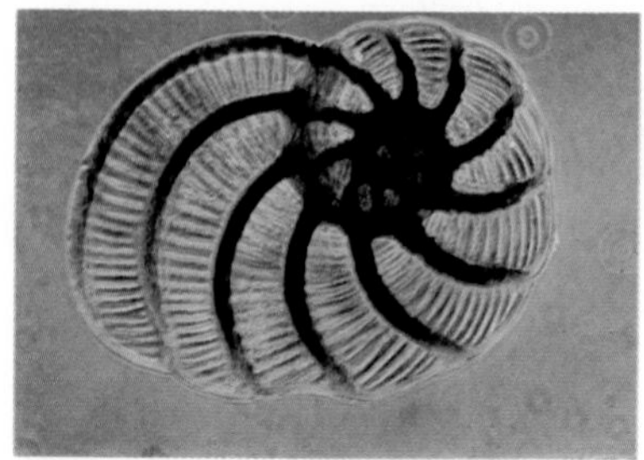

Peneroplis, a shell-forming marine protozoan with pseudopods

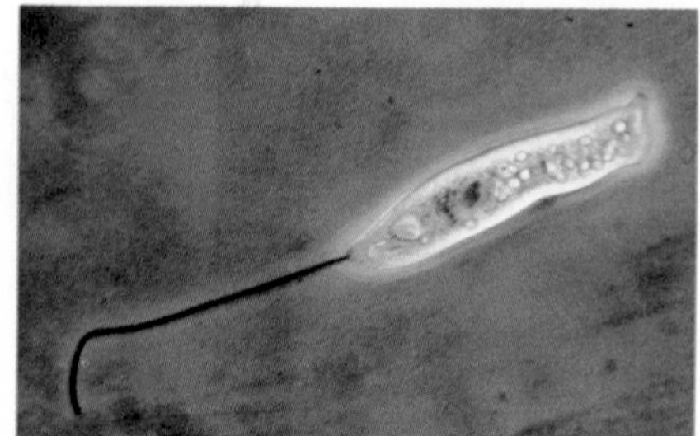

Peranema, a flagellated freshwater protozoan

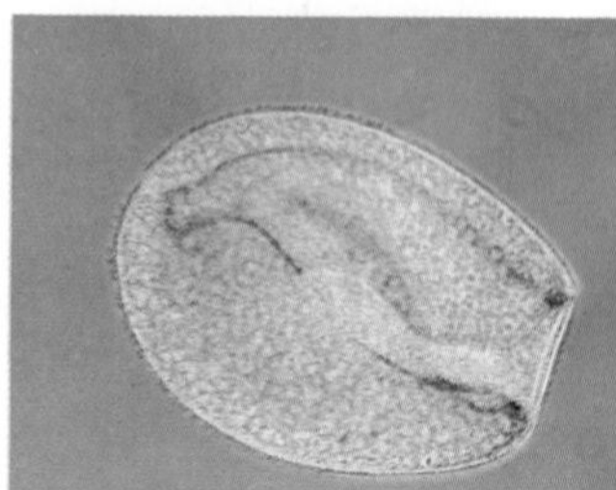

Bursaria, a freshwater ciliate

Noctiluca, marine flagellates

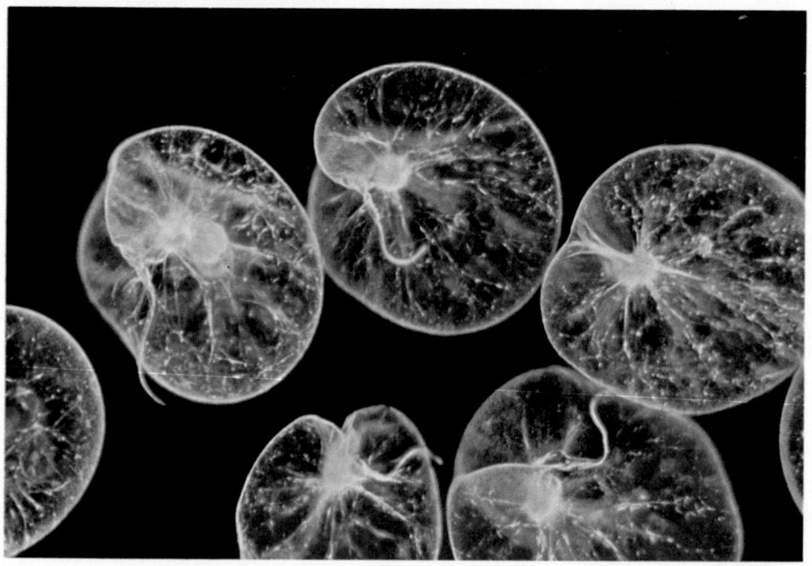

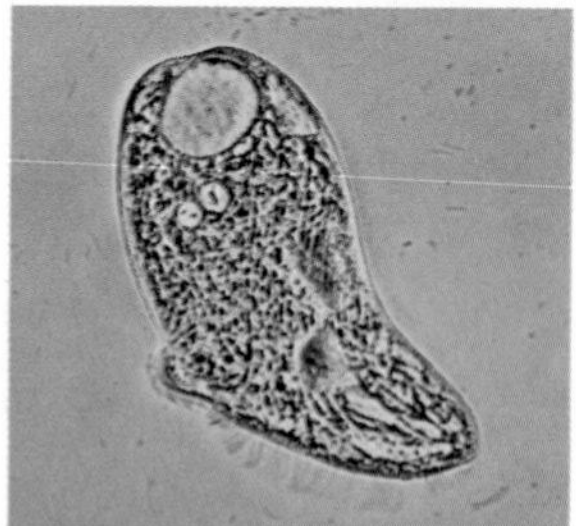

Blepharisma, a freshwater ciliate

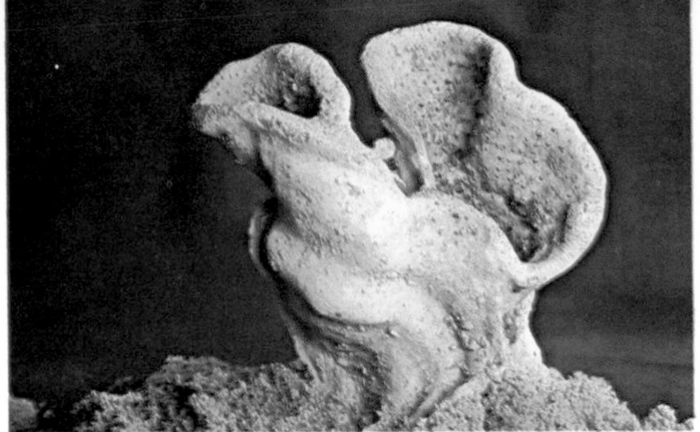

Raphidonema, a fossil sponge (Cretaceous)

PHYLUM PORIFERA—Many Cells, But Little Integration

Sponges (page 356) have many cells but no highly specialized tissues or organs. Often they do not even have a definite shape. Fossil sponges first appear in Pre-Cambrian rocks. About 2,000 species are living today.

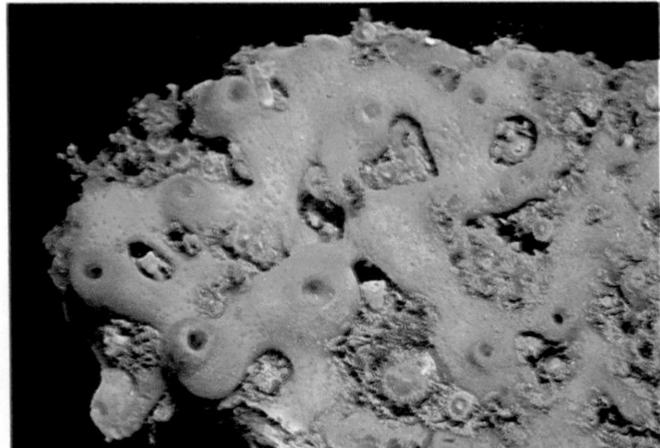

Adocia, a marine sponge, and tiny anemones

A marine sponge from the Caribbean

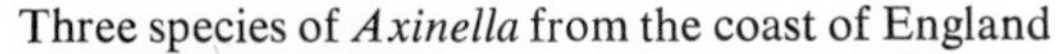

Three species of *Axinella* from the coast of England

Pennaria, a marine hydroid

PHYLUM COELENTERATA—Animals with Two Main Tissue Layers

Coelenterates have a central digestive cavity and a nervous system of a primitive kind (pages 357-58). Often they are vase-shaped, occurring singly or in colonies. The earliest fossils are in Pre-Cambrian rocks. About 4,500 living species are known. Like the sponges, all coelenterates are aquatic, and most are marine. All the species on these two pages belong to this phylum.

Astroides, a coral

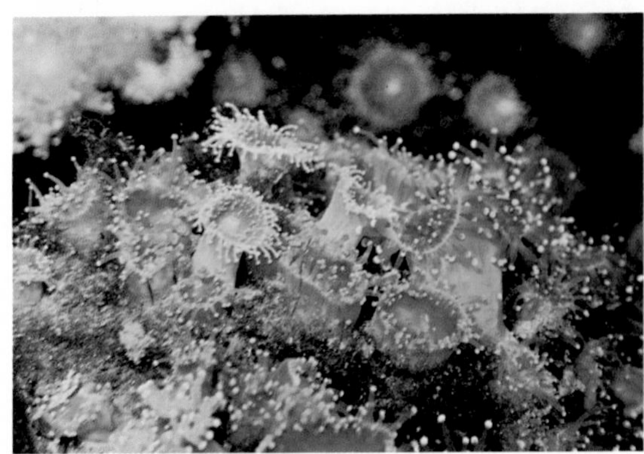

Sea anemones from the Pacific

Porpita colony

Tubularia, a marine hydroid

Physalia, or Portuguese man-o'-war

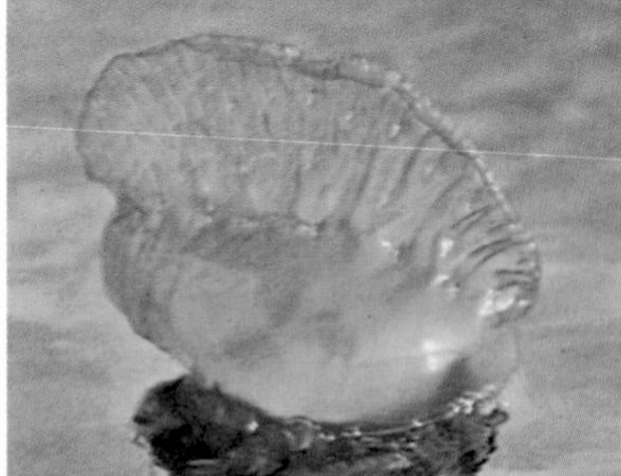

Fossil cup corals, *Thecosmilia* (Jurassic)

Caryophyllia, a living cup coral

Pre-Cambrian *Beltanella,* possibly a coelenterate

The coelenterates, though simple in anatomy, are responsible for the largest structures produced by any living organisms, including man. In the warmer seas of the earth, the corals and other coelenterates form enormous reefs. Many islands are surrounded by them; some islands were formed by them. The most spectacular construction of all is the Great Barrier Reef, which extends for more than a thousand miles along the east coast of Australia.

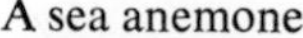

A sea anemone

Madrepora, a coral

PHYLUM PLATYHELMINTHES—Three Tissue Layers in Flattened Bodies

The flatworms (pages 359-60) are small, inconspicuous animals with digestive, nervous, excretory, and reproductive systems clearly differentiated. Little is known of fossils of these softbodied organisms, but about 6,000 species are living today. Some are free-living, and others are parasites of various animals, including man.

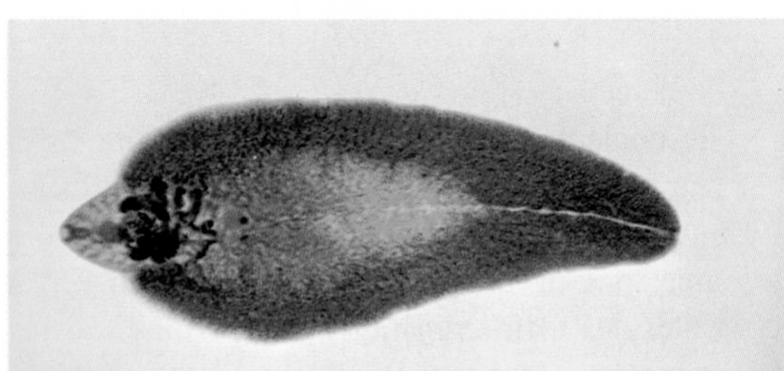

Fasciola, a sheep liver fluke

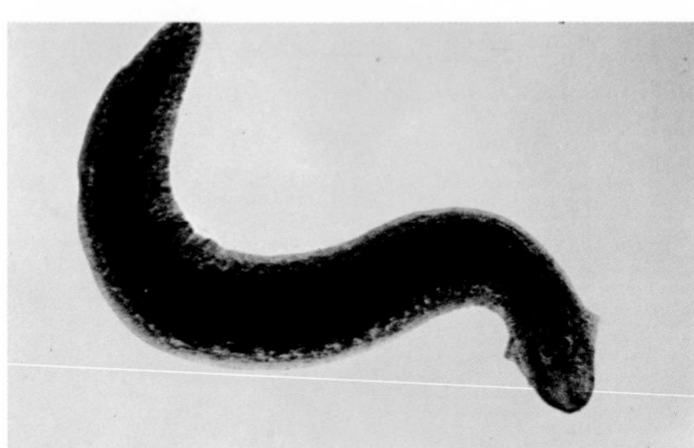

Dugesia, a freshwater planarian

A land planarian from the tropics

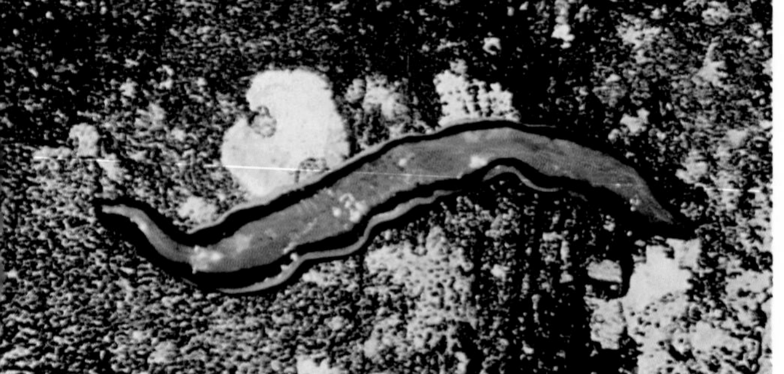

PHYLUM NEMATODA—Round Worms

The level of complexity of the round worms (pages 361-62) is about equal to that of the flatworms. The body is tubular, with an alimentary canal extending from one end of the body to the other. Fossils are almost unknown. The number of living species is at least 6,000, and possibly many more. The round worms, like the flatworms, include many species that are parasites.

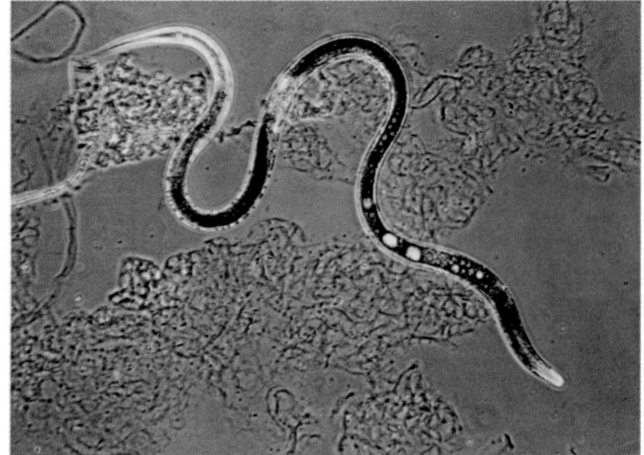

Anguillula, a round worm that lives in vinegar

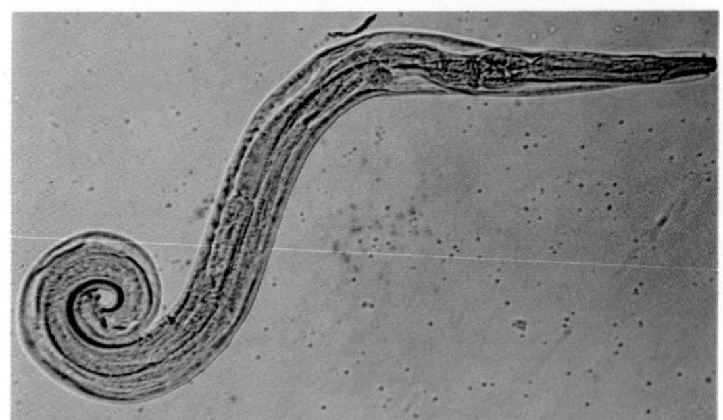

The pin worm *Enterobius,* a parasite of man

Trichuris, another parasite of man

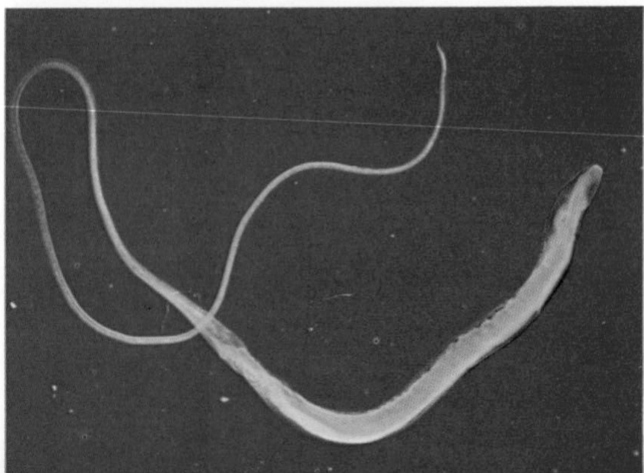

PHYLUM ANNELIDA—Segmented Worms

The annelid worms (pages 362-64) add a circulatory system and, in some species, specialized structures for respiration, to the organ systems already present in the lower animal phyla. Annelids also have a coelom, or body cavity lined with mesoderm, and their other organ systems show a higher level of complexity than in animals of lower phyla.

A few annelid fossils occur, beginning in rocks of the Cambrian period. About 6,000 species – mostly marine–live today. Some marine forms swim freely; others live in burrows, or in tubes that they secrete. (*Amphitrite,* upper right, is a tube worm that was removed from its tube to be photographed. *Bispira,* lower left, is seen in its tube, with only its tentacles exposed; these structures help in food-getting.)

A few species of annelids live in fresh water or in moist soil. Among the latter are the common earthworm (page 363) and another example (*Enchytraeus*), shown on this page.

Amphitrite, a marine annelid

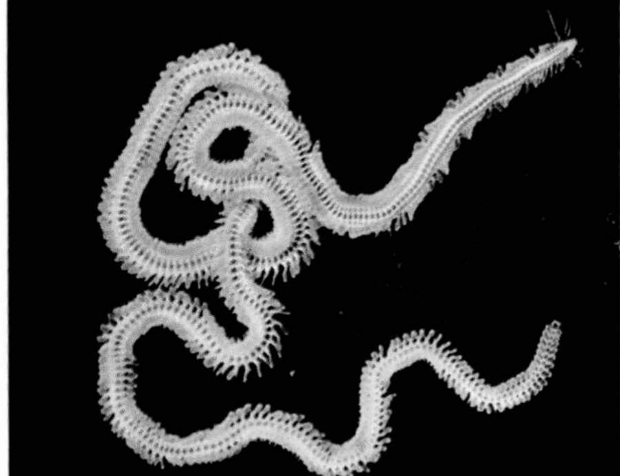

Phyllodoce, a marine annelid

Lepidonotus, a marine annelid

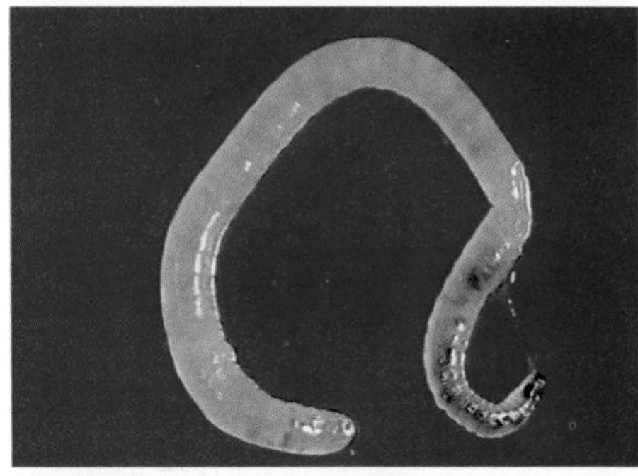

Enchytraeus, a land annelid

Bispira, a marine annelid in its tube

Fossil tubes of marine annelids (Cretaceous)

PHYLUM ECTOPROCTA—Bryozoans

Bryozoans are aquatic, mainly marine. Each little animal is part of a colony that has a supporting framework with cuplike depressions in which the individuals live. Colonies may be very large.

Bugula, a marine bryozoan colony

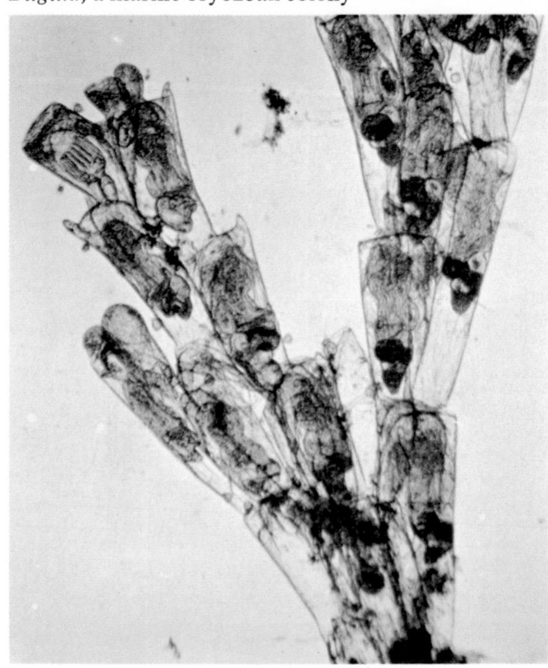

Fossil bryozoan (Carboniferous)

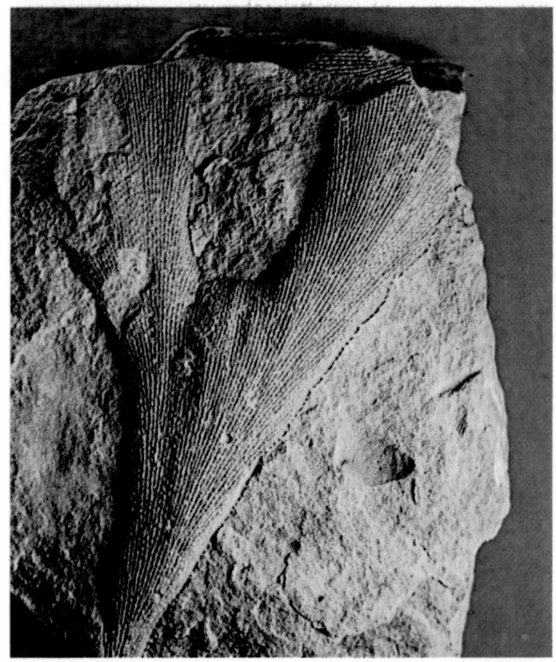

THE ROTIFERS (sometimes classified with nematodes, as Phylum Aschelminthes)

Rotifers are named for their caplike rings of cilia that in motion resemble revolving wheels. These microscopic animals live in fresh water, in the ocean, and in wet moss.

A freshwater rotifer (150 ×)

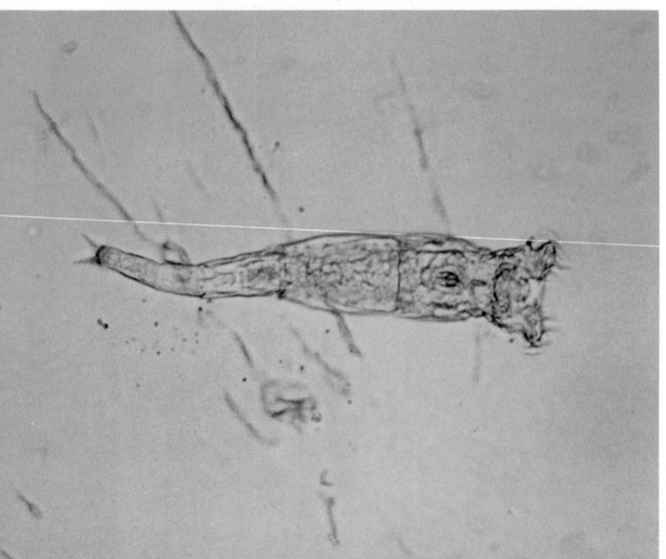

Another species of freshwater rotifer (200 ×)

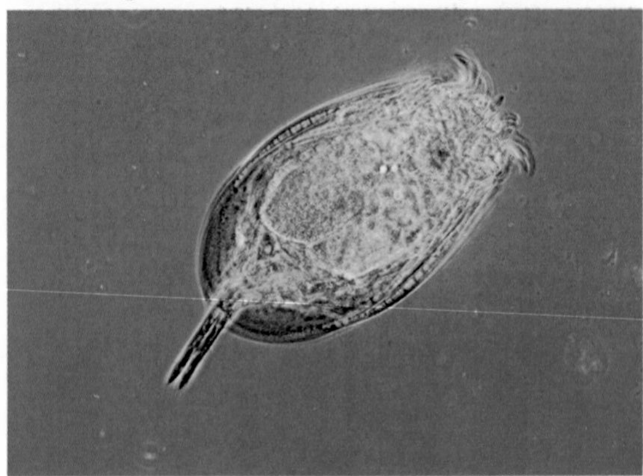

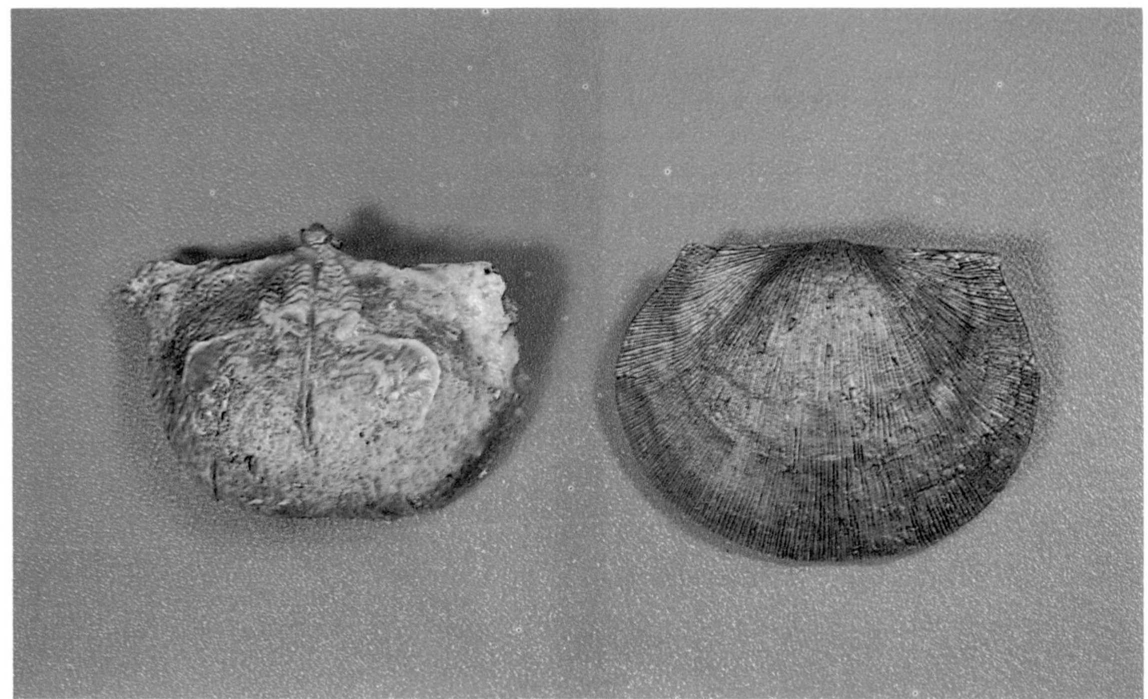

Fossil impressions of internal parts (left) and a shell (right) of Carboniferous brachiopods

PHYLUM BRACHIOPODA—Shadows of the Past

Living brachiopods are rare, but 30,000 species once inhabited the seas. Unlike mollusks, whose shells are on the right and left sides of the body, brachiopods' shells are dorsal and ventral. Internally their structure is very different from the body structure of the mollusks.

Terebratulina, a living brachiopod (right)

Lingulella, the oldest known fossil brachiopod, from Pre-Cambrian rock in Montana

PHYLUM MOLLUSCA—Animals with a Variety of Shells

The mollusks (pages 365-66) are much like the annelid worms in their general level of complexity, but the body is not segmented in the vast majority of species. Nearly all mollusks have shells, which may be single, double, composed of several parts, or small and situated within the body. Mollusks occur in the ocean, in fresh water, and on land. Their fossils first appear in Pre-Cambrian rocks, and about 75,000 living species are known today.

Mollusks have succeeded brachiopods in abundance, possibly in a direct competition.

The mollusks are the first group of animals in the phyla presented so far which have species that are regularly eaten by man. Clams, mussels, oysters, and snails are all mollusks, and even squid and octopus are used by man as food.

Most species of mollusks, especially those with heavy shells, move slowly if at all. A few, such as the squid, can swim rapidly.

Dirona, a marine nudibranch

A garden slug

Turritella, a fossil gastropod (Eocene)

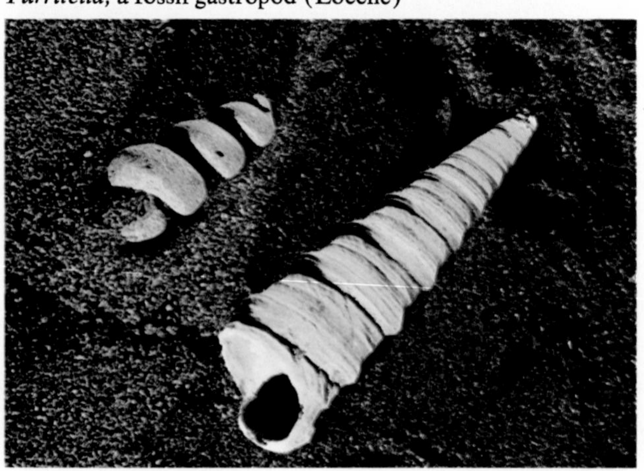

Fasciolaria, cast (left) and fossil (right)

Mya, a soft-shelled clam

Fossil (top) and contemporary (lower) cephalopods

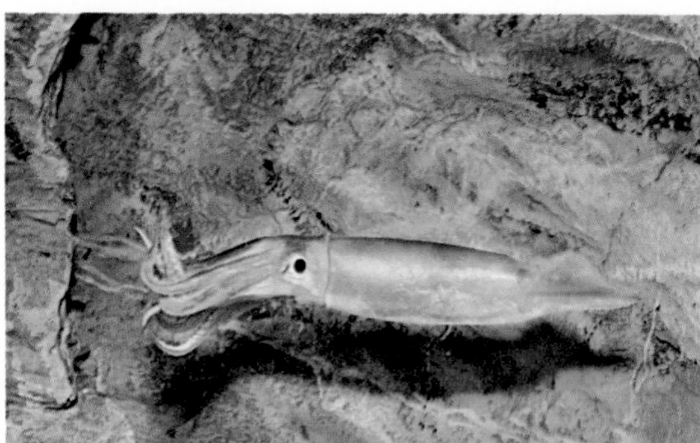

Illex, a squid

Another fossil cephalopod, *Scaphites* (Cretaceous)

A bed of marine mussels, *Mytilus*

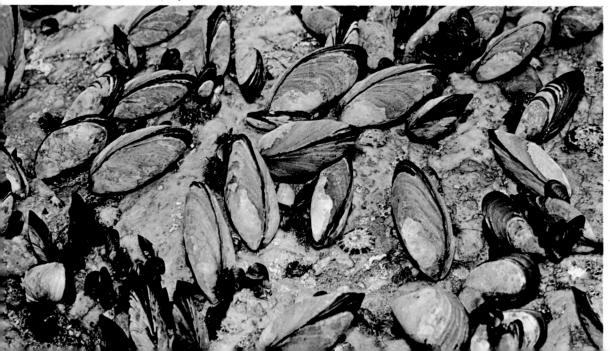

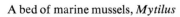

PHYLUM ARTHROPODA—Animals with Jointed Legs

The arthropods (pages 366-67) are the most advanced and the most numerous of the invertebrates. Many species have well-developed brains, complex sense organs, and complex behavior patterns. The body is enclosed in a tough exoskeleton, jointed in the legs and often in other parts of the body. There are more species of arthropods—750,000 or more—than of any other phylum.

Fossil arthropods occur in the rocks of the Cambrian and each successive period. The Cambrian arthropod *Aysheaia* and the living *Peripatus* (both at right) are related though separated almost half a billion years in time. *Peripatus* is of great interest in being a true arthropod, yet in having many of the features of the annelid worms. This is one line of evidence suggesting that the annelids and the arthropods may have had a common ancestor.

The trilobites (below) are extinct, but they were common in Paleozoic seas. The shrimp (below right) and the examples on the facing page belong to the arthropod group known as crustaceans. Three more crustaceans are shown on the succeeding page (page 788), followed by arthropods of other major groups.

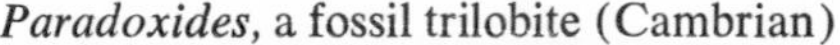

Paradoxides, a fossil trilobite (Cambrian)

Aysheaia, a fossil arthropod (Cambrian)

Peripatus, mother and newborn young

The pink shrimp *Peneus*

Aeger, a crayfish-like fossil (Jurassic)

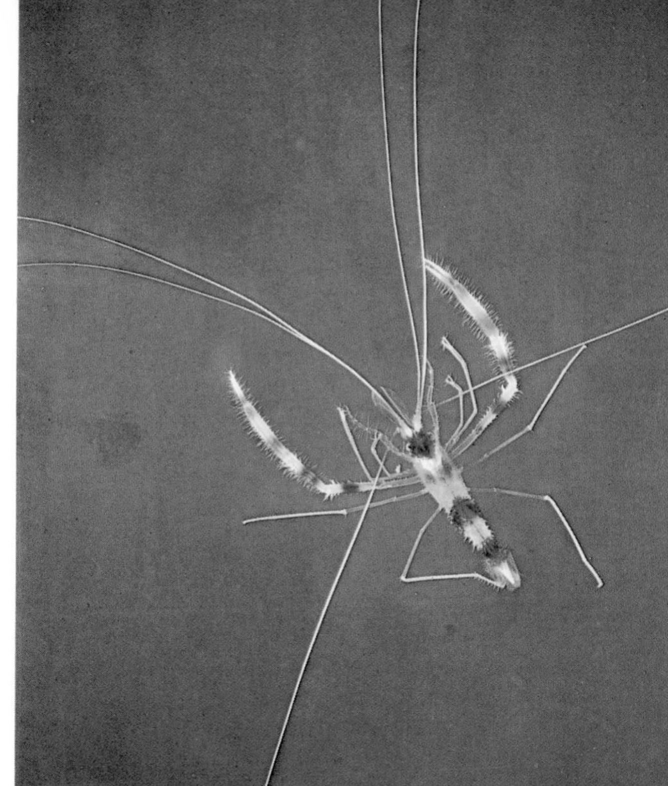

Stenopus, a coral shrimp

A group of barnacles

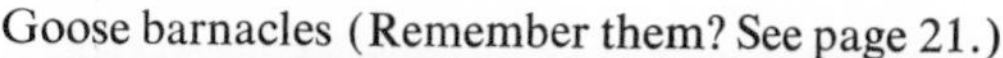

Goose barnacles (Remember them? See page 21.)

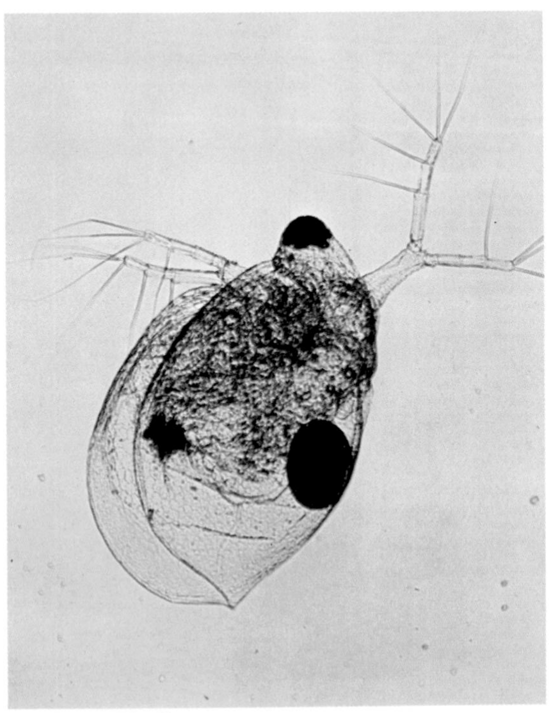

Daphnia, a freshwater crustacean

Eurypterus, a fossil arachnid (Silurian)

A marsh crab

Geocarcinus, a land crab

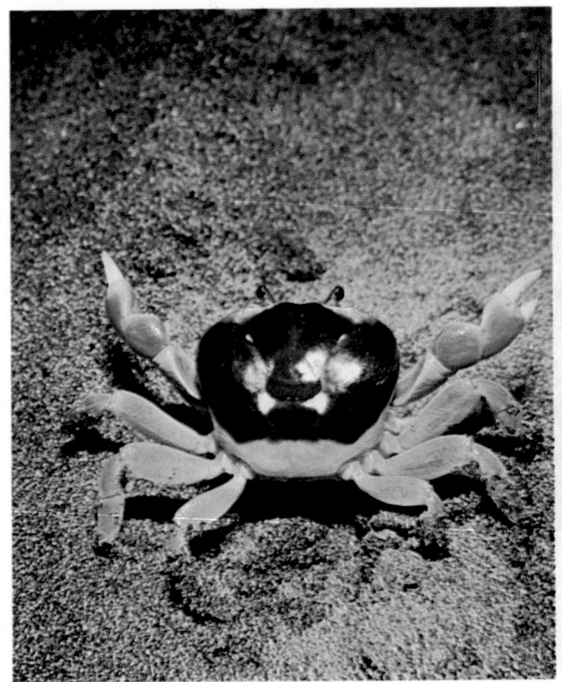

MORE ARTHROPODS

On the lefthand page are three more crustaceans (see pages 786-87) and a large eurypterid (*Eurypterus*). The eurypterid and the tick, spider, and horseshoe crabs shown on this page are members of another major arthropod group, the arachnids. Eurypterids are extinct. They often reached a length of three meters in the Paleozoic seas. The horseshoe crabs (below), another ancient line, are not extinct; they have changed little in almost 200 million years.

All arachnids have four or five pairs of legs. The ticks (upper right) are parasites of man and other animals, and some ticks transmit diseases. Most spiders (right) build webs that ensnare their prey.

Millipedes (below right) are members of another arthropod group, myriapods, meaning "many feet." Centipedes also belong to this group. The clearly segmented bodies of myriapods have one or two pairs of legs on nearly every segment.

The majority of all arthropod species belong to still another group, the insects (turn page).

The common tick

Argiope, a spider

Xiphosura, Jurassic and living horseshoe crabs

Millipedes

AND STILL MORE ARTHROPODS

The largest group of arthropods by far is the insects. All the arthropods on this and the facing page are insects.

Typically insects have two pairs of wings and three pairs of legs, but with so many species—no one knows how many – it is not surprising that many variations exist. Thus, flies have only one pair of wings, and beetles have the first pair of wings modified as hard, protective covers for the abdomen.

Although they are essential parts of the web of nature, most insects, despite their abundance, have little or no direct effect on man. Some species, however, destroy crops, transmit diseases, bite us, or are otherwise annoying.

A water strider

Honeybees

Sphecomyrma, a fossil ant (Cretaceous)

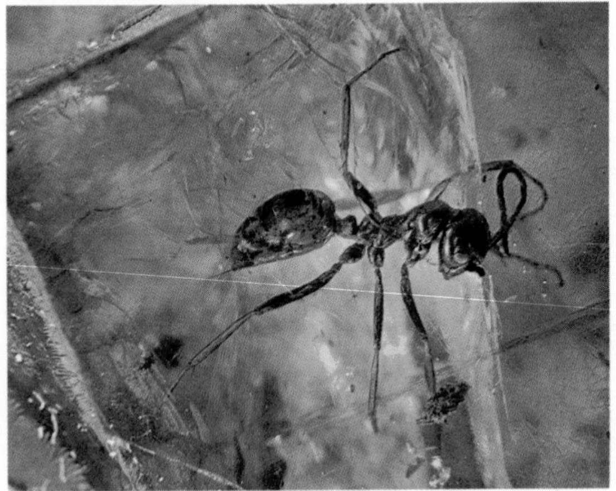

A wasp-mimicking fly

Phoracantha, a beetle

Prodryas, a fossil butterfly (Miocene)

A dragonfly

A syrphid fly

Pseudosphegina, a fossil fly (Oligocene)

Charaxes, a butterfly

Murgantia, harlequin bugs

A praying mantis

PHYLUM ECHINODERMATA—Animals with a Spiny Skin

Echinoderms (page 368) are familiar marine animals with radially symmetrical bodies that are rounded or cylindrical or starlike, with spiny projections from the surface. The body usually is divided into five parts, or some multiple of five. Organ systems are of a low level of organization, but the development of the embryo resembles to a degree the development of the chordates—and for this reason biologists believe that echinoderms are the invertebrates most closely related to the chordates. About 1,000 living species are known. Fossils date from Cambrian rocks.

Astropecten, a sea star

Echinus, a sea urchin

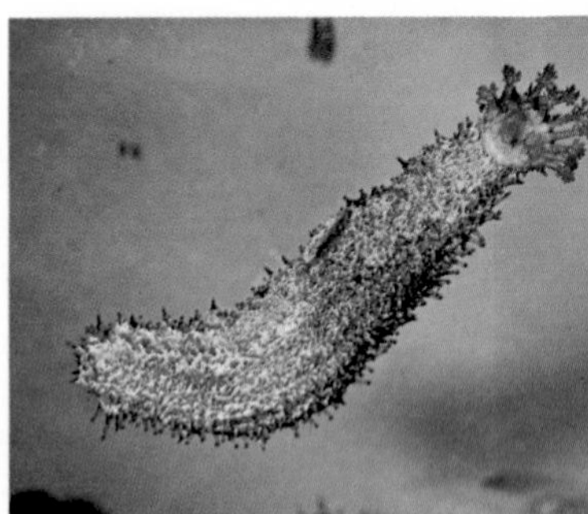

A sea cucumber

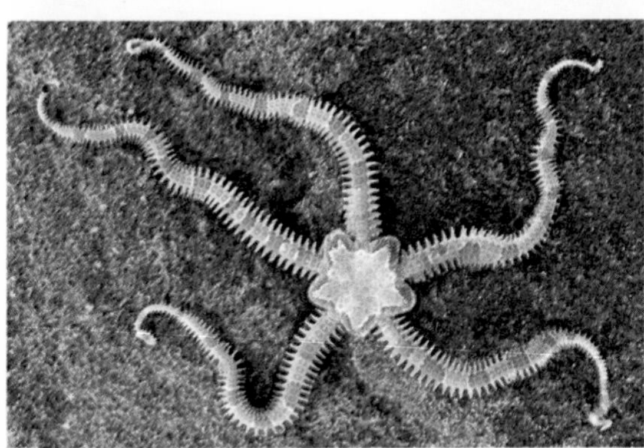

Ophiopholis, a brittle star

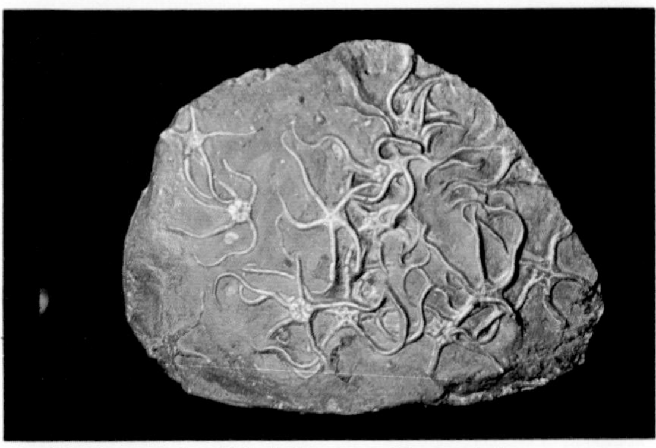

Ophioderma, fossil brittle stars (Jurassic)

Another sea urchin

Platycrinites, a fossil crinoid (Carboniferous)

PHYLUM CHORDATA—Home of the Vertebrates

This is the phylum that includes man. Chordates (pages 368-70) possess at one time or another in their lives a dorsal nerve tube, a notochord (a stiff rod of tissue below the nerve tube), and pharyngeal gill slits (which have a respiratory function in the lower chordates). The oldest known fossils are of fishlike species from the Ordovician period. About 35,000 chordate species are known in all.

Most chordates are vertebrates – that is, they have a vertebral column, or backbone. The primitive species below are exceptions.

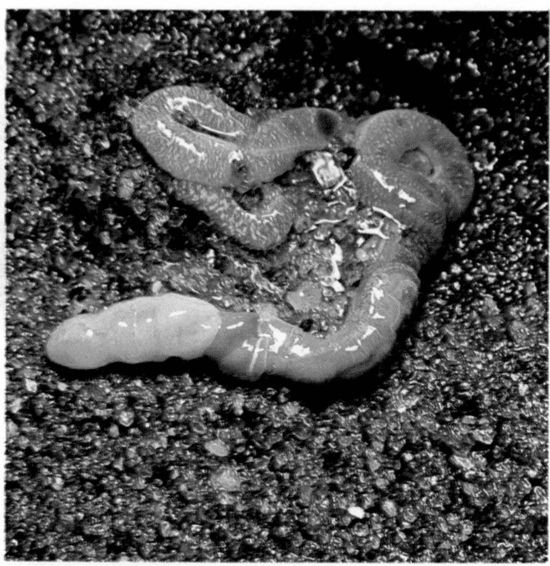

Saccoglossus, an acorn worm

A tunicate

Ciona, a tunicate

Amphioxus (stained specimen)

FISHES—Chordates That Live in Water

The fishes are the most primitive of the vertebrates. Fossils of fishlike vertebrates are first known from Ordovician rocks. Two very ancient species from the Devonian period are shown at the right.

Sharks and rays (below) have skeletons of cartilage, but most fishes have bony skeletons. You can see pectoral and pelvic fins on some of the species shown here. From such structures on early fishes like the crossopterygian at the right, the arms and legs of land-living vertebrates evolved over a period of many millions of years.

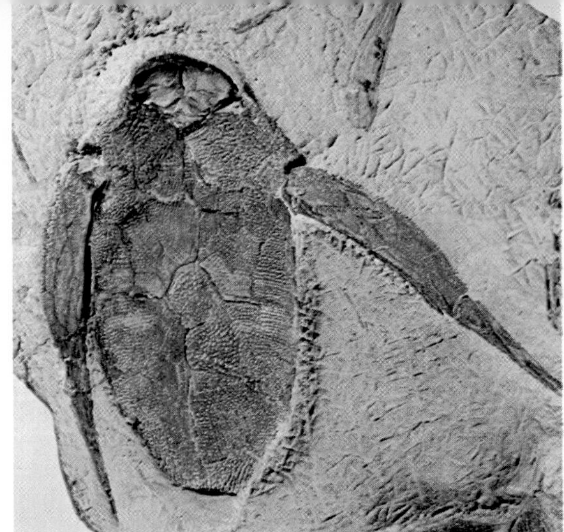

Bothriolepis, a fossil placoderm (Devonian)

Holoptychius, a fossil crossopterygian (Devonian)

Prionace, a blue shark

Raia, a ray

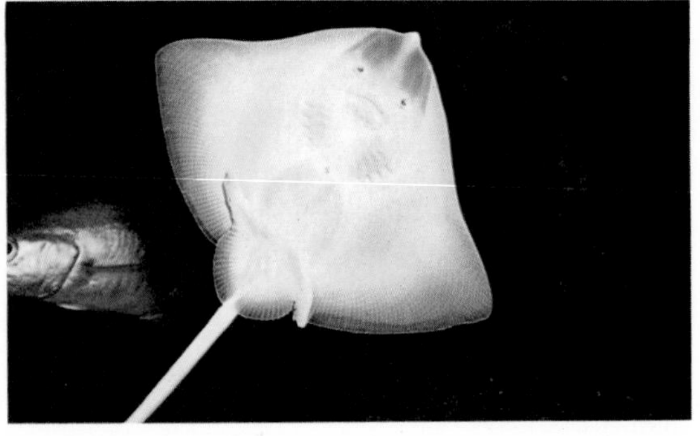

A jawfish

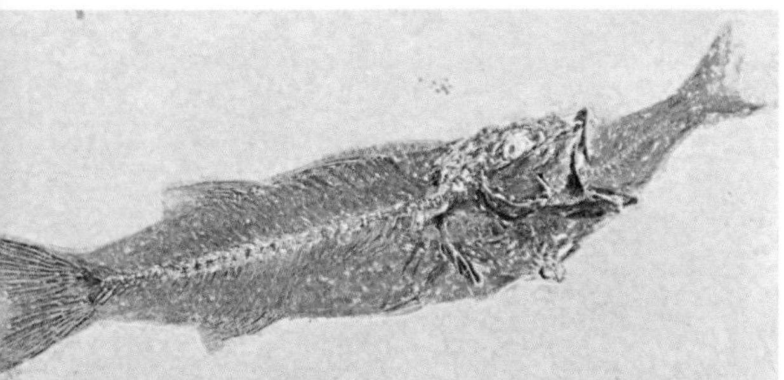
Mioplosus, a fossil perch, eating a herring (Eocene)

Trachinotus, a pompano

A male sea horse, with sea "colts" it has hatched

Gadus, a codfish

Fossil (Eocene) and model (of living) garfish

Acipenser, a sturgeon

AMPHIBIANS—Chordates That Began the Colonization of Land

During the Devonian period, some advanced species of fishes evolved into amphibians (page 377 and Figure 19-25). The pectoral and pelvic fins gradually evolved into arms and legs, gill respiration was succeeded by lung and skin respiration, and a general reorganization of the body's structure and physiology took place over countless generations.

Two main groups of amphibians survive today —those with tails (the salamanders), and those without tails, at least in the adults (frogs and froglike species). Both groups require water for part of their life cycle.

Ensatina, a California salamander that has been used to study evolution (pages 599-600)

Eryops, a primitive amphibian from the Permian rocks of Texas

The green frog *Rana*

Bufo, a toad

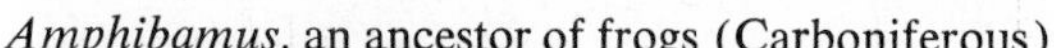

Amphibamus, an ancestor of frogs (Carboniferous)

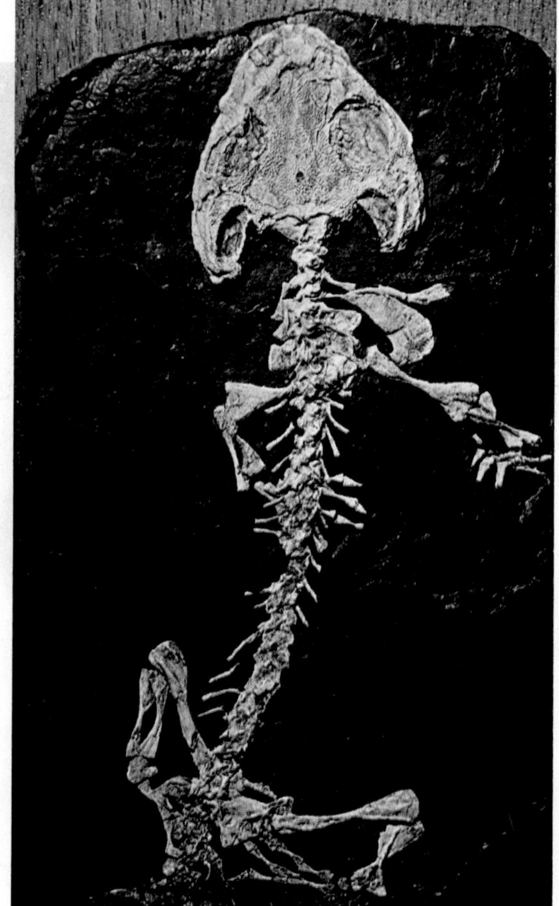

A fossil toad (Miocene)

REPTILES—At Home on Land

The slow evolution away from a dependence on water, which began with the early amphibians, was completed in approximately 40 million years with the appearance of the primitive reptiles. Unlike the amphibians, which require water for the development of their embryos, reptiles have embryos that are either kept in the mother's body until they are born, or develop in eggs laid on dry land. The outer covering of the reptilian body, frequently scales, prevents excessive loss of water in a land environment.

The oldest known reptiles are from the Carboniferous period. Some of the species illustrated (ending on page 801) are from the Age of Reptiles that began when adaptations to a variety of land environments (and some in water, too) helped the reptiles become dominant to amphibians on land (and reinvade the seas, as well).

The major groups of surviving reptiles are the turtles, the snakes and lizards, and the crocodiles (including alligators). *Sphenodon* (page 801) is the sole survivor of a group that flourished in the Mesozoic era.

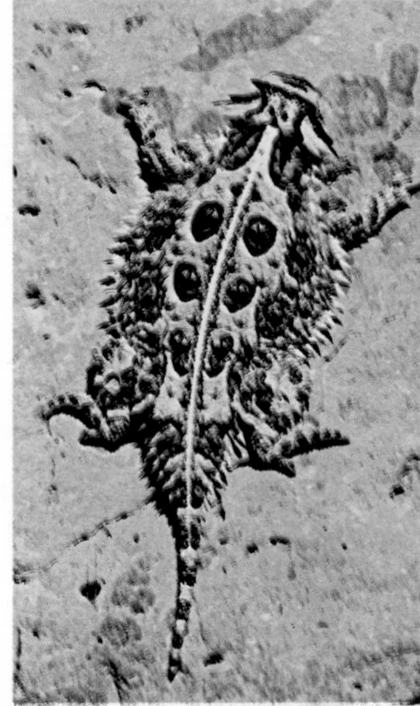

A horned lizard

A boa constrictor

A blacktailed rattlesnake

An American chameleon

Elaphe, a yellow rat snake

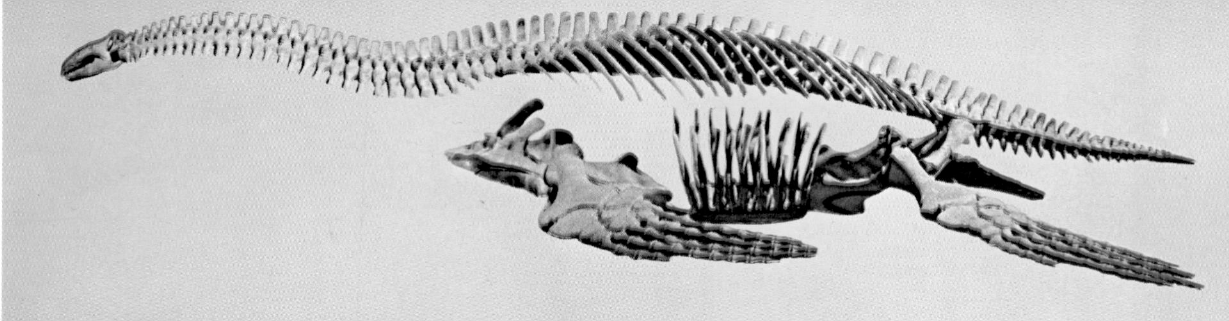

Cryptocleidus, a marine reptile of the extinct group known as plesiosaurs (Jurassic)

Gopherus, a desert tortoise

Ichthyosaurus, a marine reptile (Jurassic)

The smooth green snake

A glass snake, really a legless lizard

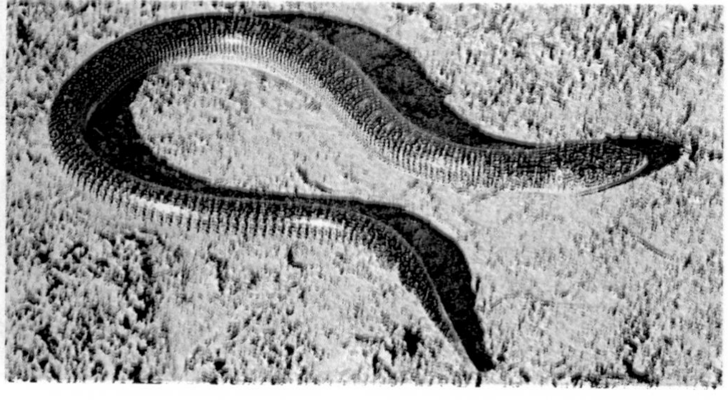

Chrysemys, a painted turtle

Brontosaurus, huge but herbivorous (Jurassic)

The living reptiles are but a shadow of their mighty ancestors. During the Mesozoic era a huge variety of dinosaurs and other reptiles evolved. Not only did they dominate the land and reinvade the seas, but they also invaded the sky. A flying reptile is illustrated at the left below, two marine species on the previous page, and three large dinosaurs, above left and on the facing page.

Some of the Mesozoic reptiles evolved into the first birds. Others, similar to the type at the bottom of this page, were ancestral to mammals.

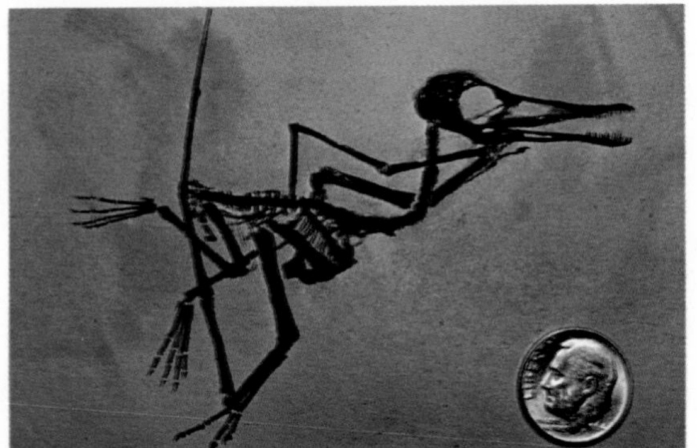

A tiny flying reptile, *Pterodactylus* (Jurassic)

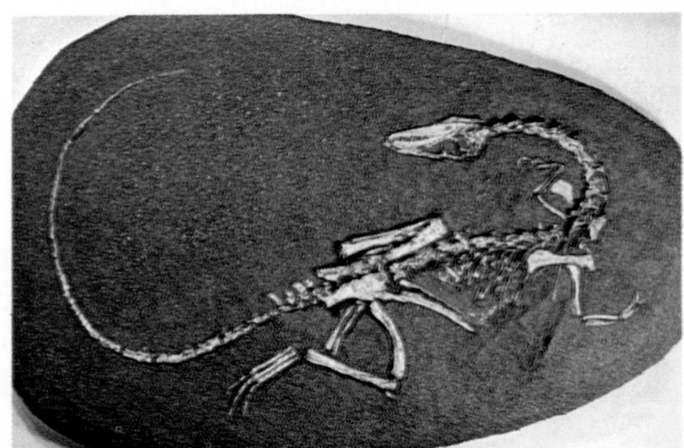

Coelophysis, a fossil reptile (Triassic)

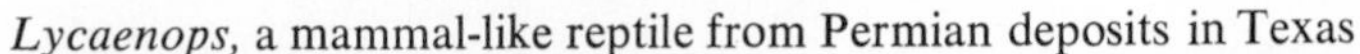

Lycaenops, a mammal-like reptile from Permian deposits in Texas

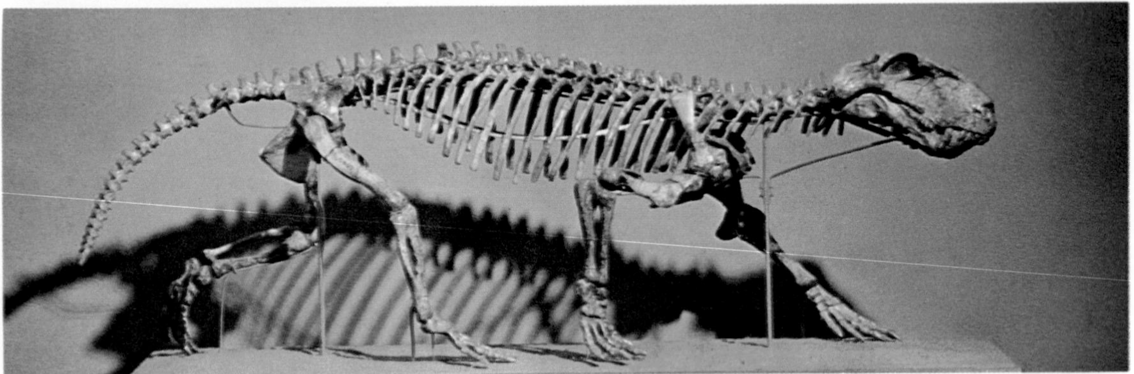

Sphenodon, a primitive living reptile

Crocodilus, a crocodile

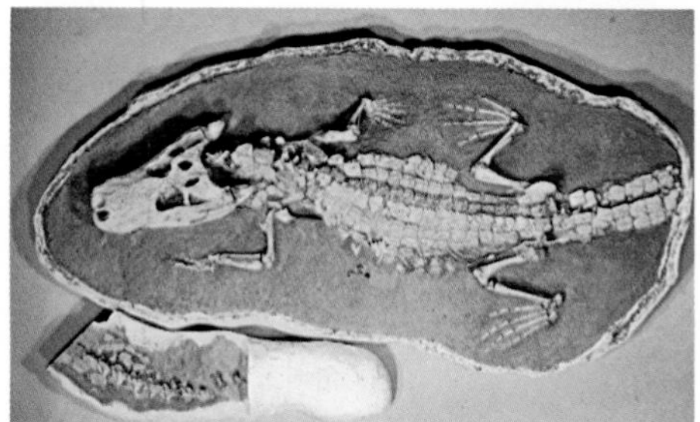
Alligator (Oligocene)

Tyrannosaurus, a huge carnivorous dinosaur (Cretaceous)

Triceratops, a large herbivorous dinosaur (Cretaceous)

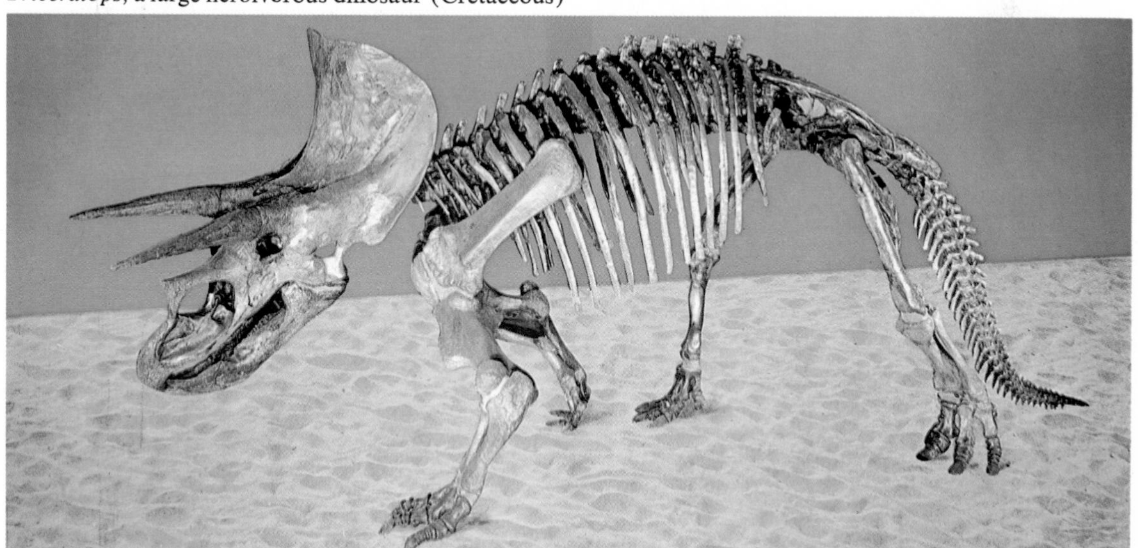

BIRDS—The Conquest of the Air

One group of invertebrates, the insects, and all the major groups of vertebrates except the amphibians, have evolved species with some ability for locomotion in air. Among the vertebrates, flying fishes can glide for hundreds of feet, flying reptiles are extinct but existed during the Mesozoic era, and flying mammals are familiar to us as bats. But it is birds that are most notable as aerial vertebrates.

The earliest known bird was *Archaeopteryx* (at right), which lived in Europe during the Jurassic period. It had many reptilian characteristics in its skeleton, such as teeth (which no recent bird has) and a long bony tail. But its body was covered with feathers, a diagnostic feature of birds.

Birds differ from lower chordates and resemble mammals in having a nearly constant body temperature. Yet, in another comparison, their embryos develop in eggs not unlike those of some reptiles. Parent birds afford their young far greater protection than is common among reptiles, however, by prolonged care and feeding after the offspring have hatched.

Birds are the only major group of animals in which nearly all the living species have been discovered and identified. Can you suggest why this would be true?

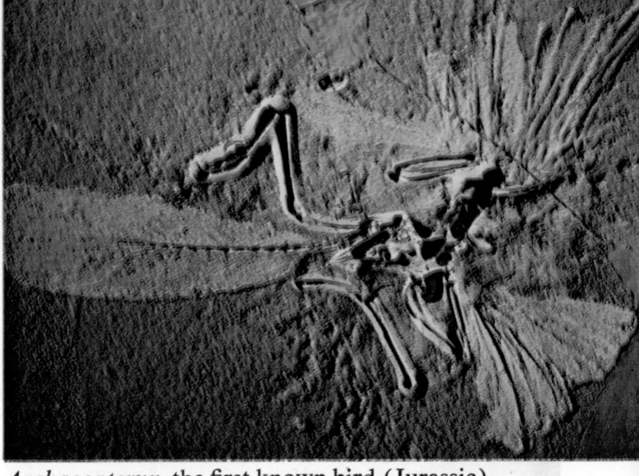

Archaeopteryx, the first known bird (Jurassic)

A reconstruction of *Andagalornis* (Oligocene)

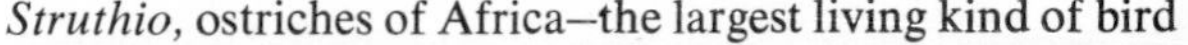

Struthio, ostriches of Africa–the largest living kind of bird

Gulls

Gallinuloides, a fossil bird (Eocene)

A parrot of Central America

An American egret

Bonasa, the ruffed grouse

Passerella, the fox sparrow

Buteo, the red-tailed hawk

In their evolution birds have capitalized on their ability to fly. *Archaeopteryx* (page 802) had a very small sternum, or breastbone. Over tens of millions of years the sternum has evolved into a much enlarged site of anchorage for powerful flight muscles. Although there are birds with a limited ability to fly (see jungle fowl, facing page), and even some flightless birds (see penguin, also facing page), sustained flight is characteristic of most living birds.

Richmondina, the cardinal

A Humboldt penguin

Pelecanus, brown pelicans

Jungle fowl

Archilochus, a hummingbird

MAMMALS—The Chordates' Milky Way

During the Mesozoic era, a group of rather primitive reptiles evolved into mammals. Fossils that are definitely mammalian begin to occur in Jurassic rocks. In many ways these small vertebrate fossils fail to suggest their relative importance, for *Brontosaurus* and other giant reptiles almost fill our capacity to imagine Jurassic events. Yet it was the little mammals, covered with hair and feeding their young with milk, that were to win the future.

Mammals today are of three major groups (see Chapter 26). Monotremes (below) lay eggs. Marsupials (at right, and facing page) have pouches in which the young are kept. Placentals (bottom of facing page and 12 following pages) have special structures for nourishing the unborn young for a longer time before birth.

Two monotremes: *Tachyglossus,* an echidna (above), and *Ornithorhynchus,* the platypus (below)

Two marsupials: *Didelphis,* an opossum with young (above), and *Phascolarctos,* the koala (below)

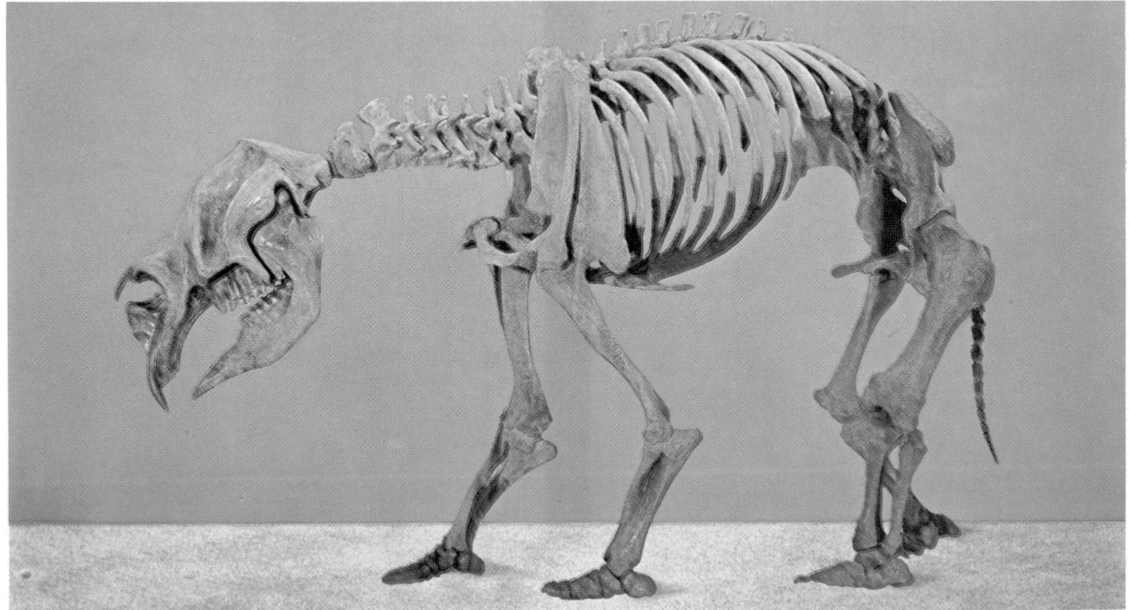

Diprotodon, a giant fossil marsupial from Australia (Pleistocene)

(Left) A wallaby of Australia, another marsupial

Three placentals: *Microgale,* an insectivore (above right); *Icaronycteris,* an Eocene bat (below); and *Myotis,* a little brown bat (below right). Other placentals are on succeeding pages.

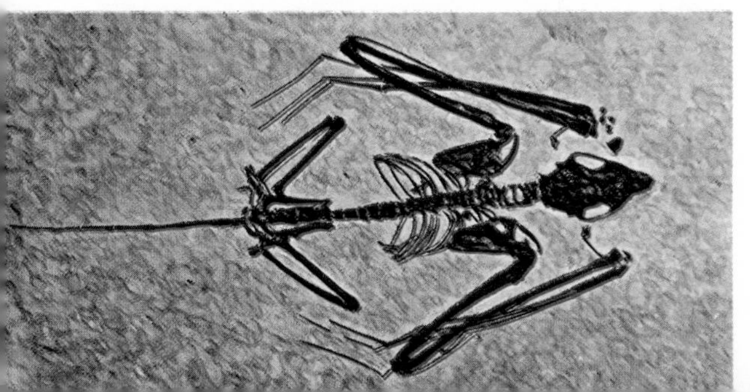

Glossotherium, two fossil giant ground sloths of Argentina (Pleistocene). They were edentates.

Dasypus, an armadillo. Like the fossil and living sloths on this page, it is an edentate.

Bradypus, a three-toed sloth—another edentate

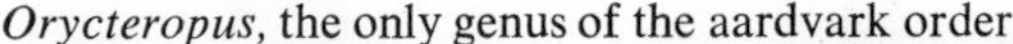

Orycteropus, the only genus of the aardvark order

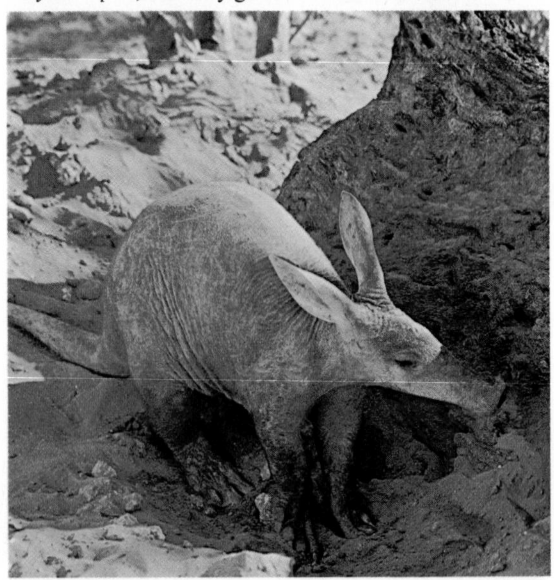

Most of the mammals with which you are familiar, including all of your friends and relatives, are placentals. The young are kept within the mother's body until they are in an advanced stage of development. During this period the placenta forms the lifeline between the embryo and the mother.

The earliest known placental mammals occurred in the Cretaceous period. They were insectivores, and like all other mammals of that time were quite small. Some insectivores closely related to these first placentals still survive (see the photograph of the insectivore *Microgale,* page 807).

Living placental mammals are placed in about 16 orders, beginning with the insectivores (which include shrews, moles, and hedgehogs). Bats, the only true flying mammals, make up another order (fossil and living examples, page 807). An order of toothless mammals, or edentates, includes anteaters, armadillos, and sloths (examples, facing page), and the aardvark order has a single genus (facing page).

The mammals on this and the following two pages belong to the order that includes you–primates. About 200 living species of primates are known. You and all other living people make up one of these species. There have been other human species, but they are now extinct.

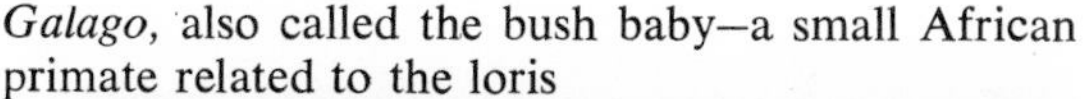

Galago, also called the bush baby–a small African primate related to the loris

Dourocoulis, a South American monkey

Megaladapsis, a giant fossil lemur (Pleistocene)

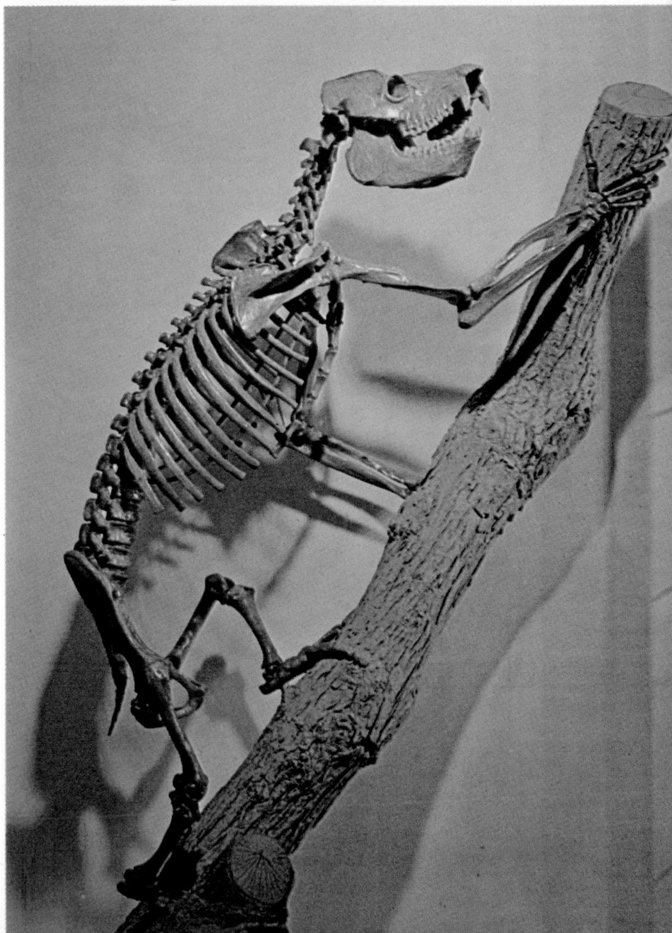

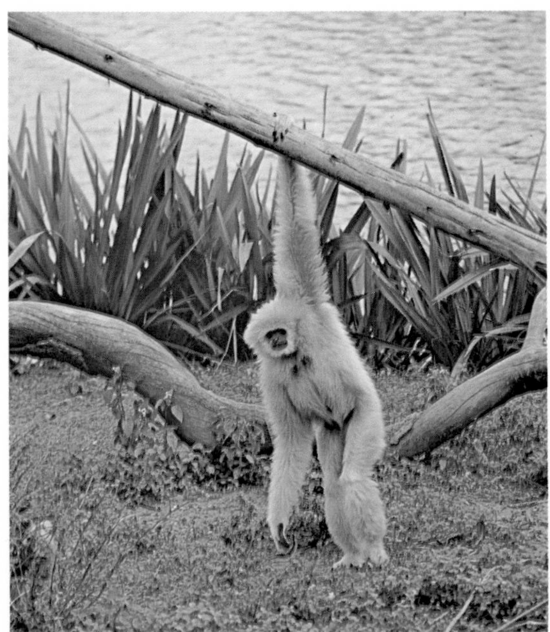

Hylobates, a gibbon of Southeast Asia

Pongo, an orangutan of Sumatra and Borneo

In many ways, the primates seem closest in relationship to the insectivores, among the orders of mammals. This implies that primates have many primitive features. Indeed, tree shrews seem so closely related to their shrewlike ancestors that many biologists disagree about whether they are primates or not. Even the human hand, on the most intelligent of all animals, has the same basic structure that is found in the most primitive mammals. (This is not true of the flipper of a seal, the hoof of a horse, or the wing of a bat.)

Lemurs, lorises, galagos, sifakas, and their relatives are among the most primitive primates alive today. Tarsiers (Figure 33-7, page 616) also are primates. There are four more advanced families of living primates: New World monkeys, Old World monkeys, the great apes, and the family of man. New World monkeys are represented by the marmoset (facing page), *Douroucoulis* (previous page), and a capuchin monkey (Figure 33-8a, page 617). Old World monkeys include baboons (below, and Figure 33-8b) and other types. The great apes are the gibbons, orangutans, chimpanzees, and gorillas (these two pages). Last is the family of man (see mirror).

Comopithecus, baboons of Africa

(Right) *Propithecus,* a sifaka of the Malagasy Republic (Madagascar)

Leontideus, a golden marmoset of South America

Pan, a chimpanzee from Africa

Gorilla, a lowland African ape

Ondatra, a muskrat

Castor, a beaver

Dipodomys, a kangaroo rat

Neotoma, a desert wood rat

The order of rodents (above and left) is in many respects the most successful order of mammals. In addition to muskrats, beavers, and rats, it includes the squirrels, chipmunks, gophers, mice, woodchucks, porcupines, and guinea pigs—and there are still others. The incisor teeth of these animals grow throughout their lives, replacing portions worn away by gnawing and cutting hard materials.

Rabbits (below) and hares are placed in a separate order of mammals—the lagomorphs.

An order to themselves—rabbits and hares

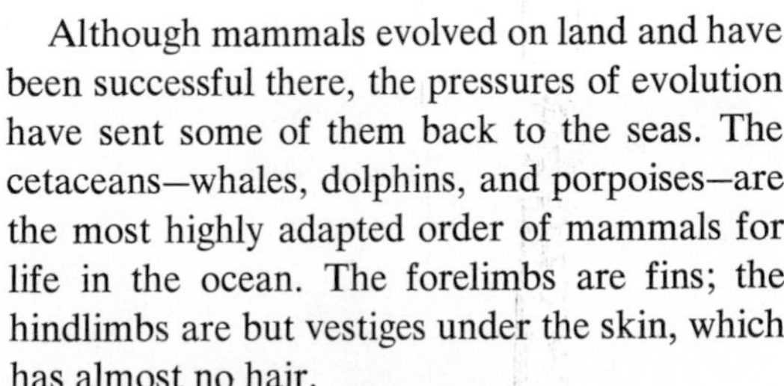

Although mammals evolved on land and have been successful there, the pressures of evolution have sent some of them back to the seas. The cetaceans—whales, dolphins, and porpoises—are the most highly adapted order of mammals for life in the ocean. The forelimbs are fins; the hindlimbs are but vestiges under the skin, which has almost no hair.

Tursiops, a bottle-nosed dolphin

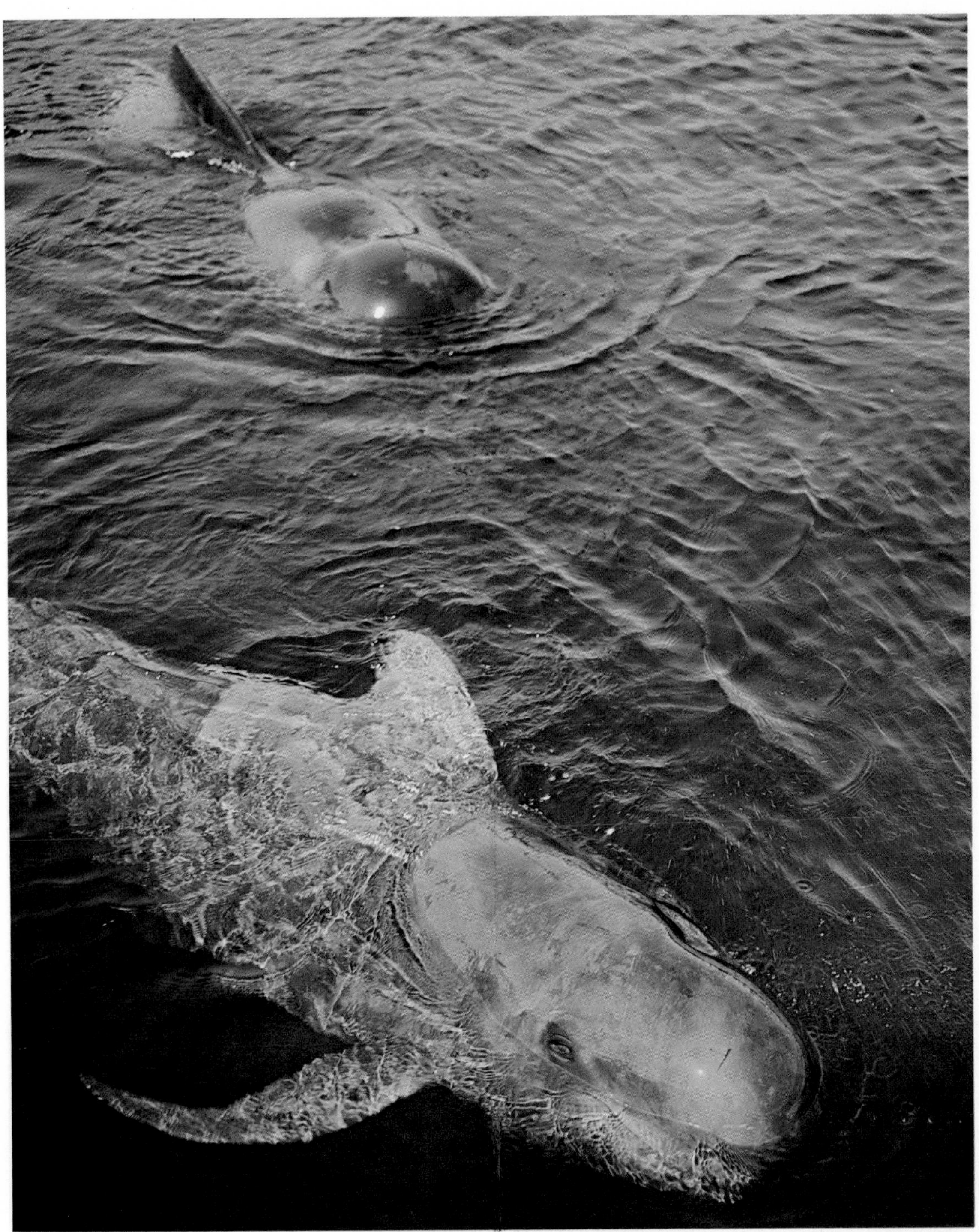

Whales are not only the largest of all mammals, but of all living animals.

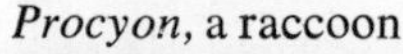
Panthera, a leopard

Ursus, a grizzly bear

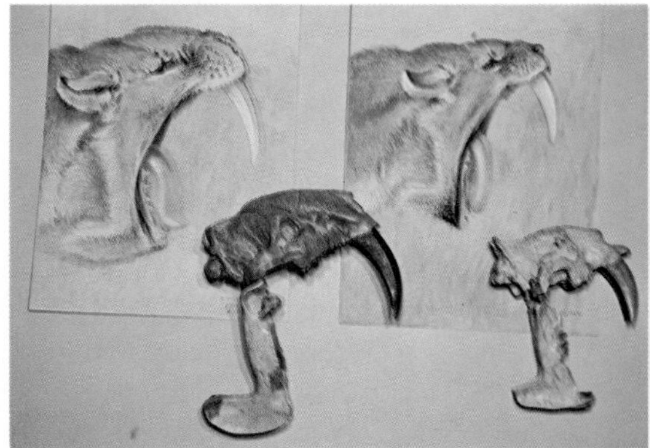

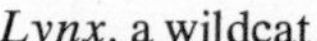
Convergent evolution in sabertooths (see text)

Procyon, a raccoon

Lynx, a wildcat

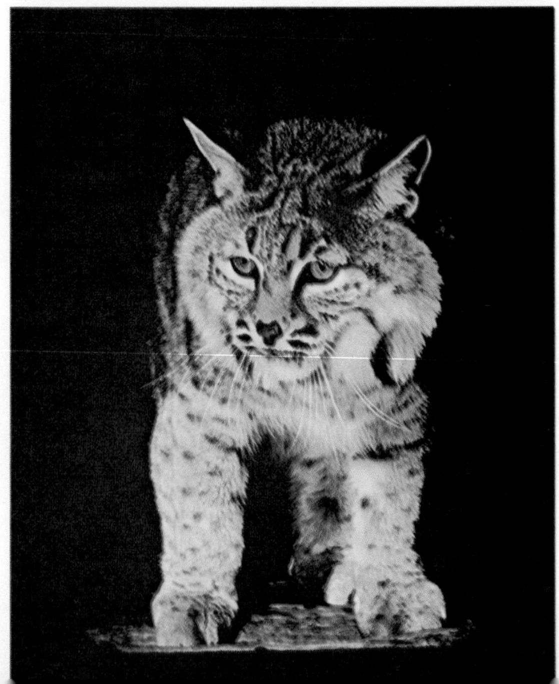

The placental mammals grouped on these two pages belong to the order carnivores, with a single exception—the extinct sabertooths illustrated on the facing page include one placental carnivore and one marsupial. The two evolved and lived quite independently of one another in North and South America when no land bridge connected the two continents. They are an example of convergent evolution in two different major groups of mammals. (The marsupial is the lefthand one, with the larger, darker fossil skull.) Most carnivores are terrestrial; a few are aquatic.

Bassariscus, a cacomistle

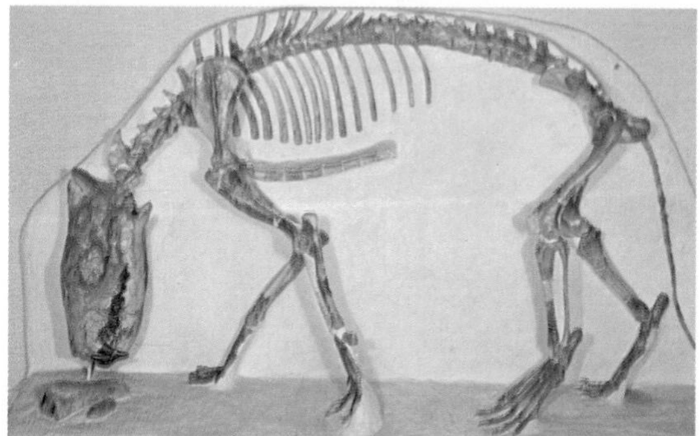

Hyaenodon, a fossil carnivore (Oligocene)

Canis, a timber wolf

Felis (or *Panthera*), lions

Odobenus, walruses

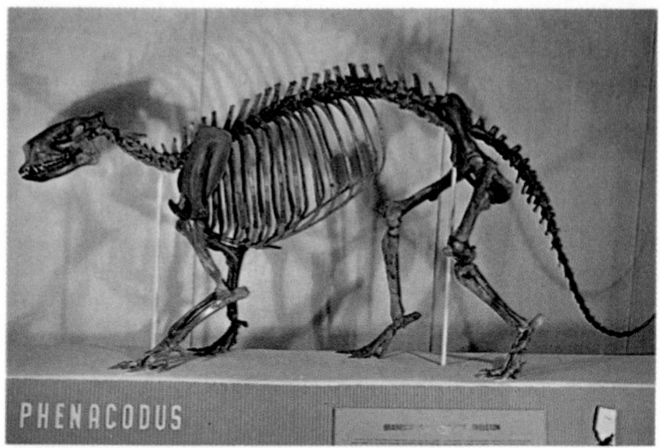

Phenacodus, an ancestral mammal type (Eocene)

Tapirus, a South American tapir

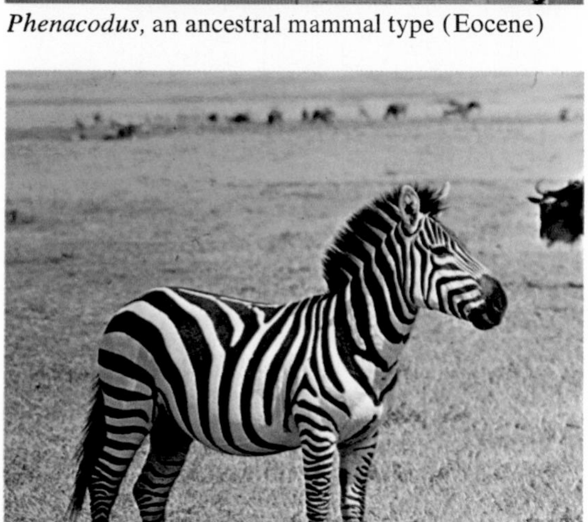

Equus, a zebra

The fossil mammal *Phenacodus,* shown at the upper left, belongs to a primitive group of early Cenozoic mammals ancestral to many of the species shown on this page and elsewhere. The remaining species on this page belong to the order of horselike mammals, or odd-toed ungulates. They are characterized by having the third toe most developed, and having, almost always, an odd number of toes. The living horses and zebras have only a single toe (see the chart on the evolution of the horse—page 581). Rhinoceroses usually have three toes.

The titanotheres (see fossil skeleton, below left) are extinct members of the same order from the Oligocene epoch of the Cenozoic.

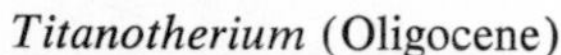

Titanotherium (Oligocene)

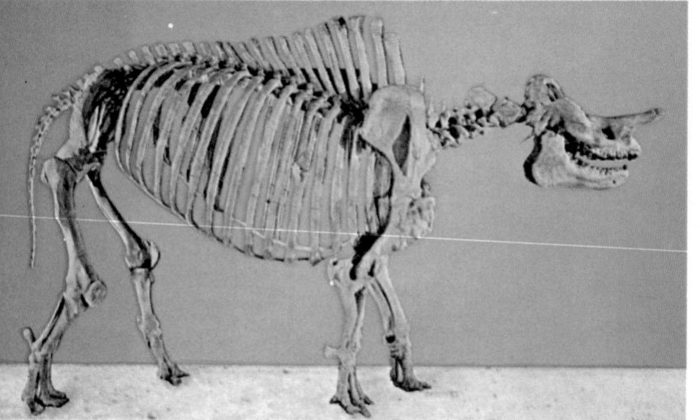

Diceros, an African rhinoceros

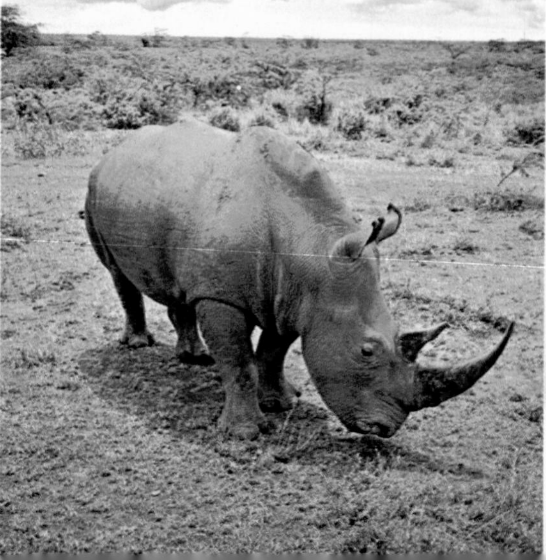

The hyrax (right) is in an order by itself, but it is related to the order of elephants. The elephant order is represented by the African elephant (below) and a fossil species of mastodon (below right). The two extinct mammals at the bottom of this page belong to different and extinct orders of South American placental mammals.

A hyrax, in an order of its own

Loxodonta, an African elephant

Mammut, a fossil mastodon (Pleistocene)

Barylambda, from an extinct order (Paleocene)

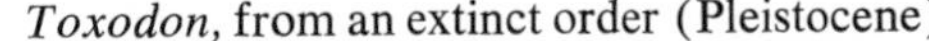

Toxodon, from an extinct order (Pleistocene)

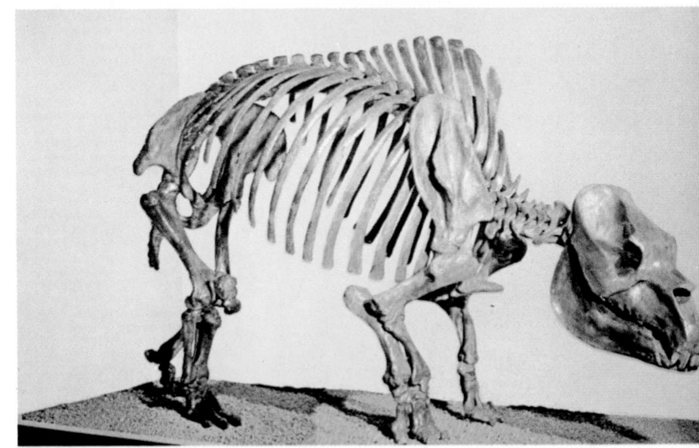

Aepyceros, impalas of Africa

Most of the species on these two pages have two functional toes; the hippopotamuses have four. All these species belong to the order of even-toed ungulates, which also includes pigs, elk, deer, llamas, gazelles, pronghorns, cattle, sheep, goats, and many others. Most of the common large mammals belong to this order. There are some superficial similarities between these even-toed ungulates and the odd-toed ungulates (page 816), but this is another example (see page 814) of convergent evolution. The most recent common ancestor was an insectivore of the ancestral order of mammals.

Alces, a bull moose

Bison of North America

Hippopotamus of Africa

Oreamnos, mountain goats

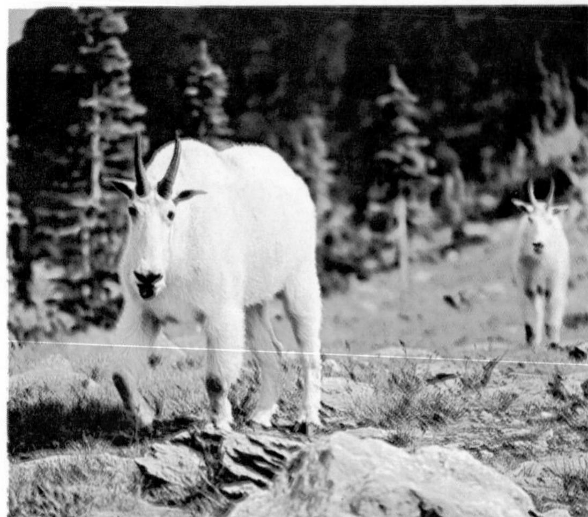

(Right) *Giraffa,* a giraffe of Africa

Stenomylus, a fossil group of small camels that once inhabited North America

Camelus, camels of the dromedarian (one-humped) type

ACKNOWLEDGMENTS FOR PHOTOGRAPHS—CHAPTER 39 (pages 757–819)

PAGE

757 Earth from space, NASA

761 Cells of fossil seeds, and spores with nuclei, ROBERT W. BAXTER; fossil fern tissue, CHESTER A. ARNOLD

762 Spirilla, cocci, bacilli, *Nostoc*, and *Oscillatoria*, Harbrace Photos; fossil blue-green algae, ELSO S. BARGHOORN

763 *Stemonitis*, two photos, and *Graterium*, CONSTANTINE ALEXOPOULOS; *Spirogyra*, Harbrace Photo made at E. Leitz, Inc; *Ischadites*, DONALD BAIRD

764 Diatoms, Harbrace Photo; *Fucus* and *Ascophyllum*, DAVID FOLLANSBEE; *Sargassum*, GEORGE WHITELEY from Photo Researchers; kelp, MARVIN WINTER from Photo Researchers

765 *Rhodymenia*, CONSTANCE MACFARLANE; *Agardhiella*, General Biological Supply House; *Stenophycus*, DONALD BAIRD; *Boletus*, *Polyporus*, and unclassified mushroom, DAVID FOLLANSBEE

766 *Marchantia*, JOHN A. MOORE; moss, CHARLES R. BELINKY from Photo Researchers; living psilopsid, Harbrace Photo; fossil psilopsid, DONALD BAIRD

767 *Equisetites*, *Lepidodendron*, and *Sphenophyllum*, DONALD BAIRD; *Equisetum*, JOHN A. MOORE; *Lycopodium*, DAVID FOLLANSBEE

768 Living tree ferns, G. R. ROBERTS; sword fern (*Nephrolepis*), RUTH KIRK; living fern showing rhizomes, Harbrace Photo; *Pecopteris*, JOHN H. GERARD from National Audubon Society; *Glossopteris* and *Archaeopteris*, DONALD BAIRD

769 *Ginkgo* branch and *Ginkgo* trees, DAVID FOLLANSBEE; fossil *Ginkgo* leaf, DONALD BAIRD; *Araucaria*, JOHN A. MOORE

770 Douglas fir-Western cedar forest, JOHN A. MOORE; *Sequoia* fossils, two photos, DONALD BAIRD

771 Living white pine, two photos, DAVID FOLLANSBEE; *Araucarioxylon* and *Proaraucaria*, DONALD BAIRD; *Microzamia*, two photos, JOHN A. MOORE

772 *Phyllostachys* and *Musa*, JANE LATTA; *Triticum*, EUGENE KEIL

PAGE

773 *Lysichiton*, JOHN A. MOORE; *Narcissus*, BETTY C. MOORE; *Thrinax*, RONA BEAME from Photo Researchers; fossil fan-palm leaf, DONALD BAIRD; wild grass, JIM THEOLOGOS; young corn plant, EUGENE KEIL; *Lilium*, DAVID FOLLANSBEE

774 *Telopea*, *Cornus*, and *Trollius*, JOHN A. MOORE; fossil *Platanus* leaf, DONALD BAIRD; living *Platanus*, JANE LATTA

775 Fossil walnut and fossil acorn, ELSO S. BARGHOORN; living black walnut tree, JANE LATTA; living white oak tree and branch, DAVID FOLLANSBEE; fossil oak leaf, DONALD BAIRD

776 *Peranema*, flagellates from the digestive system of a roach, *Peneroplis*, and *Bursaria*, ERIC V. GRAVÉ; *Noctiluca*, D. P. WILSON; *Blepharisma*, Harbrace Photo

777 *Raphidonema*, DONALD BAIRD; sponge from Caribbean, KELSO ATKINS from Photo Researchers; *Adocia* and *Axinella*, D. P. WILSON

778 *Pennaria*, WILLIAM H. AMOS; *Astroides* and *Tubularia*, D. P. WILSON; Pacific anemones, RUSS KINNE from Photo Researchers; *Porpita*, WILLIAM M. STEPHENS; *Physalia*, R. C. CARPENTER from Photo Researchers

779 *Thecosmilia*, DONALD BAIRD; *Caryophyllia* and *Madrepora*, D. P. WILSON; *Beltanella*, MARTIN F. GLAESSNER; sea anemone, WILLIAM M. STEPHENS

780 *Fasciola* and *Tricuris*, The Bergman Associates; *Dugesia*, Harbrace Photo; tropical planarian, Carolina Biological Supply Company; *Anguillula*, ERIC V. GRAVÉ; *Enterobius*, WALTER DAWN

781 *Lepidonotus*, ROBERT DUNNE from Photo Researchers; fossil tubes of marine annelids, DONALD BAIRD; *Bispira* and *Phyllodoce*, D. P. WILSON; *Amphitrite*, WALTER DAWN; *Enchytraeus*, The Bergman Associates

782 Fossil bryozoan, DONALD BAIRD; *Bugula*, WALTER DAWN; freshwater rotifers, (left) Harbrace Photo, (right) WALTER DAWN

783 Carboniferous brachiopods, Harbrace Photo; *Lingulella*, DONALD BAIRD; *Terebratulina*, WALTER DAWN

PAGE

784 *Dirona*, Carolina Biological Supply Company; *Turritella* and *Fasciolaria*, D. C. STAGER; garden slug, WALTER DAWN

785 Fossil and contemporary cephalopods, JOHN H. GERARD from National Audubon Society; *Illex* and *Mytilus*, D. P. WILSON; *Mya*, ROBERT DUNNE from Photo Researchers; *Scaphites*, DONALD BAIRD

786 *Aysheaia* and *Paradoxides*, DONALD BAIRD; *Peripatus*, JOHN A. MOORE; *Peneus*, Marineland of Florida

787 *Aeger*, DONALD BAIRD; *Stenopus*, Marineland of Florida; barnacles, JOHN A. MOORE; goose barnacles, WILLIAM H. AMOS

788 *Daphnia* and *Geocarcinus*, WALTER DAWN; *Eurypterus*, DONALD BAIRD; marsh crab, WILLIAM H. AMOS

789 Common tick, RUSS KINNE from Photo Researchers; *Argiope*, NOBLE PROCTOR from Photo Researchers; millipedes, JANE BURTON from Photo Researchers; *Xyphosura*, DONALD BAIRD

790 Water strider, HERMAN EISENBEISS from Photo Researchers; honeybees, STEPHEN COLLINS from Photo Researchers; wasp-mimicking fly, R. KOCH; *Sphecomyrma*, F. M. CARPENTER; *Phoracantha*, Australian News and Information Bureau

791 *Prodryas* and *Pseudosphegina*, F. M. CARPENTER; dragonfly, The Bergman Associates; *Charaxes*, H. UIBLE from Photo Researchers; *Murgantia*, WALTER DAWN; syrphid fly, R. KOCH; praying mantis, Carolina Biological Supply Company

792 *Astropecten*, Marineland of Florida; *Echinus*, D. P. WILSON; sea cucumber, and second sea urchin, WILLIAM M. STEPHENS; *Ophiopholis*, ROBERT DUNNE from Photo Researchers; *Ophioderma* and *Platycrinites*, DONALD BAIRD

793 *Ciona*, *Saccoglossus*, and Amphioxus, WALTER DAWN; tunicate, Ward's Natural Science Establishment, Inc.

794 Placoderm, *Bothriolepis*, and *Holoptychius*, DONALD BAIRD; *Prionace*, PETER GIMBEL; *Raia*, D. P. WILSON; jawfish, WILLIAM M. STEPHENS

795 *Mioplosus*, sea horse, and *Trachinotus*, WILLIAM M. STEPHENS; *Acipenser*, RUSS KINNE at Steinhart Aquarium from Photo Researchers; garfish, DONALD BAIRD; *Gadus*, D. P. WILSON

796 *Ensatina*, NATHAN W. COHEN from Photo Researchers; *Eryops*, DONALD BAIRD

797 *Rana*, RUSS KINNE from Photo Researchers; *Bufo*, LEONARD LEE RUE III; fossil toad and *Amphibamus*, DONALD BAIRD

798 Horned lizard and blacktailed rattlesnake, JOHN A. MOORE; boa constrictor, DADE W. THORNTON from National Audubon Society; *Elaphe*, NATHAN W. COHEN from Photo Researchers; American chameleon, WILLIAM M. STEPHENS

799 *Cryptocleidus*, AMNH, Harbrace Photo; *Gopherus*, EMIL MUENCH from Photo Researchers; *Ichthyosaurus*, DONALD BAIRD; green snake, NOBLE PROCTOR from Photo Researchers; *Chrysemys*, NORMAN R. LIGHTFOOT from Photo Researchers; glass snake, LEONARD LEE RUE III

800 *Brontosaurus* and *Lycaenops*, AMNH, Harbrace Photos; *Pterodactylus* and *Coelophysis*, DONALD BAIRD

801 *Sphenodon*, G. R. ROBERTS; *Crocodilus*, A. WILMOT JACOBSEN; *Alligator*, DONALD BAIRD; *Tyrannosaurus* and *Triceratops*, AMNH, Harbrace Photos

802 *Andagalornis*, General Biological Supply House, Inc.; *Struthio*, A. WILMOT JACOBSEN

803 Gulls, WILLIAM M. STEPHENS; *Gallinuloides*, DONALD BAIRD; parrot, GEORGE HOLTON from Photo Researchers; American egret, LEONARD LEE RUE III

804 *Bonasa* and *Richmondina*, LEONARD LEE RUE III; *Passerella*, KARL MASLOWSKI from Photo Researchers; *Buteo*, JOHN H. GERARD from National Audubon Society

805 Humboldt penguin and *Pelicanus*, LEONARD LEE RUE III; jungle fowls, J. A. HANCOCK from Photo Researchers; *Archilochus*, JOHN H. GERARD from National Audubon Society

806 *Tachyglossus*, JOHN A. MOORE; *Ornithorhynchus*, GRAHAM PIZZEY from Photo Researchers; *Didelphis*, LEONARD LEE RUE III from National Audubon Society; *Phascolarctos*, R. VAN NOSTRAND from National Audubon Society

807 *Diprotodon*, AMNH, Harbrace Photo; wallaby, WILLIS PETERSON; *Microgale*, H. UIBLE from Photo Researchers; *Icaronycteris*, DONALD

PAGE

BAIRD; *Myotis*, NOBLE PROCTOR from Photo Researchers

808 *Glossotherium*, AMNH, Harbrace Photo; *Bradypus*, ROBERT C. HERMES from National Audubon Society; *Dasypus*, WILLIS PETERSON; *Orycteropus*, RICHARD STATILE from Design Photographers International

809 *Douroucoulis*, CROSSMAN from Freelance Photographers Guild; *Megaladapsis*, AMNH, Harbrace Photo; *Galago*, WALTER DAWN

810 *Hylobates*, CARL FRANK from Photo Researchers; *Pongo*, WALTER CHANDOHA; *Comopithecus*, MYERS from Freelance Photographers Guild

811 *Leontideus*, WALTER DAWN; *Propithecus*, FREDERICK AYER III from Photo Researchers; *Pan*, Shostal; *Gorilla*, Harbrace Photo

812 *Ondatra*, LEONARD LEE RUE III; *Castor*, JAMES R. SIMON from Photo Researchers; *Dipodomys*, ALFORD W. COOPER from Photo Researchers; *Neotoma*, CORDELL ANDERSEN from National Audubon Society; rabbit, RUSS KINNE from Photo Researchers; *Tursiops*, Marineland of Florida

813 Whales, WILLIS PETERSON

814 *Panthera*, A. WILMOT JACOBSEN; *Ursus* and *Lynx*, LEONARD LEE RUE III; Sabertooths,

PAGE

DONALD BAIRD; *Procyon*, RICHARD F. TRUMP

815 *Bassariscus*, LEONARD LEE RUE III; *Canis*, JAMES R. SIMON; *Hyaenodon*, DONALD BAIRD; *Felis* (or *Panthera*), RICHARD DRANITZKE from Photo Researchers; *Odobenus*, WARD W. WELLS from Design Photographers International

816 *Phenacodus*, DONALD BAIRD; *Tapirus*, ARTHUR W. AMBLER from National Audubon Society; *Equus*, JOHN LIVINGSTON from Photo Researchers; *Titanotherium*, AMNH, Harbrace Photo; *Diceros*, GEORGE HOLTON from Photo Researchers

817 Hyrax, ANTHONY MERCIECA from National Audubon Society; *Loxodonta*, ROBERT HALMI from Design Photographers International; *Mammut*, DONALD BAIRD; *Barylambda* and *Toxodon*, AMNH, Harbrace Photos

818 *Aepyceros*, SATOUR; *Alces*, GRAHAM WILSON from LEONARD LEE RUE III; *Bison*, LEONARD LEE RUE III; *Hippopotamus*, JOHN MOSS from Photo Researchers; *Oreamnos*, WILFORD L. MILLER from National Audubon Society

819 *Stenomylus*, AMNH, Harbrace Photo; *Giraffa*, JAMES R. SIMON from Photo Researchers; *Camelus*, GEORGE DINEEN from Photo Researchers

ACKNOWLEDGMENTS TO REVIEWERS BY SOCIETIES

American Association of Physical Anthropologists

Dr. Robert Ascher, Cornell University, Ithaca, New York

Dr. William Laughlin, Center for Advanced Study in the Behavioral Sciences, Stanford, California

Dr. Lawrence Oschinsky, late of the University of Toronto, Toronto, Canada

American Physiological Society and Society of General Physiologists (Joint Review Panel)

Dr. R. R. Ronkin, University of Delaware, Newark, Delaware

Dr. Eugene M. Renkin, Duke University Medical Center, Durham, North Carolina

Dr. Robert D. Allen, Princeton University, Princeton, New Jersey

Dr. Leon Goldstein, Harvard Medical School, Boston, Massachusetts

Dr. William G. Van der Kloot, New York University School of Medicine, New York, New York

American Phytopathological Society

Dr. J. L. Dale, University of Arkansas, Fayetteville, Arkansas

Dr. Carl Boothroyd, Cornell University, Ithaca, New York

Dr. R. J. Campana, University of Maine, Orono, Maine

Dr. E. H. Barnes, Michigan State University, East Lansing, Michigan

Dr. Ralph J. Green, Jr., Purdue University, Lafayette, Indiana

American Society of Agronomy

Dr. Darrell A. Miller, North Carolina State University, Raleigh, North Carolina

American Society of Animal Science

Dr. Duane Acker, Kansas State University, Manhattan, Kansas

Dr. Gustav Bohstedt, Department of Plant and Animal Science, Stock Pavilion, Madison, Wisconsin

American Society for Horticultural Science

Dr. W. A. Sistrunk, University of Arkansas, Fayetteville, Arkansas

American Society for Microbiology

Dr. Kenneth Temple, Montana State College, Bozeman, Montana

Dr. Gordon Robertstad, South Dakota State University, Brookings, South Dakota

Dr. David E. Contois, University of Hawaii, Honolulu, Hawaii

American Society of Range Management

Dr. Wayne McCully, Texas A. and M. University, College Station, Texas

Central Association of Science and Mathematics Teachers

Mr. Louis E. Shrode, Oak Park & River Forest High School, Oak Park, Illinois

Chemical Education Materials Study

Mr. Robert L. French, Westminster High School, Westminster, California

Dr. Richard J. Merrill, Albany, California

Crop Science Society of America

Dr. A. W. Burger, University of Illinois, Urbana, Illinois

Ecological Society of America

Dr. J. Frank McCormick, University of North Carolina, Chapel Hill, North Carolina

Dr. Edward Kormondy, Oberlin College, Oberlin, Ohio

Entomological Society of America

Dr. Howard Owens, Prince Georges County Board of Education, Upper Marlboro, Maryland

Dr. Robert V. Travis, Mainesburg, Pennsylvania

Mycological Society of America

Dr. Robert W. Lichtwardt, University of Kansas, Lawrence, Kansas

Dr. A. L. Welden, Tulane University, New Orleans, Louisiana

National Science Supervisors Association

Mr. LaVar Sorensen, Salt Lake City Public Schools, Salt Lake City, Utah

Mr. John Leake, Jefferson City, Missouri

Mr. Richard Kay, Idaho State Department of Education, Boise, Idaho

Society of American Foresters

Mr. Stanley M. Jepsen, Chevy Chase, Maryland

Dr. Orie L. Loucks, University of Wisconsin, Madison, Wisconsin

ACKNOWLEDGMENTS TO HIGH SCHOOL CONSULTANTS

The following teachers met with the writing team in a series of feedback meetings. Their criticisms and constructive comments in large part guided the preparation of this revised edition.

Mrs. Iris B. Abernathy, Eastern High School, Mebane, North Carolina

Sister M. Audrey, O.P., Central High School, Anaconda, Montana

Father Donald Chigar, Mt. Carmel High School, Houston, Texas

Sister Cecilia Clare, St. Joseph's Academy, Tucson, Arizona

Mrs. Caroline P. Clarkson, Dreher High School, Columbia, South Carolina

Mr. William K. Cobbett, Jr., Marblehead High School, Marblehead, Massachusetts

Mr. Willis R. Cone, Armstrong High School, Richmond, Virginia

Miss Jean E. Cooper, East High School, Cheyenne, Wyoming

Sister Mary Corinne, O.S.B., John F. Kennedy High School, Mount Angel, Oregon

Mr. Paul C. Cottam, Miami Senior High School, Miami, Oklahoma

Mr. Glen E. Crosby, Ontario High School, Ontario, Oregon

Mr. John C. Curran, Jr., Gulf Park College, Gulfport, Mississippi

Miss Edith Curry, El Cajon Valley High School, El Cajon, California

Mr. J. Maxwell Davis, William Henry Harrison High School, Evansville, Indiana

Mr. Donald H. Dickinson, Tyee High School, Seattle, Washington

Mr. Marshall Floyd, Highland High School, Albuquerque, New Mexico

Mr. Jack Friedman, Syosset High School, Syosset, New York

Mrs. Charles Full, Moses Brown School, Providence, Rhode Island

Mr. James L. Hager, Mount St. Scholastica Academy, Atchison, Kansas

Mr. Arthur E. Haines, Bellevue Senior High School, Bellevue, Washington

Mr. Gaylord L. Hall, Mercer Island High School, Mercer Island, Washington

Miss Mary Jane Herp, Sacred Heart Academy, Louisville, Kentucky

Mr. Allen J. Hollenbeck, Boise High School, Boise, Idaho

Mr. Robert T. Kirkwood, Pine Bluff High School, Pine Bluff, Arkansas

Mr. Wilson G. Kispert, Cass Technical High School, Detroit, Michigan

Mr. Carl R. Knotts, Theodore High School, Theodore, Alabama

Mr. Leslie Kobayashi, Kalani High School, Honolulu, Hawaii

Mr. Arnold Lockett, Cooley High School, Detroit, Michigan

Mr. Robert F. McClure, Slidell High School, Slidell, Louisiana

Mr. James E. McCracken, Dixie Hollins High School, Tallahassee, Florida

Mr. William MacHardy, Ronny Eagle High School, Bustons Island, Maine

Mr. Robert E. Millett, Lincoln-Sudbury Regional High School, Sudbury, Massachusetts

Mr. Lawrence Modrich, Raton High School, Raton, New Mexico

Mr. Floyd H. Nordland, Richfield Senior High School, Minneapolis, Minnesota

Mr. Fred Olsson, Washington High School, Phoenix, Arizona

Mr. Gerald J. Perkins, Kinkaid School, Houston, Texas

Mr. Ellis Poullette, Hillsboro Union High School, Hillsboro, Oregon

Mr. Lauren D. Rice, North Thurston High School, Lacey, Washington

Mrs. Evelyn Scruggs, Luther Burbank Vocational High School, San Antonio, Texas

Mrs. Sandra Smith, Sylvan Hills High School, Atlanta, Georgia

Mr. Ralph Sonen, Northport High School, Northport, New York

Mr. William A. Spear, Senior High School, Joplin, Missouri

Mr. William H. Stewart, Sweetwater Union High School, National City, California

Mr. Richard S. Storer, Mills High School, Millbrae, California

Mrs. Florence Turek, Ketchikan High School, Ketchikan, Alaska

Miss Melba F. Turner, West High School, Salt Lake City, Utah

Mr. Joseph P. Vaughan, Brunswick High School, Brunswick, Maine

Mrs. Ina Wake, Franklin Pierce High School, Tacoma, Washington

Mr. John D. Woolever, Riverview High School, Sarasota, Florida

INDEX

Boldface numbers indicate illustrations

F 1
G 2
H 3
I 4
J 5